The Geology of North America
Volume A

The Geology of North America; An Overview

Edited by

Albert W. Bally
Department of Geology
P.O. Box 1892
Houston, Texas 77251

Allison R. Palmer
Geological Society of America
3300 Penrose Place, P.O. Box 9140
Boulder, Colorado 80301

1989

Acknowledgment

Publication of this volume, one of the synthesis volumes of *The Decade of North American Geology Project* series, has been made possible by members and friends of The Geological Society of America, corporations, and government agencies through contributions to the Decade of North American Geology fund of the Geological Society of America Foundation.

Following is a list of individuals, corporations, and government agencies giving and/or pledging more than $50,000 in support of the DNAG Project:

Amoco Production Company
ARCO Exploration Company
Chevron Corporation
Cities Service Oil and Gas Company
Diamond Shamrock Exploration Corporation
Exxon Production Research Company
Getty Oil Company
Gulf Oil Exploration and Production Company
Paul V. Hoovler
Kennecott Minerals Company
Kerr McGee Corporation
Marathon Oil Company
Maxus Energy Corporation
McMoRan Oil and Gas Company
Mobil Oil Corporation
Occidental Petroleum Corporation
Pennzoil Exploration and Production Company
Phillips Petroleum Company
Shell Oil Company
Caswell Silver
Standard Oil Production Company
Sun Exploration and Production Company
Superior Oil Company
Tenneco Oil Company
Texaco, Inc.
Union Oil Company of California
Union Pacific Corporation and its operating companies:
Union Pacific Resources Company
Union Pacific Railroad Company
Upland Industries Corporation
U.S. Department of Energy

Published by the Geological Society of America, Inc.
3300 Penrose Place, P.O. Box 9140, Boulder, Colorado 80301

Printed in U.S.A.

Front Cover: A nearly full Earth showing much of the western Hemisphere. Photo taken by astronauts on board Apollo 16, April 10, 1972. NASA image E-1358-99CT.

Library of Congress Cataloging-in-Publication Data

The Geology of North America : an overview / edited by Albert W. Bally, Allison R. Palmer.
p. cm.—(The Geology of North America ; v. A)
Includes bibliographies and index.
ISBN 0-8137-5207-8
1. Geology—North America. I. Bally, A. W. II. Palmer, Allison R. III. Series.
QE71.G48 1986 vol. A
557 s—dc20 89-7536
[557] CIP

Contents

Preface vii

Foreword ix

1. *North America; Plate-tectonic setting and tectonic elements* 1
A. W. Bally, C. R. Scotese, and M. I. Ross

2. *The Gravity Anomaly Map of North America* 17
W. F. Hanna, R. E. Sweeney, T. G. Hildenbrand, J. G. Tanner, R. K. McConnell, and R. H. Godson

3. *The Magnetic Anomaly Map of North America; A new tool for regional geologic mapping* 29
William J. Hinze and Peter J. Hood

4. *The seismic structure of the continental crust and upper mantle of North America* 39
Walter D. Mooney and Lawrence W. Braile

5. *North Atlantic Ocean basin; Aspects of geologic structure and evolution* 53
Peter R. Vogt and Brian E. Tucholke

6. *The Atlantic passive margin* 81
Robert E. Sheridan

7. *Evolution of the northern Gulf of Mexico, with emphasis on Cenozoic growth faulting and the role of salt* 97
D. M. Worrall and S. Snelson

8. *Phanerozoic evolution of the North American Cordillera; United States and Canada* 139
John S. Oldow, Albert W. Bally, Hans G. Avé Lallemant, and William P. Leeman

9. ***An outline of the geology of Mexico*** 233
Zoltan de Cserna

10. ***The northeast Pacific Ocean and Hawaii*** 265
Edward L. Winterer, Tanya M. Atwater, and
Robert W. Decker

11. ***Geologic history of the Caribbean and Central America*** 299
Thomas W. Donnelly

12. ***The evolution of the Appalachian chain*** 323
Nicholas Rast

13. ***The Arctic Islands*** 349
H. P. Trettin

14. ***The Ouachita system*** 371
J. Kaspar Arbenz

15. ***Phanerozoic basins of North America*** 397
Albert W. Bally

16. ***Precambrian geology and tectonic history of North America*** 447
Paul F. Hoffman

17. ***The Quaternary*** 513
H. E. Wright, Jr.

18. ***Fresh water of the North American continent; A profile*** 537
Gerald Meyer

19. ***North American fossil fuels*** 555
Kenneth J. Bird

20. ***Mineral resources of North America*** 575
Brian J. Skinner

Appendix A. Contents of all volumes of *The Geology of North America* 585

Appendix B. List of published COSUNA charts 600

Appendix C. Decade of North American Geology Geologic Time Scale 601

Index 603

Plates

(in accompanying slipcase)

Plate 1. Geophysical maps, scale 1:20,000,000
A. Gravity anomaly map of North America
Geological Survey of Canada
B. Magnetic anomaly map of North America
U.S Geological Survey

Plate 2. Evolution of the North Atlantic
P. R. Vogt and B. E. Tucholke

Plate 3. North Atlantic basement topography along and across the Mid-Atlantic Ridge
P. R. Vogt and B. E. Tucholke

Plate 4. Seismic line and structural cross section—Llano uplift to Sigsbee abyssal plain
D. M. Worrall and S. Snelson

Plate 5. Lithotectonic map, cross sections, and mid-Tertiary reconstruction of the Cordillera
J. S. Oldow, A. W. Bally, H. G. Avé Lallemant, and W. P. Leeman

Plate 6. Mesozoic reconstruction of the Cordillera
J. S. Oldow, A. W. Bally, H. G. Avé Lallemant, and W. P. Leeman

Plate 7. Structural cross sections across the Cordillera
J. S. Oldow, A. W. Bally, H. G. Avé Lallemant, and W. P. Leeman

Plate 8. Appalachian ultradeep core hole (ADCOH) project site investigation; Regional seismic lines and geologic interpretation
J. K. Costain, R. D. Hatcher, Jr., and C. Çoruh

Plate 9. Arctic islands, selected lithofacies maps
H. Trettin

Plate 10. Selected distribution maps, rate of accumulation maps, and lithofacies maps for the Phanerozoic of North America
A. W. Bally

Plate 11. Hydrogeologic map of North America showing the major rock units that underlie the surficial layer
R. C. Heath

Plate 12. Hydrogeologic map of North America showing the major units that comprise the surficial layer
R. C. Heath

Preface

The Geology of North America series has been prepared to mark the Centennial of The Geological Society of America. It represents the cooperative efforts of more than 1,000 individuals from academia, state and federal agencies of many countries, and industry to prepare syntheses that are as current and authoritative as possible about the geology of the North American continent and adjacent oceanic regions.

This series is part of the Decade of North American Geology (DNAG) Project which also includes eight wall maps at a scale of 1:5,000,000 that summarize the geology, tectonics, magnetic and gravity anomaly patterns, regional stress fields, thermal aspects, seismicity, and neotectonics of North America and its surroundings. Together, the synthesis volumes and maps are the first coordinated effort to integrate all available knowledge about the geology and geophysics of a crustal plate on a regional scale.

The products of the DNAG Project present the state of knowledge of the geology and geophysics of North America in the 1980s, and they point the way toward work to be done in the decades ahead.

In addition to the contributions from organizations and individuals acknowledged at the front of this book, major support has been provided to one of the editors (AWB) of this volume by Rice University, Houston, Texas.

A. R. Palmer
General Editor for the volumes
published by The Geological Society
of America

J. O. Wheeler
General Editor for the volumes
published by the Geological
Survey of Canada

Foreword

When the Decade of North America Geology Project got under way, it was planned that one of us (AWB) would write this book as a summary of all the volumes of *The Geology of North America.* As the DNAG Project evolved, it became evident that delays in the final publication of some contributions would seriously compromise this ideal plan. Also, we wanted to have some kind of overview of the geology of North America available in time for the International Geological Congress to be held in Washington in the summer of 1989. We therefore modified our original plan and prepared this multi-author volume.

Instead of a comprehensive and uniform synthesis, we now offer a series of papers that we hope cover many, if not most, key aspects of the regional geology of North America. Some of the authors of this volume are also authors and/or editors of some of the other volumes of this series. We encouraged the authors to make their chapters a personal statement, which left them free to choose their own paths between encyclopedic completeness and their own idiosyncratic perspectives. Thus, John Wheeler, in reviewing a manuscript co-authored by one of us (AWB) pointed out that some of the papers may represent more "a point of view" rather than an "overview." Fortunately, it is precisely that diversity of points of view that is the strength of earth sciences in North America!

We expect our readers to be geologically knowledgeable people who want an introduction to the geology of North America that goes beyond the boundaries of their own individual areas of specialization. We also sense that this book may help foreign geologists find useful background for analogs from North America that may help to elucidate some of their own problems. Furthermore, we hope to see this book used as base for graduate and undergraduate seminars.

We encourage readers who wish to dig deeper to consult the other volumes of *The Geology of North America.* These and their tables of contents are listed in Appendix A. All of the chapters in this overview volume are accompanied by key references; some have additional references that are listed on microfiche in the back of the volume.

We are most grateful to all the authors who were under considerable pressure to produce a summary within about 12 months time. Many authors hoped for more time, but alas, in view of the deadline given by the date of the Geological Congress, this was not possible. We thank all authors for bearing as patiently with us, as we did with them.

The Editors
March 1989

The Geology of North America
Vol. A, The Geology of North America—An overview
The Geological Society of America, 1989

Chapter 1

North America; Plate-tectonic setting and tectonic elements

A. W. Bally
Department of Geology and Geophysics, Rice University, Houston, Texas 77251
C. R. Scotese
Shell Development Company, Bellaire, Texas 77401
M. I. Ross
Department of Geology and Geophysics, Rice University, Houston, Texas 77251

INTRODUCTION

This volume is about the evolution of the North America Plate. It also briefly discusses the evolution of the Pacific Ocean and the Caribbean as they relate to North America. We will briefly sketch the present outlines of the North America Plate, review the plate-tectonic development of North America in a global context, and offer an overview of the major tectonic (Fig. 1) and geomorphic elements of our continent.

THE NORTH AMERICA PLATE TODAY. A SEISMIC PERSPECTIVE

Earthquakes are primary indicators of present plate boundaries and of plate motions that are related to these boundaries. The outline of the North America Plate is shown clearly on Figure 2, which is based only on the distribution of earthquakes occurring from 1977 to 1987. Note also the good definition of the Caribbean and Cocos Plates. In the Arctic regions (Fig. 3), earthquakes clearly outline the plate boundary along the mid-ocean ridge up to the north coast of Siberia. However, from there southward, across northeastern Siberia, the margin of the North America Plate is quite diffuse.

Substantial intraplate earthquakes (Fig. 2) have occurred particularly within the United States. The 1811 to 1812 New Madrid (Missouri) and the 1866 Charleston (South Carolina) earthquakes exceeded magnitude 7 and occurred in areas that are still active today (Seeber and Armbruster, 1988; Hinze and Braile, 1988). New England is another area of intraplate seismic activity. According to Zoback and others (1986), the midplate stress of the North America Plate is compressive, with a maximum horizontal principal stress oriented northeast to east-northeast. The stress field extends from the Rocky Mountain front to within 230 km of the Mid-Atlantic Ridge.

Focal mechanisms for large earthquakes, mostly around the North America Plate margin, between 1981 and 1985 (Fig. 4) show dominant convergence along the subduction zones of the Aleutians and Central America, while strike-slip motions dominate near the U.S. west coast, in the Caribbean region, and in the Atlantic Ocean. The neotectonic complexity of the western United States is best illustrated by Figure 5, the map of Smith and Lindh (1978). That map shows a dominant extensional motion for the Basin and Range Province and strike-slip solutions on the U.S. west coast.

GLOBAL PLATE-TECTONIC RECONSTRUCTIONS. A FOCUS ON NORTH AMERICA

Preamble

Numerous plate reconstructions have been offered over the years (e.g., Morel and Irving, 1978; Ziegler and others, 1979; Smith and others, 1981; Engebretson and others, 1985; Scotese and Sager, 1988). Jurassic to Recent reconstructions are often made by matching the magnetic lineations ("magnetic stripes") that have been mapped on the ocean floor (Larson and others, 1985). However, for the late Proterozoic to Lower Jurassic interval, reconstructions are based on a variety of evidence, including paleomagnetic data, paleoclimatology, and paleogeography. As one moves farther back in geologic time the uncertainties of reconstructions increase dramatically. Within the context of this brief introduction we cannot discuss the merits and problems of various reconstructions or review in detail the plate-tectonic history of our planet. Rather, we choose to describe the major plate-tectonic events that influenced the evolution of North America and to illustrate, in a selection of eight global reconstructions, the position of North America as it relates to the development of the world's oceans and continents.

Bally, A. W., Scotese, C. R., and Ross, M. L., 1989, North America; Plate-tectonic setting and tectonic elements, *in* Bally, A. W., and Palmer, A. R., eds., The Geology of North America—An overview: Boulder, Colorado, Geological Society of America, The Geology of North America, v. A.

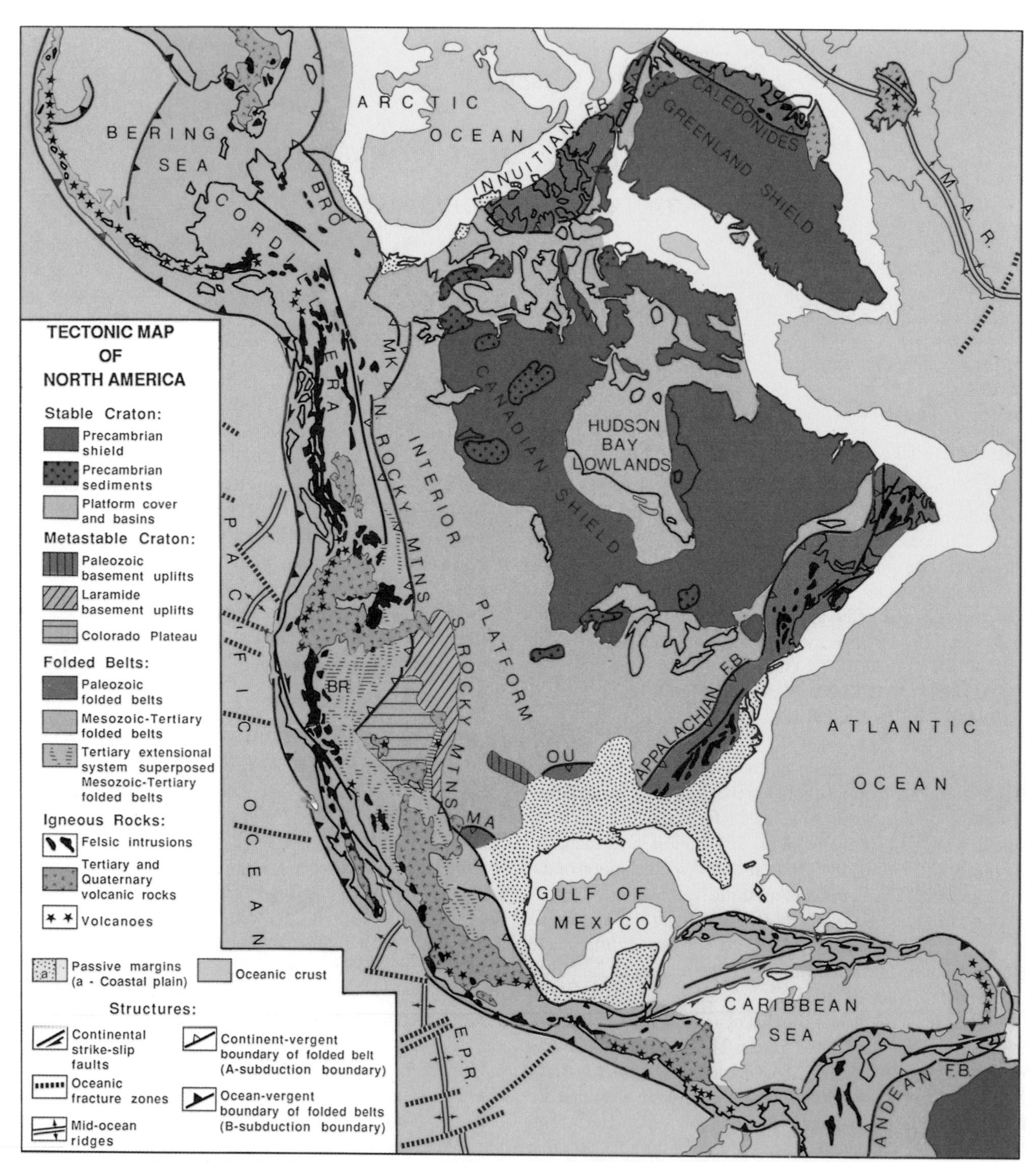

Figure 1. Simplified tectonic map of North America. BR - Basin and Range; BRO - Brooks Range; MK - Mackenzie Mountains; MA - Marathon uplift; OU - Ouachita Mountains; M.A.R. - Mid-Atlantic Ridge; E.P.R. - East Pacific Rise.

Latest Precambrian

A reconstruction at about 600 Ma, roughly corresponding to the latest Proterozoic (Fig. 6), shows North America, Baltica, and Siberia in close proximity. The relationships between each of these three continents and all the other continents are obscure. Other authors have proposed different configurations for this mythical "Precambrian Pangea" (e.g., Morel and Irving, 1978; Piper, 1983, 1987); a common feature of most Proterozoic global reconstructions is that North America lies near the center. Such a central location is also supported by the work of Bond and others (1984) who, on the basis of subsidence studies in the Cordillera and the Appalachians, suggested that during the late Proterozoic, North America was surrounded by newly formed passive margins. Hoffman (this volume, Fig. 47) offers a good perspective on the time and location of late Proterozoic rifting that formed these margins.

According to Bond and others (1984), it seems likely that continents drifted away from North America between 625 Ma and 555 Ma and were dispersed during the lower Paleozoic. Though the concept of a late Precambrian Pangea with North America at the core is accepted by many, it is difficult to make precise reconstructions because we do not know which continents originally bordered North America.

Early and middle Paleozoic

The reconstruction at 458 Ma (early Late Ordovician) shows a wide ocean (Iapetus Ocean) separating North America, Baltica (Northern Europe), and Siberia (Fig. 7). During the early Paleozoic, North America, like many of the other continents at that time, occupied equatorial latitudes. Gondwana, to which Florida and part of Mexico were still attached, straddled the South Pole.

By 425 Ma (early Late Silurian), Baltica and North America collided, forming the continent of Euramerica (Fig. 8). The Caledonian Mountains of eastern Greenland and the northern Appalachian Mountains of New England and Maritime Canada mark the zone of collision. Note the small elongated microcontinent of Avalonia (eastern New England and Maritime Canada) located off the southeast coast of North America. Avalonia was added to North America during the final phases of this continent-continent collision (Acadian orogeny).

Late Paleozoic

By the Late Permian (255 Ma), the ocean basins separating Euramerica from Gondwana and Siberia had closed, resulting in the formation of the western half of the supercontinent Pangea (Fig. 9). This Pangea configuration was already attained during the late Carboniferous and was not significantly altered until the Early Jurassic.

Ziegler (1988) illustrates how, beginning in the Carboniferous and during much of the Permian, complex rift systems develop in a zone extending from the Gulf of St. Lawrence of the Canadian Maritime provinces into eastern Greenland. During Late Permian time, a marine incursion between Greenland and Scandinavia connected the Arctic Ocean with the Zechstein basins of northeastern Europe. These rifted basins open up to the north into a wide Permian shelf area that extended from the Barents shelf into the Sverdrup basin of the northern Arctic Islands of Canada. The suggestion is that during Permian time, areas adjacent to northern North America, Baltica, and Siberia formed part of a very extended shelf area that was underlain by a basement formed of Paleozoic folded belts.

Though the precise position and orientation of northern Alaska in the Pangea reconstruction is the subject of much debate (Lawver and Scotese, 1989), most authors agree that northern Alaska was near the Canadian Arctic Islands. Note also that Florida and Yucatan were welded onto North America as a result of the late Paleozoic collision with Gondwana and that northwestern South America occupied the area of the present Gulf of Mexico.

Mesozoic

Our Mesozoic and Tertiary reconstructions are taken from Scotese and others (1988). These authors used the sea-floor map of Larsen and others (1985) as the basis for their reconstructions. The same reconstructions also serve to test the accuracy of the sea-floor map. Thus, on Figures 10 to 14 the black areas at mid-ocean ridges indicate overlap, and white areas correspond to gaps in the reconstruction.

During the Middle and Upper Triassic and the Early Jurassic a new rift system formed along the east coast of North America and into the Gulf of Mexico. This rift system was a precursor to the rifts that eventually led to the opening of the Gulf of Mexico and the central Atlantic Ocean.

The reconstruction at about 144 Ma or the beginning of the Cretaceous shows the formation of a narrow oceanic basin in the central Atlantic (Fig. 10). Following Sheridan (this volume) the breakup and the subsequent emplacement of oceanic crust occurred during the Middle Jurassic. A perhaps slightly younger, but still Middle Jurassic, age is also postulated for the central Gulf of Mexico (see Worrall and Snelson, this volume). South of the Gulf of Mexico, we see that by the Early Cretaceous the Proto-Caribbean Ocean formed in the widening gap between North America and South America.

Note also the first preserved record of magnetic lineations in the western Pacific. Perhaps more important is the observation that nearly all Paleozoic and early Mesozoic oceanic crust cannot be found today because it has been subducted. As a result, only very hypothetical reconstructions for these times are available for the Pacific Ocean and its associated plates (Farallon, Kula, and Phoenix). For additional information see Winterer and others (this volume).

At about 119 Ma (late Neocomian to early Aptian) we see a slight expansion of the central Atlantic Ocean, as well as a mod-

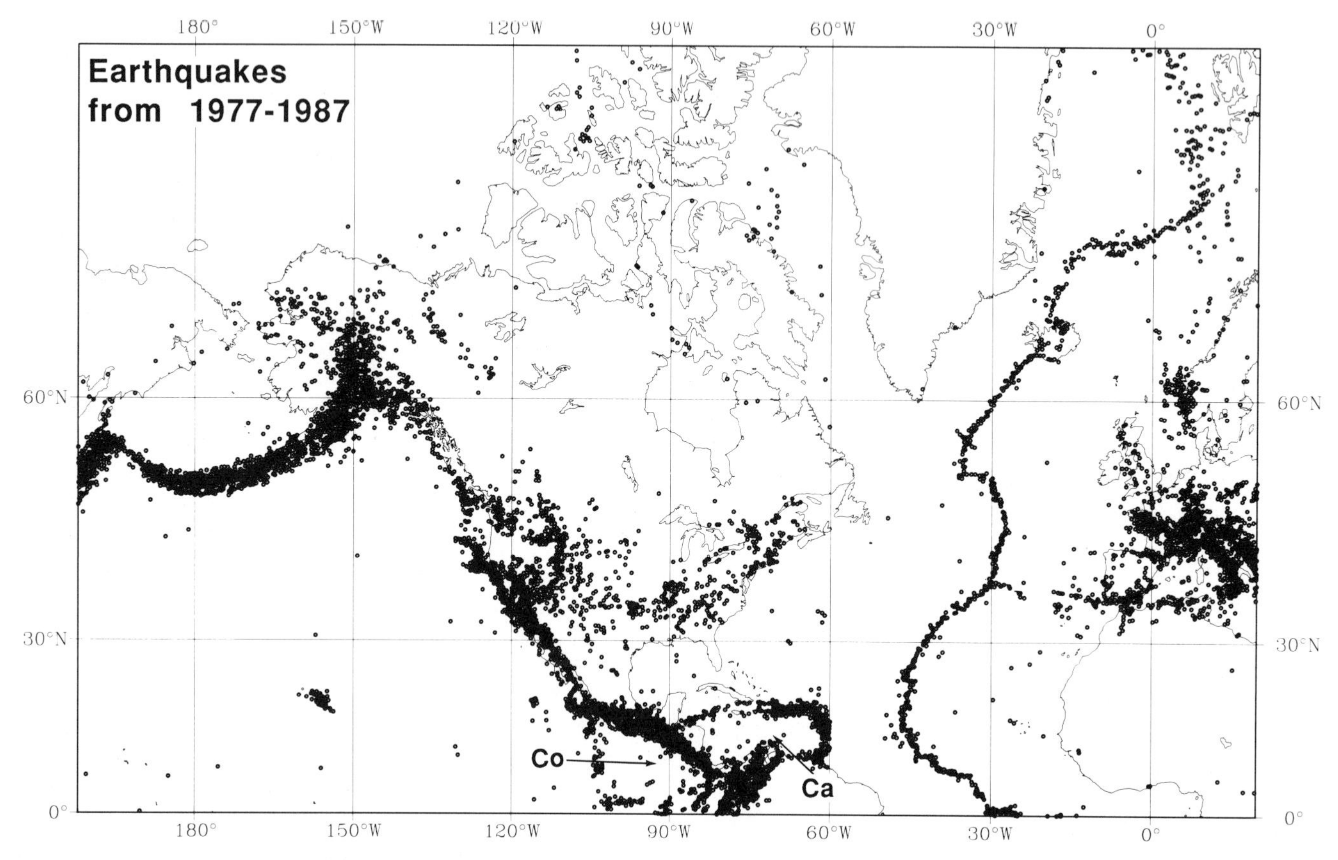

Figure 2. Present boundaries of the North America Plate, as based on a seismicity map showing earthquakes from 1977 to 1987. The map uses no earthquake magnitude cutoff. Map courtesy of S. K. Goter, Branch of Global Geology and Geomagnetism, U.S. Geological Survey, Denver. Ca - Caribbean Plate; Co - Cocos Plate.

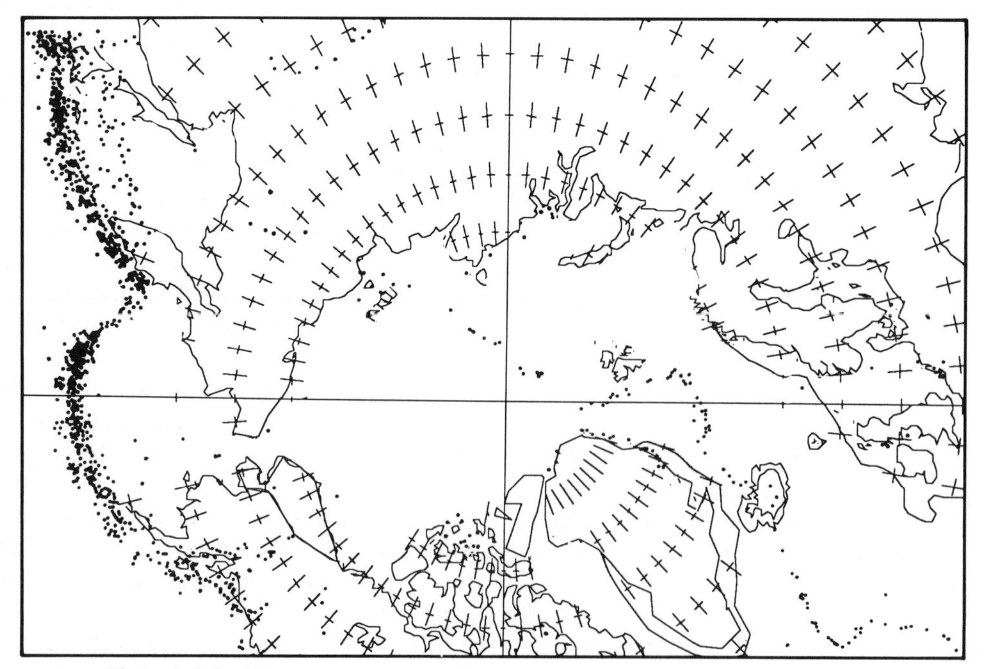

Figure 3. Seismicity map of the Arctic Ocean showing earthquakes from 1964 to 1973.

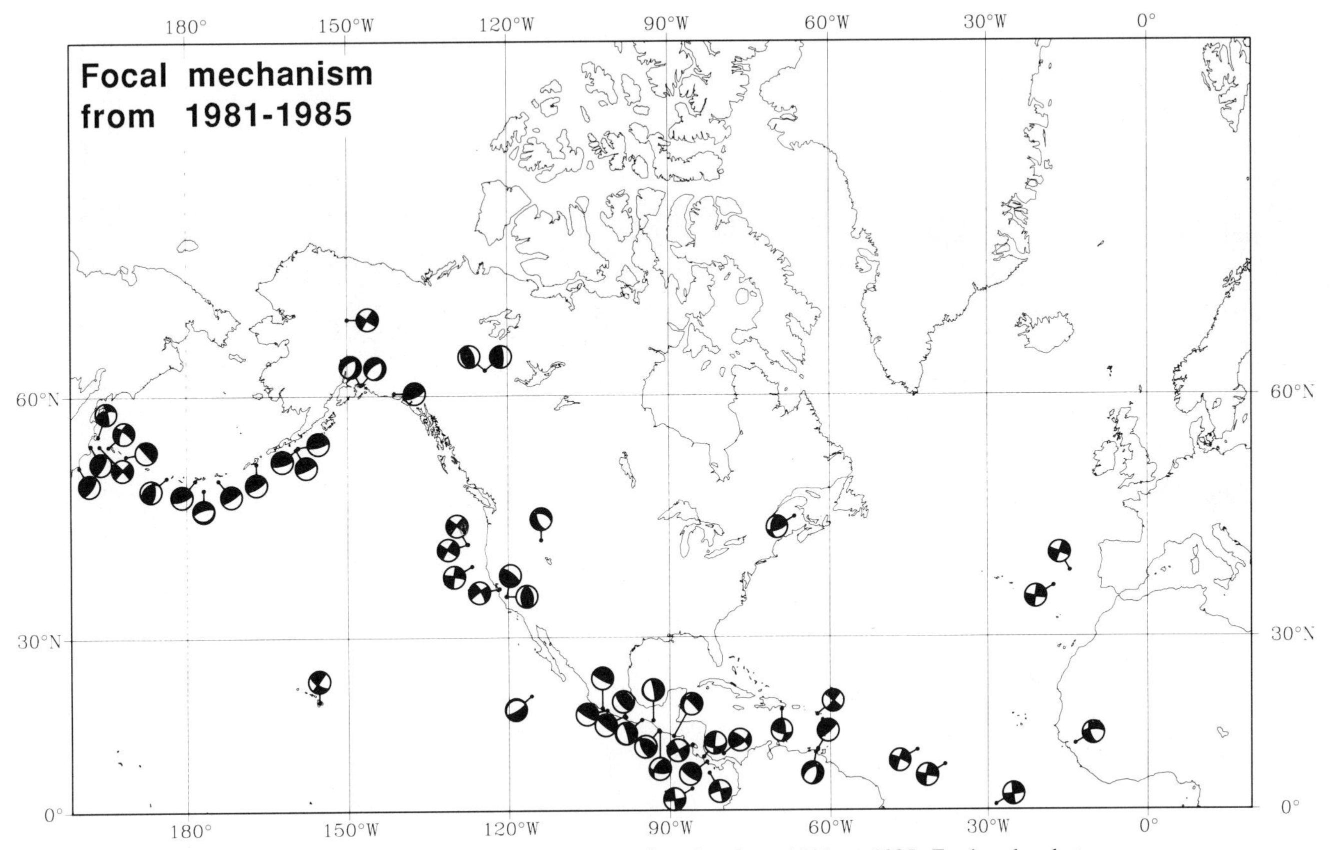

Figure 4. Focal mechanism map for large earthquakes from 1981 to 1985. Earthquakes between January 1981 and July 1982 have magnitudes of 6.5 or more. Earthquakes occurring after August 1982 have magnitudes of 5.7 or more. Focal mechanisms are taken from Needham (1986a, b). Map courtesy of S. K. Goter, Branch of Global Geology and Geomagnetism, U.S. Geological Survey, Denver.

est increase in the area of dated oceanic crust in the western Pacific (Fig. 11). Note also the appearance of a small oceanic basin between Africa and South America, and the continued expansion of the Proto-Caribbean Ocean.

During the Late Cretaceous (84 Ma, late Santonian), sea-floor spreading continued between North America and Africa, and a new rift system began to develop between North America and Europe (Fig. 12). The Proto-Caribbean stopped widening, and the Greater Antilles arc (Cuba) began to collide with the Bahama Platform (Ross and Scotese, 1988), causing the initiation of the Panamanian arc system. Note also the increased expansion of the central and South Atlantic, and the growing area of oceanic crust in the western Pacific.

Tertiary

The plate-tectonic reconstruction of the early Oligocene (38 Ma) shows the opening of Baffin Bay and the Labrador Sea, and the separation of Greenland from Norway (Fig. 13). Strike-slip motion along Nares Strait between Greenland and Ellesmere Island, and the formation of the Eurekan fold-belt in eastern Ellesmere Island, resulted from the opening of these northern seaways (see Trettin, this volume). Sea-floor spreading continued in the central and South Atlantic.

In the Caribbean, east-west rifting had begun in the Cayman Trough (late Eocene; Rosencrantz and others, 1988), and the Caribbean Plate, with its eastern island-arc systems began to acquire its modern appearance. Along the southern margin of the Caribbean, there has been a significant amount of convergence since Eocene time, leading to the collision of the South America and Caribbean Plates (Pindell and others, 1988; Ross and Scotese, 1988).

As shown in Figure 13, the leading edge of the Pacific Plate began to impinge upon the western margin of North America during the Oligocene. As a consequence the San Andreas strike-slip fault system developed and the Gulf of California opened (see Winterer and others, this volume; Oldow and others, this volume). This change in plate motions and the resulting change in stress systems may also be related to the development of the Basin and Range Province in the western United States and Mexico.

Correlation between Mesozoic-Cenozoic global plate-tectonic reorganizations and North American tectonostratigraphic events

Major changes in plate-tectonic regimes appear to coincide with major tectonostratigraphic changes in North America. Sco-

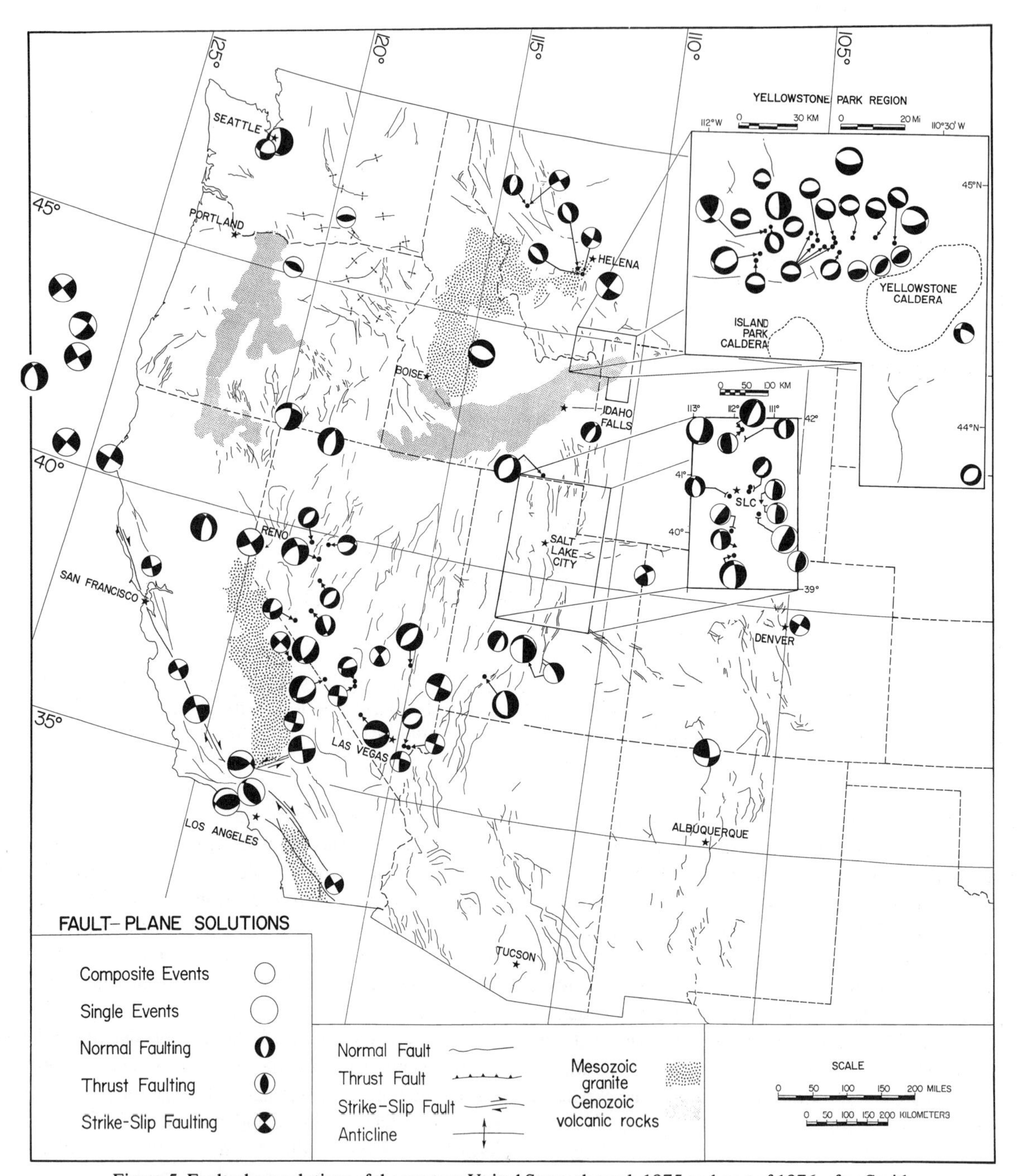

Figure 5. Fault-plane solutions of the western United States through 1975 and part of 1976, after Smith and Lindh (1978). Large symbols are single-event solutions, small symbols are composite solutions.

tese and others (1988, p. 46) identify five worldwide events that represent major changes in plate-tectonic movements during the Mesozoic and Tertiary: "(1) the breakup of Pangea and Gondwana during the Middle Jurassic (the Quiet Zone, 175 Ma), (2) the breakup of the southern continents (Africa–South America and Antarctica, Australia, and India) during the Early Cretaceous (Chron M 11, 133.5 Ma), (3) the Middle Cretaceous plate reorganization (the Quiet Zone, 95 Ma), (4) the latest Cretaceous plate reorganization (Chron 28, 65.1 Ma), and (5) the plate reorganization that followed the collision of India with Asia in the early Eocene (Chron A21, 50.3 Ma)."

There seems to be a correlation between these times of global plate reorganization and the timing of major North American tectonostratigraphic events. Thus, the first event is responsible for the beginning of the opening of the Atlantic Ocean, the Gulf of Mexico, and the Proto-Caribbean. It is followed shortly by the inception of the Rocky Mountain foredeep, which dates the beginning of the Cordilleran foreland folded belt deformation. The second event marks the beginning of the Colville foredeep on the North Slope of Alaska and the beginning of the formation of the Brooks Range in Northern Alaska. The third event is reasonably close to the formation of the widespread mid-Cretaceous unconformity of the Gulf Coast and the central Atlantic. The fourth event coincides with inception of Laramide deformation, which is responsible for the basement-involved deformation of the Southern Rocky Mountains of the United States, as well for the final phases of deformation of the Cordilleran foreland folded belts. Finally, the fifth event marks the end of the compression of the Cordilleran foreland folded belt, the inception of extensional tectonics in the Basin and Range Province, and of strike-slip tectonics in California, as well as the establishment of major drainage patterns that are responsible for the accumulation of thick Tertiary clastic sequences of the Gulf Coast.

NORTH AMERICA WITHIN A GLOBAL CONTEXT

Figure 14 is a simplified tectonic map of the world taken from Bally and Snelson (1980). The map shows that the oceans of the world are formed by Mesozoic-Cenozoic ocean spreading. The age of the Arctic Ocean floor is not really known because no drill holes have penetrated that floor; however, there is a consensus that the Amerasian Basin of the Arctic is probably underlain by Cretaceous oceanic or transitional crust.

The integrated product of all subduction processes that are coeval with Mesozoic-Cenozoic ocean spreading is the Cenozoic-Mesozoic "megasuture" shown on our map. Megasutures encompass folded belts as well as small sedimentary basins that ride piggyback on them (the successor or episutural basins of some authors). The Cenozoic-Mesozoic megasuture on our map may also be visualized as an "orogenic float" or as deformed sediments and crustal fragments that have been mechanically separated from their lithospheric roots (see Oldow and others, this volume). Important boundaries of a megasuture are (1) the Benioff (or B-) subduction boundary coinciding with the subduction of oceanic lithosphere; (2) the Ampferer (or A-) subduction boundary, or the external boundary of continent-verging folded belts, where limited amounts of continental lithosphere appear to be subducted; (3) boundaries that are dominated by strike-slip tectonics (e.g., California); and (4) an ill-defined boundary defined by felsic intrusions (e.g., China, Mongolia, and Siberia).

The Precambrian cratons of the world may be viewed as a series of peneplained Precambrian megasutures, and the Paleozoic folded belts of the world represent a Paleozoic megasuture.

Within the context of this brief description and the reconstructions presented earlier, it is clear that much of North America and Greenland (Laurentia) is underlain by Precambrian crust that may be compared to the other large Precambrian cratonic areas of the world. The Palozoic folded belts of North America find their continuation in North Africa, Europe, and Siberia. Farther south, Paleozoic folded belts form the basement that underlies much of Mexico, and the basement of the Andean Mountains of South America.

TECTONIC PROVINCES OF NORTH AMERICA

Figure 1 is a tectonic sketch of North America, Central America, and the Caribbean that serves as a simple overview of the material contained in this volume. The sketch is inspired by, but modified from, King (1977). A complementary map showing the distribution of various types of sedimentary basins is shown elsewhere (Bally, this volume, Fig. 1).

The stable craton of North America includes the Precambrian outcrops of the Canadian and Greenland Shields, their subsurface extension (see Hoffman, this volume) and their platform cover, which is subdivided into a number of sedimentary basins and arches (see Bally, this volume, Figs. 1 and 2). In the southwestern United States, the craton and its cover have been deformed and are involved in local basement uplifts of either the Paleozoic Wichita–Ancestral Rocky Mountain system, or the Laramide Southern Rocky Mountains (see Oldow and others, this volume; Arbenz, this volume). The Precambrian basement also extends well underneath the Paleozoic and Mesozoic-Cenozoic folded belts of much of North America (see Rast, this volume; Arbenz, this volume; Trettin, this volume; Oldow and others, this volume).

On Figure 1 the Phanerozoic folded belts of North America are not subdivided. However, a closer view would permit outer folded belts (Externides or the miogeosynclinal belts of earlier authors) and more internal zones (Internides) to be readily differentiated. Thus, for example, the Cordillera (see Oldow and others, this volume) has two outer folded belts with opposite vergence. These are (1) the coastal active-margin belt with its accretionary wedges, and (2) the continent-verging foreland folded belt. All Phanerozoic foreland folded belts of North America are characterized by widespread décollement structures displaying different styles of deformation that respond to ductility contrasts within now-deformed passive margin sequences. In the interior of most folded belts, however, we observe that fragments

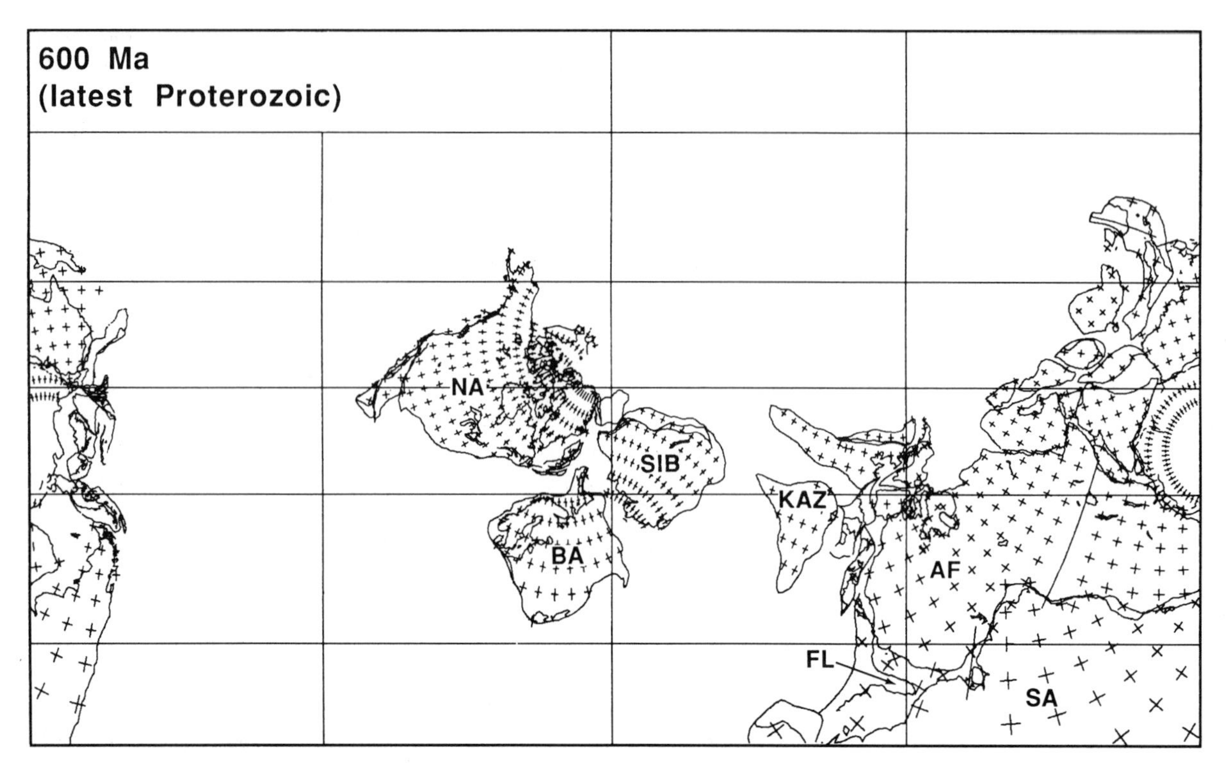

Figure 6. Plate reconstruction at about 600 Ma, or the latest Proterozoic. Abbreviations for Figures 6 to 9: AF - Africa; ANS - Alaska North Slope; AR - Armorica; AV - Avalonia; BA - Baltica; EN–B - England-Brabantia; FL - Florida; IB - Iberia; KAZ - Kazakhstania; NA - North America; SA - South America; SIB - Siberia.

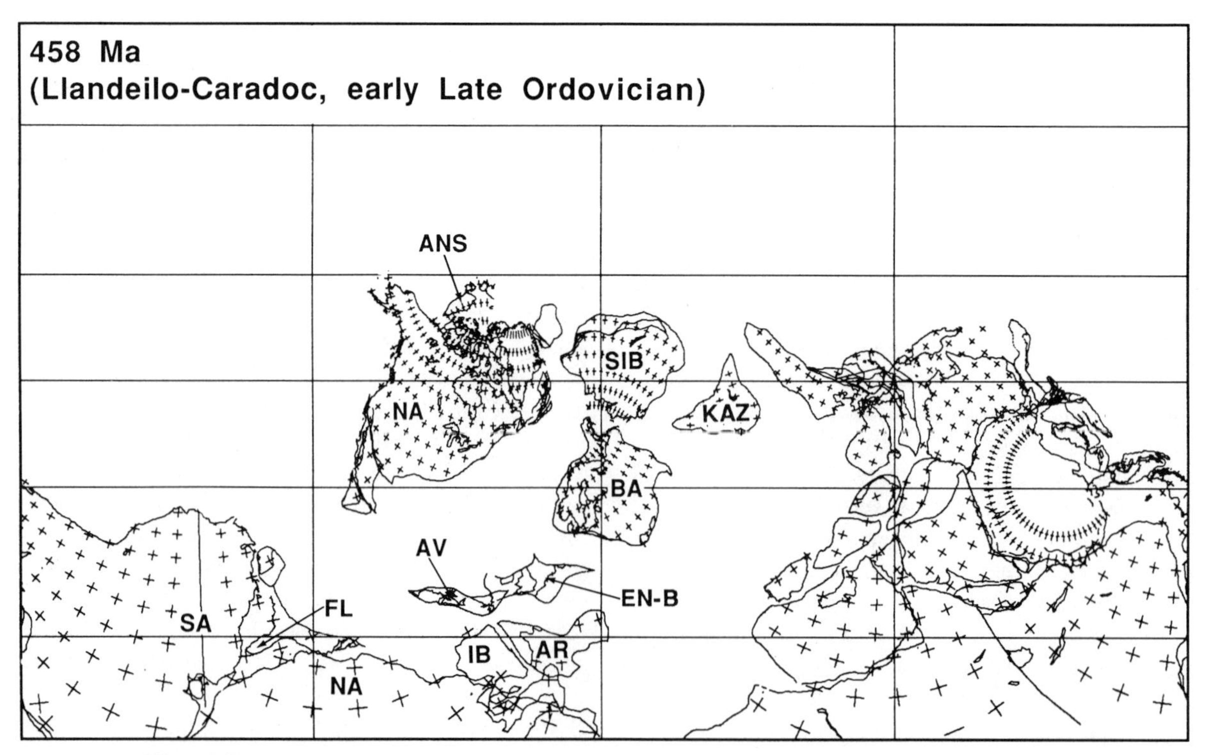

Figure 7. Reconstruction at 458 Ma, (Llandeilo/Caradoc, early Late Ordovician). For abbreviations see caption Figure 6.

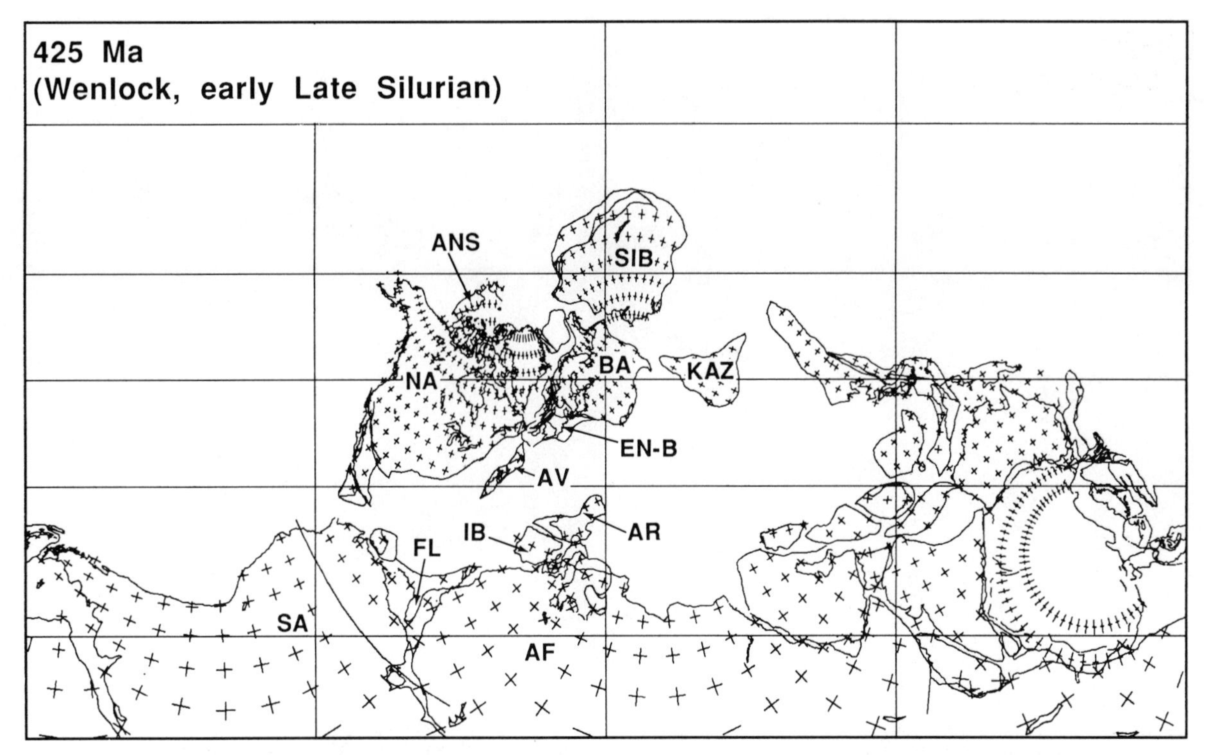

Figure 8. Reconstruction at 425 Ma, (Wenlock, early Late Silurian). For abbreviations see caption Figure 6.

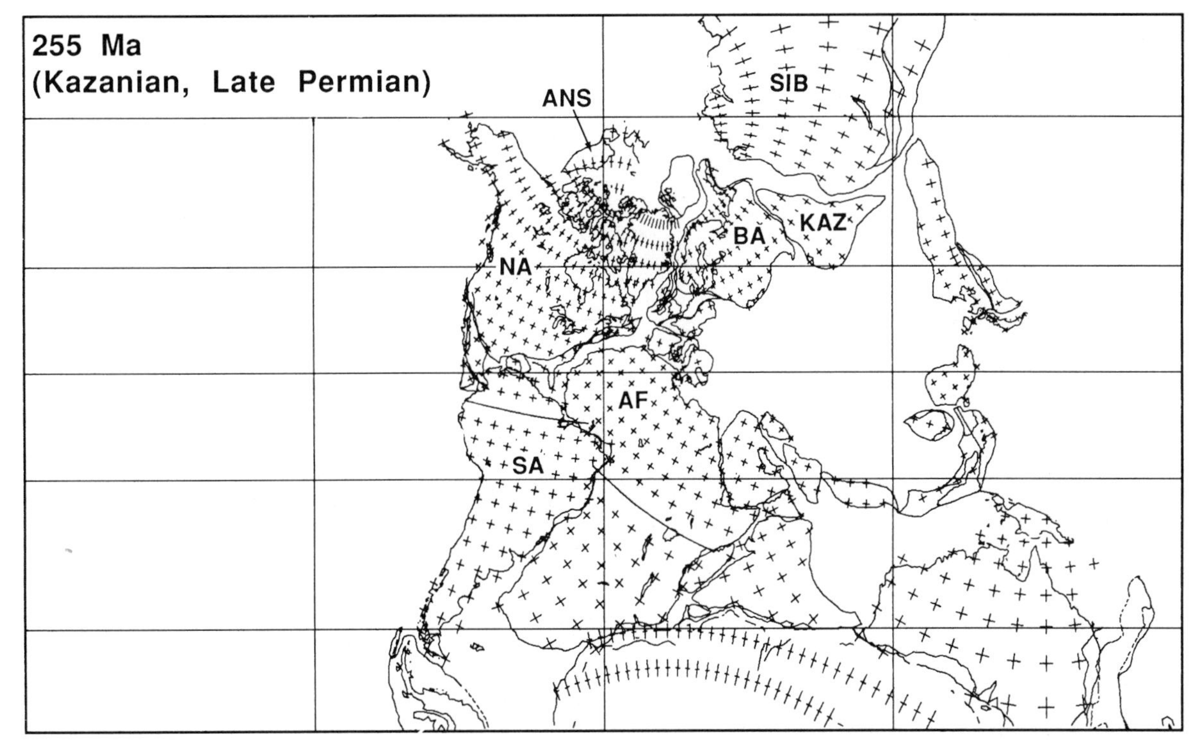

Figure 9. Reconstruction at 255 Ma, (Kazanian, Late Permian). For abbreviations see caption Figure 6.

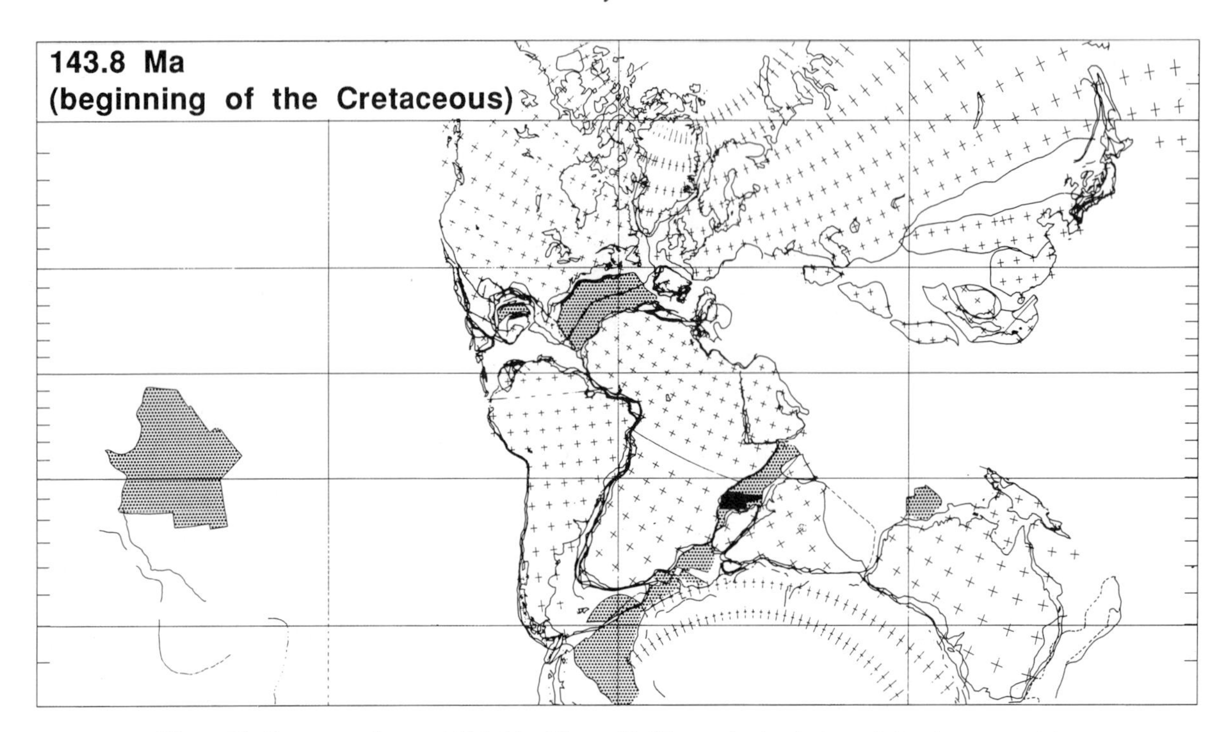

Figure 10. Reconstruction at 143.8 Ma (Chron M 17), or the beginning of the Cretaceous. The ocean-floor patterns for Figures 10 to 14 are: coarse dark stipple, chrons M0 to M 17 and earlier (Late Jurassic-Neocomian); coarse light stipple, chrons 29 to 34 (Aptian-Maastrichtian); fine dark stipple, chrons 15 to 25 (Eocene - Paleocene). (Published with permission of Elsevier.)

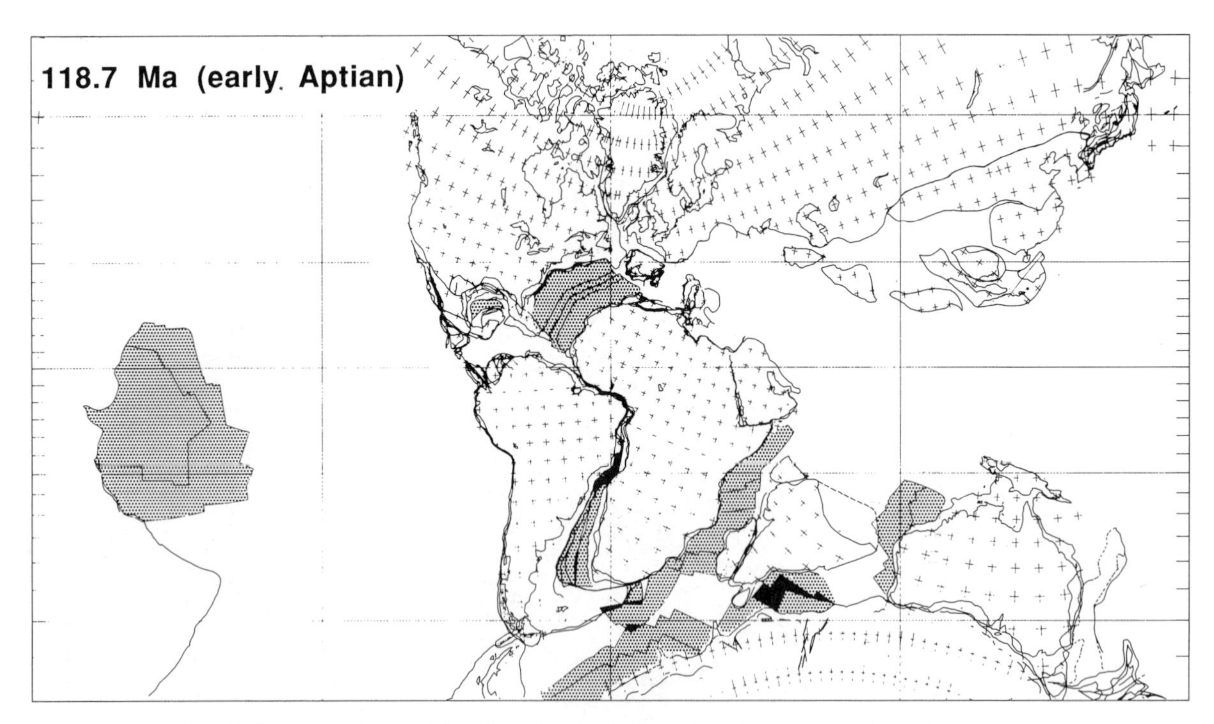

Figure 11. Reconstruction at 118.7 Ma (Chron M0 - early Aptian). For pattern legend, see Figure 10. (Published with permission of Elsevier.)

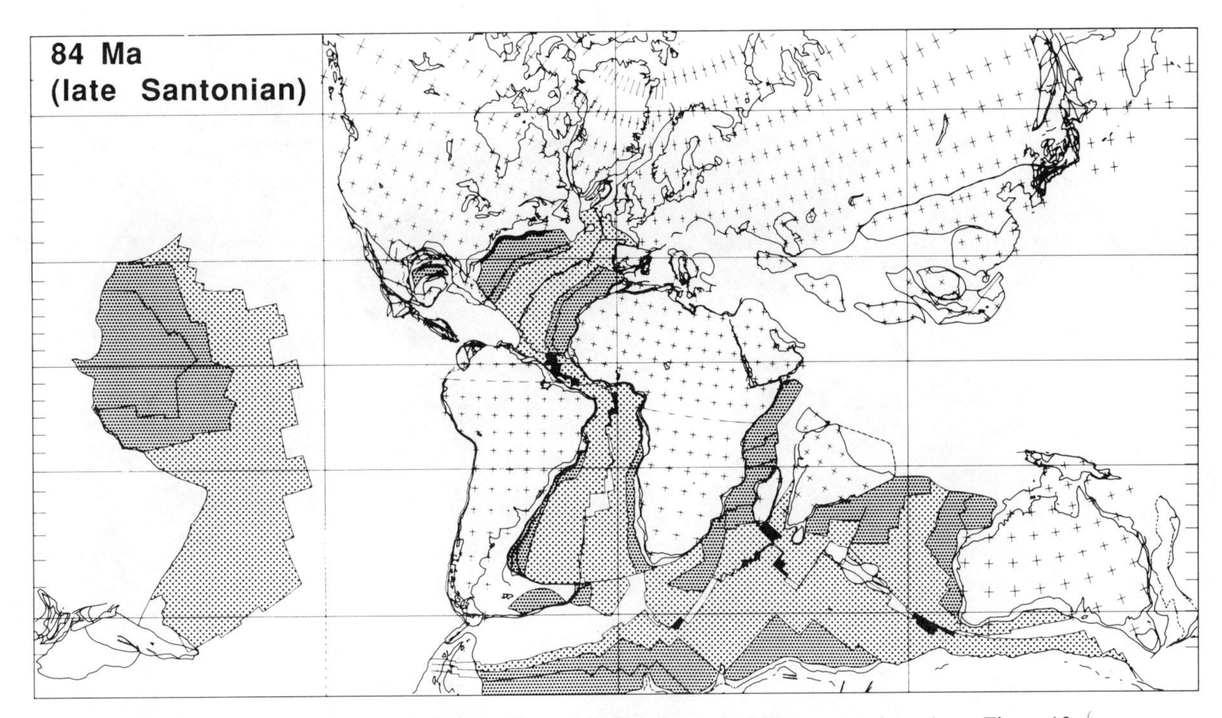

Figure 12. Reconstruction at 84 Ma (Chron 34 - late Santonian). For pattern legend, see Figure 10. (Published with permission of Elsevier.)

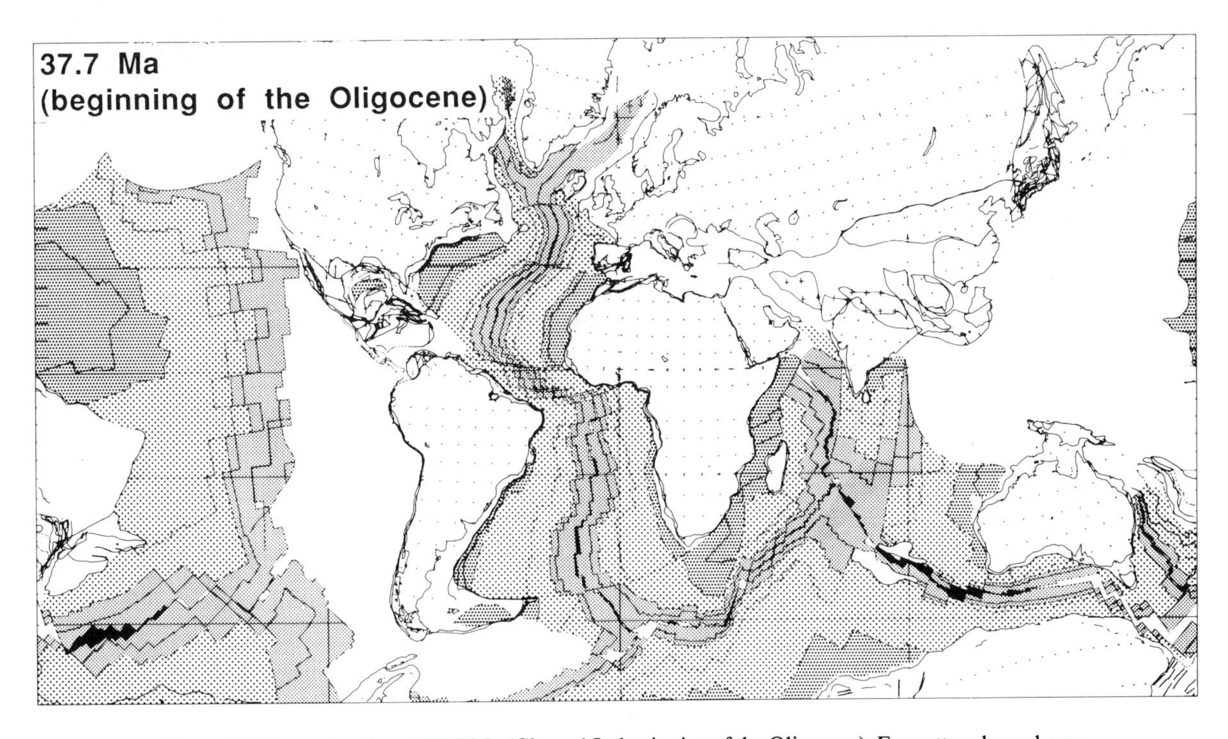

Figure 13. Reconstruction at 37.7 Ma (Chron 15 - beginning of the Oligocene). For pattern legend, see Figure 10. (Published with permission of Elsevier.)

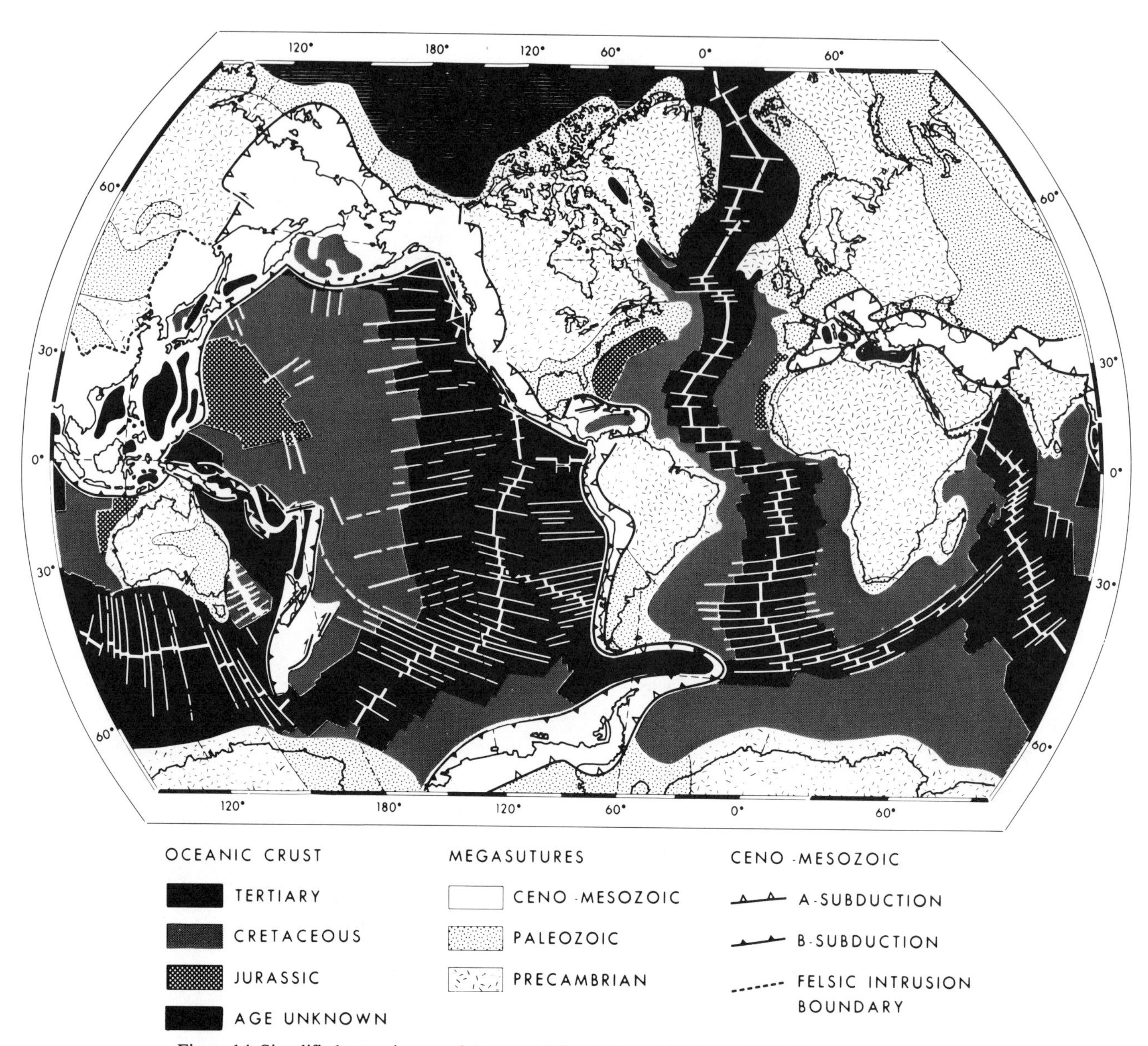

Figure 14. Simplified tectonic map of the world (after Bally and Snelson, 1980). For an explanation see text.

of the continental and transitional crust underlying the lower Paleozoic passive margins are also involved in the décollement process.

The inner portions (Internides) of the folded belts of North America are characterized by metamorphics, igneous (mostly felsic) and volcanic sequences, remnants of accretionary wedges, scarce ophiolites (the sutures of many authors), and fragments of suspect terranes that have been rafted over great distances and welded to North America by a complex docking process. These Internides often appear as complex convergent oblique-slip systems characterized by coeval strike-slip and overthrust tectonics (Oldow and others, this volume; Rast, this volume). In the Cordillera the strike component is responsible for the fragmentation and longitudinal redistribution of various terranes.

Superposed on the Mesozoic-Cenozoic Cordillera are the Tertiary extensional systems of the Basin and Range, and widespread Tertiary volcanics that extend from Central America, along the axis of the Mexican Cordillera (the Sierra Madre Occidental system), into the Basin and Range Province and southern British Columbia. Quaternary volcanoes of the Circum-Pacific ring of fire can be followed all the way from Central America into the Aleutian Island arc. Most of these volcanoes are linked to subduction of oceanic lithospheric slabs. This subduction is also accompanied by widespread Cenozoic-Mesozoic accretionary wedges and fore-arc basins, which form the west-vergent external zone of the Cordillera.

The Greater and Lesser Antilles and the Andean system of northwestern South America, together with the Caribbean Plate, are parts of a complex island-arc system. This system formed during the Paleogene-Recent convergence of North America and South America, which occurred within the context of the subduction of the Farallon and Cocos Plates of the Pacific (Winterer and others, this volume; Donnelly, this volume).

North America is surrounded by oceans (Vogt and Tucholke, this volume; Winterer and others, this volume). Of all the oceans surrounding North America, the Arctic Ocean is least known and understood (for brief discussions see Trettin, this volume; Oldow and others, this volume).

Along the Arctic and Atlantic continental shelves, and around the Gulf of Mexico, as well as offshore Honduras and Nicaragua, passive margins indicate the transition from continent to ocean. Typically these passive margins appear to be segmented by former transform zones (Sheridan, this volume). Passive margins also often display early rifting events occurring during different times (Sheridan, this volume; Bally, this volume; Ziegler, 1988), which are followed by a phase of enhanced subsidence. The Gulf of Mexico is a unique type of passive margin that no longer faces a presently spreading mid-ocean ridge (Worall and Snelson, this volume; de Cserna, this volume).

The west coast of North America is an active continental margin, which coincides with the western external zone of the Cordillera. That zone has been described either from an oceanographer's perspective (Engebretson and others, 1985; Winterer and others, this volume) or else from the perspective of structural geologists and geochemists (Oldow and others, this volume; de Cserna, this volume).

North America is best described in terms of plate-tectonic processes. The Mesozoic-Tertiary passive margins of North America serve as models for the interpretation of lower Paleozoic passive margins now involved in the deformation of the outer folded belts of the Paleozoic systems and of the Cordilleran system. In turn, the structural evolution of the Phanerozoic folded belts of North America may serve as a guide for the explanation of Precambrian evolution of North America.

Structural subdivisions of North America overlap to a large degree with the large-scale geomorphic regions of North America (Figs. 15 and 16). Of course the physiography of our continent is also the product of complex climatically controlled processes, and particularly of the Quaternary glaciation that covered large parts of the northern half of our continent (Wright, this volume). For studies of the geomorphology of North America the reader is referred to Thornbury (1965), Hunt (1974), and to Graf (1987).

TO SUM UP

North America is the product of a very long and ongoing geologic evolution that began early in the Archean. Plate-tectonic processes have dictated this evolution. The stratigraphic history of North America has been controlled by tectonic and climatic factors, and stratigraphy and climate, in turn, contribute to the wonderful diversity of tectonic and geomorphic styles we see today. We have inherited the product of more than 4 billion years of geologic history. Today mankind finds itself as a significant geologic agent, modifying the evolution not only of North America but of the Earth as a whole. A understanding of the evolution of our continent will put our own activities in a proper and responsible perspective.

Figure 15. Landform map diagram of North America by Irwin Raisz. Published with the permission of Kate Raisz.

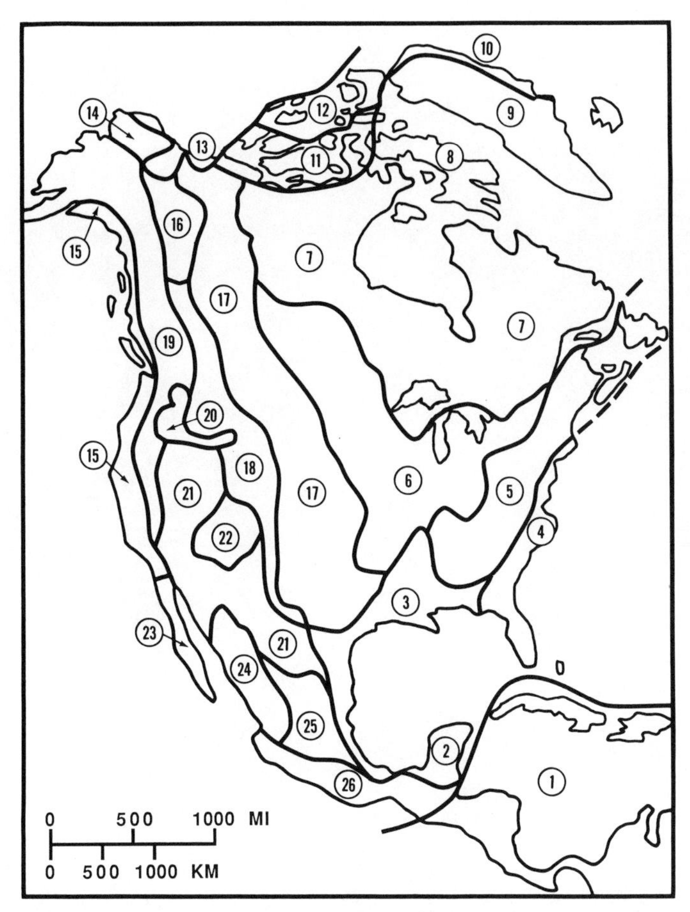

Figure 16. Generalized division of North America into geomorphic provinces, using same projection as Figure 15. 1, Central America and Caribbean (see Fig. 8); 2, Yucatan platform; 3, Gulf of Mexico Coastal Plain; 4, Atlantic Coastal Plain; 5, Appalachian Mountains and Plateaus; 6, Central Lowland; 7, Canadian Shield; 8, Baffin Island; 9, Greenland ice cap; 10, West and North Greenland Mountains and Fjords; 11, Arctic Lowland; 12, Innuitian Region; 13, Arctic Coastal Plain; 14, Brooks Range; 15, Pacific Rim and Pacific Coast Ranges; 16, Mackenzie Mountains; 17, Great Plains; 18, Rocky Mountains; 19, Interior Mountains and Plateaus; 20, Columbia Plateau; 21, Basin and Range; 22, Colorado Plateau; 23, Baja California; 24, Sierra Madre Occidental; 25, Sierra Madre Oriental; 26, Sierra Madre del Sur.

REFERENCES CITED

Balley, A. W., and Snelson, S., 1980, Realms of subsidence, *in* Miall, A. D., ed., Facts and principles of world petroleum occurrence: Canadian Society of Petroleum Geologists Memoir 6, p. 1–94.

Bond, G. C., Nickerson, P. A., and Kominz, M. A., 1984, Breakup of a supercontinent between 625 Ma and 555 Ma; New evidence and implications for continental histories: Earth and Planetary Science Letters, v. 70, no. 2, p. 325–345.

Engebretson, D. C., Cox, A., and Gordon, R. G., 1985, Relative motions between oceanic and continental plates in the Pacific Basin: Geological Society of America Special Paper 206, 59 p.

Graf, W. L., ed., 1987, Geomorphic systems of North America: Boulder, Colorado, Geological Society of America, Centennial Special Volume 2, 643 p.

Hinze, W. J., and Braile, L. W., 1988, Geophysical aspects of the craton, U.S., *in* Sloss, L. L., ed., Sedimentary cover—North American craton, U.S.: Boulder, Colorado, Geological Society of America, The Geology of North America, v. D-2, p. 5–24.

Hunt, C. B., 1974, Natural regions of the United States and Canada: San Francisco, California, W. H. Freeman, 725 p.

King, P. B., 1977, Geological evolution of North America: Princeton, New Jersey, Princeton University Press, 190 p.

Larson, R. L., and 6 others, 1985, The bedrock geology of the world: New York, W. H. Freeman, (map).

Lawver, L. A., and Scotese, C. R., 1989, A review of tectonic models for the evolution of the Canada Basin, *in* Grantz, A., Johnson, L., and Sweeney, J. F., eds., The Arctic Ocean region: Boulder, Colorado, Geological Society of America, The Geology of North America, v. L (in press).

Morel, P., and Irving, E. C., 1978, Tentative paleocontinental maps for the early Phanerozoic and Proterozoic: Journal of Geology, v. 86, no. 5, p. 535–561.

Needham, R. E., 1986a, Catalog of first-motion focal mechanisms 1981–1983: U.S. Geological Survey Open-File Report 86-285A, 250 p.

—— , 1986b, Catalog of first-motion focal mechanisms 1984–1985: U.S. Geological Survey Open-File Report 86-520, 723 p.

Pindell, J. L., and 6 others, 1988, A plate kinematic framework for models of Caribbean evolution: Tectonophysics, v. 155, p. 121–138.

Piper, J.D.A., 1983, Proterozoic paleomagnetism and single continent plate tectonics: Geophysical Journal of the Royal Astronomical Society, v. 74, no. 1, p. 163–197.

—— , 1987, Paleomagnetism and the continental crust: New York, J. Wiley and Sons, 434 p.

Ross, M. L., and Scotese, C. R., 1988, A hierarchical model of the Gulf of Mexico and Caribbean region: Tectonophysics, v. 155, p. 139–168.

Scotese, C. R., and Sager, W. W., eds., 1988, Mesozoic and Cenozoic plate reconstructions: Tectonophysics Special Issue, v. 155, 399 p.

Scotese, R. C., Gahagan, L., and Larson, R. L., 1988, Plate tectonic reconstructions of the Cretaceous and Cenozoic ocean basins: Tectonophysics, v. 155, p. 27–48.

Seeber, L., and Armbruster, J. G., 1988, Seismicity along the Atlantic seaboard of the U.S.; Intraplate tectonics and earthquake hazard, *in* Sheridan, R. E., and Grow, J. A., eds., The Atlantic continental margin, U.S.: Boulder, Colorado, Geological Society of America, The Geology of North America, v. I-2, p. 565–582.

Smith, A. G., Hurley, A. M., and Briden, J. C., 1981, Phanerozoic paleocontinental world maps: Cambridge University Press, 102 p.

Smith, R. B., and Lindh, A. G., 1978, Fault plane solutions of the western United States; A compilation, *in* Smith, R. B., and Eaton, G. P., eds., Cenozoic tectonics and regional geophysics of the western Cordillera: Geological Society of America Memoir 152, p. 107–110.

Thornbury, W. D., 1965, Regional geomorphology of the United States: New York, John Wiley and Sons, 609 p.

Ziegler, A. M., Scotese, C. R., McKerrow, W. S., Johnson, M. E., and Bambach, R. K., 1979, Paleozoic paleogeography: Annual Reviews of Earth and Planetary Sciences, v. 7, p. 473–502.

Ziegler, P. A., 1988, Evolution of the Arctic–North Atlantic and the western Tethys: American Association of Petroleum Geologists Memoir 43, 198 p.

Zoback, M. L., Nishenko, S. P., Richardson, R. M., Hasegawa, H. S., and Zoback, M. D., 1986, Mid-plate stress, deformation, and seismicity, *in* Vogt, P. R., and Tucholke, B. E., eds., The western North Atlantic region: Boulder, Colorado, Geological Society of America, The Geology of North America, v. M, p. 297–312.

MANUSCRIPT ACCEPTED BY THE SOCIETY FEBRUARY 1, 1989

ACKNOWLEDGMENTS

The authors thank Susan K. Goter for providing the seismic maps (Figs. 2 and 3) of this chapter. We also thank Ms. Chingju Liu for preparation of the frontispiece, and helping to edit all the other figures of this chapter. Terra Mobilis, a plate-tectonics program for the Macintosh computer, was used to create Figures 3 and 6 through 9.

Printed in U.S.A.

The Geology of North America
Vol. A, The Geology of North America—An overview
The Geological Society of America, 1989

Chapter 2

The Gravity Anomaly Map of North America

W. F. Hanna
U.S. Geological Survey, 927 National Center, Reston, Virginia 22092
R. E. Sweeney and T. G. Hildenbrand
U.S. Geological Survey, Box 25046, Denver Federal Center, Denver, Colorado 80225
J. G. Tanner and R. K. McConnell
Geological Survey of Canada, Ottawa, Ontario K1A 0Y3, Canada
R. H. Godson
U.S. Geological Survey, Box 25046, Denver Federal Center, Denver, Colorado 80225

INTRODUCTION

The recently developed Gravity Anomaly Map of North America is the product of a 12-year multinational effort to compile, critically edit, and merge gravity anomaly data on a continental and global scale (Gravity Anomaly Map Committee, 1987). This color-pixel map is printed on four quadrant sheets at a scale of 1:5,000,000 and includes a fifth sheet showing a color index map and data references. This map is the first at such a global scale to include several hundreds of thousands of precise bits of surface data of Canada, the United States, Mexico, and Central America, as well as other high-quality surface data from neighboring continental and oceanic areas. A 1:20,000,000 version of the map is shown on Plate 1A.

The prospect of producing a gravity anomaly map of North America was formally advanced in 1975 by way of a cooperative agreement between the U.S. Geological Survey and the Society of Exploration Geophysicists. Before these cooperators linked to specialists of Canada, Mexico, and other countries, they agreed that an updated version of the gravity anomaly map of the United States should first be developed. In 1983, following publication of the U.S. map, the Society of Exploration Geophysicists and the U.S. Geological Survey concluded that the planned Centennial Map Series of the Decade of North American Geology program would be an excellent medium for publication of the gravity anomaly map of North America as well as the magnetic anomaly map of North America. The cooperating groups subsequently coordinated with the Geological Society of America, and the map was published in 1988.

The anomaly map has a sufficiently small scale and wide enough areal coverage to be useful for correlation with known global tectonic features or identification of new ones. The map has enough detail to be useful for making correlations or new interpretations about smaller lithologic terranes and their structures. However, for such detailed analyses, the user is cautioned that the quality of the data represented is commensurate with the 1:5,000,000 scale of the map, and therefore, the map should not be correlated with features shown on any more detailed, larger scale map. For more detailed analysis at the 1:5,000,000 scale, it is sometimes useful to derive new products by computer from the available data set. For example, isostatic residual maps (Simpson and others, 1986; Goodacre and others, 1987b) or wavelength-filtered maps (Hildenbrand and others, 1982; Kane and Godson, 1985) greatly reduce the broad background effect of isostatic compensation of topographic loads. First-vertical derivative and horizontal gradient maps (Baranov, 1975; Nettleton, 1976; Hildenbrand, 1983; Thomas and others, 1987; Goodacre and others, 1987c) tend, respectively, to sharpen anomalies above abrupt density contrasts and to delineate steeply dipping lateral interfaces.

INSTRUMENTATION AND ANOMALY SIGNIFICANCE

On land, gravity measurements in North America were made as early as the 1920s in the United States (Eckhardt, 1940) and soon afterward in Canada (Miller, 1940), by using the gradient-sensing torsion balance developed by Baron Roland von Eötvös in Hungary during the 1880s. During these early years, the torsion balance survey of a subsurface domal structure in Texas led to the discovery of oil in 1926; this oil pool was probably the first to be discovered by geophysical methods in North America. The pioneering torsion balance was soon replaced by pendulums and prototype gravimeters as gravity prospecting tools (Nettleton, 1976; Dobrin, 1960) until the 1950s, when gravimeters based on the zero-length spring (LaCoste, 1934, 1988) began to replace most other instruments. At sea,

Hanna, W. F., Sweeney, R. E., Hildenbrand, T. G., Tanner, J. G., McConnell, R. K., and Godson, R. H., 1989, The gravity anomaly map of North America, *in* Bally, A. W., and Palmer, A. R., eds., The Geology of North America—An overview: Boulder, Colorado, Geological Society of America, The Geology of North America, v. A.

early pendulums used in submarines (Vening Meinesz, 1941; Heiskanen and Vening Meinesz, 1958) and surface ships (Worzel and Harrison, 1965) were also replaced by prototype static and dynamic gravimeters (Pick and others, 1973; Talwani, 1970). These gravimeters also have a modern zero-length-spring equivalent that has been used for measurements on the sea floor from surface ships (LaCoste 1967) and from the air (Hammer, 1983; Brozena, 1984). Newer surveying technologies using gravity gradiometry (Jekeli, 1988; Jordan, 1978) and a combination of inertial navigation and laser tracking ranging (Soltz and Hursh, 1985; Brown and others, 1987) are being developed for airborne and other mobile applications. However, it is notable that the venerable zero-length-spring gravimeter is the instrument used in many widely publicized geophysical tests of Newton's Gravitational Law (Stacey and others, 1987; Schwarzschild, 1988).

Over the deep oceans, the relatively new satellite altimeter has been used to map the geoid directly and has provided precise information on gravity anomalies, especially within a wavelength interval of about 100 to 2,000 km (Marsh and others, 1985; Rapp, 1981, 1984, 1986; Bowin, 1983; Haxby, 1987). First used on the National Aeronautical and Space Administrations *Skylab* satellite, the altimeter was subsequently used on the Geodynamics Experimental Ocean Satellite 3 (GEOS-3) and more recently on the SEASAT (Balmino and others, 1987) and GEOSAT (McAdoo, 1988) satellites. Free-air gravity anomalies are computed from geoidal heights derived from these altimeter measurements, which have been corrected for winds, currents, and tides affecting the ocean surface.

Although direct measurements of gravity include the effects of both gravitation and earth rotation, the computed gravity anomalies shown on the map are caused only by gravitational effects of earth masses. Whereas the gravity method, unlike electrical and seismic methods, cannot sense vertical variations of earth properties in the form of layering, it can sense lateral variations of properties from which vertical variations often can be predicted. The gravity method can sense properties throughout the deep crust and entire mantle, because unlike the magnetic method, it is not depth-restricted by the equivalent of a Curie isotherm. Thus, gravity anomalies shown on the map are caused by lateral contrasts of rock or fluid density throughout the entire range of depths beneath the Earth's surface. Bouguer gravity anomalies on land are caused not only by density contrasts underlying the sea-level geoid but also by masses above the geoid, including those within the topography that differ from the reduction density of 2.67 g/cm^3. Free-air gravity anomalies over the oceans are caused not only by density contrasts beneath the sea floor, but also by the bathymetric surface of density contrast between sea floor and seawater. Although Bouguer gravity anomalies over the oceans correct free-air gravity anomalies for the gravity defect caused by the water layer, and thus reflect the effect of sub-bottom structure more directly (Talwani, 1970), free-air gravity anomalies are shown because of the lack of precise bathymetric data and because free-air gravity anomalies were derived from satellite altimetry data.

EXAMPLES OF FREE-AIR GRAVITY ANOMALIES

The free-air anomaly part of the North American Gravity Anomaly Map displays global tectonic features in a spectacular way (Fig. 1; Plate 1A). Anomalies are associated in many places with active and passive continental margins, subduction zones, spreading ridges, sutures, lithospheric flexuring, transformly faulted fracture zones, and seamounts. Some of the more prominent features are discussed below, in an order starting from the northwest quadrant of the map, and proceeding clockwise; numbers within brackets refer to locations in Figure 1.

The Aleutian island arc–trench system vividly illustrates the negative-positive paired anomalies (1) associated with a subduction zone, as well as the broad high located seaward from the arc. The negative-positive paired features correlate approximately with the topographic features of the trench and island arc, respectively. However, these anomalies associated with subduction zones are complicated by the effects of the high density of the cold descending slab, the low density of sediments and the hot region beneath a marginal basin, and the lateral density variations of the crust (Worzel, 1976; Grow, 1973; Toksoz and others, 1973). Immediately north of the Aleutian arc, the tightly curved anomaly pair associated with the submerged Bowers ridge (2) (Kienle, 1971) is considered to be a relict subduction zone. Farther north and east in the Bering Sea, a sinuous anomaly pair is associated with deeply incised submerged canyons (3) (Childs and others, 1985). The anomaly pair has been attributed to sediment-filled depressions formed by down-faulted basement blocks (Scholl and others, 1968, 1970) but also probably marks the location of an ancient subduction zone (Ben-Avraham and others, 1981).

Seaward of the Aleutian arc, the broad region of positive anomalies (4) can be explained by regional topography and a flexuring of the oceanic lithosphere (Watts and Talwani, 1974; Watts and others, 1976; Walcott, 1970). This region of highs and similar regions beneath most plate-convergent zones worldwide were interpreted by Bowin (1985) to be associated with mass excesses that localize the driving forces at these boundaries. As noted by Cook (1970), appreciable variations of upper-mantle densities on a worldwide scale are not related to the distribution of oceans and continents but rather are related to heat flow through the Earth's surface.

Northeast of the Bering Sea in the Canada Basin, a narrow, nearly continuous positive anomaly (5) extends from the north slope of Alaska (Barnes, 1969) across the northern slope of the Canadian Arctic Archipelago (Sobczak, 1975) to the northwest slope of Greenland (Ostenso, 1962, 1968; Vogt and Ostenso, 1970). This positive feature appears to be characteristic of most passive continental margins worldwide. Over some regions, this positive anomaly is paired with a subparallel negative anomaly, although not as conspicuously as anomaly pairs along subducting active continental margins. The positive anomaly lies along the western extremity of the Atlantic Ocean, along the borders of Greenland, eastern Canada, and the eastern United States, and

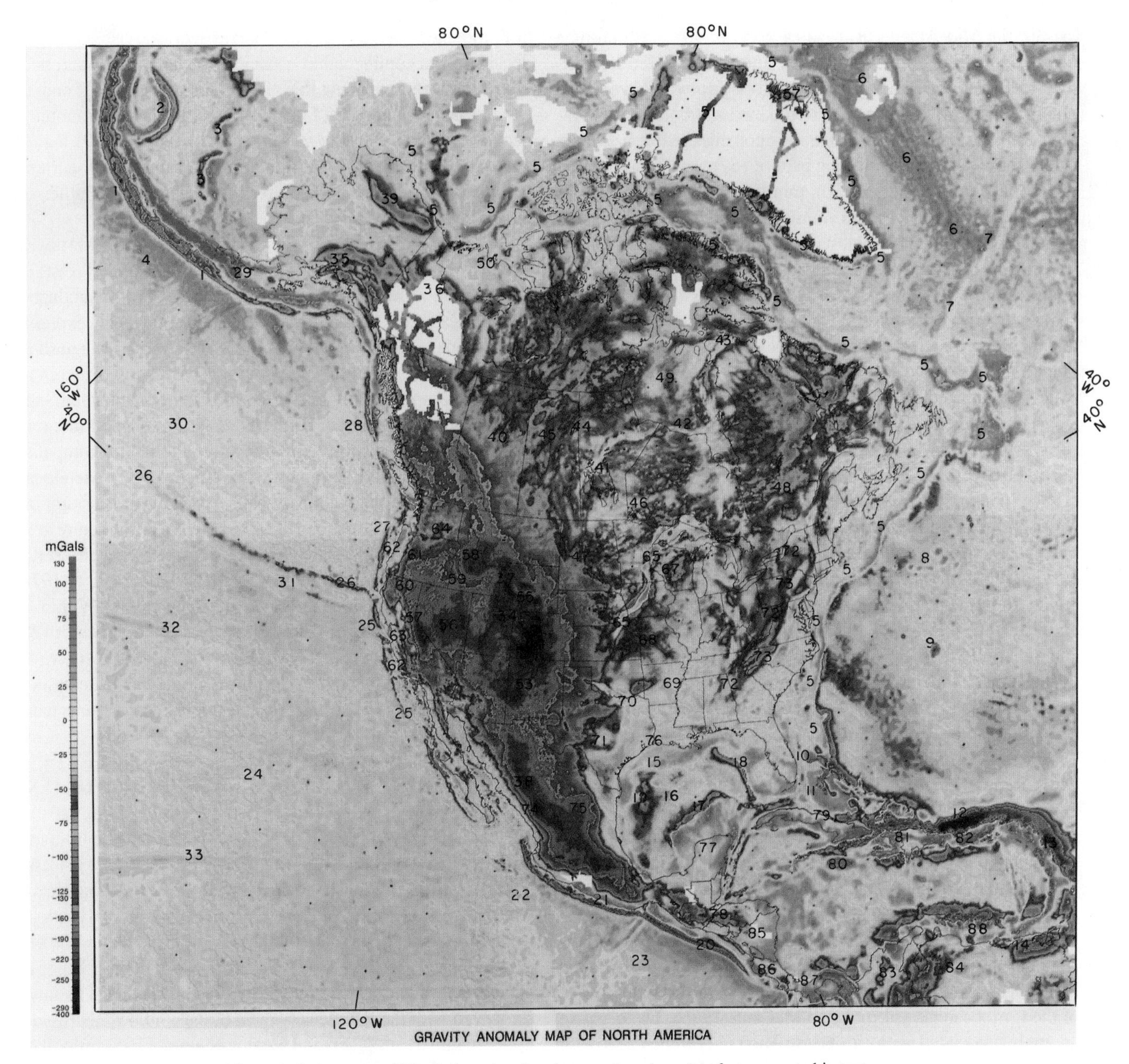

Figure 1. Index map of North America showing numbers keyed to features noted in text.

joins the conspicuous anomaly pair of the Lesser Antilles arc system. Sobczak (1975) interpreted the high in the Arctic region to be caused by thick, prograding wedges of sediments that have displaced seawater and that act as a load on the crust. Offshore eastern United States, the high lies along the edge of the continental shelf and Blake Plateau, and a parallel low traces the base of the continental slope (Grow and others, 1979). Although strongly influenced by continental slope topography and the abrupt change in crustal thickness across the margin, these maximums and minimums are interrupted by transverse basins and platforms related to differential subsidence of crustal blocks. These anomalies bordering passive continental margins need further study because they have been interpreted as caused by a buried ridge in the basement (Worzel and Shurbet, 1955), a transition zone between isostatically compensated continental and oceanic crust (Worzel, 1968), changes in mantle densities (Keen and Loncarevic, 1966; Scrutton, 1979), changes in crustal densities (Emery and others, 1975), intrabasement crustal density highs (Rabinowitz, 1974; Talwani and Eldholm, 1972), variations in sedimentary rock densities (Grow and others, 1979), flexuring at the continental edge (Walcott, 1972; Turcotte and others, 1977; Karner and Watts, 1982), and an uncompensated elevation of thickened oceanic crust adjacent to the continent (Rabinowitz and LaBrecque, 1977, 1979).

In the Mid-Atlantic Ridge area *north* of 40° north latitude on the anomaly map, free-air gravity anomalies tend to be positive, and they correlate with bottom topography (Talwani and others, 1965) and with sediment-burdened sub-bottom topography (Rabinowitz, 1974). Because the anomalies reflect bathymetry by showing a coarse striping pattern (6) parallel to the ridge axis (Collette and others, 1980), transcurrent structures such as oblique basement ridges and transformly faulted fracture zones are sharply displayed. The most conspicuous of these transcurrent features on this part of the anomaly map is the Charlie Gibbs fracture zone (7). Whereas parts of the gravity effects of fracture zones appear to be associated with topographic relief, some parts may be caused by dense ultramafic rock at shallow depth (Cochran, 1973; Robb and Kane, 1975) and by variations in density structure predicted by the thermal evolution of lithospheric plates (Sibuet and others, 1974; Sibuet and Mascle, 1978).

In the North Atlantic Ocean *south* of 40° north latitude on the anomaly map, as summarized by Rabinowitz and Jung (1986), free-air gravity anomalies tend to be negative (Kaula, 1966; Talwani and LePichon, 1969), and the long-wavelength anomalies correlate with deep-water topography (McKenzie and Bowin, 1976). Because many short-wavelength anomalies in this region do not appear to correlate with surface features (Cochran and Talwani, 1977) or with residual depth anomalies (Sclater and others, 1975), they may be caused by lateral inhomogeneities in the upper mantle. Against the background of this region of negative anomalies, local positive anomalies are associated with seamounts and guyots (8) (Uchupi and others, 1970; Walcott, 1976), the Bermuda Rise and island of Bermuda (9) (Haxby and Turcotte, 1978), the Blake-Bahama outer ridge (10) (Ewing and Ewing, 1964), and the shallow banks of the Bahamas (11) (Heezen and others, 1959), most of which correlate with some combination of topographic rises of basement, increases of uncompensated sediment thickness, and density variations near the base of the oceanic lithosphere.

Farther south, gravity anomalies similar to those of the Aleutian arc clearly mark the suture along which the Atlantic lithosphere passes beneath the leading edge of the crystalline crust of the Caribbean (Westbrook and McCann, 1986). The negative anomaly associated with the Puerto Rico (12) trench and with the seaward bulge in the oceanic lithosphere (Bunce and others, 1974; Watts and Talwani, 1974; Parsons and Molnar, 1976) does not follow the trench as it continues southward, but follows the lesser Antilles arc (13) from where the anomaly continues into eastern Venezuela (14) (Westbrook, 1982). The gravity anomalies and lithospheric bulge off Puerto Rico can be accounted for by the subduction of dense lithosphere (Molnar, 1977; Minear and Toksoz, 1970). The belts of anomalies along the Puerto Rico Trench are inferred to result from compression across a zone of transform faulting (Bowin, 1976).

Northwest of the Caribbean plate boundary in the Gulf of Mexico region, conspicuous positive and negative anomaly pairs occur over the steepest edges of the continental shelf. By using densities derived from seismic data, Dehlinger and Jones (1965) have modeled these features as changes in crustal thicknesses and densities from continental to oceanic crust, particularly across the Gulf Coast geosyncline (15), the Sigsbee Deep (16), and the Campeche (17) and West Florida (18) escarpments. Pronounced negative anomalies in the western part of the gulf (19) may be associated with massive accumulations of salt and salt-enriched sediments formed during a complex tectonic history (Buffler and others, 1980; Walper, 1980).

At the western edge of the Caribbean plate, the northwest-striking Middle America (20) and Mexico (21) underthrusts are expressed by an anomaly pair similar to those of other subduction zones. Because the East Pacific Rise (22) is not strongly expressed gravitationally, the anomaly map does not clearly distinguish the Cocos plate (23) from the areally expansive Pacific plate (24) to the east and north. Along the western border of the United States and Canada, the active or formerly active continental margin is marked most conspicuously by a negative anomaly accompanied by a broken positive anomaly (25). South of the Mendocino fracture zone (26), the anomaly pair may mark the position of a former subduction zone. North of the Mendocino fracture zone, the anomaly pair is associated with the active Cascade thrust (27) and the Queen Charlotte fault system (28) (Riddihough, 1979), where the fault system connects to the Aleutian arc. Within the Pacific Ocean, several fracture zones such as the Surveyor (29), Mendocino (30), Pioneer (31), Murray (32), and Clarion (33) fracture zones are manifested by linear, somewhat discontinous lows. Some uncharted guyots and seamouts can be detected as small circular highs (Lazarewicz and Schwank, 1982).

EXAMPLES OF BOUGUER GRAVITY ANOMALIES

The Bouguer anomaly part of the North American map is dominated by the large-amplitude negative feature (34) associated with the elevated terrain of the Cordilleran orogenic system of western North America. This negative anomaly extends from the Alaska Range (35) southeastward through the Mackenzie Mountains (36) of Canada, the Rocky Mountains (37) of the United States, and the Sierra Madre (38) of Mexico. The low is associated with the low-density mass of the continental crust and upper mantle (Heiskanen and Vening Meinesz, 1958; Woollard, 1968; Hamilton, 1978), which isostatically compensates regionally for overlying topographic loads. In the region covered by this broad low, perhaps more than any other region of the North American map, it is useful to derive an isostatic residual map or a wavelength-filtered map that more sharply delineates masses in the shallow crust.

The principal Bouguer gravity anomaly within onshore Alaska is an elliptical low associated with the Brooks Range (39), where Barnes (1977), using the technique of Woollard and Strange (1962), estimated the crustal thickness to be about 40 km. Other anomalies represent the integrated effects of local lows over poorly defined basins and of local highs over marine volcanic rocks and gabbroic intrusions.

Bouguer gravity anomalies in Canada indicate that crustal

thickness ranges from about 10 km beneath oceanic areas to 45 km beneath continental areas (Goodacre and others, 1987a). Although most topographic features are judged to be in isostatic equilibrium (Garland, 1971), the crust of the Cordillera system in Canada is inferred to be only about 30 km thick; its negative anomaly is due primarily to relatively low-density material in the upper mantle (Goodacre, 1972). Isostasy is evidenced in central Alberta (40), where raised valley rims occur over plains where active erosion is taking place (Scheidegger, 1976).

One of the most prominent regional features unrelated to topography is the curved belt of nearly continuous positive anomalies that trends northeasterly from Lake Winnipeg (41) along the southern and eastern borders of Hudson Bay (42) to northern Quebec (43) (Gibb and Thomas, 1976; Thomas, 1985). This anomaly belt marks part of the Trans-Hudson orogenic belt (44) of the Churchill craton (45), where the belt abuts against the generally older, thinner, and less-dense Superior craton (46) (Gibb and others, 1983). This boundary can be traced south (Thomas and others, 1987), using images of horizontal gradient, at least as far as North and South Dakota (47) (Dutch, 1983; Green and others, 1985; Klasner and King, 1986). Less prominent than this anomalous zone, part of the geologically important Grenville front is characterized by a belt of negative anomalies (48) (Innes and Gibb, 1970), some steep gradients of which are attributable to intrusions of anorthosite and gabbro. The mass deficiency beneath Hudson Bay (49), best seen as a negative anomaly on a free-air gravity anomaly map (Goodacre and others, 1987b), is interpreted as incomplete isostatic crustal rebound following recent glaciation (Innes and others, 1967, 1968).

Other anomalies in Canada represent the superposition of local highs associated with mapped or hidden norites, metavolcanics, granulites, and dolomitic sedimentary rocks, as well as the superposition of lows associated with glacial ice, clastic sedimentary rocks and sediments, and alkali granites, some of which are closely related to metallic mineral deposits (Innes and Gibb, 1970; Telford and others, 1976; Grant and West, 1965; Gupta and Grant, 1985). The largest single anomaly discovered in Canada is a circular high at Danley Bay (50), interpreted to be caused by a radially symmetric mafic or ultramafic body (Stacey, 1971; Hornal and others, 1970).

The neighboring continental mass of Greenland, for which relatively few gravity anomaly data have been obtained (Forsberg, 1986), is characterized by large-amplitude negative anomalies over its interior. The minimums are greatest over the Inland Ice (51) at the center of the Caledonian fold belt (52), and are consistent with a partially compensated increase in crustal thickness. A few local highs are associated with ultramafic rocks.

Some of the most prominent Bouguer gravity anomalies of the conterminous United States (Society of Exploration Geophysicists, 1982; Kerr, 1982) have been outlined by Arvidson and others (1982) and have been further discussed by O'Hara and Lyons (1983, 1985). Among these anomalies, as previously noted, the extensive negative anomaly associated with much of the western Cordillera and with connecting and adjacent terranes is by far the most conspicuous. This region of negative anomaly is influenced by many isostatic compensation mechanisms, such as crustal roots subtended into the mantle, lithosphere descending into lower mantle, regional flexure of the lithospheric plate, and lateral density contrasts within the crust and subjacent convecting mantle (Hayford and Bowie, 1912; Jeffreys, 1959; McKenzie, 1967a, 1967b; Woollard, 1968; Walcott, 1970; Kerr, 1986, 1988a, 1988b).

This vast region of negative anomalies in the western United States is associated in part with the Rio Grande rift and San Juan volcanic area (53) (Cordell and Keller, 1984), the uplifted basement terrane of Colorado (54) (Behrendt and Bajwa, 1974), the granitic and sedimentary rocks of the Laramie Range and Big Horn Mountains and neighboring basins (55), the thermally anomalous Great Basin region (56) (Eaton and others, 1978; Cook and others, 1975; Thompson and Burke, 1974; Smith and others, 1976; Sumner, 1985), and the Sierra Nevada batholith (57) (Oliver, 1977). The circular low associated with the Idaho batholith (58) is framed on its southern margin by an arcuate high associated with a broad downwarp of the Snake River Plain (59), which is filled by lava flows (Mabey, 1976). Some lows over parts of the Klamath Mountains (60) (Griscom, 1980; Blank, 1966) and Cascade Mountains (61) (LeFehr, 1965; Couch and others, 1982; Williams and Finn, 1985) are associated with serpentinized ultramafic rocks, low-density volcanic and sedimentary rocks, and concealed batholiths. Against the negative background of these regions, positive anomalies are associated with ophiolitic masses of the Coast Ranges (62) (Dehlinger and others, 1968; Bromery and Snavely, 1964; Thompson and Talwani, 1964; Riddihough, 1979) and the Great Valley of California (63) (Cady, 1975) and with basalts of the Columbia Plateau (64) (Blank, 1966; Riddihough and others, 1986). The relation between Bouguer gravity anomaly and topography in these regions bears directly on the amount of isostatic effect (McNutt, 1983). For example, the high over the Columbia Plateau is related not only to the high density of basalt but also to the low elevation of this region.

In the central United States the single most prominent anomaly is the midcontinent high (65) (Coons and others, 1967; King and Zietz, 1971), which extends from Kansas to Lake Superior and reflects dense basaltic rock in the Midcontinent rift system (Van Schmus and Hinze, 1985). This high, which is flanked by lows associated with down-faulted sedimentary rocks, turns eastward at its northern extremity. This geometry suggests that source rocks once were continuous with similar deeply buried mafic rocks associated with the mid-Michigan high (66) (Hinze and others, 1975, 1981; Klasner and others, 1985; Wold and Hinze, 1982). Centered in the inverted U-shape feature formed by the midcontinent and mid-Michigan highs is an oval low associated with less dense igneous rocks of the Wolf River batholith within the Wisconsin arch (67). Gravity anomalies constituting the Missouri gravity low (68) (Arvidson and others, 1982) and those associated with the Mississippi embayment (69) (Hildenbrand and others, 1977), although visible, are less conspicuous than the Y-shaped high (70) marking the convergence of the Ouachita and Wichita-Arbuckle orogenic belts (Keller and Cebull, 1973). This wishbone high, associated with uplifted granite and gabbro and with a graywacke-filled aulacogen, is flanked on the northeast by a low, which lies immediately south of the Ouachita Mountains where postorogenic deposits fill a deep depression. A short distance southwest of the high, one of many uplifts of Precambrian basement in the central United States is expressed by a circular high (71) over the Llano uplift in Texas.

In the eastern United States, the single most salient anomaly is an elongate low (72) that follows much of the west flank of the Appalachian Mountains. Immediately southeast of this large-amplitude low is a parallel, lower amplitude high (73) that follows much of the more elevated terrain of the Appalachian system. In the southern Appalachians the anomaly pair has been interpreted by Hutchison and others (1983) as a negative feature caused by a crustal root zone coupled with a positive feature caused possibly by a mantle upwarp or a shallow body, but probably by a suture zone. The anomaly pair has been modeled on a regional scale by Karner and Watts (1983) as a flexure of the continental lithosphere that is attributable more to subsurface loads in the forms of obducted blocks and flakes associated with continental convergence, collision, and suturing than to surface loads in the forms of fold and thrust belts. Throughout the Appalachian system, superposed effects of local highs are associated with some exposed ophiolitic rocks (Haworth and others, 1980), mafic intrusive rocks (Griscom, 1963), and carbonate sedimentary sequences (Joyner, 1963), whereas similar integrated effects of local lows correlate with some granitic plutons and basins filled with clastic sediments (Bothner and others, 1980; Diment, 1968; Kane and Bromery, 1968; Simmons, 1964).

In Mexico, the most negative parts of the Cordilleran low occur over the Sierra Madre Occidental (74) and the bordering faulted basins and mesas to the east and south (Woollard and others, 1969 a and b; Aiken and others, 1981). Much of these dissected plateaus is covered by a thick pile of lavas, which are intruded by felsic plutonic rocks along the western margin of the volcanic field. Less negative parts of the low occur over the Sierra Madre Oriental (75), much of which is underlain by thick carbonate-rich sedimentary rocks (Coney and Campa, 1984). The Gulf Coastal Plain (76) and the Yucatan Platform (77) are characterized by highs similar to those that rim the Gulf of Mexico and may result from changes in lithospheric thickness and density associated with sea-floor spreading in the Gulf. Some local gravity features have been related to mineralization (Bankey and others, 1982). Geological studies (Ruiz and others, 1988) have raised questions regarding the relation of Precambrian rocks to rocks of similar age of the Cordilleran and Appalachian systems. Future studies of gravity anomalies should contribute to deciphering these relations and those related to possible suspect terranes (Coney and others, 1980).

In Central America, the Cordilleran low becomes narrow and ends just south of the boundary (78) between Guatamala and Honduras. The Cordilleran orogenic system has been inferred to swing eastward here beneath the Caribbean plate (King, 1977) of the Greater Antilles, including the West Indian islands of Cuba (79), Jamaica (80), Hispaniola (81), and Puerto Rico (82), and emerge again in the Andean system of Colombia (83) and Venezuela (84). However, the merging of transcurrent faults, subduction thrusts forming double arcs, and transgressive zones within the mosaic of fragmented terranes in the Caribbean region (Case and Holcome, 1980; Case and others, 1984; Kellogg, 1984; Bonini and others, 1984) generates composite gravity anomalies (Bowin, 1976, 1980; Case and MacDonald, 1973) that obscure an interconnection of the Cordilleran system. The more positive gravity anomalies of Nicaragua (85), Costa Rica (86), and Panama (87) appear to be associated with arc volcanism of Pacific plate subduction on the trailing edge of the Caribbean plate, in contrast to those of the magmatic arc of the Lesser Antilles (88), which are near the leading edge of the plate. Many alternative interpretations of the plate tectonic history of the Caribbean region have been summarized by Pindell and Barrett (1988). Their summary demonstrates that, even in light of available geological and geophysical data, many complexities of this region remain to be addressed in the context of gravity and other geophysical data.

In summary, these few examples of free-air and Bouguer gravity anomalies on the North American map are among hundreds which have been or which can be interpreted in terms of subsurface lithology and structure (see, for example, bibliographies of Zwart [1986] and Keller [1988] and references in Hinze [1985]). The value of gravity-anomaly analysis as an interpretative tool increases dramatically when used jointly with magnetic, seismic, electrical, heat-flow, and physical properties data. These integrated geophysical data need to be calibrated in light of geologic mapping and drillhole information, where available. The resulting subsurface picture of lithology and structure may then be placed in a tectonic framework related to geologic hazards or to economic mineral potential (Hutchison, 1983; Guild and others, 1985; Kutina and Hildenbrand, 1987; Rowland and others, 1983). Finally, the anomaly map should prove useful as a correlation tool for planned satellite missions of the National Aeronautical and Space Administration (Geopotential Research Mission Science Steering Group, 1985; Paik and others, 1988), which will be dedicated to acquisition of gravity and magnetic data on a worldwide basis.

REFERENCES CITED

Aiken, C.L.V., Garvey, D. L., Keller, G. R., Goodell, P. C., and Fuente Duch, M. de la, 1981, A regional geophysical study of the Chihuahua City area, Mexico, *in* Goodell, P. C., and Waters, A. C., eds., Uranium in volcanic and volcaniclastic rocks: American Association of Petroleum Geologists Studies in Geology 13, p. 311–328.

Arvidson, R. E., Guinness, E. A., Strebeck, J. W., Davies, G. F., and Schulz, K. J., 1982, Image processing applied to gravity and topography data covering the continental U.S.: EOS American Geophysical Union Transactions, v. 63, no. 18, p. 261–265.

Balmino, G., Moynot, B., Sarrailh, M., and Vales, N., 1987, Free-air gravity anomalies over the oceans from SEASAT and GEOS 3 altimeter data: EOS (American Geophysical Union Transactions), v. 68, p. 17–19.

Bankey, V. L., Fuente Duch, M. F. de la, and Kleinkopf, M. D., 1982, Principal facts for gravity stations near Alcaparroso, Sonora, Mexico: U.S. Geological Survey Open-File Report 82–890, 6 p.

Baranov, W., 1975, Potential fields and their transformations in applied geophysics: Berlin, Gebruder Borntraeger, Geoexploration Monographs, ser. 1, no. 6, 121 p.

Barnes, D. F., 1969, Lack of isostatic adjustment on two Alaskan continental margins: Geological Society of America Abstracts with Programs, v. 1, p. 254–256.

—— , 1977, Bouguer gravity map of Alaska: U.S. Geological Survey Geophysical Investigations Map GP–913, scale 1:2,500,000.

Behrendt, J. C., and Bajwa, L. Y., compilers, 1974, Bouguer gravity map of Colorado: U.S. Geological Survey, prepared in cooperation with the Colorado Mining Industrial Development Board and the Colorado Geological Survey, scale 1:500,000.

Ben-Avraham, Z., Nur, A. M., Jones, D. L., and Cox, A. V., 1981, Continental accretion—From oceanic plateaus to allochthonous terranes: Science, v. 213, no. 4503, p. 47–54.

Blank, H. R., 1966, Geological features of the Bouguer field in southwestern Oregon: U.S. Geological Survey Professional Paper 550, p. C113–C119.

Bonini, W. E., Hargraves, R. B., and Shagam, R., editors, 1984, The Caribbean–South American plate boundary and regional tectonics: Geological Society of America Memoir 162, 421 p.

Bothner, W. A., Simpson, R. W., and Diment, W. H., compilers, 1980, Bouguer anomaly map of the northeastern United States and adjacent Canada: U.S. Geological Survey Open-File Report 80–2012, scale 1:1,000,000.

Bowin, C. O., 1976, Caribbean gravity field and plate tectonics: Geological Society of America Special Paper 169, 79 p.

—— , 1980, Gravity and geoid anomalies of the Caribbean: Transactions of the 9th Caribbean Geological Conference 1980, Santo Domingo, Dominican Republic, v. 2, p. 527–538.

—— , 1983, Depth of principal mass anomalies contributing to the Earth's geoidal undulations and gravity anomalies, *in* Saxena, N. K., ed., Marine geodesy—an international journal of ocean surveys, mapping and sensing: New York, Crane, Russak & Co., v. 7, no. 1–4, p. 61–100.

—— , 1985, Global gravity maps and the structure of the Earth, *in* Hinze, W. J., ed., The utility of regional gravity and magnetic anomaly maps: Society of Exploration Geophysicists, p. 88–101.

Bowin, C. O., Warsi, W., and Milligan, J., 1983, Free-air gravity anomaly [map] of the world: Geological Society of America Map Chart Series MC–45 [now referenced as MCH045], scale approximately 1:22,000,000, two sheets.

Bromery, R. W., and Snavely, P. D., 1964, Geologic interpretation of reconnaissance gravity and aeromagnetic surveys in northwestern Oregon: U.S. Geological Survey Bulletin 1181–N, p. N1–N13.

Brown, R. H., Chapman, W. H., Hanna, W. F., Mongan, C. E., and Hursh, J. W., 1987, Inertial instrument system for aerial surveying: U.S. Geological Survey Professional Paper 1390, 103 p.

Brozena, J. M., 1984, A preliminary analysis of the NRL airborne gravimetry system: Geophysics, v. 49, p. 1060–1079.

Buffler, R. T., Watkins, J. S., Shaub, F. J., and Worzel, J. L., 1980, Structure and early geologic history of the deep central Gulf of Mexico Basin, *in* Pilger, R. H., ed., The origin of the Gulf of Mexico and the early opening of the central North Atlantic Ocean: Baton Rouge, Louisiana State University School of Geoscience, p. 3–16.

Bunce, E. T., Phillips, J. D., and Chase, R. L., 1974, Geophysical study of Antilles Outer Ridge and northeast margin of the Caribbean Sea: American Association of Petroleum Geologists Bulletin, v. 58, no. 1, p. 106–123.

Cady, J. W., 1975, Magnetic and gravity anomalies in the Great Valley and western Sierra Nevada metamorphic belt, California: Geological Society of America Special Paper 168, 56 p.

Case, J. E., and Holcombe, T. L., 1980, Geologic-tectonic map of the Caribbean region: U.S. Geological Survey Miscellaneous Investigations Map I–1100, scale 1:2,500,000, three sheets.

Case, J. E., and MacDonald, W. D., 1973, Regional gravity anomalies and crustal structure in northern Colombia: Geological Society of America Bulletin, v. 84, p. 2905–2916.

Case, J. E., Holcombe, T. L., and Martin, R. G., 1984, Map of geologic provinces in the Caribbean region, *in* Bonini, W. E., Hargraves, R. B., and Shagam, R., eds., The Caribbean–South American plate boundary and regional tectonics: Geological Society of America Memoir 162, p. 1–30.

Childs, J. R., Magistrale, H. W., and Cooper, A. K., 1985, Free-air gravity anomaly map, Bering Sea: U.S. Geological Survey Miscellaneous Field Studies Map MF–1728, scale 1:2,500,000.

Cochran, J. R., 1973, Gravity and magnetic investigations in the Guiann Basin, western equatorial Atlantic: Geological Society of America Bulletin, v. 84, p. 3249–3268.

Cochran, J. R., and Talwani, M., 1977, Free-air gravity anomalies in the world's oceans and their relationship to residual elevation: Royal Astronomical Society Geophysical Journal, v. 50, p. 495–552.

Collette, G. J., Verhoef, J., and de Mulder, A.F.J., 1980, Gravity and a model of the median valley: Journal of Geophysics, v. 47, p. 91–98.

Coney, P. J., and Campa, M. F., 1984, Lithotectonic terrane map of Mexico: U.S. Geological Survey Open-File Report 84–523, p. D1–D14.

Coney, P. J., Jones, D. L., and Monger, J.W.H., 1980, Cordilleran suspect terranes: Nature, v. 30, p. 606–611.

Cook, A. H., 1970, Geodesy, *in* Tucker, R. H., Cook, A. H., Iyer, H. M., and Stacey, F. D., Global geophysics: New York, Elsevier, p. 25–66.

Cook, K. L., Montgomery, J. R., and Smith, J. T., 1975, Structural trends in Utah as indicated by gravity data: Geological Society of America Abstracts with Programs, v. 7, p. 598.

Coons, R. L., Woollard, G. P., and Hershey, G., 1967, Structural significance and analysis of the Mid-continent gravity high: American Association of Petroleum Geologists Bulletin, v. 51, p. 2381–2399.

Cordell, L. E., and Keller, G. R., 1984, Regional structural trends inferred from gravity and aeromagnetic data in the New Mexico–Colorado border region: New Mexico Geological Society Guidebook, 35th Field Conference, p. 21–23.

Couch, R. W., Pitts, G. S., Gemperle, M., Braman, D. E., and Veen, C. A., 1982, Gravity anomalies in the Cascade Range in Oregon—Structural and thermal implications: Oregon Department of Geology and Mineral Industries Open-File Report O–82–9, 66 p.

Dehlinger, P., and Jones, B. R., 1965, Free-air gravity anomaly map of the Gulf of Mexico and its tectonic implications (1963 edition): Geophysics, v. 30, no. 1, p. 102–110.

Dehlinger, P., Couch, R. W., and Gemperle, M., 1968, Continental and oceanic structure from the Oregon coast westward across the Juan de Fuca Ridge: Canadian Journal of Earth Sciences, v. 5, p. 1079–1090.

Diment, W. H., 1968, Gravity anomalies in northwestern New England, *in* Zen, E-an, White, W. S., Hadley, J. B., and Thompson, J. B., Jr., eds., Studies of Appalachian geology—Northern and maritime: New York, Interscience Publishers, p. 399–413.

Dobrin, M. B., 1960, Introduction to geophysical prospecting: New York, McGraw-Hill Book Company, 446 p.

Dutch, S. I., 1983, Proterozoic structural provinces in the north-central United States: Geology, v. 11, p. 478–481.

Eaton, G. P., Wahl, R. R., Prostka, H. J., Mabey, D. R., and Kleinkopf, M. D., 1978, Regional gravity and tectonic patterns—Their relation to late Cenozoic epeirogeny and lateral spreading in the western Cordillera, *in* Smith, R. B., and Eaton, G. P., eds., Cenozoic tectonics and regional geophysics of the western Cordillera: Geological Society of America Memoir 152, p. 51–91.

Eckhardt, E. A., 1940, History of gravity methods of prospecting for oil: Geophysics, v. 3, pt. 1, p. 231–242.

Emery, K. O., Uchupi, E., Bowin, C. O., Phillips, J. D., and Simpson, E.S.W., 1975, Continental margin off western Africa—Cape St. Francis (South Africa) to Walvis Ridge (South-West Africa): American Association of Petroleum Geologists Bulletin, v. 59, no. 1, p. 3–59.

Ewing, M., and Ewing, J. I., 1964, Distribution of oceanic sediments: Japan, University of Tokyo Geophysical Institute Studies of Oceanography, p. 525–537.

Forsberg, R., 1986, Gravity measurements in Jameson Land and neighboring parts of East Greenland: Meddelelser om Gronland, Geoscience 15, published by The Commission for Scientific Research in Greenland, 24 p.

Garland, G. D., 1971, Introduction to geophysics—Mantle, core, and thrust: Philadelphia, Pennsylvania, W. B. Saunders Company, 420 p.

Geopotential Research Mission Science Steering Group, 1985, Geopotential Research Mission—Scientific Rationale: Washington, D.C., National Aeronautics and Space Administration Report, 25 p.

Gibb, R. A., and Thomas, M. D., 1976, Gravity signature of fossil plate boundaries in the Canadian Shield: Nature, v. 262, p. 199–200.

Gibb, R. A., Thomas, M. D., Lapointe, P. L., and Mukhopadhyay, M., 1983, Geophysics of proposed Proterozoic sutures in Canada: Precambrian Research, v. 19, p. 349–384.

Goodacre, A. K., 1972, Generalized structure of the deep crust and upper mantle in Canada: Journal of Geophysical Research, v. 77, p. 3146–3161.

Goodacre, A. K., Grieve, R.A.F., and Halpenney, J. F. compilers, 1987a, Bouguer gravity anomaly map of Canada: Geological Survey of Canada Canadian Geophysical Atlas Map 3, scale 1:10,000,000.

——, 1987b, Isostatic gravity anomaly map of Canada: Geological Survey of Canada Canadian Geophysical Atlas Map 4, scale 1:10,000,000.

——, 1987c, Horizontal gradient of the Bouguer gravity anomaly map of Canada: Geological Survey of Canada Canadian Geophysical Atlas Map 5, scale 1:10,000,000.

Grant, F. S., and West, G. F., 1965, Interpretation theory in applied geophysics: New York, McGraw-Hill Book Company, 583 p.

Gravity Anomaly Map Committee, 1987, Gravity anomaly map of North America: Boulder, Colorado, Geological Society of America, 5 sheets, scale 1:5,000,000.

Green, A. G., Hajnal, Z., and Weber, W., 1985, An evolutionary model of the western Churchill province and western margin of the Superior province in Canada and the north-central United States: Tectonophysics, v. 116, p. 281–322.

Griscom, A., 1963, Tectonic significance of the Bouguer gravity field of the Appalachians [abs.]: Geological Society of America Special Paper 73, p. 163.

——, 1980, Klamath Mountains province, *in* Oliver, H. W., ed., Interpretation of the gravity map of California and its continental margin: California Division of Mines and Geology Bulletin 205, p. 34–36.

Grow, J. A., 1973, Crustal and upper mantle structure of the central Aleutian arc: Geological Society of America Bulletin, v. 84, p. 2169–2192.

Grow, J. A., Bowin, C. O., and Hutchinson, D. R., 1979, The gravity field of the U.S. continental margin: Tectonophysics, v. 59, p. 27–52.

Guild, P. W., Lee, M. P., McKelvey, V. E., Piper, D. Z., Swint, T. R., and Addicott, W. O., 1985, Explanatory notes for the mineral-resources map of the Circum-Pacific region, Northeast Quadrant: American Association of Petroleum Geologists, 48 p.

Gupta, V. K., and Grant, F. S., 1985, Mineral-exploration aspects of gravity and aeromagnetic surveys in the Sudbury–Cobalt area, Ontario, *in* Hinze, W. J., ed., The utility of regional gravity and magnetic anomaly maps: Society of Exploration Geophysicists, p. 392–412.

Hamilton, W. B., 1978, Mesozoic tectonics of the western United States: Pacific Section, Society of Economic Paleontologists and Mineralogists, Pacific Coast Paleogeography Symposium 2, p. 33–70.

Hammer, S., 1983, Airborne gravity is here!: Geophysics, v. 48, no. 2, p. 213–223.

Haworth, R. T., Daniels, D. L., Williams, H., and Zietz, I., 1980, Bouguer gravity anomaly map of the Appalachian orogen: St. Johns, Newfoundland, Canada, Memorial University Map no. 3, scale 1:1,000,000.

Haxby, W. F., 1987, Gravity field of the world's oceans—A portrayal of gridded geophysical data derived from SEASAT radar altimeter measurements of the shape of the ocean surface: National Geophysical Data Center and World Data Center A Report MGG-3, scale approximately 1:40,000,000, published jointly by the Office of Naval Research, the National Geophysical Data Center, and the Lamont–Doherty Geological Observatory of Columbia University.

Haxby, W. F., and Turcotte, D. L., 1978, On isostatic geoid anomalies: Journal of Geophysical Research, v. 83, p. 5473–5478.

Hayford, J. F., and Bowie, W., 1912, The effect of topography and isostatic compensation upon the intensity of gravity: U.S. Coast and Geodetic Survey Special Publication 10, 132 p.

Heezen, B. C., Tharp, M., and Ewing, M., 1959, The floors of the ocean; 1, The North Atlantic: Geological Society of America Special Paper 65, p. 1–122.

Heiskanen, W. A., and Vening-Meinesz, F. A., 1958, The earth and its gravity field: New York, McGraw-Hill Book Company, 470 p.

Hildenbrand, T. G., 1983, FFTFIL—A filtering program based on two-dimensional Fourier analysis of geophysical data: U.S. Geological Survey Open-File Report 83–237, 61 p.

Hildenbrand, T. G., Kane, M. F., and Stauder, W. V., 1977, Magnetic and gravity anomalies in the northern Mississippi embayment and their spatial relation to seismicity: U.S. Geological Survey Miscellaneous Field Studies Map MF–914, with 18-page text, scale 1:1,000,000.

Hildenbrand, T. G., Simpson, R. W., Godson, R. H., and Kane, M. F., 1982, Digital colored residual and regional Bouguer gravity maps of the conterminous United States with cut-off wavelengths of 250 km and 1,000 km: U.S. Geological Survey Geophysical Investigations Map GP–953–A, scale 1:7,500,000.

Hinze, W. J., editor, 1985, The utility of regional gravity and magnetic anomaly maps: Society of Exploration Geophysicists, 454 p.

Hinze, W. J., Kellogg, R. L., and O'Hara, N. W., 1975, Geophysical studies of basement geology of Southern Peninsula of Michigan: American Association of Petroleum Geologists Bulletin, v. 59, p. 1562–1584.

Hinze, W. J., Wold, R. J., and O'Hara, N. W., 1982, Gravity and magnetic studies of Lake Superior, *in* Wold, R. J., and Hinze, W. J., eds., Geology and tectonics of the Lake Superior basin: Geological Society of America Memoir 156, p. 203–221.

Hornal, R. W., Sobczak, L. W., Burke, W.E.F., and Stephens, L. E., 1970, Preliminary results of gravity surveys of the Mackenzie Basin and Beaufort Sea (with maps 117, 118, and 119): Ottawa, Department of Energy, Mines and Resources Gravity Map Series of the Earth Physics Branch, 12 p., scale 1:1,000,000.

Hutchinson, C. S., 1983, Economic deposits and their tectonic setting: New York, John Wiley and Sons, 365 p.

Hutchinson, D. R., Grow, J. A., and Klitgord, K. D., 1983, Crustal structure beneath the Southern Appalachians, nonuniqueness of gravity modeling: Geology, v. 11, no. 10, p. 611–615.

Innes, M.J.S., and Gibb, R. A., 1970, New gravity anomaly of Canada—an aid to mineral exporation, *in* Morley, L. W., ed., Mining and Groundwater Geophysics 1967: Geological Survey of Canada Economic Geology Report 26, p. 238–248.

Innes, M.J.S., Goodacre, A. K., Weber, J. R., and McConnell, R. K., 1967, Structural implications of the gravity field in Hudson Bay and vicinity: Canadian Journal of Earth Sciences, v. 4, p. 977–993.

Innes, M.J.S., Goodacre, A. K., Argun-Weston, A., and Weber, J. R., 1968, Gravity and isostasy in the Hudson Bay region, *in* Beals, C. S., and Shenstone, D. A., eds., Science, history, and Hudson Bay: Ottawa, Department of Energy, Mines and Resources, v. 2, p. 703–728.

Jeffreys, H., 1959, The Earth: London, Cambridge University Press, 420 p.

Jekeli, C., 1988, The Gravity Gradiometer Survey System (GGSS): EOS (American Geophysical Union Transactions), v. 69, no. 8, p. 105, 116–117.

Jordan, S. K., 1978, Moving-base gravity gradiometer surveys and interpretation: Geophysics, v. 43, no. 1, p. 94–101.

Joyner, W. B., 1963, Gravity in north-central New England: Geological Society of America Bulletin, v. 74, p. 831–858.

Kane, M. F., and Bromery, R. W., 1968, Gravity anomalies in Maine, *in* Zen, E-an, White, W. S., Hadley, J. B., and Thompson, J. B., Jr., eds., Studies in Appalachian geology—Northern and maritime: New York, Interscience Publishers, p. 415–423.

Kane, M. F., and Godson, R. H., 1985, Features of a pair of long-wavelength (>250 km) and short-wavelength (<250 km) Bouguer gravity maps of the United States, *in* Hinze, W. J., ed., The utility of regional gravity and magnetic anomaly maps: Society of Exploration Geophysicists, p. 46–61.

Karner, G. D., and Watts, A. B., 1982, On isostasy at Atlantic-type continental margins: Journal of Geophysical Research, v. 87, p. 2923–2948.

——, 1983, Gravity anomalies and flexure of the lithosphere at mountain ranges: Journal of Geophysical Research, v. 88, no. B12, p. 10449–10477.

Kaula, W. M., 1966, Tests and combination of satellite determinations of the gravity field with gravimetry: Journal of Geophysical Research, v. 71, p. 5303–5314.

Keen, C., and Loncarevic, B. D., 1966, Crustal structure on the eastern seabord of Canada—Studies on the continental margin: Canadian Journal of Earth Sciences, v. 3, p. 65–76.

Keller, G. R., 1988, The development of gravity and magnetic studies, emphasizing articles published in the *Geological Society of America Bulletin:* Geological Society of America Bulletin, v. 100, p. 469–478.

Keller, G. R., and Cebull, S. E., 1973, Plate tectonics and the Ouachita system in Texas, Oklahoma, and Arkansas: Geological Society of America Bulletin, v. 83, p. 1659–1666.

Kellogg, J. N., 1984, Cenozoic tectonic history of the Sierra de Perija, Venezuela-Colombia and adjacent basins, *in* Bonini, W. E., Hargraves, R. B., and Shagam, R., eds., The Caribbean-South American plate boundary and regional tectonics: Geological Society of America Memoir 162, p. 239–261.

Kerr, R. A., 1982, New gravity anomalies mapped from old data: Science, v. 215, no. 4537, p. 1220–1222.

——, 1986, The continent plates are getting thicker: Science, v. 232, p. 933–934.

——, 1988a, Geophysics; The slower side of the sciences: Science, v. 240, p. 1734–1735.

——, 1988b, Making mountains with lithospheric drips: Science, v. 239, p. 978–979.

Kienle, J., 1971, Gravity and magnetic measurements over Bowers ridge and Shirshov ridge, Bering Sea: Journal of Geophysical Research, v. 76, no. 29, p. 7138–7153.

King, E. R., and Zietz, I., 1971, Aeromagnetic study of the midcontinent gravity high of central United States: Geological Society of America Bulletin, v. 82, p. 2187–2208.

King, P. B., 1977, The evolution of North America: Princeton, New Jersey, Princeton University Press, 197 p.

Klasner, J. S., and King, E. R., 1986, Precambrian basement geology of North and South Dakota: Canadian Journal of Earth Sciences, v. 23, p. 1083–1102.

Klasner, J. S., King, E. R., and Jones, W. J., 1985, Geologic interpretation of gravity and magnetic data for northern Michigan and Wisconsin, *in* Hinze, W. J., ed., The utility of regional gravity and magnetic anomaly maps: Society of Exploration Geophysicists, p. 267–286.

Kutina, J., and Hildenbrand, T. G., 1987, Ore deposits of the western United States in relation to mass distribution in the crust and mantle: Geological Society of America Bulletin, v. 99, no. 1, p. 30–41.

LaCoste, L.J.B., 1934, A new type long period vertical seismograph: Physics, v. 5, p. 178–180.

——, 1967, Measurement of gravity at sea and in the air: Reviews of Geophysics, v. 5, p. 477–526.

——, 1988, The zero-length spring gravity meter: Geophysics: The Leading Edge of Exploration, v. 7, no. 7, p. 20–21.

La Fehr, T. R., 1965, Gravity, isostasy, and crustal structure in the southern Cascade Range: Journal of Geophysical Research, v. 70, p. 5581–5597.

Lazarewicz, A. R., and Schwank, D. C., 1982, Detection of uncharted seamounts using satellite altimeter data: Geophysical Research Letters, v. 9, p. 385.

Mabey, D. R., 1976, Interpretation of a gravity profile across the western Snake River Plain, Idaho: Geology, v. 4, p. 53–55.

Marsh, J. G., Koblinsky, C. J., Brenner, A., Beckley, B. D., and Martin, T. V., 1985, Global mean sea surface computation based upon a combination of SEASAT and GEOS-3 satellite altimeter data [abs.]: Geopotential Research Mission (GRM), National Aeronautical and Space Administration Conference Publication 2390, p. 77.

McAdoo, D. C., 1988, Marine gravity—GEOSAT's Exact Repeat Mission (ERM): EOS (American Geophysical Union Transactions), v. 69, no. 46, p. 1569.

McKenzie, D. P., 1967a, Some remarks on heat-flow and gravity anomalies: Journal of Geophysical Research, v. 72, p. 6261–6273.

——, 1967b, The viscosity of the mantle: Royal Astronomical Society Geophysical Journal, v. 14, p. 297–305.

McKenzie, D. P., and Bowin, C. O., 1976, The relationship between bathymetry and gravity in the Atlantic Ocean: Journal of Geophysical Research, v. 81, p. 1903–1915.

McNutt, M. K., 1983, Influence of plate subduction on isostatic compensation in northern California: Tectonics, v. 2, no. 4, p. 399–415.

Miller, A. H., 1940, Invetigations of gravitational and magnetometric methods of geophysical prospecting: Ottawa, Publications of the Dominion Observatory, v. 11, 6 p.

Minear, J. W., and Toksoz, M. N., 1970, Thermal regime of a downgoing slab and new global tectonics: Journal of Geophysical Research, v. 75, p. 1397–1419.

Molnar, P. H., 1977, Gravity anomalies and the origin of the Puerto Rico trench: Royal Astronomical Society Geophysical Journal, v. 51, p. 701–708.

Nettleton, L. L., 1976, Gravity and magnetics in oil prospecting: New York, McGraw-Hill Book Company, 464 p.

O'Hara, N. W., and Lyons, P. L., 1983, New map updates gravity data: Geotimes, v. 28, p. 22–27.

——, 1985, Preparation and overview of the gravity-anomaly map of the United States, *in* Hinze, W. J., ed., The utility of regional gravity and magnetic anomaly maps: Tulsa, Oklahoma, Society of Exploration Geophysicists, p. 33–37.

Oliver, H. W., 1977, Gravity and magnetic investigations of the Sierra Nevada batholith: Geological Society of America Bulletin, v. 88, p. 445–461.

Ostenso, N. A., 1962, Geophysical investigation of the Arctic Ocean Basin: University of Wisconsin Polar Research Center Research Report 62–4, 124 p.

——, 1968, Geophysical studies in the Greenland Sea: Geological Society of America Bulletin, v. 79, p. 107–131.

Paik, H. J., Leung, J.-Sun, Morgan, S. H., and Parker, J., 1988, Global gravity survey by an orbiting gravity gradiometer: EOS (American Geophysical Union Transactions), v. 69, no. 48, p. 1601 and 1610–1611.

Parsons, B. E., and Molnar, P. H., 1976, The origin of outer topographic rises associated with trenches: Royal Astronomical Society Geophysical Journal, v. 45, p. 707–712.

Pick, M., Picha, J., and Vyskocil, V., 1973, Theory of the Earth's gravity field: New York, Elsevier, 538 p.

Pindell, J. L., and Barrett, S. F., 1988, Geological evolution of the Caribbean region—A plate tectonic perspective, *in* Dengo, G., and Case, J. E., eds., The Caribbean region: Boulder, Colorado, Geological Society of America, The Geology of North America, v. H (in press).

Rabinowitz, P. D., 1974, The boundary between oceanic and continental crust in the western North Atlantic, *in* Burk, C. A., and Drake, C. L., eds., The geology of continental margins: New York, Springer-Verlag, p. 67–84.

Rabinowitz, P. D., and Jung, W.-Y., 1986, Gravity anomalies in the western North Atlantic Ocean, *in* Vogt, P. R., and Tucholke, B. E., eds., The western North Atlantic region: Boulder, Colorado, Geological Society of America, The Geology of North America, v. M, p. 205–213.

Rabinowitz, P. D., and LaBrecque, J. L., 1977, The isostatic gravity anomaly—A key to the evolution of the ocean-continent boundary: Earth and Planetary Science Letters, v. 35, p. 145–150.

——, 1979, The Mesozoic South Atlantic Ocean and evolution of its continental margins: Journal of Geophysical Research, v. 84, p. 5973–6002.

Rapp, R. H., 1981, The earth's gravity field to degree and order 180 using SEASAT altimeter data, terrestrial gravity data and other data: Columbus, Ohio State University Department of Geodetic Science 322, 53 p.

——, 1984, Free-air gravity anomalies, *in* Moore, G. W., ed., Geodynamic map of the Circum-Pacific region, northeast quadrangle: American Association of Petroleum Geologists, scale 1:10,000,000.

——, 1986, Gravity anomalies and sea surface heights derived from a combined GEOS 3/SEASAT altimeter data set: Journal of Geophysical Research, ser. B, v. 91, no. 5, p. 4867–4876.

Riddihough, R. P., 1979, Gravity and structure of an active margin—British Columbia and Washington: Canadian Journal of Earth Sciences, v. 16, p. 350–363.

Riddihough, R. P., Finn, C., and Couch, R. W., 1986, Klamath–Blue Mountain lineament, Oregon: Geology, v. 14, p. 528–531.

Robb, J. M., and Kane, M. F., 1975, Structure of the Vema fracture zone from gravity and magnetic intensity profiles: Journal of Geophysical Research, v. 80, p. 441–445.

Rowland, R. W., Goud, M. R., and McGregor, B. A., 1983, The U.S. Exclusive Economic Zone—A summary of its geology, exploration, and resource potential: U.S. Geological Survey Circular 912, 29 p.

Ruiz, J., Patchett, P. J., and Ortega-Gutierrez, F., 1988, Proterozoic and Phanerozoic basement terranes of Mexico from Nd isotope studies: Geological Society of America Bulletin, v. 100, p. 274–281.

Scheidegger, A. E., 1976, Foundations of geophysics: New York, Elsevier, 238 p.

Scholl, D. W., Buffington, E. C., and Hopkins, D. M., 1968, Geologic history of the continental margin of North America in the Bering Sea: Marine Geology, v. 6, no. 4, p. 297–330.

Scholl, D. W., Buffington, E. C., Hopkins, D. M., and Alpha, T. R., 1970, The structure and origin of the large submarine canyons of the Bering Sea: Marine Geology, v. 8, no. 2, p. 187–210.

Schwarzschild, B., 1988, From mine shafts to cliffs—The "Fifth Force" remains elusive: Physics Today, v. 41, no. 7, p. 21–24.

Sclater, J. G., Lawver, L. A., and Parsons, B. E., 1975, Comparison of long-wavelength residual elevation and free-air gravity anomalies in the North Atlantic and possible implications for the thickness of the lithospheric plate: Journal of Geophysical Research, v. 80, p. 1031–1052.

Scrutton, R. A., 1979, Structure of the crust and upper mantle at Goban Spur, southwest of the British Isles—Some implications for margin studies: Tectonophysics, v. 59, p. 201–215.

Sibuet, J. C., and Mascle, J., 1978, Plate kinematic implications of Atlantic equatorial fracture zone trends: Journal of Geophysical Research, v. 83, p. 3401–3421.

Sibuet, J. C., LePichon, X., and Goslin, J., 1974, Thickness of lithosphere deduced from gravity edge effects across the Mendocino Fault: Nature, v. 252, p. 676–679.

Simmons, G., 1964, Gravity survey and geological interpretation, northern New York: Geological Society of America Bulletin, v. 75, p. 81–98.

Simpson, R. W., Jachens, R. C., Saltus, R. W., and Blakely, R. J., 1986, Isostatic residual gravity, topographic, and first-derivative gravity maps of the conterminous United States: U.S. Geological Survey Geophysical Investigations Map GP–975, scale 1:7,500,000.

Smith, R. B., Mabey, D. R., and Eaton, G. P., 1976, Regional geophysics and tectonics of the Intermountain West: Geology, v. 4, p. 437–438.

Sobczak, L. W., Gravity and deep structure of the continental margin of Banks Island and MacKenzie Delta: Canadian Journal of Earth Sciences, v. 12, p. 378–394.

Society of Exploration Geophysicists, 1982, Gravity anomaly map of the United States (exclusive of Alaska and Hawaii): Tulsa, Oklahoma, Society of Exploration Geophysicists, scale 1:2,500,000.

Soltz, J. A., and Hursh, J. W., 1985, An APTS gravity mapping experiment: Proceedings of AIAA Guidance, Navigation and Control Conference, Snowmass, Colorado, August 1985 (Addendum), p. 1–11.

Stacey, F. D., Tuck, G. J., Moore, G. I., Holding, S. C., Goodwin, B. D., and Zhou, R., 1987, Geophysics and the law of gravity: Reviews of Modern Physics, v. 59, no. 1, p. 157–174.

Stacey, R. A., 1971, Interpretation of the gravity anomaly at Darnley Bay, N.W.T.,: Canadian Journal of Earth Sciences, v. 8, p. 1037–1042.

Sumner, J. S., 1985, Crustal geology of Arizona as interpreted from magnetic, gravity, and geologic data, *in* Hinze, W. J., ed., The utility of regional gravity and magnetic anomaly maps: Society of Exploration Geophysicists, p. 164–180.

Talwani, M., 1970, Gravity, *in* Maxwell, A. E., ed., The sea: New York, John Wiley and Sons, Wiley-Interscience, p. 251–297.

Talwani, M., and Eldholm, O., 1972, Continental margin off Norway; A geological study: Geological Society of America Bulletin, v. 83, p. 3575–3608.

Talwani, M., and LePichon, X., 1969, Gravity field over the Atlantic Ocean, *in* Hart, P. J., ed., The earth's crust and upper mantle: American Geophysical Union, p. 341–351.

Talwani, M., LePichon, X., and Ewing, M., 1965, Crustal structure of the mid-ocean ridges—Pt. 2, Computed model from gravity and seismic refraction data: Journal of Geophysical Research, v. 70, p. 341–352.

Telford, W. M., Geldart, L. P., Sheriff, R. E., and Keys, D. A., 1976, Applied geophysics: New York, Cambridge University Press, 860 p.

Thomas, M. D., 1985, Gravity studies of the Grenville province—Significance for Precambrian plate collision and the origin of anorthosite, *in* Hinze, W. J., ed., The utility of regional gravity and magnetic anomaly maps: Society of Exploration Geophysicists, p. 109–123.

Thomas, M. D., Sharpton, V. L., and Grieve, R.A.F., 1987, Gravity patterns and Precambrian structure in the North American Central Plains: Geology, v. 15, p. 489–492.

Thompson, G. A., and Burke, D. B., 1974, Regional geophysics of the Basin and Range province: Annual Review of Earth and Planetary Science, v. 2, p. 213–238.

Thompson, G. A., and Talwani, M., 1964, Crustal structure from the Pacific Basin to central Nevada: Journal of Geophysical Research, v. 69, p. 4813–4837.

Toksoz, M. N., Sleep, N. H., and Smith, T. A., 1973, Evolution of the downgoing lithosphere and mechanisms of deep focus earthquakes: Royal Astronomical Society Geophysical Journal, v. 35, p. 285–310.

Turcotte, D. L., Ahern, J. L., and Bird, J. M., 1977, The state of stress at continental margins: Tectonophysics, v. 42, p. 1–28.

Uchupi, E., Phillips, J. D., and Prada, K. E., 1970, Origin and structure of the New England Seamounts chain: Deep-Sea Research, v. 17, p. 483–494.

Van Schmus, W. R., and Hinze, W. J., 1985, The Midcontinent rift system: Annual Review of Earth and Planetary Sciences, v. 13, p. 345–383.

Vening-Meinesz, F. A., 1941, Theory and practice of pendulum observations at sea, part 2: Delft, Waltman, 146 p.

Vogt, P. R., and Ostenso, N. A., 1970, Magnetic and gravity profiles across the Alpha Cordillera and their relation to sea-floor spreading: Journal of Geophysical Research, v. 75, p. 4925–4937.

Walcott, R. I., 1970, Flexural rigidity, thickness, and viscosity of the lithosphere: Journal of Geophysical Research, v. 75, p. 3941–3954.

——, 1972, Gravity, flexure, and the growth of sedimentary basins at a continental edge: Geological Society of America Bulletin, v. 83, p. 1845–1848.

——, 1976, Lithospheric flexure, analysis of gravity anomalies, and the propagation of seamount chains, *in* Sutton, G. H., Manghnani, M. H., and Moberly, R., eds., The geophysics of the Pacific Ocean basin and its margin: American Geophysical Union Geophysical Monograph 19, p. 431–438.

Walper, J. L., 1980, Tectonic evolution of the Gulf of Mexico, *in* Pilger, R. H., ed., The origin of the Gulf of Mexico and the early opening of the central North Atlantic Ocean: Baton Rouge, Louisiana State University School of Geoscience, p. 87–98.

Watts, A. B., and Talwani, M., 1974, Gravity anomalies seaward of deep-sea trenches and their tectonic implications: Geophysical Journal of the Royal Astronomical Society, v. 36, p. 57–90.

Watts, A. B., Talwani, M., and Cochran, J. R., 1976, Gravity field of the northwest Pacific Ocean basin and its margin, *in* Sutton, G. H., Manghnani, M. H., and Moberly, R., eds., The geophysics of the Pacific Ocean basin and its margin: American Geophysical Union Geophysical Monograph 19, p. 17–34.

Westbrook, G. K., 1982, The Barbados Ridge Complex—Tectonics of a mature forearc system, *in* Leggett, J. K., ed., Trench and forearc geology; Sedimentation and tectonics in ancient and modern plate margins: Geological Society of London Special Publication 10, p. 261–276.

Westbrook, G. K., and McCann, W. R., 1986, Subduction of Atlantic lithosphere beneath the Caribbean, *in* Vogt, P. R., and Tucholke, B. E., eds., The western North Atlantic region: Boulder, Colorado, Geological Society of America, The Geology of North America, v. M, p. 341–350.

Williams, D. L., and Finn, C., 1985, Analysis of gravity data in volcanic terrain and gravity anomalies and subvolcanic intrusions in the Cascade Range, U.S.A., and at other selected volcanoes, *in* Hinze, W. J., ed., The utility of regional gravity and magnetic anomaly maps: Society of Exploration Geophysicists, p. 361–374.

Wold, R. J., and Hinze, W. J., editors, 1982, Geology and tectonics of the Lake Superior Basin: Geological Society of America Memoir 156, 280 p.

Woollard, G. P., 1968, The interrelationship of the crust, the upper mantle, and isostatic gravity anomalies in the United States: American Geophysical Union Geophysical Monograph 12, p. 312–341.

Woollard, G. P., and Strange, W. E., 1962, Gravity anomalies of the crust of the earth in the Pacific basin, *in* Macdonald, G. A., and Kuno, H., eds., The crust of the Earth: American Geophysical Union Geophysical Monograph 6, p. 60–80.

Woollard, G. P., Caldera, J. M., and Machesky, L., 1969a, Gravity relations in Mexico: Mexico City, Proceedings of the Pan American Symposium on the upper mantle, March, 1968, v. 1, p. 43–48.

Woollard, G. P., Machesky, L., and Caldera, J. M., 1969b, A regional gravity survey of northern Mexico and relations of Bouguer anomalies to regional gravity and elevation in Mexico: Hawaii Institute of Geophysics Data Report, HIG-69-13, 53 p.

Worzel, J. L., 1968, Advances in marine geophysical research of continental margins: Canadian Journal of Earth Sciences, v. 5, p. 963–983.

——, 1976, Gravity investigations of the subduction zone, *in* Sutton, G. H., Manghnani, M. H., and Moberly, R., eds., The geophysics of the Pacific Ocean basin and its margin: American Geophysical Union Geophysical Monograph 19, p. 1–15.

Worzel, J. L., and Harrison, J. C., 1965, Gravity at sea, *in* Hill, M. N., ed., The sea: New York, John Wiley and Sons, Wiley-Interscience, p. 134–174.

Worzel, J. L., and Shurbet, G. L., 1955, Gravity anomalies at continental margins: National Academy of Sciences Proceedings, v. 41, p. 963–983.

Zwart, W. J., editor, 1986, Cumulative index of Geophysics (1936–1985), Geophysical Prospecting (1953–1985), and Geophysics: The Leading Edge of Exploration (1982–1985): Geophysics, v. 51, no. 10A, 636 p., published jointly by the Society of Exploration Geophysicists and the European Association of Exploration Geophysicists.

MANUSCRIPT ACCEPTED BY THE SOCIETY JANUARY 30, 1989

ACKNOWLEDGMENTS

We thank Robert C. Jachens and H. Richard Blank, U.S. Geological Survey, and William J. Hinze, Purdue University, for their thoughtful reviews of the manuscript.

Printed in U.S.A.

The Geology of North America
Vol. A, The Geology of North America—An overview
The Geological Society of America, 1989

Chapter 3

The Magnetic Anomaly Map of North America; A new tool for regional geologic mapping

William J. Hinze
Department of Earth and Atmospheric Sciences, Purdue University, West Lafayette, Indiana 47907
Peter J. Hood
Geological Survey of Canada, Energy, Mines, and Resources Canada, Ottawa, Ontario K1A 0E8, Canada

INTRODUCTION

Although the charting of anomalous variations in the Earth's magnetic field to aid in the mapping of the Earth's crust has been practiced for over a century, the development of aeromagnetic-surveying technology has made it possible in recent decades to conduct surveys of extensive regions efficiently and precisely. These improvements in surveying instrumentation, procedures, and data processing made it possible to move from magnetic "anomaly hunting" to the preparation of regional total field contour maps. Aeromagnetic surveys have been conducted over limited areas for specific geologic objectives, with little attention paid to the possibility of compositing individual surveys into regional, small-scale maps for the study of continental-scale geologic features. However, interpretation of compilations of simplified near-surface, aeromagnetic anomaly maps (e.g., MacLaren and Charbonneau, 1968), and high-level, broadly spaced profile surveys (e.g., Zietz and others, 1969; Sexton and others, 1982) has shown that small-scale, low-resolution magnetic anomaly maps of extensive regions can be very useful in mapping continental-scale geologic features.

Since the mid-1940s, airborne magnetic surveys have been conducted over vast regions of North America. The public availability of many of these surveys led to the preparation of national maps by Canada and the United States. The first 1:5,000,000-scale colored magnetic anomaly map of Canada (Morley and tohers, 1968) was prepared with hand-compilation techniques by the Geological Survey of Canada (GSC). Subsequent editions of the map have provided greater coverage and improved detail, leading to the fifth edition (Dods and others, 1987), which was produced by machine-compilation of digital data. The United States magnetic anomaly map was published in two parts in 1982 and 1984 from hand-compiled data at a 1:2,500,000 scale as a result of a joint effort of the U.S. Geological Survey (USGS) and the Society of Exploration Geophysicists (SExG). The digitized versions of the Canadian and U.S. maps form the nucleus of the *Magnetic Anomaly Map of North America* (Committee for the Magnetic Anomaly Map of North America, 1987).

The *Magnetic Anomaly Map of North America* was the responsibility of an international committee chaired by William J. Hinze (Purdue University) and Peter J. Hood (GSC). Members of the committee and their affiliations during the preparation of the map were William E. Bonini (Princeton University), James E. Case (USGS), Mauricio F.J. De La Fuente (Geosciencias Aplicadas SA, Mexico), Richard H. Godson (USGS), Stuart A. Hall (University of Houston), William F. Hanna (USGS), James R. Heirtzler (Woods Hole Oceanographic Institution), Robert H. Higgs (U.S. Naval Oceanographic Office), M. Dean Kleinkopf (USGS), Herbert J. Meyers (U.S. National Geophysical Data Center), Allison R. Palmer (Geological Society of America), Norman W. Peddie (USGS), Mike S. Reford (Geoterrex Limited), Dennis J. Teskey (GSC), Leif Thorning (Geological Survey of Greenland), and Isidore Zietz (Phoenix Corporation). Mike S. Reford served as the liaison with the SExG. James R. Heirtzler acted as the coordinator in the collection of the marine magnetic data for the map. Richard H. Godson was responsible for preparing the digital data set of the United States to the specifications required for the map. The Aeromagnetic Data Processing Section of the GSC was responsible for digitization of magnetic anomaly maps as required and composing the final version of the map. The USGS did the cartographic work and the actual printing of the map.

The *Magnetic Anomaly Map of North America* is the first international map of such data over a continent-scale region. It is useful for studying the distribution and character of regional geologic features that contrast magnetically with their surrounding rocks, for providing a regional framework for the interpretation of magnetic studies of limited areas, for selecting areas for more detailed magnetic investigations, and for indexing available magnetic-map coverage. It is particularly useful because it provides continuous coverage across international boundaries and the continent-ocean interface. The map is an important new tool for regional geological mapping, but caution is recommended in the use of the map and the associated digital data set at scales

Hinze, W. J., and Hood, P. J., 1989, The Magnetic Anomaly Map of North America; A new tool for regional geologic mapping, *in* Bally, A. W., and Palmer, A. R., eds., The Geology of North America—An overview: Boulder, Colorado, Geological Society of America, The Geology of North America, v. A.

larger than 1:5,000,000. The specifications of the data and the compilation process are designed for the portrayal of anomalies that are broader than tens of kilometers and greater in amplitude than a few hundred nanoteslas (nT). Original data sources should be used for quantitative interpretation of individual anomalies. These sources are identified in indexes prepared by individual nations. Equal care must be exercised in interpreting anomalies at the long-wavelength end of the spectrum. Although improvements have been made in this map by minimizing errors of previous national maps in mapping anomalies that exceed 1,000 km in horizontal dimensions, undoubtedly errors remain in these anomalies due to problems in tying together individual surveys and specifying the core-derived, main magnetic field that is used in defining the anomalous field from the observed data.

MAP PREPARATION

The continental areas of the *Magnetic Anomaly Map of North America* have been largely drawn from published map sources that were digitized and processed in preparation for compositing. The marine areas of the map were prepared from digital data tracks, except in the Gulf of Mexico, Caribbean Sea, and the continental shelf of Alaska, where data were obtained from digitized maps. The continental areas of Canada and the United States were tied together first, and the remainder of the map areas adjusted to this nucleus.

Canada

Roughly 70 percent of the land area of Canada is covered by anomaly data, and the vast majority of these data, except for mountainous areas, were acquired with constant flight specifications; flight lines spaced at 800 m (one-half mile) at an elevation above the ground surface of 300 m (1,000 ft).

The GSC digitized the Canadian magnetic anomaly maps of areas not surveyed with digital recording techniques by digitizing contour intersections with flight lines on 1:50,000-scale aeromagnetic maps. The observed digital and digitized analog data were interpolated on a 2-km grid and levelled using data obtained from long control lines specially flown by the GSC and the National Aeronautical Establishment of the Canadian National Research Council (NRC). The latter agency also observed control lines across the Caribbean Sea for data levelling purposes. The Atlantic Geoscience Center of the GSC processed data off the east coast of Canada, and the Pacific Geoscience Center provided marine data off the west coast and from Hudson Bay.

The absolute value of the anomaly field for the entire map was established by tying the GSC data to the Bourget, Quebec, calibration range that is referenced to the Blackburn Geomagnetic Observatory near Ottawa, Canada.

United States

The United States magnetic anomaly data are, in general, neither as detailed nor as consistent in survey specifications and reduction procedures as the Canadian data set. The U.S. surveys were designed by numerous organizations and individuals to achieve specific geological objectives, but the majority of the observations were made within 300 m of the ground surface and at spacings of 1.6 km or less. The U.S. data were originally compiled at a 1:1,000,000 scale for the preparation of USGS GP (Geophysical) Maps 954A and 954B from roughly 700 separate magnetic anomaly maps. The areal limits and specifications of the surveys are referenced in texts that accompany the U.S. Magnetic Anomaly Map (USGS and SExG, 1982 and 1984). The compilation and data sources of the U.S. maps are discussed for Alaska and Hawaii by Godson (1985) and for the conterminous United States by Hinze and Zietz (1985). Contours for the eastern half of the conterminous United States were digitized at 200 nT(γ) intervals from Map GP 954A at a 1:2,500,000 scale, and for the western half the contours were digitized at 100 nT(γ) intervals from 1:1,000,000-scale maps used in preparation of USGS Map GP 977 (Bond and Zietz, 1987). Alaskan data were obtained by digitizing contours at 200 nT(γ) intervals from USGS Map GP 954B at a scale of 1:2,500,000. The U.S. anomaly maps were compiled on a nationwide base net of data collected from 1975 through 1981 by the U.S. Department of Energy's National Uranium Resource Evaluation program. The aeromagnetic data were reduced utilizing the updated 1975.0 version of the International Geomagnetic Reference Field (IGRF). Unfortunately, studies subsequent to the preparation of the U.S. maps showed that this version of the reference field caused a spurious regional gradient in the anomaly field. Over the conterminous United States the result is a positive gradient of several hundred nanoteslas from the southeast to the northwest. Thus, in the compilation of the North American map, the IGRF originally removed from the observed data was added back into the data set, and the appropriate (corrected) Definitive Geomagnetic Reference Field (DGRF) was removed. As a result, the long-wavelength gradient increasing from southeast to northwest on the U.S. map has been eliminated. Similarly, the appropriate DGRF has been used in reducing the Canadian and Alaska data. These three data sets—conterminous United States, Canada, and Alaska, which form the nucleus of the map—fit together with a minimum of adjustment by simple level shifts to a precision that is commensurate with the scale and contour interval of the map. Exceptions do occur locally, and appropriate adjustments were made to minimize these.

Offshore

The extensive ship-track data used in the map were supplied primarily by the U.S. National Geophysical Data Center (NGDC) from data originating with the U.S. Navy and Scripps and Woods Hole Oceanographic Institutions. The appropriate DGRF was removed from the observations of individual cruises. The resulting data were sorted into convenient-sized areas, gridded a 2-km intervals, and plotted in map form. Individual cruises that showed level problems with coexisting data were adjusted, or removed if the data could not be tied with a low-order correction surface. No attempt was made to remove the small (several tens of nanoteslas) residual differences that occur at some track intersections. This procedure was used even for those areas for which compiled maps exist, such as the west coast of the United States, the Caribbean Sea, and the Gulf of Mexico, and the resulting data were used as a reference for the final levelling of these areas. The resulting offshore data presented in color-swath form tie in smoothly to the map nucleus.

Flight-track data in the Arctic and eastern Atlantic Oceans from the U.S. Navy also were used in the map preparation. These data were observed at a wide line-spacing (10 to 30 km) and are unlevelled. Thus, they were processed in the same manner as the ship-track data. The Kane Basin–Nares Strait data observed from the Canadian NRC's aircraft also were included.

Greenland

Digital aeromagnetic data for Greenland and environs, provided by the Geological Survey of Greenland, were gridded, an appropriate DGRF removed, and amalgamated with the North American nucleus. A swath of aeromagnetic data across southern Greenland, observed in a Canadian NRC's aircraft in a joint Canadian-Greenland program on behalf of the Geological Survey of Greenland, were reduced and compiled with adjacent data by the GSC. Control lines of aeromagnetic data acquired by the Canadian NRC along Baffin Bay, the Labrador Sea, and around the southern tip of Greenland to Iceland were used to level the data in this region.

Other regions

The remainder of the data shown on the map were obtained by digitizing existing maps made available to the project. These include Siberia, a number of areas along the west coast of the United States, Mexico, and Central America. These offshore data were levelled to the adjacent conterminous United States and digital ship-track data provided by NGDC. Numerous attempts to obtain regional aeromagnetic data from Mexico were unsuccessful.

Several areas were covered by preexisting composite maps such as the Hall and others (1984) and Pilger and others (1984) maps in the Gulf of Mexico, the Hall and Westbrook (1989) map in the Caribbean Sea, the Westbrook (1984) map of the eastern Caribbean Sea, and the Roberts and Jones (1984) map in the northeast Atlantic Ocean. Other areas in which digitized data were used were Project Magnet data of the U.S. Navy off the east coast of the United States, eastern Siberia, the North Atlantic in the vicinity of Iceland, Venezuela, and several small areas in the Caribbean Sea not covered by the Hall and Westbrook (1989) map.

All composited and levelled data were gridded at a 2-km interval using the minimum curvature method employing the North American transverse mercator projection with a central meridian of longitude 100° west, a scale factor of 0.926 and an Earth radius of 6,371.024 km. In most cases this gridding led to acceptable data presentation, except where anomaly trends were at a small angle to ship or aircraft tracks and the line spacing was measured in tens of kilometers. An example is shown in the area south of Alaska where an obvious linear trend has been broken up into a series of separate anomalies. In areas where data are sparse, only the actual data are shown; all gridded data beyond a chosen radius from an actual data point were blanked out on the map.

Color-separates of the four quadrants forming the map were prepared from the gridded data set by the GSC using an Optronics wide-format laser plotter. These were sent to the USGS for final cartographic work and printing at a scale of 1:5,000,000. The magnetic values are presented in 16 colors representing 100 nT (γ) intervals. Another form of this map is the shaded-relief map presented in Figure 1. In this map, magnetic anomaly values are assigned a vertical scale to represent topography and illuminated from a light source at an azimuth of 315° and an inclination of 40°. This form of presentation emphasizes shorter wavelength anomalies, particularly those trending nearly perpendicular to the azimuth of the light source. This map, and the colored version of the map at a scale of 1:20,000,000 on Plate 1B, can be used to identify anomalies discussed in the text.

ANOMALY SOURCES

The broad spectrum of magnetic anomaly patterns and types observed over North America and environs is indicative of the wide variety of geologic features and terranes that are present and the complex history of the continent and adjacent oceanic crust. These anomalies are caused by lateral variations in the magnetic polarization of the lithosphere, which reflect the nature, history, and distribution of the ferrimagnetic minerals, primarily magnetite. The anomalies of small-scale maps, such as the map of North America, largely originate within the igneous/metamorphic basement rocks that are mostly hidden by nonmagnetic sediments. Thus, the anomalies are more complex than would be anticipated from the nonmagnetic surface formations. Locally, anomalies occur due to igneous rocks that have intruded or extruded onto the sedimentary rock section.

Lateral magnetic polarization variations, and thus anomaly sources, occur throughout the crust due to structural disturbances, intrusions, metamorphism, and alteration. Petrological studies and magnetization measurements on rock samples derived from the upper mantle suggest that ferrimagnetic minerals, and thus anomaly sources, are limited to the crust (Wasilewski and others, 1979). However, the existence of deeper sources cannot be ruled out because of the possible presence of serpentinized zones within the upper mantle and ferrimagnetic elemental iron that may occur in the deep crust or upper mantle (Haggerty, 1978). Prominent long-wavelength anomalies are anticipated from the lower crust because the magnetization of these rocks, although highly variable, is on the average an order of magnitude greater than the upper crust (e.g., Hall, 1974). In tectonically active regions the

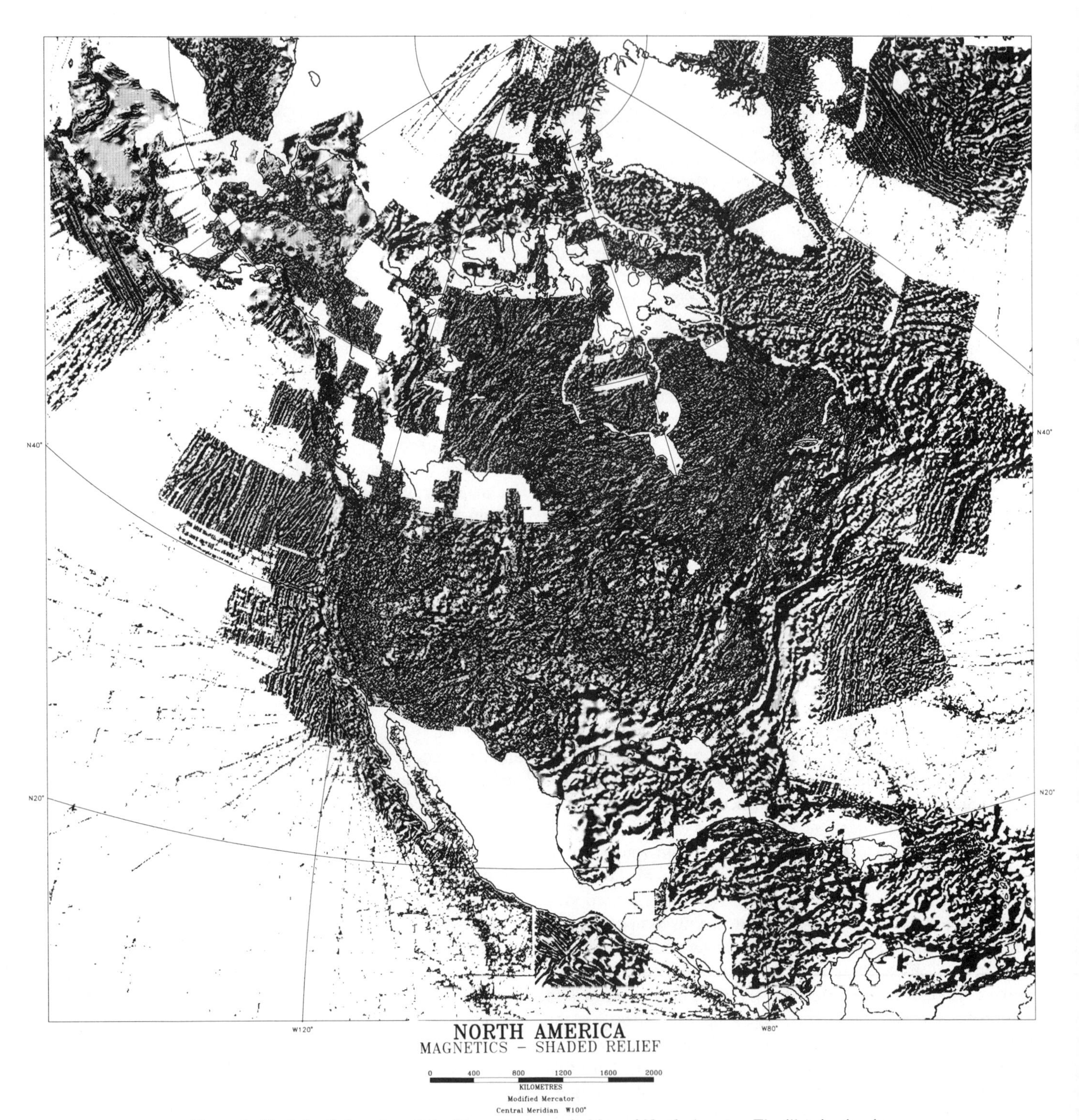

Figure 1. Shaded-relief version of the *Magnetic Anomaly Map of North America*. The illumination is from a light source at an azimuth of 315° and an inclination of 40°.

Curie isotherm of magnetite (≈580°C), the temperature at which this mineral loses its ferrimagnetic properties and thus its intense magnetization, may be warped upward into the crust by increased heat transfer from the mantle into the crust. The result is a decrease in the thickness of the magnetic layer and a negative magnetic anomaly. The prominent magnetic anomaly anticipated at the continental margin due to the profound change in thickness of the crust between the continent and ocean is not observed, probably because the long-wavelength (i.e., continent/ocean) anomalies may be removed with the main, core field of the Earth (Meyer and others, 1983).

The magnetic polarization of crustal rocks is caused by induction in the Earth's current magnetic field and remanent magnetization reflecting ancient or modern geomagnetic fields. The majority of the anomalies on the North American continent are believed to be caused by induction because the character of the anomalies is generally consistent with the direction of the Earth's field (Hinze and Zietz, 1985). Furthermore, most of the anomalies outside of the Cordillera on the western portion of the continent are derived from ancient rocks that have largely lost their original remanence by long-term decay or alteration by subsequently superimposed processes. However, this generalization must be used with caution because of notable exceptions. For example, the 1,100-Ma Keweenawan mafic volcanic rocks of the Lake Superior region contain a strong remanent component from the time of their origin. The Tertiary and Quaternary volcanic rocks of western North America also carry a strong remanence, and the higher temperature rocks of the lower crust probably have a prominent viscous remanent magnetization directed along the current geomagnetic field.

The magnetic anomaly caused by induced magnetic polarization of a specific geologic feature will vary over the North American map because of the spatial difference in the direction and intensity of the inducing geomagnetic field. The intensity of the field, and thus the resulting magnetic polarization, increases by roughly one-third from the southern to the northern portions of the map. The inclination of the field varies from 40° in the south to 90° at the north magnetic pole in northern Canada, and the declination varies greatly as the magnetic pole is approached, although over the vast majority of the continent the change is less than ±30°. As a result of these variations, the anomaly from a specific positive magnetic polarization contrast within the Earth will increase in amplitude and symmetry from the southern to the northern portions of the map. The anomaly maximum will shift to the north, and the polarization minimum on the north side of the maximum will decrease with increasing magnetic latitude. The imaginary line connecting the centers of the maximum and minimum of the anomaly will change with the declination of the geomagnetic field.

Typical magnetic anomalies derived from a geologically reasonable, but idealized, model centered over a Paleozoic cratonic basin in mid–North America are illustrated in Figure 2. The figure shows the two-dimensional geological model from the surficial Paleozoic sedimentary rocks to the upper mantle along a west-to-east profile. Anomalies originating with sources in the basin and the topography on the basement, as well as lower crustal sources and variations due to the depth of the Moho, have amplitudes of at most a few tens of nanoteslas. In contrast, upper crustal–source anomalies dominate the profile and are likely to do so on the *Magnetic Anomaly Map of North America.* This total intensity magnetic profile also illustrates the profound effect of source depth on magnetic anomalies. The two anomalies at the western margin of the upper crustal–features profile are from equivalent sources, but the amplitude of the easternmost anomaly is greatly diminished and the anomaly broadened by only a few kilometers of increased depth. The marked effect of source depth is increased as the source shape approaches a concentrated three-dimensional element.

The amplitude of the anomalies derived from induced magnetization is also a function of the contrast in the magnetic minerals, primarily magnetite. Unfortunately, magnetite is a minor component of most rocks and thus is only indirectly related to lithology and rock-classification schemes. The relationship between magnetic-mineral content (and thus magnetic anomaly

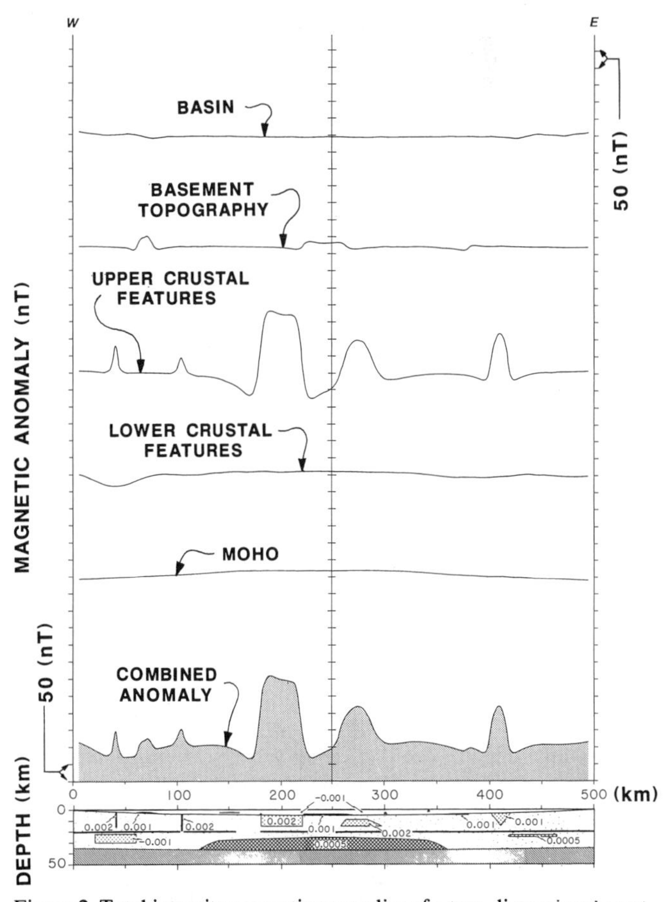

Figure 2. Total intensity magnetic anomalies of a two-dimensional crustal geologic model illustrating individual anomalies and the combined anomaly from all sources. Numbers on model indicate magnetic susceptibility contrasts in emu/cm^3, and tic marks on vertical scale are 50 nT(γ) intervals. Model is positioned in the central Midcontinent (after Hinze and Hildenbrand, 1989).

intensity) is tenuous. Broad generalizations are used in interpretation, but the exceptions to these limit their usefulness. For example, mafic rocks are generally more magnetic than felsic rocks, yet there are excellent examples of granites that cause positive magnetic anomalies. Sedimentary rocks are considered to be magnetically transparent, but Precambrian sedimentary iron formations of the Canadian Shield produce some of the most intense magnetic anomalies in North America. Additional discussions on the problems of relating magnetic anomalies to specific geologic sources are discussed by Hinze and Zietz (1985).

Marine magnetic anomalies are dominated by the linear striping produced by rocks alternately magnetized by polarity reversals of the geomagnetic field as mantle rocks are intruded into and extruded onto the oceanic crust as part of the sea-floor–spreading process. Other, unlineated magnetic anomalies of the oceans are related to sea mounts, structural features such as ridges, plateaus, and faults, and perhaps to geochemical alteration of the oceanic crust. Harrison (1987a, b) presents a comprehensive review of the nature and source of marine magnetic anomalies.

GEOLOGIC SIGNIFICANCE OF SELECTED ANOMALIES

The previous discussion points out the complexity of relating magnetic anomalies to specific geologic features. However, continental-scale magnetic anomaly maps can be extremely useful even where the specific lithology and geometry of the source are not interpretable. Because the primary source of anomalies on these maps is the upper crust, magnetic anomalies can be used to identify steeply dipping structural disturbances such as faults, patterns of anomalies can be mapped to characterize and identify specific basement rock terranes with generally consistent structures and lithologies, and specific anomalies can be interpreted in terms of geologic units and their magnetic characteristics. The effectiveness of these interpretations is in large measure a function of the amount of collateral geologic and geophysical information available. The interpretation of the *Magnetic Anomaly Map of North America* will be most successful where the anomaly can be identified with a known geologic feature and extrapolated with the magnetic anomaly into areas where limited geologic information is available. To illustrate the potential of the North American map, we briefly review a range of magnetic anomalies apparent on the map. Comprehensive analysis and interpretation of the map await integration of available geological and geophysical data in selected regions and quantitative modeling of data derived from larger scale maps.

Marine magnetic stripes

Pervasive alternating bands or stripes of positive and negative anomalies is the distinctive feature of the ocean basins on the *Magnetic Anomaly Map of North America.* Vine and Matthews (1963) suggested that these anomalies record the reversal history of the Earth's magnetic field preserved in the oceanic rocks as they are emplaced in oceanic rifts. Dating of these reversals of the geomagnetic field (Heirtzler and others, 1968) showed that much of the ocean crust could be dated. Furthermore, oceanic crustal rocks, as they upwelled at mid-oceanic ridges, moved away from the ridges at speeds from 1 to 10 cm/yr. The study of these anomalies thus led to the confirmation of sea-floor spreading and the concept of plate tectonics that has so totally revolutionized the Earth sciences. Investigation of individual magnetic striping patterns can be used to establish sea-floor–spreading directions, rates of movement, and the locations of faults.

Modeling of marine magnetic anomalies and consideration of the measurements of the magnetization of oceanic crustal samples indicates that the source of the anomalies is not limited to the upper volcanic rock layers, but probably involves sources within most of the oceanic crust (Harrison, 1987a). In general, the younger magnetic anomalies are greater in amplitude than the older anomalies more distant from mid-oceanic ridges. This decay in amplitude with age probably results from low-temperature oxidation of the ferrimagnetic minerals and thus a decrease in magnetization of the source rocks, although other processes may be involved, including increasing source depth as the rocks move away from the inflated ridge, and are covered by an increasing thickness of sediments.

East Coast magnetic anomaly

One of the truly prominent anomalies of the North American map is the East Coast magnetic anomaly (ECMA), a linear positive magnetic anomaly that crudely coincides with the edge of the continental shelf over much of its length from Nova Scotia to Georgia (Fig. 1; Plate 1B). The anomaly turns into the continent at roughly 31°N latitude and continues with a strong minimum to the north in an arcuate fashion across Georgia into Alabama. The continental portion is referred to as the Brunswick magnetic anomaly. The ECMA is a typical feature of rifted passive continental margins in contrast to transform fault or subduction margins as found along the west coast of North America (Heirtzler, 1985).

Taylor and others (1968), after reviewing previous studies of ECMA and modeling it, favored a felsic basement-intrusive source along the pre-Paleozoic continent/ocean boundary. Other workers (e.g., Behrendt and Klitgord, 1980) support an origin associated with the continental-edge effect. Alsop and Talwani (1984) and Behrendt and Grim (1985) suggest that the anomaly is the sum of effects from the continental edge and volcanic rocks along the edge associated with the rifting of the original continental mass. McBride and Nelson (1988) show that both the ECMA and the Brunswick anomaly can be accounted for with an oceanward dipping, positive-magnetization-contrast source. They suggest that this source may be lower continental or oceanic crust thrust upward during Alleghanian continental collision or mafic igneous rocks intruded during Mesozoic rifting. Oceanward of the ECMA the magnetic anomaly field is featureless as a result of the constant magnetic-field polarity during Jurassic time (Larson and Hilde, 1975) when the crust originated and acquired its remanent magnetization or because of subsequent modification of preexisting remanent magnetization (Bleil and Peterson, 1983).

Oceanic crust between Baffin Island and Greenland

Geologic history of the rupture of continental blocks can be deciphered from magnetic striping anomalies that are produced in the intervening ocean by sea-floor spreading, and preserved by the increasing separation of the ruptured blocks and reversals of the geomagnetic field. Such is the case for the separation of Greenland from North America and Baffin Island. Although earlier workers identified the marked striping anomalies of the Labrador Sea off the northeast coast of Labrador and their use in dating the opening of this segment of the Atlantic Ocean, Srivastava (1978) was able to use both airborne and shipborne magnetic observations to map subtle magnetic striping anomalies northward across the Davis Straits into Baffin Bay, and between Baffin Island and Greenland (Fig. 1). Dating of the striping led him to suggest that whereas the Labrador Sea opened between 75 and 60 Ma, Baffin Bay and the Davis Straits opened from 60 to 40 Ma.

Grenville basement province magnetic pattern

Within the North American craton, magnetic anomaly patterns can be grouped into segments with relatively consistent anomaly characteristics that are identified with basement terranes. In addition, linear anomalies transect the more pervasive anomaly patterns. These are associated with faults and rifts that postdate the basement construction and predate extensive incursions of seas with their related sediments that hide the terranes from direct view.

An example of the use of magnetic anomaly patterns in mapping basement terranes occurs in the eastern craton where rocks involved in the 1,150- to 1,000-Ma Grenvillian Orogeny crop out on the Canadian Shield and extend southerly into the subsurface of the United States. Numerous subdivisions of this Grenville basement province in the outcrop region have been defined by detailed geological mapping and are supported by magnetic anomaly patterns (e.g., Moore, 1986; Forsyth and others, 1989), although the boundaries of these terranes are seldom marked by specific anomalies. The anomaly patterns have been used to extrapolate outcropping terranes beneath the Phanerozoic cover of the craton of the United States and to identify terranes that do not crop out (Lidiak and Hinze, 1989). The availability of the North American map has been particularly useful in this regard (Fig. 1; Plate 1B).

Over the Grenville Province of the Canadian Shield the magnetic anomalies occur in belts, made up of an intricate "birdseye" pattern, that trend north to northeast. These same trends are identified east of the New York–Alabama Lineament (King and Zietz, 1978) in the eastern United States where they are broadened and attenuated and thus mark the southerly continuation of the Grenville Province beneath the only mildly deformed Phanerozoic sedimentary rocks of the craton. The western edge of the Grenville Province in Canada where the rocks involved in the Grenville Orogeny have been thrust over the older Superior Province rocks (Green and others, 1988) is dominated by a paired curvilinear anomaly consisting of a sharp high on the northwest, and a less intense, broad minimum on the southeast. This pattern can be traced from Labrador across Quebec and Ontario to the north shore of Lake Huron and is related to the westernmost subprovince or terrane of the Grenville Province, the Grenville Front tectonic zone. The magnetic anomaly pattern is associated with the high-grade metamorphic rocks of this zone and the adjacent segment of the Central Gneiss Belt. It can be traced south across Lake Huron into northern Ohio where the westernmost Grenville Province is reflected in a series of relatively narrow and complex north-trending magnetic highs and lows. These are believed to be associated with a terrane that extends south into Kentucky and Tennessee, but does not crop out on the Canadian Shield (Lidiak and Hinze, 1989). Farther south in the United States, the magnetic anomalies do not provide a definitive clue to the continuation of the Grenville Province and location of the Grenville Front.

Midcontinent Rift System

One of the more prominent magnetic anomalies in central North America is the western limb of the Midcontinent Rift (MCR) System (Fig. 1; Plate 1B). The rift is notable for its great length, extending from eastern Kansas to western Lake Superior and south from eastern Lake Superior to southeastern Michigan, and the manner in which it transects the pervasive magnetic patterns of the region. This 1,100-Ma paleorift (Halls, 1978; Green, 1983; Van Schmus and Hinze, 1985) crops out in the Lake Superior region; elsewhere along its length it is known only from occasional drill holes and geophysical information. The related magnetic anomalies are primarily due to mafic igneous rocks; largely basalts, that have a strong remanent component and are magnetized both positively and negatively. The resulting magnetic anomalies are complex, especially because deformation of the volcanic rocks was subsequent to their acquisition of strong remanence. Despite this complexity, magnetic modeling has been useful (e.g., McSwiggen and others, 1987; Chandler and others, 1989), together with gravity and seismic-reflection studies, in showing that the thickness of the volcanic rocks is generally between 10 and 20 km and they are overlain by as much as 10 km of rift-related clastic sedimentary rocks (Cannon and others, 1989). The nature of the MCR and character of the rift-related rocks are important constraints on continental crustal evolution (Hinze and Kelly, 1988).

New Madrid rift complex

Not all identified paleorifts of the North American midcontinent have as profound an anomaly as the MCR. Such is the case with the New Madrid rift complex that has been identified underlying the northern Mississippi Embayment on the basis of combined magnetic, gravity, and seismic data interpretation (Ervin and McGinnis, 1975; Hildenbrand and others, 1977; Braile and others, 1986). A sediment-filled graben extending from east-central Arkansas into western Kentucky and southeastern Missouri along the axis of the embayment was mapped on the basis of two parallel, linear northeast trends of magnetic anomalies (Fig. 1; Plate 1B) that are interpreted as having originated from mafic intrusives along the graben-margin faults, and attenuated anomalies over the graben. Braile and others (1982), using detailed maps, suggest that this late Precambrian or early Paleozoic feature continues into southwest Indiana and breaks up into a complex of similar features in southern Illinois, with one limb extending into Kentucky and another continuing up the Mississippi River toward St. Louis, Missouri. The rift complex and particularly the graben in Arkansas, Tennessee, and Missouri is one of the most intensely earthquake-active intracratonic regions of North America (Hinze and Hildenbrand, 1989).

Great Valley, California magnetic anomaly

Perhaps the most conspicuous magnetic anomaly in the western United States occurs over the sediments of the Great Valley of central California (Fig. 1; Plate 1B). The anomaly extends from the Garlock fault in southern California north to near the Oregon border. However, it is displaced a few tens of kilometers to the west near 40°N latitude along a west-northwest strike-slip fault (Hamilton, 1987) and is split into two parallel segments south of roughly 36°N latitude. Basement drillhole data together with magnetic and gravity modeling show that the source of the anomaly is a complex of mafic igneous rocks: gabbro, diabase, diorite, andesite, and schist (Thompson and Talwani, 1964; Griscom, 1966; Cady, 1975). These mafic rocks are identified as a westward-dipping Jurassic ophiolite that was attached to the continent during Mesozoic subduction of oceanic lithosphere beneath the western United States. North of the Great Valley the magnetic anomaly pattern follows the exposed Paleozoic-Mesozoic ophiolite thrust slices in the Klamath Mountains of northern California (Hamilton, 1987). Perhaps the north-striking regional magnetic maximum in the Coast Ranges of Oregon and Washington also is related to ophiolitic rocks. Interpretation of the Great Valley magnetic anomaly is an illustration of the use of the *Magnetic Anomaly Map of North America* to map buried rock units that are significant in developing the accretionary history of the continent.

Great Slave Lake shear zone

Perhaps the most obvious fault system apparent on the North American map (Fig. 1; Plate 1B) from its linearity, great length (≈1,300 km), and disruption of adjacent magnetic anomaly patterns is the Great Slave Lake shear zone (McDonald fault), which extends from within the Thelon Basin through the exposed Precambrian Shield on the East Arm of Great Slave Lake in the Canadian Northwest Territories in a southwesterly direction under the Phanerozoic sedimentary rocks of the Interior Plains to the foothills of the Cordillera in British Columbia. It is identified as a continental transform fault that accommodated eastward motion of the Slave Craton as it collided obliquely with the western margin of the Churchill Province during Early Proterozoic time (Hoffman, 1987, 1988; Hanmer, 1988). Interpretation of the magnetic anomaly data has played an important part in recognizing the fault and the associated 300 to 700 km of dextral displacement.

Central western United States quiet zone

One of the prominent features of the North American map is a broad northeasterly striking region of few magnetic anomalies that extends from central Nevada into Wyoming. The southeastern margin of this zone coincides with the Cheyenne Belt in southeastern Wyoming that has been recognized by Houston and others (1979) as a shear zone that marks the boundary between Archean, Wyoming Province, rocks to the north and the accreted Proterozoic rocks to the south. This margin also coincides with the northern and western margin of the Early Proterozoic Yavapai-cycle rocks (Hoffmann, 1988) that are interpreted as island arcs and associated sedimentary basins accreted onto the Wyoming Province. The northwestern margin coincides with the southern boundary of the Snake River Plain in Idaho. Mabey and others (1978) define this zone of attenuated anomalies where basement magnetic anomalies are largely absent as the "quiet basement zone." They point out that although the quiet zone could be in part related to the deep burial of the basement crystalline rocks by the thrust-thickened sedimentary rocks of the Cordilleran system, the change in anomaly character is probably due to a variation in the nature of the crust. The change in magnetic anomaly pattern also has been related to a thinned crust, perhaps a thinned magnetic crust owing to an elevated Curie isotherm. The latter hypothesis is untenable as a result of filtering of the magnetic anomaly data of Nevada by Blakely (1988), which shows numerous deep magnetic sources. He argues that the quiet zone, at least in Nevada, is the result of limited basaltic volcanism dating from 17 Ma in this region compared to the surrounding region and possibly to igneous rocks that contain less magnetite; for example, the presence of S-type granites with probable sedimentary sources rather than magnetic, I-type granites, derived from igneous rocks. The full story on the source of this anomaly pattern awaits further investigation and correlation with the crustal geology.

Caribbean Basin

The magnetic anomaly pattern over the Caribbean Sea consists mostly of elliptical anomalies of moderate amplitude reflecting the nature of the underlying continental crust. Linear anomalies also indicate major fault zones. Distinct anomalies occur over most of the islands in the Lesser Antilles chain, indicative of the volcanic rocks that underlie many of the islands at no great depth; Barbados is an exception. The anomalous field of the Gulf of Mexico is especially flat, reflecting the great thickness of sediment present over much of the Gulf.

SUMMARY

The *Magnetic Anomaly Map of North America,* the first such map of a complete continent, is an important new tool for regional geological mapping. It is particularly useful when combined with geologic information and other geophysical data. It is obvious on viewing the map that data gaps for significant geologic regions seriously detract from its usefulness. We await the cooperation of government agencies and the geoscience community in filling these gaps and the preparation of a revised, improved edition of the map.

REFERENCES CITED

Alsop, L. E., and Talwani, M., 1984, The East Coast magnetic anomaly: Science, v. 226, p. 1189–1191.

Behrendt, J. C., and Grim, M. S., 1985, Structure of the U.S. Atlantic continental margin from derivative and filtered maps of the magnetic field, *in* Hinze, W. J., ed., The Utility of Regional Gravity and Magentic Anomaly Maps: Society of Exploration Geophysicists, p. 325–338.

Behrendt, J. C., and Klitgord, K. D., 1980, High resolution aeromagnetic survey of the U.S. Atlantic Continental margin: Geophysics, v. 45, p. 1813–1846.

Blakely, R. J., 1988, Curie temperature isotherm analysis and tectonic implications of aeromagnetic data from Nevada: Journal of Geophysical Research, v. 93, p. 11817–11832.

Bleil, V., and Petersen, N., 1983, Variations in magnetization intensity and low-temperature titanomagnetite oxidation of ocean floor basalts: Nature, v. 301, p. 384–388.

Bond, K. R., and Zietz, I., 1987, Composite Anomaly Map of the Conterminous United States, west of 96° longitude: U.S. Geological Survey Geophysical Investigations Map GP-977, 2 sheets, scale 1:2,500,000.

Braile, L. W., Keller, G. R., Hinze, W. J., and Lidiak, E. G., 1982, An ancient rift complex and its relation to contemporary seismicity in the New Madrid seismic zone: Tectonics, v. 1, p. 225–237.

Braile, L. W., Hinze, W. J., Keller, G. R., Lidiak, E. G., and Sexton, J. L., 1986, Tectonic development of the New Madrid Rift Complex, Mississippi Embayment, North America: Tectonophysics, v. 131, p. 1–21.

Cady, J. W., 1975, Magnetic and gravity anomalies in the Great Valley and western Sierra Nevada metamorphic belt, California: Geological Society of America Special Paper 168, 56 p.

Cannon, W. F., and 11 others, 1989, The Midcontinent Rift beneath Lake Superior from GLIMPCE seismic reflection profiling: Tectonics (in press).

Chandler, V. W., McSwiggen, P. L., Morey, G. B., Hinze, W. J., and Anderson, R. L., 1989, Interpretation of seismic reflection, gravity, and magnetic data across the middle Proterozoic Midcontinent Rift System in western Wisconsin, eastern Minnesota, and central Iowa: American Association of Petroleum Geologists Bulletin, (in press).

Committee for the Magnetic Anomaly Map of North America, 1987, Magnetic anomaly map of North America: Boulder, Colorado, Geological Society of America, CSM-3, 4 sheets, scale 1:5,000,000.

Dods, S. D., Teskey, D. J., and Hood, P. J., 1987, Magnetic Anomaly Map of Canada: Geological Survey of Canada Map 1255A (5th ed.), scale 1:5,000,000.

Ervin, C. P., and McGinnis, L. D., 1975, Reelfoot Rift—Reactivated Precursor to the Mississippi Embayment: Geological Society of America Bulletin, v. 86, p. 1287–1295.

Forsyth, D. A., Thomas, M. D., Real, D., Abinett, D., Broome, J., and Halpenny, J., 1989, Geophysical investigations of the central metasedimentary belt, Grenville Province—Quebec to northern New York State: Proceedings of the 7th International Basement Tectonics Meeting (in press).

Godson, R. H., 1985, Preparation of magnetic-anomaly maps of Alaska and Hawaii, *in* Hinze, W. J., ed., The Utility of Regional Gravity and Magnetic Anomaly Maps: Society of Exploration Geophysicists, p. 25–32.

Green, A. G., and nine others, 1988, Crustal structure of the Grenville Front and adjacent terranes: Geology, v. 16, p. 788–792.

Green, J. C., 1983, Geologic and geochemical evidence for the nature and development of the Middle Proterozoic (Keweenawan) Midcontinent Rift of North America: Tectonophysics, v. 94, p. 413–437.

Griscom, A., 1966, Magnetic data and regional structure in northern California: California Division of Mines and Geology Bulletin, v. 94, p. 407–417.

Haggerty, S. E., 1978, Mineralogical constraints on Curie isotherms in deep crustal magnetic anomalies: Geophysical Research Letters, v. 5, p. 105–108.

Hall, D. H., 1974, Long-wavelength aeromagnetic anomalies and deep crustal magnetization in Manitoba and northwestern Ontario, Canada: Pure and Applied Geophysics, v. 40, p. 403–430.

Hall, S. A., and Westbrook, G. K., 1989, Magnetic anomaly map of the Caribbean region, *in* Dengo, G., and Case, J. E., eds., The Caribbean region: Boulder, Colorado, The Geological Society of America, The Geology of North America, v. H (in press).

Hall, S. A., Shepherd, A. V., Titus, M. W., and Snow, R. L., 1984, Magnetic total intensity anomalies east of 90 degrees, *in* Buffler, R. T., Locker, S. D., Bryant, W. R., Hall, S. A., and Pilger, R. H., Jr., eds., Gulf of Mexico: Woods Hole, Massachusetts, Marine Science International, Ocean Drilling Program Regional Atlas 6, scale 1:3,000,000 at 24°N.

Halls, H. C., 1978, The late Precambrian central North America rift system—A survey of recent geological and geophysical investigations, *in* Neumann, E. R., and Ramberg, I. B., eds., Tectonics and Geophysics of Continental Rifts: Hingham, Massachusetts, NATO Advanced Study Institute Series C, v. 37, p. 111–123.

Hamilton, W., 1987, Plate-tectonic evolution of the western U.S.A.: Episodes, v. 10, p. 271–277.

Hanmer, S., 1988, Great Slave Lake shear zone, Canadian Shield—Reconstructed vertical profile of a crustal-scale fault zone: Tectonophysics, v. 144, p. 245–264.

Harrison, C.G.A., 1987a, Marine magnetic anomalies—the origin of stripes: Annual Reviews of Earth and Planetary Science, v. 15, p. 505–543.

—— , 1987b, The crustal field, *in* Jacobs, J. A., ed., Geomagnetism, v. 1: Orlando, Florida, Academic Press, p. 513–610.

Heirtzler, J. R., 1985, The change in the magnetic anomaly pattern at the ocean-continent boundary, *in* Hinze, W. J., ed., The Utility of Regional Gravity and Magnetic Anomaly Maps: Society of Exploration Geophysicists, p. 339–346.

Hiertzler, J. R., Dickson, G. O., Herron, E. M., Pitman, W. C., and LePichon, X., 1968, Marine magnetic anomalies, geomagnetic reversals, and motions of the ocean floor and continents: Journal of Geophysical Research, v. 73, p. 2119–2136.

Hildenbrand, T. G., Kane, M. F., and Stauder, W., 1977, Magnetic and gravity anomalies in the northern Mississippi Embayment and their spatial relation to seismicity: U.S. Geological Survey Miscellaneous Field Studies Map MF-914, scale 1:1,000,000.

Hinze, W. J., and Hildenbrand, T. G., 1989, The utility of geopotential field data in seismotectonic studies in the eastern United States: Seismological Research Letters (in press).

Hinze, W. J., and Kelly, W. C., 1988, Scientific drilling into the Midcontinent Rift Systems; Probing the processes and products of an ancient continental crustal rupture: EOS Transactions of the American Geophysical Union, v. 69, p. 1646, 1656–1657.

Hinze, W. J., and Zietz, I., 1985, The composite magnetic-anomaly map of the conterminous United States, *in* Hinze, W. J., ed., The Utility of Regional Gravity and Magnetic Anomaly Maps: Society of Exploration Geophysicists, p. 1–24.

Hoffman, P. F., 1987, Continental transform tectonics, Great Slave Lake shear zone (ca. 1.9 Ga), northwest Canada: Geology, v. 15, p. 785–788.

—— , 1988, United plates of America, the birth of a craton—Early Proterozoic assembly and growth of Laurentia: Annual Reviews of Earth and Planetary Sciences, v. 16, p. 543–604.

Houston, R. S., Karlstrom, K. E., Hills, F. A., and Smithson, S. B., 1979, The Cheyenne Belt—the major Precambrian crustal boundary in the western United States: Geological Society of America Abstracts with Programs, v. 11, p. 446.

King, E. R., and Zietz, I., 1978, The New York–Alabama lineament—Geophysical evidence for a major crustal break in the basement beneath the Appalachian basin: Geology, v. 6, p. 312–318.

Larson, R. L., and Hilde, T.W.C., 1975, A revised time scale of magnetic reversals for the Early Cretaceous and Late Jurassic: Journal of Geophysical Research, v. 80, p. 2586–2594.

Lidiak, E. G., and Hinze, W. J., 1989, Proterozoic rocks east and southeast of the Grenville Front (subsurface Grenville age rocks between the Adirondack Massif and the Black Warrior Basin), *in* Reed, J. C., Jr., and 6 others, eds., Precambrian–Conterminous U.S.: Boulder, Colorado, Geological Society of America, The Geology of North America, v. C–2, (in press).

Mabey, D. R., Zietz, I., Eaton, G. P., and Kleinkopf, M. D., 1978, Regional magnetic patterns in part of the Cordillera in the western United States, *in* Smith, R. B., and Eaton, G. P., eds., Cenozoic Tectonics and Regional Geophysics of the Western Cordillera: Geological Society of America Memoir 152, p. 93–106.

MacLaren, A. S., and Charbonneau, B. W., 1968, Characteristics of magnetic data over major subdivisions of the Canadian Shield: Geological Association of Canada Proceedings, v. 19, p. 57–65.

McBride, J. H., and Nelson, K. D., 1988, Integration of COCORP deep reflection and magnetic anomaly analysis in the southeastern United States; Implications for the origin of the Brunswick and East Coast magnetic anomalies: Geological Society of America Bulletin, v. 100, p. 436–445.

McSwiggen, P. L., Morey, G. B., and Chandler, V. W., 1987, New model of Midcontinent Rift in eastern Minnesota and western Wisconsin: Tectonics, v. 6, p. 677–685.

Meyer, J., Hufen, J.-H., Siebert, M., and Hahn, A., 1983, Investigations of the internal field by means of a global model of the Earth's crust: Zeitschrift Geophysika, v. 52, p. 71–84.

Moore, J. M., 1986, Introduction; "The Grenville problem" then and now, *in* Moore, J. M., Davidson, A., and Baer, A. J., eds., The Grenville Province: Geological Association of Canada Special Paper 31, p. 1–11.

Morley, L. W., MacLaren, A. S., and Charbonneau, B. W., 1968, Magnetic anomaly map of Canada: Geological Survey of Canada Map 1255A, 1st ed., scale 1:5,000,000.

Pilger, R. H., Jr., Rubin, D. S., and Kauth, L. M., 1984, Magnetic total intensity anomalies west of 90 degrees, *in* Buffler, R. T., Locker, S. D., Bryant, W. R., Hall, S. A., and Pilger, R. H., Jr., eds., Gulf of Mexico: Woods Hole, Massachusetts, Marine Science International, Ocean Margin Drilling Program Regional Atlas 6, scale, 1:3,000,000 at 24°N.

Roberts, I. G., and Jones, M. T., 1980, Magnetic anomalies in the northeast Atlantic: United Kingdom Institute of Oceanographic Sciences.

Sexton, J. L., Hinze, W. J., von Frese, R.R.B., and Braile, L. W., 1982, Long-wavelength aeromagnetic anomaly map of the conterminous United States: Geology, v. 10, p. 364–369.

Srivastava, S. P., 1978, Evolution of the Labrador Sea and its bearing on the early evolution of the North Atlantic: Geophysical Journal of the Royal Astronomical Society, v. 52, p. 313–357.

Taylor, P. T., Zietz, I., and Dennis, L. S., 1968, Geologic implications of aeromagnetic data for the eastern continental margin of the United States: Geophysics, v. 3, p. 755–780.

Thompson, G. A., and Talwani, M., 1964, Crustal structure from Pacific basin to central Nevada: Journal of Geophysical Research, v. 64, p. 49–59.

U.S. Geological Survey and Society of Exploration Geophysicists, 1982, Composite Magnetic Anomaly Map of the United States, Part A—Conterminous United States: U.S. Geological Survey Geophysical Investigations Map GP-954A, scale 1:2,500,000.

—— , 1984, Composite Magnetic Anomaly Map of the United States, Part B, Alaska and Hawaii: U.S. Geological Survey Geophysical Investigations Map GP-954B, scale 1:2,500,000.

Van Schmus, W. R., and Hinze, W. J., 1985, The Midcontinent Rift System: Annual Reviews of Earth and Planetary Sciences, v. 13, p. 345–383.

Vine, F. J., and Matthews, D. H., 1963, Magnetic anomalies over ocean ridges: Nature, v. 199, p. 947–949.

Wasilewski, P. J., Thomas, H. H., and Mayhew, M. A., 1979, The Moho as a magnetic boundary: Geophysical Research Letters, v. 6, p. 541–544.

Westbrook, G. K., 1984, Magnetic total intensity anomalies in Lesser Antilles in Arc and Adjacent Terranes, *in* Speed, R. C., and Westbrook, G. K., Ocean Margin Drilling Program Regional Atlas 1: Woods Hole, Massachusetts, Marine Science International, p. 4.

Williams, H., and Hatcher, R. D., Jr., Appalachian suspect terranes, *in* Hatcher, R. D., Jr., Williams, H., and Zietz, I., eds., Contributions to the Tectonics and Geophysics of Mountain Chains: Geological Society of America Memoir 158, p. 33–53.

Zietz, I., and 6 others, 1969, Aeromagnetic investigations of crustal structure for a strip across the western United States: Geological Society of America Bulletin, v. 80, p. 1703–1714.

Manuscript Accepted by the Society February 1, 1989

Printed in U.S.A.

The Geology of North America
Vol. A, The Geology of North America—An overview
The Geological Society of America, 1989

Chapter 4

The seismic structure of the continental crust and upper mantle of North America

Walter D. Mooney
U.S. Geological Survey, MS 977, 345 Middlefield Road, Menlo Park, California 94025
Lawrence W. Braile
Department of Earth and Atmospheric Sciences, Purdue University, West Lafayette, Indiana 47907

INTRODUCTION

The seismic structure of the crust and upper mantle provides critical information regarding lithospheric composition and evolution. There are large variations in fundamental properties such as crustal thickness, crustal and upper-mantle velocity structure, and the depth to the lithosphere/asthenosphere boundary, which are interpretable in terms of processes that have formed and modified the lithosphere. Much of what we know about the seismic structure of the lithosphere has been accumulated over the past 30 years from seismic refraction profiles and surface-wave studies. Modern seismic refraction studies use denser arrays of seismic sources and recorders, improving the resolution and reliability of crustal models. Within the last 15 years, the deep-seismic reflection technique has been widely applied and has provided fundamental new insights into the structure and physical properties of the crust. Recently, seismic investigations have provided a fresh look at the properties of the Moho and the upper mantle where we may discover the "driving forces" of continental tectonics.

In this discussion we define the lithosphere as the crust and the portion of the upper mantle above the seismic low-velocity layer (asthenosphere) that occurs at a depth of 60 to 200 km and is generally more evident in the shear-wave structure than in the compressional-wave structure. The low-velocity layer contrasts with the base of the crust (Moho), which is very pronounced in compressional-wave structure and is defined as the depth below which the seismic velocity (measured on a reversed seismic refraction profile) is greater than 7.6 km/s. Where the crust/mantle boundary has been examined in detail, it appears to consist of a laminated transition zone with a thickness of 2 to 5 km. The thickness of the Earth's crust is highly variable; typical oceanic crust has a thickness of about 7 ± 3 km (excluding the water column), and continental crust typically has a thickness of 25 to 50 km. "Transitional crust" is a useful term for the crust that links the oceans and the continents. It has a highly variable seismic velocity structure depending on whether it was formed at a rifted, accreted, stretched, or strike-slip continental margin. The boundaries between transitional crust and continental or oceanic crust are, by definition, gradational. The transitional crust of the continental margins of North America has been well studied and is described elsewhere (Keen and Hyndman, 1979; Keen and de Voogd, 1988; Trehu and others, 1989; Couch and Riddihough, 1989).

This chapter summarizes the seismic properties of the crust and upper mantle of North America, with particular emphasis on crustal thickness and seismic velocity structure, and the properties of the crust as revealed by seismic reflection profiles. In addition, we discuss such critical seismic features as crustal reflectivity, the nature of the Moho, and the depth to the lithosphere/asthenosphere boundary. Unfortunately, the physical interpretation of the seismic structure of the crust and upper mantle is highly ambiguous without supporting evidence from geological and geochemical studies, complementary geophysical data, and laboratory measurements of rock properties. While a comprehensive discussion of the geophysics of the crust and upper mantle is not possible in the space available, both accepted and currently debated theories are discussed.

CRUSTAL THICKNESS OF NORTH AMERICA

The thickness of the crust of North America is known primarily from seismic refraction profiles, although recent seismic reflection data have contributed additional estimates based on the "reflection Moho"; the latter is defined as the two-way traveltime to the last clear reflections above a seismically transparent upper mantle. Where seismic-reflection profiles are coincident with refraction profiles, the reflection Moho is nearly always at the same depth as the refraction Moho (Mooney and Brocher, 1987).

A new contour map of crustal thickness of North America has been compiled from all published seismic refraction and most deep reflection profiles (Fig. 1A). Most references for the United

Mooney, W. D., and Braile, L. W., 1989, The seismic structure of the continental crust and upper mantle of North America, *in* Bally, A. W., and Palmer, A. R., eds., The Geology of North America—An overview: Boulder, Colorado, Geological Society of America, The Geology of North America, v. A.

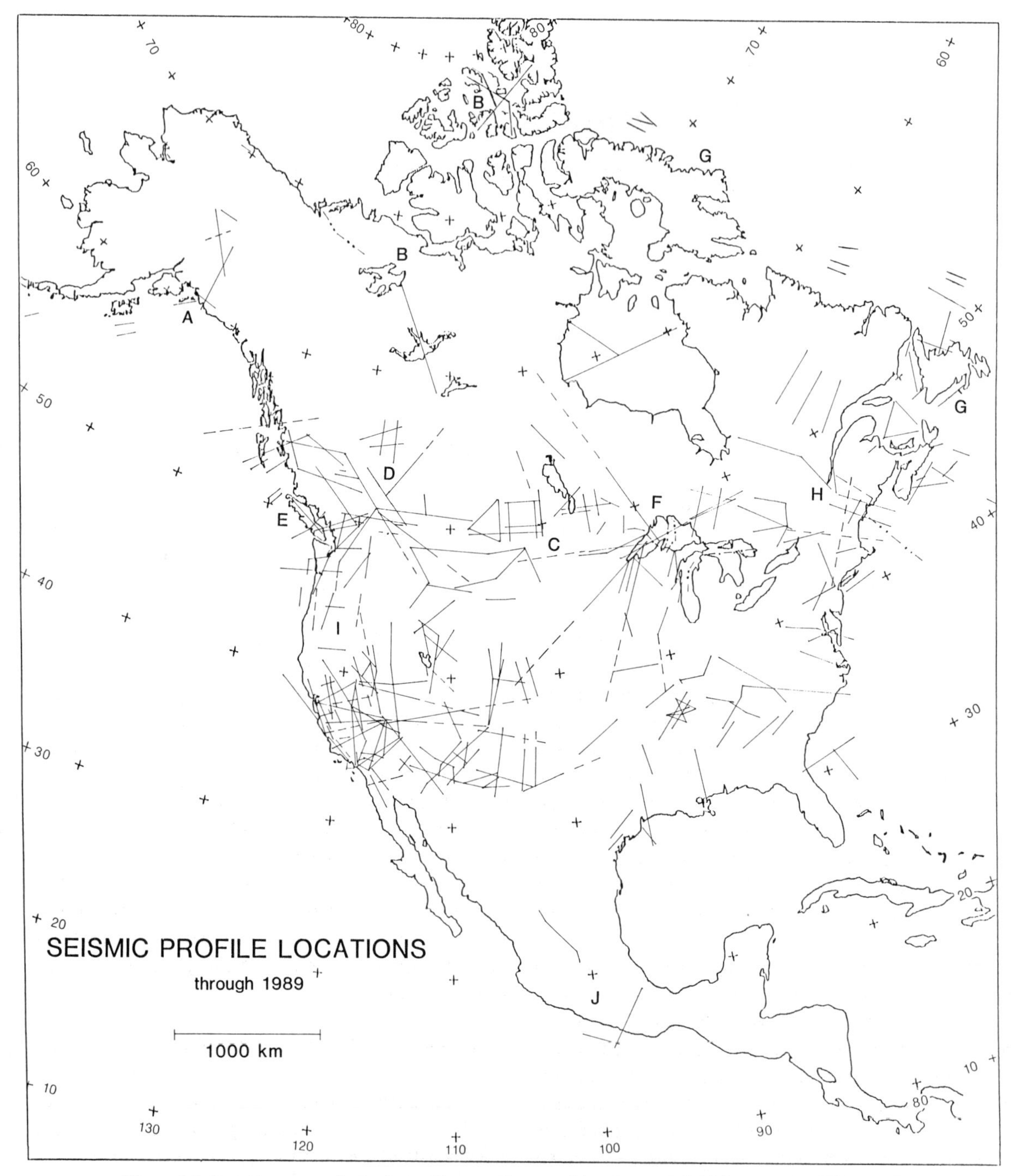

Figure 1A. Location map of seismic profiles used in compiling the crustal thickness map of Figure 1B. The profiles are concentrated in southern Canada and the United States. Key: solid lines, seismic-refraction profiles; dashed lines, unreversed portions of seismic-refraction profiles; dash-dot lines, seismic-reflection profiles. Most of the seismic-refraction profiles in southern Canada and the United States are identified and tabulated in Braile and others (1989); additional profiles used for this compilation are in the areas indicated by capital letters and are tabulated in Table 1.

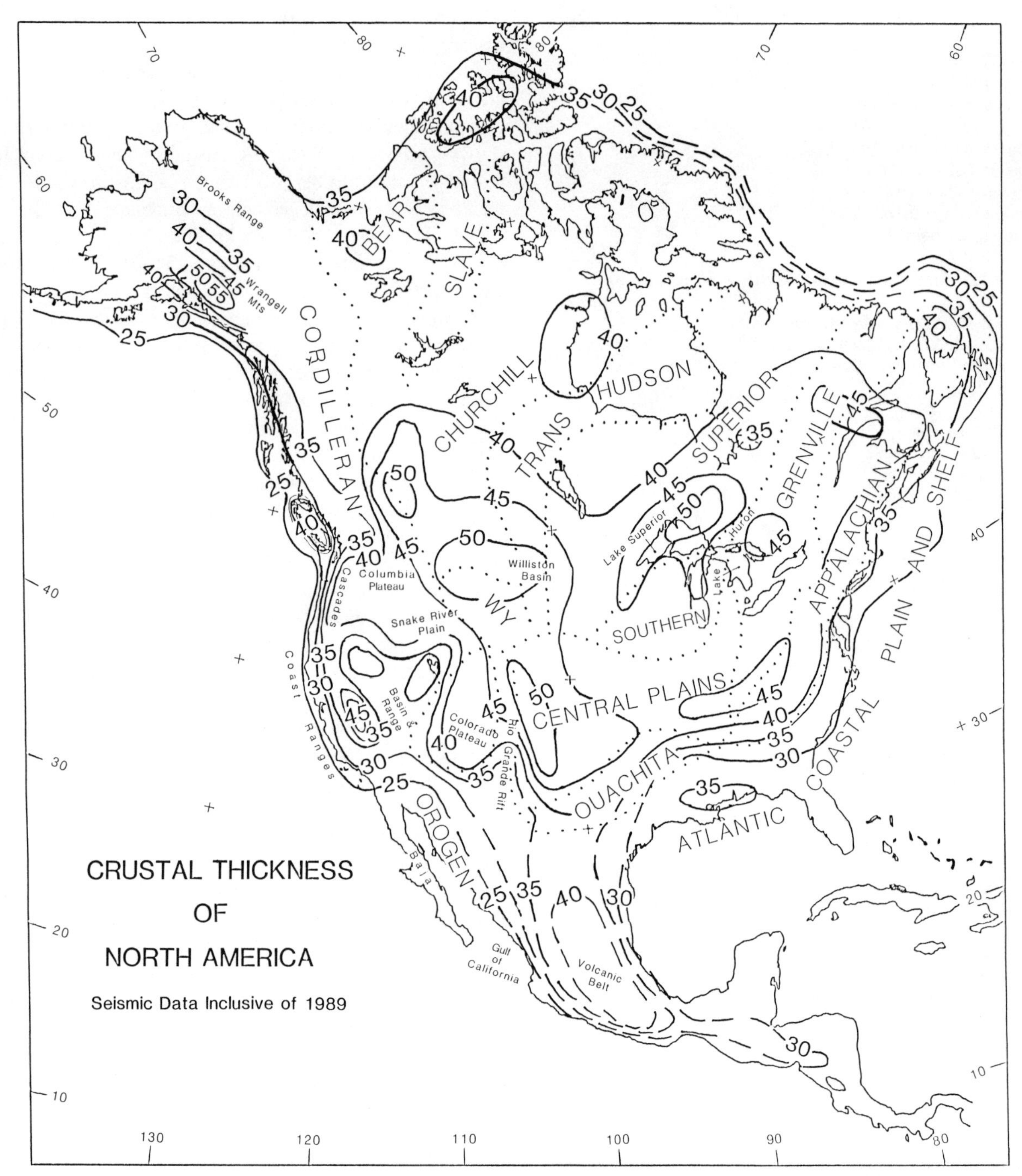

Figure 1B. Contour map of the crustal thickness (km) of North America superimposed on a simplified geologic province map. Seismic control is indicated in Figure 1A. The average crustal thickness is about 36 km, and varies from as little as 25 km at the coast to 55 km within the continental interior. The contours have been smoothed to better present the regional patterns. Variations in crustal thickness are poorly known for Mexico, central and northern Canada, and much of Alaska. There is a clear pattern of crustal thickening from the coasts to the interior, where the crust is generally 40 km thick or greater.

TABLE 1. SEISMIC PROFILE REFERENCES FOR NORTH AMERICA*

ALASKA (A)†
Shor, 1962
Hansen and others, 1968
Berg, 1973
Beaudoin and Fuis, 1988
Fuis and others, 1989
Ambos and others, 1989
Goodwin and others, 1989
Flueh and others, 1989

ARCTIC AND NORTHWESTERN CANADA (SOUTH OF 80°N LAT.) (B)
Barr, 1971
Sander, G. W., annd Overton, A., 1965
Sobczak, L. W., and Overton, A., 1984
Keen and Hyndman, 1979
Cook, 1988

CENTRAL CANADA (C)
Hall and Brisbin, 1965
Green and Hall, 1978
Kanasewich and others, 1987

SOUTHWEST CANADA (D)
Clowes and others, 1968
Cook and others, 1988
Zelt and Ellis, 1989

WEST COAST ISLANDS, CANADA (E)
Clowes and others, 1981
Clowes and others, 1987
Mackie and others, 1989

GREAT LAKES REGION (F)
Green and others, 1988
Boland and Ellis, 1989
Behrendt and others, 1988
Green and others, 1989

EASTERN SEABOARD (G)
Keen and Hyndman, 1979

QUEBEC TO GULF OF MAINE, U.S.A. (H)
Luetgert and others, 1987
Hutchinson and others, 1988
Spencer and others, 1989

OREGON (I)
Catchings and Mooney, 1988

MEXICO (J)
Meyer and others, 1961
Valdez and others, 1986

*Included here are only those references *not* cited in the summary of the conterminous U.S.A. and southern Canada by Braile and others (1989).
†Letter designations (A, B, C, etc.) following location refer to Figure 1A.

States and southern Canada are given in Braile and others (1989); additional references, particularly for Canada, Alaska, and Mexico, appear in Table 1.

Crustal thickness in North America varies by more than a factor of two, from about 25 to 55 km (Fig. 1B). The crust generally thickens from the coast to the continental interior, showing an overall increase in thickness with age. Some important observations to be made from a comparison of the crustal thickness contours with geologic age provinces (Fig. 1B) are:

1. The crust is 30 to 35 km thick along most of the east coast of North America but is about 25 to 30 km thick along the west coast. This difference reflects the contrasting processes of margin evolution by rifting (involving extension and magmatic inflation) on the east coast, versus accretion on the west coast.

2. Going from the near-shore to the continental interior, there is a continuous, gradual crustal thickening from about 30 km to 40 to 45 km in eastern North America, but a more complex pattern in western North America where magmatic and tectonic processes have more recently been active.

3. Volcanic regions (Cascade Range, Columbia Plateau, Snake River Plain, Mexican volcanic belt, Wrangell Mountains, Alaska) are characterized by a crust 40 to 45 km thick, even when surrounding regions have significantly thinner crust. This suggests that magmatic processes result in a characteristic crustal structure (both in terms of thickness and crustal velocities). This characteristic structure is probably a product of the thermal regime below a magmatic arc: crustal materials at depths greater than 45 km are above the solidus for basalt and therefore melt back into the mantle; conversely, thin crust (less than about 40 km) is thickened by intrusion of basaltic melts (Mooney and Weaver, 1989).

4. Despite an elevation of 1.0 to 2.5 km (which implies a crustal root), the Basin and Range of the western United States is characterized by a crustal thickness of only 30 to 35 km. This thickness is similar to that of extended crust worldwide (including the eastern margin of North America) and suggests that continental extension produces a characteristic crustal structure. This hypothesis is further supported by global seismic reflection data, which show similar features in the deep crust of extended terrains (Klemperer, 1988; McCarthy and Thompson, 1988). An important exception is the Keweenawan rift (1,100 Ma), which does not have a crustal structure similar to modern rift zones (see below).

5. The Archean and Proterozoic crust of the continental interior has a crustal thickness that ranges from 35 to 55 km (Fig. 1B), with an average thickness greater than the North American mean of 36 km. There is no simple correlation between crustal thickness and surface geology or age; the areas with the thickest crust (50 km or more) include the Williston Basin (intracratonic basin), western Great Plains (platform), and Lake Superior (Keweenawan rift). Several distinct mechanisms of crustal thickening must operate to explain the pattern of crustal thickness in North America.

STATISTICS OF THE CRUST AND UPPERMOST MANTLE

Statistics on crustal thickness, average crustal velocity, and Pn (upper mantle) velocity have been compiled by Braile and others (1989) for the United States and southern Canada where the most complete coverage of seismic lines exists (Fig. 1A). These statistics represent seismic properties versus number of observations and are biased by the nonuniform coverage of the North American continent. They therefore do *not* represent the average seismic properties per square kilometer, nor do they adequately sample all geologic and age provinces. Additional profiles are needed to obtain a more representative geological and geographical sample of North America.

From 337 seismic profiles, the mean crustal thickness is 36.1 km, with a standard deviation of 9 km (Fig. 2A). Onshore the thinnest and thickest crustal measurements are 18 km (coastal Oregon) and 58 km (eastern Montana), respectively, a variation of over 300 percent. (These single-point measurements do not appear on the contour map of Figure 1B, which has been smoothed.) Using Figure 2A as a guide we may view crustal thickness greater than 50 km or less than 25 km as "anomalous" and indicative of unusual crustal evolution. In the case of very thick crust, there must almost certainly have been an unusual tectonic history (e.g., major crustal overthrusting or voluminous magmatic additions to the crust). Thin crust has either been recently accreted (west coast margin) or has been rifted at an oceanic margin (Baja, California). Rifting within the continental interior does *not* typically produce crustal thicknesses less than 25 km.

Compared with North America, the continental crust of eastern and western Europe (Russian Platform to Atlantic Ocean, and Baltic Shield to Mediterranean Sea) has roughly the same average thickness (36 km) and variation in thickness (20 to 55 km; Meissner and others, 1987). Oceanic crust averages only 7 km in thickness, or 20 percent that of continental crust. Although the oceans cover more than 70 percent of the Earth's surface, there is a greater overall volume of continental crust due to its greater average thickness. This may not have been the case throughout the Earth's history because the continental crust has grown substantially in the past 2.5 b.y. (Meissner, 1986; Reymer and Schubert, 1987).

Mean crustal velocity is an important indicator of average crustal density and composition (e.g., Smithson and others, 1981). The mean crustal compressional wave (P-wave) velocity from 255 measurements is 6.44 km/s, with a standard deviation of 0.24 km/s (Fig. 2B). The mean P-wave velocity corresponds to a density of about 2.75 (±0.1) g/cc, a shear wave velocity of 3.7 (± 0.1) km/s (Gebrande, 1982) and an intermediate SiO_2 composition (e.g., quartz-diorite or diorite). The narrow range in average crustal velocity and density, amounting to a standard deviation of only 4 percent, is a remarkable observation and indicates that the formation of continental crust is firmly con-

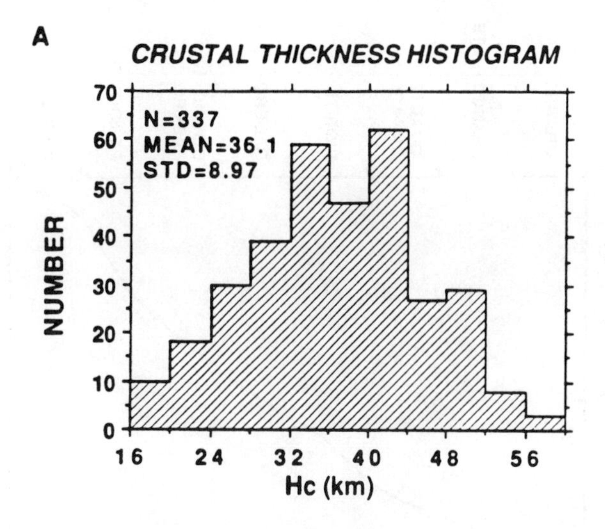

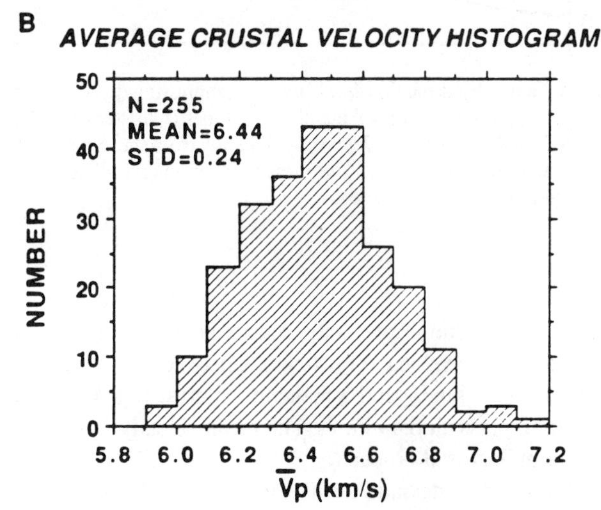

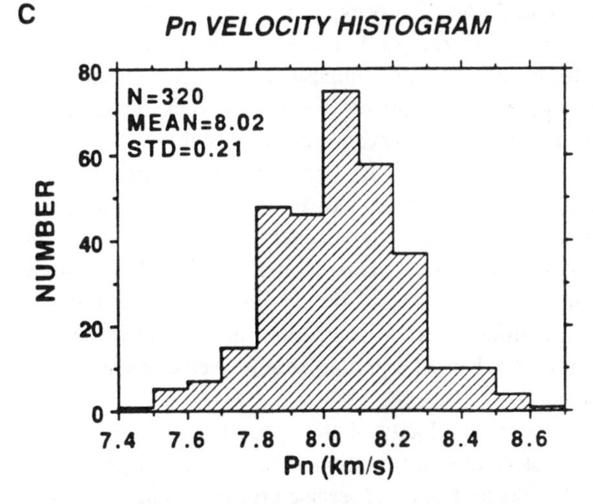

Figure 2. Histograms of crustal properties derived for the United States and southern Canada, where the majority of well-determined measurements are available. The histograms portray crustal properties versus number of measurements, and are therefore biased geographically by the data base (c.f., Fig. 1A).

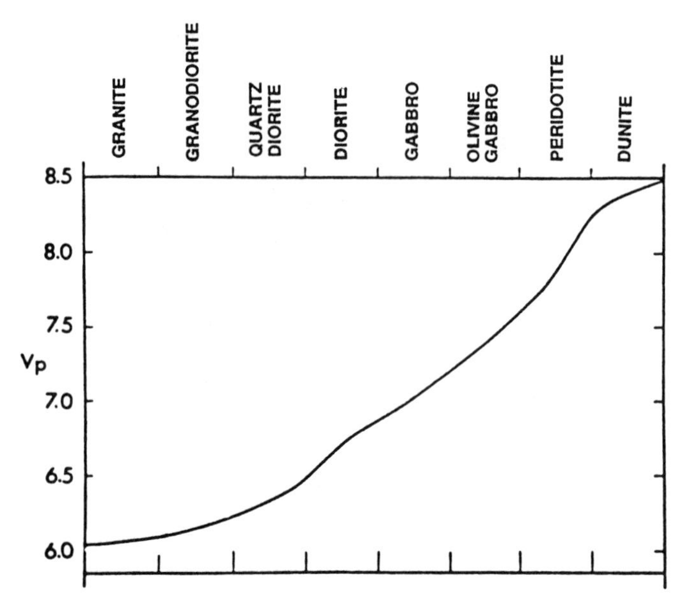

Figure 3. Generalized relationship between compressional wave seismic velocity and crustal and upper mantle rock types (Christensen, 1965). Individual rock samples may deviate significantly from the curve, but the velocity range and pattern of seismic measurements in crystalline rocks at 5 km depth or greater is depicted.

trolled to stay within this velocity/density parameter. Note that a crust with a mean velocity of 6.44 km/s may consist of a granitic upper crust (6.1 km/s) and a mafic lower crust (6.8 km/s), but *no* crustal layer with 6.44 km/s. The mean velocity is indicative only of a bulk crustal property.

One standard deviation in average crustal velocity does correspond to a significant difference in mean crustal composition. A low value (6.2 km/s) corresponds to a dominantly felsic crust, a high value (6.7 km/s) to a dominantly mafic crust, and the mean value to an intermediate composition. This relationship can be seen in a generalized comparison of seismic velocities with typical rock types (Fig. 3). However, average crustal velocity (and particularly the velocity of the lower crust) may be significantly reduced by temperature effects. In areas of high heat flow the lower crust may be 400° hotter than in regions of average heat flow, giving a temperature correction of 0.05 to 0.2 km/s or more (Christensen, 1979). Therefore, the thermal regime of the crust must be considered when comparing middle and lower crustal velocities or when interpreting seismic velocities in terms of composition.

The seismic velocity of the upper mantle (Pn) is also an indicator of mantle composition, density, and temperature. The mean Pn velocity from 320 seismic profiles is 8.02 km/s, with a standard deviation of 0.21 km/s (Fig. 2C). Some of the distribution in measured velocity may be caused by seismic anisotropy of olivine-rich upper-mantle rocks (Bamford, 1977; Christensen, 1984) and by temperature effects. The effect of variations in the temperature of the upper mantle can be seen by comparing heat flow, crustal age (i.e., time since the last major thermal event), and Pn velocity (Fig. 4). This comparison shows that high heat flow, recent thermal events (e.g., volcanism or crustal extension), and low Pn velocity are correlated. The thermal state of the lithosphere is therefore a major factor in determining the Pn velocity; other contributing factors are variations in composition and seismic anisotropy.

VELOCITY STRUCTURE OF THE CRUST

Below supracrustal sedimentary and volcanic rocks, the crystalline continental crust shows a remarkably varied seismic velocity structure that is indicative of variations in crustal composition and evolution. However, caution must be used when interpreting regional differences in crustal structure for at least two reasons. First, the limited coverage of seismic refraction profiles in some portions of North America (Fig. 1A) makes it impossible to assemble reliable statistics regarding crustal properties for many geologic or age provinces. Secondly, the available profiles span a time period of over 25 years and were recorded for a variety of purposes. Some early profiles succeed in outlining crustal thickness and average crustal velocity on a regional scale but are less reliable in showing the details of crustal velocity structure. Since the mid-1970s, data density on seismic refraction profiles has increased by about an order of magnitude, with shot-point intervals of 10 to 20 km and recorder spacings of 0.2 to 2.0 km commonly used (Mooney, 1989). In the discussion below we emphasize the observations supported by the highest quality data, but additional modern profiles are needed to establish a firm relationship between crustal velocity structure and crustal evolution in North America.

We begin by summarizing the crustal velocity structure of the Archean and Proterozoic crust (Fig. 5a to 5f). Crustal thickness in these areas is equal to or greater than the continental average of 36 km, and the average crustal velocity is always greater than the continental average of 6.44 km/s. However, the oldest crust—the Archean Superior Province—is not the thickest crust, as would be expected if the continental crust thickened with age. In fact, outside of the Keweenawan rift beneath Lake Superior, the Superior Province appears to have a relatively thin crust compared to the Archean Baltic Shield (Fig. 5b). The differences between these two Archean provinces are important because they demonstrate that great diversity in crustal evolution dates back to earlier than 2.5 Ga. The difference in crustal structure is so large it suggests either that portions of the crust in the Superior Province have been thinned (by Archean or Proterozoic extension?), or that the crust of the Baltic Shield has been thickened by overthrusting or magmatic inflation.

Four examples of Proterozoic crust, three from North America and one from the Saudi Arabian Shield, are compared in Figure 5c to 5f. Several features are common to all four regions: (1) the top of the middle crust (6.6 km/s) is everywhere at a depth of 19 ± 4 km; (2) a mafic lower crust (7.0 to 7.6 km/s) is present in each case with a thickness of 7 to 15 km; and (3) the

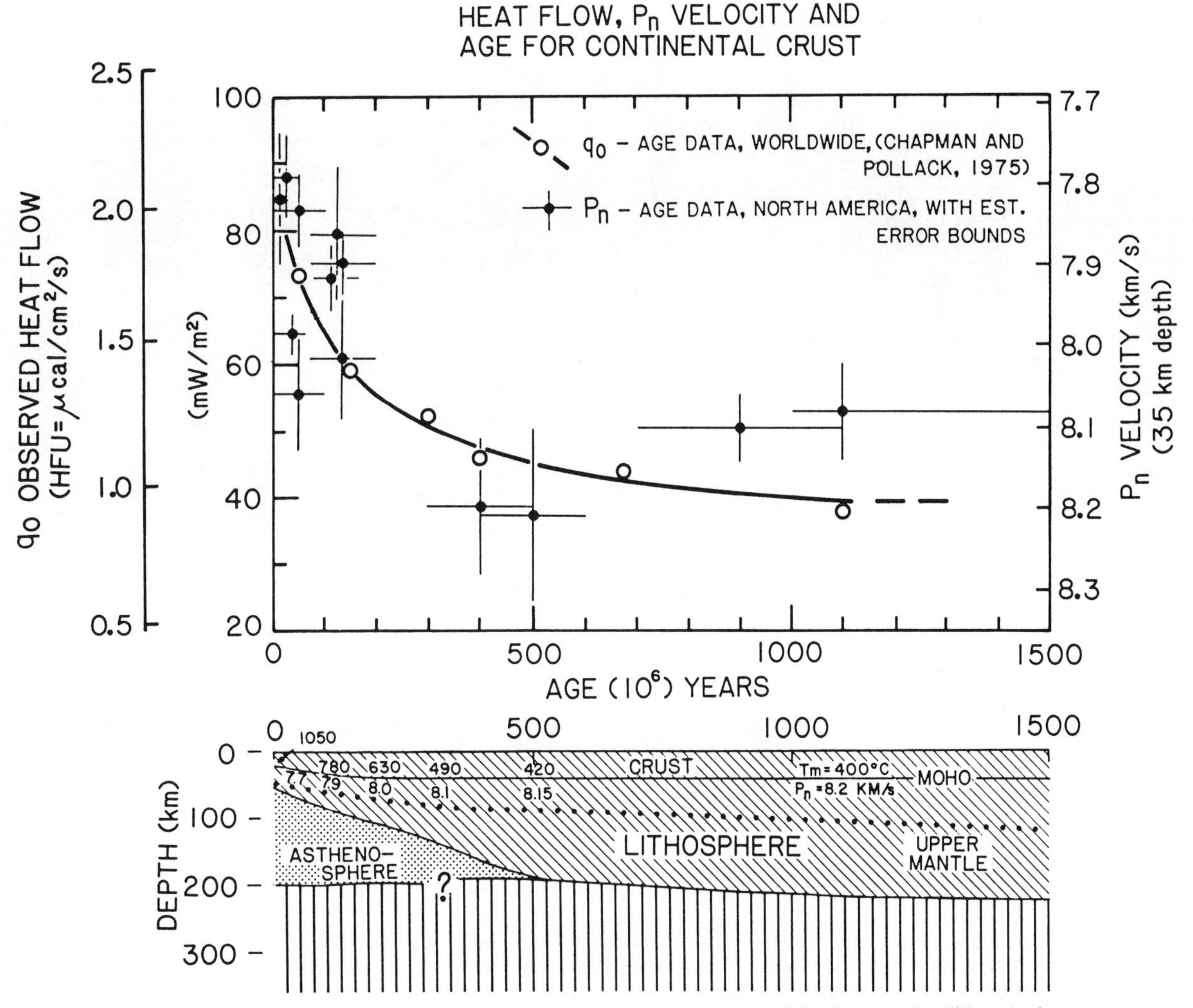

Figure 4. Relationship between heat flow (Chapman and Pollack, 1975), Pn velocity, lithospheric thickness, and time since the last thermal event effecting the continental lithosphere (Black and Braile, 1982). Low Pn velocity (7.9 km/s and less) and thin lithosphere (100 km or less) correlate with high heat flow (70 mW/m^2 and greater). In the diagram the upper mantle low-velocity layer (stipple) corresponds to the asthenosphere, and is well developed in P-wave structure for a lithosphere with thermal disturbances younger than about 500 Ma. A well-developed asthenosphere and low Pn velocity are characteristic of Cordilleran North America, whereas central and eastern North America have a higher average Pn velocity and a thin or nonexistent P-wave low-velocity layer (Iyer and Hitchcock, 1989). Tm, temperature at the top of the mantle. Pn, seismic velocity.

crust is 45 ± 5 km thick. If we include the Archean crust in the comparison, then the top of the middle crust (6.6 km/s) occurs at a depth of 19 ± 4 km for all examples. This commonality argues in favor of retaining the concept of a "Conrad" discontinuity, defined as the depth below which the seismic velocity increases rapidly to 6.6 km/s or greater. The cause of the velocity increase may be a change in composition, metamorphic grade, or physical properties (such as reduced pore pressure). The lower crustal layer (7.0 to 7.6 km/s) often has a high-velocity gradient and sometimes grades smoothly into the upper mantle. This layer most likely consists of high-grade intermediate-to-mafic composition metamorphic rocks (Fountain and Christensen, 1989).

A comparison of six regions of Phanerozoic North American crust shows great variability in crustal thickness and seismic velocity structure (Fig. 5g to 5l). The western Cordillera of Idaho and Wyoming has a crustal structure very similar to that beneath the northwest Canadian Platform (Fig. 5d), an observation consistent with geological arguments that the Cordilleran fold and thrust belt is underlain by Proterozoic North American crust (see below). The three examples of magmatic provinces—the Mexican volcanic belt, Wrangell arc, and the Cascades Range (Fig. 5h to 5j)—all show a similar velocity structure, a crustal thickness of about 45 km, and are typified by a thick lower crustal layer with a seismic velocity of about 7.0 km/s. It is inferred that this lower crustal layer consists of mafic igneous rocks at amphibolite-to-granulite metamorphic grade.

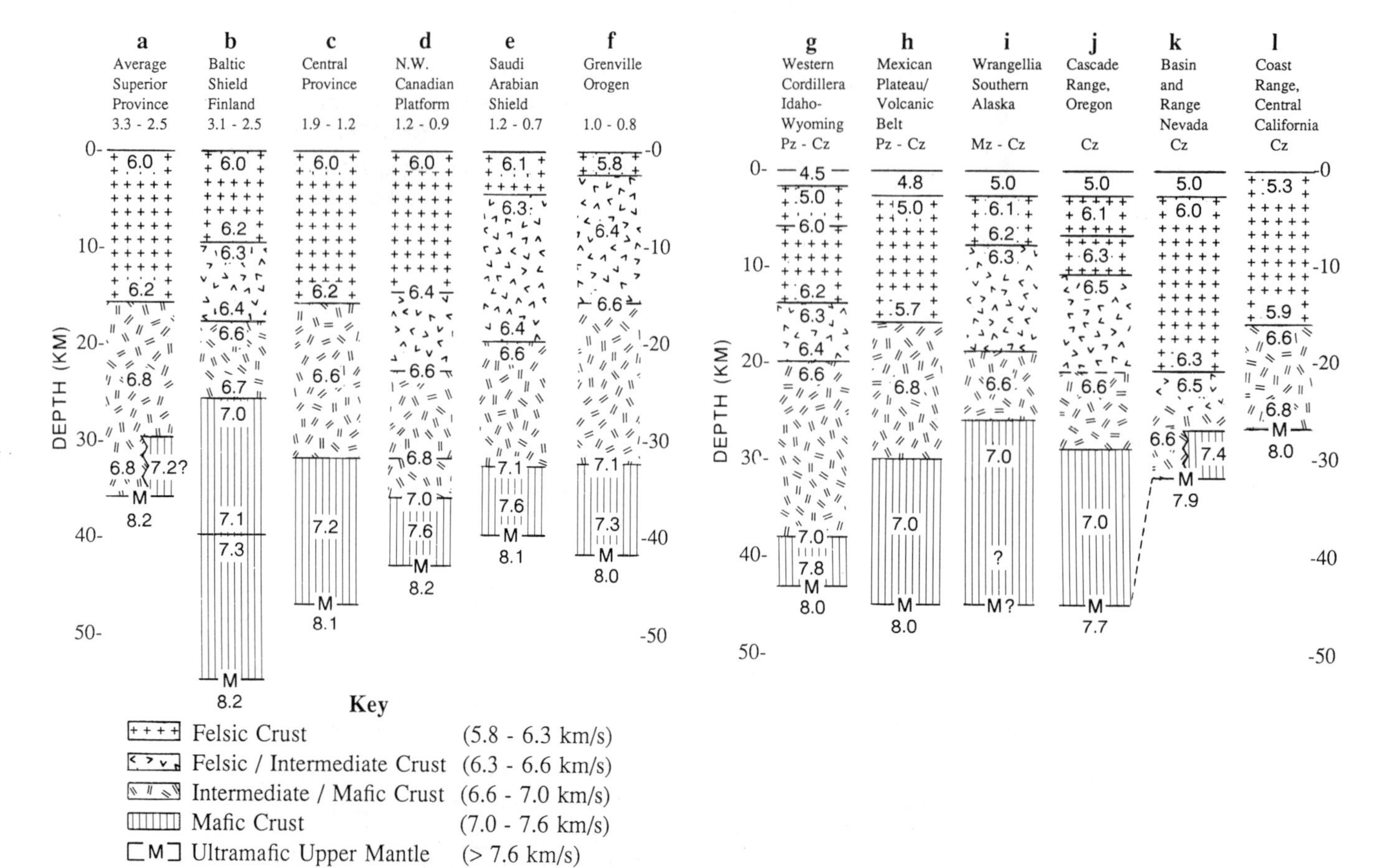

Figure 5. Representative seismic velocity-depth functions for ten regions of North America and two elsewhere (Baltic and Saudi Arabian Shields). North American Archean and Proterozoic crust (a, c, d, f) averages 40 km in thickness, volcanic provinces (h, i, j) average 45 km, and the Basin and Range (k) and Coast Ranges (1) of the western United States are less than 35 km thick. The Archean Baltic shield (b) is significantly thicker than the Superior Province (a). The Saudi Arabian shield has a crustal structure comparable with the Grenville Orogen (f). The crustal structure of the western Cordillera (g) is very similar to the northwest Canadian Platform (d). The majority of the crustal columns show a "Conrad discontinuity" (6.6 km/s or greater) at about 20 km depth, and a high-velocity (7.0 km/s or greater) basal crustal layer (high-grade igneous rocks?). The average Superior Province crustal column does not include the thickened crust beneath the Keweenawan Rift of Lake Superior. Sources: a, Braile, 1989; b, Grad and Luosto, 1987; c, Braile, 1989; d, Zelt and Ellis, 1989; e, Mooney and others, 1985; f, Mereu and others, 1986; g, Prodehl, 1979; h, Meyer and others, 1961; Valdez and others, 1986; i, Goodwin and others, 1989; j, Leaver and others, 1984; k, Prodehl, 1979; 1, Walter and Mooney, 1982.

The Basin and Range of the western United States and the Coast Ranges of California, Oregon, and Washington have crustal thicknesses less than the continental average of 36 km. The Basin and Range of Nevada is an area of continental extension, with a crustal thickness of about 32 km. The mean crustal seismic velocity (6.2 km/s) is significantly less than the continental average of 6.44 km/s, but a high-velocity basal crustal layer (7.3 to 7.5 km/s) is locally present. The Basin and Range is an area of high heat flow (80 mW/m^2 and greater), and temperature effects certainly play a role in lowering the mean crustal velocity.

The crustal structure of the Coast Ranges may be described, in simplest terms, in two layers: an upper crust of marine metasediments (5.7 to 5.9 km/s), and a lower crust of tectonically underplated igneous oceanic crust (6.6 to 6.8 km/s). This accreted crust is among the youngest and thinnest in North America.

STRUCTURE OF THE CRUST FROM SEISMIC-REFLECTION PROFILES

Seismic-reflection profiles provide the highest resolution of the structure within the crust. Deep-reflection profiles have been collected in North America over a broad geographic area and contribute a great deal to our knowledge of continental structure and tectonics (e.g., Brown and others, 1986; Green and others, 1986; Matthews and Smith, 1987; Phinney and Roy-Chowdhury, 1989; Smithson and Johnson, 1989). Seismic-reflection profiling is also highly effective in the marine environment, due to the excellent coupling of the source (air guns) with the water medium and the relatively uniform bottom conditions that minimize static corrections. High-quality marine data exist for both the Atlantic and Pacific margins of North America (e.g., Talwani and others, 1987; Hutchinson and others, 1988; Keen and de Voogd, 1988), and recently, deep-reflection data were collected on the Great Lakes in a joint U.S.–Canadian project (Behrendt and others, 1988; Green and others, 1989).

Deep-seismic reflection profiles have identified several important characteristic features of the continental crust (Mooney and Brocher, 1987). These include (1) a commonly (but certainly not universally) transparent upper crust, (2) inferred widespread low-angle faulting in the upper and middle crust, (3) a moderate to highly reflective lower crust, (4) a discontinuously reflective and often flat Moho, and (5) a seismically transparent upper mantle (with a few exceptions). These observations are consistent with a physical model of the crust involving several key features:

- A crystalline upper crust characterized by brittle deformation and steeply dipping, short scale-length features (with the exception of high-angle faults) that do not produce coherent seismic reflections.
- A lower crust characterized by ductile deformation in areas of moderate to high heat flow. Upper crustal normal faults often terminate in the middle or lower crust as listric faults. The high seismic reflectivity of the lower crust is consistent with the presence of a network of shear zones and laminated high- and low-velocity layers consisting of alternating felsic and mafic (intruded) rocks.
- A Moho that has been reworked during thermal disturbances and has reformed at a nearly constant depth in the case of crustal extension.
- An upper mantle that appears to be relatively homogeneous at seismic reflection wavelengths (50 to 500 m) and lacks the ductile shear zones or igneous laminations inferred for the lower crust.

Particularly in thermally active regions, the general properties of the crust have sometimes been compared to a "toasted jelly sandwich," with the ductile lower crust being the filling (Matthews and Cheadle, 1986). In cold crust, temperatures will not be high enough for ductility, and the observed seismic reflections may largely record deformation (or igneous intrusions) dating from the last thermal event. Where the last thermal event is 700 Ma or older, as for the platforms and shields, lower-crustal reflections are often weak and of short scale-length, probably due to brittle deformation of the lower crust in the Phanerozoic.

Complementing these generalized seismic reflection observations are the results obtained from investigations of specific geologic targets. Reflection profiles have illuminated the internal structure of several orogenic belts. Both the southern Appalachians and the southern Canadian Cordillera provide strong support for thin-skinned tectonics along major décollements (Fig. 6). In the southern Appalachians, reflections from a low-angle thrust fault may be followed from the Valley and Ridge Province eastward beneath the Blue Ridge and Piedmont Provinces to a zone of dipping reflections that lies beneath the Charlotte belt, a possible root zone for the thrusts and detachments to the west (Fig. 6A; Cook and others, 1981). These data are interpreted in terms of an allochthonous crystalline thrust sheet that has overthrust the passive continental margin and continental basement. Overthrusting is also observed in the northern Appalachians of southern Quebec and Maine (Green and others, 1986; Stewart and others, 1986) where the Appalachian allochthon overlies Grenville basement. Similar results have been obtained in the southern Cordillera, Canada; here the dominant structural style of the fold and thrust belt is "thin skinned," with the deformation largely confined to the supracrustal sedimentary wedge above autochthonous North American basement (Price, 1981; Cook and others, 1988; Fig. 6B).

Some of the most important seismic reflection results have come from the continental interior, where the last major tectonic events occurred between 700 and 1,500 Ma. The midcontinental geophysical anomaly has been investigated with reflection profiles in Kansas (Serpa and others, 1984) and in the Great Lakes (Behrendt and others, 1988). Interpretations of seismic-reflection data recorded in Lake Superior and Lake Michigan show that the rift basin extends to great depth (more than 20 km) and is filled with interbedded volcanic and sedimentary rocks (Behrendt and others, 1988; Fig. 7A). This may be the greatest thickness of intracratonic rift deposits on Earth. The reflection data also indicate that the Midcontinent rift system differs from Phanerozoic rifts in having total crustal thickness equal to or greater than the surrounding (presumably unextended) regions (Behrendt and others, 1988).

Seismic reflection data have begun to push back the earliest time for which we can describe the deep crustal expression of ancient collisional events. Data collected in Lake Huron across the Grenville front reveal a 32-km-thick package of strong, moderately east-dipping reflections (Fig. 7B). East of the Grenville front the seismic data image a series of gently east-dipping reflections at about 20 km depth that separate a highly reflective lower crust from a moderately reflective upper crust (Green and others, 1988). These data are consistent with a model that calls for the progressive stacking of microterranes at the margin of the Superior Province during the Penokean Orogeny (1.83 to 1.89 Ga). The steeply dipping reflection events recorded across the Grenville front originate from ductilely deformed rocks dating from this collision (Green and others, 1988).

The evolution of the crust during continental extension has been documented by seismic reflection profiles in the western United States and western Europe (Matthews and Smith, 1987; McCarthy and Thompson, 1988). One of the most important observations of these studies is a relatively flat-lying reflection Moho at a depth of about 30 km for broad (500 km or more) areas of extension. This observation has led some authors to argue

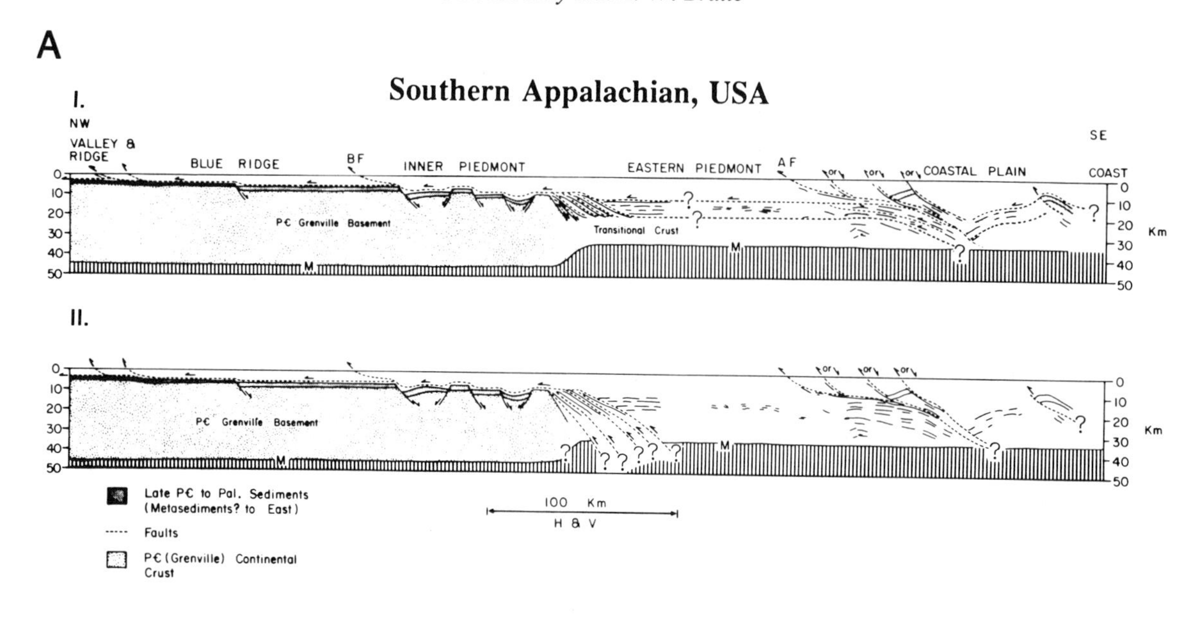

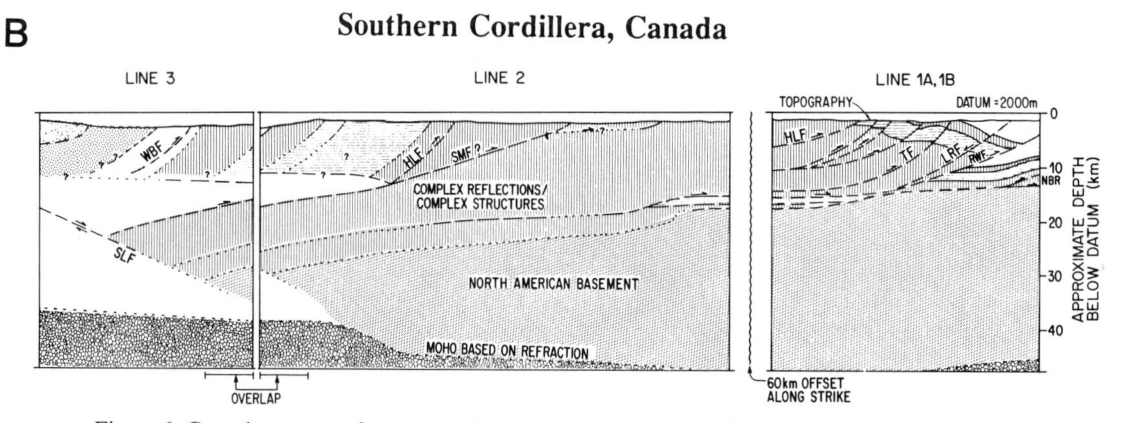

Figure 6. Crustal structure of two orogenic belts from seismic-reflection data: (A) southern Appalachians (Cook and others, 1981) and (B) southern Cordillera, Canada (Cook and others, 1988). Both are examples of thin-skinned tectonics with deformation largely confined to the supracrustal sedimentary wedge above a Precambrian basement. Abbreviations for faults: (A) BF, Brevard fault; AF, Augusta fault. (B) VSZ, Valkyr shear zone; VR, Valhalla reflection; SLF, Slocan Lake fault; WBF, West Brevard fault; HLF, Hall Lake fault; SMF, St. Mary fault; TF, Torrent fault; LRF, Lussier River fault; RWF, Redwall fault; NBR, near-basement reflections.

that the Moho in extensional regimes is a relatively young feature "reworked" by deformational and igneous processes. Gans (1987) argues on the basis of geologic and geophysical evidence that during extension, lower crustal materials may flow laterally along a network of shear zones from areas of less extension to areas of higher extension. Such a process would produce a flat Moho where extension varies laterally.

LITHOSPHERIC THICKNESS

The lithosphere extends to the top of the upper-mantle seismic low-velocity layer (the asthenosphere), a layer that has been identified at regionally variable depth by long-range seismic refraction and surface wave profiles. Seismic models for the upper mantle beneath North America can be divided into shield models that apply to central and eastern North America, and tectonic models for western North America (Iyer and Hitchcock, 1989). Shield models exhibit higher P- and S-wave velocities in the upper half of the upper mantle than tectonic models, which have pronounced low-velocity zones in the top 200 km of the upper mantle (Fig. 8). Shield models and tectonic models primarily reflect differences in the thermal regime and composition of the mantle. It is clear that the tectonically active western portion of North America is underlain by a hotter, more mobile upper mantle at a depth of 70 to 100 km. The evolution of the upper mantle from a tectonic model to a shield model is illustrated in

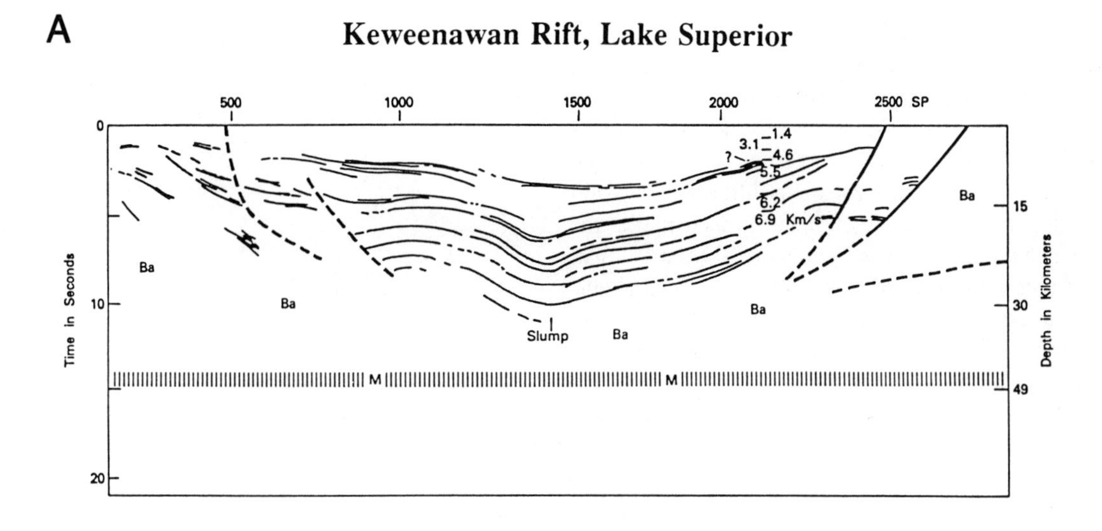

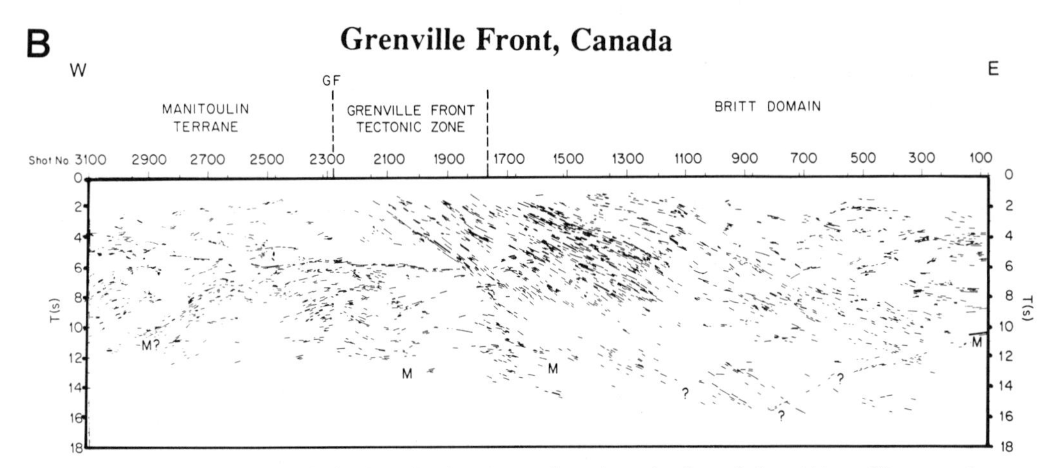

Figure 7. Line drawings of seismic-reflection data collected on the Great Lakes: (A) profile across the Keweenawan rift beneath Lake Superior showing a thick sequence of volcanic and sedimentary rocks (Behrendt and others, 1988), and (B) profile across the Grenville Front beneath Lake Huron showing prominent east-dipping reflections beneath the Britt Domain (Green and others, 1988). These reflections are interpreted as ductilely deformed rocks dating from the Penokean orogeny (1.83 to 1.89 Ga). Abbreviations: (A) SP, shot point; Ba, basement; M, Moho. (B) GF, Grenville fault.

Figure 4 (bottom), which depicts lithospheric thickening (and asthenospheric thinning) with increased time since the last major thermal event. A shallow asthenosphere (70 km) has been identified beneath the Basin and Range Province, Rio Grande Rift, and the Gulf of California (Iyer and Hitchcock, 1989), and a plume-shaped upper-mantle low-velocity anomaly has been identified beneath the Yellowstone hotspot (Evans, 1982). However, the lithosphere/asthenosphere boundary cannot be reliably contoured beneath North America with the data presently available.

DISCUSSION AND CONCLUSIONS

There are wide variations in the seismic structure of the continental crust and upper mantle of North America that result from the complex processes of continental growth and modification. Seismic investigations conducted within the past 25 years are beginning to show consistent patterns that, if studied in further detail and over a wider geographic area, may enable us to reconstruct the major processes of lithospheric evolution in North America.

There is an overall trend of crustal thickening with age, but the oldest crust is not always the thickest. What processes determine crustal thickness? In addition to overthrusting at collision zones, a favorable comparison between Proterozoic crust and that of modern continental magmatic arcs, such as the Cascade Range, indicates that magmatic processes do result in a crustal thickness and seismic-velocity structure typical of the continental interior. Regional variations in Proterozoic magmatism may explain many of the variations in crustal structure for the shield and platform.

The observation of a nearly horizontal seismic reflection Moho has revised thinking about this important boundary. It is likely that the Moho is reformed by deformational and igneous processes during major lithospheric thermal disturbances. Further comparisons of the Moho's seismic properties in various geologic settings are needed to understand its role in lithospheric evolution. In addition, the Conrad discontinuity, which marks the depth below which the seismic velocity rises rapidly to more than 6.6 km/s, is present in most North American crust, yet its significance and role in crustal evolution has received little attention. Coincident seismic reflection and refraction profiles are the most productive method for investigating the properties of these discontinuities and of the entire crust. Complementary geological investigations of exposed deep crustal rocks are also a vital ingredient.

How thick is the North American lithosphere? Seismic studies have identified a shallow asthenosphere beneath the tectonically active western Cordillera of North America, with the minimum depths (100 km or less) beneath thermally disturbed regions, including the Rio Grande Rift and the Basin and Range. At present, however, we are unable to contour the lithosphere/asthenosphere boundary beneath North America; our knowledge of how the lithosphere has evolved is scant below the Moho discontinuity. Further studies of the subcrustal lithosphere are needed if we are to understand fundamental questions, such as: Why are there platforms? Why are there exposed shields? What are the driving forces of plate motions?

Seismic reflection profiles have been successful in revealing the architecture of the continental crust and in defining the basic "reflection character" of shields, continental margins, terrane boundaries (old and young), and mountain belts. Future work will focus on understanding the origin of deep-crustal reflections in a physical and geologic context. Why is the lower crust often highly reflective? How does composition, mineralogy, and seismic anisotropy effect the crustal "image"?

Finally, as the seismic profile location map (Fig. 1A) makes clear, many important geologic and age provinces have had few or no deep seismic investigations, and it is therefore imperative that high-quality data be collected over the broadest possible area so that firm conclusions can be arrived at regarding lithospheric evolution.

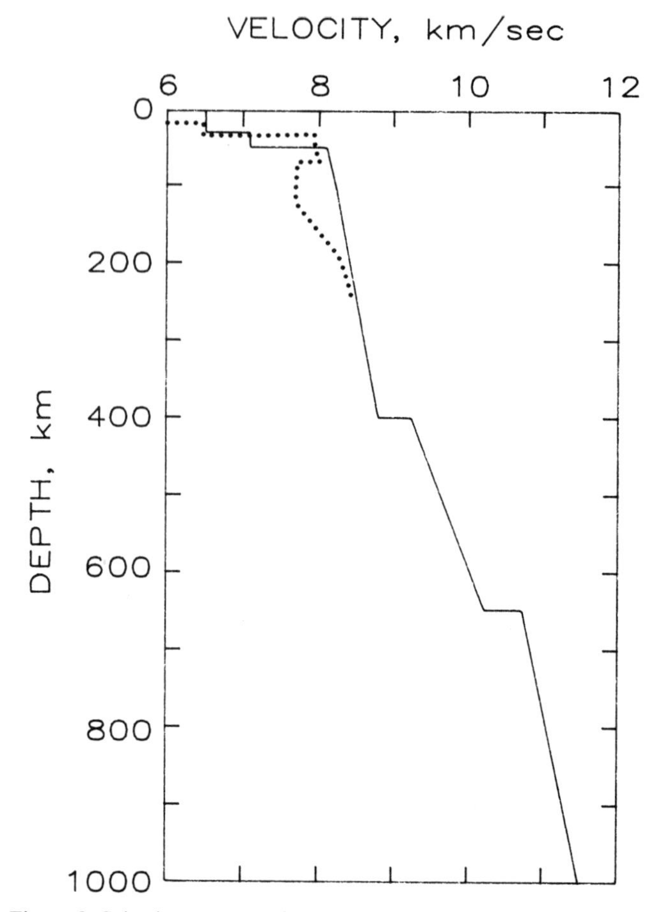

Figure 8. Seismic structure of the upper mantle for shield areas (solid line) and tectonic areas (dotted line) (Iyer and Hitchcock, 1989). The tectonic model shows a well-developed low-velocity layer (asthenosphere), while this layer may be absent (in the compressional wave structure) beneath shields. The evolution of the asthenosphere from tectonic to shield provinces is depicted in Figure 4 (bottom).

REFERENCES

Ambos, E. L., Mooney, W. D., and Fuis, G. S., 1989, Seismic refraction measurements within the Wrangellia–Peninsular (composite) terranes, south-central Alaska: Journal of Geophysical Research (in press).

Bamford, D., 1977, Pn-velocity anisotropy in a continental upper mantle: Geophysical Journal of the Royal Astronomical Society, v. 49, p. 29–48.

Barr, K. G., 1971, Crustal refraction experiment—Yellowknife: Journal of Geophysical Research, v. 76, p. 1929–1948.

Beaudoin, B. C., and Fuis, G. S., 1988, Crustal structure of Yukon–Tanana Uplands, central Alaska from refraction/wide-angle reflection seismic data, TACT 1987 [abs.]: EOS Transactions of the American Geophysical Union, v. 69, p. 1457.

Behrendt, J. C., and 7 others, 1988, Crustal structure of the Midcontinent rift system—Results from the GLIMPCE deep seismic reflection profiles: Geology, v. 16, p. 81–85.

Berg, E., 1973, Crustal structure in Alaska: Tectonophysics, v. 20, p. 165–182.

Black, P. R., and Braile, L. W., 1982, Pn velocity and cooling of the continental lithosphere: Journal of Geophysical Research, v. 87, p. 10557–10568.

Boland, A. V., and Ellis, R. M., 1989, Velocity structure of the Kapuskasing Uplift, northern Ontario, from seismic refraction studies: Journal of Geophysical Research (in press).

Braile, L. W., 1989, Crustal structure of the continental interior, *in* Pakiser, L. C., and Mooney, W. D., eds., Geophysical Framework of the Continental United States: Geological Society of America Memoir 172 (in press).

Braile, L. W., Hinze, W. J., von Frese, R.R.B., and Keller, G. R., 1989, Seismic properties of the crust and upper-most mantle of the conterminous United States and adjacent Canada, *in* Pakiser, L. C., and Mooney, W. D., eds., Geophysical Framework of the Continental United States: Geological Society of America Memoir 172 (in press).

Brown, L., Barazangi, M., Kaufman, S., and Oliver, J., 1986, The first decade of COCORP; 1974–1984, *in* Barazangi, M., and Brown, L., eds., Reflection seismology—A Global Perspective: American Geophysical Union Geodynamics Series, v. 13, p. 107–120.

Catchings, R. C., and Mooney, W. D., 1988, Crustal structure of east-central Oregon—relationship between Newberry Volcano and regional crustal structure: Journal of Geophysical Research, v. 93, p. 10081–10094.

Chapman, D. S., and Pollack, H. N., 1975, Global heat flow—a new look: Earth and Planetary Science Letters, v. 28, p. 23–32.

Christensen, N. I., 1965, Compressional wave velocities in metamorphic rocks at 10 kilobars: Journal of Geophysical Research, v. 70, p. 6147–6164.

——, 1979, Compressional wave velocities in rocks at high temperatures and pressures, critical thermal gradients, and crustal low-velocity zones: Journal of Geophysical Research, v. 84, p. 6849–6857.

——, 1984, The magnitude, symmetry, and origin of upper mantle anisotropy based on fabric analyses of ultramafic tectonites: Geophysical Journal of the Royal Astronomical Society, v. 76, p. 89–111.

Clowes, R. M., Kanasewich, E. R., and Cumming, G. L., 1968, Deep crustal seismic reflections at near-vertical incidence: Geophysics,v. 33, p. 441–451.

Clowes, R. M., Thorleifson, A. J., and Lynch, S., 1981, Winona Basin, west coast Canada—Crustal structure from marine seismic studies: Journal of Geophysical Research, v. 86, p. 225–247.

Clowes, R. M., and 6 others, 1987, LITHOPROBE – southern Vancouver Island—Cenozoic subduction complex imaged by deep seismic reflections: Canadian Journal of Earth Sciences, v. 24, p. 31–51.

Cook, F., 1988, Middle Proterozoic compressional orogen in northwestern Canada: Journal of Geophysical Research, v. 93, p. 8985–9005.

Cook, F. A., Brown, L. D., Kaufman, S., Oliver, J. E., and Petersen, T. A., 1981, COCORP seismic profile of the Appalachian orogen beneath the central plain of Georgia: Geological Society of America Bulletin, part 1, v. 92, p. 738–748.

Cook, F. A., and 9 others, 1988, Lithoprobe seismic reflection structure of the southeastern Canadian Cordillera—initial results: Tectonics, v. 7, p. 157–180.

Couch, R. W., and Riddihough, R. P., 1989, The crustal structure of the western continental margin of North America, *in* Pakiser, L. C., and Mooney, W. D., eds., Geophysical Framework of the Continental United States: Geological Society of America Memoir 172 (in press).

Evans, J. R., 1982, Compressional wave velocity structure of the upper 350 km under the eastern Snake River Plain near Rexburg, Idaho: Journal of Geophysical Research, v. 87, p. 2654–2670.

Flueh, E. R., Mooney, W. D., Fuis, G. S., and Ambos, E. L., 1989, Crustal structure of the Chugach Mountains, southern Alaska—a study of pegleg multiple from a low-velocity zone: Journal of Geophysical Research (in press).

Fountain, D. M., and Christensen, N. I., 1989, Composition of the continental crust and upper mantle—a review, *in* Pakiser, L. C., and Mooney, W. D., eds., Geophysical Framework of the Continental United States: Geological Society of America Memoir 172 (in press).

Fuis, G. S., Ambos, E. L., Mooney, W. D., and Christensen, N. I., 1989, Crustal structure of accreted terranes in the Chugach Mountains and Cooper River Basin, Southern Alaska, from seismic-refraction results: Journal of Geophysical Research (in press).

Gans, P. G., 1987, An open-system, two-layer crustal stretching model for the eastern Great Basin: Tectonics, v. 6, p. 1–12.

Gebrande, H., 1982, Elastic wave velocities and constants of elasticity of rocks and rock forming minerals, *in* Angenheister, G., ed., Physical properties of rocks: Berlin, Landolt-Bornstein, Springer-Verlag, band 1, v. b, p. 1–99.

Goodwin, E. L., Fuis, G. S., Ambos, E. L., and Nokleberg, W. J., 1989, The crustal structure of Wrangellia along the Tok Highway, eastern southern Alaska: Journal of Geophysical Research (in press).

Grad, M., and Luosto, U., 1987, Seismic models of the crust of the Baltic Shield along the SVEKA profile in Finland: Annales Geophysicae, v. 6, p. 639–649.

Green, A. G., and Hall, D. H., 1978, A sub-critical seismic crustal reflection survey over the Aulneau batholith, Kenora region, Ontario: Canadian Journal of Earth Sciences, v. 15, p. 301–315.

Green, A. G., and 9 others, 1986, Recent seismic reflection studies in Canada, *in* Barazangi, M., and Brown, L., eds., Reflection Seismology—A Global Perspective: American Geophysical Union Geodynamics Series, v. 13, p. 85–97.

Green, A. G., and 9 others, 1988, Crustal structure of the Grenville front and adjacent terranes: Geology, v. 16, p. 788–792.

Green, A. G., and 9 others, 1989, A 'Glimpce' of the deep crust beneath the Great Lakes: American Geophysical Union Geodynamics Series (in press).

Hall, D. H., and Brisbin, W. C., 1965, Crustal structure from converted head waves in central western Manitoba: Geophysics, v. 30, p. 1053–1067.

Hanson, K., Berg, E., and Gedney, L., 1968, A seismic refraction profile and crustal structure in central interior Alaska: Bulletin of the Seismological Society of America, v. 58, p. 1657–1665.

Hutchinson, D. R., Klitgord, K. D., Lee, M. W., and Trehu, A. M., 1988, U.S. Geological Survey deep seismic reflection profile across the Gulf of Maine: Geological Society of America Bulletin, v. 100, p. 172–184.

Iyer, H. M., and Hitchcock, T., 1989, Upper mantle velocity structure in continental U.S. and Canada, *in* Pakiser, L. C., and Mooney, W. D., eds., Geophysical Framework of the Continental United States: Geological Society of America Memoir 172 (in press).

Kanasewich, E. R., and 10 others, 1987, Seismic studies of the crust under the Williston Basin: Canadian Journal of Earth Sciences, v. 24, p. 2160–2171.

Keen, C. E., and Hyndman, R. D., 1979, Geophysical review of the continental margins of eastern and western Canada: Canadian Journal of Earth Sciences, v. 16, p. 712–736.

Keen, C. E., and de Voogd, B., 1988, The continent-ocean boundary at the rifted margin off eastern Canada—new results from deep seismic reflection studies: Tectonics, v. 7, p. 107–124.

Klemperer, S. L., 1988, Crustal thinning and nature of extension in the northern North Sea from deep seismic reflection profiling: Tectonics, v. 7, p. 803–821.

Leaver, D. S., Mooney, W. D., and Kohler, W. M., 1984, A seismic refraction study of the Oregon Cascades: Journal Geophysical Research, v. 89, p. 3121–3134.

Luetgert, J. H., Mann, C. E., and Klemperer, S. L., 1987, Wide-angle deep crustal reflections in the northern Appalachians: Geophysical Journal of the Royal Astronomical Society, v. 89, p. 183–188.

Matthews, D. H., and Cheadle, M. J., 1986, Deep reflections from the Caledonides and Variscides west of Britain and comparison with the Himalayas, *in* Barazangi, M., and Brown, L. D., eds., Reflection Seismology—A Global Perspective: American Geophysical Union Geodynamics Series,v. 13, p. 5–19.

Matthews, D., and Smith, C., eds., 1987, Deep seismic profiling of the continental lithosphere: Royal Astronomical Society Journal Special Issue, v. 89, p. 1–447.

Mackie, D. J., Clowes, R. M., Dehler, S. A., and Ellis, R. M., 1989, The Queen Charlotte Islands refraction project: Part II–structural model for transition from Pacific Plate to North American Plate: Canadian Journal of Earth Sciences (in press).

McCarthy, J., and Thompson, G. A., 1988, Seismic imaging of extended crust with emphasis on the western United States: Geological Society of America Bulletin, v. 100, p. 1361–1374.

Meissner, R., 1986, The continental crust, a geophysical approach: Orlando, Florida, Academic Press, 426 p.

Meissner, R., Wever, T., and Flueh, E. R., 1987, The Moho in Europe—Implications for crustal development: Anneles Geophysicae, v. 87/04B, p. 357–364.

Mereu, R., and 11 others, 1986, The 1982 COCRUST seismic experiment across the Ottawa–Bonnechere graben and Grenville Front in Ottawa and Quebec: Geophysical Journal of the Royal Astronomical Society, v. 84, p. 491–514.

Meyer, R. P., Steinhart, J. S., and Woollard, G. P., 1961, Central plateau, Mexico, 1957, *in* Steinhart, J. S., and Meyer, R. P., eds., Explosion studies of continental structure: Washington, D.C., Carnegie Institute, p. 199–225.

Mooney, W. D., 1989, Seismic methods for the determination of earthquake source parameters and lithospheric structure, *in* Pakiser, L. C., and Mooney,

W. D., eds., Geophysical Framework of the Continental United States: Geological Society of America Memoir 172 (in press).

Mooney, W. D., and Brocher, T. M., 1987, Coincident seismic reflection/refraction studies of the continental lithosphere—a global review: Reviews of Geophysics, v. 25, p. 723–742.

Mooney, W. D. and Weaver, C. S., 1989, Regional crustal structure and tectonics of the Pacific Coastal States—California, Oregon and Washington, *in* Pakiser, L. C. and Mooney, W. D., eds., Geophysical Framework of the Continental United States: Geological Society of America Memoir 172 (in press).

Mooney, W. D., Gettings, M. E., Blank, H. R., and Healy, J. H., 1985, Saudi Arabian seismic refraction profile—a traveltime interpretation of crustal and upper mantle structure: Tectonophysics, v. 111, p. 173–246.

Phinney, R. A., and Roy-Chowdhury, K., 1989, Reflection seismic studies of crustal structure in the eastern United States, *in* Pakiser, L. C., and Mooney, W. D., eds., Geophysical Framework of the Continental United States: Geological Society of America Memoir 172 (in press).

Price, R. A., 1981, The Cordilleran foreland thrust and fold belt in the southern Canadian Rocky Mountains, *in* McClay, K. R., and Price, R. A., eds., Thrust and Nappe Tectonics: Geological Society of London Special Publication 9, p. 427–488.

Prodehl, C., 1979, Crustal structure of the western United States: U.S. Geological Survey Professional Paper 1034, 74 p.

Reymer, A.P.S., and Schubert, G., 1987, Phanerozoic and Precambrian crustal growth, *in* Kroener, A., ed., Proterozoic Lithospheric Evolution: American Geophysical Union Geodynamics Series, v. 17, p. 1–9.

Sander, G. W., and Overton, A., 1965, Deep seismic refraction investigation in the Canadian Arctic Archipelago: Geophysics, v. 30, p. 87–96.

Serpa, L., and 6 others, 1984, Structure of the southern Keweenawan rift from COCORP surveys across the Midcontinent Geophysical Anomaly in northeastern Kansas: Tectonics, v. 3, p. 367–384.

Shor, G. G., 1962, Seismic refraction studies off the coast of Alaska: Bulletin of the Seismological Society of America, v. 52, p. 37–57.

Smithson, S. B., and Johnson, R., 1989, Crustal structure of the western U.S. based on reflection seismology, *in* Pakiser, L. C., and Mooney, W. D., eds., Geophysical Framework of the Continental United States: Geological Society of America Memoir 172 (in press).

Smithson, S. B., Johnson, R. A., and Wong, Y. K., 1981, Mean crustal velocity—a critical parameter for interpreting crustal structure and crustal growth: Earth and Planetary Science Letters, v. 53, p. 323–332.

Sobczak, L. W. and Overton, A., 1984, Shallow and deep crustal structure of the western Sverdrup Basin: Canadian Journal of Earth Sciences, v. 21, p. 902–919.

Spencer, C., and 7 others, 1989, Allochthonous units in the northern Appalachians—results from the Quebec–Maine seismic reflection and refraction surveys: Tectonics (in press).

Stewart, D. B., and 8 others, 1986, The Quebec–western Maine seismic reflection profile—setting and first year results, *in* Barazangi, M., and Brown, L., eds., Reflection Seismology, The Continental Crust: American Geophysical Union Geodynamics Series, v. 14, p. 189–199.

Talwani, M., and 6 others, 1987, EDGE and related seismic projects—onshore, offshore California [abs.]: EOS Transactions of the American Geophysical Union, v. 68, p. 1365.

Trehu, A. M., Klitgord, K. D., Sawyer, D. S., and Buffler, R. T., 1989, Regional investigations of crust and upper mantle—Atlantic and Gulf of Mexico continental margins, *in* Pakiser, L. C., and Mooney, W. D., eds., Geophysical Framework of the Continental United States: Geological Society of America Memoir 172 (in press).

Valdez, C. M., and 8 others, 1986, Crustal structure of Oaxaca, Mexico, from seismic refraction measurements: Bulletin of the Seismological Society of America, v. 76, p. 547–563.

Walter, A. W. and Mooney, W. D., 1982, Crustal structure of the Diablo and Gabilan ranges, central California—a reinterpretation of existing data: Seismological Society of America Bulletin, v. 72, p. 1567–1590.

Zelt, C., and Ellis, M. A., 1989, Seismic structure of the crust and upper mantle in the Peace River Arch region, Canada: Journal of Geophysical Research (in press).

Manuscript Accepted by the Society February 1, 1989

ACKNOWLEDGMENTS

A broad summary such as this draws on the data and ideas of many people, most of whom are referenced in the text. We thank A. G. Green and P. Morel-a-l'Huissier for providing references and preprints of several papers by themselves and their Canadian colleagues. M. Goldman assisted in the preparation of Figures 1 and 5. A. W. Bally, T. M. Brocher, R. C. Catchings, M. Goldman, J. McCarthy, and A. R. Palmer provided insightful and timely review comments.

Printed in U.S.A.

The Geology of North America
Vol. A, The Geology of North America—An overview
The Geological Society of America, 1989

Chapter 5

North Atlantic Ocean basin; Aspects of geologic structure and evolution

Peter R. Vogt
Naval Research Laboratory, Washington, D.C., 10375-5000
Brian E. Tucholke
Woods Hole Oceanographic Institution, Woods Hole, Massachusetts 02543

INTRODUCTION

In creating Volume M, the Western North Atlantic region (Vogt and Tucholke, 1986a) for the Geology of North America series, we deemed it best from both oceanographic and plate-tectonic viewpoints to deal with the entire North Atlantic spreading system from the equator to the Arctic (Figs. 1 and 2), rather than limiting treatment to the western half of the ocean basin. Even so, the scope in some places had to be expanded. The Atlantic, like other ocean basins, did not evolve in isolation from global changes in tectonic regime, oceanic circulation, or climate patterns (Fig. 3). The development of plate-tectonic theory since the late 1960s clearly has emphasized the importance of these large-scale linkages.

The present chapter continues this philosophy, summarizing the geology of the North Atlantic but noting linkages to areas outside this ocean basin. The synthesis is based largely on material presented in Volume M. The citation or lack of citation of Volume M references here, however, reflects only the thematic fabric of the present synthesis, not the scientific merit of the chapters. We refer the reader to original sources in Volume M for more complete treatment. We begin this chapter by noting ties between Volume M and several other Geology of North America volumes, and we continue with some "vital statistics" that describe three basic components of the Atlantic in space and time: igneous crust, sediments, and ocean waters. This is followed by a discussion of scales of spatial and temporal variability, with emphasis on the latter. The chapter concludes with a summary of some of the important advances that have occurred in the three years since Volume M was published.

The bare essence of North Atlantic geology is distilled in Plate 2, which provides a highly condensed summary of many Atlantic and global parameters against time, starting at the Triassic-Jurassic boundary. Plate 3 shows basement topography along the Kane Fracture Zone corridor from North America to near Africa, and it also provides an index map for numerous geologic features and geographic provinces discussed in this text, and locations of sea-floor areas illustrated in the figures. These plates and the text figures with their captions convey graphically a large amount of data that cannot be fully discussed in the limited space of this chapter. It should be kept in mind that Plate 2 has limitations: (a) the Atlantic has strong asymmetries in oceanographic and geologic architecture across both latitude and longitude; (b) for a given time slice, some properties such as sediment composition vary significantly with water depth across the ocean basin; (c) for parameters like volcanism and sea-floor erosion by bottom currents, only subjective estimates of intensity presently are available; (d) high-frequency variability (e.g. Milankovitch cycles) cannot be displayed at this scale; and (e) sampling of paleoenvironments still is very fragmentary because of wide spacing and limited penetration of drill sites, incomplete core recovery, and numerous hiatuses.

COMMON GROUND

Volume M shares common ground, in some cases literally, with several other volumes in the Geology of North America series. The link with Volumes I-1 (Keen and Williams, 1989) and I-2 (Sheridan and Grow, 1988) (the Atlantic continental margin) is particularly strong. The Atlantic margin volumes primarily describe gestation and birth of the North Atlantic basins, whereas Volume M documents their growth and maturation. However, the margin volumes also discuss the landward ends of the same sedimentary "drift supersequence" (Emery and Uchupi, 1984) whose vast seaward tail is analyzed in Volume M. Clearly, the margin has exerted control on sediment delivery to the adjacent deep basin, through variables as diverse as climate, topographic relief, presence or absence of barrier reefs, and even seismicity, which can trigger slumps and turbidity flows (Embley and Jacobi, 1986). Another thread of commonality is that during post-breakup times, igneous and tectonic episodes that affected eastern North America (deBoer and others, 1988) may have similarly affected the deep western Atlantic Ocean basin. Seismicity of the western North Atlantic (Zoback and others, 1986), formation of

Vogt, P. R., and Tucholke, B. E., 1989, North Atlantic Ocean basin; Aspects of geologic structure and evolution, *in* Bally, A. W., and Palmer, A. R., eds., The Geology of North America—An overview: Boulder, Colorado, Geological Society of America, The Geology of North America, v. A.

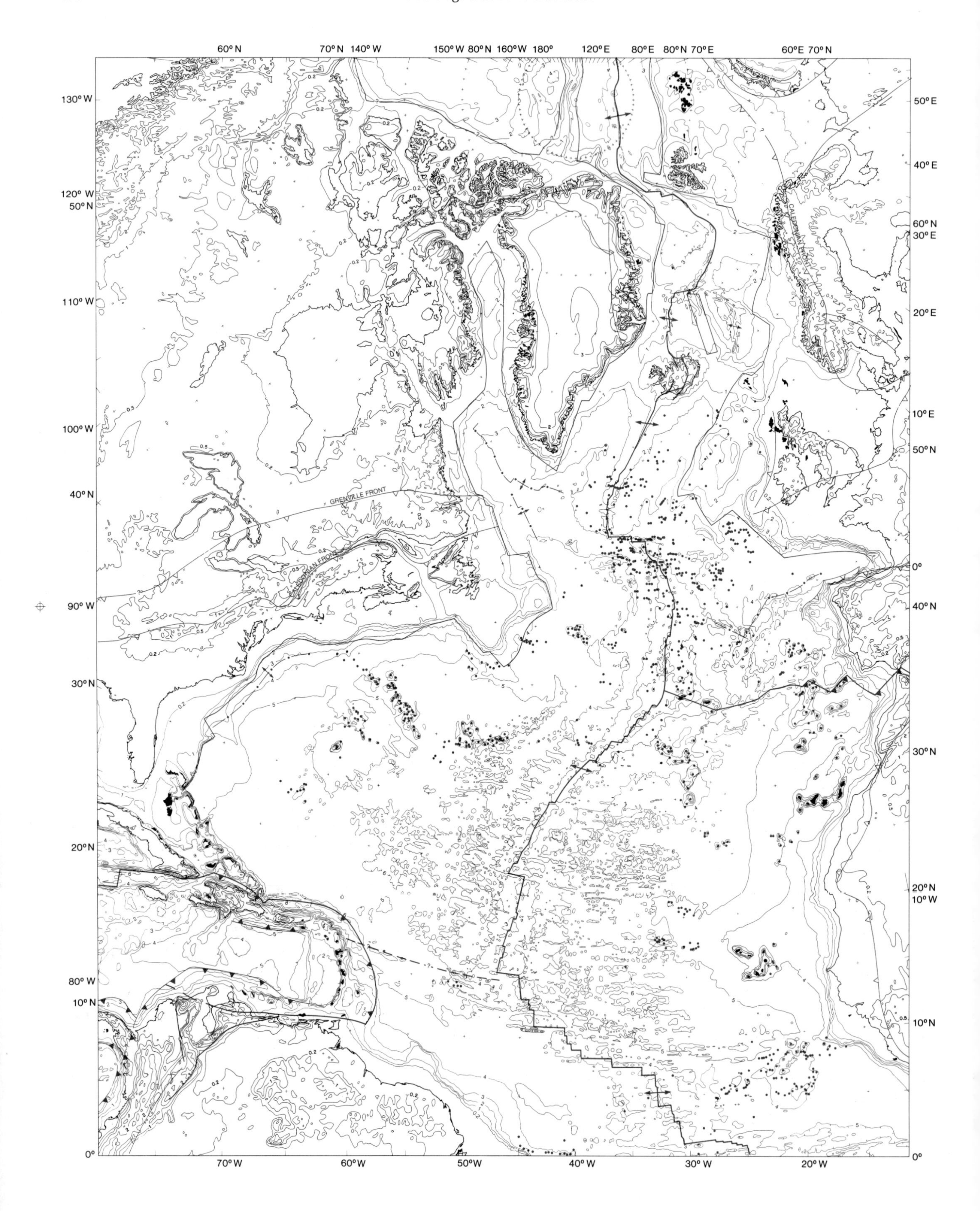
60° N
70° N 140° W
150° W 80° N 160° W 180°
120° E
80° E 80° N 70° E
60° E 70° N
130° W
120° W
50° N
110° W
100° W
40° N
90° W
30° N
20° N
80° W
10° N
0°
50° E
40° E
60° N
30° E
20° E
10° E
50° N
0°
40° N
30° N
20° N
10° W
10° N
0°
70° W
60° W
50° W
40° W
30° W
20° W
GRENVILLE FRONT
CALEDONIAN FRONT

the Bermuda Rise (Sclater and Wixon, 1986), and construction of Bermuda, the New England seamounts, and other volcanic edifices (Saemundsson, 1986) probably are linked to the same deep-seated processes and events that affected the margins. Also, as first noted by Vogt and Ostenso (1967), processes such as thermal subsidence and isostasy control margin evolution (Steckler and others, 1988) just as they do the regional depth distribution of the Mid-Atlantic Ridge and Bermuda Rise (Sclater and Wixon, 1986). More speculatively, post-rift uplift and magmatism in the Appalachians and in the western North Atlantic (Bermuda Rise) may reflect paired asthenosphere upwellings associated with sinking under the margins (Vogt, in preparation).

Of the submarine regions common to both the Atlantic margins and basins, the oldest oceanic, or possibly "transitional," crust next to the continent-ocean boundary is one of the most intriguing (Figs. 1 and 2). Where the oceanic crust reaches beneath upper continental rises and continental slopes, the ~6.8-km/s P-wave velocities that typically define the top of oceanic Layer 3 often give way to values of 7.0 to 7.2 km/s (e.g., Fig. 4 of Grow and Sheridan, 1988). North Atlantic examples of this phenomenon occur on the "normally sedimented" U.S. East Coast margin (Diebold and others, 1988), the volcanic Hatton Bank margin (White and others, 1987), and the obliquely rifted Barents Sea margin (Myhre and Eldholm, 1988). The velocity change and other peculiarities of such marginal oceanic crust commonly are attributed to unique rift-stage processes such as massive "underplating" by mafic intrusions near the locus of breakup (LASE Study Group, 1986; Diebold and others, 1988). Such underplating is most plausible where unusual circumstances are independently suggested; examples include greatly thickened crust, such as along USGS seismic line 25 and LASE (Large Aperture Seismic Experiment) line 6 across Baltimore Canyon Trough (Diebold and others, 1988), and where upper crust is both thickened and composed of dipping reflectors (Greenland and Eurasian margins, 55° to 70°N; White and others, 1987).

The underplating explanation is less attractive where the upper crust has constant thickness or actually thins landward across the zone of velocity transition from 6.8 to 7.2 km/s. This is the case on the Barents Sea margin (Myhre and Eldholm, 1988) and along USGS seismic line 25 across the Baltimore Canyon Trough. Two kinds of simple explanations deserve exploration: (1) Ophiolites suggest that the upper part of the sheeted dike unit, roughly equivalent to oceanic layer 3, normally is brecciated (e.g., Salisbury and Christensen, 1978). It is possible that high overburden pressures (150 to 175 MPa) along thickly sedimented margins could close these cracks. For rocks metamorphosed to the amphibolite-epidote level, crack closure could raise velocities to the observed 7.0 to 7.2 km/s. (2) Rapid sediment input may cause the earliest ocean crust to form by intrusion into or below the sediment pile. This would prevent the formation of a low-velocity, extrusive upper crust, and by damping hydrothermal circulation, could prevent brecciation in the top of layer 3. Slow cooling in the absence of hydrothermal metamorphism might result in a crust predominantly of pyroxene gabbro, which also would fit the observed seismic-velocity distribution.

Apart from the margins, the North Atlantic also shares common elements with the Arctic Ocean basin (Volume L; Grantz and others, 1989). In particular, the mid-ocean-ridge/transform-fault system has been connected through both ocean basins since about Campanian time, first via the Labrador Sea, and later (post-Paleocene) through the Norwegian-Greenland Sea (Srivastava and Tapscott, 1986; Vogt, 1986a, b). The opening of these northern oceans, together with that of the South Atlantic in mid- to Late Cretaceous time, reconfigured the North Atlantic from a latitudinally oriented to a longitudinally oriented ocean. The new ocean-basin configuration permanently altered sedimentation and circulation patterns in the North Atlantic, particularly when marine connections allowed introduction of cool Arctic water into the deep Atlantic at the beginning of Oligocene time (Tucholke and Mountain, 1986).

Important, but less direct, connections link the western Atlantic region to the Appalachians (Volumes F1, F2; Williams and Neale, 1989; Hatcher and others, 1989), for example, through structural control of the Appalachians on the modern shape of the North Atlantic Ocean and through Appalachian exposures of ocean crust. Although asymmetric spreading and ridge jumps have changed the detailed shape of the plate boundary at the Mid-Atlantic Ridge (Vogt, 1986c; Klitgord and Schouten, 1986), the plate boundary in plan view still bears an unmistakable resemblance to the form of the continent-ocean crustal boundary (Figs. 1 and 2). In fact, the boundary shape of the Mid-Atlantic Ridge axis also broadly replicates the suture zone of the Paleozoic Iapetus Ocean and even the Proterozoic Grenville front (Fig. 1). The present plate boundary thus retains a dim structural memory of tectonic events more than 1 b.y. in the past. This continuous, if imprecise, replication of plate-boundary shape even through successive Wilson cycles (e.g., Nance and others, 1988) must be related to distribution of plate strength. Just as rifting and magmatism now continue at the warm, thin, and weak Mid-Atlantic Ridge axis, the newly rifting ocean basins tended to follow the warm, weak, fractured lithosphere of the previous orogen.

Scattered along the Appalachian orogen are exposed, but usually altered and deformed, oceanic crustal remnants of the Iapetus Ocean or its associated marginal basins. A particularly complete crustal section is the Blow-Me-Down Massif in western Newfoundland (Fig. 1). Available data show that crust now forming at the Mid-Atlantic Ridge axis is strikingly similar to this

Figure 1. Bathymetry (isobaths and elevations in km, with addition of ±200 m contours) for Atlantic Ocean area north of the Equator (simplified from Vogt and Tucholke, 1986b, Plate 2, with addition of land elevations courtesy of P. Sloss). Red dots show all known seamounts (>50 fms, or 92 m high) except north of Iceland and in Caribbean area (from Epp and Smoot, 1989). Plate boundaries based on Vogt (1986c, Plate 8B). Continent–ocean boundary from Plate 5 of Tucholke (1986) and other sources. Major pre-Mesozoic deformation fronts and other tectonic lineaments simplified from numerous sources.

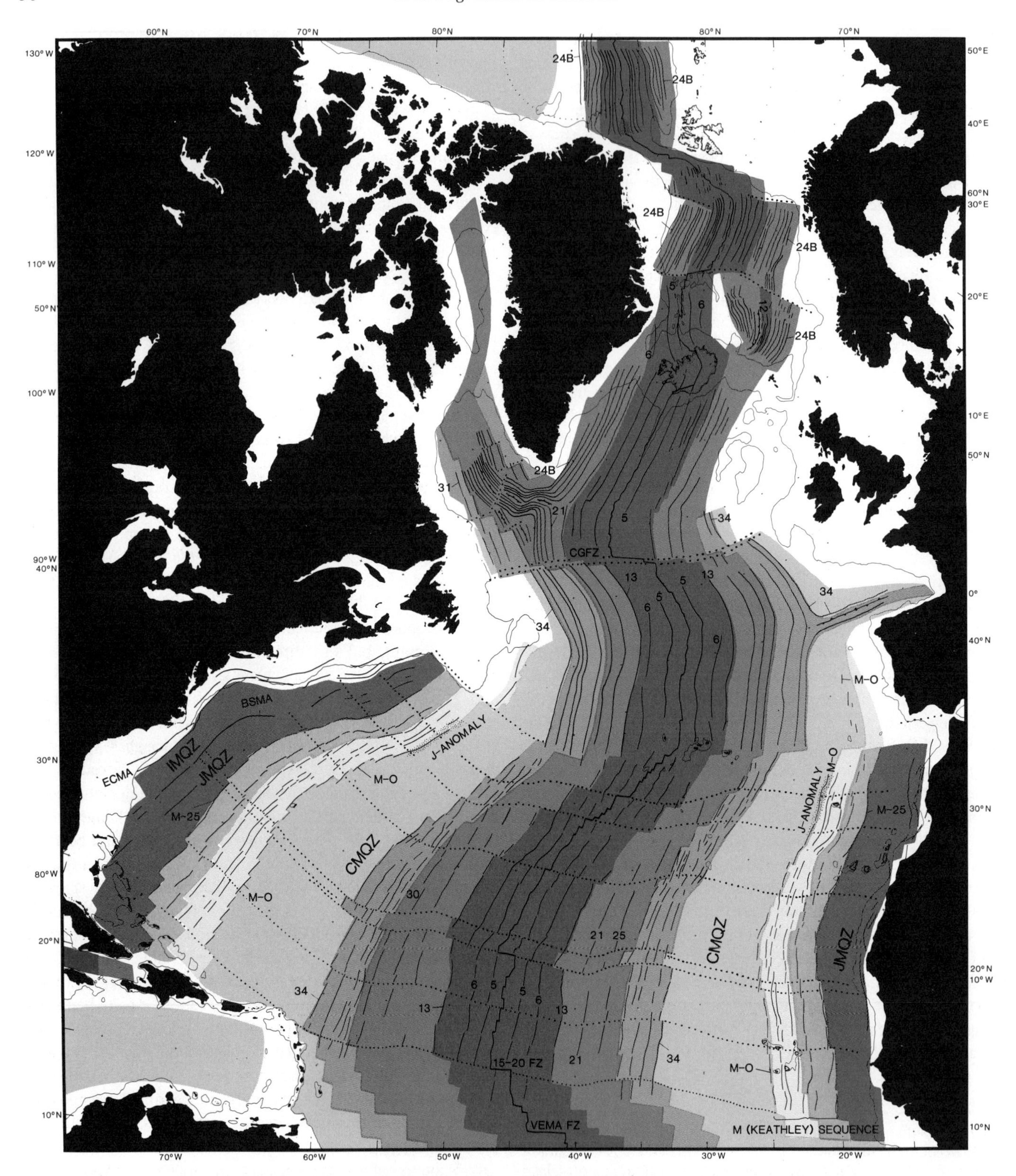

Figure 2. Magnetic lineations and oceanic crustal ages of North Atlantic area (from Vogt, 1986e, Plate 3). Color boundaries are at anomalies M25 (157 Ma), Cretaceous/Jurassic boundary (144 Ma), M0 (118 Ma), 34 (84 Ma), Cretaceous/Tertiary boundary (66.4 Ma), and 13 (35.5 Ma). See Srivastava and Tapscott (1986), Klitgord and Schouten (1986), Tucholke and Vogt (1986, Plates 9 and 10) and Plate 2 (this volume) for details and plate-tectonic reconstructions.

lower Paleozoic Iapetan ocean crust. With the current absence of drillholes into the oceanic mantle, and the scarcity of submarine outcrops that expose modern Atlantic mantle rocks (a rare exception is found in the Vema Fracture Zone; Auzende and others, 1988), Iapetan ocean slivers such as the Blow-Me-Down Massif constitute excellent and accessible ground truth for geophysically derived crustal structure of the modern ocean (e.g., Salisbury and Christensen, 1978).

VITAL STATISTICS

Basin characteristics

The greater Atlantic Ocean from 60°S northward, including the Mediterranean, the Gulf of Mexico, the Caribbean, and the Arctic Ocean, covers roughly 94 × 10^6 km^2, about a quarter of the global ocean area (Emery and Uchupi, 1984). Total volume is 355 × 10^6 km^3, the immensity of which can be appreciated by the 45,000 years it would take the world's most copious river, the Amazon, to fill this basin at its mean annual discharge rate of 8,000 km^3/yr. Ninety percent of greater Atlantic Ocean waters are contained in the region between 60°S and 60°N, excluding the Mediterranean, the Gulf of Mexico, and the Caribbean Sea. The ocean's median depth of 4,170 m (60°N to 60°S) compares closely to that of the global ocean (4,150 m).

The North Atlantic Ocean (0° to 60°N; Fig. 1) contains approximately 147 × 10^6 km^3 of sea water and has a median depth of 3,910 m (Emery and Uchupi, 1984). The area underlain by oceanic crust can be approximated by subtraction of 5 × 10^6 km^2 of continental shelf area. This "oceanic North Atlantic" happens to have the same surface area as the moon (31 × 10^6 km^2) and is larger than the North American continent. Although the ca. 75-Ma median basement age of the North Atlantic is far less than that of North America (1,000 to 1,500 Ma) and the moon (3,000 to 4,000 Ma), the North Atlantic shares with the lunar surface a basaltic composition. Both crusts are draped with fine debris and have been little eroded or tectonized by endogenic forces since they were formed.

In the most fundamental sense, the structure and evolution of the oceanic Atlantic can be described in terms of three components: (1) the oceanic crust and mantle lithosphere, which has evolved by sea-floor spreading and plate motions; (2) the oceanic sediments, accumulated primarily from continental erosion, volcanism, biologic processes, mass wasting, and bottom currents; and (3) the ocean waters, which form the culture medium for biologic processes, erode and redeposit sediments, and interact chemically with the oceanic crust and sediments. Each of these components, as well as the structure and content (or even absence) of the rock record which remains today, ultimately is linked to rates and patterns of tectonism and volcanism (Fig. 3; Tucholke and McCoy, 1986). Exceptions are caused by extraterrestrial effects, which typically are fine-scale (e.g., orbital forcing) or geologically instantaneous (e.g., bolide impacts). We use the term "tectonism" in the broad sense to refer to plate motions and their geologic manifestations in the form of crustal deformation, including weak strains like thermal expansion or subsidence. Most volcanism is genetically associated with plate boundaries, typically spreading ridges or the volcanic arcs landward of subduction zones. Volcanism also is generated in plate interiors, however, particularly above asthenospheric temperature anomalies, such as mantle plumes that appear to be independent of plate motion; many of the larger seamounts shown in Figure 1 were formed in this manner. Below, we summarize the three components of the Atlantic Ocean through time and in relation to the record of tectonism and volcanism.

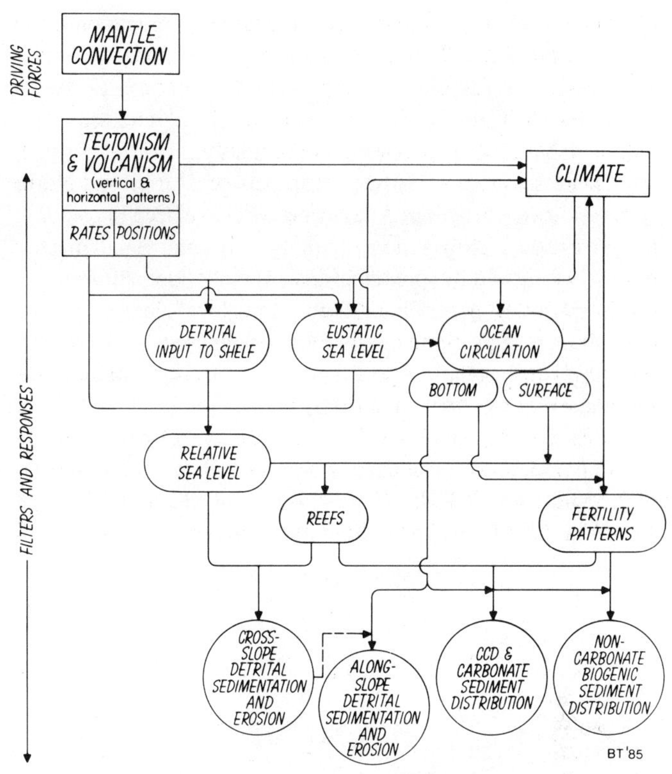

Figure 3. Whole-earth wiring diagram summarizing the hierarchy and interaction of the most direct controls on sedimentation and erosion in the North Atlantic basins. Exogenic effects and numerous less-direct controls and interactions are not included. Pathways for atmospheric dispersal of sediment (e.g., ash, eolian dust) involve an additional branch of tectonics/climate interaction that is not shown here. Reproduced from Tucholke and McCoy (1986).

Ocean crust

Sea-floor spreading adds lithosphere to the Atlantic trailing end of the North American plate, while sedimentation adds layers on top. The actual geometric relationships may be better described in terms of basalt flows "off-lapping" the top of the growing plate (e.g., Pálmason, 1986); lithosphere "off-lapping" the bottom of the plate (e.g., Sclater and Wixon, 1986); and sediments lapping onto the continental margins (or off-lapping, depending on relative sea-level fluctuations) and lapping onto the Mid-Atlantic Ridge flanks. Because subduction along the Scotia and Lesser Antilles island arcs is relatively minor (e.g., Westbrook and McCann, 1986), the volumes of Atlantic crust and sediment have been increasing continuously, albeit at varying rates, since sea-floor spreading began between Africa and North America. Rate changes in Atlantic growth have been in response to: (a) episodic propagation of rifting into continental masses, normally followed by spreading; and (b) other fluctuations in the rate of spreading, generally attributable to global changes in plate dynamics. Atlantic mantle lithosphere volume also has increased, but it may have temporary reversals; e.g., if information of the Bermuda Rise was accompanied by plate thinning.

Sea-floor spreading widens the Atlantic Ocean basin by addition of new crust in a narrow plate-boundary zone at the axis of the Mid-Atlantic Ridge (Figs. 2, 4 and 5). Chapters 4 through 12 of Volume M (see Appendix A at the end of this volume) deal with this crustal factory mostly as it has been operating in the geologic present, i.e., the last 1 m.y. or so. Vital statistics for the spreading process, averaged over the past 3 m.y., are given in Table 1. They were computed from the NUVEL-1 model (DeMets and others, 1989) for the three major sections of the Mid-Atlantic Ridge. More refined estimates of crustal production north of the equator are attempted in Figure 5, where along-strike variations in crustal thickness are taken into account. However, actual physical data supporting such variability in crustal thickness are still very limited (Purdy and Ewing, 1986).

Triassic to Early Jurassic rifting of Africa from North America culminated in formation of the first North Atlantic ocean crust by sea-floor spreading about Bathonian time (Klitgord and Schouten, 1986). Age limits on this stage have been estimated variously at 169 to 176 Ma (Kent and Gradstein, 1986) to 157 to 165 Ma (Haq and others, 1987), to name only two time scales published in recent years. Large uncertainties in time scales intro-

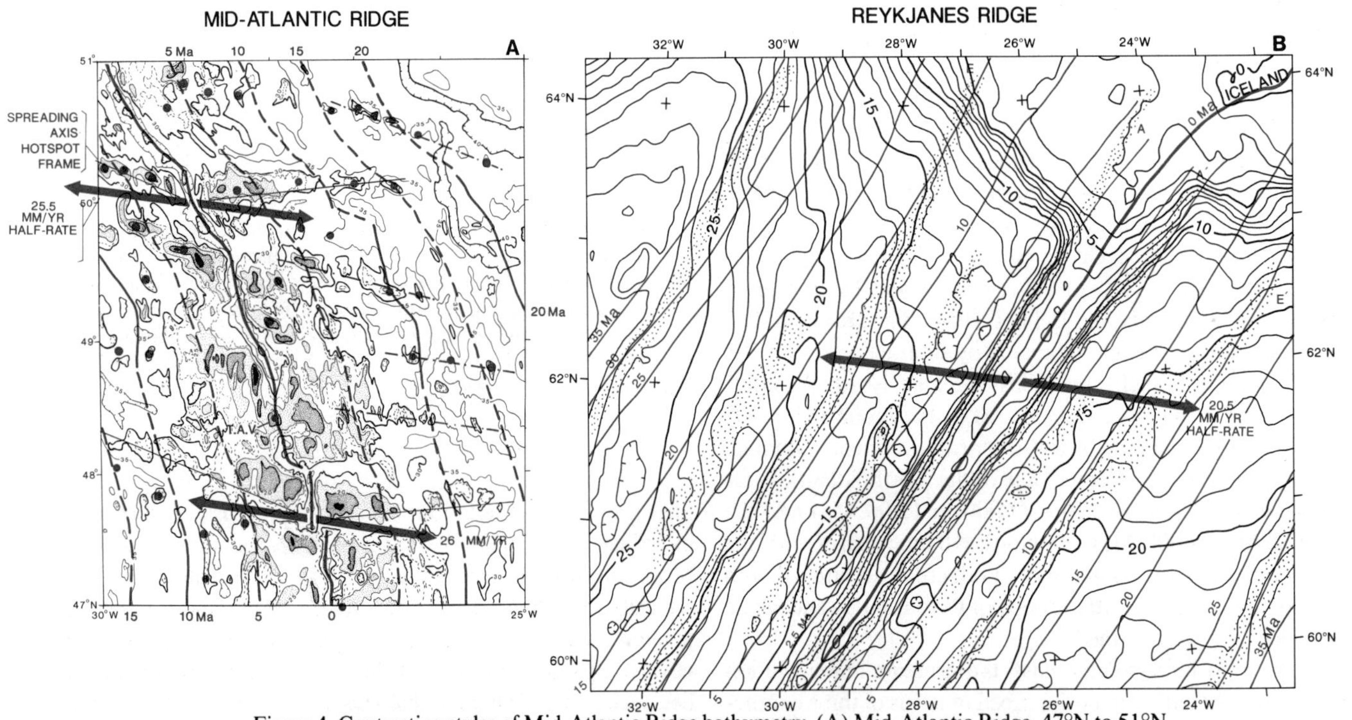

Figure 4. Contrasting styles of Mid-Atlantic Ridge bathymetry. (A) Mid-Atlantic Ridge, 47°N to 51°N, Mercator projection, with 500-m contours (locally 250-m) from Johnson and Vogt (1973). Topography shallower than 1,500 m is solid black, 1,500 to 2,000 m is thickly stippled and 2,000 to 2,500 m is lightly stippled. T.A.V. denotes Telegraph Axial Volcano, a rare example of a major volcanic edifice filling the rift valley. Red: dots are seamounts according to Epp and Smoot (1989); thick arrows show present directions of relative plate motion labeled in mm/yr half-rate (based on DeMets and others, 1989); thin solid lines, (labeled axis/hotspot frame) indicate predicted motion between accreted crust and hotspots fixed to mesosphere (based on Schouten and others, 1987); dashed lines are linear seamount alignments approximately parallel to direction of relative plate motion; and red lines give crustal isochrons (dashed where inferred; based on Klitgord and Schouten, 1986, and Srivastava and Tapscott, 1986). (B) Reykjanes Ridge on polar stereographic projection, with 100-m contours based on DBDB-5 global bathymetric data base. Red stippling shows basement topographic highs and/or escarpments, labeled by letter according to Vogt (1971, 1983). Red arrows give present direction of relative plate motion with half-rates based on DeMets and others (1989). Red isochrons are based on Nunns and others (1983). Note that topographic features are slightly diachronous (younger towards the southwest), implying southwestward propagation of some anomaly that controls spreading-axis elevation.

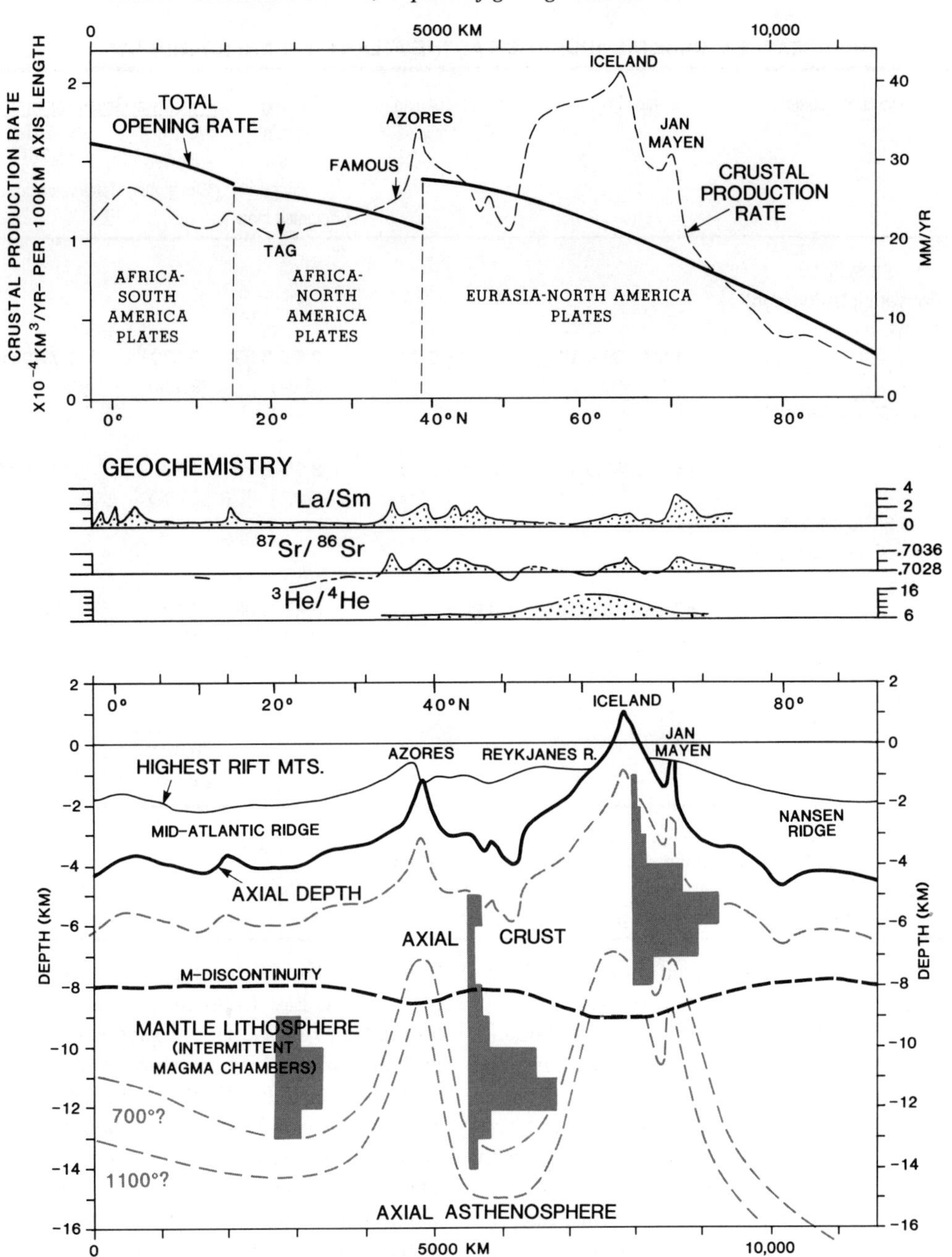

Figure 5. Along-strike Mid-Atlantic Ridge variations in opening rate (based on DeMets and others, 1989; see Table 1) and crustal production rate. Middle: geochemical parameters (La/Sm, $^{87}Sr/^{86}Sr$, and $^{3}He/^{4}He$; generalized from Schilling, 1986, and Plate 8AB of Vogt and Tucholke, 1986a; La/Sm peaks near 15°N and 4°N from Bougault and others, 1988, and Schilling and others, 1988). Bottom: In black, along-strike variations in axial topography (simplified from Plate 3, and Vogt and Tucholke, 1986a, Plate 8B) and depth of M-discontinuity (estimated using Figs. 2 and 14 of Klein and Langmuir, 1987). Superimposed in red are conjectural along-strike variations in rheology, inferred mainly from earthquake focal-depth distributions (Einarsson, 1986, p. 113) and, on Iceland, also from magnetotellurics (Hermance, 1981). Histograms (red) show earthquake hypocenter distributions at 23°N (Toomey and others, 1985), at 45°N (Lilwall and others, 1978), and on Iceland for the Krafla rift-zone event in February 1980. Although brittle, the crust above the upper dashed line is intensely fissured, weak, unable to support large stresses, and thus low in earthquake activity. The next deeper dashed line (based in part on Solomon and others, 1988) approximates the brittle–ductile transition, ca. 600° to 800°C. Significant seismicity does not occur below that depth. Average depth of basalt solidus (ca. 1,100°C) must be greater still and must extend into upper mantle along much of the Mid-Atlantic Ridge axis. Based on arguments of Vogt and others (1969) and consistent with available constraints, the average solidus is placed coincident with Moho wherever a pronounced rift valley is lacking (mainly on Iceland).

TABLE 1. CRUSTAL ACCRETION AT THE ATLANTIC PLATE BOUNDARY*

Plate-Boundary Segment	Limits of Segment	Rotation Pole	Angular Opening Rate°/m.y.	Opening Rate in cm/yr Range (Weighted mean)	Crustal Generation Rate: Area in km^2/yr (% of global)	Crustal Generation Rate: Volume† in km^3/yr Total/Volcanics only	Lithosphere accretion rate§ in km^3/yr
	55°S, 1°W (Bouvet triple Junction)						
Africa–South America		61.5°N, 39.4°W	0.32 ± 0.01	2.59–3.59 (3.34)	0.273 (9.1%)	1.77/041	27.2
	15.25°N, 44.9°W**						
Africa–North America		78.8°N, 38.3°W	0.25 ± 0.02	2.05–2.75 (2.45)	0.72 (2.4%)	0.47/0.11	7.2
	39.38°N, 29.72W (Azores triple junction)						
Eurasia–North America		62.4°N, 135.8°E	0.22 ± 0.01	0.47–2.68 (1.76)	0.122 (4%)	0.79/0.18	12.2
	~77.5°N, 128.3°E (limit of spreading on Siberian margin)						
Total					0.467 (16%)	3.03/070	46.6

*Based on DeMets and others, 1989.
†For an assumed mean crustal thickness of 6.5 km, including 1.5 km of extrusives.
§For a 100-km-thick equilibrium lithosphere.
**Exact triple junction location indeterminate, see e.g., Roest and Collette (1986).

duce large uncertainties into Atlantic (and global) sea-floor–spreading rate estimates and, therefore, into derived quantities such as predicted sea level (Plate 2). But time-scale uncertainties are only part of the problem of dating the onset of Atlantic spreading. As reviewed by Sheridan and Grow (1988), there are ambiguous hints that under Georges Bank, rocks as old as Upper Triassic might overlie the "breakup unconformity," presumably formed at the time of incipient sea-floor spreading, and some authors suggest Lower Jurassic drift-stage sediments. Such an early onset of spreading would be more consistent with the pronounced magmatic event observed ca. 190 ± 10 Ma, as opposed to the more subdued, even questionable, event at 175 ± 5 Ma (deBoer and others, 1988). To fully document North Atlantic evolution, one certainly needs to know when sea-floor spreading actually began, but this will remain elusive until the oldest deeply buried oceanic crust is dated.

Subsequent to initial opening, growth of the North Atlantic is commonly described by a sequence of rotation stage poles and angles between selected magnetic lineations (Klitgord and Schouten, 1986; Srivastava and Tapscott, 1986). These poles and angles were used to make the paleogeographic base maps in Plate 2 (see also Plates 9 and 10, Vogt and Tucholke, 1986a). As shown in Plate 2 (lower left), the original Atlantic (Klitgord and Schouten, 1986) was a narrow low-latitude seaway extending from the Gulf of Mexico through present south Florida, along the present U.S. East Coast margin, and into the Ligurian Tethys (Gibraltar to Italy). The Mojave-Sonora megashear in Mexico probably was a long transform fault connecting the Atlantic spreading axis to Pacific plate boundaries. After generating a Red Sea–sized ocean basin ca. 150 km wide, the accreting plate boundary jumped east into the paleo-African plate (Vogt, 1973). The time of this jump is estimated with considerable uncertainty as late Bathonian (170 Ma). Opening then proceeded at a relatively rapid (but not well constrained) rate of ca. 40 mm/yr (Plate 2). At anomaly M21 time (Tithonian, ca. 150 Ma), Klitgord and Schouten (1986) believe the Gulf of Mexico rift jumped southeastward, splitting Yucatan–Guatemala from South America and, by abandoning the Mojave-Sonora megashear, established a new plate-boundary connection to the Pacific. At that time, the ca. 25-m.y.-old Atlantic–Gulf of Mexico ocean basin was roughly 1,000 km wide and 4,000 km long, comparable in size and shape to the present Atlantic extension north of 55°N into the Arctic.

By anomaly M10N time (132 Ma) the Atlantic was experiencing the first of several expansions, which 100 m.y. later would make it a true Arctic-to-Antarctic ocean basin. At about 132 Ma (late Valanginian) sea-floor spreading was initiated in the Argentina–South Africa part of the South Atlantic (Austin and

Uchupi, 1982; Sibuet and others, 1984), while continental crust remained in sheared contact in the equatorial Atlantic. Rifting between Iberia and the Grand Banks, first concentrated in a Late Triassic phase, recommenced in the Late Jurassic through Early Cretaceous (Tankard and Welsink, 1987), and it probably extended north into intercontinental rift zones that would eventually form the Labrador and Norwegian-Greenland Seas.

About anomaly M0 time (118 Ma), an Iceland-like hot spot developed at the juncture of the Mid-Atlantic Ridge and the rift zone between Iberia and the Grand Banks. Magmas vented by this hot spot now form the J-Anomaly Ridge, the Madeira-Tore Rise, and probably the Southeast Newfoundland Ridge in the North Atlantic (Plate 2; Tucholke and Ludwig, 1982). Perhaps as a result of this hot-spot activity, sea-floor spreading extended northward at anomaly M0 into the Bay of Biscay. By anomaly 33 time (80 Ma), rifting had ended in Rockall Trough, and spreading axes in the Caribbean and Bay of Biscay were abandoned, but spreading was underway in the Labrador Sea. Propagation of the spreading system through the Norwegian-Greenland Sea into the Arctic (Srivastava and Tapscott, 1986) and massive widespread volcanism, associated with the birth (or great intensification) of the Iceland hot spot, occurred at anomaly 25/24 (~59 Ma) (see Vogt, 1986b for a review).

The Atlantic finally became the Arctic-to-Antarctic ocean it is today near the time of anomaly 13 (36 Ma) when sea-floor spreading ceased in the Labrador Sea, and the North American plate abruptly grew 10 percent in size by annexing the 3.5×10^6 km^2 Greenland plate. As a direct geometric consequence of this annexation, strike-slip motion was replaced by spreading between Greenland and Spitsbergen, opening the first deep-water connection from the North Atlantic to the Arctic Basin. The spectacular "pulse" of bottom-current erosion over much of the western North Atlantic (Plate 2; Tucholke and McCoy, 1986; Tucholke and Mountain, 1986) may have been a result of this tectonically induced connection. However, causality is difficult to prove; numerous regional and global (e.g., $\delta^{18}O$, Plate 2) geologic changes occurred at nearly the same time, and their interrelations are still poorly understood. Nevertheless, underlying links to tectonism probably form the basis for the changes observed in the rock record (Fig. 3).

Subsequent geometry of Atlantic opening changed episodically but less dramatically. About 32 Ma, the spreading axis (Aegir Ridge) in the Norway Basin was abandoned, and a new rift began to propagate northeastward along the east Greenland margin, splitting off a probable microcontinent, the Jan Mayen Ridge. Sea-floor spreading became fully established on the new Kolbeinsey Ridge axis ca. 20 Ma (anomaly 6; Vogt, 1986b). As the Aegir Ridge became defunct, so did the King's Trough–Biscay plate boundary, which shifted south to the Gibraltar-Azores line (ca. 28 Ma; Klitgord and Schouten, 1986). Up to this time, Iberia had been part of the Africa plate for at least 90 m.y., since the initial separation of Iberia from North America at anomaly M0.

Generally similar timing of plate-motion changes during opening of the Atlantic, but at higher resolution, has been inferred from basement morphology along the trace of the Kane Fracture Zone, which approximates plate-flow lines (Plate 3; Tucholke and Schouten, 1989). The major plate-motion changes indicated by fracture-zone orientation, and the events with which they correlate, are: ~136 Ma (M14/13 to M12; latest stage South Atlantic rifting), ~102 Ma (within Cretaceous Magnetic Quiet Zone), ~92 Ma (CMQZ; rift-drift transition in Labrador Sea), ~59 Ma (anomaly 25/24; opening of Norwegian-Greenland Sea), ~22 Ma (pre-anomaly 6; ? shift of Iberian plate from Africa to Eurasia, Kolbeinsey Ridge spreading established), and 17 Ma. The last time corresponds to the extrapolated origin time of the "E" diachronous escarpments on Iceland (Plate 2; Vogt, 1971; see Fig. 4 and later discussion). Klitgord and Schouten (1986) also infer "a reorganization of spreading direction and rate along the entire Atlantic sea-floor spreading system" at 2.5 Ma (see also Vogt, 1986c, d). This reorganization, which corresponds to elevation of the Reykjanes Ridge along the "A" escarpments (Fig. 4), may have been a tectonic stimulus that is interrelated with onset of major Northern Hemisphere glaciation and a 3 to 2 Ma pulse of Atlantic sea-floor erosion by bottom currents (Tucholke and Mountain, 1986).

Sedimentary sequences

Greater Atlantic Ocean sediments (60°N to 60°S) have a volume of 137×10^6 km^3 and occupy an average 30 percent of the space between basement and sea level (Emery and Uchupi, 1984). These deposits, volumetrically 10 to 15 percent of the global total, can be subdivided into "rift" and "drift" supersequences, the latter including everything deposited since sea-floor spreading began. The rift supersequence on continental crust is surprisingly voluminous (Sheridan and Grow, 1988), and the rift-plus-drift sediment volume that resides on continental crust along the eastern margin of North America (23×10^6 km^3) exceeds the volume of drift sediments on oceanic crust west of the Mid-Atlantic Ridge (20×10^6 km^3; Emery and Uchupi, 1984).

The drift supersequence is split by the Mid-Atlantic Ridge into eastern and western limbs, and sediment thickness is zero along the ridge axis. In the western North Atlantic basin the 1-km isopach is reached 500 to 1,000 km from the North American (U.S.) shelf edge. Sediments closer to the margin thicken abruptly; for example, Jurassic oceanic crust in the Baltimore Canyon Trough area is covered by up to 13 km of sediments. The concentration of sediments along the margin primarily reflects proximity to continental sediment sources, and secondarily the great age of the marginal oceanic crust. Very thick sediments (7 to 20 km) also occur seaward of the Lesser Antilles in a tectonically thickened accretionary-wedge complex (Westbrook and McCann, 1986). Of the greater Atlantic Ocean, the northwest quadrant (including South America north of the equator) contains a disproportionately large share of Atlantic sediments, 37 of 68×10^6 km^3 of sediments lying on pre-rift continental crust, and 36 of 69×10^6 km^3 of overlying oceanic crust (Emery and Uchupi, 1984). Of the 36×10^6 km^3 of sediments overlying northwest Atlantic oceanic crust, 14×10^6 km^3 were deposited during the Neogene and 22×10^6 km^3 are of Mesozoic and Paleogene age (~175 to 22 Ma). The larger Neogene Atlantic has naturally accumulated more pelagic material, and large volumes of detritus were shed from North America during the Plio-Pleistocene glaciations. However, the large post–22 Ma sediment volume is inflated relative to older sediments by two additional factors: (1) compaction has reduced the volume of older, more deeply buried sediments, and (2) pre-Neogene sediments that have been eroded and redeposited by bottom currents or mass wasting are reassigned younger ages according to the time of their final redeposition. For the most part, sediments that are missing at Mesozoic-Paleogene unconformities were not physically transported from the Atlantic basin, although an unknown volume of biogenous (siliceous and calcareous) sediment was chemically removed by dissolution.

The annual mass of sediment accreted to the top of western North Atlantic lithosphere in the Holocene has been 0.34×10^9 tons/yr (1.05×10^9 tons/yr for the Neogene-Quaternary), which is comparable to the ca. 0.4×10^9 tons/yr of volcanic material accreted to the North America plate at the Mid-Atlantic Ridge. The annual tonnage of suspended sediment carried into the western North Atlantic by North American rivers is 0.75×10^9 tons/yr (Emery and Uchupi, 1984), more than enough to account for the sediment accumulation rate in the western North Atlantic basins. Average long-term sedimentation rates across the North Atlantic have been remarkably uniform (ca. 3 to 5 mg/cm^2/yr) over the history of the ocean (Emery and Uchupi, 1984). However, there have been some significant variations. The Late Cretaceous deep North Atlantic, for example, accumulated pelagic red shales at very low rates of 0.2 to 0.7 mg/cm^2/yr. In contrast, Paleogene and Pleistocene deep-basin turbidites accumulated at rates faster by a factor of ten or more (Jansa and others, 1979). Large geographic variations in sedimentation rate also have persisted through time, from <0.3 mg/cm^2/yr in the mid-Atlantic pelagic province, to 3 to 10 mg/cm^2/yr along continental slopes and rises, and up to more than 30 mg/cm^2/yr on tropical carbonate platforms. Large areas of the western Atlantic, particularly the continental margins, also have experienced erosion by bottom currents, i.e., negative accumulation rates (Fig. 6B and 7A, B). Volumetrically, most such erosion has occurred since the time that significant deep-water circulation developed in the early Oligocene (Mountain and Tucholke, 1985; Tucholke and Mountain, 1986). The other principal mechanisms of sediment removal and redistribution are slumps, slides, and debris flows (Embley and Jacobi, 1986), which have been active on the continental margins and other submarine slopes throughout the history of the basin (Fig. 8).

North Atlantic paleosedimentation patterns, paleobiogeography, and paleoenvironment are discussed in detail in chapters 31 to 38 of Vogt and Tucholke (1986a, see Appendix A), and the highlights are summarized in Plate 2 of this volume. The oldest sedimentary rocks recovered in boreholes in the deep western North Atlantic basin are Middle Jurassic (Callovian) dark-colored mudstones, although Triassic and Lower Jurassic sediments have been drilled in the deep eastern North Atlantic and in shallow-water areas of the continental margins (Jansa, 1986). The latter deposits record the birth of the North Atlantic in the form of rift-stage, typically red-bed clastics, and in evaporites deposited as marine waters entered the restricted rift zone. Very limited deep circulation in the young, Middle Jurassic ocean basin is suggested by the dark shales and marls. By Late Jurassic time, more open-marine conditions prevailed, resulting in deposition of green-gray and reddish shales and marls. Much of the North Atlantic margin was rimmed by Jurassic carbonate reefs and banks, which persisted into the Cretaceous and which controlled or modulated the flux of both continental clastics and detrital carbonates to the basin.

In the latest Jurassic and Early Cretaceous (Neocomian) the North Atlantic was a carbonate ocean, accumulating limestones and marls across all parts of the basin (Plate 2; Jansa and others, 1979). A dramatic change to deposition of black and gray-green shales occurred in Hauterivian-Barremian time, and deposition of these sediments continued through the Cenomanian (Arthur and Dean, 1986). The anoxic to low-oxygen conditions of the deep basin during this period may have been caused by tectonic isolation of the deep North Atlantic, with barriers to deep circulation developed in the region of the present Caribbean and probably in the Eurasian Tethys seaway. Deep-water connections, which developed between the North and South Atlantic in the Late Cretaceous, again oxygenated the North Atlantic basin, but elevated eustatic sea level (Plate 2) trapped most continental clastics in shallow water; the deep basin consequently accumulated mainly pelagic, red-brown shales (Arthur and Dean, 1986). The close of the Cretaceous was preceded by a sharp pulse of increased surface-water productivity and carbonate accumulation in the deep basin, indicated in Plate 2 by a temporary depression and rise of the calcite compensation depth (CCD).

Lowered eustatic sea levels in the Cenozoic triggered flux of continental-margin clastic and biogenic detritus to the deep North Atlantic basins, and widespread abyssal fan/plain systems developed (Tucholke and Mountain, 1986). Open-ocean productivity of biosiliceous organisms was particularly high in early to middle Eocene time, and the diagenetically altered remains of these organisms now form widespread chert beds in almost all provinces of the North Atlantic (Horizon A^c, Fig. 7C). The development of strong deep-ocean circulation about early Oligocene time, presumably in response to tectonic opening of a deep-water Arctic–North Atlantic passage, permanently transformed the depositional environment of the North Atlantic. Subsequent episodes of deep current-controlled erosion and deposition sculpted much of the upper Paleogene and Neogene sedimentary record, particularly along western margins of the basins (Fig. 6B). Although the western North Atlantic basins and margins commonly are considered to be tectonically "passive," their sedimentation history has been geologically dynamic.

Ocean waters

Atlantic Ocean waters are a low-viscosity convecting fluid, and they consequently have a very short memory. Nevertheless, the present properties and motions of this complex fluid body must be understood before the record of past oceans can be properly interpreted from sea-floor sediments. Conversely, models of global atmospheric/ocean circulation are untrustworthy if, upon entry of reasonable boundary conditions and forcing functions, they are incapable of reproducing paleoenvironments recorded by the sediments.

Physical oceanography is generally treated as a separate subject in the ocean sciences, and because of space limitations, Volume M did not contain a chapter on this aspect of the present Atlantic Ocean. Even so, aspects of the modern deep circulation (McCave and Tucholke, 1986) and the paleo-physical oceanography (derived from interpretation of paleoenvironments; Chapters 31 through 38 of Vogt and Tucholke, 1986a, see Appendix A) are treated in that volume. Marine geologists have inferred from the chemistry, mineralogy, and fossil assemblages of sea-floor sediments how the Atlantic Ocean evolved throughout its 180+-m.y. history: its temperature and salinity; its surface and deep currents; its organic productivity and oxygen content; and its floral/faunal populations, which have shifted and evolved (Plate 2) in response to water temperature/chemistry and at times have suffered catastrophic extinctions (Gradstein, 1986; Premoli-Silva and Boersma, 1986; Poag and Miller, 1986; Berggren and Olsson, 1986). The potential for reconstructing global paleoenvironments from the sedimentary record in a rigorous, quantitative fashion is very high. Although most such work has been conducted on higher-resolution records of the Quaternary (see e.g., Ruddiman and Wright, 1987), quantitative paleoceanography of the older oceans will improve as better sedimentary records are recovered for study.

Fundamental to Atlantic environments and paleoenvironments are the ocean's internal motions—both wind-driven surface currents like the Gulf Stream (Fig. 6A) and thermohaline-driven bottom currents like the Western Boundary Undercurrent (Fig. 6B)—and its enormous heat capacity (and hence climatic buffering effects). The ocean currents, as well as atmospheric circulation, are strongly influenced by the Earth's rotation; acting on an ocean with north-south boundaries, this rotational influence (Coriolis force) imparts a strong east-west asymmetry to the ocean circulation. The Coriolis effect deflects the tradewinds toward the west, piling up surface waters along the central American margin. These waters re-enter the Atlantic through the Florida Straits to form the Gulf Stream, a geostrophic current in which Coriolis force and pressure gradient are in balance. The Coriolis effect is also responsible for steering the deep, southward-flowing thermohaline currents into the western Atlantic (Fig. 6B). Along the oceanographically active western margins of the basins, abyssal-current speeds average 10 to 20 cm/s and intermittently reach >30 cm/s. In certain deep conduits, such as the Faeroe-Shetland Channel, which links the Norwegian-Greenland Sea to the North Atlantic (DSOW, WTRO, Fig. 6B), flow speeds can reach 200 cm/s (Roberts and others, 1983). At current speeds of several tens of cm/s or more, the typically fine-grained sea-floor sediments are readily eroded and redistributed. Westward-intensified surface currents such as the Gulf Stream reach much higher speeds (several knots, >100 to 200 cm/s), and their rapid transport of unique water properties (temperature, salinity, etc.) is fundamental to biogeographic provinciality. For all these reasons, western North Atlantic sediments typically record a much more interesting, but also more complex, geologic history than those of the eastern Atlantic or the Pacific margin of North America.

Water-volume transport in the oceans is so staggering that a special unit, the Sverdrup (Sv, 1×10^6 m^3/s), has come into use. The greatest Atlantic flow involves the Gulf Stream, which carries 30 Sv through the Florida Straits. Transport increases downstream to ~70 Sv off the mid-Atlantic states and ~100 Sv at 55°W (Richardson, 1985). This increase is balanced by flanking and underlying countercurrents, however, and the net eastward flow is not increased. By contrast the Amazon and Mississippi Rivers together average only 0.75 Sv. Volume transport of Gulf Stream magnitude is briefly (for a few hours) approached only by truly catastrophic events. For example, the late Pleistocene Spokane flood in Washington state (Anonymous, 1976) and the 1929 Grand Banks (Clarke, 1988) turbidity-current event involved flows on the order of 10 Sv. However, these events involved flow speeds up to 1,000 to 2,000 cm/s, much faster and, therefore, much more erosive than even the Gulf Stream in the Florida Straits.

The Gulf Stream is but one element of a large North Atlantic circulation system that involves both shallow and deep waters (Fig. 6A, B). Accurate measurements of transport for the different branches of this system are difficult to make, since the oceanic current field is dominated by mesoscale eddies and meanders (e.g., Krauss and Meincke, 1982), rather than by large-scale steady flows as had earlier been supposed. Approximately 16 Sv of the Gulf Stream water moving eastward across the Atlantic at 40° to 50°N turns south to form the Canary Current in the eastern North Atlantic (Sverdrup and others, 1942). About 26 Sv of eastern and equatorial Atlantic water enters the Caribbean from the east, contributing to the volume transport of the Gulf Stream. North of 50°N, the North Atlantic Current extension of the Gulf Stream carries ~10 Sv northward; about 3 to 6 Sv of that reaches into the Norwegian Sea, keeping that ocean ice-free to 80°N. The 10-Sv northward flow of the North Atlantic Current past 50°N is only partly compensated by southward surface recirculation; 2 to 4 Sv of Arctic water that flows south along the east coast of Greenland is mostly recirculated in the Greenland-Norwegian Sea. The remaining return flow is composed of former North Atlantic Current water that has fairly high salinity, and cools and sinks in the Greenland-Norwegian Sea during winters. Exiting through several gaps in the Iceland-Greenland and Greenland-Scotland Ridges (Fig. 6B), the deep flow eventually combines to 10 Sv along the southeast Greenland continental rise and be-

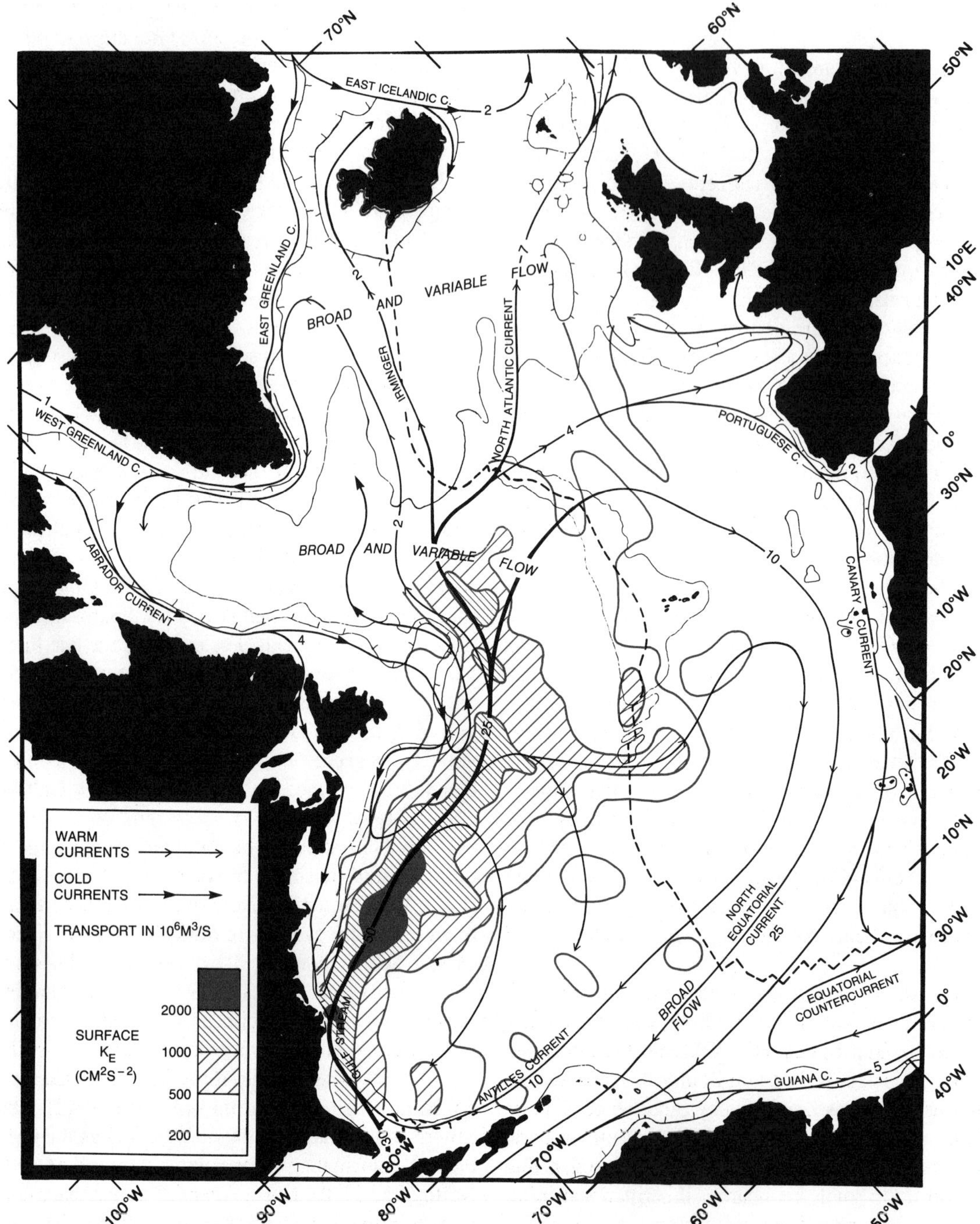

Figure 6A. Generalized surface-water circulation (less than 700 m) in the North Atlantic, on Mercator projection, modified from Sverdrup and others (1942) and Dietrich and others (1980). Approximate transports are given in units of Sverdrups (1×10^6 m^3/s). Surface eddy kinetic energy (red) from Richardson (1983). Approximate location of continental shelf edge, and 3 km isobath indicated by thin lines.

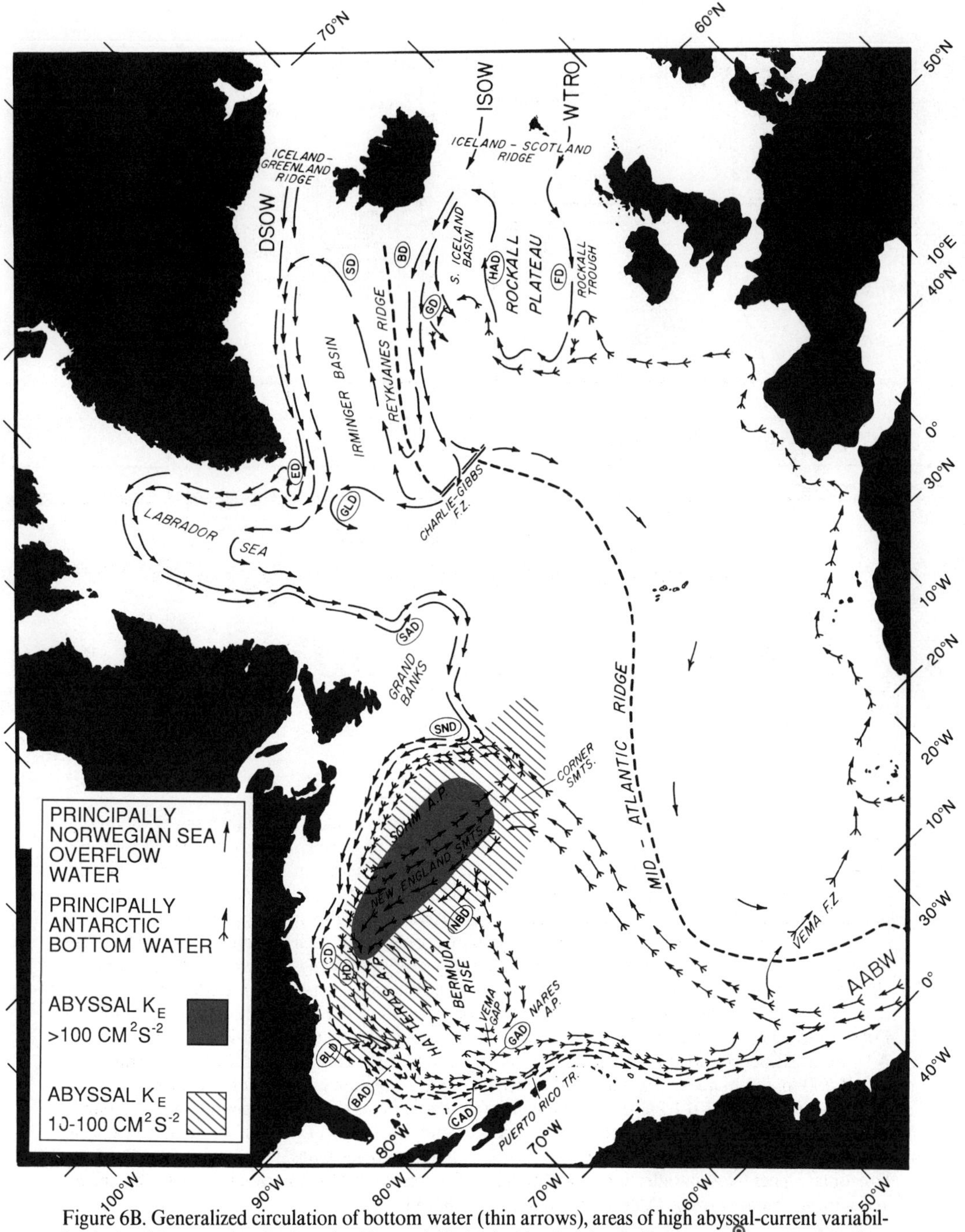

Figure 6B. Generalized circulation of bottom water (thin arrows), areas of high abyssal-current variability (red solid or crosshatched) and sediment drifts in the North Atlantic Ocean, on mercator projection. Thin red arrows show currents with a significant component of Antarctic Bottom Water (AABW). Thin black arrows show circulation of principally Norwegian Sea origin (DSOW, Denmark Strait overflow water; ISOW, Iceland–Scotland overflow water; and WTRO, Wyville-Thomson Ridge overflow water), which combine to form the North Atlantic deep water (NADW) and the Western Boundary Undercurrent. Solid red indicates K_E ("eddy kinetic energy per unit mass, a measure of abyssal "storminess") exceeding 100 cm^2/s^2, and red cross-hatching denotes K_E of 10 to 100 cm^2/s^2. Circled labels give locations of sediment drifts. In order along path of abyssal boundary currents (generally north to south), these are: FD, Feni Drift; HAD, Hatton Drift; BD, Bjorn Drift; GD, Gardar Drift; GLD, Gloria Drift; SD, Snorri Drift; ED, Eirik Drift; SAD, Sackville Spur Drift; SND, Southeast Newfoundland Ridge Drift; CD, Chesapeake Drift; HD, Hatteras (Gulf Stream Outer Ridge) Drift; BLD, Blake Drift; BAD, Bahama Drift; GAD, Greater Antilles Drift; and NBD, Northern Bermuda Rise Drift. Based on McCave and Tucholke (1986).

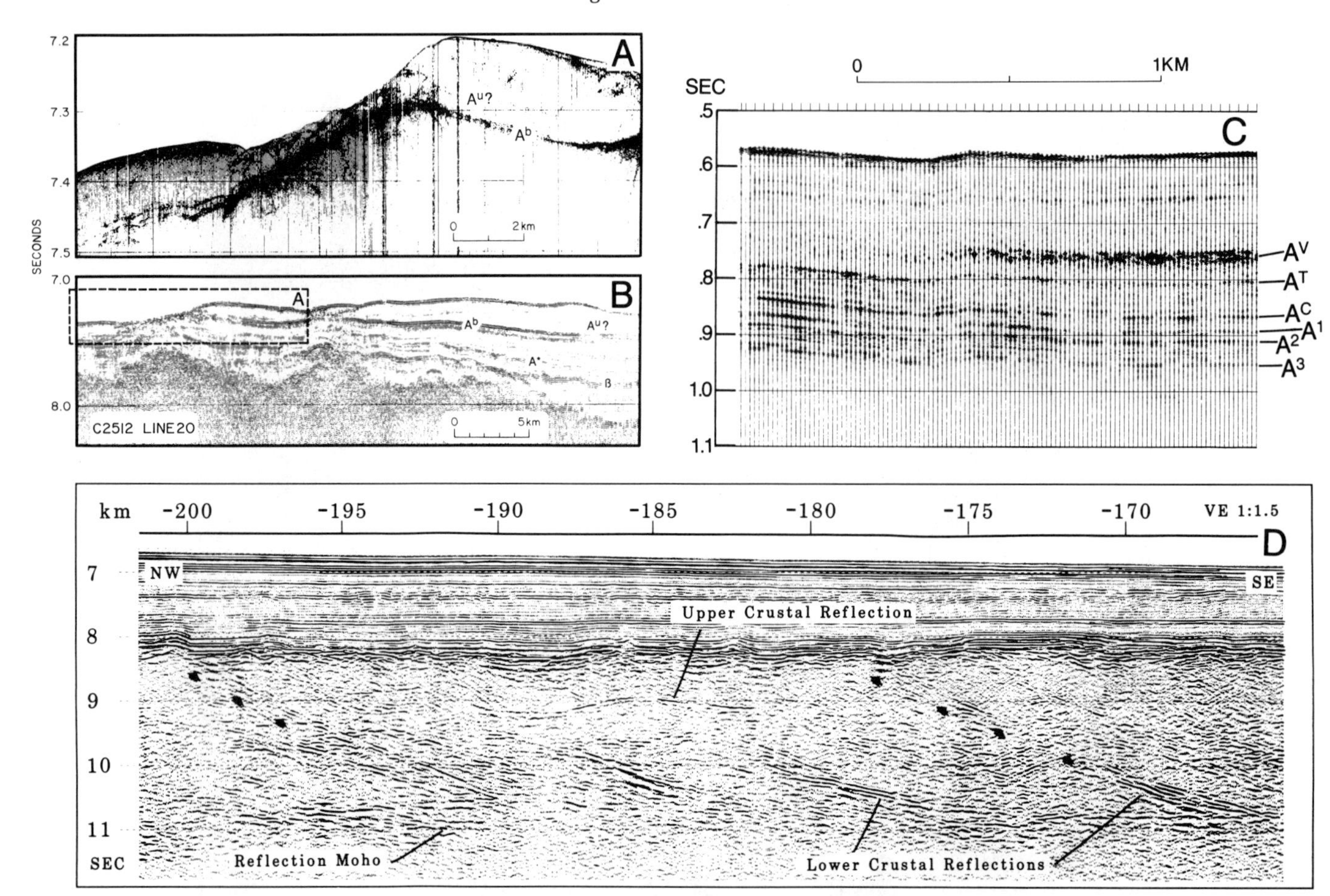

Figure 7. The Western Atlantic subbottom at different scales of seismic penetration and resolution (see Plate 3 for profile locations and Plate 2 for geologic correlation of seismic reflections). (A) 3.5-kHz, and (B) digitally processed, single-channel (50 to 100 Hz, ca. 1-s penetration) watergun profiles showing outcrop of reflections on southern Bermuda Rise (Mountain and others, 1985). Along the U.S. Atlantic margin reflector A^u is a lower Oligocene erosional surface; A^b in this profile is an erosional surface thought to date to the early to middle Eocene, based on correlation to DSDP Hole 417D. (C) Segment of Deep Towed Array Geophysical System (DTAGS) profile showing numerous reflections of the Horizon A Complex on the central Bermuda Rise (Gettrust and others, 1988). Reflectors are: A^v—upper Oligocene volcaniclastic turbidites derived from erosion of Beruda pedestal; A^t - top of middle Eocene turbidites originating from U.S. Atlantic margin; A^c—lower to middle Eocene cherts; A^1 to A^3—intra-Paleocene surfaces. DTAGS employs a 250 to 650 Hz source and a 24-channel array, both towed 500 to 700 m above sea floor, and it provides high-resolution estimates of structure and elastic properties in the upper 0.4 km of the sediments. (D) Part of two-ship, wide-aperture, North Atlantic Transect, multichannel, seismic profile (time-variable bandpass with 15 to 50 Hz passband at sea floor, decreasing to 5 to 22 Hz at base of crust) showing dipping Lower Crustal Reflections (arrows) and horizontal Upper Crustal Reflection, in addition to reflections from M-discontinuity, oceanic basement, and intra-sediment horizons (McCarthy and others, 1988, Fig. 4).

Figure 8. Summary map showing some of the downslope (gravity-dominated) dispersal routes for North America–derived sediments deposited in western North Atlantic basins. Debris flows (screened red), blocky slides (solid red), and submarine canyons (submarine red arrows) showing mass-wasting areas on U.S. continental margin are from Figure 6 of Embley and Jacobi (1986), modified using Anonymous (1988) and Clarke (1988). On land, major rivers draining into the Atlantic between Florida and New England are indicated by red dashed lines and arrows. Glacial-age buried river valleys crossing shelf (red dash–dot arrows) and shelf-edge sediment deltas (red stippled) are from Emery and Uchupi (1984). Selected 100-m bathymetric contours (red dashes) indicate slopes of abyssal plains and thus general direction of turbidity flows. Open red stippling shows extent of the 1929 Grand Banks turbidite on the Sohm Abyssal Plain (Clarke, 1988).

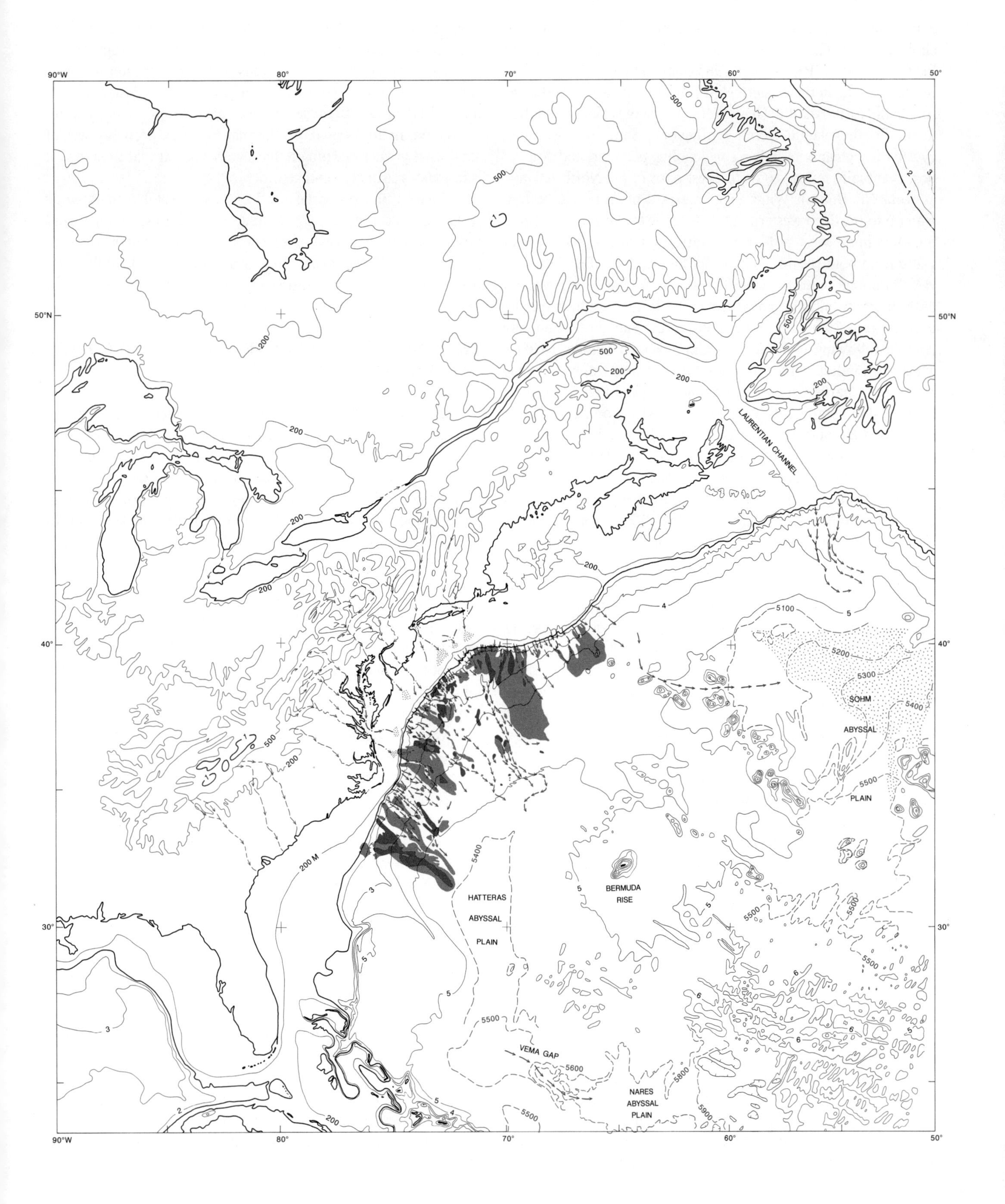
90°W
80°
70°
60°
50°
50°N
40°
30°
LAURENTIAN CHANNEL
SOHM
ABYSSAL
PLAIN
BERMUDA
RISE
HATTERAS
ABYSSAL
PLAIN
VEMA GAP
NARES
ABYSSAL
PLAIN
200 M
5100
5200
5300
5400
5500
5600
5800
5900

comes the Western Boundary Undercurrent (McCave and Tucholke, 1986). This deep flow, estimated at 10 to 15 Sv north of the Grand Banks (Richardson, 1985), has constructed most of the sediment drifts in the western North Atlantic (Fig. 6B) and is the source of North Atlantic Deep Water, much of which is exported to the South Atlantic Ocean and beyond. Some of this water, cycled through another mixing and cooling phase around Antarctica, eventually returns to the deepest parts of the North Atlantic as Antarctic Bottom Water. The transport of Antarctic bottom water into the deep western North Atlantic basins is about 1 to 2 Sv. Only in the western North Atlantic do significant volumes of water from both polar regions sculpt the sea floor (Fig. 6B).

Although bottom-water flow is concentrated along western basin margins, intra-oceanic topography further controls the details of the deep flow, and bottom currents are essentially contour-following currents (McCave and Tucholke, 1986). Thus, even individual features of submarine topography, e.g., the Vema and Charlie-Gibbs fracture zones, Rockall Plateau, and the New England seamounts, have profound effects on deep circulation (Fig. 6B). Surface currents also may be "anchored" by sea-floor topography; for example the East Greenland Current is confined to the continental shelf, the Iceland front is positioned on the Iceland–Faeroe Ridge crest, and the Arctic Polar Front tends to overlie Mohns Ridge (see Vogt, 1986a for a review). Given the profound influence of sea-floor topography on ocean currents, it is to be expected that paleobathymetric changes brought on paleoceanographic changes. Even simple eustatic changes (up to 50 to 100 m) could have major effects on surface currents; they could also influence overflow across shallow sills such as the Greenland-Scotland Ridge, just as sea-floor uplift and subsidence would do (Tucholke and Mountain, 1986). Better constraining the geologic history of such gateways, and quantitatively defining their control on ocean circulation, will become increasingly important to our understanding of North Atlantic paleoceanography.

Massive northward transport of heat by Atlantic Ocean currents and the overlying atmosphere represents perhaps the single greatest factor that has controlled Atlantic climates and biogeography. At 10-degree intervals of latitude beginning at the equator, the combined poleward heat flux in the Atlantic is 2.9, 5.8, 7.7, 9.2, 4.6, 4.4, and 1.9×10^{14}W (von Arx, 1962). The Gulf Stream–North Atlantic Current provides a significant part of this flux; for example, the Norwegian–Atlantic current (Fig. 6A) advects 10^{14}W northward across the Iceland-Scotland Ridge. Such heat fluxes, however, can vary dramatically over geologically short times; as recently as the 18-ka glacial maximum, the Norwegian-Atlantic current was virtually nonexistent (Kellogg, 1980).

Geothermal heat flux into the ocean across its lower boundary layer is comparatively trivial. Roughly 3×10^{12}W is emitted into the entire North Atlantic Ocean basin from below (see e.g., Sclater and Wixon, 1986); if evenly distributed, this would merely heat a 70-cm layer of water by 1°C per year. However, hydrothermal vents along the mid-oceanic ridge axis may affect abyssal circulation (Stommel, 1982), and transients caused by submarine volcanism could create local upwelling (Vogt, 1989). Average geothermal heat flow must have been greater and volcanism more intense during the mid-Cretaceous fast-spreading interval (Plate 2). Because this was also a time of deep-water stagnation, hydrothermal/geothermal heat flux probably was of somewhat greater oceanographic significance at that time than it is in today's strongly ventilated ocean.

Clearly, the properties and circulation of North Atlantic surface and deep waters are intimately linked to sea-floor topography, oceanic gateways, and continental positions at local to global scales. These linkages are yet another example of the roles that tectonism and volcanism play in controlling processes that formed the geologic record (Fig. 3).

TEXTURE OF THE MARINE GEOLOGIC RECORD: VARIABILITY IN SPACE AND TIME

The North Atlantic oceanic crust and its sediment cargo are "textured" with spatial variability of many sorts. Lateral variability, as well as the geophysical survey systems currently used to map that variability across a wide spectrum of scales (millimeters to hundreds of kilometers and more), were summarized by Vogt and Tucholke (1986b, Fig. 1A, B). The part of the spectrum of lateral variability that presently is the least understood is at scales of meters to tens of kilometers. This is not because of a lack of appropriate survey tools, but because the detailed survey characterization that is required is both time consuming and expensive. Much of the marine geological research currently underway concentrates on these scales, however, and it can be expected that in the not-too-distant future we will gain significant new insights into the fine-scale workings of tectonic, volcanic, and sedimentary processes.

Our knowledge of vertical spatial variability comes primarily from boreholes, from seismic-reflection/refraction data, from deeper rocks exposed by erosion or faulting, and to a lesser extent, from other geophysical data. This knowledge falls off rapidly with subbottom depth. The highest resolution is provided by core analysis, outcrops, and borehole logging, but the typically wide spacing between drill sites severely limits lateral interpolation of fine-scale vertical variability (<tens of meters). Seismic-reflection data (Fig. 7) provide ties between drill sites, but seismic resolution is frequency-dependent, and the "earth filter" consequently dictates a progressive loss of resolution with increasing depth. Increased attenuation with increasing acoustic frequency is a fact of nature, so the Moho, unlike the ocean floor, can never be mapped in kilohertz. Nevertheless, with new acquisition and processing techniques the mapping of finer-scale intra-crustal and upper-mantle structure has now begun (Fig. 7D; McCarthy and others, 1988; White and others, 1988), and methods for seismically mapping the sedimentary subbottom are continually being improved (e.g., Gettrust and others, 1988; Fig. 7C).

Rates of processes are derived from the geologic record when time scales are attached to spatial variability. This immediately raises the difficulty of lack of time resolution at fine scales. We consequently are forced to describe processes in terms of average rates, but such averaging tends to obscure the fact that most geologic processes are episodic. Two examples are instructive: Turbidites in the Quaternary abyssal plains next to North America accumulated at ca. 100 m/m.y. (Fig. 8; Pilkey and Cleary, 1986). Yet 0.1 m or even 1 m of sand or silt may have been deposited within a few hours, covering sea floor over tens of thousands of square kilometers, with millenia then passing before the next event. In another example, we calculate that, on average, the North America plate gains 1 to 2×10^8 m^3 of new extrusives along its 8,000-km Mid-Atlantic Ridge edge each year, as a consequence of ~2 cm/yr plate separation (Table 1). Yet at any one location the plate boundary may rupture suddenly after centuries of quiescence, causing rapid changes of stress and strain over many tens of kilometers. As much as 10^8 or even 10^{10} m^3 of basalt may erupt at a site over a few weeks, representing centuries or even millenia of "average" contribution on that segment of the spreading axis. Only the great lithospheric plates creep along reliably from day to day and year to year, with any short-period kinematic jitter being suppressed by the staggering viscosity (10^{19} to 10^{20} P) of the subjacent mantle.

Variability in time ranges from cyclic to irregularly episodic. Orbital (Milankovitch) forcing, for example, is caused by planetary motions and thus is cyclic, with cycle periods that are nearly constant even on geologic time scales. The variations in insolation affect the entire ocean environment and typically leave a complex but cyclic signal in the chemical, biogenic, or mineralogic record of sea-floor sediments. However, the signals commonly are laterally diachronous, being created as current systems, oceanographic fronts, and faunal assemblages slowly shift in response to environmental change. Event correlation from site to site thus requires very accurate time scales (which is difficult for the pre-Quaternary sedimentary record) or it must rely on identification of unique "fingerprints" of individual cycles, or independent episodic markers, like volcanic ash horizons, that can be traced from one location to another.

Compiled in Fig. 9 are examples of temporal variability (both cyclic and episodic) showing recurrence times of 440 m.y. (Wilson cycle inset) down through 0.01 m.y. (graphs A through M). The 400 to 500-m.y. Wilson cycle (Nance and others, 1988) is so long that the ~175-m.y. history of central North Atlantic widening, plus the preceding ~50 m.y. of intracontinental rifting, scarcely represent half of one cycle (but if the past is any indication, the central North Atlantic should begin to close within the next few tens of millions of years). Somewhat shorter-term (50 to 100-m.y.) fluctuations in geomagnetic reversal frequency, sea level, and plate speed may be intercorrelated (Fig. 9A, B; Plate 2; see e.g., Vogt, 1975; Sheridan, 1986). The central North Atlantic has recorded approximately one complete cycle in this part of the spectrum, consisting of the mid-Cretaceous interval of high sea level, rapid spreading, and constant normal geomagnetic polarity, which separated regimes of lower sea level, slower spreading, and rapid polarity reversals in the Jurassic and Neogene. Mantle convection, including the lithospheric plate-boundary layer, must be the process underlying most temporal variability on time scales of 50 to 500 m.y.

Next higher in frequency are global extinction rates (Fig. 9C) and intermediate-term sea-level fluctuations (Fig. 9D). Extinction-rate peaks have been attributed to periodic (~26 m.y.) bolide impacts (e.g., Raup and Sepkoski, 1986) and as such would represent exogenic forcing. However, the possible role of sea-level fluctuations in expanding and contracting ecologic niches is suggested by the closely similar "cycle" lengths. Flood-basalt episodes also recur quasi-periodically with a mean cycle time of 32 ± 1 m.y. (Rampino and Stothers, 1988). Whether all these phenomena are linked, and if linked, whether they relate to impact periodicity or other factors such as mantle-plume episodicity (Vogt, 1972), remains to be determined.

Next up in frequency is the intensity of sea-floor erosion induced by bottom currents (Fig 9F; see also Plate 2), and variability in rate of volcanic input above a mantle plume (Vogt, 1972, 1979), suggested here by topographic variability on the flank of the Reykjanes Ridge southwest of Iceland (Fig. 9E). There is a possible correlation between these two parameters in the late Neogene; increased elevation of the Reykjanes Ridge or Greenland-Scotland Ridge by volcanic accretion or thermal uplift would cause these areas to act as "valves" for bottom water crossing from east to west (Tucholke and Mountain, 1986b). The Reykjanes Ridge depth fluctuations also may correlate with plate-kinematic fluctuations on 1- to 10-m.y. scales (Vogt, 1986d). If so, the observed late Paleogene-Neogene variability in intensity of erosion by bottom currents may be closely linked to both tectonic and volcanic influences (Fig. 3). Other parameters have similar recurrence times during the pre-Neogene. For example, Schlanger (1987) noted a recurrence time of 5.1 ± 1 m.y. for Albian-Maastrichtian flooding of craton edges, which could reflect either tectonic or eustatic forcing. This period is also very similar to the "Grand Cycles" of the Cambrian (Palmer and Halley, 1979).

The short-term sea-level fluctuations of Haq and others (1987; see Plate 2) are rather irregularly spaced (Fig. 9G), with a post–200 Ma mean of about 2 m.y. Comparable scales of variability (1 to 2 m.y.) characterize Mid-Atlantic Ridge basement topography (Figs. 4A, 9H, and 10), but this most likely represents local tectono-magmatic processes and may have little global synchronism. The 413,000-yr-long eccentricity cycle (Berger, 1980) also appears in this band of the temporal spectrum, where orbital influences overlap with volcano-tectonic influences on the environment.

Oceanic variability at 10^4 to 10^5-yr scales clearly is dominated by orbital (Milankovitch) effects on insolation, and by the way the atmosphere-cryosphere-hydrosphere responds to such exogenic forcing. Effects on the Neogene North Atlantic have been numerous, pronounced, and wide-ranging. Modulated parameters include frequency of occurrence of ice-rafted and windblown material, $CaCO_3$ content, productivity, sea level, faunal/floral assemblages, bottom-current intensity, the oxygen

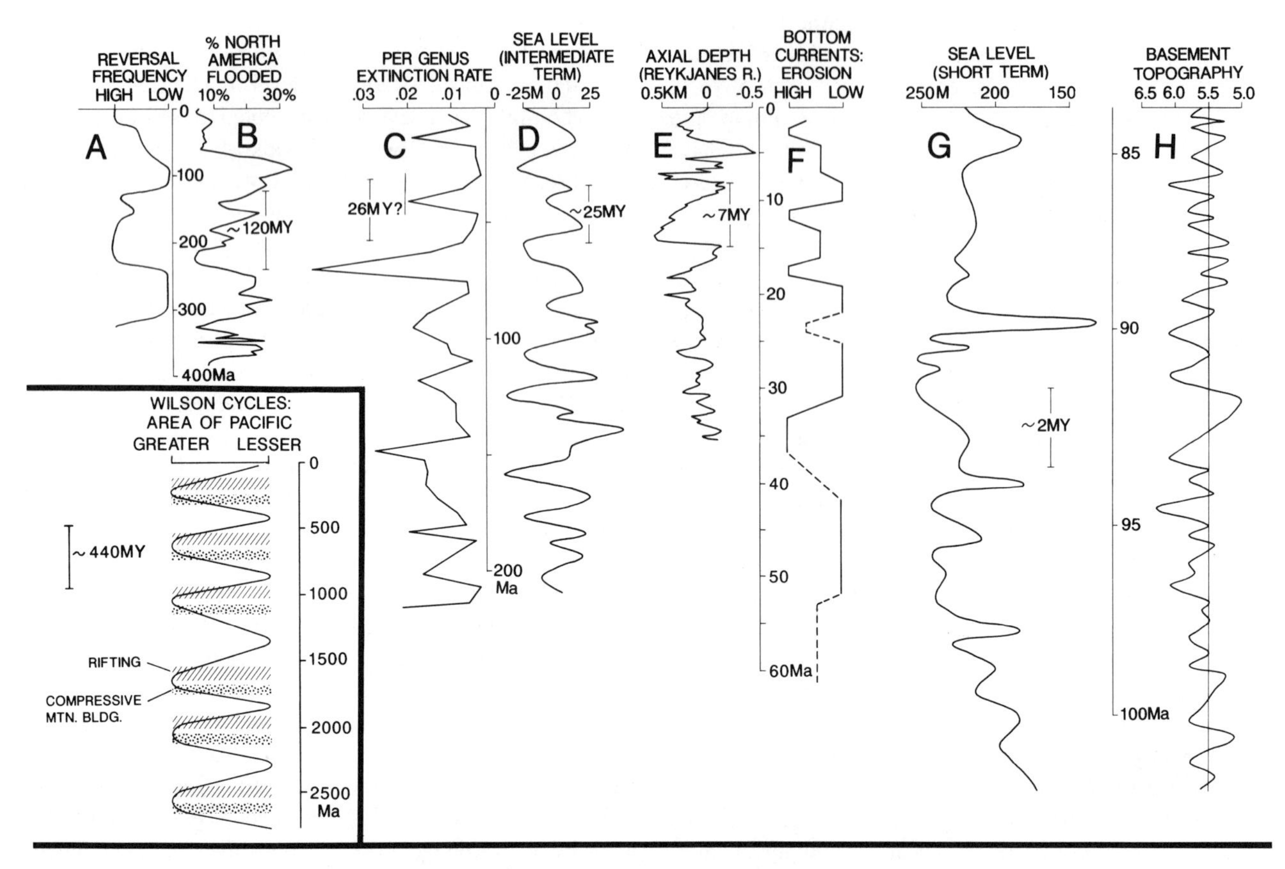

MAINLY GEOGENIC (ENDOGENIC) INFLUENCES
REVERSAL FREQUENCY
HIGH LOW
% NORTH AMERICA FLOODED
10% 30%
A
B
100
200
~120MY
300
400Ma
PER GENUS EXTINCTION RATE
.03 .02 .01 0
C
26MY?
100
200 Ma
SEA LEVEL (INTERMEDIATE TERM)
-25M 0 25
D
~25MY
AXIAL DEPTH (REYKJANES R.)
0.5KM 0 -0.5
E
~7MY
BOTTOM CURRENTS: EROSION
HIGH LOW
F
0
10
20
30
40
50
60Ma
SEA LEVEL (SHORT TERM)
250M 200 150
G
~2MY
BASEMENT TOPOGRAPHY
6.5 6.0 5.5 5.0
H
85
90
95
100Ma
WILSON CYCLES: AREA OF PACIFIC
GREATER LESSER
~440MY
RIFTING
COMPRESSIVE MTN. BLDG.
0
500
1000
1500
2000
2500 Ma

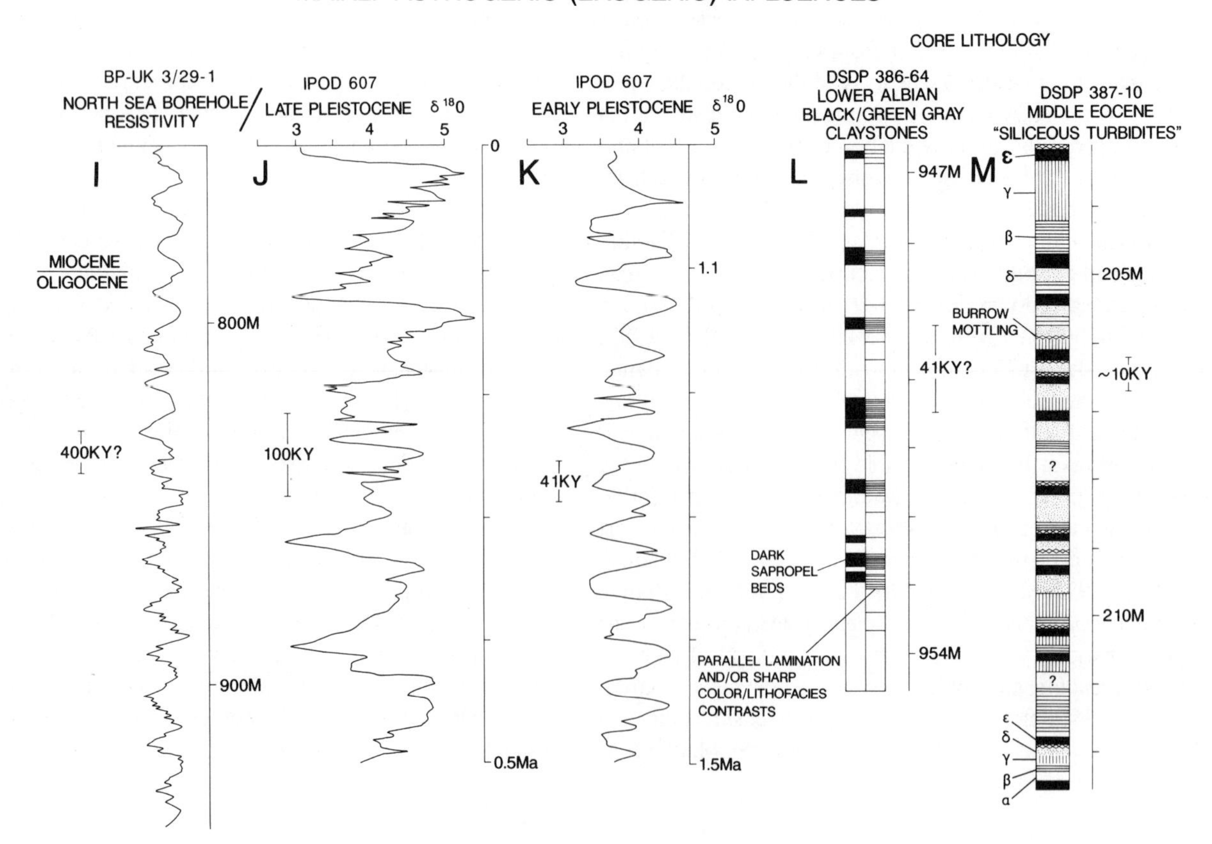

MAINLY ASTROGENIC (EXOGENIC) INFLUENCES
BP-UK 3/29-1
NORTH SEA BOREHOLE RESISTIVITY
I
MIOCENE
OLIGOCENE
800M
400KY?
900M
IPOD 607
LATE PLEISTOCENE δ18O
3 4 5
J
100KY
0
0.5Ma
IPOD 607
EARLY PLEISTOCENE δ18O
3 4 5
K
1.1
41KY
1.5Ma
CORE LITHOLOGY
DSDP 386-64
LOWER ALBIAN
BLACK/GREEN GRAY CLAYSTONES
L
947M
41KY?
DARK SAPROPEL BEDS
PARALLEL LAMINATION AND/OR SHARP COLOR/LITHOFACIES CONTRASTS
954M
DSDP 387-10
MIDDLE EOCENE
"SILICEOUS TURBIDITES"
M
ε
γ
β
δ
205M
BURROW MOTTLING
~10KY
?
210M
?
ε
δ
γ
β
α

Figure 9. Examples of environmental variability on different geologic time scales (5×10^8 yr to 10^4 yr recurrence times), including phenomena that are nearly periodic (I through L, and perhaps C), others that are more broadly rhythmic (inset, B, C, D, M), and some that are simply recurrent with poorly understood statistical properties and physical origins (E, F, H). Data locations for items H through M shown on Plate 3. Inset—Area of Pacific, a measure of opening and closing of Atlantic-type oceans (based on Nance and others, 1988). A—Average geomagnetic reversal frequency (Harland and others, 1982). B—Percent flooding of North America (from Vogt, 1975). C—Frequency of generic extinction in the oceans from Late Triassic to present, showing purported 26 Ma periodicity. From COSOD-II report (Anonymous, 1987) and based on Sepkoski (1986). D—Intermediate-term sea-level fluctuations, obtained by graphically "band-passing" sea-level curves of Haq and others (1987). Note similarity in period to extinction record (C). E—Fluctuations in Reykjanes Ridge axial depths with time, based on ridge-flank topography (from Luyendyk and others, 1979; see also Plates 2 and 3). F—Pulses of bottom-current activity and seafloor erosion in North Atlantic (schematic, based on Tucholke and McCoy, 1986; see also Plate 2). Note correlation with Reykjanes Ridge crestal depths. G—Short-term sea-level fluctuations (section of unfiltered curve of Haq and others, 1987; see also Plate 2). H—Basement topography along portion of Kane Fracture Zone corridor, eastern Mid-Atlantic Ridge flank (constructed from Tucholke and Schouten, 1989; see also Plate 3). I—Resistivity variations in Oligocene–Miocene muds of the North Sea (British Petroleum U.K. 3/29-1) possibly representing 400-k.y.-long eccentricity cycle (from R. Fischer, in COSOD-II report; Anonymous, 1987). J—Stable-isotopic (δ^{18}O) record from benthonic foraminifera at North Atlantic DSDP Site 607 (41°N, 33°W), showing 100-k.y. cycles (Ruddiman and others, 1987). K—As in J, showing 41-k.y. cycles for 1.0 to 1.5 Ma in same core. L—Sediment rhythmicity of probable Milankovitch origin (41-k.y. orbital forcing?), Lower Albian, DSDP Site 386 (Tucholke and Vogt, 1979a). M—Sediment rhythmicity believed to represent turbidites emplaced at ca. 10-k.y. intervals, middle Eocene, DSDP site 387 (Tucholke and Vogt, 1979a).

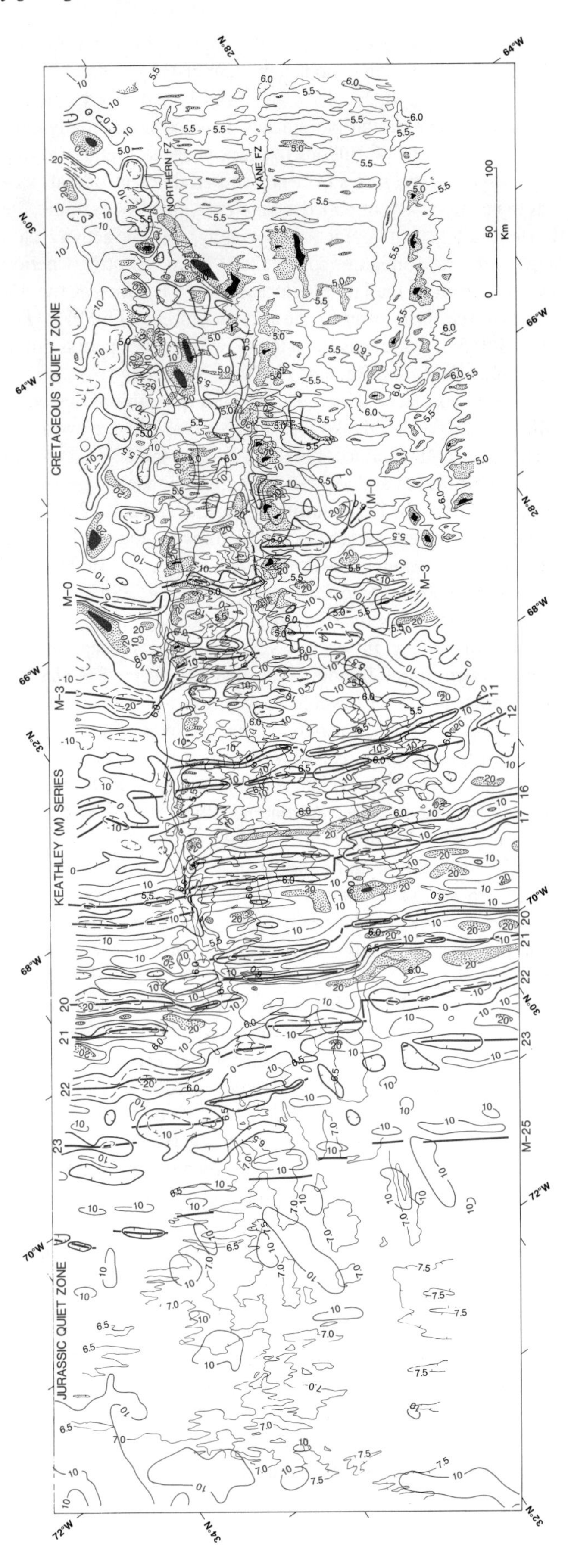

Figure 10. Crustal structure and magnetic anomalies across southern Bermuda Rise. Red: magnetic anomaly contours and identifications; contours in units of 10 nT, with values above +300 nT solid and 200 to 300 nT stippled (from Vogt, 1986e, Plate 3, and unpublished data). Black: structure contours on basement surface in km below sea level (0.5-m contour interval) with depths <4.5 km solid and 4.5 to 5 km stippled (simplified from Tucholke and Schouten, 1989).

isotope makeup of sea water (Fig. 9J, K), and physical properties of sediment. Dominant periodicities occur at 413 k.y. and 101 k.y. (eccentricity; Fig. 9I, J), 41 k.y. (tilt), and 19 and 21 k.y. (precession). While the orbital periodicities have been essentially constant for hundreds of millions of years, geogenic factors varying over >1-m.y. time scales evidently caused different orbital periods to be selectively amplified at different times. For example, the Earth's geologic environment (topography, volcanic activity, etc.) apparently was configured so that the 101-k.y. eccentricity period was dominant in the late Pleistocene (Fig. 9J), whereas the 41-k.y. tilt cycle held sway in the mid-Pleistocene (Fig. 9K). The interval 0.5 to 1 Ma was transitional, with neither period dominant (Ruddiman and Raymo, 1988).

Plio-Pleistocene (Fig. 9J, K) and probably Oligocene-Miocene (Fig 9I) Milankovitch cycles involve the growth and melting of continental ice sheets, reflected in the $\delta^{18}O$ record of ocean temperature and ice volume. Large ice sheets were probably absent from the Earth during Cretaceous and early Paleogene times. Nevertheless, variability on Milankovitch time scales is still observed, for example in the alternating oxic-anoxic bottom-water conditions at Deep Sea Drilling Project site 386 in the deep western North Atlantic (Fig. 9L), which suggest a periodicity close to the 41-k.y. tilt cycle. Cyclic input to the deep basin of dense, warm, saline bottom water that was formed in shallow marginal seas is one possible explanation for the intermittent ventilation. Although quantitative understanding of nonglacial orbital responses remains primitive, orbital forcing is nowadays commonly invoked to explain rhythmic stratigraphy throughout the geologic record (e.g., Barron and others, 1985; Arthur and Garrison, 1986; Fischer, 1986; van Tassel, 1987).

Sedimentary rhythms shorter in duration than the 19 k.y. precession period so far have received little attention, in part because they are seldom resolved in deep-sea cores. At typical hemipelagic sedimentation rates of 1 to 2 cm/k.y., the sediment-mixing activity of benthic organisms usually limits the resolving power of ocean-floor sediments to a few thousand years. In expanded sections, however, sub-Milankovitch cycle lengths of ca. 10 k.y. can be observed. At Ocean Drilling Project site 645 in Baffin Bay where sedimentation rates exceeded 10 cm/k.y., for example, variability at this scale was observed through much of the Plio-Pleistocene (Srivastava and others, 1987).

Still shorter-period events are recorded in deposits of slumps (Fig. 8), turbidity currents, and other catastrophic phenomena; the sediments can also reflect intra-event transient activity at scales of hours (e.g., subunits α, β, δ, γ, and ϵ in Fig. 9M), many orders of magnitude shorter than the recurrence time of the events. Less violent events, including "benthic storms," diurnal tidal currents, and possible multiannual influences such as El Niño, usually do not leave high-amplitude signatures; therefore, they do not normally survive the blurring effects of benthic bioturbation or erasure by subsequent events. Even though only the cumulative effect of such processes is finally recorded in the sedimentary record, the short time scale of the events does make it possible to study them directly (e.g., McCave and Tucholke, 1986).

During the Early Cretaceous—and even today in unusual settings like the Cariaco trench and Black Sea—the abyss was calm, anoxic, and therefore not bioturbated (Arthur and Dean, 1986). Sediments deposited under such circumstances are ideal for recording events of short duration, as suggested by the fine-scale laminations in Fig. 9L. Conceivably, thin partings of carbon-rich shale can resolve oceanic variability on time scales of decades or even years (Hay, 1987), but new techniques will be required to establish the space-time relations of such short-period variability in the deep ocean basins. Even if such ultra-fine-scale stratigraphy proves unfeasible, there is promise that sufficiently dense borehole/logging grids can yield an ocean-wide "cyclostratigraphy" based on orbitally forced variability on 10^4 to 10^5-yr time scales. This would better magnetostratigraphic resolution by an order of magnitude!

NEW ACCRETIONS TO THE KNOWLEDGE BODY: A CENTENNIAL SNAPSHOT

New research published since Vogt and Tucholke's (1986a) volume reflects North Atlantic studies with greatest current vitality. From the U.S. margin eastward, six topics of particular interest are: acoustic imaging of the continental rise, deep seismic-reflection work on old oceanic crust and upper mantle, basin-wide studies using multibeam bathymetry, plate kinematics, deep drilling, and the plate-boundary zone of the Mid-Atlantic Ridge.

Acoustic imaging

Acoustic imaging of the U.S. and adjacent Canadian continental slope and rise (Fig. 8) has been carried out mainly with the GLORIA long-range sidescan sonar system (Clarke, 1988; Anonymous, 1988). Mapping the Exclusive Economic Zone (EEZ; see Knauss, 1986, for juridical aspects) was the incentive for this imaging program. The new data show a large variety of "morphoacoustic" provinces and features, including areas dominated by slumping, others incised by prominent channels, and still others devoid of either. The effect of contour-following bottom currents is faint, with the backscatter texture of the surficial sediments being dominated by features related to downslope sedimentary processes. This new imaging will greatly extend and refine previous knowledge synthesized by Embley and Jacobi (1986).

Seismic profiles

Two-ship multichannel seismic profiles over Jurassic oceanic crust near the Blake Spur Fracture Zone revealed discontinuous reflections that apparently arise from the extrusive/sheeted-dike transition, as well as inclined intra-crustal reflections that dip toward younger crust and reflections from the M-discontinuity (Fig. 7D; McCarthy and others, 1988). A more recent grid-type experiment in the same area (White and others, 1988) revealed another set of inclined reflections, roughly one every 30 km, that parallels the fracture zone trend. The M-discontinuity was found to consist of not one but a band of reflections. Strong discontinuous reflections and anomalous velocity structure characterize crust beneath the fracture zone itself. The dipping reflections were not predicted by models of spreading-ridge crustal accretion, but will now find their way into such models. Ophiolites will be searched for possible exposures of dipping features (thrust faults related to thermal contraction? intrusions? magma-chamber bottoms?), which might account for the reflections. In any case, such experiments open the door to more detailed seismic mapping of oceanic crustal and uppermost mantle structure. While the Blake Spur Fracture Zone region was experimentally ideal (sediment layer overlying a relatively smooth basement), it remains to be seen whether comparable results can be obtained over the bare flank of the rugged and reverberant Mid-Atlantic Ridge.

Basin-wide studies using multibeam bathymetry

Two large-area studies based on multibeam bathymetry have been completed, both relying in part on U.S. Navy data collected over the last two decades. Epp and Smoot (1989) identified more than 800 seamounts (>50 fm, or 92 m high) in the North Atlantic between Iceland and the equator (Figs. 1 and 4A). The distribution is non-uniform and includes clusters or chains of major seamounts, presumably generated by mantle hotspots, as well as widely scattered small seamounts near the Mid-Atlantic Ridge crest. Remarkably, the section of ridge crest from the Azores north to the southern Reykjanes Ridge has been the principal small-seamount factory, with the Mid-Atlantic Ridge south of 35°N virtually devoid of such features. As noted by Epp and Smoot (1989), there is some correlation of ridge-crest seamount density with the geochemical anomalies revealed by ridge-crest sampling (Fig. 5). The small-seamount province also corresponds to that part of the ridge where (1) a rift valley is present, and (2) the regional gravity anomaly exceeds +30 mgals (e.g., Vogt, 1986c, Plate 8). The latter observation suggests a correlation between seamount density and mantle conditions. Within the small-seamount province, the seamounts appear to be randomly scattered except for a line along the south edge of the Charlie-Gibbs Fracture Zone and two broadly V-shaped lines that intersect the Mid-Atlantic Ridge axis at 50° and 56°N (Fig. 1). These lines have seemingly recorded the motion of the accreting plate boundary relative to magma sources in a fixed mesospheric reference frame (Fig. 4A; Schouten and others, 1987). However, Figure 4A also shows other seamounts that apparently originated from magma sources fixed to the accreting plate boundary or to other reference frames.

Tucholke and Schouten (1989) used seismic-reflection and multibeam bathymetric data to map a ca. 300-km-wide swath of basement topography extending along the Kane Fracture Zone from near Cape Hatteras across the Mid-Atlantic Ridge to Africa. A simplified version, with the regional (crustal-age-dependent) effect of the Mid-Atlantic Ridge removed, is shown in Plate 3. In Figure 10, the section crossing the southern Bermuda Rise is reproduced in more detail and with associated magnetic anomaly contours (based on Vogt, 1986e, Plate 3). Geophysical data coverage is only now, in some areas, dense enough for such contour representation over a large area of old Atlantic crust. The detailed study shows major changes in relative plate motion as discussed earlier in this chapter. During the changes at ca. 102 and 92 Ma, the Kane transform was forced to make severe adjustments that involved formation of new transform faults and abandonment of old ones (Plate 3). More frequent, smaller-scale structural irregularities along the Kane Fracture Zone may record numerous minor changes in rotation pole. If so, they must be recorded in other fracture zones as well, and inter–fracture zone comparison of this kind of detailed structure will be a fruitful avenue of future research. Step-by-step plate reconstructions (e.g., Klitgord and Schouten, 1986) using magnetic lineations cannot resolve plate-kinematic detail.

Migration of small-offset discontinuities along the Mid-Atlantic Ridge axis was first noted by Johnson and Vogt (1973; Fig. 4A). Tucholke and Schouten (1989) found that small-offset discontinuities north of the Kane Fracture Zone began to migrate northward away from the large-offset transform about 22 Ma (Plate 3). One discontinuity, the Northern Fracture Zone, also shows earlier migration as a small offset, but as a large-offset fracture zone in the M-series anomalies, it follows plate flow lines (Plate 3; Fig. 10). The Kane Fracture Zone was a small-offset discontinuity across the Jurassic magnetic quiet zone and the M-series anomalies, and it has little structural definition there; the trace of its continuation back across Jurassic crust to the continent-ocean crustal boundary is uncertain.

Plate kinematics

Plate-kinematic models continue to be refined. The utility of large-offset fracture zones, such as the Kane Fracture Zone, as recorders of numerous changes in relative plate-rotation pole (Tucholke and Schouten, 1989) was mentioned above. Srivastava and Roest (1988) have refined Greenland–North America motion, which began ~92 Ma, from Srivastava and Tapscott's (1986) synthesis. Cronin (1987) has proposed that, in general, relative plate motions are more accurately described by cycloids rather than small circles. Various types of space-based geodesy (Anderle, 1986) are increasingly being analyzed for improved estimates of present intra-plate deformation and relative plate motions (Stein, 1987; Jordan and Minster, 1989), while fracture-zone traces inferred from satellite radar altimetry are being used to better constrain plate-kinematic models (Shaw, 1987; Cande and others, 1988).

Deep drilling

The latest round of deep-sea drilling (Ocean Drilling Project) began in the Atlantic in 1985 and, by coinciding with the final preparation of Volume M, could not contribute to the synthesis. The new drill ship JOIDES *Resolution* began by coring a drowned mid-Cretaceous megabank in the Bahamas (Leg 101). It then reoccupied Site 418 on the Bermuda Rise (Leg 102), testing a new suite of logging tools and making that site a natural laboratory and reference section for old (118 Ma) oceanic crust. Leg 103 examined the sediment-starved, tectonically thinned, continental crust of the Galicia margin and continent-ocean boundary, coring the breakup unconformity. The *Resolution* then examined a volcanic continental margin, the Voring Plateau, which was influenced by the Iceland hot spot during continental breakup (Leg 104); seaward-dipping subbasement reflectors observed there were identified as subaerial basalt flows, including an andesitic "Upper Series" that overlies submarine tholeiites of a "Lower Series."

Drilling in the Labrador Sea and Baffin Bay (Leg 105) confirmed that the latter basin opened between 55 and 36 Ma. Plio-Pleistocene sedimentation rates were higher and intrasediment seismic reflections younger than expected. Northern hemisphere glaciation intensified about 2.5 Ma, but may have begun as early as 3.4 Ma; isolated glacial dropstones were found in sediments as old as upper Miocene. Similarly, in the Norwegian Sea (Leg 104), climatic cooling began about 2.8 to 2.9 Ma (possibly as early as 4.5 Ma), with warm/temperate water masses briefly present at 2.2 and 0.98 Ma. Evidence for major glaciation in the northeast Atlantic generally begins at 2.5-Ma levels in the cores (e.g., Leg 94, 35° to 55°N), although low-amplitude, quasiperiodic surface-water temperature oscillations, possibly related to small, high-latitude ice sheets, extend back to ca. 3.3 Ma. Leg 108 examined the evolution of Neogene paleoclimate in the *low*-latitude eastern North Atlantic; in that region, higher-amplitude, ca. 20- to 40-k.y. sediment cycles, increased flux of eolian dust, and higher productivity/upwelling began at 2.5 to 3.0 Ma.

Leg 106 tested bare-rock drilling techniques on the Mid-Atlantic Ridge axis south of the Kane Fracture Zone, and hydrothermal deposits were discovered and cored near an active vent. The ship returned to the area on Leg 109 and logged 500 m in previously drilled Site 395 on the Mid-Atlantic Ridge flank, but technical problems were encountered in attempting to core young, rubbly basalt in the Mid-Atlantic rift valley. A peridotite intrusion extending to at least 92 m subbottom was cored only 5 km from the rift axis. The final North Atlantic Leg (110) examined the tectonic development of the Barbados accretionary wedge. The décollement was penetrated, and major fluid flow was found to be associated with fault zones.

Plate-boundary zone

The Mid-Atlantic Ridge plate-boundary region continues to attract research attention, and the launching of a decade-long RIDGE initiative by the National Science Foundation promises to ensure a continuation of activity. Recent advances can be grouped under hydrothermal vents, basalt geochemistry, imaging, crustal structure, and earthquake seismology.

Hydrothermal vents. Hydrothermal activity on Iceland has been studied for a long time, and "black smoker" vents were found in the Pacific more than a decade ago. Numerous clues also suggested that such vents were present along the submerged Mid-Atlantic Ridge, so the first discovery (at 26°N; Klinkhammer and others, 1986; Fig. 11), followed by a second discovery at 23°N, was no surprise. Further vents are certain to be found, and they may prove to be most readily identifiable by obtaining continuous thermistor tows like those conducted along the East Pacific Rise. Transient but more energetic "megaplumes," such as those discovered on the Juan de Fuca Ridge (Baker and others, 1987), will no doubt be found as well. Known megaplumes have topped out about 1,000 m above the sea floor, versus only 200 to 400 m for typical "smokers" (Fig. 11). The importance of hydrothermal venting (Edmond, 1986) for the heat budget of the mid-ocean ridges, ocean-water geochemistry, long-term geochemical budgets, and oceanic crustal structure is well established. Hydrothermal plumes may even play an active role in abyssal circulation (Stommell, 1982), and during times of basin-wide deep-water stagnation they may have carried anoxic deep water to the ocean surface (Vogt, 1989).

Basalt geochemistry. Since the syntheses by Schilling (1986) and Melson and O'Hearn (1986), additional dredging expeditions have filled in much of the sampling gap on the equatorial Mid-Atlantic Ridge. Hot-spot–type La/Sm highs (Fig. 5) were found north of the St. Paul Fracture Zone (3° to 5°N; Schilling and others, 1988) and near the triple junction between North America, South America, and Africa (Bougalt and others, 1988). Compared to basalts dredged to the north, those from the equatorial and southern Mid-Atlantic Ridge axis (south of 12°N) reveal geologically recent mantle-source depletions by melt extraction. The hot-spot geochemical signature north of the St. Paul Fracture Zone (Fig. 5) corresponds to the intersection of a band of seamounts with the equatorial Mid-Atlantic Ridge.

A synthesis of major-element basalt chemistry along the entire mid-oceanic ridge system (Klein and Langmuir, 1987) uncovered systematic geochemical relations to axial depth (Fig. 12) and crustal thickness. The simplified zero-age portrait of the Mid-Atlantic Ridge plate boundary (Fig. 5) incorporates the relation between crustal thickness and axial depth implied by their findings. Although basalt geochemistry, axial depth, and crustal thickness do not correlate systematically with spreading rate, the variability in these parameters does correlate (Klein and Langmuir, 1987). Klein and Langmuir's results and other data are used to illustrate this point in Fig. 13, which shows the high along-strike relief of the Mid-Atlantic Ridge axis (ca. 5 km; see also Plate 3). Vogt (1976) suggested that the relation between along-strike variability in relief and spreading rate (Fig. 13) could be explained in terms of how subaxial flow from plume centers affects the axial lithosphere; under slow-spreading ridges, partial

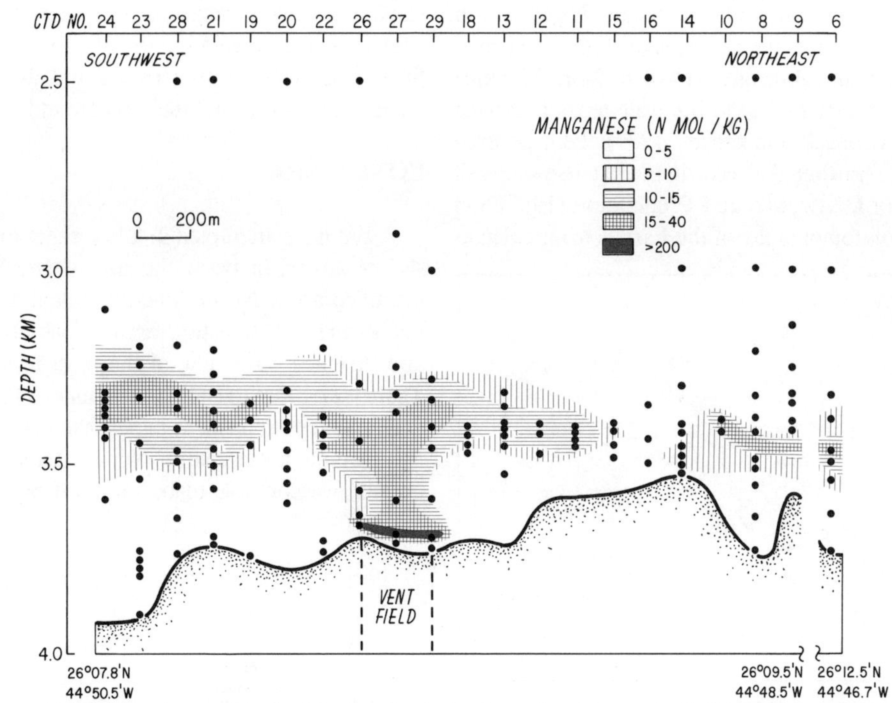

Figure 11. Geochemical section for Mn showing hydrothermal activity at the 26°N TAG area on the Mid-Altantic Ridge. Mn particles discharged into water column by thermal plume indicate a maximum plume height of 300 to 400 m above sea floor. Redrawn from Klinkhammer and others (1986).

melting would be restricted to pipe-like zones, causing upwelled mantle materials to pile up in the asthenosphere and thus create high relief at plume centers like Iceland.

Imaging. Large-area imaging of the submarine Mid-Atlantic Ridge plate-boundary zone began with GLORIA backscatter imagery and U.S. Navy SASS multibeam bathymetry (e.g., Vogt and Tucholke, 1986b, Fig. 8). New work includes Sea Beam bathymetry, SeaMARC I and II backscatter imagery, and deep-towed instrument studies; concomitant gravity and seismic-refraction studies have led to new models of crustal structure. The field work has focused on major transforms (e.g., the Kane Fracture Zone, Abrams and others, 1988; Pockalny and others, 1988; and the Vema Fracture Zone, Macdonald and others, 1986) and adjacent spreading axes such as the MARK area south of the Kane Fracture Zone (Kong and others, 1989) and the TAG area to the north.

Crustal structure. Advances in understanding of crustal structure (Purdy and Ewing, 1986) have been reported by Purdy (1987), Calvert and Whitmarsh (1986), and Bowen and White (1986), among others. The latter authors used near-bottom hydrophones together with a surface-towed airgun array to image the strike-slip fault in the sediment-filled transform valley of the Vema Fracture Zone. Purdy (1987) used fixed sea-floor hydrophones and a controllable explosive source towed a few tens of meters above the Mid-Atlantic Ridge flank at 23°N to study the top 200 to 300 m of oceanic crust. Due to age-related processes not yet fully understood, the average P-wave velocities increase dramatically, from 2.1 km/s in the rift valley (4 s^{-1} gradient) to 4.1 km/s (0.5 s^{-1} gradient) on 7-Ma crust.

Earthquake seismology. Mid-Atlantic Ridge earthquakes (Einarsson, 1986) continue to attract study, both teleseismically (e.g., Huang and others, 1986; Engeln and others, 1986; Bergman and Solomon, 1988) and by deployment of ocean-bottom seismographs (e.g., Lilwall and Kirk, 1985). Inversion of teleseismic long-period (ca. 10 s) P and SH waveforms (Huang and others, 1986) has shown that events arise on ridge-axis–parallel fault planes dipping 45°; the water-column reverberation period places most events below the median valley, showing for example that the east-west scatter and westward displacement of reported ridge-crest shocks at 47°51′N (Vogt, 1986d, Fig. 4) is an artifact. Maximum source depths increase with decreasing spreading rate (Solomon and others, 1988); results also imply that, away from hot spots, maximum depths of seismic faulting increase northward from about 6 km at the equator to 12 km in the central Eurasia Basin (Fig. 5). Maximum depths of faulting (seismic behavior) also constrain our knowledge of thermal structure, although the seismic threshold occurs at higher temperatures at plate boundaries, where strain rates are high, than it does in plate interiors. Estimates of threshold temperatures along Mid-Atlantic Ridge transforms range from 400°C (Engeln and others, 1986) to 600° to 900°C (Bergman and Solomon, 1988).

In coming years, oceanic borehole seismometers and generally improved global teleseismic networks will further advance our knowledge of earthquake-generating mechanisms and tectonic structures both in the Atlantic and elsewhere. Together with borehole stress measurements, the earthquake studies will map the state of stress within the submerged part of the North America plate and will relate this stress field to the plate-tectonic driving and resisting forces (Zoback and others, 1986). Perhaps even more exciting, future earthquake recordings of teleseisms will build on the results of Dziewonski and Woodhouse (1987) and lead to high-resolution tomography of the Earth's mantle. High-resolution (in the range of 50 to 100 km) images of mantle-velocity structure below Bermuda, the Azores, and Iceland may finally establish the true nature and depths of origin of these Atlantic anomalies and their kin around the world.

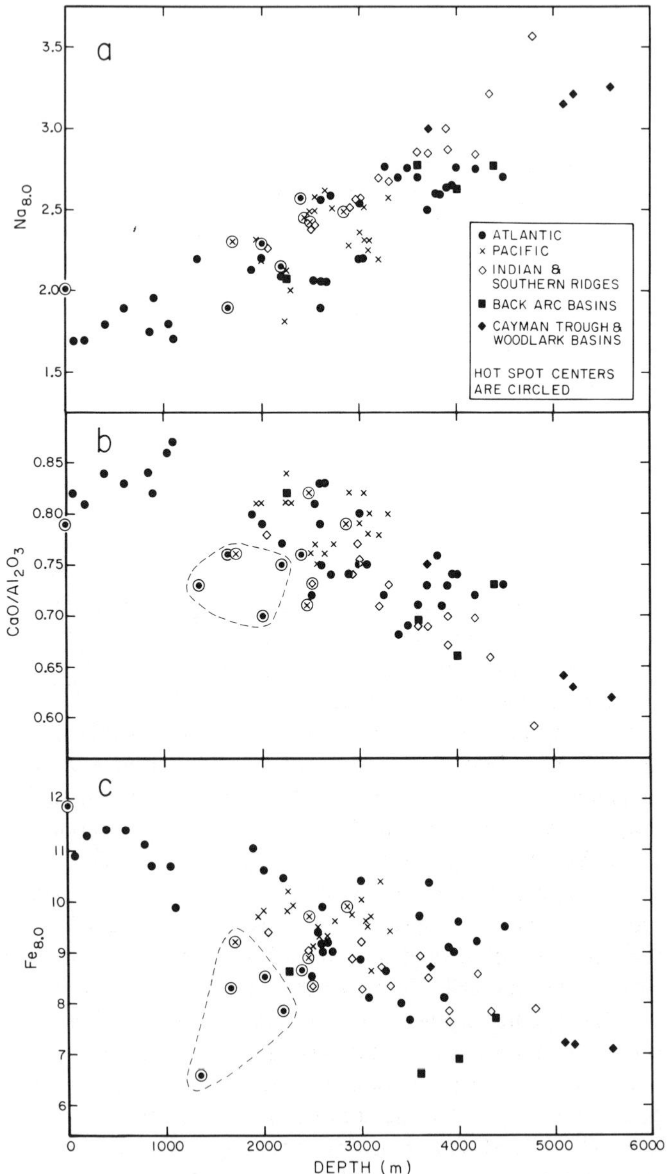

Figure 12. Regional averages of axial depth (versus (a) $Na_{8.0}$, (b) CaO/Al_2O_3, and (c) $Fe_{8.0}$ for samples from Mid-Atlantic Ridge (solid dots) and other spreading axes as noted in legend. Data points from the Azores, Jan Mayen, and Galapagos hotspot centers are enclosed by dashed lines. $Na_{8.0} = Na_2O + 0.373 \times (MgO) - 2.98$; $Fe_{8.0} = FeO + 1.664 \times (MgO) - 13.313$. $Na_{8.0}$ and $Fe_{8.0}$ are calculated for samples with 5.0 to 8.5 wt % MgO; CaO/Al_2O_3 are calculated for samples with >5.0 wt % MgO. Reproduced from Figure 2 of Klein and Langmuir (1987) by permission. Note that variability of axial depth and probably variability of geochemical parameters is inversely related to opening rate (Fig. 13).

CONCLUSION

We have attempted in a few pages to "synthesize a synthesis" of an ocean basin the size of North America itself. We identified a few North America–Atlantic connections, reviewed the ocean's vital statistics, discussed variability in space and time, and sketched out a few of the most recent research advances. There is no room to elaborate on many of the figures and Plates 2 and 3, which supplement rather than complement the text.

Although the central North Atlantic has become a "type ocean," we continue to be surprised by new field observations

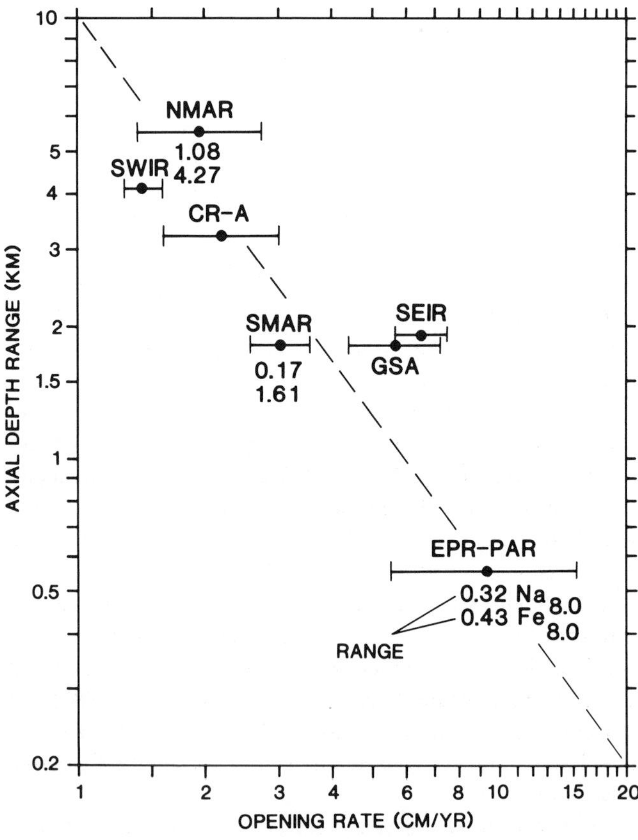

Figure 13. Along-strike depth range of spreading axis versus spreading rate. Depth varies less on fast-spreading ridges than on slow-spreading ridges (Vogt, 1976; Klein and Langmuir, 1987). The northern Mid-Atlantic Ridge (NMAR) exhibits the greatest depth range. Other major parts of the mid-ocean ridge system are the Southwest Indian Ocean Ridge (SWIR), Carlsberg Ridge to Afar area (CR–A), Southern Mid-Atlantic Ridge (SMAR), Southeast Indian Ocean Ridge (SEIR), Galapagos spreading axis (GSA), and East Pacific Rise–Pacific Antarctic Ridge (EPR–PAR). Geochemical variability also appears to decrease with increasing spreading rate, as indicated by known range (maximum–minimum) of $Na_{8.0}$ and $Fe_{8.0}$. Constructed from Table 1 of Klein and Langmuir (1987) and other sources.

that were unpredicted by any theory or model. Uneven small-seamount distribution (Epp and Smoot, 1989), fine-scale plate-kinematic structural effects on transforms (Tucholke and Schouten, 1989), and dipping intracrustal seismic reflections in ocean crust (McCarthy and others, 1988; White and others, 1988) are but three examples. Clearly there will be more surprises, and scientific advances will continue to be driven primarily by new field data, particularly those acquired using new technology and research teams with diverse expertise. High-resolution seismic tomography (beyond Dziewonski and Woodhouse, 1987) of the upper mantle below the North Atlantic and North America is one of the brightest geophysical lights on the horizon.

Notwithstanding the torrent of new observations, comparatively little progress has been made on causalities. The Cretaceous/Tertiary boundary has become the type impact signature (Alvarez, 1987), yet detailed understanding of its effect on extinctions has proved elusive, and some still argue for a mantle-plume origin (Officer and others, 1987). If impacts, extinctions and flood basalts really all march to the same drummer—at 1 beat per ca. 30 m.y. (Rampino and Stothers, 1988)—much paleoenvironmental and even tectonic variability must be of cosmic origin. Is this possible? Consider the consequences: If an impact triggered the Thulean (Brito-Arctic) flood-basalt episode (conveniently landing in a shallow marine basin with weakened crust) it must also be held responsible for the initiation of spreading between Greenland and Eurasia, while an earlier impact (130 to 135 Ma) presumably broke Africa from South America. The close correspondence (Plate 2) between igneous events on the eastern North American margin (190 ± 10, 175 ± 5, 135 ± 5, and 100 ± 10 Ma; deBoer and others, 1988) and the onset of distant flood basalts (190 ± 5, 170 ±5, 135 ± 5, and 110 ± 5 Ma; Rampino and Stothers, 1988) would necessarily give distant impacts an indirect role in shaping North Atlantic evolution as well. To be sure, nature is notorious for her surprises and false clues, yet we find it easier to suppose that the Earth's mantle is capable of producing widely separated, synchronous, quasi-periodic tectonic-magmatic episodes (e.g., Vogt, 1972, 1979) than to do it all with bolides.

A factor of 10 greater in frequency is the seemingly step-wise climatic deterioration and ice-sheet development, a central theme of Cenozoic Atlantic paleoenvironments (Plate 2). Deep-sea drilling suggests that the most recent steps occurred in the latest Miocene, again at 3.3(?) and 2.5 Ma, and in the mid-Pleistocene. Do these steps reflect sudden tectonic accidents, such as closing of the Panamanian isthmus or opening of the Fram Strait; are they responses to step-wise increases in orographic relief or volcanic discharge; or do they represent threshold responses by the ocean/atmosphere/cryosphere to more gradually changing forcing? Whether or not there are are enough data in hand to answer these questions, it seems clear that they cannot be answered without extensive planet-wide numerical modeling of climate and oceanic circulation. Until this succeeds, the prospects for truly understanding variability in the Cenozoic or Mesozoic Atlantic seem dim.

As the above examples suggest, 1989 is really too early to draw conclusions about the Atlantic Ocean.

REFERENCES CITED

Chapters in Volume M of *The Geology of North America* that are cited in this chapter are listed below, along with the full citation for the volume.

Vogt, P. R., and Tucholke, B. E., eds., 1986a, The Western North Atlantic Region: Boulder, Colorado, Geological Society of America, The Geology of North America, v. M.

Anderle, R. J., 1986, Space systems as marine geologic sensors, p. 651–660.

Arthur, M. A., and Dean, W. E., 1986, Cretaceous paleoceaography of the western North Atlantic Ocean, p. 617–630.

Berggren, W. A., and Olsson, R. K., 1986, North Atlantic Mesozoic and Cenozoic paleobiogeography, p. 565–587.

Edmond, J. M., 1986, Hydrothermal activity in the North Atlantic, p. 173–188.

Einarsson, P., 1986, Seismicity along the eastern margin of the western North Atlantic Plate, p. 99–116.

Embley, R. M., and Jacobi, R., 1986, Mass wasting in the western North Atlantic, p. 479–490.

Gradstein, F. M., 1986, Northwestern Atlantic Mesozoic biostratigraphy, p. 507–526.

Jansa, L. F., 1986, Paleoceanography and evolution of the North Atlantic Ocean basin during the Jurassic, p. 603–616.

Kent, D. V., and Gradstein, F. M., 1986, A Jurassic to recent chronology, p. 45–50.

Klitgord, K. D., and Schouten, H., 1986, Plate kinematics of the central Atlantic, p. 351–378.

Knauss, J. A., 1986, The juridicial ocean basin, p. 677–687.

McCave, I. N., and Tucholke, B. E., 1986, Deep current-controlled sedimentation in the western North Atlantic, p. 451–468.

Melson, W. G., and O'Hearn, T., 1986, "Zero-age" variations in the composition of abyssal volcanic rocks along the axial zone of the Mid-Atlantic Ridge, p. 117–136.

Pálmason, G., 1986, Model of crustal formation in Iceland, and application to submarine mid-ocean ridges, p. 87–97.

Pilkey, O. H., and Cleary, W. J., 1986, Turbidite sedimentation in the northwestern Atlantic Ocean basin, p. 437–450.

Poag, C. W., and Miller, K. G., 1986, Neogene marine microfossil biofacies of the western North Atlantic, p. 547–564.

Premoli-Silva, I., and Boersma, A., 1986, Paleogene biofacies of the western North Atlantic Ocean, p. 527–546.

Purdy, G. M., and Ewing, J., 1986, Seismic structure of the ocean crust, p. 313–330.

Saemundsson, K., 1986, Subaerial volcanism in the western North Atlantic, p. 69–86.

Schilling, J.-G., 1986, Geochemical and isotopic variation along the Mid-Atlantic Ridge axis from 79°N to 0°N, p. 137–156.

Sclater, J. C., and Wixon, L., 1986, The relationship between depth and age and heat flow and age in the western North Atlantic, p. 257–270.

Srivastava, S. P., and Tapscott, C. R., 1986, Plate kinematics of the North Atlantic, p. 379–404.

Tucholke, B. E., 1986, Structure of basement and distribution of sediments in the western North Atlantic Ocean, p. 331–340.

Tucholke, B. E., and McCoy, F. W., 1986, Paleogeographic and paleobathymetric evolution of the North Atlantic Ocean, p. 589–602.

Tucholke, B. E., and Mountain, G. S., 1986, Tertiary paleoceanography of the western North Atlantic Ocean, p. 631–650.

Vogt, P. R., 1986c, The present plate boundary configuration, p. 189–204.

——, 1986d, Plate kinematics during the last 20 m.y., and the problem of "present" motions, p. 409–425.

——, 1986e, Magnetic anomalies and crustal magnetization, p. 229–256.

Vogt, P. R., and Tucholke, B. E., 1986b, Imaging the ocean floor; History and state of the art, p. 19–44.

Westbrook, G. K., and McCann, W. R., 1986, Subduction of Atlantic lithosphere beneath the Caribbean, p. 341–350.

Zoback, M. L., and 4 others, 1986, Mid-plate stress, deformation, and seismicity, p. 297–312.

Abrams, L. J., Detrick, R. S., and Fox, P. J., 1988, Morphology and crustal structure of the Kane Fracture Zone transverse ridge: Journal of Geophysical Research, v. 93, p. 3195–3210.

Alvarez, L. W., 1987, Mass extinctions caused by large bolide impacts: Physics Today, v. 40, p. 24–33.

Anonymous, 1976, The channeled scablands of eastern Washington: U.S. Geological Survey Publication INF–72–2 (R–1), 24 p.

Anonymous, 1987, Report of the Second Conference on Scientific Ocean Drilling (COSOD II), Strasbourg, 6–8 July 1987: Joint Oceanographic Institutions for Deep Earth Sampling, and European Science Foundation, 142 p.

Anonymous, 1988, GLORIA reveals rise: Geotimes, v. 33, no. 3, p. 22–24.

Arthur, M. A., and Garrison, R. E., eds., 1986, Milankovitch cycles through geologic time: Paleoceanography, v. 1, p. 359–586.

Arthur, M. A., Dean, W. E., and Schlanger, S. O., 1985, Variations in the global carbon cycle during the Cretaceous related to climate, volcanism, and changes in atmospheric CO_2, *in* Sundquist, E. T., and Broecker, W. S., eds., The carbon cycle and atmospheric CO_2—natural variations Archean to present: American Geophysical Union Geophysical Monograph Series, v. 32, p. 504–530.

Austin, J. A., Jr., and Uchupi, E., 1982, Continental-oceanic crustal transition off Southwest Africa: American Association of Petroleum Geologists Bulletin, v. 66, p. 1328–1347.

Auzende, M., and 8 others, 1988, Complete section of slow spreading crust from the Vema Fracture Zone in the Atlantic: EOS Transactions of the American Geophysical Union, v. 69, p. 1440.

Baker, E. T., Massoth, G. J., and Feely, R. A., 1987, Cataclysmic hydrothermal venting on the Juan de Fuca Ridge: Nature, v. 329, p. 149–151.

Barron, E. J., Arthur, M. A., and Kauffman, E. G., 1985, Cretaceous rhythmic bedding sequences—a plausible link between orbital variations and climate: Earth and Planetary Science Letters, v. 72, p. 327–340.

Berger, A. L., 1980, The Milankovitch astronomical theory of paleoclimates—a modern review: Vistas in Astronomy, v. 24, p. 103–122.

Bergman, E. A., and Solomon, S. C., 1988, Transform fault earthquakes in the North Atlantic—source mechanisms and depth of faulting: Journal of Geophysical Research, v. 93, p. 9027–9057.

Bougalt, H., Dimitriev, L., Schilling, J. G., Sobolev, A., Joron, J. L., and Needham, H. D., 1988, Mantle heterogeneity from trace elements—MAR triple junction near 14°N: Earth and Planetary Science Letters, v. 88, p. 27–36.

Bowen, A. N., and White, R. S., 1986, Deep-tow seismic profiles from the Vema transform and ridge-transform intersection: Journal of the Geological Society of London, v. 143, p. 807–817.

Calvert, A. J., and Whitmarsh, R. B., 1986, The structure of the Charlie-Gibbs Fracture Zone: Journal of the Geological Society of London, v. 143, p. 819–821.

Cande, S. C., LaBrecque, J. L., and Haxby, W. F., 1988, Plate kinematics of the South Atlantic, chron C34 to present: Journal of Geophysical Research, v. 93, p. 13479–13492.

Clarke, J. E., 1988, The geological record of the 1929 "Grand Banks" earthquake and its relevance to deep-sea clastic sedimentation [Ph.D. thesis]: Halifax, Nova Scotia, Dalhousie University, 171 p.

Cronin, V. S., 1987, Cycloid kinematics of relative plate motion: Geology, v. 15, p. 1006–1009.

deBoer, J. Z., McHone, J. G., Puffer, J. H., Ragland, P. C., and Whittington, D., 1988, Mesozoic and Cenozoic magmatism, *in* Sheridan, R. E., and Grow, J. A., eds., The Atlantic continental margin: Boulder, Colorado, Geological Society of America, The Geology of North America, v. I–2, p. 217–241.

DeMets, C., and 10 others, 1989, Current plate motions: Journal of Geophysical Research (in press).

Diebold, J. B., Stoffa, P. L., and LASE Study Group, 1988, A large aperture seismic experiment in the Baltimore Canyon Trough, *in* Sheridan, R. E., and Grow, J. A., eds., The Atlantic continental margin: Boulder, Colorado, Geological Society of America, The Geology of North America, v. I–2, p. 387–398.

Dietrich, G., Kalle, K., Krauss, W., and Siedler, G., 1980, General oceanography: New York, Wiley-Interscience, 626 p.

Dziewonski, A. M., and Woodhouse, J. H., 1987, Global images of the earth interior: Science, v. 236, p. 37–48.

Emery, K. O., and Uchupi, E., 1984, The geology of the Atlantic Ocean: New York, Springer-Verlag, 1050 p.

Engeln, J. F., Wiens, D. A., and Stein, S., 1986, Mechanism and depths of Atlantic transform earthquakes: Journal of Geophysical Research, v. 91, p. 548–577.

Epp, D., and Smoot, N. C., 1989, Distribution of seamounts in the North Atlantic: Nature, v. 337, p. 254–257.

Fischer, A. G., 1986, Climatic rhythms recorded in strata: Annual Reviews of Earth and Planetary Sciences, v. 14, p. 315–376.

Gettrust, J. F., Grimm, M., Madoski, S., and Rowe, M., 1988, Results of a deep-tow multichannel survey on the Bermuda Rise: Geophysical Research Letters, v. 15, p. 1413–1416.

Grantz, A., Sweeney, J. F., and Johnson, G. L., eds., 1989, The Arctic Ocean Region: Boulder, Colorado, Geological Society of America, The Geology of North America, v. L (in press).

Grow, J. A., and Sheridan, R. E., 1988, U.S. Atlantic continental margin; A typical Atlantic-type or passive continental margin, *in* Sheridan, R. E., and Grow, J. A., The Atlantic continental margin: Boulder, Colorado, Geological Society of America, The Geology of North America, v. I–2, p. 1–7.

Haq, B. U., Hardenbol, J., and Vail, P. R., 1987, Chronology of fluctuating sea levels since the Triassic: Science, v. 235, p. 1156–1167.

Harland, W. B., Cox, A. V., Llewellyn, P. G., Pickton, C.A.G., Smith, A. G., and Walters, R., 1982, A geologic time scale: Cambridge, England, Cambridge University Press, 128 p.

Hatcher, R. D., Jr., Viele, G. W., and Thomas, W. A., eds., 1989, The Appalachian–Ouachita orogen in the United States: Boulder, Colorado, Geological Society of America, The Geology of North America, v. F–2 (in press).

Hay, B. J., 1987, Particle flux in the western Black Sea in the present and over the last 5000 years—temporal variability, sources, transport mechanisms [Ph.D. thesis]: Woods Hole Oceanographic Institution–Massachusetts Institute of Technology Joint Program in Oceanography, 201 p.

Hermance, J. F., 1981, Crustal genesis in Iceland—geophysical constraints on crustal thickening with age: Geophysical Research Letters, v. 8, p. 203–206.

Huang, P. Y., Solomon, S. C., Bergman, E. A., and Nabelek, J. L., 1986, Focal depths and mechanisms of Mid-Atlantic Ridge earthquakes from body waveform inversion: Journal of Geophysical Research, v. 91, p. 579–598.

Jansa, L. F., Enos, P., Tucholke, B. E., Gradstein, F. M., and Sheridan, R. E., 1979, Mesozoic–Cenozoic sedimentary formations of the North American basin; western North Atlantic, *in* Talwani, M., Hay, W., and Ryan, W.B.F., Deep drilling results in the Atlantic Ocean—continental margins and paleoenvironment: American Geophysical Union, Maurice Ewing Series, v. 3, p. 1–57.

Johnson, G. L., and Vogt, P. R., 1973, Mid-Atlantic Ridge from 47° to 51°N:

Geological Society of America Bulletin, v. 84, p. 3443–3462.

Jordan, T. H., and Minster, J. B., 1989, Beyond plate tectonics—looking at plate deformation with space geodesy, *in* Reid, M. H., and Moran, J. M., eds., The impact of VLBI on astrophysics and geophysics; Proceedings International Astronomical Union Symposium 129: Dordrecht, Netherlands, Reidel (in press).

Keen, M. J., and Williams, G. L., eds., 1989, Geology of the continental margin of eastern Canada: Ottawa, Geological Survey of Canda, Geology of Canada series, v. 7 (Geological Society of America, The Geology of North America, v. I-1) (in press).

Kellogg, T. B., 1980, Paleoclimatology and paleo-oceanography of the Norwegian and Greenland Seas; Glacial-interglacial contrasts: Boreas, v. 9, p. 115–137.

Klein, E. M., and Langmuir, C. H., 1987, Global correlations of ocean ridge basalt chemistry with axial depth and crustal thickness: Journal of Geophysical Research, v. 92, p. 8089–8115.

Klinkhammer, G., Elderfield, H., Greaves, M., Rona, P., and Nelsen, T., 1986, Manganese geochemistry near high-temperature vents in the Mid-Atlantic Ridge rift valley: Earth and Planetary Science Letters, v. 80, p. 230–240.

Kong, L., Detrick, R. S., Fox, P. J., Mayer, L. A., and Ryan, W.B.F., 1989, The morphology and tectonics of the MARK area from SEABEAM and SEA MARC I observations (Mid-Atlantic Ridge 23°N): Marine Geophysical Researches (in press).

Krauss, W., and Meincke, J., 1982, Drifting buoy trajectories in the North Atlantic Current: Nature, v. 296, p. 737–740.

LASE Study Group, 1986, Deep structure of the U.S. east coast passive margin from large aperture seismic experiments (LASE): Marine and Petroleum Geology, v. 3, p. 234–242.

LeDouaran, S., Needham, H. D., and Francheteau, J., 1982, Pattern of opening rates along the axis of the Mid-Atlantic Ridge: Nature, v. 300, p. 254–257.

Lilwall, R. C., and Kirk, R. E., 1985, Ocean-bottom seismograph observation of the Charlie-Gibbs Fracture Zone: Geophysical Journal of the Royal Astronomical Society, v. 80, p. 195–208.

Lilwall, R. C., Francis, T.J.G., and Porter, I. T., 1978, Ocean-bottom seismograph observations on the Mid-Atlantic Ridge near 45°N—further results: Geophysical Journal of the Royal Astronomical Society, v. 55, p. 255–262.

Luyendyk, B. P., Shor, A., and Cann, J. R., 1979, General implications of the Leg 49 drilling program for North Atlantic Ocean geology, *in* Luyendyk, B. P., and Cann, J. R., eds., Initial reports of the Deep Sea Drilling Project: Washington, D.C., U.S. Government Printing Office, v. 49, p. 825–839.

Macdonald K. C., and 5 others, 1986, Deep-tow studies of the Vema Fracture Zone. 1. Tectonics of a major slow slipping transform fault and its intersection with the Mid-Atlantic Ridge: Journal of Geophysical Research, v. 91, p. 3334–3354.

McCarthy, J., Mutter, J. C., Morton, J. L., Sleep, N. H., and Thompson, G., 1988, Relic magma chamber structures preserved within the Mesozoic North Atlantic crust?: Geological Society of America Bulletin, v. 100, p. 1423–1436.

Metcalf, T. P., 1982, Intraplate tectonics of the Appalachians in post-Triassic time [M.S. thesis]: Middletown, Connecticut, Wesleyan University, 238 p.

Miller, K. G., Fairbanks, R. G., and Mountain, G. S., 1987, Tertiary oxygen isotope synthesis, sea level history, and continental margin erosion: Paleoceanography, v. 2, p. 1–19.

Mountain, G. S., and Tucholke, B. E., 1985, Mesozoic and Cenozoic geology of the U.S. Atlantic continental slope and rise, *in* Poag, C. W., ed., Geologic evolution of the United States Atlantic margin: New York, Van Nostrand Reinhold, p. 293–341.

Mountain, G. S., Driscoll, N. W., and Miller, K. G., 1985, Cenozoic seismic stratigraphy of the SW Bermuda Rise: Geological Society of America Abstracts with Programs, v. 17, p. 670.

Myhre, A. M., and Eldholm, O., 1988, The western Svalbard margin (74°–80°N): Marine and Petroleum Geology, v. 5, p. 134–156.

Nance, R. D., Worsley, T. R., and Moody, J. B., 1988, The supercontinent cycle: Scientific American, v. 259, p. 72–79.

Nunns, A. G., and 7 others, 1983, Magnetic anomalies over Iceland and surrounding seas, *in* Bott, M.H.P., Saxov, S., Talwani, M., and Thiede, J., eds., Structure and development of the Greenland–Scotland Ridge, new methods and concepts: New York, Plenum Press, map, scale 1:2,000,000 at 64.5°N.

Officer, C. B., Hallam, A., Drake, C. L., and Devine, J. D., 1987, Late Cretaceous and paroxysmal Cretaceous/Tertiary extinctions: Nature, v. 326, p. 143–149.

Palmer, A. R., and Halley, R. B., 1979, Physical stratigraphy and trilobite biostratigraphy of the Carrara Formation (Lower and Middle Cambrian) in the southern Great Basin: U.S. Geological Survey Professional Paper 1047, 162 p.

Pockalny, R. A., Detrick, R. S., and Fox, P. J., 1988, Morphology and tectonics of the Kane transform from Sea Beam bathymetry data: Journal of Geophysical Research, v. 93, p. 3179–3193.

Purdy, G. M., 1987, New observations of the shallow seismic structure of young oceanic crust: Journal of Geophysical Research, v. 92, p. 9351–9362.

Rampino, M. R., and Stothers, R. B., 1988, Flood basalt volcanism during the past 250 million years: Science, v. 241, p. 629–760.

Raup, D. M., and Sepkoski, J. J., Jr., 1986, Periodic extinction of families and genera; Science, v. 231, p. 833–836.

Richardson, P. L., 1983, Eddy kinetic energy in the North Atlantic from surface drifters: Journal of Geophysical Research, v. 88, p. 4355–4367.

——, 1985, Average velocity and transport of the Gulf Stream near 55°W: Journal of Marine Research, v. 43, p. 83–111.

Roberts, D. G., Bott, M.H.P., and Uruski, C., 1983, Structure and origin of the Wyville–Thomson Ridge, *in* Bott, M.H.P., Saxov, S., Talwani, M., and Thiede, J., eds., Structure and development of the Greenland–Scotland Ridge, new methods and concepts: New York, Plenum, p. 133–158.

Roest, W. R., and Collette, B. J., 1986, The Fifteen Twenty Fracture Zone and the North American–South American Plate boundary: Journal of the Geological Society of London, v. 143, p. 833–843.

Rosencrantz, E., Ross, M. I., and Sclater, J. G., 1988, Age and spreading history of the Cayman Trough as determined from depth, heat flow, and magnetic anomalies: Journal of Geophysical Research, B, Solid Earth and Planets, v. 93, p. 2141–2157.

Ruddiman, W. F., and Raymo, M. E., 1988, Northern hemisphere climate regimes during the past 3 Ma—possible tectonic connections: Philosophical Transactions of the Royal Society of London, B, v. 318, p. 411–430.

Ruddiman, W. F., and Wright, H. E., Jr., eds., 1987, North America and adjacent oceans during the last deglaciation: Boulder, Colorado, Geological Society of America, The Geology of North America, v. K-3, 501 p.

Ruddiman, W. F., McIntyre, A., and Raymo, M., 1987, Paleoenvironmental results from North Atlantic sites 607 and 609, *in* Ruddiman, W. F., and Kidd, R. B., eds., Initial reports of the Deep Sea Drilling Project, v. 94, Part 2: Washington, D.C., U.S. Government Printing Office, p. 855–878.

Salisbury, M. H., and Christensen, N. I., 1978, The seismic velocity structure of a traverse through the Bay of Islands ophiolite complex, Newfoundland, an exposure of oceanic crust and upper mantle: Journal of Geophysical Research, v. 83, p. 805–817.

Schilling, J. G., Hanan, B. B., and McCully, B., 1988, MAR volcanism from 3°S to 5°N; Pb isotope evidence: EOS Transactions of the American Geophysical Union, v. 69, p. 1426.

Schlanger, S. O., 1987, High frequency sea-level fluctuations in Cretaceous time; An emerging geophysical problem, *in* Hsü, K. J., ed., Mesozoic and Cenozoic oceans: American Geophysical Union Geodynamics Series, v. 15, p. 61–74.

Schouten, H., Dick, H.J.B., and Klitgord, K. D., 1987, Migration of mid-ocean ridge volcanic segments: Nature, v. 326, p. 835–839.

Sepkoski, J. J., Jr., 1986, Global bioevents and the question of periodicity, *in* Walliser, O., ed., Global bio-events: Berlin, Springer, p. 47–61.

Shaw, P. R., 1987, Investigations of relative plate motions in the South Atlantic using Seasat altimeter data: Journal of Geophysical Research, v. 92, p. 9363–9375.

Sheridan, R. E., 1986, Pulsation tectonics as the control of North Atlantic paleoceanography, *in* Summerhayes, C. P., and Shackleton, N. J., eds., North Atlantic palaeoceanography: Blackwell Scientific Publications, Geological

Society Special Publication 21, p. 255–275.

Sheridan, R. E., and Grow, J. A., 1988, Synthesis and unanswered questions, *in* Sheridan, R. E., and Grow, J. A., eds., The Atlantic continental margin: Boulder, Colorado, Geological Society of America, The Geology of North America, v. I-2, p. 595–599.

Sibuet, J.-C., Hay, W. W., Prunier, A., Montadert, L., Hinz, K., and Fritsch, J., 1984, Early evolution of the South Atlantic Ocean—role of rifting episode, *in* Hay, W. W., and Sibuet, J.-C., eds., Initial reports of the Deep Sea Drilling Project: Washington, D.C., U.S. Government Printing Office, v. 75, p. 469–481.

Solomon, S. C., Huang, P. Y., and Meinke, L., 1988, The seismic moment budget of slowly spreading ridges: Nature, v. 334, p. 58–61.

Srivastava, S. P., and Roest, W. R., 1988, Evolution of the North Atlantic—new constraints from the Labrador Sea and northwest Atlantic magnetic data: EOS Transactions of the American Geophysical Union, v. 69, p. 1431.

Srivastava, S. P., Arthur, M. A., Clement, B., and others, 1987, Proceedings of the Ocean Drilling Program, Part A—Initial report: College Station, Texas, Ocean Drilling Program, v. 105, 917 p.

Steckler, M. S., Watts, A. B., and Thorne, J. A., 1988, Subsidence and basin modeling at the U.S. Atlantic passive margin, *in* Sheridan, R. E., and Grow, J. A., eds., The Atlantic continental margin: Boulder, Colorado, Geological Society of America, The Geology of North America, v. I-2, p. 399–416.

Stein, R. S., 1987, Contemporary plate motion and crustal deformation: Reviews of Geophysics, v. 25, p. 855–863.

Stommel, H., 1982, Is the South Pacific helium-3 plume dynamically active?: Earth and Planetary Science Letters, v. 61, p. 63–67.

Sverdrup, H. U., Johnson, M. W., and Fleming, R. H., 1942, The oceans. Their physics, chemistry, and general biology: Englewood Cliffs, New Jersey, Prentice-Hall, 1087 p.

Tankard, A. J., and Welsink, H. J., 1987, Extensional tectonics and stratigraphy of Hibernia oil field. Grand Banks, Newfoundland: American Association of Petroleum Geologists Bulletin, v. 71, p. 1210–1232.

Toomey, D. R., Solomon, S. C., Purdy, G. M., and Murray, M. H., 1985, Microearthquakes beneath the median valley of the Mid-Atlantic Ridge near 23°N: hypocenters and focal mechanisms: Journal of Geophysical Research, v. 90, p. 5443–5458.

Tucholke, B. E., and Ludwig, W. J., 1982, Structure and origin of the J-Anomaly Ridge, western North Atlantic Ocean: Journal of Geophysical Research, v. 87, p. 9389–9407.

Tucholke, B. E., and Schouten, H., 1989, Kane Fracture Zone: Marine Geophysical Researches (in press).

Tucholke, B. E., and Vogt, P. R., eds., 1979a, Initial reports of the Deep Sea Drilling Project, Volume 43: Washington, D.C., U.S. Government Printing Office, 1115 p.

——, 1979b, Western North Atlantic—sedimentary evolution and aspects of tectonic history, *in* Tucholke, B. E., and Vogt, P. R., eds., Initial reports of the Deep Sea Drilling Project, Volume 43: Washington, D.C., U.S. Government Printing Office, p. 791–825.

van Tassel, J., 1987, Upper Devonian Catskill Delta margin cyclic sedimentation; Brallier, Scherr, and Foreknobs Formations of Virginia and West Virginia: Geological Society of America Bulletin, v. 99, p. 414–426.

Vogt, P. R., 1971, Asthenosphere motion recorded by the ocean floor south of Iceland: Earth and Planetary Science Letters, v. 13, p. 153–160.

——, 1972, Evidence for global synchronism in mantle plume convection, and possible significance for geology: Nature, v. 240, p. 338–342.

——, 1973, Early events in the opening of the North Atlantic, *in* Tarling, D. H., and Runcorn, S. K., eds., Implications of continental drift to the earth sciences: New York, Academic Press, p. 691–712.

——, 1975, Changes in geomagnetic reversal frequency at times of tectonic change; Evidence for coupling between core and upper mantle processes: Earth and Planetary Science Letters, v. 25, p. 313–321.

——, 1976, Plumes, subaxial pipe flow, and topography along the mid-oceanic ridge: Earth and Planetary Science Letters, v. 29, p. 309–325.

——, 1979, Global magmatic episodes—new evidence and implications for the steady-state mid-oceanic ridge: Geology, v. 7, p. 93–98.

——, 1983, The Iceland plume—status of the hypothesis after a decade of new work, *in* Bott, M.H.P., Saxov, S., Talwani, M., and Thiede, J., eds., Structure and development of the Greenland–Scotland Ridge, new methods and concepts: New York, Plenum, p. 191–213.

——, 1986a, Seafloor topography, sediments, and paleoenvironments, *in* Hurdle, B. G., ed., The Nordic Seas: New York, Springer, p. 237–410.

——, 1986b, Geophysical and geochemical signatures and plate tectonics, *in* Hurdle, B. G., ed., The Nordic Seas: Springer, New York, p. 413–662.

——, 1989, Volcanogenic upwelling of anoxic nutrient-rich water—a possible factor in carbonate bank/reef demise and benthic faunal extinctions?: Geological Society of America Bulletin (in press).

Vogt, P. R., and Ostenso, N. A., 1967, Steady state crustal spreading: Nature, v. 215, p. 810–817.

Vogt, P. R., and Tucholke, B. E., eds., 1986a, The western North Atlantic region: Boulder, Colorado, Geological Society of America, The Geology of North America, v. M, 696 p.

Vogt, P. R., Schneider, E. D., and Johnson, G. L., 1969, The crust and upper mantle beneath the sea, *in* Hart, P., ed., The earth's crust and upper mantle: American Geophysical Union Geophysical Monograph 13, p. 557–617.

Vogt, P. R., Johnson, G. L., Holcombe, T. L., Gilg, J. G., and Avery, O. E., 1971, Episodes of sea-floor spreading recorded by North Atlantic basement: Tectonophysics, v. 12, p. 211–234.

von Arx, W. S., 1962, An introduction to physical oceanography: Reading, Massachusetts, Addison-Wesley, 422 p.

White, R. S., Spence, G. D., Fowler, S. R., McKenzie, D. P., Westbrook, G. K., and Bowen, A. D., 1987, Magmatism at rifted continental margins: Nature, v. 330, p. 439–444.

White, R. S., Detrick, R. S., Mutter, J., Buhl, P., Minshull, T. A., and Morris, E., 1988, Lower crustal layering, dipping reflectors and fracture zone structure in Mesozoic oceanic crust: EOS Transactions of the American Geophysical Union, v. 69, p. 1440.

Williams, H., and Neale, E.R.W., eds., 1989, Appalachian orogen; Canada and Greenland: Ottawa, Geological Survey of Canada, Geology of Canada series, v. 5 (Geological Society of America, The Geology of North America, v. F-1) (in press).

Manuscript Accepted by the Society February 23, 1989

ACKNOWLEDGMENTS

We thank D. Epp and N. C. Smoot for their seamount locations (Fig. 1) and G. Mountain, J. McCarthy and J. Gettrust for permission to reproduce seismic-reflection profiles. Peter Sloss (NGDC) contributed the land elevation contours on Fig. 1, and Michael Max advised on placement of suture zones. For illustrations and manuscript preparation we thank I. Jewett, L. Maiden, J. Zwinakis, and K. Lilly. Research support during preparation of this chapter was provided by the U.S. Navy, Naval Research Laboratory and Office of Naval Research, and by the National Science Foundation. Elements of this chapter dealing with linkages of the geologic record to tectonism and volcanism were presented by one of us (B.E.T.) at the Geological Society of America Centennial Symposium in October 1988. Contribution No. 7041 of Woods Hole Oceanographic Institution.

Printed in U.S.A.

The Geology of North America
Vol. A, The Geology of North America—An overview
The Geological Society of America, 1989

Chapter 6

The Atlantic passive margin

Robert E. Sheridan
Department of Geological Sciences, Rutgers University, New Brunswick, New Jersey 08903

INTRODUCTION

The eastern North American passive margin includes the Atlantic continental margin from the Bahamas to Baffin Bay. Formed by the rifting, breakup, and drift of North America away from Africa and Europe, the margin's thick sedimentary cover of Mesozoic to Cenozoic age lying over the Coastal Plain, continental shelf, slope, and rise straddles three distinct basement types: continental, transitional, and oceanic. The emerged Coastal Plain, which is a seaward-thickening wedge of sediments 1 to 2 km thick, extends from Florida to Long Island (Fig. 1). It exists as a submerged wedge off Canada (Fig. 2). The continental crust under the inner continental shelf, Coastal Plain, and landward is marked by exposed and buried rift basins formed by asymmetric half grabens (Fig. 1). The continental crust consists of three grossly different ages and terranes: the Precambrian shield from Labrador northward (Fig. 2); the Paleozoic orogenic belt from Newfoundland to Georgia (Figs. 1 and 2); and the African Precambrian and Paleozoic Terranes of Florida (Fig. 1). The transitional crust under the outer continental shelves and marginal plateaus is deeply subsided and underlies major sedimentary basins. These deep sedimentary basins are: (1) South Florida–Bahamas Basin, (2) Blake Plateau Basin, (3) Carolina Trough, (4) Baltimore Canyon Trough, (5) Georges Bank Basin (Fig. 1), (6) Scotian Shelf Basin, (7) Grand Bank Basins, and (8) Labrador Shelf Basins (Fig. 2). The boundary between the transitional crust and the true oceanic crust is marked by the linear East Coast magnetic anomaly north of Florida, and farther east by the Blake Spur magnetic anomaly in the Blake-Bahamas region (Fig. 1). Off Canada similar slope anomalies mark the continent/ocean boundary (c/o, Fig. 2). The thick sediments of the continental rise are laid on oceanic crust (Sheridan and others, 1979; Klitgord and Hutchinson, 1985; Grow and others, 1983; Fig. 2).

The chapter will discuss the major features of the Atlantic margin describing the character of the rocks present and the interpreted geologic origin and history. The discussion will proceed from the simpler southern basins to the more complex northern basins. Recent interpretations on basin modeling and paleogeographic reconstructions will be discussed.

RIFT-STAGE BASINS

In the United States and Nova Scotia, narrow, linear rift-stage basins generally parallel the northeast-southwest strike of the prevailing grain of the Appalachian orogen basement (Fig. 1). The sediments in the exposed rift basins range from Triassic to Middle Jurassic in age (Manspeizer, 1985) and reach up to 10 km in thickness. Off the Grand Banks, east Newfoundland, and Labrador margins the latest rift basin ages are younger, and sediment ages range from Triassic to Cretaceous (McWhae, 1981; Tankard and Welsink, 1987; Keen and others, 1987; Keen and deVoogd, 1988). The structure of the basins is dominantly one of half grabens with a major listric normal fault as a border fault. Offshore, these rift-basin structures are well observed seismically (Figs. 3 to 7; McWhae, 1981; Grow and others, 1983; Klitgord and Hutchinson, 1985; Keen and others, 1987; Keen and de-Voogd, 1988). In some cases the border faults dip eastward, while in others they dip landward.

In the exposed rift basins, the sedimentary deposits are generally nonmarine fluvial and lacustrine in nature (Manspeizer, 1985). Fanglomerates grade basinward from the border fault margin into fine-grained, lacustrine, organic-rich black shales and argillites; the lake deposits are interlayered with fluvial sandstones and shales.

Recent seismic profiles across the U.S. rift basins onshore (Ratcliffe and others, 1986) and in the U.S. offshore (Hutchinson and others, 1986) reveal that the border faults are dipping at low angles (~30°) and apparently reoccupy deep-penetrating Paleozoic thrust faults. Consequently the Mesozoic rift basins are oriented and positioned by the preexisting basement structure of the Appalachian orogen (Fig. 1).

Offshore, the synrift structures of the half grabens and the enclosed tilted sediments are truncated by a major discontinuity with the overlying through-going reflectors of the onlapping drift stage sequences (Figs. 3, 4, and 5). This discontinuity is often a hiatus called the post-rift unconformity (Grow and others, 1983) or the breakup unconformity (Falvey, 1974). Beneath the unconformity the truncated tilted reflectors of the synrift sedimentary sequences are revealed seismically.

Sheridan, R. E., 1989, The Atlantic passive margin, *in* Bally, A. W., and Palmer, A. R., eds., The Geology of North America—An overview: Boulder, Colorado, Geological Society of America, The Geology of North America, v. A.

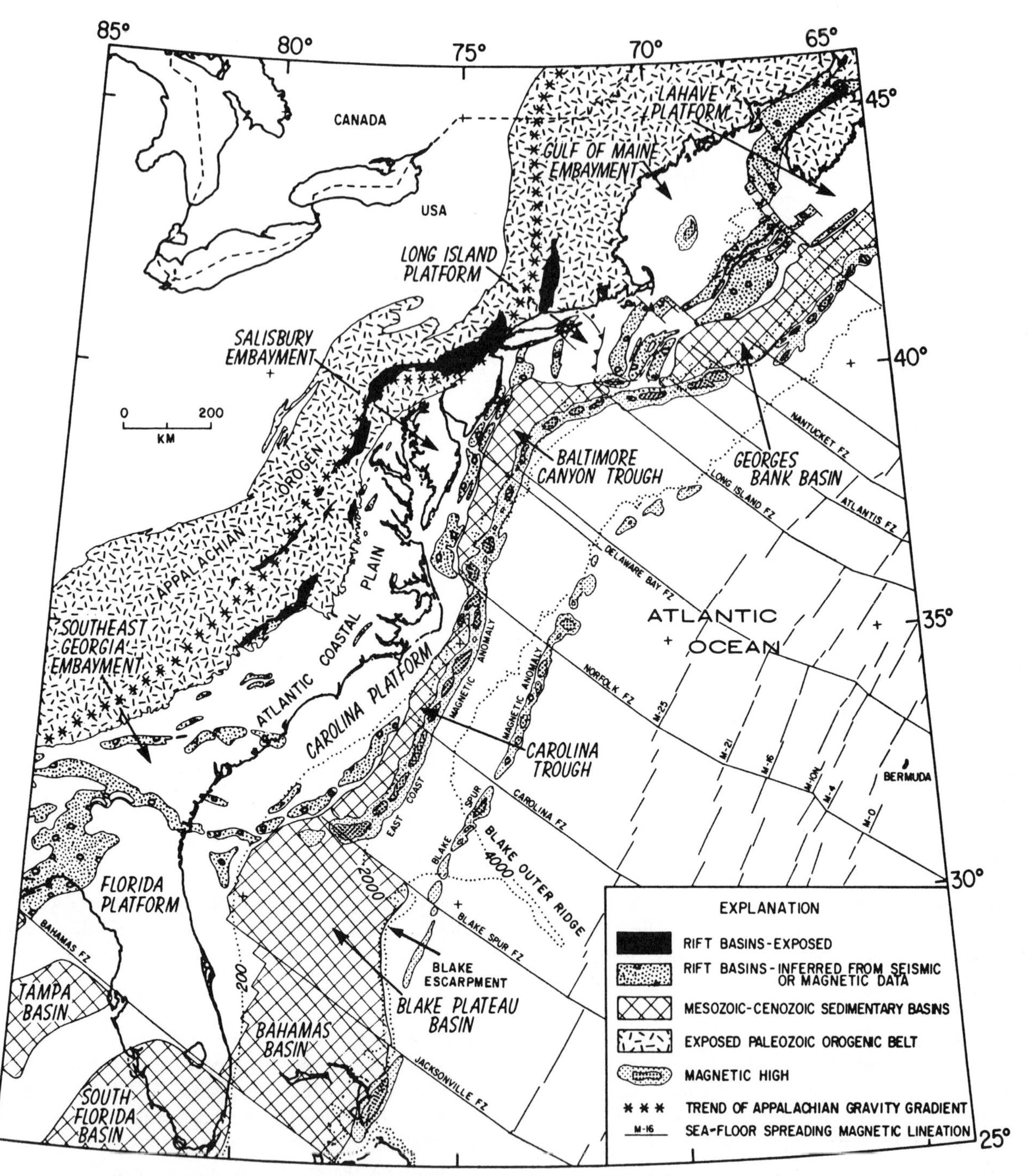

Figure 1. First-order structural and geophysical features of the United States passive Atlantic continental margin (from Hutchinson and Kiltgord, 1988; Grow and Sheridan, 1988).

Near the transitional-crust/oceanic-crust boundary under the East Coast magnetic anomaly, thick wedges of seaward-dipping reflectors commonly occur (Fig. 5; Klitgord and Hutchinson, 1985). These have been found on other passive margins (Mutter, 1985), and have been drilled (Roberts and others, 1984). They are interpreted to be thick wedges of intercalated sedimentary rocks and basalts formed at the time of breakup. The wedge apparently straddles the transitional crust/oceanic crust boundary (White and others, 1987).

The Canadian Atlantic margin is more complex than that of the United States because of the presence of a triple point in the North Atlantic spreading center and the headward propagation of that spreading center over several sets of spreading-center jumps. The Canadian margin is subdivided into a series of segments bounded by major transform faults (McWhae, 1981; Fig. 2). The transform faults played important roles in controlling the timing of spreading and breakup in the individual segments, and controlling the major changes in direction of breakup and spreading.

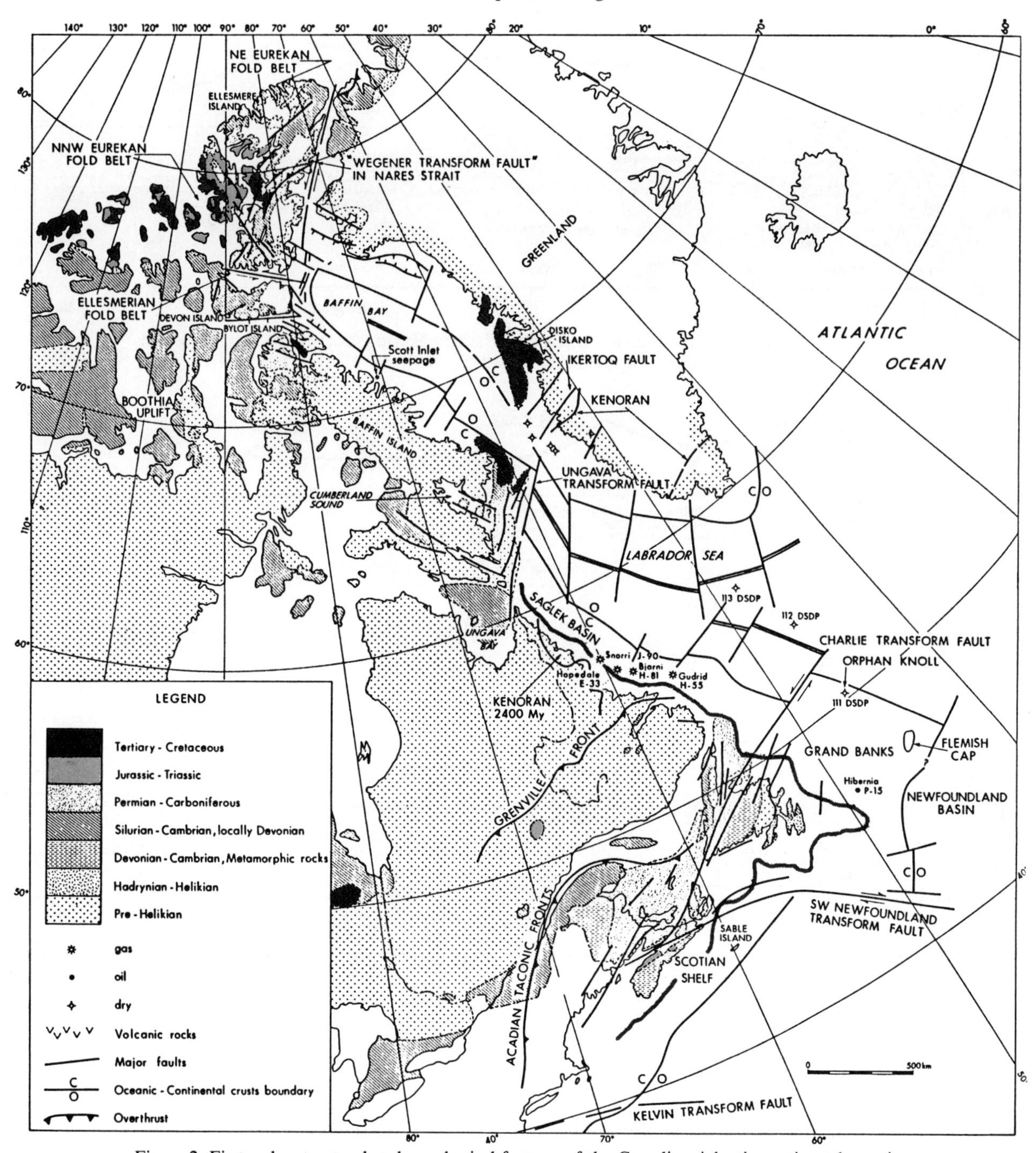

Figure 2. First-order structural and geophysical features of the Canadian Atlantic continental margin (from McWhae, 1981). The gray line following the hinge line of the continental margin marks the onlap of Tertiary and Cretaceous sediments.

South of the southwest Newfoundland transform fault (Fig. 2), the Scotian shelf margin underwent breakup in the Middle Jurassic along with the U.S. passive margin to the south (Wade, 1981). And similar to the U.S. passive margin, decreasing thermal subsidence during the Late Jurassic to Holocene controlled the thick accumulation of the drift-stage sedimentary wedge that onlapped the southeast-tilting basement. A simple pull-apart margin existed along the Scotian Shelf (McWhae, 1981; Wade, 1981).

In contrast, the Grand Banks (Fig. 2) was undergoing rifting in the Triassic-Jurassic as an extension of the northeast-southwest–trending rift basins then forming along the Appalachian structural grain. Major fault structures, such as the Chedabucto fault (Fig. 6), extended across the Scotian Shelf and Grand Banks area during the late Paleozoic. These faults, active in Paleozoic time as terrane boundaries and major wrench faults, were reactivated to bound deeply subsiding rift basins in Triassic-

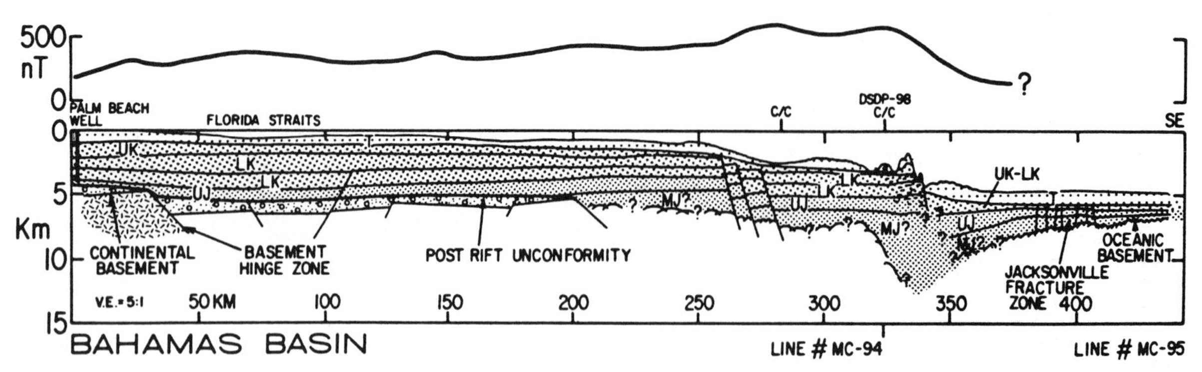

Figure 3. Interpreted cross section across the Bahama Platform, Bahamas Basin, and the Blake-Bahama Basin (from Sheridan and others, 1981; Klitgord and others, 1988).

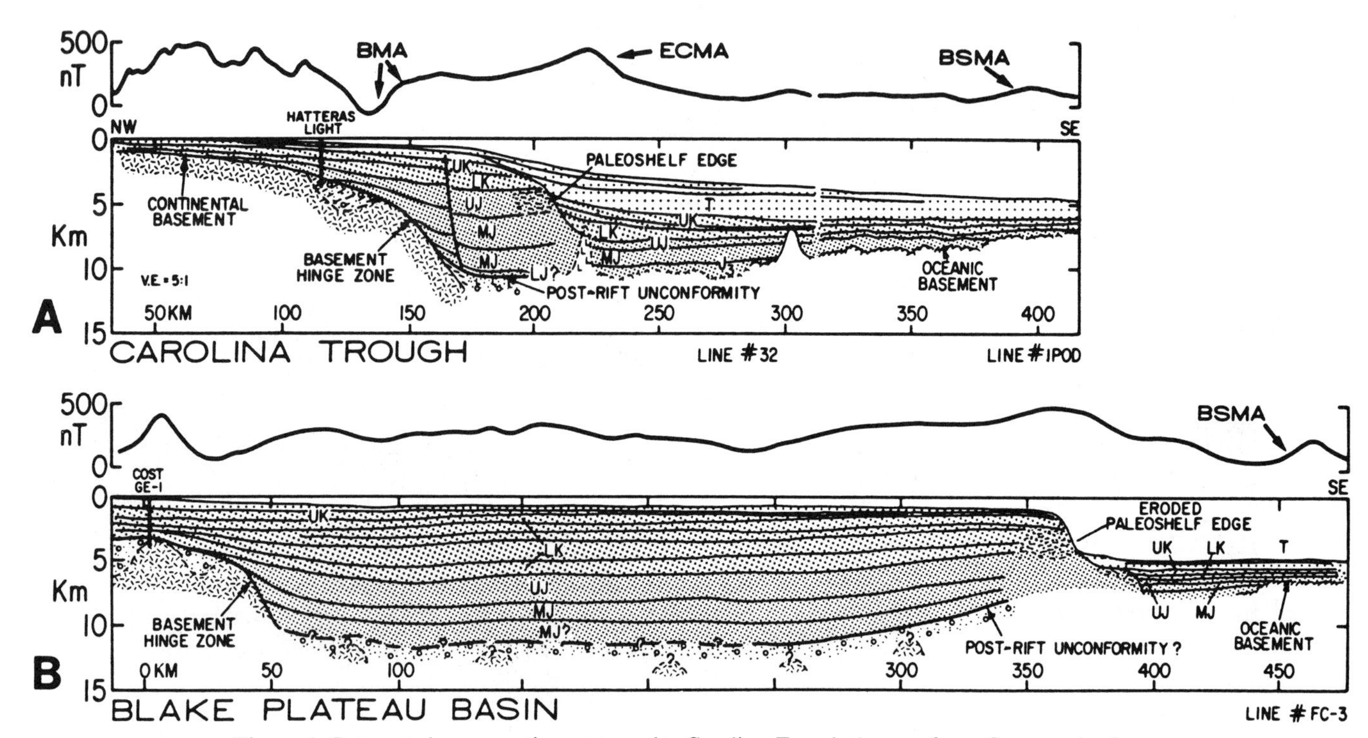

Figure 4. Interpreted cross sections across the Carolina Trough (upper; from Grow and others, 1983; Klitgord and others, 1988), and the Blake Plateau (lower; from Dillon and others, 1979; Klitgord and others, 1988).

Jurassic time. The Orpheus Trough (Fig. 6), striking northeast across the Scotian Shelf, is one of these reactivated fault basins.

In fact, reactivation of the Paleozoic Chedabucto fault may have influenced the location of the southwest Newfoundland transform fault, which was an active plate margin during the Jurassic–Early Cretaceous as Africa slid past the southern boundary of the Grand Banks (Figs. 2, 6, and 7; McWhae, 1981; Wade, 1981). This action and the transform led to a major 500-km right-lateral offset in the continent/ocean boundary along the southern margin of the Grand Banks (Fig. 2).

Under the Grand Banks proper, crustal extension and rotation on rift faults led to extensive crustal thinning and basin subsidence (McWhae, 1981; Wade, 1981; Tankard and Welsink, 1987; Keen and deVoogd, 1988; Figs. 7 and 8). Many of the rift basins of the Grand Banks were active as basins in the Carboniferous, and sedimentary rocks of these ages fill the bottom of the rifts (Fig. 7). Unlike the exposed Triassic-Jurassic rift basins to the south in the United States, where the sedimentary rocks are entirely nonmarine in origin, there are Upper Triassic to Lower Jurassic salt deposits and Jurassic–Lower Cretaceous marine carbonates and shales in the Grand Banks rift basins. This reflects the transgression of the Tethyan seaway from an easterly direction (Wilson, 1981). As much as 5 to 10 km of sedimentary rocks fill the Grand Banks rift basins (Figs. 7, 8, and 9; McWhae, 1981; Wade, 1981; Tankard and Welsink, 1987).

In the Early Cretaceous, the northeast-striking rifting on

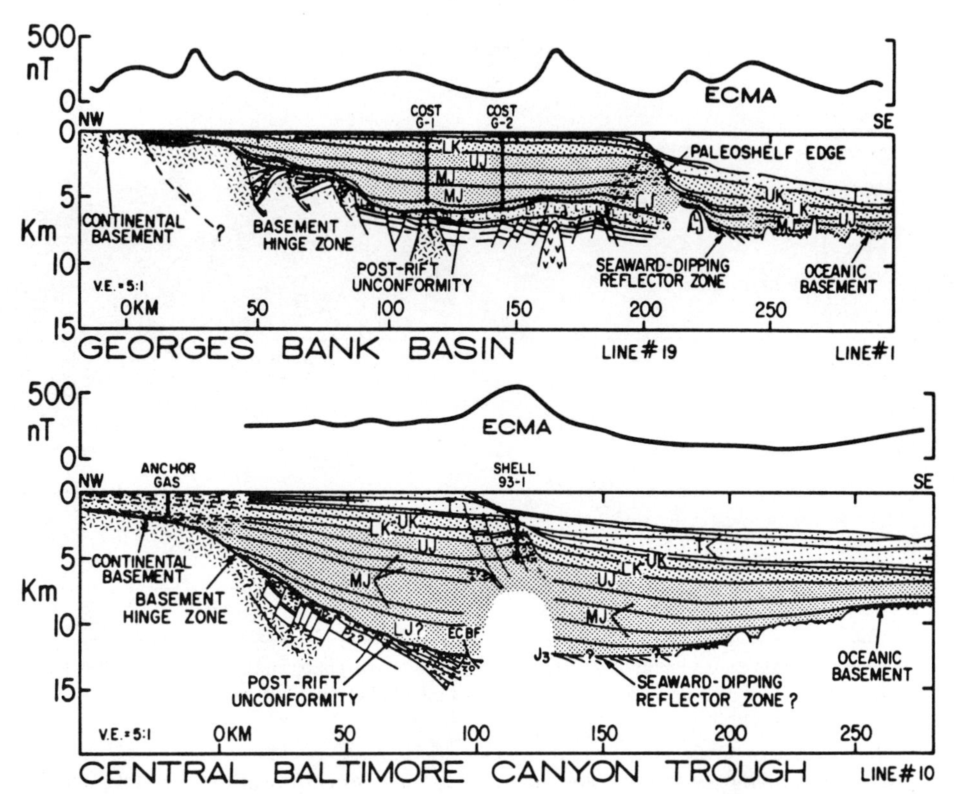

Figure 5. Interpreted cross sections across the Georges Bank Basin (upper), and the central Baltimore Canyon Trough (lower), (from Klitgord and Hutchinson, 1985; Klitgord and others, 1988). ECBF = East Coast boundary fault; J_3 = deepest Atlantic continental rise reflection.

Grand Banks gave way to breakup and formation of the continent/ocean boundary along the east margin of the Grand Banks (Fig. 2). The oldest magnetic anomaly along this margin is M0 (Keen and de Voogd, 1988), which was formed in Aptian time when Iberia and Grand Banks began spreading apart.

During the Middle Cretaceous, extension of Grand Banks took a new direction with a northwest-southeast strike, oriented by the reactivation of ancient Paleozoic terrane boundaries as transform faults. The major terrane boundary fault between the Gander and Avalon terranes (Williams, 1979) was reactivated to become the Charlie Transform fault (Fig. 2). This new direction of rifting developed as a northwest-trending arm of a triple junction involving the newly opening North Atlantic Ocean in the region of the Iberian-Biscay margin. Eventually this northwest-striking rifting of Grand Banks led to breakup and the development of the continent/ocean boundary along the northeast margin of the banks (Fig. 2). New Atlantic Ocean crust formed as the Irish margin spread from that marked by Flemish Cap and Orphan Knoll (Fig. 2). The oldest magnetic anomaly along this segment of the Canadian passive margin is identified as anomaly 34, indicating a breakup age of possibly Santonian (Srivastava and others, 1981).

The northwest-striking arm of the new North Atlantic spreading center propagated northwest of Charlie Transform fault to create the Labrador Sea and the Canadian Labrador passive margin (Fig. 2). Magnetic anomalies 31 to 28 are identified near the continent/ocean boundary, indicating a breakup of the Labrador margin in the Late Cretaceous to early Paleocene (Srivastava and others, 1981).

In early Paleocene, North Atlantic spreading began east of Greenland to form the Norwegian Sea (Roberts and others, 1984), and eventually the Labrador Sea spreading ceased in the Tertiary. This left the Canadian Atlantic margin in a passive state after a relatively long period of recurring rifting and breakup. At least three major transform and breakup events affected the three sides of Grand Banks: (1) Middle Jurassic, (2) Early Cretaceous, and (3) Late Cretaceous. The Grand Banks basins, therefore, have a complex history of tectonic rejuvenation over a long period of time.

MESOZOIC-CENOZOIC DRIFT-STAGE BASINS

After breakup in the Middle Jurassic, the newly formed central North Atlantic Ocean invaded the U.S. and eastern Canadian continental margins. As the basement subsided with thermal cooling of the lithosphere, the shallow-marine sedimentary rocks progressively onlapped the post-rift unconformity (Figs. 3, 4, and 5) (Dillon and others, 1979; Sheridan and others, 1981; Grow and others, 1983; Klitgord and Hutchinson, 1985). Where the earliest drift-stage and latest rift-stage rocks are drilled on the central Atlantic continental margin, such as in Georges Bank Basin (Fig. 5) (Poag, 1982) and the Bahamas (Fig. 3) (Sheridan

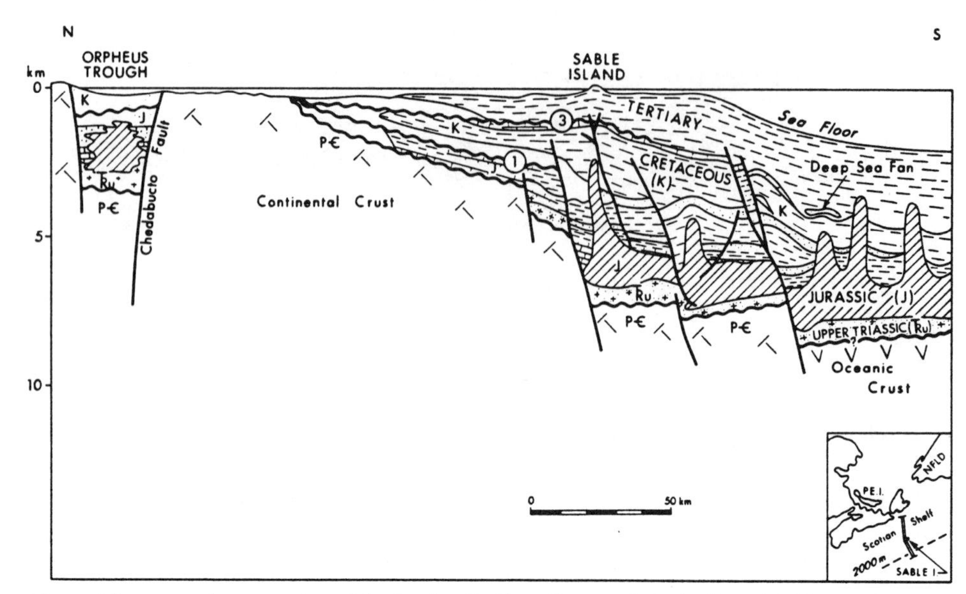

Figure 6. Interpreted cross section of the Scotian Shelf passive margin basin (from McWhae, 1981). 1 = regional Lower Cretaceous unconformity; 3 = regional middle Paleocene unconformity.

others, 1981), the earliest onlapping sediments are interbedded limestone, dolomite, and anhydrite. These evaporites and carbonates were deposited in warm, shallow seas overlying the post-rift unconformity or a late rift-stage halite deposit. The salt layer just beneath these onlapping beds sourced several zones of salt diapirs in the Grand Banks basins, Scotian Basin, Baltimore Canyon Trough, and the Carolina Trough. Salt has been drilled beneath the Grand Banks, Scotian, Georges Bank, and Baltimore Canyon Basins (McWhae, 1981; Wade, 1981; Poag, 1982; Grow and others, 1983).

All along the passive margin from the Bahamas to the Grand Banks, the Middle Jurassic through earliest Cretaceous was a time of carbonate deposition. The carbonate deposits formed a formidable, seismically identifiable structure along a paleoshelf edge from the Bahamas to the Scotian Shelf (Figs. 3, 4, 5, and 6). This carbonate bank was eroded periodically since at least in the Jurassic, so that steep escarpments are now buried under the continental slope (Mattick and others, 1978; Sheridan and others, 1981; Jansa, 1981). Jansa (1981) points out that drift of the North American Plate carried the eastern North American Atlantic margin progressively north of 30°N latitude from earliest Cretaceous time. Thus, the carbonate banks terminated earlier on the Scotian Shelf and Georges Bank Basin (Neocomian), later on the Blake Plateau Basin (Cenomanian), and still exist in the Bahamas today (Jansa, 1981).

As sea-floor spreading and continental drift continued and North America moved away from the hot spreading center, the thermal cooling of the North American lithosphere caused crustal subsidence. Along the U.S. margin by latest Jurassic time, the sediment load on the cooling lithosphere caused flexural downbending of the adjacent unthinned continental crust to form the Coastal Plain landward of the hinge zone (Figs. 4 and 5) (Watts, 1981). Continued cooling, subsidence, and flexure increased the width and thickness of the Coastal Plain wedge. Off Canada, this wedge, caused by flexure landward of the hinge line, is totally submerged (Fig. 6) (Wade, 1981; McWhae, 1981).

Mechanical stretching by viscous processes, crustal thinning by brittle, listric normal fault rotations, and intrusion and underplating of the transitional crust all are factors contributing to drastic subsidence seaward of the hinge zone (Watts, 1981; White and others, 1987; Keen and others, 1987; Keen and deVoogd, 1988). Off the United States the subsidence varied along strike to produce five distinct and individualized depositional basins. The Georges Bank Basin, which is the shallowest of the basins off the coast of the United States, subsided some 6 to 7 km (Fig. 5). This contrasts with the deeper basin of the Baltimore Canyon Trough, which reaches 12 to 14 km. The shallow, positive basement of the Long Island Platform (Fig. 1) separates the deeper parts of these two major basins. Similarly the Carolina and Florida Platforms separate the deeper parts of the Baltimore Canyon and Carolina Troughs and the Blake Plateau and South Florida–Bahama Basins, respectively (Fig. 1).

The individualization of these basins and their variations in depth and width relate to preexisting weaknesses and rheological behavior of the North American basement rocks. The Paleozoic Appalachian orogen was marked by major suture zones and promontories and reentrants. For example, the Long Island Platform forms a major offset in the modern passive margin that mimics the major curvature of the Appalachian structures between the New York promontory and the Pennsylvania reentrant. Similarly the Florida Platform and the Blake Plateau are southeast of the Appalachian sutures where they swing westward

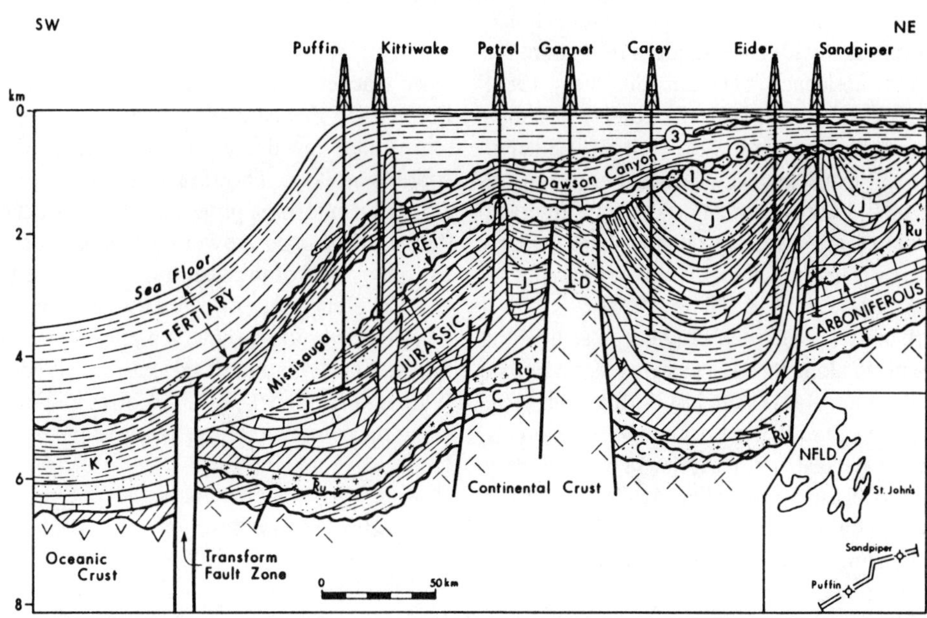

Figure 7. Interpreted cross section of the Grand Banks basins showing the southern transform fault margin (from McWhae, 1981). 1 = regional Lower Cretaceous unconformity; 2 = regional Upper Cretaceous unconformity; 3 = regional middle Paleocene unconformity; C = Carboniferous; D = Devonian.

across Georgia (Fig. 1), and therefore the Florida Platform and Blake Plateau crusts originated on African basement with perhaps different rheologic behavior (Sawyer, 1985). These dominant offsets in Paleozoic basement are inherited in the Mesozoic passive margin, and eventually in the major fracture zone offsets in the modern Atlantic (Fig. 1).

Indeed, these basement rheologic differences controlled by Paleozoic structures even had subtle influences landward of the hinge line. There, the flexing lithosphere varied in subsidence along strike so that slightly deeper (2 to 3 km) depressions of the basement occurred, as in the Southeast Georgia and Salisbury Embayments (Fig. 1). Magnetic anomalies associated with Paleozoic terrane sutures bound the centers of these embayments.

The particular geologic features of the seven major basins off the Atlantic passive margin are discussed below.

South Florida–Bahamas Basin

Seismic data indicate thicknesses of from 5 to 12 km of Jurassic to Holocene sedimentary rocks in this basin (Sheridan and others, 1966, 1981; Fig. 3). Drilling of a few wells on the Bahama Banks has penetrated these Upper Jurassic and younger sedimentary rocks. They are consistently shallow-water limestones and dolomites, evaporites, and deep-water limestones. However, in one of the channels some middle Cretaceous dark shales have been recovered in drilling by the ODP (Ocean Drilling Program; Austin and others, 1986). Seismic reflection profiles reveal a faulted, rifted basement under the western Bahamas extending from Florida to a point in the Bahamas where the Blake Spur magnetic anomaly projects inland (Sheridan and others, 1981). On seismic profiles southeast of this point the basement no longer appears to be faulted, but instead is a hummocky reflecting surface interpreted to be oceanic crust. Upper Cretaceous reflection horizons appear offset by faults that might extend into the Tertiary. These relatively young faults are attributed to stresses related to effects of the Cuban orogeny in the Late Cretaceous and Early Tertiary. Faults and folds are known to exist in the southern Bahamas just north of Cuba, and faults as far north as Little Bahama Bank have now been found (Fig. 3). This faulting, in the Late Cretaceous and Tertiary, apparently segmented what was once a broader megabank beneath the Florida/Blake Bahamas area. Then isolated banks developed, surrounded by the deeper channels through which the Gulf Stream and Antilles currents flowed. Later, some of the Upper Cretaceous channels were filled in and some isolated banks coalesced (Ladd and Sheridan, 1987).

Blake Plateau Basin

This basin is one of the widest along the U.S. passive margin, reaching nearly 300 km, compared to 100 to 150 km for the basins to the north. Sedimentary rocks reach to depths of 12 km in the basin (Fig. 4). Jurassic to Cretaceous carbonates persist over the plateau, and Lower Cretaceous and Upper Cretaceous limestones and dolomites have been dredged and sampled by submersibles along the Blake Escarpment (Sheridan and others,

1966; Dillon and others, 1985). Seismic data do not image the basement very well beneath the carbonates, but the transitional crust must be heavily intruded with basaltic rocks to account for the crustal thickness and subsidence (Sheridan and others, 1981; Sawyer, 1985). After Cenomanian time, the continued subsidence of the plateau with the beginning of the Gulf Stream led to starvation and erosion of the plateau. This caused a deepening of the plateau to more than 1,000 m. In the same time interval, several processes, including mass wasting, chemical and biological corrosion, and current erosion, caused the Blake Escarpment to retreat several kilometers (Paull and Dillon, 1980).

Besides the width of the basin, the Blake Plateau is different from the basins to the north along the U.S. passive margin in that the East Coast magnetic anomaly dies out just north of this area. Another magnetic anomaly, the Blake Spur magnetic anomaly near the seaward edge of the Blake Plateau, marks the boundary between transitional and oceanic crust (Fig. 4). This magnetic anomaly is thought to mark a basement-ridge structure formed by extrusions along a spreading center. This was a new spreading center formed by a spreading-center shift, leaving an extinct center in the East Coast–Blake Spur magnetic anomaly corridor (Fig. 1). Consequently, the broad Blake Plateau Basin has no equivalent on the African side of the Atlantic.

Carolina Trough

One of the narrowest basins of the U.S. passive margin, this basin reaches 11 to 12 km in thickness (Grow and others, 1983; Fig. 4). At the base of the section, Jurassic salt is identified seismically, and this layer sources a ridge of diapirs under the continental slope. The Jurassic to lowermost Cretaceous carbonate platform forms a pronounced paleoshelf edge (Fig. 4). One of the best-developed growth faults along the margin occurs under the outer shelf of the Carolinas. It can be traced for more than 100 km along strike. Apparently, movement of the flowing salt beneath the brittle carbonate platform has allowed slipping along the fault and rotation of the entire shelf-edge block as one piece (Dillon and others, 1979). Correspondingly, the diapir ridge along the continental slope is one of the best developed along the U.S. passive margin.

Baltimore Canyon Trough

Drift-stage sediments are up to 12 to 14 km thick in the outer part of this basin, and synrift sediments and dipping reflector wedges could reach greater thicknesses below that (Grow and others, 1983; Fig. 5). Jurassic salt at the base of the drift-stage

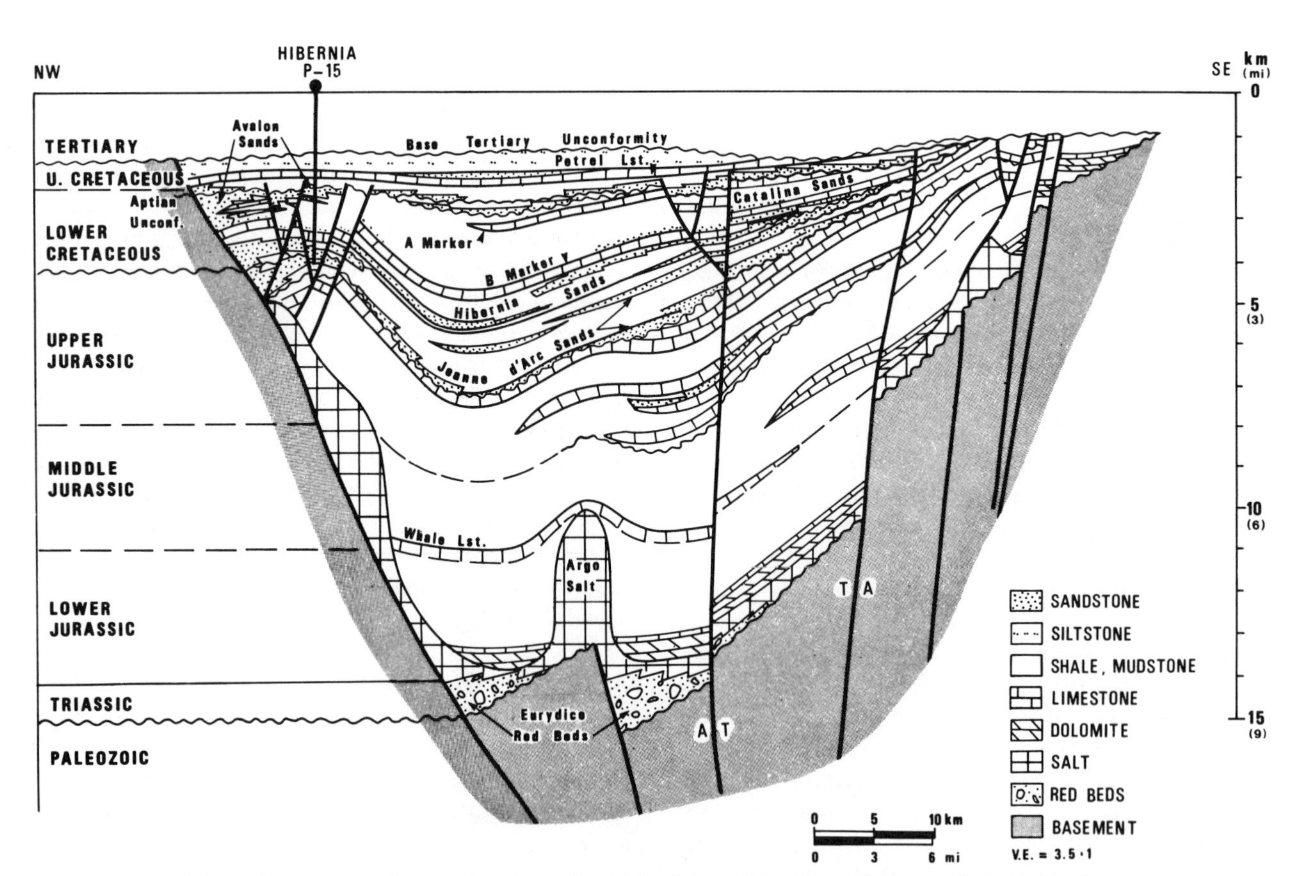

Figure 8. Diagrammatic geologic cross section of the Jeanne d'Arc Basin of the Grand Banks showing the recent Hibernia field discovery well (located on Fig. 2). Hydrocarbons occur in Upper Jurassic–Lower Cretaceous synrift sediments (from Tankard and Welsink, 1987).

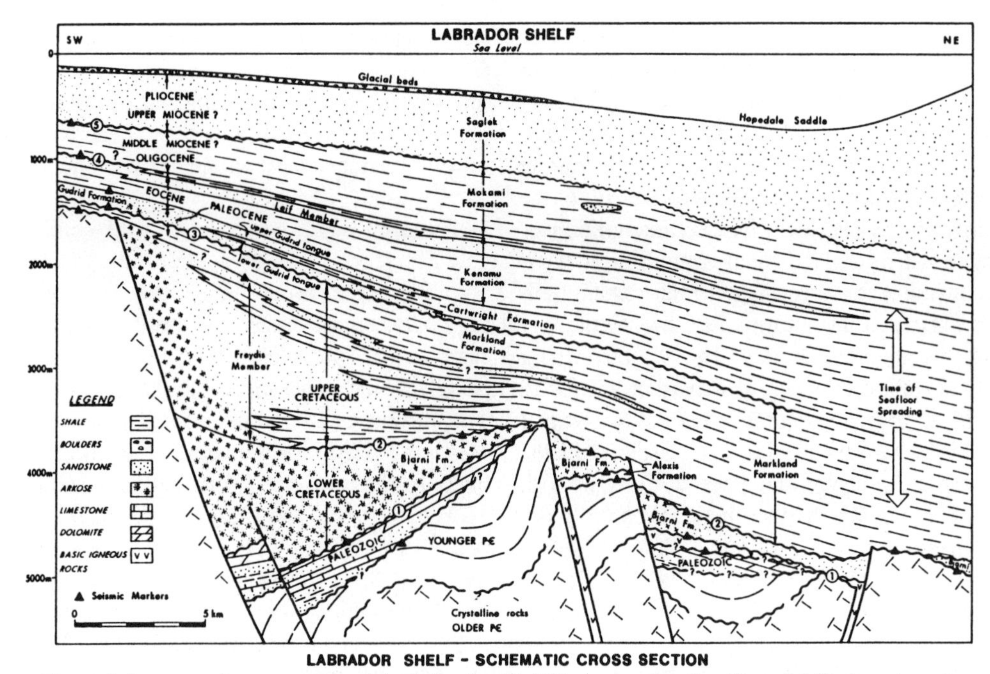

Figure 9. Interpreted cross section of the Labrador Shelf Basin showing the rift- and drift-stage deposits (from McWhae, 1981). 1 = regional Lower Cretaceous unconformity; 2 = regional Upper Cretaceous unconformity; 3 = regional Paleocene unconformity.

sequence has formed salt pillows and diapirs that have penetrated to within 5 km of the surface. Jurassic through lowermost Cretaceous carbonates cover the lower part of the basin and have prograded eastward to form a prominent carbonate platform edge. Erosion along the platform edge has created a steep escarpment, which is now buried by Upper Cretaceous marine sediments. Near the edge of the continental shelf there occur a number of deep-penetrating listric growth faults that probably do not involve the underlying basement. Motions along this fault have caused rotation of the older carbonate platform edge. This created a large structural closure in carbonate rocks, which was tested unsuccessfully in recent petroleum exploration wells by Shell (Fig. 5). In the Late Cretaceous and Early Tertiary, the siliciclastic deposits draped the carbonate platform edge. Through the Early Tertiary the continental shelf deepened as sediment influx slackened with continued subsidence; the starved-margin sedimentation was dominated by chemical deposition of glauconite and diatomite (Olsson, 1978). In the Late Tertiary, the deep shelf was filled in with prograding sequences of sands and gravels to build the shelf edge out to its present position. Meanwhile, canyon cutting and other deep-marine erosional processes sculptured the continental slope and upper continental rise.

Georges Bank Basin

This is the shallowest of the basins, and the entire drift-stage sequence has been penetrated by the Continental Offshore Stratigraphic Test (COST) G1 and G2 wells (Poag, 1982; Fig. 5). Drift-stage sediments reach 6 to 7 km, but there are well-defined synrift and prerift sedimentary basins below these depths. Jurassic or Triassic salt has been penetrated in a COST well and appears as a seismic layer across the base of the basin. Few piercing diapirs are found in the basin, but more diapirs form a ridge province under the continental slope. Jurassic through lowermost Cretaceous carbonates and evaporites cover most of the basin and pass seaward into a major carbonate platform edge under the continental slope. Smaller isolated carbonate banks are found in the interior of the basin as well (Poag, 1982). During the Late Cretaceous and Tertiary, siliclastic deposition dominated to build the shelf to its present form. Quaternary deposition of thick glacial sands, gravels, and tills topped the shelf in this area to form the Georges Bank, which was further defined by glacial erosion of the adjacent Gulf of Maine and Northeast Channel (Fig. 1).

Scotian Basin

Drift-stage sequences reach 10- to 12-km depths in this basin (Fig. 6). Triassic nonmarine red beds are overlain by Lower Jurassic salt that has formed into piercing diapirs under the continental shelf. The diapirs form a more continuous salt ridge or wall under the continental slope. Under the shelf the Middle Jurassic to Lower Cretaceous drift-stage sediments above the salt are dominated by carbonate platform deposits (Eliuk, 1978; Jansa, 1981). Erosional carbonate escarpments occur along the ancient Jurassic–Lower Cretaceous paleoshelf edge. Seaward of this escarpment under the present slope and rise are Jurassic–Lower Cretaceous off-bank shales (Fig. 6; McWhae, 1981). A major regional unconformity (1, Fig. 6) separates the Jurassic–

Lower Cretaceous carbonates from the middle and Upper Cretaceous sands and shales that overwhelm the Scotian Basin (McWhae, 1981). This unconformity may correspond to one of Vail and others (1977) and be related to a global sea-level fluctuation, or it may be related to uplift and thermal events during the recurring breakup of nearby Grand Banks. At the end of the Cretaceous and early Paleocene, a prominent limestone layer covered the Scotian Shelf region, indicating a return to a clear-water environment without the overwhelming siliciclastic sediment input. Another regional unconformity (3, Fig. 6) of early Paleocene age tops this limestone marker. This too could be a Vail and others (1977) sea-level event, or it may be related to recurring breakup in the region at a time when the Norwegian Sea was opening east of Greenland. Tertiary clastics built the Scotian Shelf to its present depth, and these are topped with Quaternary glacial deposits which contribute to minor topographic banks and channels.

Grand Banks basins

Several important subbasins controlled by bounding faults from the rifting of Grand Banks contain 5 to 8 km of Triassic–Lower Cretaceous rift-stage sediments (McWhae, 1981; Wade, 1981; Tankard and Welsink, 1987; Keen and deVoogd, 1988). These subbasins are named the Jeanne d'Arc, Horseshoe, Carson-Bonnition, and Orphan basins. These basins are reoccupations of even older, upper Paleozoic, fault-bounded troughs that contain Carboniferous red beds, limestones, and salt deposits (McWhae, 1981; Fig. 7). The Upper Triassic to Lower Jurassic salt under the Grand Banks basins has formed into pronounced diapiric structures. These structures have been drilled in petroleum exploration, and recently a major field has been discovered on the Grand Banks. The Hibernia well (Figs. 2 and 8) discovered a major field, which could yield several billion barrels of oil (McWhae, 1981; Tankard and Welsink, 1987). The salt diapirs penetrate the overlying Jurassic and Lower Cretaceous limestones and marine shales, and Lower Cretaceous marginal marine and nonmarine sandstones. The limestones and marine shales reflect the invasion of the newly formed central North Atlantic Ocean south of the Grand Banks across the Jurassic–Lower Cretaceous transform plate margin (Fig. 7). The marginal marine and nonmarine Lower Cretaceous sandstone (Fig. 8) reflects the influx of siliciclastics from the northeast onto the Grand Banks from the rifted and uplifted Irish Sea region (McWhae, 1981; Tankard and Welsink, 1987). A major regional unconformity (1, Fig. 7) truncates the rift basins and qualifies as the breakup unconformity (Falvey, 1974) caused by the onset of spreading east of Grand Banks. Above this unconformity are drift-stage marine sandstones and shales. In the Late Cretaceous, a second regional unconformity cut the Grand Banks (2, Fig. 7). This is related to the breakup and onset of spreading along the northeast margin of Grand Banks. Yet another unconformity exists across the Grand Banks above the Upper Cretaceous limestones, which also extend to the Scotian Shelf (Fig. 6). This could relate to the even younger breakup and onset of spreading along the Labrador margin or even eastern Greenland. So the Grand Banks sequences are bounded by major unconformities that might be thought of as "stacked" breakup unconformities related to the many recurrences of uplift and rifting and thermal events on the nearby continental margins.

Labrador Shelf Basin

This area of the Canadian passive margin has well-developed synrift basins overlain by a seaward-thickening drift-stage wedge (McWhae, 1981; Fig. 9). One of the sedimentary troughs of the Labrador Shelf is called the Saglek Basin (Fig. 2). The breakup unconformity truncates the synrift basins (2, Fig. 9), which are filled with Lower Cretaceous arkosic sediments. This unconformity correlates with that on the Grand Banks (2, Fig. 7; McWhae, 1981), and is about Santonian age, equivalent to just before magnetic anomaly 34. Siliclastic sediments drape the margin with the slow thermal subsidence of the drift stage. The drift-stage wedge is punctuated by regional unconformities (3, 4, 5, Fig. 9), which might be related to local breakup events such as that east of Greenland (early Paleocene, 3), or global sea-level events (Vail and others, 1977). Thick sandstone, deposited in the late Miocene and Pliocene across the Labrador Shelf, is topped by Quaternary glacial deposits. Longitudinal channels related to erosion and glacial deposition on the shelf form distinct topography on the Labrador Shelf (Fig. 9).

PASSIVE MARGIN SUBSIDENCE MODELING

The passive margin of North America has been an ideal place to practice basin modeling. Given the wealth of new seismic reflection data calibrated with COST (Continental Offshore Stratigraphic Test) and commercial wells, and the latest DSDP (Deep Sea Drilling Program) drilling dates for the East Coast and Blake Spur magnetic anomalies and the anomalies along the continent/ocean boundary off Canada, geohistory curves of subsidence can be established across many parts of the margin (Steckler and others, 1988; Keen and others, 1987).

The initial subsidence (S_i) during rifting, and subsequent thermal subsidence (S_t) during drifting, combine to give the total subsidence (S_{tot}) of the basement. Both these components of subsidence (S_i and S_t) are dependent on the amount of extension, and therefore, thinning that the crust and lithosphere have undergone during the rift stage. This extension is generally denoted by the stretching factor, $\beta = H_o/H$, where H_o is the initial crustal thickness and H is the stretched crustal thickness. Thinning of the crust and lithosphere causes heating, a thermal event, that must cool. Upon cooling, the crust and lithosphere thicken, become more dense, and therefore, sink.

The sediment load caused by the infill on the subsiding basement also contributes to the subsidence. Depending on the variable strength of the crust with time and depth, the sediment loading will be distributed laterally to cause flexural subsidence. This is what causes the crustal subsidence landward of the hinge line even where the crust has not been thinned (Steckler and others, 1988; Fig. 10). Flexural subsidence is largely responsible for the deposition of a coastal-plain wedge on passive margins.

From the observational data of the stratigraphy and basement faullt structures on the North American passive margin the conclusion has been made that simple "uniform" stretching does not apply (Steckler and others, 1988; Keen and others, 1987). In uniform stretching, both the crust and lithosphere (upper mantle) are taken to stretch an equal amount and to be described by a single β factor. Crustal stretching can be estimated by the fault

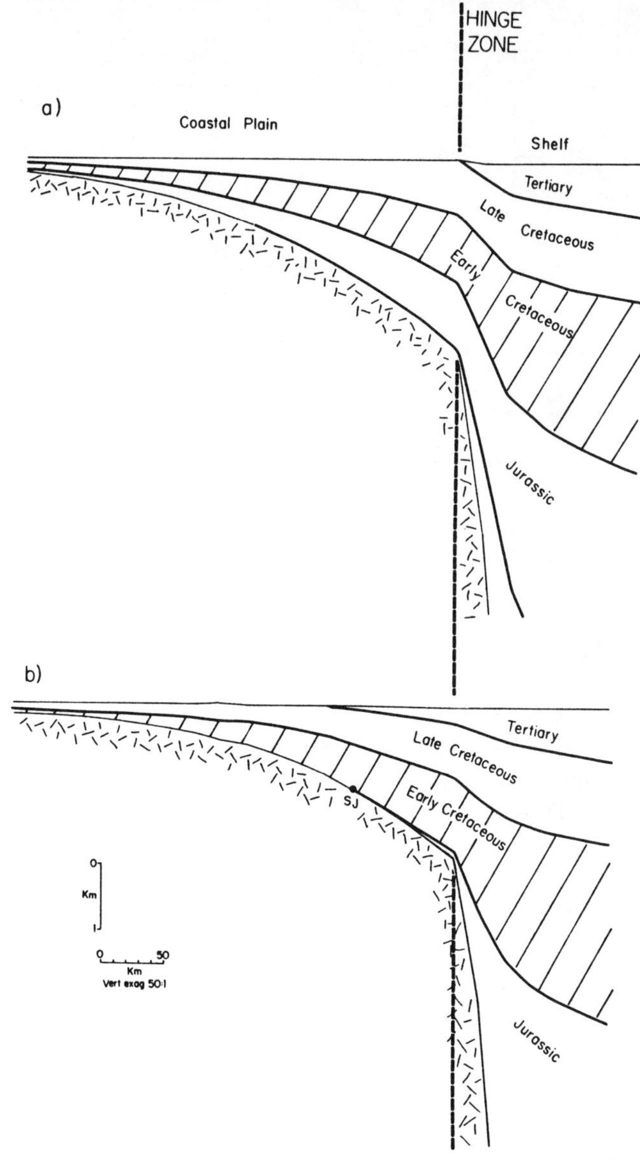

Figure 10. Synthetic stratigraphic cross section of coastal plain and continental shelf of central portion of Baltimore Canyon Trough using flexural loading model. a). "One Layer" model in which the crust and lithosphere are extended by equal amounts. b). "Two layer" model in which the crust and lithosphere are extended equal amounts seaward to the hinge zone, and only the lithosphere is extended landward of the hinge. Note differences in onlap of Tertiary and Jurassic in the two models. "Two layer" model gives better "stratigraphy" (from Steckler and others, 1988).

rotations of the rifted basement (Keen and others, 1987), and on the North American passive margin these estimates have generally been too low to explain the total subsidence (S_{tot}) when corrected for sediment loading. Consequently, satisfactory models of the subsidence had to invoke a "two layer" or "nonuniform" stretching in which the upper layer crust had a different stretching factor, β, from the lower-layer lithosphere with its own stretching factor, δ.

These nonuniform stretching models have been successful. For example, Steckler and others (1988) have shown two models (Fig. 10), one for a uniform single-layer case and one for a nonuniform two-layer case, that were applied to create the synthetic stratigraphy of Baltimore Canyon Trough. They concluded that the two-layer model better predicts the onlap of the Tertiary and Upper Jurassic sediments in the Coastal Plain (Fig. 10). The single-layer model gives a totally incorrect result for these two ages of sediments.

Similarly, Keen and others (1987) modeled three separate regions of the Orphan Basin where the total subsidence was significantly different. Deep seismic-reflection data revealed rift-related faults, so that the crustal thinning β factor could be estimated in the three regions. It was required to invoke thinning of a deep layer with a stretching factor of δ to explain the total observed subsidence (Fig. 11).

Another complication in the Orphan Basin, and the Grand Banks in general, is that there has been a more complex rifting and stretching history than on the margin off the central North Atlantic. Given the stratigraphic data and crustal data, Keen and others (1987) have produced subsidence models for Orphan

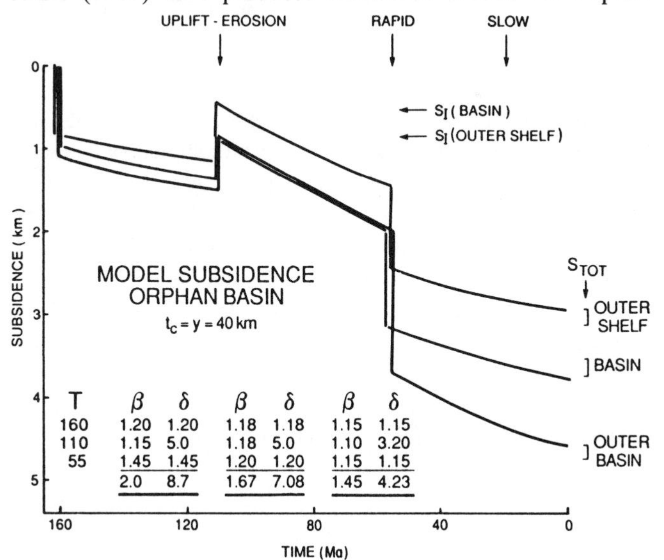

Figure 11. Predicted subsidence based on two layer (β, δ) stretching for Orphan Basin on Grand Banks. Three different regions (located on Fig. 13), outer shelf, basin, and outer basin, are modeled, with three different stretching events, at 160, 110, and 55 m.y. The observed initial subsidence (S_i) and total subsidence (S_{tot}) are shown (from Keen and others, 1987).

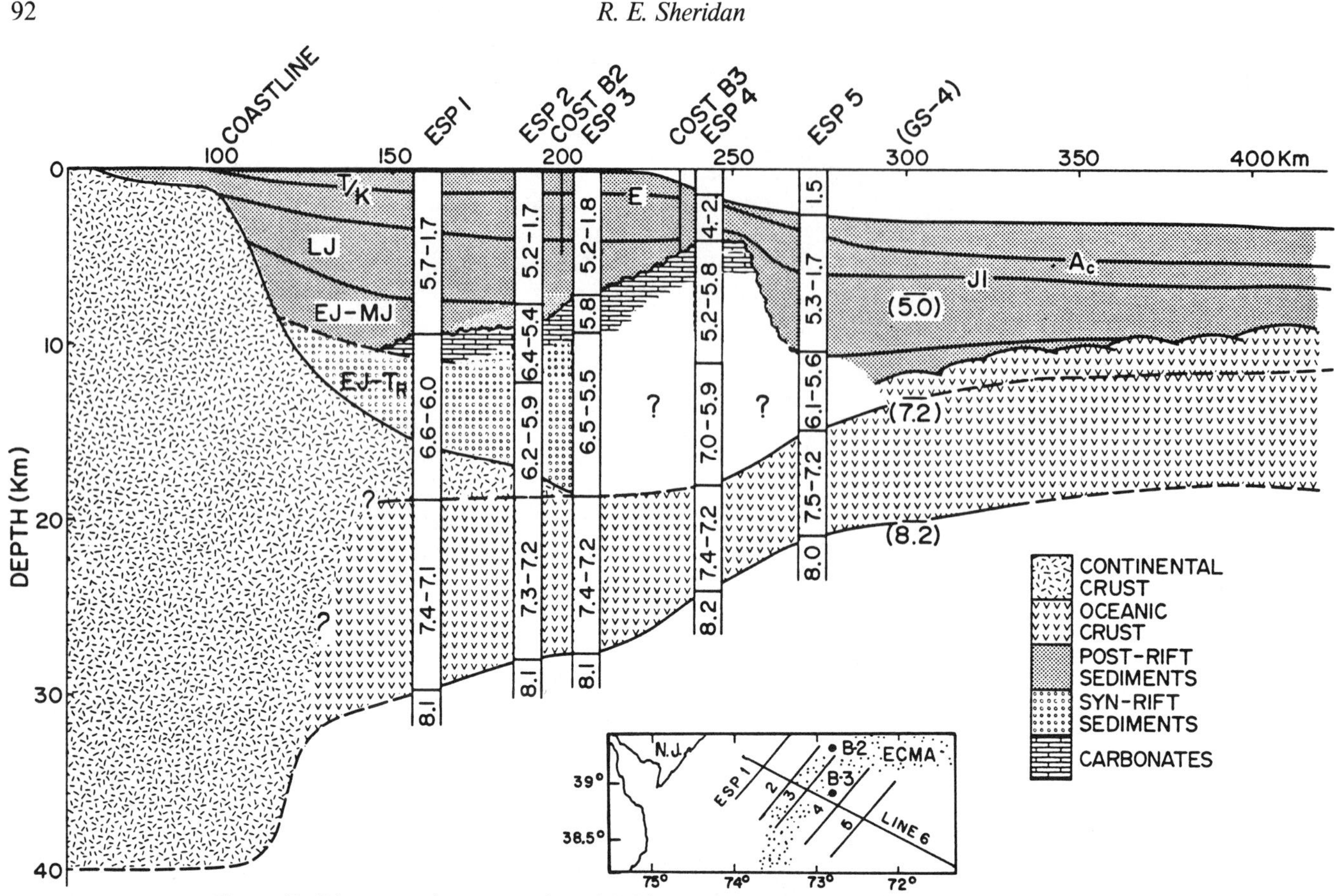

Figure 12. Diagrammatic cross section of Baltimore Canyon Trough of the United States passive continental margin showing deep crustal seismic velocity structure (from Diebold and others, 1988). Note the 7.1 to 7.5 km/sec crustal layer under the trough proper landward of the East Coast Magnetic Anomaly (ECMA, insert). Here, this layer is indicated as an extension of the oceanic crust, but its origin is problematic.

Basin that generally reproduce the geohistory curves of wells, and the total basement subsidence, by varying the stretching factors β and δ through time (Fig. 11). The major breakup events at 160, 110, and 55 Ma were taken to have different β and δ factors for the Orphan Basin. In so doing, Keen and others (1987) were able to explain the subsidence, followed by uplift and erosion, followed by subsidence, that resulted in Orphan Basin, and on Grand Banks in general, where there are "stacked" breakup unconformities from several distinct events (Fig. 11).

DEEP CRUSTAL STRUCTURE AND MOHO

One of the most important new discoveries on the North American passive margin was due to the Large Aperture Seismic Experiment (LASE) (LASE Study Group, 1986; Diebold and others, 1988; Fig. 12). Several expanded-spread profiles were run in a strike-parallel pattern across the Baltimore Canyon Trough, and a long-aperture vertical profile was run as a dip section.

The expanded-spread profile results showed the Moho at around 30-km depths under the Baltimore Canyon Trough landward of the East Coast magnetic anomaly, and then the Moho gradually shallowing from 30 to 20 km under the general region of the East Coast magnetic anomaly (Fig. 12). Another remarkable discovery was the measurement of a lower crustal layer 5 to 10 km thick with a relatively high seismic velocity of 7.1 to 7.5 km/sec (Diebold and others, 1988).

The origin of the 7.1 to 7.5 km/sec layer is problematic because this layer is found under the Baltimore Canyon Trough itself and landward of the East Coast magnetic anomaly (Fig. 12). A similar velocity layer at nearly similar depths was measured just seaward of the East Coast magnetic anomaly by seismic refraction techniques (Sheridan and others, 1979). Seaward of the East Coast magnetic anomaly these kinds of velocities, 7.1 to 7.5 km/sec, are generally interpreted as the lower oceanic crustal layer, 3b (Sheridan and others, 1979).

Now, however, with the presence of the 7.1 to 7.5 km/sec layer landward of the East Coast magnetic anomaly, several interpretations are possible:

1. Oceanic crustal layer 3b continues landward under the Baltimore Canyon Trough, and the East Coast magnetic anomaly is related to shallower magnetic contrasts and fault structures in the crust (Alsop and Talwani, 1984; LASE Study Group, 1986).

2. Magmatic underplating during the rift stage created a new lower crust under the stretched and faulted continental

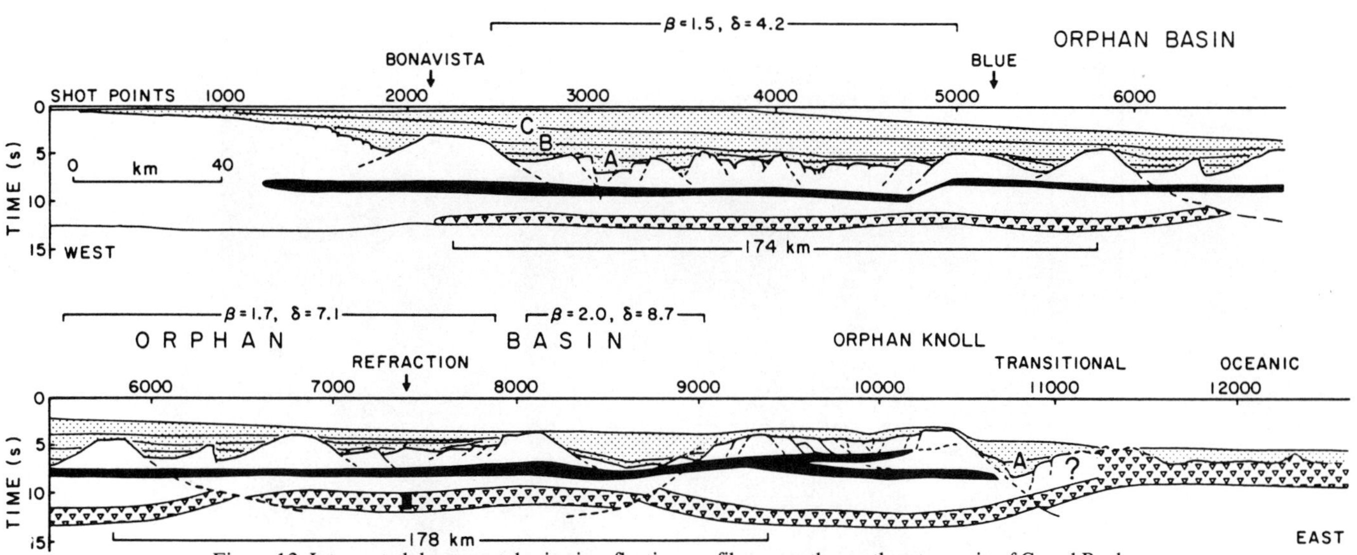

Figure 13. Interpreted deep crustal seismic reflection profile across the northeast margin of Grand Banks through Orphan subbasin and Orphan Knoll. Note the deep crustal layer depicted as equivalent to oceanic crust is a layer with the high velocity of 7.1 to 7.5 km/sec as measured with refraction profiles. Its origin is problematic. Note the β and δ cumulative stretching values based on models of Figure 11 are indicated in the three regions of this profile (from Keen and others, 1987).

basement under the Baltimore Canyon Trough (LASE Study Group, 1986; White and others, 1987; Diebold and others, 1988).

3. Obducted Paleozoic ophiolitic crust related to the Alleghanian suture is preserved under the Atlantic margin basins, such as Baltimore Canyon Trough (McBride and Nelson, 1988).

The Canadian passive margin is one of the best-studied passive margins for deep crustal structure. Four long dip-section seismic lines were run using large air gun capacity and long offset seismic streamers. This was called the LITHOPROBE project (Keen and others, 1987; Keen and deVoogd, 1988). Reflections were recorded for up to 20 sec of two-way travel time, and the Moho reflection was observed.

One of these deep-penetration seismic lines, across the Grand Banks' northeast margin through Orphan Knoll (located on Fig. 2), shows the detailed crustal structure across the passive margin (Fig. 13; Keen and others, 1987). The rifted and stretched, thinned and subsided crust of the Orphan subbasin is seen well on the profile, underlying a thick drift-stage cover. The listric border faults of the rifted basement, in most cases, seem to sole out in a basal detachment zone at 7 to 8 sec of reflection time

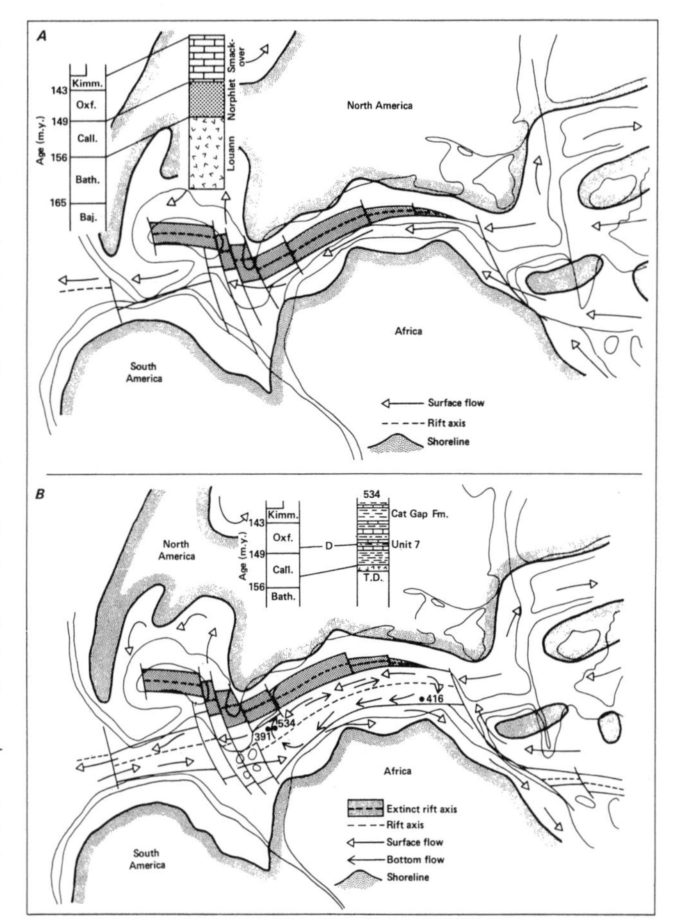

Figure 14. Continental reconstructions and paleogeography during the earliest Callovian (middle Jurassic) at the time of formation of the Blake Spur magnetic anomaly (upper) and during mid-Oxfordian (Late Jurassic), the age of magnetic anomaly M 26 (lower). Note that the proto-Atlantic/Gulf of Mexico spreading centers are extinct and isolated on North America in the lower figure (from Sheridan, 1983).

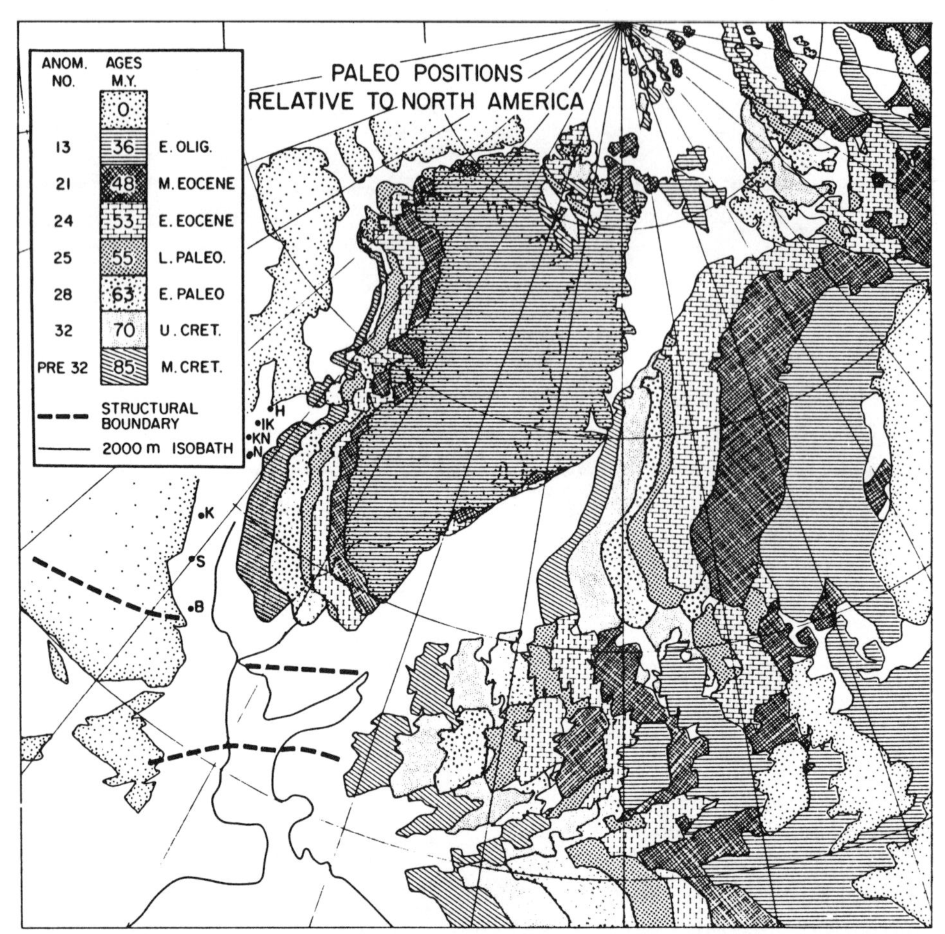

Figure 15. Plate reconstructions for key geologic times (magnetic anomaly numbers) relevant to the complex breakup and spreading of the Canadian Atlantic passive margin and Labrador Sea (from Srivastava and others, 1981). The lettered dots refer to wells on the Labrador and western Greenland Shelves restored to the predrift location.

across the profile. In three places the listric border faults of the rifted crust appear to extend to the lower crust and may offset the Moho reflection (Fig. 13).

Strike-parallel refraction profiles (Fig. 13) reveal that the lower crust has a relatively high-velocity seismic layer (7.1 to 7.5 km/sec) beneath the thinned, rifted transitional crust. This is similar to the 7.1 to 7.5 km/sec velocity layer found under the Baltimore Canyon Trough (LASE Study Group, 1986; Fig. 12). Again, the origin of this layer is problematic and might be one of several suggestions:

1. Magmatic underplating created during rift and breakup of the passive margin (Keen and others, 1987).

2. Remnants of an original Paleozoic ophiolitic oceanic crust that has been preserved beneath overthrusted continental crust (Sheridan and Drake, 1968; Sheridan, 1974).

Resolving the origin of the 7.1 to 7.5 km/sec layer is most critical for the understanding of the origin of the North American passive margin, and indeed for the origin of passive margins in general.

PLATE RECONSTRUCTIONS AND PALEOGEOGRAPHY

DSDP results at Site 534 east of Florida (Fig. 14) yield a more precise age for the breakup of North America and Africa, and evidence on the paleogeography of the earliest central North Atlantic Ocean (Sheridan, 1983). The age of the basement at Site 534 and projections of constant spreading rates to the Blake Spur magnetic anomaly and the East Coast magnetic anomaly date these anomalies as earliest Callovian and Bathonian (Middle Jurassic), respectively. These ages are younger than previously thought, and similar to the ages interpreted for the breakup of the Gulf of Mexico and Yucatán Caribbean margin. This simplifies the breakup history of these three ocean margins. Both the U.S. Atlantic margin and the Gulf of Mexico had initial breakup in the Bathonian (Fig. 14) with the creation of a small strip of oceanic crust. This formed the East Coast magnetic anomaly on the Atlantic margin. A few million years later in earliest Callovian, a spreading-center shift occurred to create the Blake Spur magnetic anomaly on the Atlantic margin and to begin the breakup of the Yucatán Caribbean margin (Fig. 14). With the spreading-center jump to the Blake Spur magnetic anomaly, the extinct spreading center and older oceanic crusts in the Blake Spur–East Coast magnetic anomaly corridor off the U.S. passive margin and under the Gulf of Mexico were left isolated on the North American plate. This contributed to the asymmetry in width of the Jurassic magnetic quiet zone crusts in the North Atlantic, being wider off the U.S. margin and narrower off Africa. Thus, this extinct oceanic-crust spreading center was attached to the North American plate and drifted away from Africa.

The paleoenvironmental data from Site 534 (Sheridan, 1983) and other data in the circum-Atlantic region for the Jurassic (Manspeizer, 1985) indicate that the early Atlantic Ocean was more latitudinal and equatorial in nature. Consequently, easterly trade winds and currents dominated at the surface. With the breakup and initiation of the Jurassic Caribbean, complicated Tethyan circulation to the Pacific occurred, and bottom currents began to flow, perhaps salinity driven (Sheridan, 1983). Several lines of evidence suggest bottom-current flow from the African margin at Site 534 during the Jurassic (Fig. 14). As North America drifted, the United States passive margin moved north of 30°N latitude, and then westerly currents dominated with evolution of the Gulf Stream circulation. This fundamental change in paleoenvironment occurred around middle Cretaceous time.

The pre–magnetic anomaly 32 reconstruction of the Labrador Sea brings about the elimination of oceanic crust and the juxtaposition of the Irish Sea and Orphan Knoll continental crusts (Fig. 15; Srivastava and others, 1981). The orientation of the northeast-southwest–striking Paleozoic Gander/Avalon terrane boundary and the Precambrian Grenville front (Figs. 15 and 2) controlled the direction of spreading of the Labrador Sea (Srivastava and others, 1981). These predrift structures were inherited as major offset oceanic fracture zones (Fig. 2).

Opening of the Labrador Sea in Late Cretaceous–early Paleocene (anomalies 32 to 28) follows these old Paleozoic orientations. Then in Paleocene-Eocene time (anomalies 28 to 24), the Norwegian Sea began to open east of Greenland. Finally, the Labrador Sea ceased spreading in the Eocene (anomaly 21), and all the plate motion was shifted to the opening of the Norwegian Sea. These motions seem to require several hundred kilometers of left-lateral shear in Nares Strait (Fig. 2) between Greenland and North America. However, this is much in debate; some geologists disagree with this offset (Kerr, 1981), and others accept this shearing (McWhae, 1981).

OVERVIEW

The North American Atlantic continental margin is the archetype passive margin formed by the rifting, breakup, and spreading apart of three continents. Rifting has resulted in exemplary rift half-graben basins and crustal stretching that controlled drift-stage subsidence. Stretching, thinning, and igneous intrusions formed the transitional crust under the thick sediments of the continental margin basins. As much as 10 to 14 km of sediments are found in individualized basins along the margin. The central North Atlantic opened first, separating Africa and North America in Middle Jurassic. Later separation of Iberia in middle Cretaceous, and Europe and Greenland in Late Cretaceous, formed the Grand Banks and Labrador margin of the North Atlantic.

The wealth of data on the North American passive margin has led to a better understanding of passive margin processes in general. Yet questions still remain about those processes. Deeper seismic data and deeper drilling in the future might answer these questions.

REFERENCES

Austin, J. A., Jr., Schlager, W., Palmer, A. A., and others, 1986, Part A, Initial reports of the Ocean Drilling Program: Washington, D.C., U.S. Government Printing Office, v. 101, 569 p.

Alsop, L. E., and Talwani, M., 1984, The East Coast magnetic anomaly: Science, v. 226, p. 1189–1191.

Diebold, J. B., Stoffa, P. L., and others, 1988, A large aperture seismic experiment in the Baltimore Canyon Trough, *in* Sheridan, R. E., and Grow, J. A., eds., The Atlantic Continental Margin: Boulder, Colorado, Geological Society of America, The Geology of North America, v. I-2, p. 387–398.

Dillon, W. P., Paull, C. K., Dahl, A. G., and Patterson, W. C., 1979, Structure of the continental margin near the COST GE-1 well site from a common depth point seismic reflection profile, *in* Scholle, P. A., ed., Geological studies of the COST GE-1 well, U.S. South-Atlantic Outer Continental Shelf area: U.S. Geological Survey Circular 800, p. 97–107.

Dillon, W. P., Paull, C. K., and Gilbert, L. E., 1985, History of the Atlantic continental margin off Florida; The Blake Plateau basin, *in* Poag, C. W., ed., Geologic evolution of the United States Atlantic margin: New York, Van Nostrand Reinhold, p. 189–215.

Eliuk, L. S., 1978, The Abenaki Formation, Nova Scotia shelf, Canada: A depositional and diagenetic model for a Mesozoic carbonate platform: Bulletin of Canadian Petroleum Geology, v. 26, p. 425–514.

Falvey, D. A., 1974, The development of continental margins in plate tectonic theory: Australian Petroleum Exploration Journal, v. 14, p. 95–106.

Grow, J. A., and Sheridan, R. E., 1988, U.S. Atlantic continental margin; A typical Atlantic-type or passive continental margin, *in* Sheridan, R. E., and Grow, J. A., eds., The Atlantic Continental Margin; U.S.: Boulder, Colorado, Geological Society of America, The Geology of North America, v. I-2, p. 1–7.

Grow, J. A., Hutchinson, D. R., Klitgord, K. D., Dillon, W. P., and Schlee, J. S., 1983, Representative multichannel seismic profiles over the U.S. Atlantic margin, *in* Bally, A. W., ed., Seismic expression structural styles: American Association of Petroleum Geologists Studies in Geology Series, no. 15, v. 2, p. 2.2.3-1–2.2.3-19.

Hutchinson, D. R., and Klitgord, K. D., 1988, Deep structure of the rift basins from the continental margin around New England: U.S. Geological Survey Bulletin 776, p. 211–219.

Hutchinson, D. R., Klitgord, K. D., and Detrick, R. S., Jr., 1986, Rift basins of the Long Island Platform: Geological Society of America Bulletin, v. 97, p. 688–702.

Jansa, L., 1981, Mesozoic carbonate platforms and banks of the eastern North American margin: Marine Geology, v. 44, p. 97–117.

Keen, C. E., and deVoogd, B., 1988, The continent-ocean boundary at the rifted margin off eastern Canada; New results from deep seismic reflection studies: Tectonics, v. 7, p. 107–124.

Keen, C. E., Stockmal, G. S., Welsink, H., Quinlan, G., and Mudford, B., 1987, Deep crustal structure and evolution of the rifted margin northeast of Newfoundland; Results from LITHOPROBE East: Canadian Journal of Earth Sciences, v. 24, p. 1537–1549.

Kerr, J. W., 1981, Stretching of the North American plate by a now-dormant Atlantic spreading center: Canadian Society of Petroleum Geologists Memoir 7, p. 245–278.

Klitgord, K. D., and Hutchinson, D. R., 1985, Distribution and geophysical signatures of early Mesozoic rift basins beneath the U.S. Atlantic continental margin, *in* Robinson, G. R., Jr., and Froelich, A. J., eds., The early Mesozoic basins of the eastern United States: U.S. Geological Survey Circular 946, p. 45–53.

Klitgord, K. D., Hutchinson, D. R., and Schouten, H., 1988, U.S. Atlantic continental margin; Structural and tectonic framework, *in* Sheridan, R. E., and Grow, J. A., eds., The Atlantic Continental Margin; U.S.: Boulder, Colorado, Geological Society of America, The Geology of North America, v. I-2, p. 19–55.

Ladd, J. W., and Sheridan, R. E., 1987, Seismic stratigraphy of the Bahamas: American Association of Petroleum Geologists Bulletin, v. 71, p. 719–736.

LASE Study Group, 1986, Deep structure of the U.S. east coast passive margin from large aperture seismic experiments (LASE): Marine Petroleum Geology, v. 3, p. 234–242.

Manspeizer, W., 1985, Early Mesozoic history of the Atlantic passive margin, *in* Poag, C. W., ed., Geologic evolution of the United States Atlantic Margin: New York, Van Nostrand Reinhold, p. 1–23.

Mattick, R. E., Girard, O. W., Jr., Scholle, P. A., and Grow, J. A., 1978, Petroleum potential of the U.S. Atlantic slope, rise, and abyssal plain: American Association of Petroleum Geologists Bulletin, v. 62, p. 592–608.

McBride, J. H., and Nelson, K. D., 1988, Integration of COCORP deep reflection and magnetic anomaly analysis in the southeastern United States; Implications for origin of the Brunswick and East Coast magnetic anomalies: Geological Society of America Bulletin, v. 100, p. 436–445.

McWhae, J.R.H., 1981, Structure and spreading history of the northwestern Atlantic region from the Scotian shelf to Baffin Bay: Canadian Society of Petroleum Geologists Memoir 7, p. 299–332.

Mutter, J. C., 1985, Seward dipping reflectors and the continent-ocean boundary at passive continental margins: Tectonophysics, v. 114, p. 117–131.

Olsson, R. K., 1978, Summary of lithostratigraphy and biostratigraphy of Atlantic coastal plain (northern part), *in* Initial reports of the Deep Sea Drilling Project: Washington, D.C., U.S. Government Printing Office, v. 44, p. 941–947.

Paull, C. K., and Dillon, W. P., 1980, Erosional origin of the Blake Escarpment; An alternative hypothesis: Geology, v. 8, p. 538–542.

Poag, C. W., 1982, Stratigraphic reference section for Georges Bank Basin; Depositional model for New England passive margin: American Association of Petroleum Geologists Bulletin, v. 66, p. 1021–1041.

Ratcliffe, N. M., Burton, W. C., D'Angelo, R. M., and Costain, J. K., 1986, Low-angle extensional faulting, reactivated mylonites, and seismic reflection geometry of the Newark Basin margin in eastern Pennsylvania: Geology, v. 14, p. 766–770.

Roberts, D. G., Morton, A. C., and Backman, J., 1984, Late Paleocene–Early Eocene volcanic events in the northern North Atlantic Ocean, *in* Initial reports of the Deep Sea Drilling Project: Washington, D.C., U.S. Government Printing Office, v. 81, p. 913–923.

Sawyer, D. S., 1985, Total tectonic subsidence; A parameter for distinguishing crustal type at the U.S. Atlantic continental margin: Journal of Geophysical Research, v. 90, p. 7751–7769.

Sheridan, R. E., 1974, Atlantic continental margin of North America, *in* Burke, D. C., and Drake, C. D., eds., The geology of continental margins: New York, Springer-Verlag, p. 391–407.

——, 1983, Phenomenon of pulsation tectonics related to the breakup of the eastern North American continental margin, *in* Initial reports of the Deep Sea Drilling Project: Washington, D.C., U.S. Government Printing Office, v. 76, p. 897–909.

Sheridan, R. E., and Drake, C. L, 1968, Seaward extension of the Canadian Appalachians: Canadian Journal of Earth Sciences, v. 5, p. 337–373.

Sheridan, R. E., Drake, C. L., Nafe, J. E., and Hennion, J., 1966, Seismic refraction study of the continental margin east of Florida: American Association of Petroleum Geologists Bulletin, v. 60, p. 1972–1991.

Sheridan, R. E., Grow, J. A., and Bayer, K. C., 1979, Seismic refraction study of the continental edge off the eastern United States: Tectonophysics, v. 59, p. 1–26.

Sheridan, R. E., Crosby, J. T., Bryan, G. M., and Stoffa, P. L., 1981, Stratigraphy and structure of southern Blake Plateau, northern Florida Straits, and northern Bahama Platform from multichannel seismic reflection data: American Association of Petroleum Geologists Bulletin, v. 65, p. 2571–2593.

Srivastava, S. P., Falconer, R.K.H., and MacLean, B., 1981, Labrador Sea, Davis Strait, Baffin Bay; Geology and geophysics, a review: Canadian Society of Petroleum Geologists Memoir 7, p. 333–398.

Steckler, M., Watts, A. B., and Thorne, J. A., 1988, Subsidence and basin modeling at the U.S. Atlantic passive margin, *in* Sheridan, R. E., and Grow, J. A., eds., The Atlantic Continental Margin: Boulder, Colorado, Geological Society of America, The Geology of North America, v. I-2, p. 399–416.

Tankard, A. J., and Welsink, H. J., 1987, Extensional tectonics and stratigraphy of Hibernia oil field, Grand Banks, Newfoundland: American Association of Petroleum Geologists Bulletin, v. 71, p. 1210–1232.

Vail, P. R., Mitchum, R. M., Todd, R. G., Widmier, J. M., Thompson, S., Sangree, J. B., Bubb, J. N., and Hatfield, W. F., 1977, Seismic stratigraphy and global changes in sea-level: American Association of Petroleum Geologists Memoir 26, p. 49–212.

Wade, J. A., 1981, Geology of the Canadian Atlantic margin from Georges Bank to The Grand Banks: Canadian Society of Petroleum Geologists Memoir 7, p. 447–460.

Watts, A. B., 1981, The U.S. Atlantic continental margin; Subsidence history, crustal structure, and thermal evolution, *in* Bally, A. W., ed., Geology of passive continental margins (with special emphasis on the Atlantic Margin): American Association of Petroleum Geologists Educational Course Notes Series 19, p. 2-1–2.75.

White, R. S., Westbrook, G. K., Fowler, S. R., and others, 1987, Hatton Bank (Northwest U.K.) continental margin structure: Geophysical Journal of the Royal Astronomical Society, v. 89, p. 265–272.

Williams, H., 1979, Appalachian orogen in Canada: Canadian Journal of Earth Sciences, v. 16, p. 792–807.

Wilson, L. M., 1981, Circum-North Atlantic tectono-stratigraphic reconstruction: Canadian Society of Petroleum Geologists Memoir 7, p. 167–184.

Manuscript Accepted by the Society October 18, 1988

Printed in U.S.A.

The Geology of North America
Vol. A, The Geology of North America—An overview
The Geological Society of America, 1989

Chapter 7

Evolution of the northern Gulf of Mexico, with emphasis on Cenozoic growth faulting and the role of salt

D. M. Worrall
Shell Offshore Incorporated, P.O. Box 60193, New Orleans, Louisiana 70160
S. Snelson
Shell Oil Company, P.O. Box 2463, Houston, Texas 77001

INTRODUCTION

The northern Gulf of Mexico Basin, although one of the most intensely studied and explored regions in North America, is also one of the most structurally complex (Figs. 1 and 2). Cenozoic depocenters contain abundant growth faults of a variety of shapes, orientations, sizes, and complexities. In addition, salt domes, flows, and massifs combine to form a complex near-surface pattern that tends to mask the origins of many structures. Not surprisingly, a number of contrasting hypotheses have been proposed to explain the growth faults of this region, among them theories invoking shale diapirism, shale compaction, gravity gliding, salt diapirism, and salt flow. Clearly, the best way to understand the various origins of these features is to observe their structural underpinnings at depth; unfortunately, most of the large growth fault systems of the Texas and Louisiana shelf project below the bottoms of seismic lines of 6- or 7-sec record length. However, as will be discussed in this chapter, deep seismic data now available from the Louisiana slope greatly illuminate the spectacular structural development of this province. In addition, palinspastic reconstructions are useful for analyzing the structural development of these features, and for constraining hypotheses on their origins.

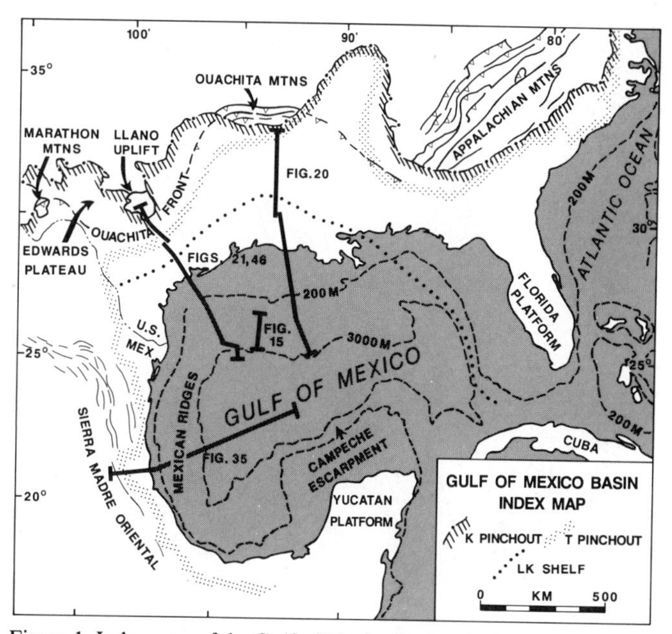

Figure 1. Index map of the Gulf of Mexico Basin with locations of cross sections discussed in text.

Prior to discussing the Cenozoic tectonic development of the northern Gulf of Mexico—the main focus of this chapter—we will briefly review the pre-Cenozoic framework and basic Cenozoic depositional patterns of the Gulf of Mexico Basin, both of which influenced Cenozoic structural styles.

PRE-CENOZOIC FRAMEWORK

The Gulf of Mexico Basin (Fig. 1) was initiated in the late Middle to early Late Jurassic as a result of crustal attenuation and sea-floor spreading associated with the breakup of the supercontinent Pangea. Although authors differ on the original position and translation paths of South America, Yucatan, and other crustal elements, there is general agreement that the Gulf of Mexico and the central Atlantic developed at the time North America separated from South America and Africa (Pindell, 1985, and many others).

The basement terrain affected by this rifting event was the late Paleozoic Appalachian-Mauritanide megasuture, an orogenic belt generally believed to have resulted from the closing of a proto–Atlantic Ocean (Wilson, 1966).

Following the suturing of this basement terrain and prior

Worrall, D. M., and Snelson, S., 1989, Evolution of the northern Gulf of Mexico, with emphasis on Cenozoic growth faulting and the role of salt, *in* Bally, A. W., and Palmer, A. R., eds., The Geology of North America—An overview: Boulder, Colorado, Geological Society of America, The Geology of North America, v. A.

to the development of the Cenozoic Gulf of Mexico Basin, five main episodes are recorded in the northern Gulf of Mexico Basin (Fig. 3): (1) Late Triassic–Early Jurassic terrestrial synrift deposition (Eagle Mills Formation) during crustal attenuation; (2) late Middle Jurassic evaporite (Louann) and aeolian sand deposition (Norphlet) over a major regional unconformity; (3) Late Jurassic–earliest Cretaceous carbonates (e.g., Smackover) and updip evaporite deposition (Buckner) followed by progradation of terrigenous clastics (Cotton Valley and Hosston); (4) two major shelf-margin reef cycles during the Early (e.g., Sligo) and Middle Cretaceous (e.g., Stuart City); and lastly; (5) widespread Late Cretaceous drowning of reefs and associated extensive sedimentation of chalks, marls, and shales, following some broad upwarping of the shelf region, local intrusives (e.g., Monroe Uplift and Jackson Dome), and the development of a post–"mid-Cretaceous" unconformity. In the western Gulf region of northeastern Mexico, the early Tertiary was a time of compressional folding and local volcanism associated with the Laramide orogeny.

Paleozoic orogenic framework

The southern Appalachians, the Ouachitas, and the Marathon uplift are outcropping remnants of an extensive, now largely concealed, late Paleozoic thrust belt which rims, and forms the basement to, the northern flank of the Gulf of Mexico Basin (Fig. 2). On a gross scale, the fold belt is the northwestern flank of the Appalachian-Mauritanide megasuture. Evidence as to the location of the axis of this megasuture is obscured by younger deposits of the Gulf and Atlantic Coastal Plains; however, some Ordovician to Devonian deposits in the subcrop of northern Florida possess fauna of African and Eu-

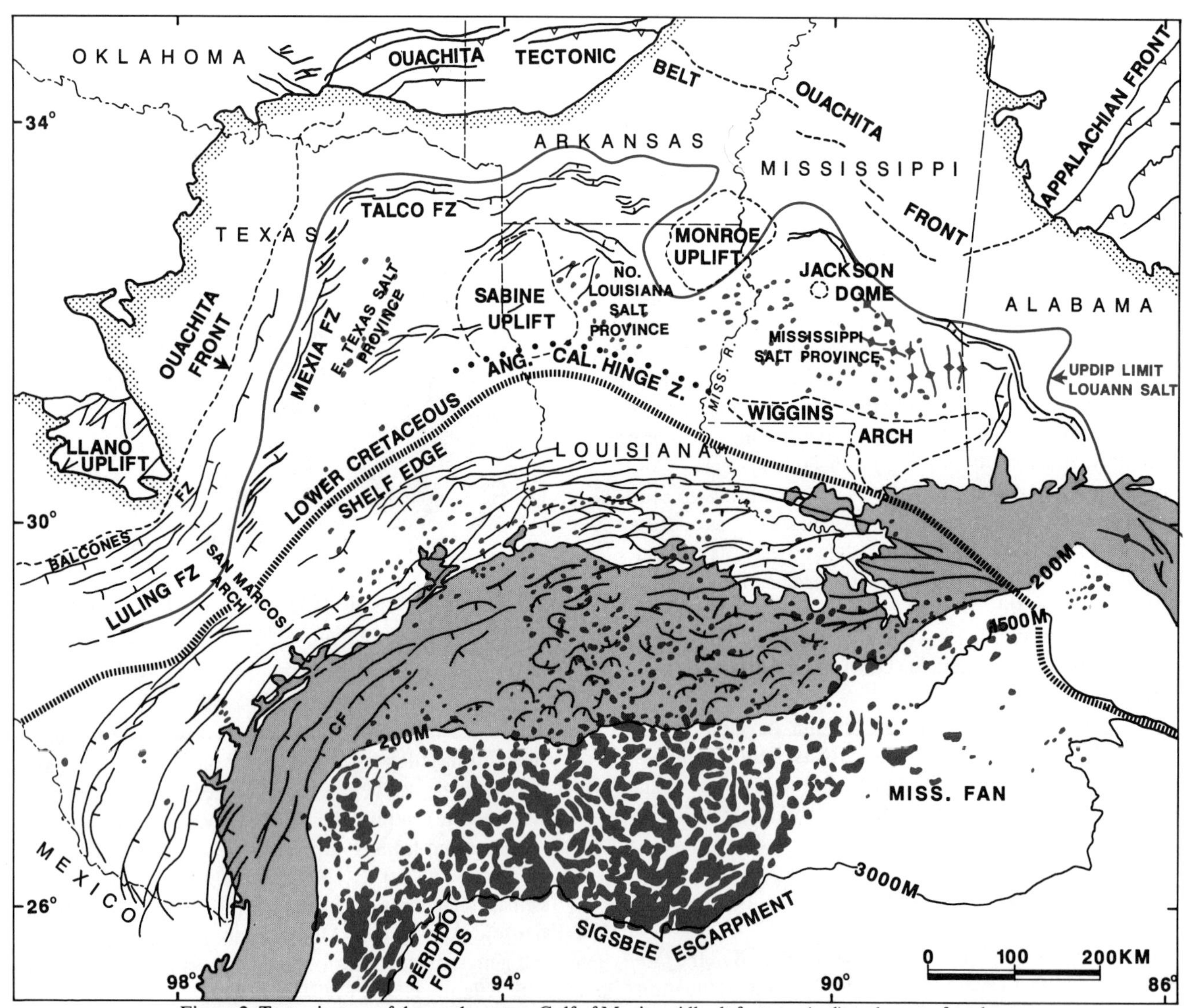

Figure 2. Tectonic map of the northwestern Gulf of Mexico. All salt features (red) and most of onshore structural trends based on compilation by R. G. Martin (1978). Generalized offshore structures supplemented with other published and unpublished sources. Shelf area (0 to 200 m water depths) is gray. CF = Corsair fault system discussed later in text.

ropean affinities (Flawn and others, 1961), and it is clear that at least a portion of the megasuture axis passes through the southeastern United States. It has been postulated by McBride and Nelson (1988) that the axis of the megasuture is represented by the very prominent Brunswick magnetic anomaly (Zietz, 1982), which passes east-westerly across central Georgia and Alabama from its Atlantic offshore continuation, the East Coast magnetic anomaly, and is overprinted by the South Georgia rift basin. These and other authors (e.g., Swanson, 1986) have postulated that the suture zone acted as a zone of crustal weakness in the early Mesozoic, a period of widespread crustal attenuation and ensuing sea-floor spreading, leading to the breakup of the Pangean supercontinent and the opening of the Gulf of Mexico and Central Atlantic ocean basins.

Exterior thrusting along the north flank of the fold belt was diachronous and ranges in age from Late Mississippian (Chesterian) to Late Pennsylvanian in the southern Appalachians (Thomas, 1976), mid-Pennsylvanian (Atoka-Desmoines) in the Ouachitas (Arbenz, this volume), and latest Pennsylvanian (Virgilian) to earliest Permian (Wolfcampian) in the Marathon region (King, 1975).

In the subsurface south of the outcropping Ouachita fold belt, wells have penetrated mid-Pennsylvanian (Desmoinesian) and Late Permian (Wolfcampian) shallow-marine sediments that presumably post-date Ouachita thrusting and pre-date Late Triassic rifting (Vernon, 1971; Woods and Addington, 1973).

The late Permian configuration

Restoration of the supercontinent Pangea by the closure of the Central and South Atlantic Oceans presents serious overlap problems in the Gulf and Caribbean regions (Ball and Harrison, 1969; Dietz and Holden, 1970; Wood and Walper, 1974; Moore and del Castillo, 1974; Pilger, 1978; Dickinson and Coney, 1980; Salvador and Green, 1980; White, 1980; White and Burke, 1980; Buffler and others, 1981; Walper, 1981; Pindell and Dewey, 1982; Anderson and Schmidt, 1983; Pindell, 1985; Klitgord and Schouten, 1986; Ross and Scotese, 1988; Dunbar and Sawyer, 1988; and others). It is clear that some crustal elements (e.g., Yucatan block and eastern Mexico) must have moved into place when North and South America separated from Africa, and crustal attenuation and sea-floor spreading presumably began concomitantly in the Gulf region.

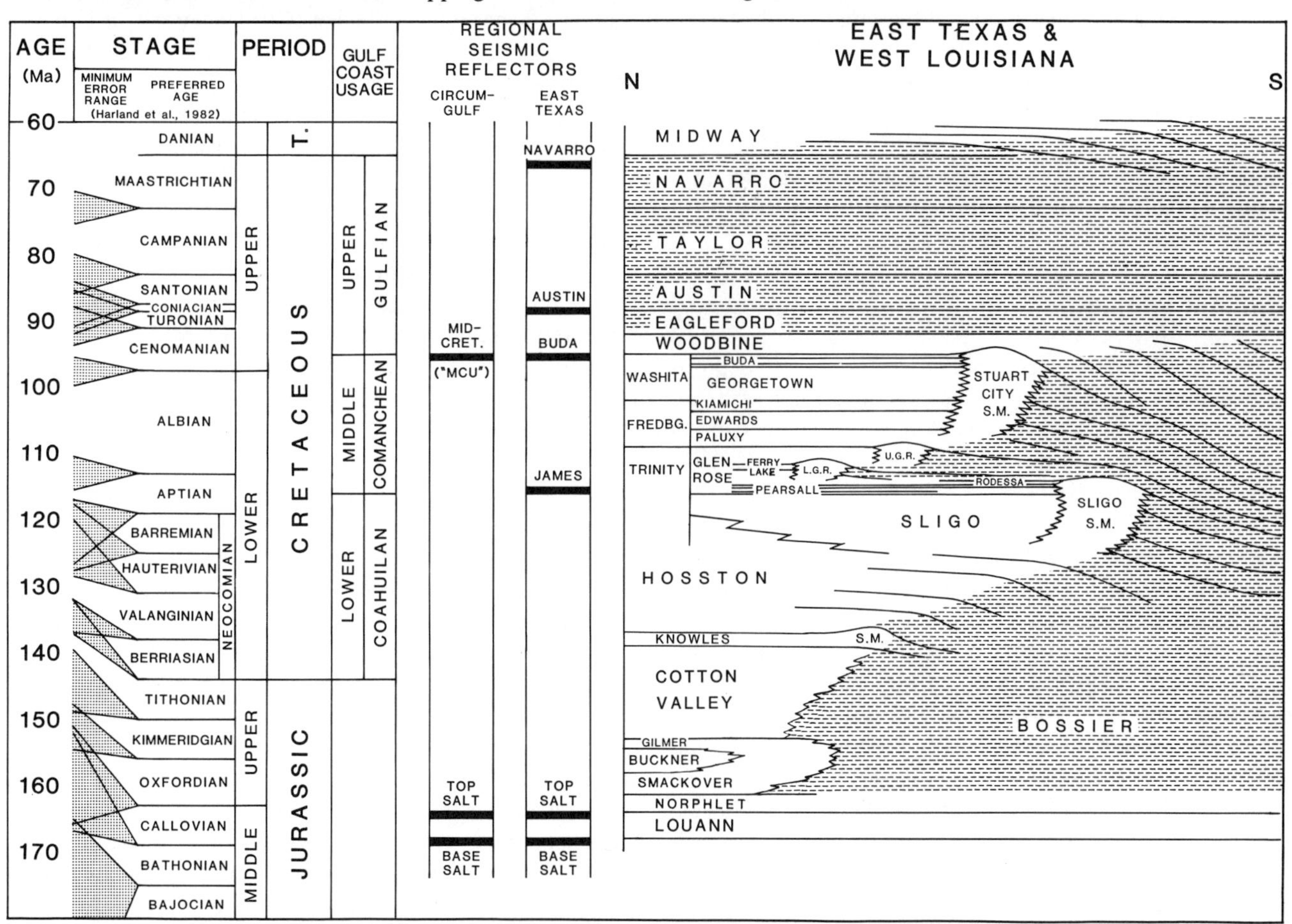

Figure 3. Jurassic and Cretaceous stratigraphic chart, east Texas and western Louisiana (from Winker and Buffler, 1988).

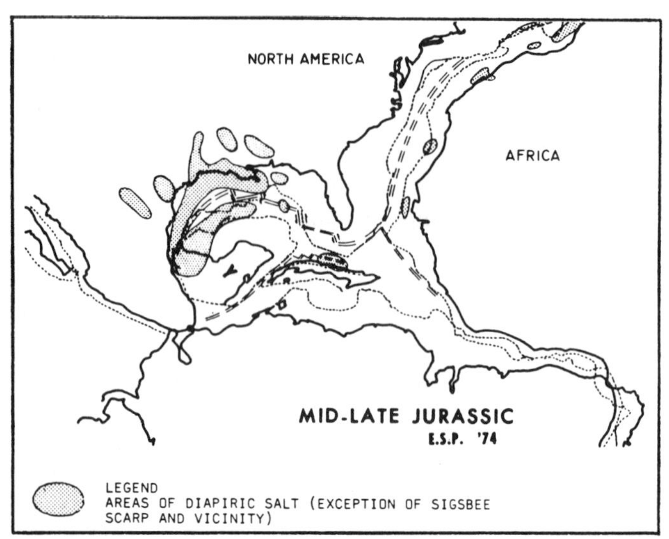

Figure 4. Reconstruction of the Gulf of Mexico and Caribbean region at the beginning of postulated late Jurassic seafloor spreading (from Humphris, 1978, 1979).

The myriad of pre-opening Pangean fits proposed by various authors (Fig. 4 is an example) differ largely in the "tightness" of the Permian fit, and in the original position, shape, and nature of rotation of individual crustal elements. The evaluation of all the different Late Permian reconstructions for the circum-Gulf Basin is beyond the scope of this introductory section, and the reader is invited to review the above references for more insights into the complexities of the problem.

Late Triassic–Early Jurassic rifting and crustal attenuation

The late Triassic–Early Jurassic terrestrial rift deposits and basic intrusions exposed in the central and northern Appalachians, and subcropping beneath the Atlantic Coastal Plain, are known to extend southwesterly beneath Mesozoic strata of the northern Gulf of Mexico Basin (Fig. 1). According to Salvador (1987), Lower and Middle Triassic deposits are absent in the region, and it can be assumed that much of the northern Gulf region was an eroding land mass during this time interval.

In the subsurface, presumed Upper Triassic to Lower Jurassic red beds (Scott and others, 1961) of the Eagle Mills Formation, with locally associated diabase and basalt, have been encountered in numerous wells in southern Georgia and Alabama, northwesternmost Florida, west-central Mississippi, northern Louisiana (see Plate 4), and east Texas. These deposits are usually correlated with the Newark Group of the eastern United States (Cornet and Traverse, 1975; Manspeizer, 1982) and the La Boca Formation of Mexico (Mixon and others, 1959); however, faunal data in these nonmarine deposits are very sparse. The strike of the red-bed subcrop closely parallels the Ouachita fold belt (Vernon, 1971). Isotopic dates of associated dikes and sills typically are Early Jurassic in age, ranging from 180 to 200 Ma (van Houten, 1977; Chowns and Williams, 1983; Dooley and Wampler, 1983).

Late Middle Jurassic evaporite deposition, present-day morphology, and distribution

Following widespread continental conditions in the Late Triassic through Middle Jurassic, broad regional subsidence and associated widespread marine incursions resulted in the deposition of evaporites over much of the Gulf region. Because of their incompetence and ductility, these evaporites played a major role in determining the later, highly variable tectonic and stratigraphic character of the region.

Based on well and seismic reflection data, two major evaporite belts in the circum-Gulf region can be mapped (Fig. 5): (1) a northern region, which includes much of the coastal plain and offshore regions of northeastern Mexico, Texas, Louisiana, southern Arkansas, Mississippi, and the Florida Panhandle, characterized by Louann Salt (Hazzard and others, 1947) deposition; and (2) a southern, eastward-concave belt along the west and northwest flank of the Yucatan Peninsula. The southern belt occupies a portion of the southern deep Gulf of Mexico (Challenger salt of Ladd and others, 1976), the Bay of Campeche, and adjacent onshore Mexico to the south (Isthmian salt). Separating these two major areas is the Sigsbee abyssal plain, a deep, structure-free area underlain by presumed oceanic crust and apparently devoid of salt (Buffler and others, 1981). Humphris (1978, 1979) postulated that these two major salt regions were originally contiguous, but later separated as a result of late Middle to early Late Jurassic sea-floor spreading (Fig. 4).

In the onshore portions of the northern Gulf salt basin are three areas cratonward of the Early and Middle Cretaceous shelf margins where salt structuring is particularly prominent: the East Texas, North Louisiana, and Mississippi salt structure provinces (Fig. 2).

In the East Texas province, it is estimated that the original thickness of salt was between 1,500 m (5,000 ft) and 2,100 m (7,000 ft) (Jackson and Seni, 1984). In this area, as in the two other onshore salt structure provinces, classical salt "rollers" (Fig. 6), pillows, salt domes (Fig. 7), salt walls, and "turtle structures" variously occur. (See Jackson and Seni, 1983, for a review of the distribution and morphology of these salt structures.) Likewise, in the southern salt belt, north of the Campeche escarpment offshore northwestern Yucatan, are numerous examples on seismic lines of pillows, massive salt domes, and "turtle structures" (Buffler, 1983). In both the southern and northern evaporite belts, seismic data reveal the gradual thinning and ultimate pinching out of evaporites updip toward the basin margins. Typically, these updip pinchout regions are characterized by basin-rimming, often listric and en echelon, extensional fault systems (e.g., Mexia-Talco fault system of east Texas, Fig. 2).

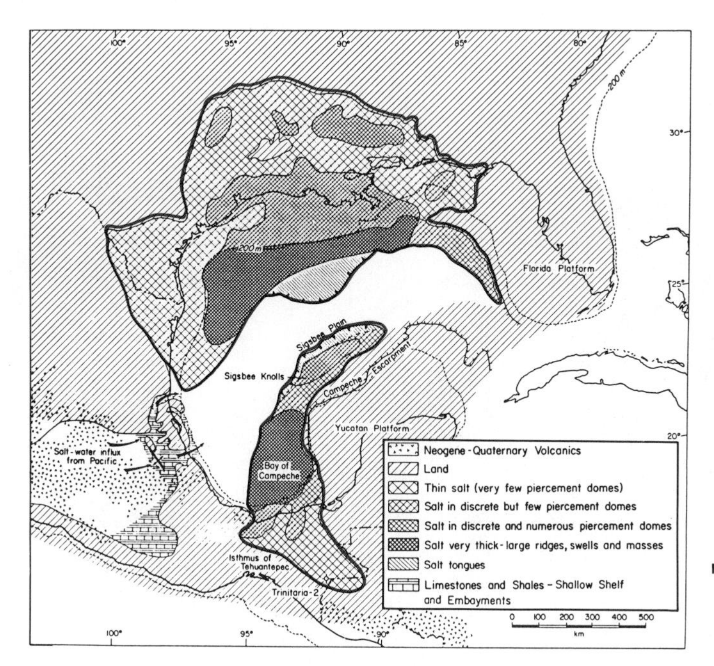

Figure 5. Present-day distribution of salt and other mid-late Jurassic deposits in the Gulf of Mexico region (Salvador, 1987). Red line delimits maximum extent of salt.

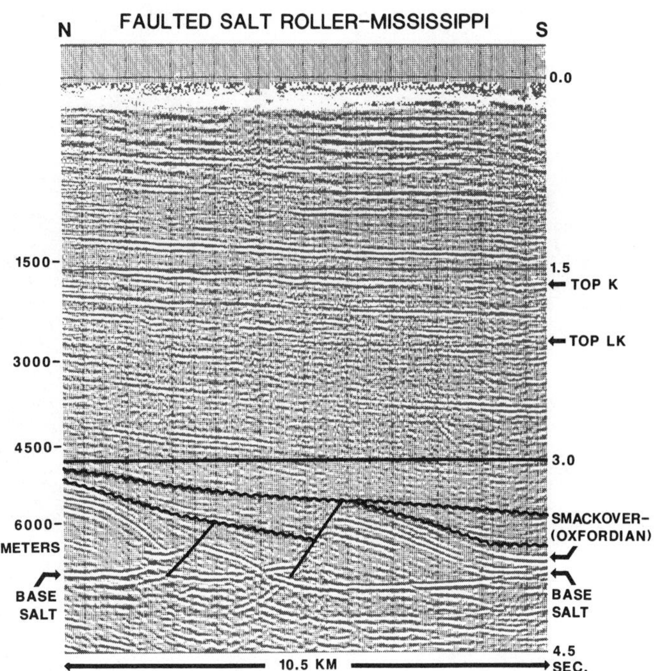

Figure 6. Seismic section showing faulted salt "rollers" in the Mississippi salt structure province (from Bally, 1981).

Although in substantial portions of the northern and southern Gulf evaporite belts, salt structures clearly "root" into a late Middle Jurassic (Callovian) (Imlay, 1980; Salvador, 1987) autochthonous "mother" salt horizon, in other large areas of the Gulf region, seismic data indicate salt to be clearly allochthonous. One of the more dramatic manifestations of allochthonous salt is along the Sigsbee Escarpment, an area discussed later in this chapter. Both autochthonous and allochthonous salt profoundly influenced the structural development of the Mesozoic and Cenozoic Gulf of Mexico Basin. One cannot assume that present-day distribution and thickness of salt reflects original depositional thicknesses and basinal outlines because post-depositional displacements of salt were often quite substantial.

Late Jurassic–earliest Cretaceous sedimentation and salt deformation

Following Louann Salt deposition, quartzose sandstones, red beds, and conglomerates of the Norphlet Formation were deposited (Fig. 3). This nonmarine clastic unit contains aeolian sandstones, which have been the focus of oil industry activity in recent years as a result of significant hydrocarbon discoveries in offshore Alabama (Mancini and others, 1985). The type Norphlet Formation and, in fact, all succeeding type sections of Late Jurassic age in the northern Gulf region are based entirely on well control. All Jurassic units wedge out updip beneath the Cretaceous strata seen at the surface along most of the northern Gulf rim (see Plate 4).

The first major Mesozoic marine transgression to affect the Gulf of Mexico Basin region occurred during the Late Jurassic Oxfordian Stage, presumably as widening oceanic crust moved Yucatan into its present position and more open marine conditions were established within the proto-Caribbean and newly developing central Atlantic Ocean (e.g., Pindell and Dewey, 1982). The transgression is recorded in most areas of the northern Gulf by shallow-water, heterogeneous carbonates of the Smackover Formation (Fig. 3), which lies at the base of the Smackover–Buckner–Gilmer (Haynesville) seismically defined stratigraphic sequence of Todd and Mitchum (1977).

The Smackover is an important hydrocarbon source and reservoir rock in the Gulf Coast with a laminated organic-rich mudstone at its base (Sassen and Moore, 1988), and an upper member characterized by oolitic carbonate grainstones (indicative of an environment of shallow bars and shoals). The Buckner is an evaporitic and red bed facies that overlies and is in part laterally equivalent to the upper Smackover Formation. The overlying upper Kimmeridgian Gilmer Limestone (Forgotson and Forgotson, 1976) in east Texas represents the late transgressive culmination to the Smackover–Buckner–Gilmer cycle. In central Mississippi, north Louisiana, and southeast Arkansas, portions of these facies are replaced by terrigenous clastics known as the Haynesville Formation (Salvador, 1987).

The next overlying sequence in the northern Gulf, originally named the Cotton Valley Formation (Mann and Thomas, 1964; Collins, 1980) reflects a major clastic influx

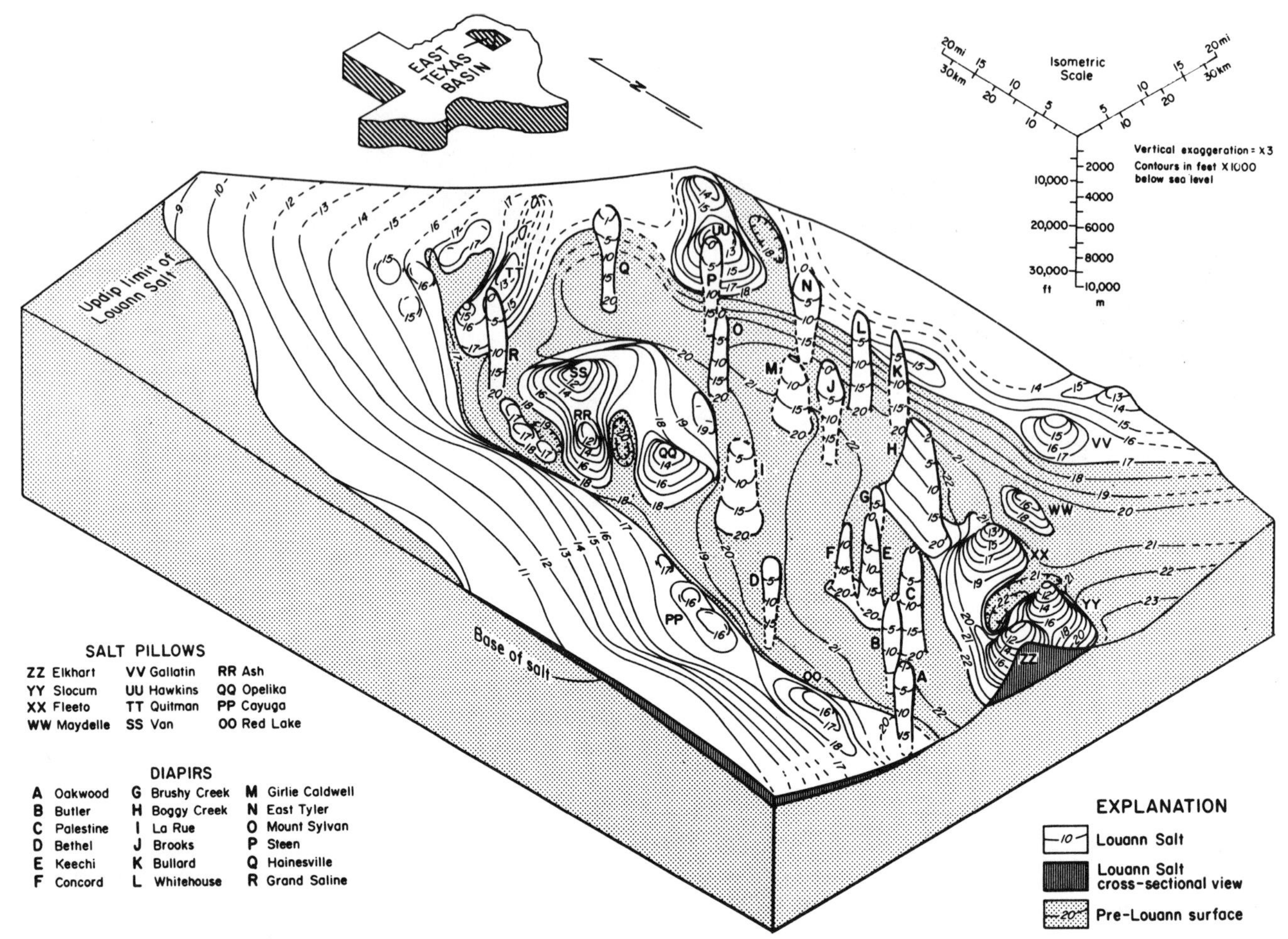

Figure 7. Isometric diagram showing salt domes and pillows in the East Texas salt structure province (from Seni and Jackson, 1983).

into the region. This uppermost Jurassic (Tithonian)–earliest Cretaceous (Berriasian) sequence (Fig. 3) is typically much thicker than underlying units. It is characterized by a basinal Bossier shale facies that passes laterally and vertically into coarser-grained marine clastics and finally into nonmarine deposits. In east Texas and northern Louisiana, a carbonate facies (Knowles Limestone) punctuates this overall classic regressive sequence.

There is abundant evidence on seismic data of faulting and folding associated with salt deformation during the deposition of the Smackover–Buckner–Gilmer (Haynesville) and overlying Cotton Valley sequences (McGowen and Harris, 1984). In the onshore East Texas salt structure province (Fig. 2), for example, salt appears to have moved at different times. Deformation around the margins of the basin began as early as Smackover time, coincident with pull-apart deformation along the updip, basin-rimming Mexia-Talco fault zone. More extensive salt movement with associated listric faults, "rollers," pillows, and domes occurred during the influx of Cotton Valley clastics (Jackson and Harris (1981). Seismic data often illustrate faults rooting into mobile salt above a gently southward-dipping planar detachment surface.

The basic stratigraphic, tectonic, and geographic framework of the Gulf was established by the end of the Jurassic (Salvador, 1987). A deep central Gulf was surrounded by stable platform terrains (Yucatan and Florida), and there were open marine connections with the central Atlantic and probably the Pacific Ocean as well.

Early and Middle Cretaceous shelf margins, tectonic and volcanic activity

During the Early and Middle Cretaceous (as defined in Fig. 3), the deep Gulf was essentially a deep-water basin surrounded by the steep carbonate platforms of Florida and Yucatan to the northeast and south, and by gentler carbonate shelves to the north and northwest. These carbonate shelves of the northern Gulf are underlain by 2,700 to 3,700 m (8,000 to 11,000 ft) of Lower and Middle Cretaceous strata (McFarlan and Menes, personal communication, 1988). Abyssal sediments of the same age averaging 2,000 m (6,500 ft) in thickness overlie presumed Late Jurassic oceanic crust and sediments beneath the Sigsbee plain in the deep Gulf of Mexico (Schaub and others, 1984).

According to Winker and Buffler (1988), the shelf margins of the Early and Middle Cretaceous that surround the Gulf of Mexico Basin exhibit a variety of architectural styles. Two cycles of progradation characterize the northern Gulf, each terminated by drowning events. For example, in Texas, the Lower Cretaceous (Coahuilan) Hosston-Sligo progradational cycle is followed by the Middle Cretaceous (Comanchean) Trinity–Fredericksburg–Washita cycle with its associated Glen Rose and Stuart City ("Edwards") reefs (Fig. 3). A single cycle of progradation exists to the southwest along north-northwest–trending platforms in onshore Mexico. Continuous aggradation occurred in the eastern and southern Gulf along the present-day margins west of Florida and the Campeche Escarpment (Fig. 1).

The Early and Middle Cretaceous two-cycle shelf margins can be mapped on the basis of seismic and well data rather continuously from the Laramide fold belt of northwestern Mexico into Louisiana. Lower Cretaceous outcrops are not widespread in Texas, but extensive exposures of Middle Cretaceous (Comanchean) strata in the Edwards Plateau (Fig. 1) and along the Balcones fault zone (Fig. 2) of west Texas (e.g., Trinity, Fredericksburg, and Washita groups) have received a great deal of study (e.g., Bebout and Loucks, 1977). All of these outcropping Middle Cretaceous rocks represent facies deposited landward of the coeval, progradational Glen Rose–Stuart City ("Edwards") shelf margin complex, which is known only in the subsurface of Texas and Louisiana.

In the northern Gulf of Mexico Basin, the lower cycle of Winker's two-cycle margin, the Lower Cretaceous (Coahuilan) Hosston-Sligo cycle, was drowned roughly in the early Aptian (Fig. 3). The upper cycle, the Middle Cretaceous (Comanchian) Glen Rose–Stuart City ("Edwards") cycle, an important gas producer in Texas, was drowned in the early Cenomanian (about 97 m.y. ago), following development of a "mid-Cretaceous" circum-Gulf unconformity ("MCU" of Buffler and others, 1980), and prior to the onset of Late Cretaceous (Gulfian) clastic sedimentation.

Although much of the Gulf region behaved as a passive Atlantic-type margin during Early and Middle Cretaceous shelf deposition, some tectonic and volcanic activity affected the region. In the north-central Gulf, landward of the Early and Middle Cretaceous shelf margins, several localized uplifts developed, namely the Sabine Uplift in northeastern Texas and northwesternmost Louisiana, the Monroe Uplift in northeastern Louisiana (Johnson, 1958), the Wiggins arch in southern Mississippi (Cagle and Khan, 1983), and the Jackson Dome in central Mississippi (Fig. 2). Each of these has its own unique history (see Murray, 1964).

The Sabine Uplift is the largest and economically one of the most significant positive features in the northern Gulf. It was a very broad, exceedingly low-relief, often submerged structure in the Early and Middle Cretaceous. But as a result of tectonic upwarping in the mid-Cenomanian, the upper Albian to lower Cenomanian strata on its western flank became prominently truncated beneath a mid-Cretaceous unconformity. The giant East Texas oil field owes its origin to the uplift (Halbouty and Halbouty, 1982; Hamberg, 1983; Galloway and others, 1983). The Sabine Uplift also has a younger history, as evidenced by its present-day arcuate outline in surface exposures of lower Eocene strata.

The Sabine Uplift was in part responsible for modifying the Mesozoic shelf of the northern Gulf, separating it into what are now termed the East Texas and Northern Louisiana salt structure provinces. These two shelfal sags, as well as the central Mississippi shelfal sag to the east, have preserved Louann Salt at their base, and as a result of differential subsidence, in part due to salt withdrawal during the Cretaceous, have developed a full spectrum of often hydrocarbon-bearing salt tectonic features (e.g., Wood and Giles, 1982; Jackson and Seni, 1984).

At the southern margin of the Sabine Uplift is the westerly-trending Angelina-Caldwell hinge zone (Fig. 2) where gently south-dipping lower Tertiary strata rather abruptly thicken. This hinge zone marks the southern limit of the East Texas and Central Louisiana shelfal sags. It roughly parallels the Middle Cretaceous Stuart City (Edwards) carbonate shelf edge. To the east, this hinge zone projects into the southern border of the Wiggins Arch (see Walper and others, 1979, Fig. 2), a presently south-dipping feature which in the late Mesozoic formed the southern flank of the central Mississippi salt structure province. The Angelina-Caldwell hinge zone may reflect an underlying crustal thickness change from more normal continental crust to the north to a thinner transitional crust to the south.

Late Cretaceous volcanic activity occurs along the northern rim of the Gulf of Mexico Basin (Kidwell, 1951), including the Monroe Uplift and the Jackson Dome areas. In Arkansas, nepheline syenites, pyroxenites, carbonatites, kimberlites, and the famous Murfreesboro diamond-bearing lamproite have produced various mid-Cretaceous age dates ranging from 87 to 101 Ma (Zartman, 1977; G. R. Byerly, personal communication, 1988).

Late Cretaceous sedimentation

After the mid-Cretaceous carbonate shelf edge was drowned, the Late Cretaceous became a time of widespread chalk, marl, and shale sedimentation. In ascending order, the Woodbine, Eagle Ford, Austin, Taylor, and Navarro groups make up the classic Upper Cretaceous (Gulfian) stratigraphy of the Gulf Coast (Fig. 3). This terminology was derived from outcrop studies in a narrow belt that extends from east Texas to Mexico. East of the Mississippi Embayment, roughly coeval units crop out and have such names as Tuscaloosa (= Woodbine), Eutaw (= Austin), and Selma or Ripley (= Taylor and Navarro). In much of the northern Gulf of Mexico Basin, the Cenomanian-Turonian base of the Upper Cretaceous section is largely characterized by economically important terrestrial and marine clastics, but these rapidly pass upward into the volumetrically more significant and very widespread heterogeneous assemblages of marine shales, marls, and chalks.

The Woodbine Formation, the most prolific hydrocarbon-producing interval in the East Texas basin, in outcrop overlies a major unconformity at the base of the Upper Cretaceous section. In the subsurface region, "updip" of the mid-Cretaceous shelf margin, basal Woodbine and Eagle Ford strata are largely concordant with underlying units. South of the margin, the Woodbine displays pronounced progradational downlap geometries (Siemers, 1978). The "updip" facies are characterized by fluvial, deltaic, and shelf strandplain deposits (Oliver, 1971), some containing volcanic detritus. In the Tyler County region of northeastern Texas this "updip" interval is less than 16 m thick (Siemers, 1978), but south of the Edwards reef trend and Angelina-Caldwell hinge zone, over a distance of 25 km, the interval thickens to about 500 m. The "downdip" Woodbine–Eagle Ford is here interpreted by Siemers (1978) to be a mud-dominated clastic wedge containing fine- to very fine-grained reservoir sands 5 to 13 m thick with features indicative of both turbidity and traction currents.

To the east, in Louisiana and Mississippi, the coeval Tuscaloosa Formation shares a somewhat similar history to that of the Woodbine, with a "shallow Tuscaloosa" trend north of the buried mid-Cretaceous shelf and a "deep Tuscaloosa" trend south of the shelf. In contrast to the Woodbine, however, the deltaic shoreline of the Tuscaloosa reached the shelf edge (Winker, 1982). Smith (1985) reports lower Tuscaloosa thicknesses of 100 to 165 m above the carbonate shelf and over 1,500 m, 20 km to the south. Whereas the "shallow Tuscaloosa" has produced hydrocarbons since the 1940s, "deep Tuscaloosa" gas was not found until 1975. Since that time, numerous gas fields have been discovered, most on east-west–trending closures associated with the downward side of down-to-the-basin growth faults.

In summary, with the exception of the Rio Grande region of west Texas where terrestrial to shallow marine sedimentation and submarine volcanism occurred in the upper Taylor and overlying Navarro groups (Indest and McPherson, 1985), most of the northern Gulf in post-Woodbine–Eagle Ford, Late Cretaceous time was blanketed by deeper water marine chalks, marls, and shales; well-defined shelf margins did not reappear in the northern Gulf until the early Tertiary.

CENOZOIC DEPOSITIONAL SETTING

Overview of Cenozoic depositional patterns

During the Cenozoic, the Gulf of Mexico Basin was fed by sediments from the west, northwest, and north from a complex system of shifting alluvial source areas which variously provided coastal deposits along migrating, typically unstable, faulted shelf margins (Fig. 8). Depocenters shifted throughout the Cenozoic, with upward of 16 km (50,000 ft) of cumulative sediment deposited (McGookey, 1975). The shelves variously prograded, aggraded, or retreated; they record numerous regressive and transgressive cycles that reflect the complex interplay of sediment supply, eustacy, and the instability of underlying salt. Individual depositional cycles typically consist of (1) a sandy continental to deltaic sequence, (2) a "sand-shale" sequence of coastal-deltaic or strand-plain deposits, and (3) "shale" composed of prodelta and more distal marine deposits (Curtis and Picou, 1978). Associated with these cycles were periods of slope collapse with glacier-like mass flow, growth faulting, canyon cutting, deep-sea fan deposition, and salt flow.

The classic Gulf Coast Paleocene and Eocene section (see generalized columnar section in Fig. 21), which crops out along most of the northern Gulf rim (Midway, Wilcox, Claiborne, Jackson), comprises: (1) a basal, mud-dominated stable progradational system (i.e., not accompanied by growth faulting), which in the Paleocene (Midway) prograded over the Late Cretaceous clastic margin; (2) unstable, progradational, lower Eocene Wilcox deltaic systems (e.g., in Texas the Rockdale Delta of Fisher and McGowen, 1967) characterized by growth faulting, as well as by a major submarine canyon (Yoakum Canyon of Hoyt, 1959; location on Fig. 8); and (3) middle to late Eocene (Clairborne and Jackson) regressive sequences, with the exception of the Yegua in east Texas where unstable progradational conditions associated with salt withdrawal prevailed. (See Winker, 1982, for fuller discussion of Cenozoic shelf margin character and terminology.)

The Oligocene, divided into the Vicksburg, Frio, and Anahuac (see Fig. 21), reaches its greatest thickness in southwest Texas. (1) The lowermost unit, the Vicksburg, is similar to the underlying upper Eocene Jackson Formation, consisting largely of marine shales and interbedded sands in southeast Texas. The sequence thickens greatly across a major northeast-trending growth fault in south Texas (Vicksburg fault). There, the fault system is clearly listric, with pronounced rollover of faulted strata (up to 50 degrees) above an underlying detachment surface (see Fig. 48). (2) The Frio Formation was deposited during a largely progradational event on an unstable margin reaching thicknesses of over 4,500 m (15,000 ft). In Texas, it contains both deltaic and interdeltaic facies (Bebout and others, 1978). It is economically one of the most important formations in the Texas Gulf Coast, with gas and oil production to date (1981) equivalent to 16 billion barrels of oil (Dupre, 1987). (3) The Anahuac Formation was deposited during an overall late Oligocene regional transgression with a largely mud-dominated shelf margin similar to the middle to late Eocene Clairborne and Jackson Formations (Winker, 1982).

The stratigraphically and structurally complex Neogene

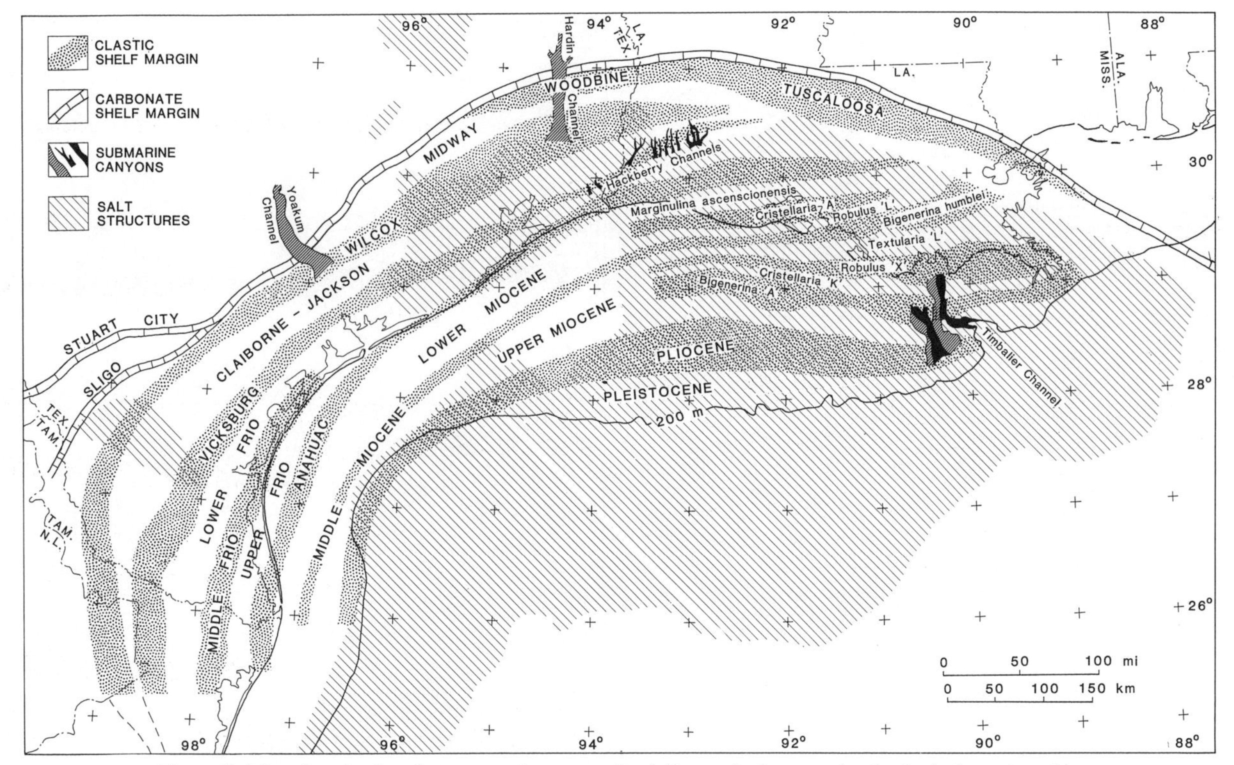

Figure 8. Map showing bands representing generalized Cenozoic depotrends of principal stratigraphic units and submarine channels seaward of the mid-Cretaceous carbonate shelf margin in the northern Gulf of Mexico (from Winker, 1982).

section is responsible for most of the hydrocarbons in the offshore northern Gulf. Miocene depocenters developed over unstable shelf margins in onshore southern Louisiana (Curtis, 1970) as well as offshore Texas, where, for example, along the major Corsair fault, sandy middle to upper Miocene regressive deposits expand from 915 to 1,220 m (3,000 to 4,000 ft) updip to more than 4,600 m (15,000 ft) in the downthrown block (Vogler and Robison, 1987). Thick Plio-Pleistocene depocenters are restricted to the easternmost Texas and Louisiana offshore (Woodbury and others, 1973) where thousands of meters of sediment prograded gulfward (Lehner, 1969). The Pleistocene depocenter is located near the present shelf edge off central Louisiana along the so-called "flexure trend" (Pearcy and Ray, 1986), where shallow-water sediments may exceed thicknesses of 6 km (20,000 ft) (Foote and Martin, 1981). Much of the modern outer slope is characterized by a hummocky topography (Bouma and Coleman, 1986), with huge, bathymetrically high salt masses separated by bathymetrically lower "mini-basins" containing thick accumulations of Plio-Pleistocene and Miocene sediment (Forrest, 1986).

CENOZOIC TECTONICS

Introduction

Fundamental differences in the style of growth faulting exist between many of the progradational Cenozoic shelf margins of Louisiana and Texas. The faults downdip from the Cretaceous reef trend form two distinct types, as shown on the tectonic map (Fig. 2). (1) Very long fault systems predominate in onshore Texas, the Texas shelf, and parts of western Louisiana. These dip basinward and strike parallel to the present coast, and are not generally associated with near-surface salt piercements, although a few salt piercements are present in far south Texas (Fig. 2). (2) Shorter, more arcuate-shaped fault systems in much of coastal Louisiana, the Louisiana shelf, and parts of easternmost Texas dip both landward and basinward, and are spatially associated with abundant near-surface salt bodies. This close relationship with shallow salt has been interpreted by most workers as strong evidence that their origin is due to salt movement by sedimentary loading (e.g., Quarles, 1953; Woodbury and others, 1973; Spindler, 1977; and many others). For convenience, these two fundamentally different fault types will be termed "Texas style" and "Louisiana style" in the remainder of this chapter, although of course, the two styles are not confined to either state.

The scarcity of shallow salt features beneath the coastal plain and continental shelf of Texas and coastal western Louisiana, plus the existence there of long, linear trends of listric, regularly basinward-dipping faults, have evoked hypotheses that the origin of these "Texas-style" growth faults is a result of either: (1) gravity sliding caused by rapid sedimentary loading of prodelta shales near the shelf margin (Bornhauser, 1958;

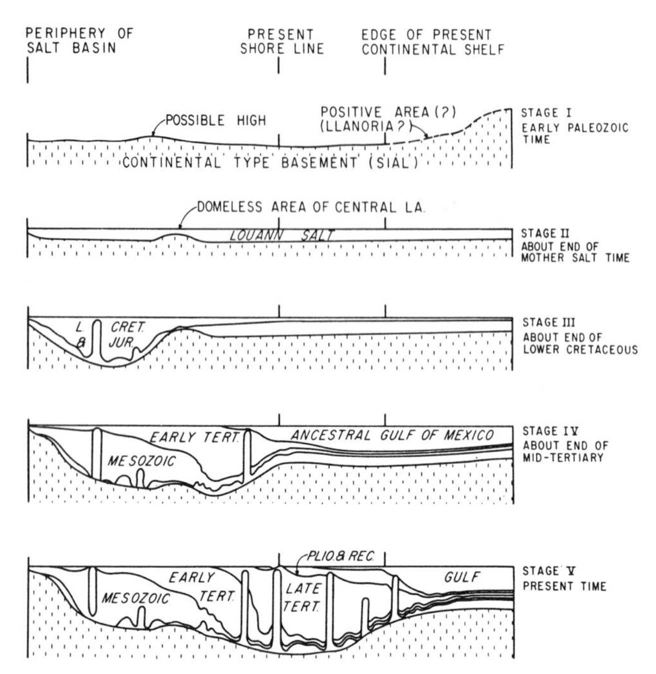

Figure 9. Development of interior and northern coastal plain salt basins as envisioned by Ocamb (1961).

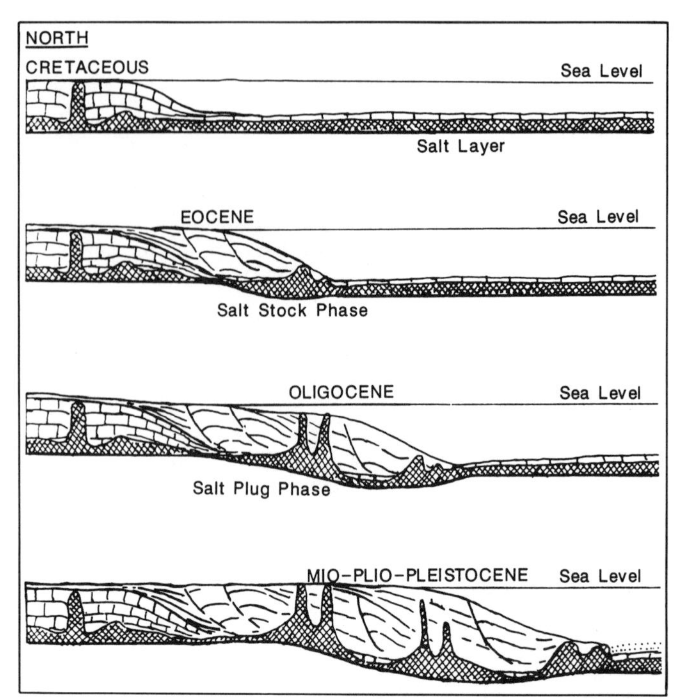

Figure 10. Hypothesis for the development of gravity-induced growth faults on a deep mobile salt layer, northern Gulf of Mexico (from Wilhelm and Ewing, 1972).

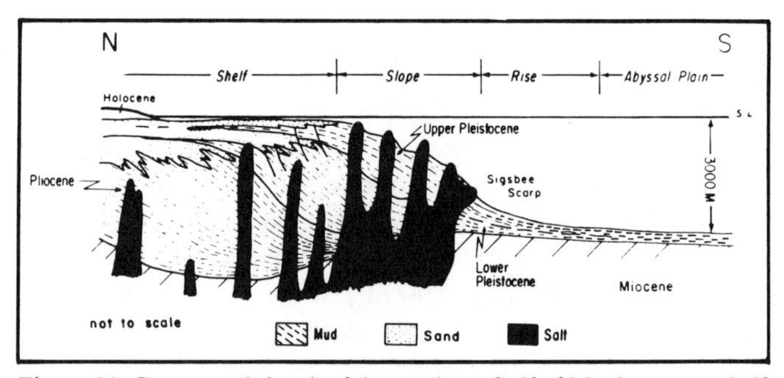

Figure 11. Conceptual sketch of the northern Gulf of Mexico, outer shelf to abyssal plain, as drawn by Stuart and Caughey (1977).

Cloos, 1968; Berg and others, 1979; R. G. Martin, Jr., 1978; Edwards, 1981; Winker and Edwards, 1983; Humphris, 1984, 1985; and many others) or (2) differential shale compaction (Honea, 1965; Carver, 1968; Bruce, 1973, 1983).

Along the east coast of Mexico, updip listric growth faults have been related to the downdip Mexican Ridges fold belt and postulated as due to a gravity slide (Garrison and Martin, 1973; Buffler and others, 1979). This region will be discussed later.

Historical perspective of ideas on growth faulting in the Gulf region

The development of ideas on Cenozoic tectonics for the Louisiana and Texas Gulf Coast has taken place over a long period of time in which geological data have only very slowly accumulated. Subsurface data were limited in the early days; good seismic control of structure at moderate depth is a fairly recent phenomenon. The result has been a slowly evolving set of tectonic concepts. It perhaps is useful to review this evolutionary growth of ideas to check the basis for current understanding.

The most common early view in the literature is that Cenozoic shelf margins in the northern Gulf developed as a series of thick Tertiary clastic accumulations that prograded onto a continuous layer of Jurassic salt, which emplaced itself upward in a series of diapiric intrusions (Fig. 9; see also Halbouty, 1967). Ocamb (1961) and Quarles (1953) thought that upward emplacement of salt was a cause of growth faulting, noting the common presence of crestal growth faults over salt domes.

In the 1960s, the gravity slide hypothesis for growth faulting at shelf margins became very popular, spurred on to some extent by the clay modeling work of Cloos (1968; discussed later). One result of this school of thought was a conceptual model by Wilhelm and Ewing (1972; shown in Fig. 10) where growth faults utilized autochthonous salt as a detachment surface. They envisioned basinward gravity sliding toward a basin floor deep enough to permit such massive downslope transport. Other workers considered shale to be the main detachment surface for these faults. In the 1960s and 1970s, many geologic sketches of the Gulf margin depicted salt masses as

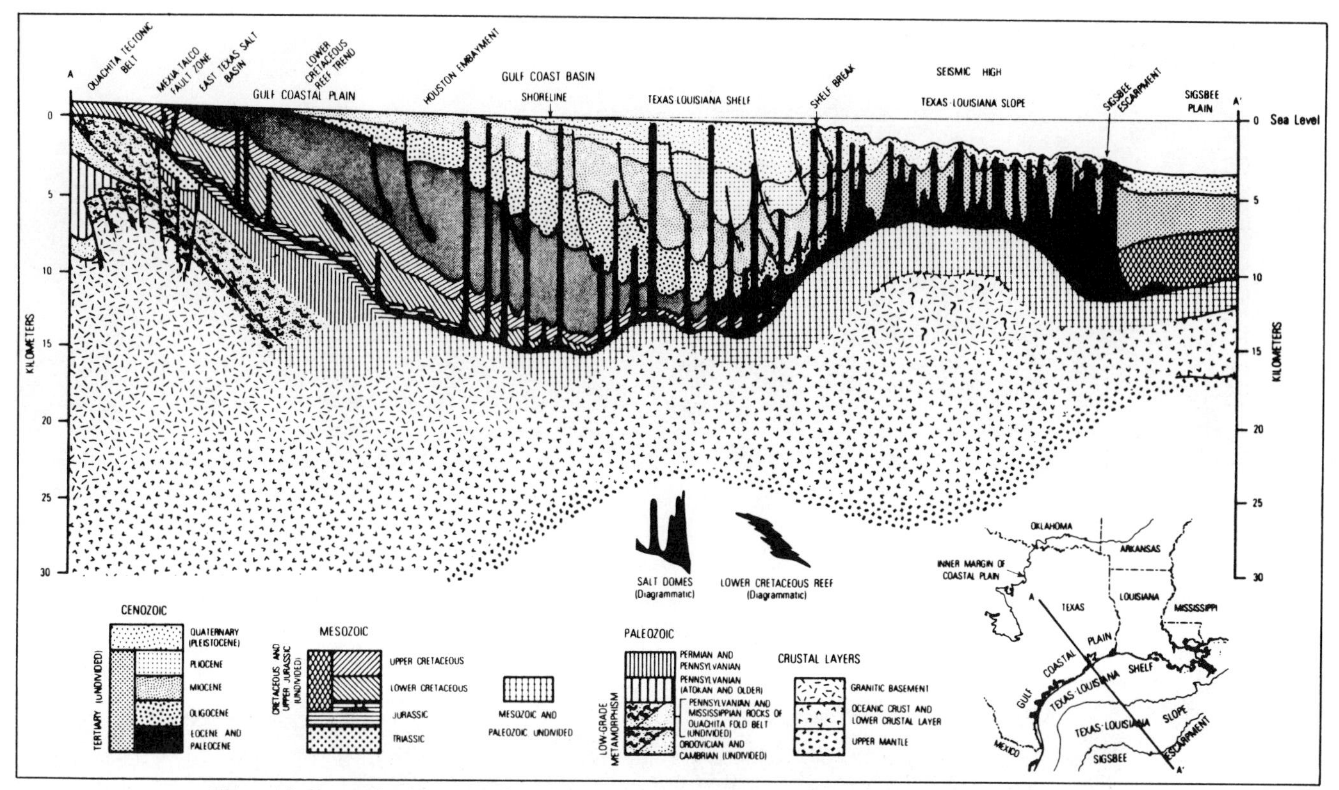

Figure 12. Generalized cross section of the northern Gulf of Mexico margin (from R. G. Martin, 1978, modified from earlier interpretations of Lehner, 1969; Dorman and others; 1972, Antoine and others, 1974; and Martin and Case, 1975).

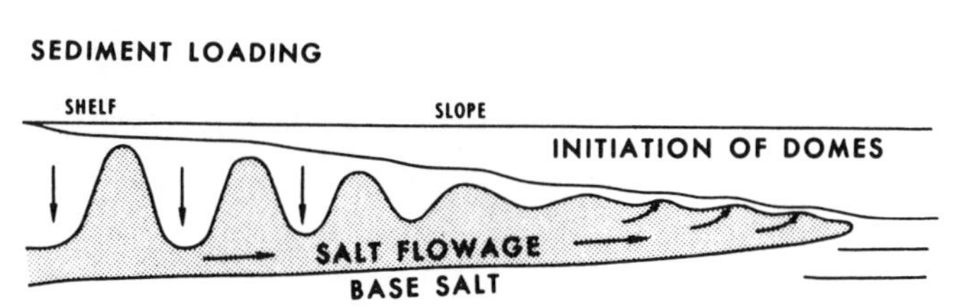

Figure 13. Diagrammatic representation of the initiation of salt dome growth on the continental slope as a result of sediment loading on the shelf–upper slope (from Humphris, 1978, 1979).

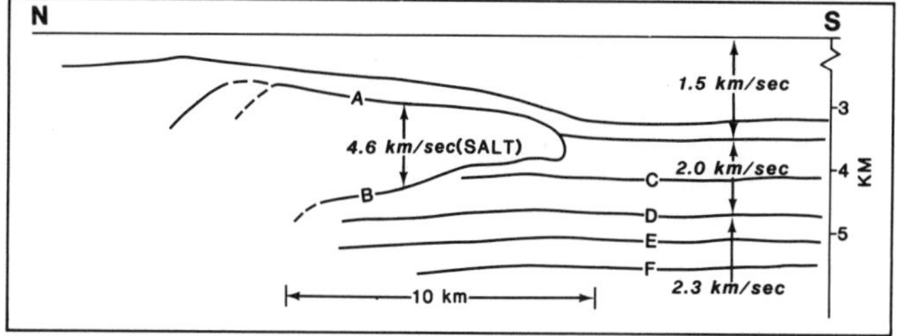

Figure 14. Reflections from a sparker profile across the Sigsbee Escarpment (from Amery, 1969). Reflectors beneath the salt have been corrected for salt velocity pull-up.

rather passive, upward growing diapirs without any apparent causative link with regional-scale growth faulting (e.g., Figs. 11 and 12).

In the late 1970s and 1980s, a very different model emerged for the structure of this region. This new thinking was based on better quality seismic data from exploration activity on the Louisiana shelf that showed: (1) not all Louisiana growth faults dip basinward (many dip landward); and (2) these faults are typically short and arcuate in map view, intimately related with salt (Fig. 2), and form small "mini-basins" between shallow salt features (e.g., Seglund, 1974; Spindler, 1977). Humphris (1978, 1979), using mostly palinspastic logic, reasoned that thick clastic strata in these basins displaced thick salt; moreover, he hypothesized that the salt displaced by advancing clastic deposition moved basinward into the slope as an allochthonous nappe of flowing salt (Fig. 13).

The hypothesis of large-scale lateral displacement of this salt into the slope was a dramatically new idea. Although a few kilometers of lateral salt flow at the toe of the slope was demonstrated by Amery (1969; Fig. 14), regional deep-record seismic data were not available at the time to demonstrate an actual base to the hypothetical salt nappe beneath the middle and lower slope. Humphris based his ideas of a northward-thickening wedge of allochthonous salt on the basis of a perceived thickening of salt-floored basins (which overlie the nappe), northward from the Sigsbee Escarpment.

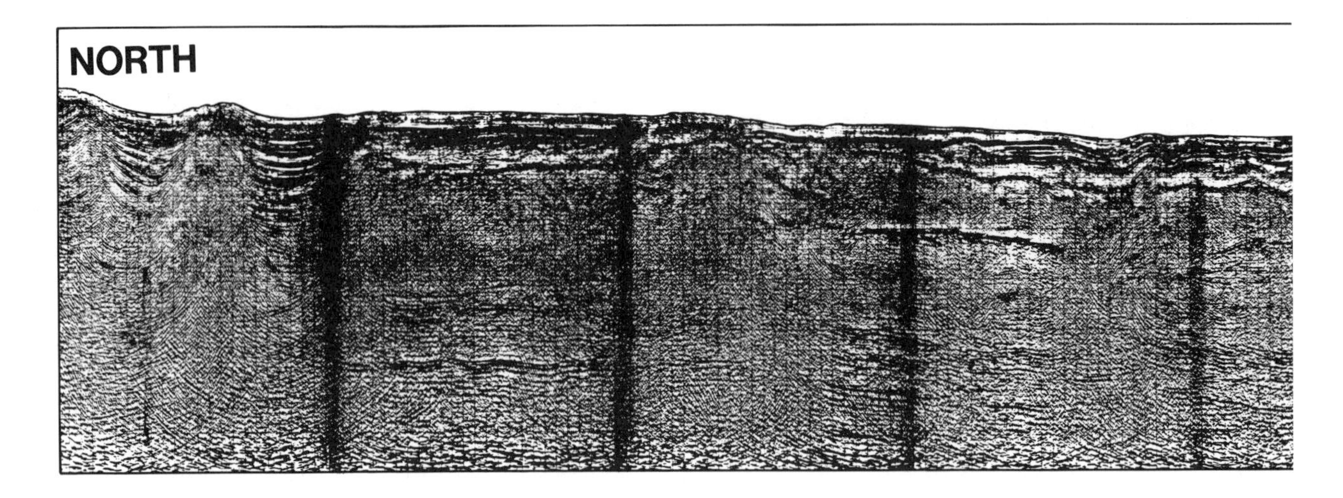
NORTH

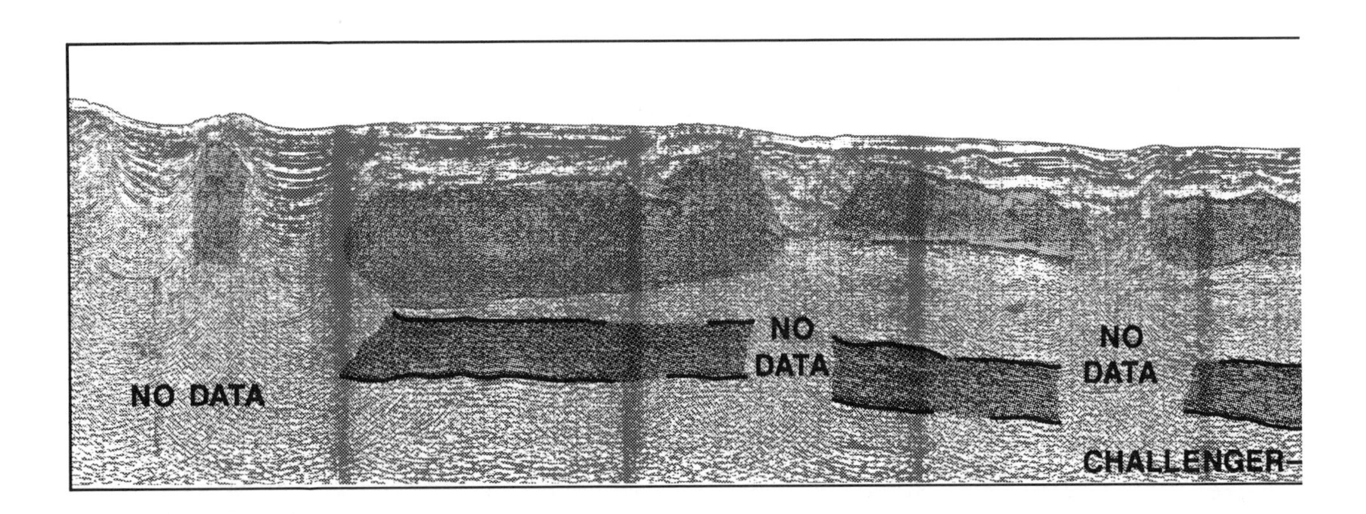
NO DATA
NO DATA
NO DATA
CHALLENGER-

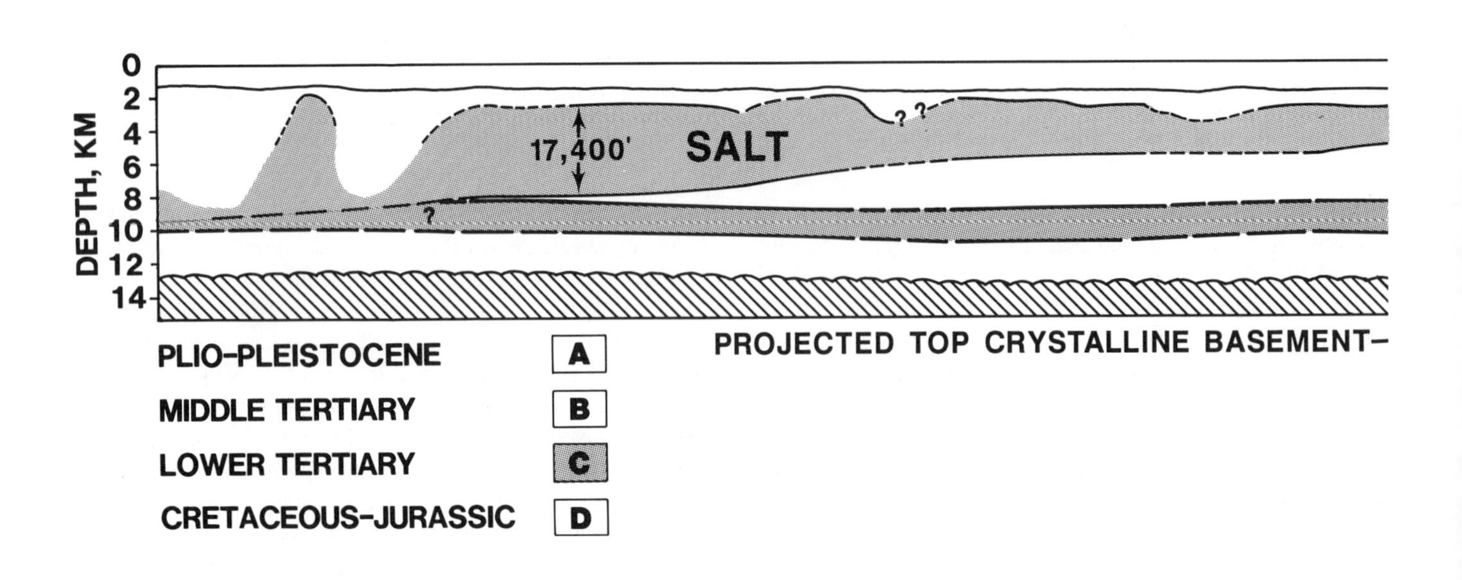
DEPTH, KM
0
2
4
6
8
10
12
14
17,400'
SALT
?
PROJECTED TOP CRYSTALLINE BASEMENT-
PLIO-PLEISTOCENE A
MIDDLE TERTIARY B
LOWER TERTIARY C
CRETACEOUS-JURASSIC D

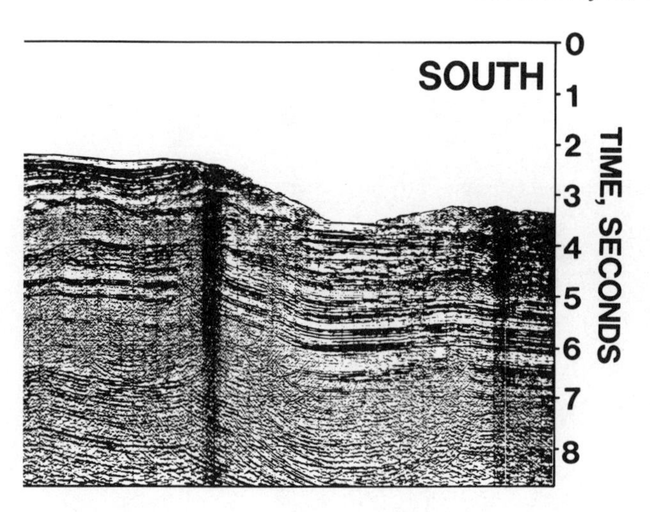

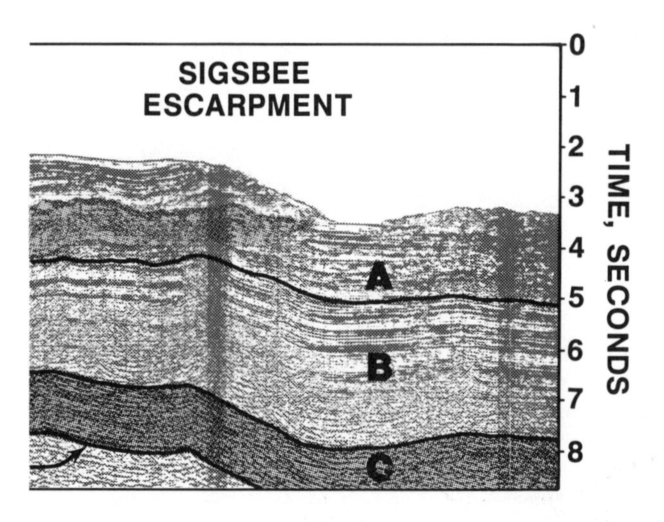

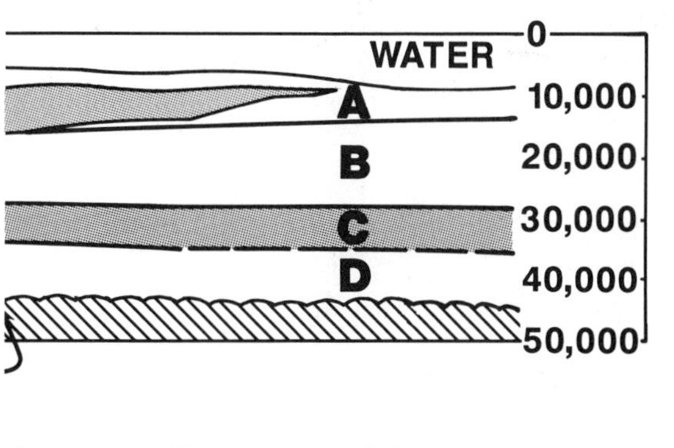

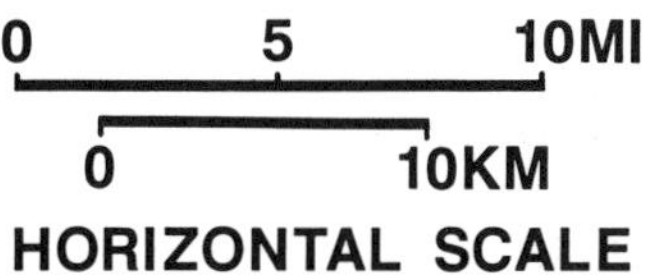

A corollary of the above hypothesis is the idea that salt ridges and domes adjacent to slope basins, rather than being late-piercing diapiric structures rooting vertically below in the Jurassic salt horizon, are actually preserved remnants of large, thick, allochthonous salt masses. A non-diapiric origin for such salt structures draws on the "downbuilding" concept of salt dome growth originally proposed by Barton (1933).

Louisiana structural style

The Sigsbee salt nappe complex. Amery (1969) published seismic data showing that the Sigsbee Escarpment at the base of the Louisiana slope consists of salt that is, at least locally, "overthrusting" sediment of the abyssal plain at least 10 km (Fig. 14). As has been discussed, Humphris (1978, 1979) used this as evidence of a hypothesized regional "overthrust" of salt. R. G. Martin, Jr. (1978), however, interpreted this same overthrust toe as a minor local feature (see Fig. 12), as did Amery (1978). In recent years, however, the concept of a regional salt nappe has gradually gained adherents.

Seismic data shown in Figure 15 confirm the regional extent of this salt nappe. Clearly visible on this north-south seismic line from the middle to lower central Louisiana slope (see Fig. 1 for location) is the "overthrust" at the toe of the slope, as well as the top and base of salt for more than 80 km updip to the middle slope. Abyssal strata beneath the allochthonous salt exhibit up to 2 seconds of relative pull-up in time due to the fast velocity of the massive salt tongue relative to surrounding strata, as well as to the varying bathymetry. This velocity effect is corrected in the underlying depth section; Tertiary and Mesozoic strata underlying the salt are almost flat. The velocity contrast between salt and shallow sediments is large, and explains why long seismic lines clearly showing this feature are somewhat rare: to see the salt base, the salt top must typically be relatively flat. Where sedimentary basins have loaded the top of the salt, the resulting strong velocity contrast usually destroys lower reflection quality (the "no data" zones are marked on Fig. 15).

The wedge of allochthonous salt thickens northward to over 5.2 km (17,000 ft) on the seismic section. Its base dips northward, and truncates successively older strata. At the northern observed limit, the nappe truncates the top of probable lower Tertiary strata. This means that this massive salt "overthrust" has been moving slowly to the south probably

Figure 15. Seismic section across the Sigsbee salt nappe, lower slope offshore Louisiana (location shown in Fig. 1). Length of section is nearly 110 km (70 mi). Top section is uninterpreted seismic data. Middle section shows interpretation. Bottom section is an interpreted depth section with no vertical exaggeration. The term "no data" refers to loss of base-salt reflector where thick sedimentary basins overlie salt. Note projected truncation of probable top of lower Tertiary strata (top Eocene?) by base of salt nappe at left side of section.

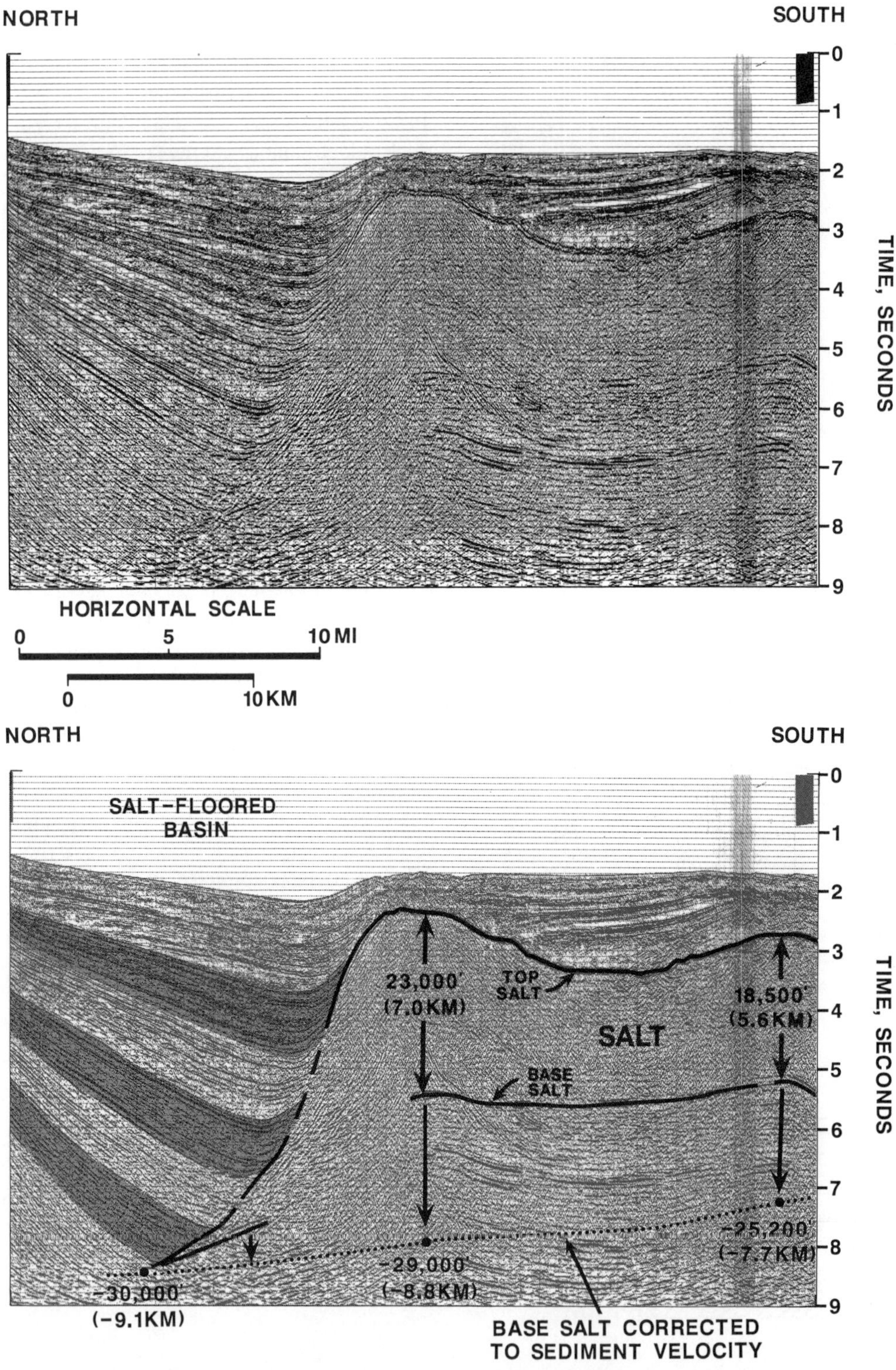

Figure 16. Thick, allochthonous, slope salt mass and adjacent Plio-Pleistocene basin, Louisiana slope (uninterpreted and interpreted versions). This section is parallel to and near the northern end of Figure 15. The base-salt shown is part of the same regional base-salt surface shown in Figure 15. The salt is here up to 7 km thick and exhibits a velocity pull-up of nearly 2.5 seconds. The base-salt has been corrected (dotted line) to the same time horizon as if the salt had the same velocity as the adjacent basin, allowing a quick assessment of relative geometry. Base-salt dips northward and projects beneath the basin to the left. Extremely fast, asymmetric subsidence in the salt-floored basin is largely due to rapid displacement of massive salt. The basin is bounded by a growth fault that terminates at depth against the base of the salt nappe, placing Plio-Pleistocene strata against underlying, probably lower Tertiary strata.

since at least late Eocene time. The landward dip of the basal salt surface shows that this is not a downward-gliding gravity flow, but rather a gravity-spreading feature (in the sense of Ramberg, 1981) that reflects the dynamic interaction of three principal factors: tectonic subsidence rate, deposition rate of abyssal strata, and displacement rate of the salt (related to sedimentary loading updip).

A second north-south seismic line (Fig. 16), located near and east of the basins shown at the north end of Figure 15, illustrates the relations among the base-salt surface, a growth fault, and a sedimentary mini-basin in its early stage. The allochthonous salt is even thicker on this line, reaching a thickness here up to 7 km (23,000 ft). The adjacent mini-basin to the north is subsiding as a wedge against this salt, truncating against an immense landward-dipping growth fault at the salt interface. At first glance, the base-salt surface to the south seems perched high relative to the base of the mini-basin, but this is the result of several seconds of velocity pull-up. The differential velocity effect has been corrected on this time section, and the base salt surface has been redrawn relative to the velocity of adjacent sediments. Thus, the corrected surface shows where the surface would be in time if the salt had the same velocity as adjacent mini-basin strata. This "corrected" base-salt surface projects beneath the adjacent mini-basin, shown near the northern terminus of a growth fault, at a depth of about 9 km (30,000 ft).

Mini-basin strata deposited on the salt, while not penetrated here by drilling, are most likely Plio-Pleistocene in age. The basal sediments in this mini-basin now appear to rest essentially upon probable late Eocene–early Oligocene(?) abyssal plain strata visible beneath a presumably evacuated allochthonous salt layer. The intervening hiatus between the basal Plio-Pleistocene mini-basin strata and underlying early Tertiary abyssal plain sequences represents the time interval required for the salt nappe to progressively spread laterally across this area, build up in thickness, and be displaced by the strata deposited within the overlying mini-basin.

"Down-building" origin of certain salt domes as determined by palinspastic analysis. Most salt domes and massifs flanking mini-basins like the one described above appear to owe their origin mainly to a "down-building" mechanism rather than diapirism, piercement, or "up-building." (For a discussion on terminology and mechanisms of salt dome emplacement, see Barton, 1933, and Jackson and others, 1988.) This conclusion is based partly on seismic data in the region of the salt nappe, and partly on palinspastic analyses. To illustrate this process, a simple reconstruction of a shelf salt dome will be discussed below, and will be followed by a reconstruction of part of the upper Louisiana continental slope showing the relationship between growth faulting and salt.

A north-south cross section through a Louisiana salt dome (Eugene Island Block 175) is shown in Figure 17a. The south flank is steeply dipping, but the north flank is more gently inclined. Surrounding strata range from older bathyal (dark gray) to younger, middle neritic deposits. Strata on the north side dip regionally southward toward the dome and are deeper than equivalent strata on the south side. Two large, east-west–striking, landward-dipping faults that terminate against the dome accommodate this displacement out of the plane of this section.

On the gently dipping north flank, a thin "sheath" of geopressured bathyal shale extends up the flank. Overlying neritic strata disconformably onlap this sheath. Such sheaths were at one time thought to be portions of older bathyal shales "dragged up" by upward-moving diapiric salt. A palinspastic reconstruction of this dome by a proprietary computer-assisted palinspastic program (PREP) suggests a different origin (Fig. 18). (The techniques employed by PREP are discussed in the Appendix.) The bottom reconstruction shows conditions at the time this area was on the continental slope. The "dome" was at this time a broad, flat-topped slope salt mass, of the type common on the present Louisiana slope (e.g., see Fig. 15). The shale "sheath" reconstructs as the thin cover of this flat-topped mass (an idea earlier suggested by Johnson and Bredeson, 1971). The dome evolves as the north flank of the slope salt mass collapses at the onset of neritic sedimentation.

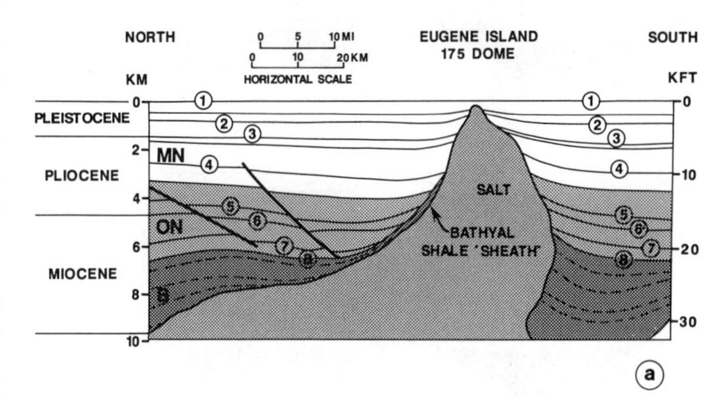

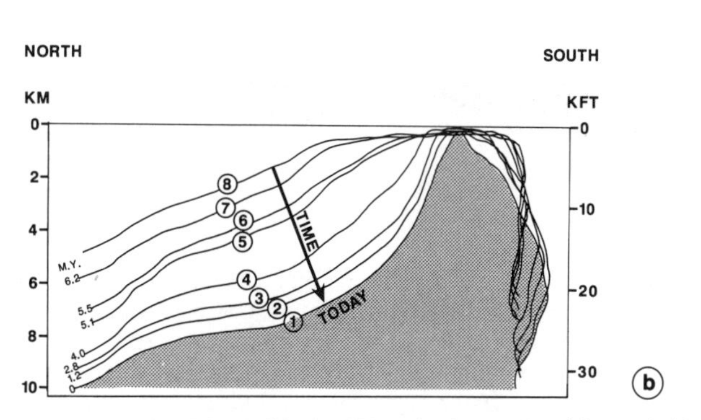

Figure 17. Eugene Island Block 175 salt dome, Louisiana shelf: (A) Depth cross section without vertical exaggeration. MN = middle neritic; ON = outer neritic; B = bathyal. Note shale "sheath" on northern flank. (B) Relative position of top-salt for eight reconstructed time intervals (see Fig. 18); note collapse of north flank of original slope massif through time. Also note lack of "upward diapiric" motion in this dome; the dome has always been high since the earliest stage of reconstruction shown.

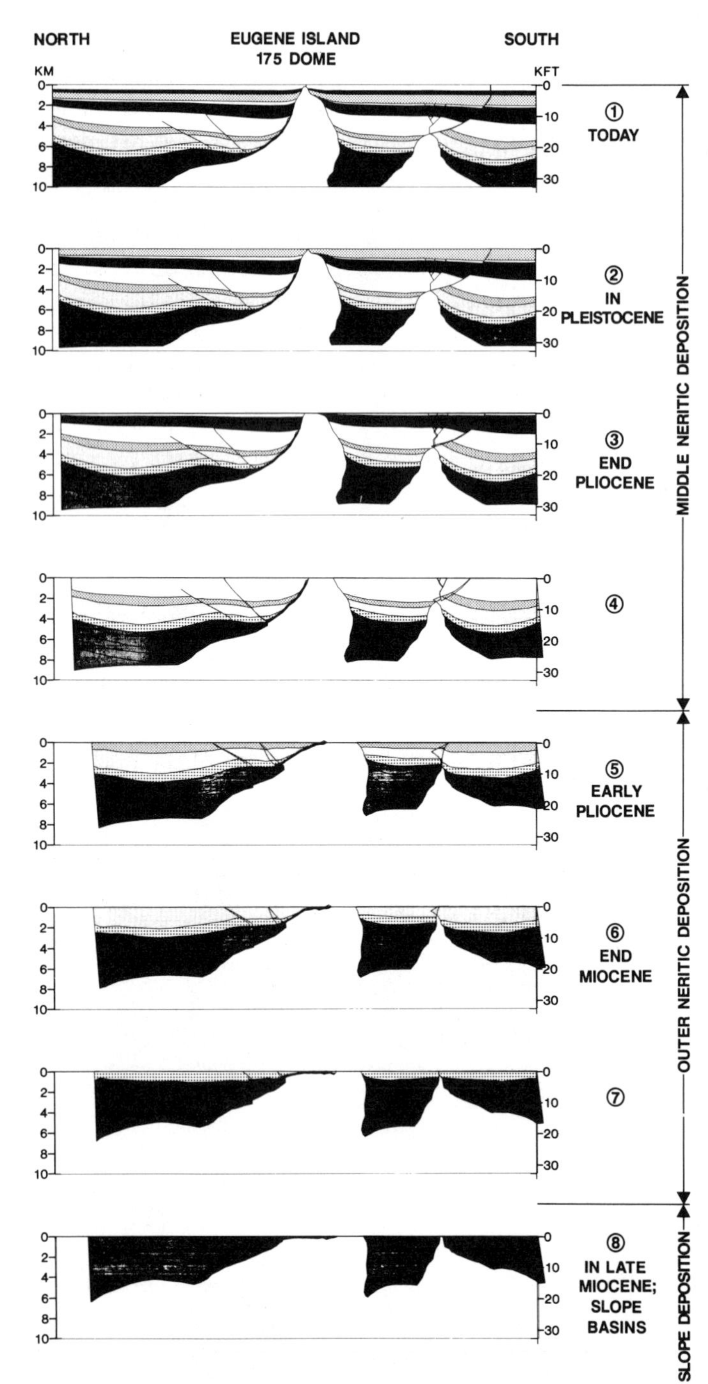

Figure 18. PREP-drawn palinspastic reconstructions, Eugene Island Block 175 dome. No vertical exaggeration. Compare with Figure 17 for strata correlations (circled numbers refer to reconstructions at stratal datums numbered in Fig. 17a). Not corrected for bathymetry. Note that the shale sheath in frame 1, present-day, is the remnant of a thin cover over what was once a large, flat-topped slope salt massif (bottom frame). Base of section (frame 1) is at an arbitrary depth.

The rapid collapse of the north flank of the massif is represented by a tracing of the top-salt surface through time (Fig. 17b). The motion of the top-salt surface in this dome is generally downward, not upward or "diapiric" relative to the sea floor. In like manner, the shale sheath has not been dragged up from depth, but has, in fact, always moved downward from its origin as a thin shale veneer deposited over the thick slope-salt mass. The basin directly south of the dome appears in its early stages (bottom reconstruction) as a slope basin bounded by a fault contact against salt, and appears to be subsiding into salt. Because the base of the system is not here observable, we cannot speculate as to the thickness of the original salt body, which was presumably at least in part evacuated to form this mid-Tertiary slope basin. Clearly, however, this basin is mainly the result of "downbuilding" of the salt, and in no way can this particular present-day dome be described as an upward-moving, narrow-piercement diapir that simply intrudes surrounding basins and faults. Most offshore Gulf of Mexico geologists are quite familiar with the "down-building" concept. Unfortunately, however, the term "diapir" very often continues to be used as a synonym for "salt dome" in the region regardless of the wide variety of emplacement mechanisms known to occur.

The similar development of an incipient dome near the present shelf-slope break is shown in a second reconstruction (Fig. 19). This figure illustrates better the dependence of growth faults on salt displacement in this province. Like the Eugene Island 175 dome, the gently dipping north flank of this salt dome originated from the collapse of the north flank of an originally more extensive slope salt mass. Auxiliary growth faults on the north flank terminate at depth against, and displace, salt. In older systems on the middle and inner shelf as well as onshore, similar faults are more deeply buried, and hence, their downdip termini are not always observable. Nonetheless, palinspastic logic suggests a common origin. The base of the salt is not observable here; that indicated by the base of shading in Figure 19 is arbitrary. The basin to the south of the dome, like its counterpart in Eugene Island 175, is fault-bounded on either side against salt, and as reconstructed appears to be subsiding into a sea of salt.

An important observation to be made from this section involves the change with time in the reconstructed area of salt. Using the arbitrary base of salt shown, several times as much salt appears to have existed on this section in Pliocene time as exists now. Because the base of the salt cannot actually be observed, salt volume cannot be reconstructed and conclusions must be tentative. However, this situation is not unique in this province, and, in fact, represents the norm in making reconstructions in the central Louisiana offshore. It is inferred that at least some of this apparent "excess" salt was involved in the basinward shifting of the Sigsbee salt nappe. Sedimentary loading in basins adjacent to salt domes like those discussed is inferred to provide the dominant driving force behind the nappe.

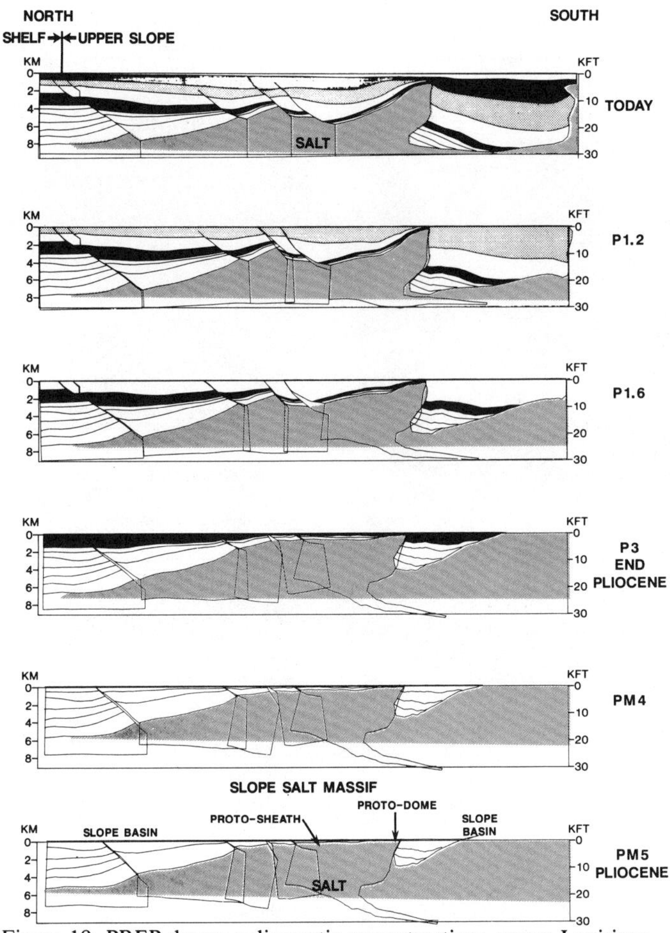

Figure 19. PREP-drawn palinspastic reconstructions, upper Louisiana slope. Note similarities with development of Eugene Island 175 dome. This slope dome, however, is not as structurally mature. Note collapse of the north flank of slope massif with attendant development of dome and accompanying compressed "sheath" section. Note also decreasing amount of salt in cross section through time (although base of salt here is not known or implied).

Regional cross section and discussion. The regional context of the Sigsbee salt nappe, as well as its extraordinary scale, is displayed in a regional cross section through onshore and offshore Louisiana (Fig. 20a). The south end of the line is located at the extreme southward bulge of the Sigsbee Escarpment, geographically well to the east of the seismic line shown in Figure 15 (see Fig. 1 for location). The interpretation is based on reflection and refraction seismic data. Speculative interpretations in poorly resolved or unresolved regions of seismic reflection data are dashed and are undoubtedly more complex than shown. In the vicinity of this section, allochthonous salt as thick as 7.6 km (25,000 ft) has been observed on seismic data, and projections of the landward-dipping base of allochthonous salt suggest even greater thicknesses to the north. As previously mentioned, available data indicate that this salt mass has been moving southward probably since at least late Eocene time.

Truncated sub-nappe strata are nearly flat in the above regional section (Fig. 20a), similar to the sub-nappe strata observed in Figure 15. However, in areas to the east, these same strata become involved in deep folds at the base of the slope, reportedly rooting in autochthonous Jurassic salt (Martin, 1984).

What was the configuration of the northern Gulf at the end of Louann Salt deposition? Simple palinspastic logic suggests a Late Jurassic reconstruction similar to that shown in Figure 20b, where a thick salt-filled basin rests landward of an active spreading center. Such a scenario was suggested by Humphris (1978, 1979), who noted an analogy with the Miocene salt deposits of the Red Sea. Following the Late Cretaceous drowning of mid-Cretaceous carbonate margins in the northern Gulf, progradational unstable shelf edges and slope mini-basins, like those on today's slope, built out over autochthonous salt. This progradation displaced the salt in a myriad of complex ways and resulted in the creation of a giant allochthonous salt nappe, which progressively overrode penecontemporaneous abyssal plain sediments at its distal termination.

Summary. The immense scale of the Sigsbee salt nappe is unique among described geometries in the world's salt basins, and is one of the largest single structural features of the North American continent. As a comparative aid, a cross section through the more familiar, but of course structurally dissimilar, Swiss Alps is included in Figure 20c. The large Helvetic and Pennine nappes are dwarfed in size by the Sigsbee salt nappe. Subsidence rates within the mini-basins above this thick allochthonous salt are among the highest on earth. In local places on the Louisiana upper slope, Pleistocene strata reach thicknesses of over 7.6 km (25,000 ft). The conceptualization of the Sigsbee nappe by Humphris and its substantiation by regional seismic data over the past ten years have marked a most exciting development in regional geological concepts in the Gulf of Mexico.

In addition to the tectonic phenomena in the Louisiana offshore described above, many other salt-related structural features exist that are beyond the scope of this chapter. In fact, very little data has as yet been published for much of the region. What is clear is that the Louisiana continental margin is not simply a progradational delta where salt plays a passive, largely intrusive role unrelated to sedimentation and growth faulting. Salt has been fundamental to the evolution of growth faults, mini-basins, and in fact, most tectonic phenomena. Scaled cross sections and palinspastic analysis demonstrate load-induced growth faulting and gravity spreading (see later discussion) above a mobile substratum, rather than growth faulting related to purely down-slope gravitational gliding.

Texas structural style

Introduction. The unifying concepts of underlying deep structure so clear in "Louisiana-style" structure are not so obvious for "Texas-style" growth faults for a variety of rea-

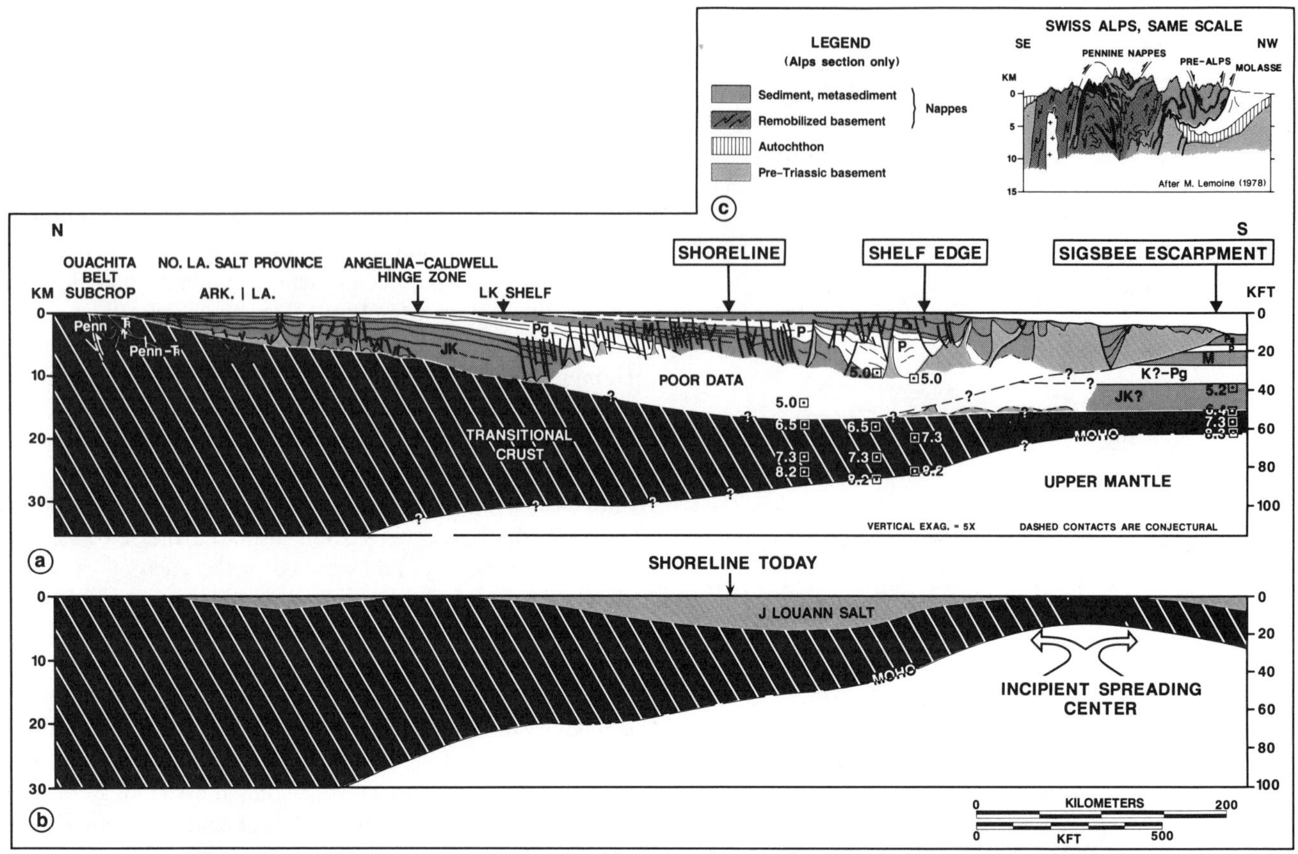

Figure 20. (a) North-south cross section, Louisiana; location on Figure 1. Vertical exaggeration = 5×. Dashed contacts highly conjectural. Northern half of section from A. D. Scardina (Shell Development Company, 1983). Refraction data in km/sec from Shell files. JK = Jurassic–Cretaceous; Pg = Paleogene; M = Miocene; P = Pliocene; Ps = Pleistocene. (b) Hypothetical reconstruction, mid-Jurassic time; (c) (upper right) Cross section of Swiss Alps after M. Lemoine (1978) drawn to same scale for comparison. The Sigsbee salt nappe is one of the largest structural features in North America and is apparently unique in scale if not structural style among the world's salt basins.

sons. The geology of much of the Texas slope is less well known, and is further complicated by the compressional, deeply rooted Perdido folds at the base of the continental slope (Fig. 2; Martin, 1984). In Texas, growth faults are longer in plan view, more regular, and outwardly do not appear to be salt-related. This has led to several hypotheses for their origin, including gravity sliding. However, very little of the deep structural underpinnings of these systems is visible on presently available seismic data, and very few palinspastic reconstructions have been attempted to test structural interpretations.

This section attempts to address the origin of "Texas-style" growth-fault systems and will proceed in the following order: (1) a brief review of the regional setting as well as the development of "peripheral" fault zones; (2) a review of the development of concepts regarding these "Texas-style" listric growth faults; and (3) a discussion of a palinspastic reconstruction of one of these fault systems, the Corsair fault of the Texas shelf, as well as a discussion of a regional seismic and structural cross section and its implications for the development of "Texas-style" growth faults.

Regional setting and peripheral fault zones. A vertically exaggerated but scaled structural cross section (Fig. 21), from the Llano uplift in central Texas southeast to the abyssal plain (see Fig. 1 for location), constructed from surface, seismic, and well data, constitutes the basis for the following discussion. Only subsurface structural and stratigraphic features that are reasonably well observed on the seismic lines or in nearby wells are shown; the lack of extrapolation allows a relatively unbiased appraisal of what is known about the deep structure of the region underlying the San Marcos arch. This cross section and an accompanying composited seismic line are shown in detail on Plate 4.

Regional setting. Early Gulf of Mexico history is reflected on Plate 4 by lower Paleozoic strata and Precambrian granite of the North American craton and low-grade metamorphic rocks of the Ouachita system, which underlie Cretaceous strata in central Texas. On this section, seismic data show minor imbrication of Precambrian basement rocks with a structural culmination similar to that drilled along strike to the northeast near Waco, Texas (Nicholas and Rozendal, 1975). Postorogenic, latest Paleozoic marine deposits (Vernon, 1971) as well as Permian–Triassic–earliest Jurassic red beds have been penetrated by drilling in the region (Woods and Addington, 1973), and are weakly visible on the seismic data. These strata are thickening southeastward where last observed, but it is unknown how thick they are beneath the Gulf Coastal Plain. They are overlain by Jurassic Louann Salt southeast of the subcropping Ouachita-Marathon system.

Basin-rimming fault zones. A number of relatively minor fault zones lie northwest of the Lower Cretaceous shelf margin. The origin of these fault zones, which are peripheral to much larger growth faults downdip, is germane to the overall topic of growth fault mechanics. From the Llano uplift seaward (see Figs. 2, 21, and Plate I), one crosses the: (1) Balcones and Luling fault zones; (2) Mexia-Talco and Fashing fault zones; (3) unnamed faults expanding Late Jurassic Cotton Valley strata; and finally, (4) faulting affecting the Lower and Middle Cretaceous carbonate shelf margin. The origins of these peripheral fault zones are generally well understood relative to the much larger growth faults farther downdip:

(1) The northeast-southwest–trending Balcones fault system is paralleled immediately to the southeast by the Luling fault zone. Both fault systems have relatively minor displacement (usually much less than 300 m) and define the flanks of a regional graben. Seismic and well data indicate that these systems cut lower Tertiary, Mesozoic, and late Paleozoic strata of the Ouachita fold belt without any apparent expansion of Mesozoic or earliest Tertiary strata. This and similar graben systems occur along a hinge zone at the northern rim of the Gulf basin that typically separates flat-lying Lower Cretaceous strata northwest of the zone from strata to the southeast, which dip gently gulfward (Fig. 21). It seems plausible that this fault system developed in Tertiary time as a tensional phenomenon associated with crustal downwarping related to differential tectonics, as well as load-induced subsidence, of the Gulf basin (Walthall and Walper, 1967; Holcomb, 1971; Dunbar and Sawyer, 1988).

(2) The Mexia-Talco fault system, lying structurally basinward from the trends of the Luling and Balcones fault systems, occupies a position near the updip limit of the Jurassic Louann Salt (Figs. 2 and 5). Seismic data indicate that it is essentially a salt withdrawal–induced graben with faults terminating on the pre-salt surface (Fig. 21). This salt-controlled basin-rimming fault system extends into southern Arkansas (Hughes, 1968; Bishop, 1973) and forms the northern flank of the well-known and highly structured shelfal salt provinces of east Texas, northern Louisiana, and central Mississippi.

The Fashing fault zone (Karnes trough) is similar to the Mexia-Talco zone in that it, too, is salt controlled. A well adjacent to the composite seismic line shown in Plate 4 penetrated a Jurassic sequence several hundred meters thinner than normal before penetrating Jurassic Louann Salt; the missing section was faulted out by a listric down-to-the-coast fault that terminates in salt. Along the line of the regional section, displacement is greater than the Mexia-Talco system, perhaps indicating a slight thickening of the original Louann Salt in the seaward direction.

(3) Listric, down-to-the-coast, pre-Cretaceous growth faults transecting Jurassic Cotton Valley strata occur seaward of the Karnes trough and terminate on the pre-salt surface. These faults, too, seem to be related to early salt displacement, and are quite similar to the salt "rollers" shown in Figure 6.

(4) At the Lower Cretaceous shelf margin are faults that display somewhat larger amounts of displacement and were active during Cretaceous and early Tertiary time. Although the seismic data are much less definitive than for the previous systems, it seems likely that these faults also terminate at the pre-salt surface.

Texas growth faults. Seaward of the Lower Cretaceous carbonate shelf margin, extending across both the coastal plain and the Texas continental shelf, are numerous large, listric, basinward-dipping growth faults with attendant minor structures such as rollover folding and antithetic faulting (Fig. 21 and Plate 4). These faults differ from the previously discussed basin-rimming fault zones in several ways. Whereas these peripheral faults show modest amounts of slip, the growth fault systems downdip show thousands of meters of slip. For example, dip-slip in the lower part of the offshore Corsair system is greater than 10 km, as opposed to a hundred meters or so of dip-slip in the Mexia-Talco zone. Accompanying this spectacular increase in fault displacement is related contemporaneous thickening of strata of large proportions. These downdip fault systems also differ from the more peripheral faults in that much less is known about the basal terminations of these larger growth faults, because the greater depth of burial has in most places obscured these relationships. These systems are progressively younger basinward, and successively younger strata are involved in the stratal thickening across faults. Thus, older rocks are successively faulted below the limits of seismic resolution or basinward well-log correlation.

Historical perspective. Before proceeding with a detailed discussion of some of the very large Cenozoic listric faults shown on this section, it is necessary to place the various concepts regarding the origin of these features in a historical perspective. Because these are purely subsurface features, with little or no surface expression, concepts as to their shape or origin have only slowly evolved with the equally slow accumulation of well and seismic control.

The flexure concept. In the 1930s, W. S. Adkins (unpublished) among others, observed zones of rapid thickening in the Vicksburg, Frio, and Anahuac Formations in the Texas Coastal Plain. These zones occurred downdip from areas in which there was only very gradual basinward thickening. Adkins thought the rapid thickening of Tertiary strata in these zones reflected prior basin bathymetric relief, caused by "flexuring with probable faulting." Lohse (1958, Shell Oil Company, unpublished) showed this flexure concept in a regional stratigraphic section (Fig. 22) that depicted each successively more seaward zone of flexuring as representing progradation over an older shelf margin.

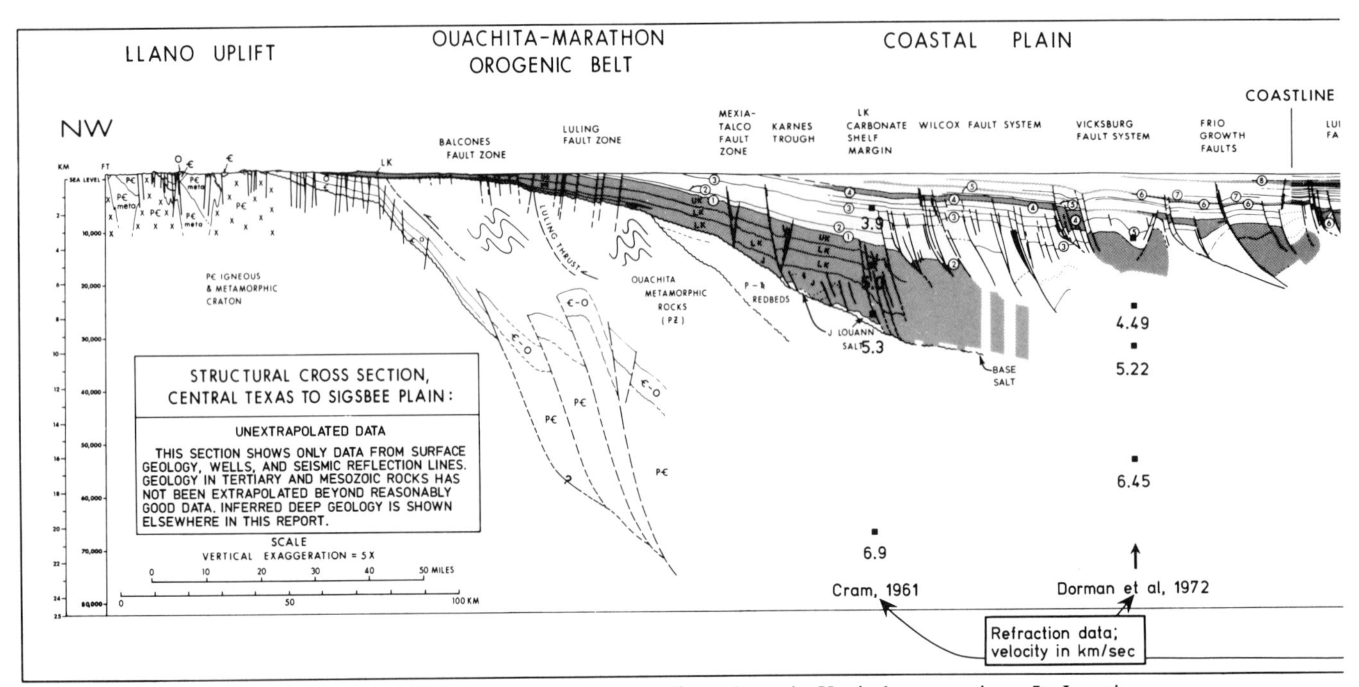

Figure 21. Structural cross section across Texas continental margin. Vertical exaggeration = 5×. Location shown on Figure 1. Plate 4 contains a true scale, more detailed version with seismic data. Mesozoic and Cenozoic geology not extrapolated beyond reasonably good control. The position of the Luling thrust and an unnamed thrust to the west are taken from well control discussed by Flawn and others (1961).

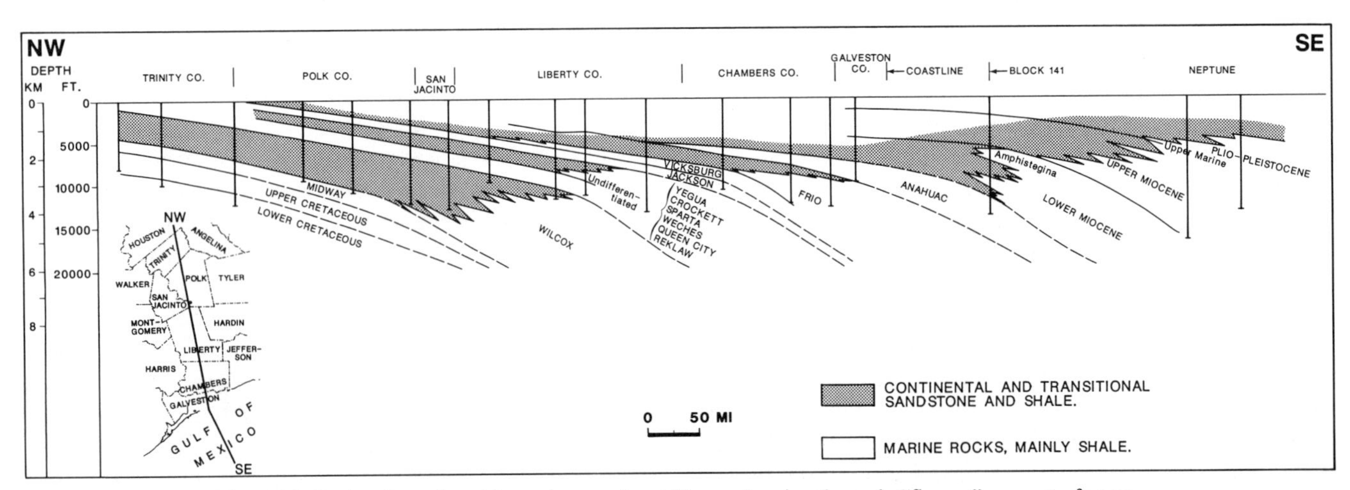

Figure 22. Regional stratigraphic section, southeast Texas, showing the early "flexure" concept of zones of rapid stratigraphic thickening (from E. A. Lohse, Shell Oil Company, 1958, unpublished).

With increasingly better subsurface data in the late 1950s and early 1960s, Hardin and Hardin (1961) observed, "The accentuated rate of dip found on regional cross sections downdip is commonly more apparent than real. Much of the increase in depth of sediments downdip from flexures is caused by contemporaneous faulting rather than warping of the sediments." They believed that so-called "flexures" were really syndepositional faults that formed at the shelf edge by gravitational sliding (Fig. 23).

Although the flexure concept was thus quickly replaced by the idea of growth faulting as the cause of such rapid stratal thickening, it nevertheless has left a large but subtle impact on the thinking of many geologists to the present day. Note, for example, that Hardin and Hardin's schematic representation (Fig. 23), while providing a much more plausible mechanism for large-scale stratal thickening, nonetheless shows a "locus of accentuated dip" (paleoslope) much steeper than the present-day, 1.5- to 2-degree, bathymetric upper slope in offshore Texas. Many, if not most,

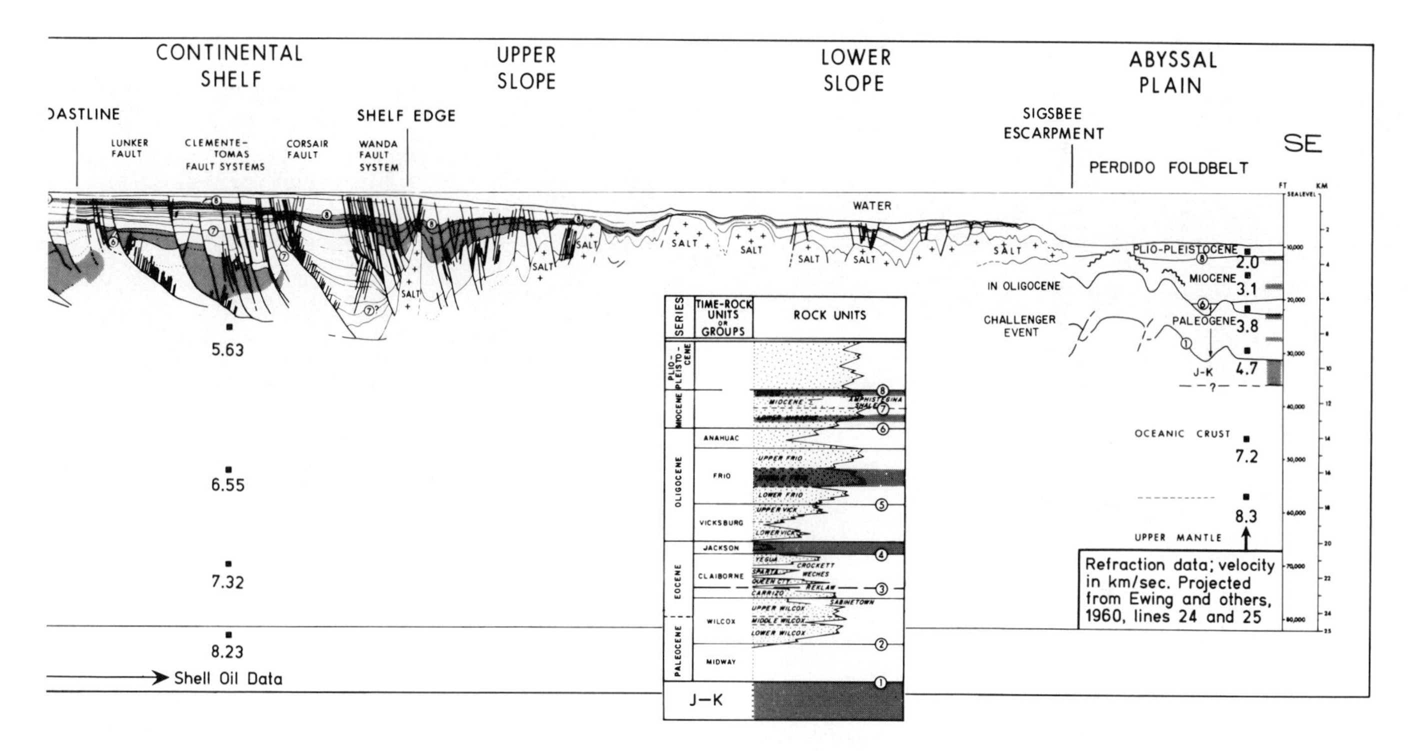

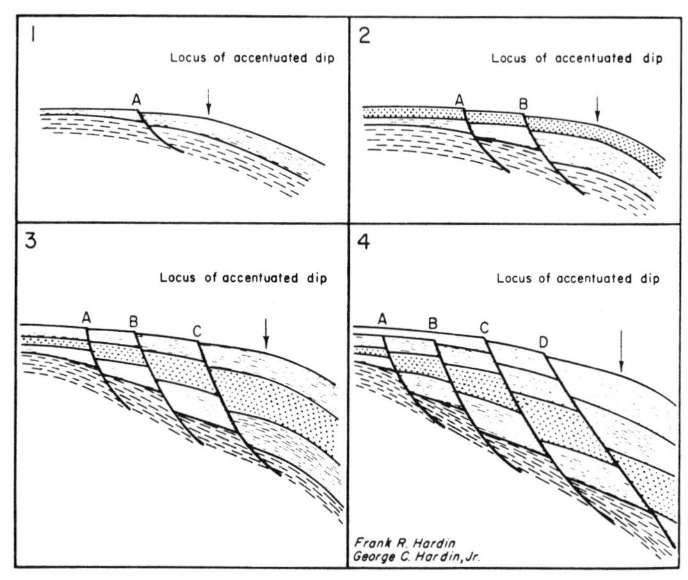

Figure 23. Stratigraphic thickening by development of growth faults at the shelf-slope break, as interpreted by Hardin and Hardin (1961). Compare with Figure 22.

conceptual and cartoon cross sections in the literature showing either the development of growth faults or gross regional relationships show a bathymetric slope much steeper than the present-day slope (i.e., see Figs. 10, 11, 23, 29, and 32). The common tendency to conceptualize a steep slope can be explained by a perceived requirement to have a downward-sloping glide plane of sufficient relief to cause growth faulting (discussed below), and evokes, in a subtle way, the original flexure concept. The vestigial term "flexure" has descended to this day as reflected in the commonly used names for major onshore growth fault systems—the "Wilcox flexure," the "Vicksburg flexure," etc.

Shale flow and differential compaction. Many workers have proposed that rapid local subsidence associated with growth faulting is due to flow of a ductile material (either salt or shale) at depth. In Texas, the relative absence of near-surface salt features has been cited as evidence for thin or absent salt at depth (e.g., Halbouty, 1967). As was pointed out by Harding and Lowell (1979), this lack of near-surface salt has also been used by many as a reason to invoke shale as the ductile and compressible material responsible for a variety of structural phenomena instead of mobile salt.

Berg and others (1979), for example, hypothesized that the uplift of ductile geopressured shale induced gravity sliding in the Vicksburg fault system in south Texas (Fig. 24). Honea (1956), Carver (1968), and Bruce (1973, 1983) favored compaction of thick geopressured shales as a mechanism to accommodate greatly thickened strata downdip from Texas growth faults. Bruce (1973) discussed a similar concept whereby thick masses of overpressured shale are overridden by regressive and eustatic still-stand pulses of clastic sediments that formed growth fault systems "primarily by differential compaction with some gravity adjustment" (Figs. 25 and 26). Bruce envisioned that "regional contemporaneous fault systems are formed on the seaward side of underlying shale masses, where all down-to-basin faults flatten and converge with depth" and that growth faults "die out at or near the depositional axis of the adjacent syncline."

Although shale compaction clearly plays some role in the formation of space for thickened strata in the downthrown block of growth faults, data shown on the regional seismic line and

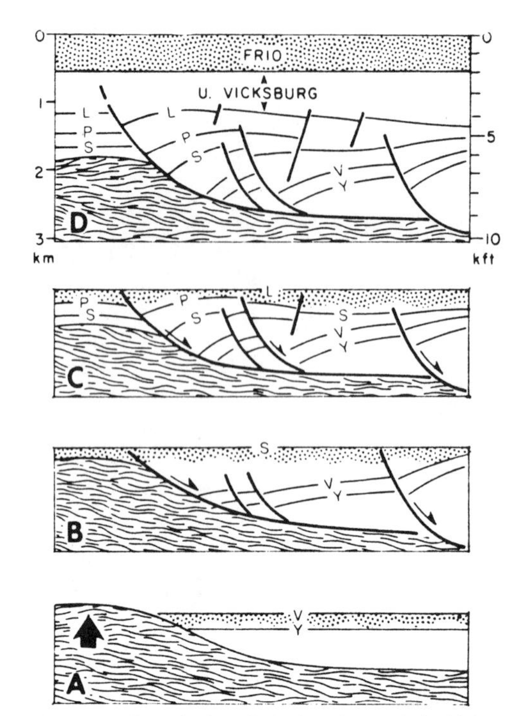

Figure 24. Concept of gravitationally induced growth faulting and sliding caused by shale uplift (wavy pattern) as proposed by Berg and others (1979). (L, P, S, V, and Y are producing Oligocene lower Vicksburg sandstones in the West McAllen Ranch field of south Texas.)

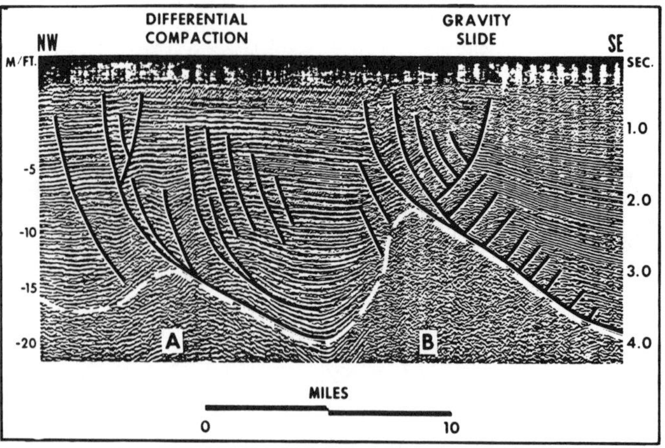

Figure 25. Seismic time section offshore Texas with interpretation of growth faults (from Bruce, 1973). Four-second record length.

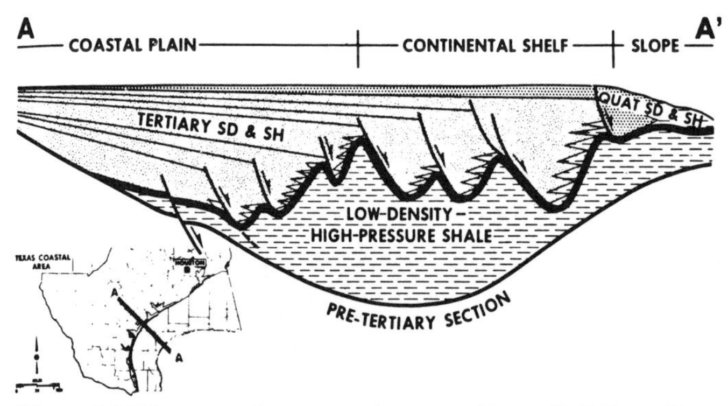

Figure 26. Diagrammatic cross section across Texas Gulf Coast (from Bruce, 1973), showing concept of thick shale masses underlying growth fault packages.

cross section (Plate 4) suggest that growth faulting in Texas may have another explanation. A segment of the regional seismic line (reproduced as Fig. 27) is very close to the location of that line used by Bruce (Fig. 25) but is of more recent vintage with somewhat better resolution at depth. The fault zone labeled "differential compaction" in Figure 25 is the Clemente-Tomas fault (Fig. 27); the fault labeled "gravity slide" is the Corsair fault. Note that these newer data reach significantly below the 4-second record of Figure 25, and the better resolution shows that these faults do not terminate in the adjacent synclines at 4 seconds, but rather extend into a near-flat horizon at 5 seconds or more (more than 7.6 km [25,000 ft] in depth). Thus, although the growth faults indeed flatten at depth, the sedimentary section deposited (envisioned by Bruce to have been accommodated by differential compaction of underlying geopressured shale) is considerably thicker than shown in Figure 25. Moreover, the interpreted relict shale mass at A on Figure 25 between 3 and 4 seconds is better resolved on the more recent data (Fig. 27). These data show that the growth faults transect folded and faulted, but nevertheless, coherent sedimentary strata rather than amorphous flowing shale.

The amount of stratal thickening across these regional growth-fault systems is very large; for example, the Corsair fault system discussed below exhibits greater than 4 km of stratal expansion across the fault. (Compare the upper to middle Miocene interval [horizons "M-2" to "M-11"] on either side of the fault on Plate 4.) If the growth faults were accommodated by shale compaction, space would need to be created by compaction of shales beneath the fault system. However, the magnitude of compaction possible for even geopressured shales at depths greater than a kilometer or so is small (Baldwin and Butler, 1985; Perrier and Quiblier, 1974); hence, compaction seems an unlikely mechanism to handle this magnitude of stratal expansion (e.g., 4 km).

Gravitational mechanisms. It will be useful for the remainder of this chapter to differentiate between two basic classes of gravity phenomena that develop under slope conditions (Ramberg, 1981; see Fig. 28): (1) gravity gliding—the downslope sliding of rock masses; and (2) gravitational collapse and spreading—the slow, plastic vertical collapse and complementary lateral spreading of rock masses. By far the most common hypothesis for Texas growth faulting cited in the literature has been that of gravity gliding. Although gravity gliding is a common shear-surface phenomenon in the region, we will

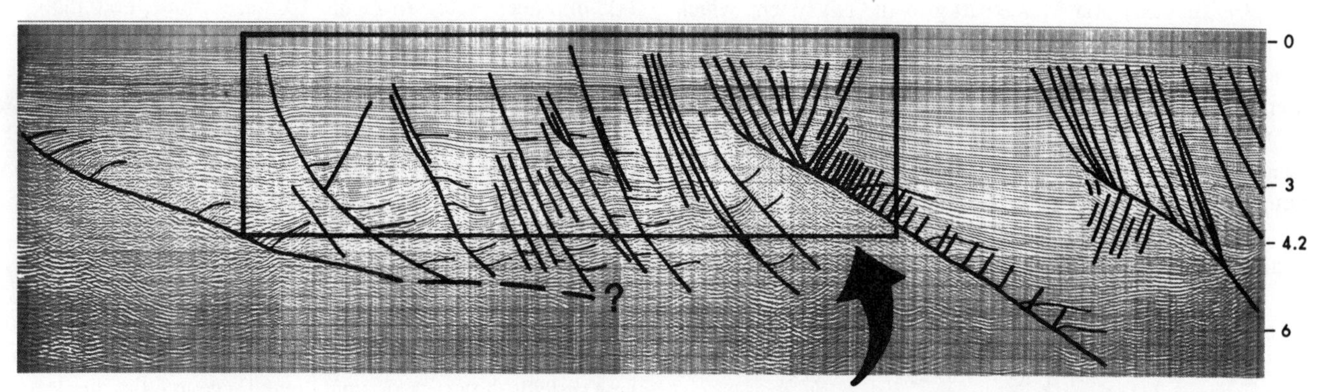

Figure 27. A portion of regional seismic section (Plate 4) that is parallel to and a few miles from the section shown in Figure 26. Seven-second record length allows considerably better resolution of the deeper portions of the growth-fault systems.

attempt to document that it is not a viable mechanism to account for most of the large growth faults of this province.

Gravity gliding as a growth fault mechanism is implicit in the early work of Hardin and Hardin (1961; see Fig. 23) and Bornhauser (1958). The concept was further advanced by the clay model studies of Cloos (1968). Cloos assumed that Gulf Coast growth faults represented "regional gravity creep of the sedimentary blanket into the basin." To model this, he placed a slab of wet clay over a layer of paraffin wax. When heated, the paraffin became ductile and allowed the overlying clay to slide when the layers were inclined. The result was a normal fault. Cloos reasoned that if fault movement happened during deposition, the units would, of course, be thicker on the downthrown side. When Cloos repeated the experiment on a larger inclined slab, an arcuate fracture pattern resulted, which Cloos thought was similar to that of the Gulf basin in plan view. Cloos' paraffin wax acted as a mobile detachment horizon, which in the "real world" would be salt according to some workers (e.g., Wilhelm and Ewing, 1972; Fig. 10), and shale according to others.

The type of detachment surface most typically invoked for Texas growth faults involves down-slope slippage on a geopressured shale surface that has been buried by rapidly prograding sands (Fig. 29). Low-angle detachment faults above shale, known to occur in the Vicksburg system of portions of onshore south Texas (Berg and others, 1979; Edwards, 1981; Erxleben and Carnahan, 1983), have been explained as due to gravitational gliding (see later discussion related to Fig. 48). Edwards (1981) states that the growth faults "were maintained by gulfward gravity sliding of the upper layer of Wilcox deltaic and upper slope sediments over deeper, geopressured slope shales."

The work of Crans and others (1980) and Crans and Mandle (1980) explored the mechanics of growth faulting

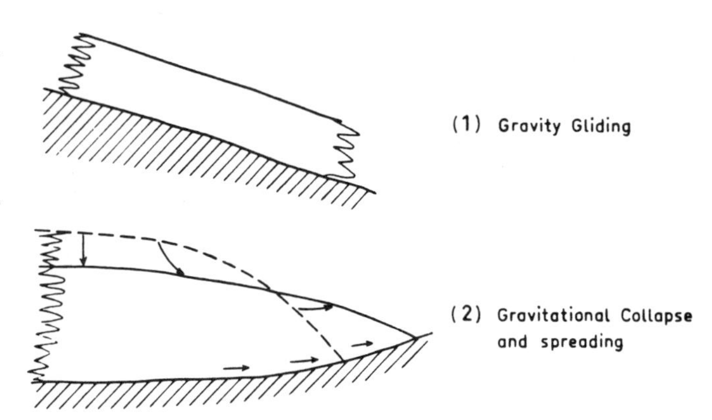

Figure 28. Two gravitational transport mechanisms (from Ramberg, 1981).

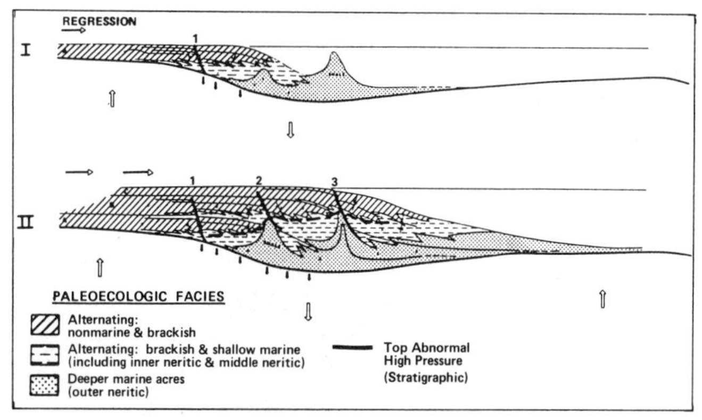

Figure 29. Hypothetical section showing gravity faulting on deep shale substrate (from G. B. Martin, 1978).

not specific to the Gulf of Mexico. Their studies suggest that growth faults could originate on slump surfaces parallel to the slope where the slope is underlain by geopressured deltaic shales (Fig. 30). They envision a three-part growth-fault system, which like some of the above examples, essentially slumps into deeper water, displacing the water column (Fig. 31): (1) an updip extensional region; (2) a downdip compressional toe, consisting of either folds or thrusts that balance updip extension; and (3) a "rigid block" in between 1 and 2 that is simply translated with the slumping mass.

As previously mentioned, most conceptual gravity gliding models of "Texas style" growth faults are illustrated with a nonscaled diagrammatic representation of a much steeper slope than actually exists (e.g., Figs. 10, 23, 29, and 32), usually with the implicit inference that most sediments variously build out and glide into deep water. In Figure 10, for example, note that the water column above the abyssal plain is envisioned as high enough to accommodate the total thickness of sediment above the basinward-slumping fault system. This and other similar diagrams that exaggerate the dip of the slope infer that the space required for the sediment involved in the basinward slumping is created mainly by the displacement of an equivalent volume of water.

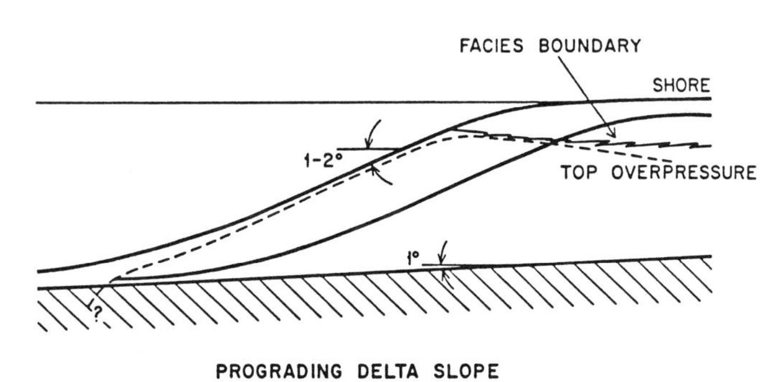

Figure 30. Schematic cross section of prograding delta front, with top of geopressures (shown as a dashed line) envisioned to control the formation of a parallel but deeper glide plane for gravity sliding (from Mandl and Crans, 1981).

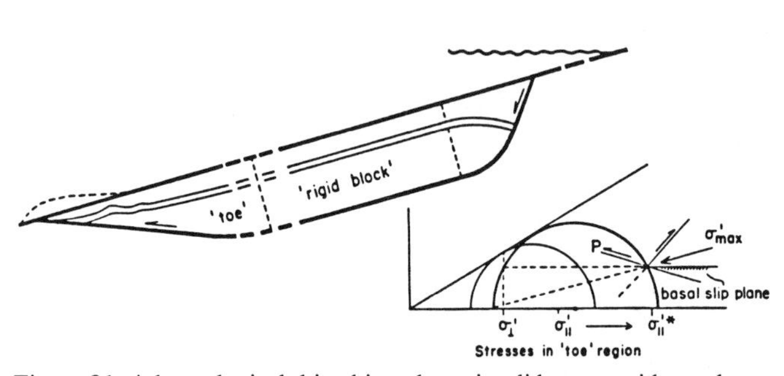

Figure 31. A hypothetical thin-skinned gravity slide mass with toe thrust (from Mandl and Crans, 1981). A detachment surface is hypothesized to develop below the top of geopressures (see Fig. 24).

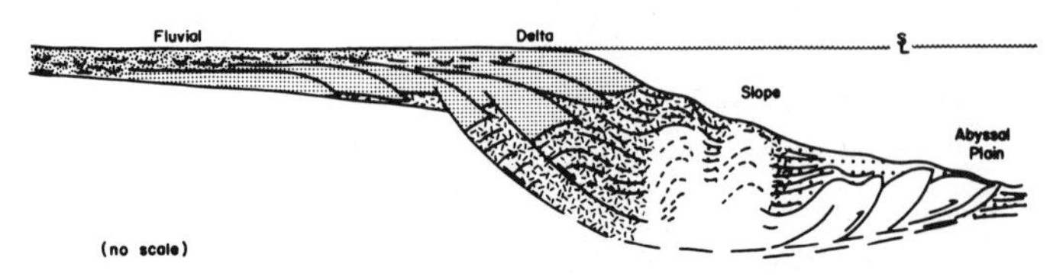

Figure 32. Sketch section showing hypothetical Gulf-like margin with growth faults and compressional features (from Galloway, 1986).

Growth fault geometries.

Miocene to Recent systems. In Texas, references to gravity gliding as a growth fault mechanism have been applied mainly to earlier Tertiary onshore systems (i.e., Wilcox and Vicksburg). In these systems, however, original downdip geometries are deeply buried and obliterated by younger fault systems, making the model difficult to evaluate. For this reason, it may be more illuminating to look at some younger Texas growth-fault systems where evolving structural geometries can be more completely visualized. We recognize that this approach, of course, carries the implicit risk that the present is not always the key to the past.

The geometries of Miocene to Recent fault systems offshore Texas are highlighted in Figure 33 (modified from the regional 1:1 cross section in Plate 4). Immediate differences with some of the models depicted in Figures 10, 23, 29, and 32 are clear. (1) The present slope has an extremely gentle, not steep, inclination. The youngest fault system at the present shelf-slope break cuts both steeply and deeply into the upper slope. The inclinations of the faults are not subparallel to the very gently inclined upper slope, and clearly these are not thin-skinned gravity glides of the sort pictured in Figure 31. (2) The listric faults, which expand Miocene to Pleistocene strata, cut deeply to depths of around 10,000 m (33,000 ft), several times as deep as the abyssal plain water depth of less than 3,000 m (10,000 ft). Whatever the mechanisms of faulting here, these faults are not simply shifting sediments downslope into deep water and displacing the water column. (3) The present slope is not the simple prograding delta system envisioned in many gravity slide models (e.g., Fig. 29), but a complex mass of shallow salt masses and intervening slope basins, not unlike the Louisiana slope in many respects.

This is not to say, however, that thin-skinned gravity gliding phenomena of the sort envisioned by Crans and Mandl do not exist on the continental slope. Such mass-wasting features are common; Figure 34 is an example (from Berryhill and others, 1987). These slumps from the Texas upper slope are shown here with a large, 16×, vertical exaggeration. They are clearly gravitational and develop parallel to inclined bedding. However, they are typically 50 to 100 m thick, roughly two orders of magnitude thinner than typical regional Texas growth-fault systems.

To sum up, the regional geology, drawn to scale, is quite different from that schematically shown in many growth fault models in the literature describing this region. These faults are

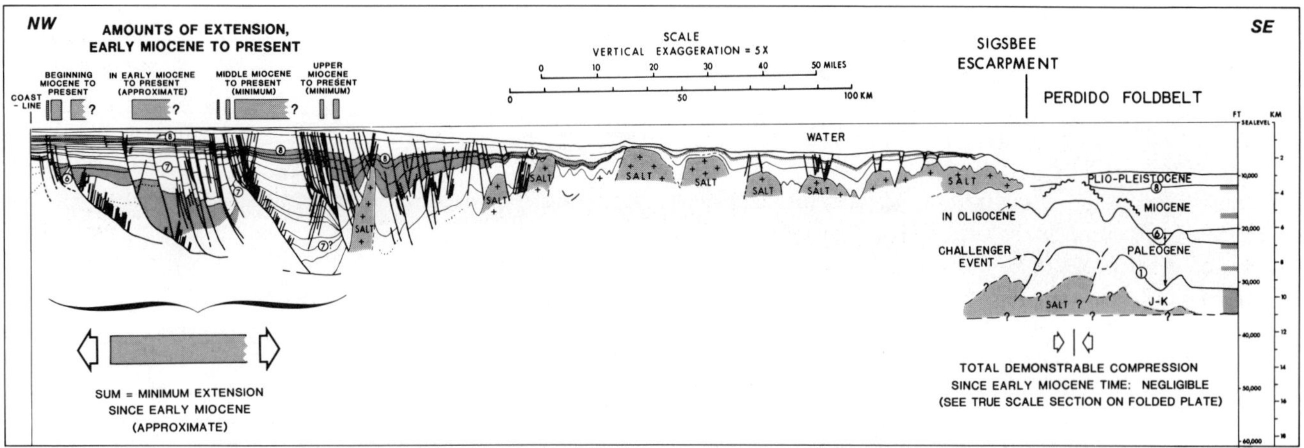

Figure 33. Structural cross section, Texas coastline to the Sigsbee abyssal plain (from Fig. 21), showing minimum amounts of Miocene to Recent extension on Texas shelf (as measured by horizontal separation of correlated beds) compared with the smaller amount of coeval extension in the Perdido foldbelt. Growth-fault extension of this age is not accommodated in the Perdido foldbelt of mostly pre-Miocene age and must be accommodated in the salt-rich slope region. Vertical exaggeration = 5×.

clearly not simple basinward slumps, and the role gravity plays in the development of these systems must be evaluated along with the complex geology of the slope region. We will next consider two areas: the central Mexican Ridges area, and the more complex systems of offshore Texas. These two provinces represent variations on two end-member types of gravity spreading in the Gulf of Mexico. Updip extension in both is accommodated downdip by a rather plastic style of deformation. In one end-member, downdip compensation is by folding over a deep detachment surface, and in the other end-member, flow of mobile salt occurs in the downdip region (as in the Louisiana cross section previously discussed).

Mexican Ridges fold belt. An example of a thick, large-scale gravity-spreading system where downdip compensation for updip extension is accomplished by folding of strata occurs in the central Mexican Ridges area in the western Gulf of Mexico (Figs. 1 and 35). The Mexican Ridges is the physiographic name for an extensive set of north-northeast- to north-northwest-trending ridges along the sea floor of the western Gulf of Mexico between the latitudes of 25N and 19N, which were first described by Bryant and others (1968). Seismic data from south of 22.5N studied by Buffler and others (1979) and Pew (1982) show that the bathymetric ridges reflect underlying low-relief folds of Neogene strata with wavelengths averaging 10 to 12 km, and with structural relief from 300 m to as much as 1 km. These folds underlie the western continental slope in water depths from 1,500 to more than 3,000 m.

The folds appear to root into an underlying detachment surface probably within the Paleogene section (Fig. 35). Updip, near the coastline, a master listric fault system may project downward toward this detachment surface. Although the rollover wedge of Neogene strata in the downthrown block has not been dated, it is a reasonable assumption that it represents the expanded Pliocene to Holocene section, which developed along this clearly unstable shelf margin. Although deep data from the upper slope east of the Mesozoic Golden Lane (Tuxpan) platform are lacking, the profile can be interpreted as a single gravitationally driven system (Garrison and Martin, 1973) with updip growth faulting and expansion and downdip compression above a deep detachment within the Paleogene(?) section. The detachment is well below the sea-bottom depth of the abyssal plain. Hence, rather than downslope gravity gliding in the sense of Mandl and Crans, a type of gravity spreading more aptly describes the role of gravity in this deep-seated detachment-based

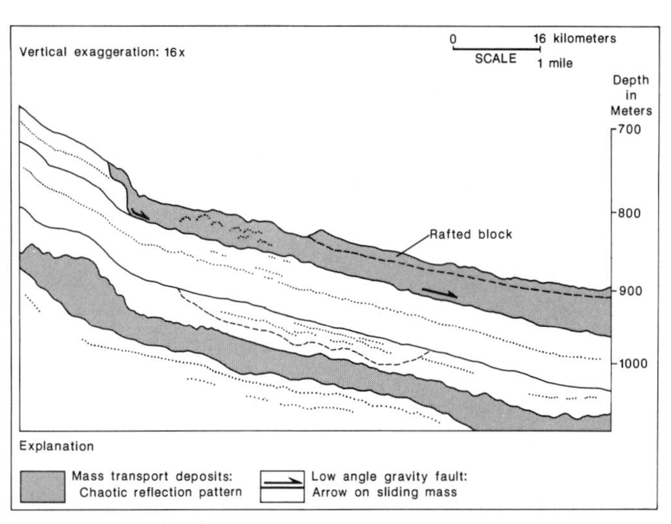

Figure 34. Tracing from seismic section showing thin gravity slide sequences, East Breaks area, Texas slope (from Berryhill and others, 1987). Note scale and large 16× vertical exaggeration. These are relatively minor near-surface features.

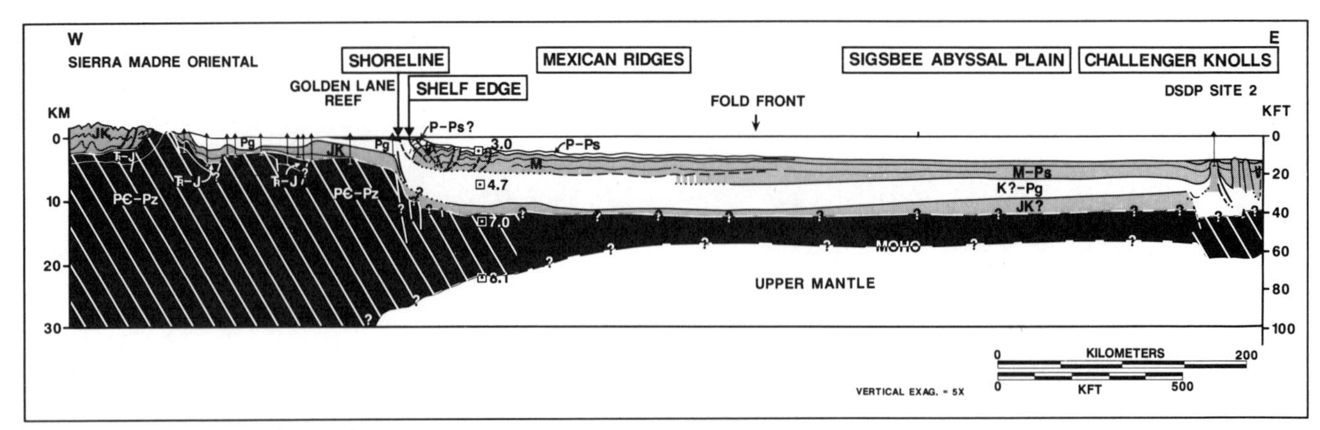

Figure 35. Regional structural cross section of the central Mexican Ridge areas extending to the Challenger Knolls (location on Fig. 1). Vertical exaggeration = 5×. Offshore geology modified from unpublished sources including interpretations by M. T. Roberts (Shell), and S. Goetsch (Shell), based on University of Texas seismic data studied by Buffler and others (1979) and Pew (1982).

system. In contrast to the northern Mexican offshore area, this central Mexican Ridges province appears to generally lack salt involvement.

Offshore Texas. In comparing the central Mexican Ridges area to offshore central Texas, one notes the Perdido fold belt (Fig. 33) at the base of the Texas slope (Martin, 1984). Are these compressional "toe" folds similar in origin to the folds of the central Mexican Ridges (Fig. 35)? Could this compression be the direct result of updip Miocene to Recent growth fault extension, as implied in the model shown in Fig. 32? The following points argue against this conclusion. (1) The Perdido folds at the base of the slope are typically onlapped by flat-lying Miocene to Recent strata (Martin, 1980). Thus, these folds are mainly pre-Miocene (Oligocene?) in age (Blickwede and Queffelec, 1988), and although a gravity spreading origin is likely, they are clearly too old to accommodate Miocene to Recent extension. (2) The Perdido folds along the line of section shown only involve about 2 km of observed minimum shortening (best seen in the true-scale depth section, Plate 4). In contrast, a *minimum* value of horizontal extension since early Miocene time is about 30 to 40 km, as shown in Figure 33. In summary, there is no balance (in terms of age or distance) in offshore Texas between shortening in the Perdido fold belt and Miocene to Recent extension farther updip.

Clearly, the Miocene to Recent extension in this offshore Texas area has been accommodated in the area between the Miocene to Recent updip growth faults and the downdip Perdido folds—namely, the area of the middle and lower Texas slope. This slope interval differs dramatically from that of the Mexican Ridges cross section. The Texas slope contains abundant shallow salt features and complex inter-salt basins, rather than the simple, low-amplitude folds of the Mexican slope. These shallow salt features obscure much of the underlying structure.

Gravity models of both types (gliding and spreading) for major growth faulting along the Texas Gulf coast have largely overlooked the role and significance of the large quantities of shallow salt that exist on the present-day slope. What role, if any, does this salt play in the formation of growth faults? Although we do not know what the Paleogene Texas slope looked like, it seems unlikely that it was as devoid of salt as most growth-fault models imply. In order to gain possible mechanical insight into the development of these growth-fault systems, palinspastic analysis of one of the Miocene systems of the Texas offshore will next be presented, followed by a more regional Miocene to Recent reconstruction.

Corsair fault system. The Corsair fault system is a very large listric growth-fault system that stretches over 320 km in map view along the Texas shelf (Fig. 2). Its overall features have been described by Christensen (1983) and Vogler and Robison (1987), among others. Figure 36 is a seismic line showing both the Corsair system and the downdip Wanda fault system (see also Plate 4). The Corsair fault is a deep-cutting feature, extending to depths of more than 9 km (28,000 ft), well below the present abyssal plain depth of approximately 3 km (10,000 ft).

Two-stage system. The Corsair system, defined as the Corsair and Wanda faults and the invervening rock package, displays a rich variety of internal structures and a history that can be separated into two very distinct stages (Fig. 36). In the early stage, strata thin basinward; later-stage strata thicken basinward. Near the Corsair fault, early-stage strata terminate against the gently inclined master fault in a series of short antithetic faults and rollover folds. Later-stage strata truncate against a much steeper fault and are involved in a large updip graben that clearly developed during the late stage. Downdip structures also are of two different types. Near the Wanda fault, early-stage strata are cut by numerous, small, landward-dipping normal faults. Later-stage strata, in contrast, are cut by equally numerous basinward-dipping faults. These faults locally sole into a shale detachment surface near the interface between the two different stratal sequences. Interestingly, the upper, later faults show cross-fault stratal thickening, and are clearly growth faults; the lower ones (early stage) do not show such growth.

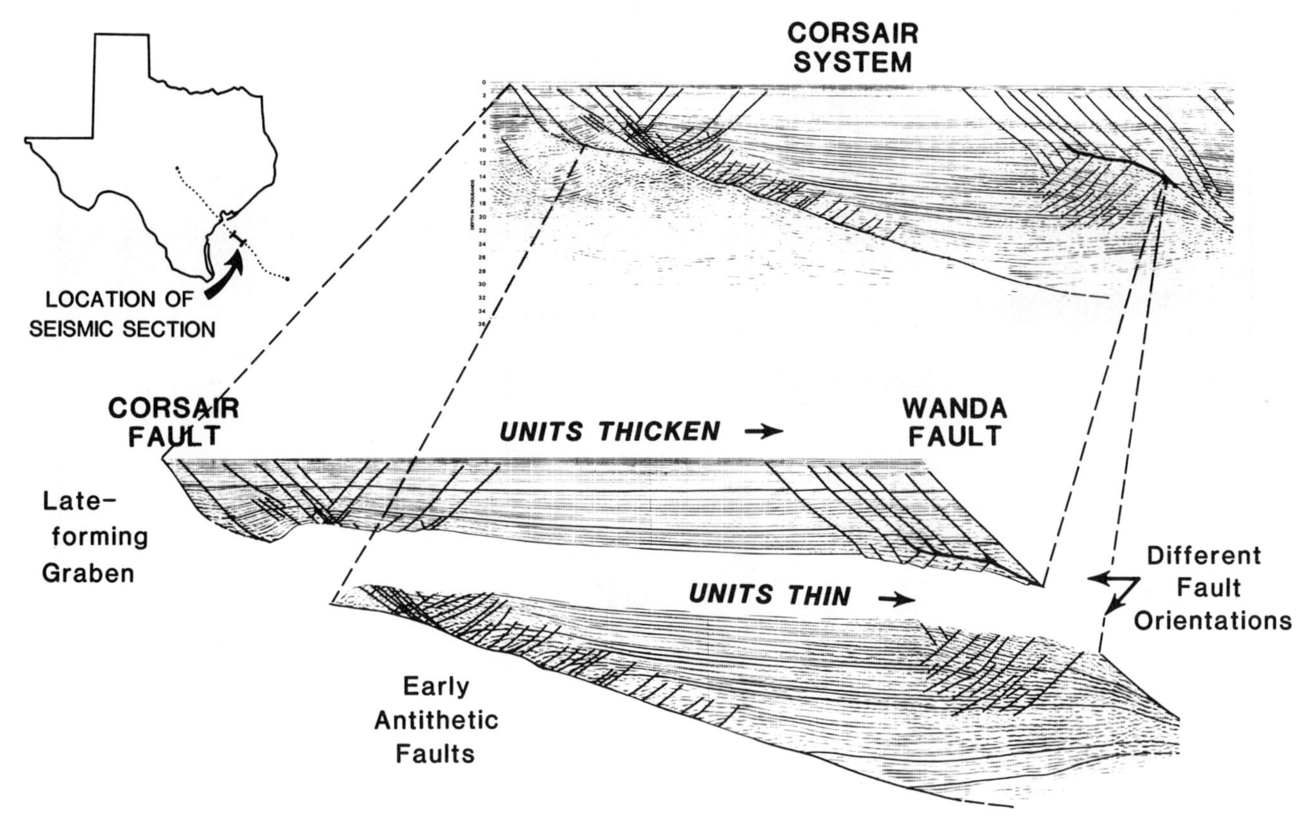

Figure 36. Seismic data illustrating two-part history of the Corsair system. Lower strata thin basinward, and the main fault surface is gently dipping with early-formed antithetic faults. Upper strata thicken basinward, and the main fault surface is steeper and is associated with a late-forming graben system. Downdip fault orientations differ at the same early–late boundary.

Reconstruction. A computer-assisted palinspastic reconstruction (Fig. 37) of the seismic line through the Corsair fault (Plate 4 and Fig. 21) was constructed using our proprietary program, PREP. Restored paleobathymetric relief honored paleontologic control where present; a 1.5-degree slope was inferred for earliest strata. These PREP reconstructions show numerous gaps, overlaps, and artificial vertical block boundaries, which are artifacts of the program's reconstruction method (discussed in the Appendix). A smoothed and corrected set of reconstructions using an expanded version of Figure 37 as a base will be discussed later.

In early frames, the reconstruction shows a developing wedge of material that expands landward into the master fault (Fig. 37, frames L, K, and I). The downdip "tail" of this early wedge subsides under later-stage deposition, and a listric fault system develops on top of the early wedge. This downdip thinning "tail" occurs adjacent to a known shallow salt mass and is clearly related to mobile salt.

A reconstruction of a nearby seismic section (Fig. 38), displayed a 5× vertical exaggeration, emphasizes a change in the sense of rotation of early strata during the history of the system. The lines are drawn through the endpoints of the lowest digitized horizon in each frame. During the early phase, rotation is counterclockwise as the early wedge of updip-thickening strata forms. Later, the sense of rotation changes to clockwise as downdip-thickening late-stage strata are deposited. This change is also coincident with the transition at the updip end of the system from early small antithetic faulting to late updip graben development. The style of structure developed southeast of the Corsair fault is rather like a half-turtle structure and is strongly suggestive of the involvement of deep mobile material during deformation. Based on the proximity of an adjacent salt dome and its connection to this half-turtle, such mobile material is likely to be salt.

How mobile material like salt could be involved in such a system is shown in cartoon fashion in Figure 39. The amount of space created for local stratal thickening across a growth-fault system, where such thickening occurs in a very short period of time, is primarily dependent on two factors: (1) the amount of total extension, which creates space by *lateral* displacement of material basinward; and (2) the original thickness of displaced mobile material at depth, which creates space in a *vertical* sense by load-induced displacement (the previously discussed Louisiana mini-basin growth faults are examples). For the purpose of discussion, the cartoon shown is not to scale and is vertically exaggerated to emphasize the vertical component of space

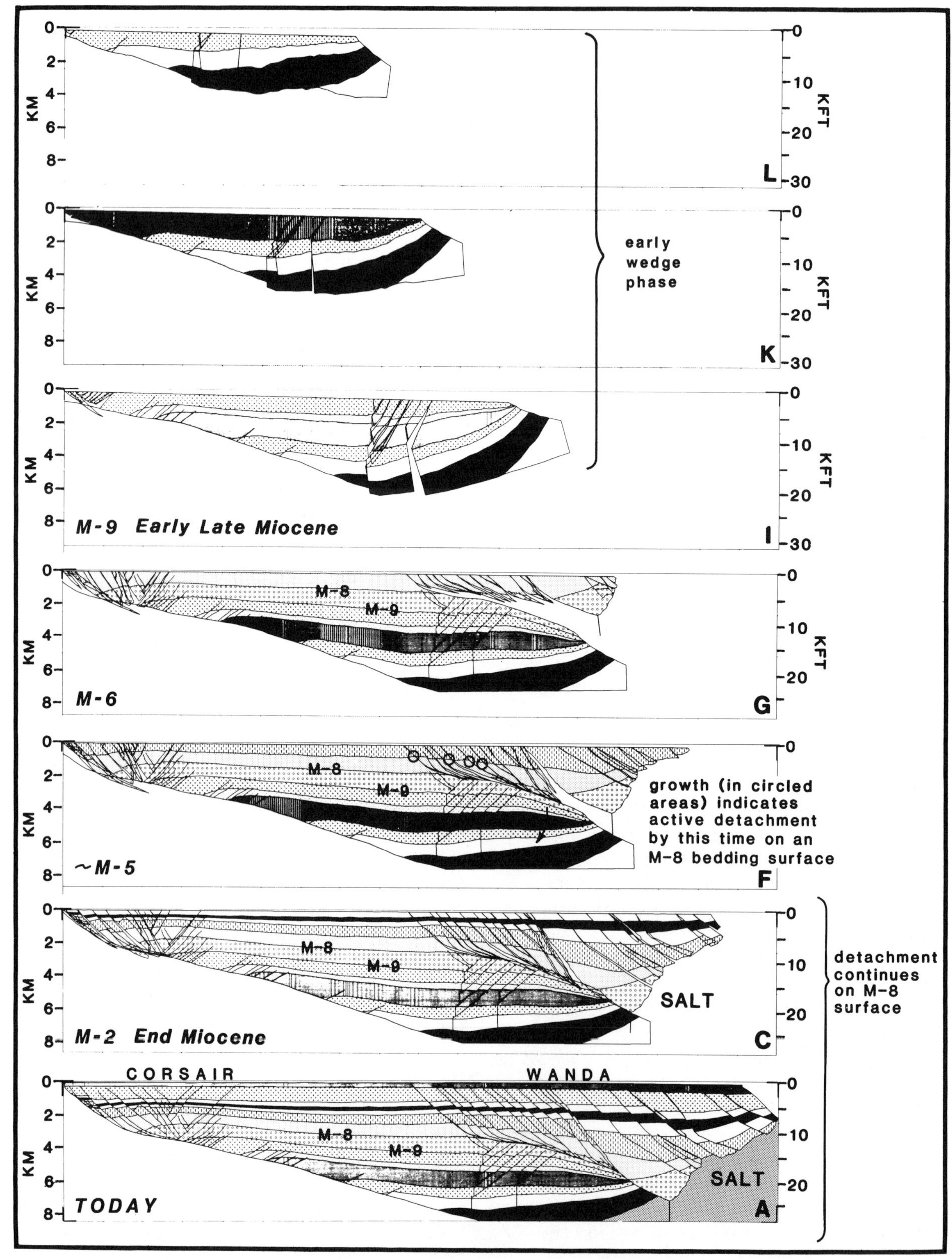

Figure 37. PREP-generated palinspastic reconstruction of the Corsair system. Inferred paleobathymetry added. See Plate 4 for seismic data used and an explanation of "M" horizon terminology. No vertical exaggeration. Gaps in frames G and I are artifacts of reconstruction method, as are vertical lines extending downward from some fault termini.

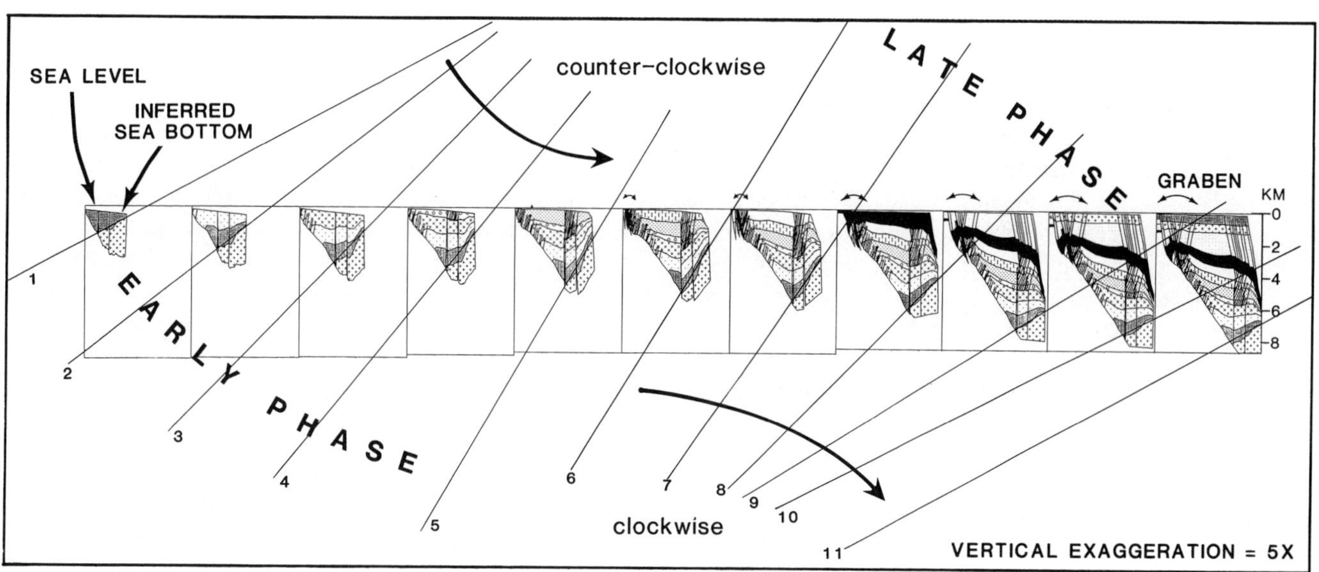

Figure 38. PREP-generated palinspastic reconstruction of the Corsair system. Vertical exaggeration = 5×. Lines 1 through 11 are drawn through the end points of the lowest horizon in each frame. Lines 1 through 5 describe a counter-clockwise sense of rotation as the early wedge forms. The sense of rotation changes to clockwise in frames 6 through 11; the graben appears when the sense of rotation changes. Seismic data used are shown in Figure 36.

generation over the easier-to-visualize lateral extension component. *Frame 1:* Early-stage strata, shaded gray, accumulate in an updip-thickening wedge that displaces salt at depth. *Frame 2:* Eventually this wedge "bottoms out" (locally displaces all the salt), ending local rapid accumulation and extension. The shelf edge, marked by a triangle, then migrates seaward to the next area where salt remains, namely to the downdip, thin "tail" of the early wedge. *Frame 3:* This tail rotates and subsides under increased sedimentary loading, and small landward-dipping faults form due to tension caused by related bending. Seaward-dipping faults develop above the "tail" as the locus of extension and salt displacement moves seaward. On a larger scale, the clockwise rotation of the early wedge may cause tension around the upper portion of the system, resulting in the late-forming updip graben. Ultimately, the locus of deposition and growth fauting moves seaward.

This basic structural pattern of alternating downdip thinning and thickening is repeated in other Texas fault systems, as is indicated in the seismic section in Figure 40. Note that the Corsair fault's downdip-thinning early stage, comprising a mid-Miocene marker (M-9) and older strata, is equivalent in time to a downdip-thickening late stage in the older Clemente-Tomas system (M-9 to a lower Miocene marker, M-14). Although broken by numerous faults, strata older than the lower Miocene marker (M-14) in this older Clemente-Tomas system seem to reflect a basinward-thinning early stage as seen in the Corsair system.

Lateral extension. Figure 41 shows a reconstruction of a small area of the Corsair system through time, and emphasizes the rapid early-stage lateral extension. After the transitional period of

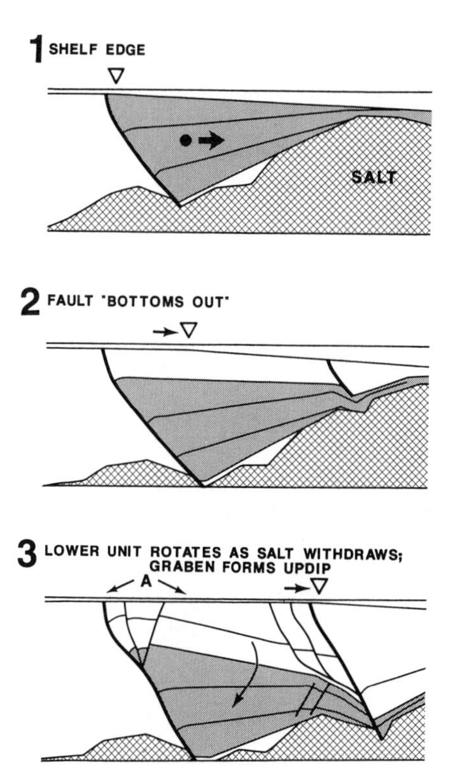

Figure 39. Schematic sections showing the hypothetical development of a Corsair-like fault. Not to scale.

bottoming out, lateral extension nearly ceases, and the vertical subsidence rate is greatly reduced, presumably as the locus of salt displacement has shifted farther to the southeast. (Note: Although the reconstruction shows a continuing, but reduced, horizontal component of translation of the reconstructed segment during the late stage, most of the apparent lateral extension at this stage is not real. Extension has actually nearly ceased. In the late stages of development, the updip terminus of the by then nearly inactive fault tends to "grow" landward, with only minor displacement during continued subsidence.)

The Wanda fault. The structural development of the downdip "tail" is well displayed in the Corsair system reconstruction of Figure 37. The late-stage seaward-dipping faults shown in frame 3 of Figure 39 make up the Wanda fault system, which in this vicinity soles into a detachment surface parallel to the bedding surfaces in the underlying lower wedge. Its development began when the thin downdip "tail" of the early wedge was forced downward, as has been discussed, in a clockwise rotation against salt under the load of prograding post–M-8 strata (frames G and F). In the vicinity of this seismic section, the Wanda fault system developed as a bedding plane detachment above, and parallel to bedding in, the early wedge. The development of the Wanda fault is particularly noteworthy because it demonstrates how underlying and downdip salt displaced by loading can provide a mechanism for bedding-plane "shale-detachment" faults.

Whereas the landward-dipping faults seen beneath the Wanda detachment surface could be interpreted as earlier features related to the formation of an early wedge (pre-middle Miocene M-8 marker), they are not accompanied by any obvious stratal growth in transected strata. Therefore, it seems likely that these landward-dipping faults formed as a response to the later clockwise flexing of the early wedge that produced local extension.

Antithetic faults and rollover folds. Antithetic faults and rollover folds are common in growth-fault systems such as the Corsair system and develop in a narrow zone adjacent to the master fault (Fig. 36). Although not central to the issue of the origin of the regional fault systems, these features are of considerable economic importance and merit discussion. The idea that rollover folding (termed "reverse drag" in early literature) is the result of extensional collapse with depth was proposed by Quarles (1953). Bruce (1973) elaborated on Quarles' concept and showed that antithetic faults are also the result of extension generated by downward motion on a listric fault surface. More recently, Ellis and McClay (1988) have successfully modeled such rollover anticlines and associated crestal collapse structures in their experiments with listric extensional fault systems.

The formation of rollover folds and antithetic faults is continuous throughout the early stage of the Corsair system, and is a consequence of continuous motion on a listric master fault. The process is diagrammatically shown in Figure 42. Given a fault shape as in frame A, downward motion of the hanging wall would result in a hypothetical gap as shown in frame B. Such a gap, of course, would not exist in nature, and would be filled in as fast as the gap formed, by collapse of the hanging-wall material—either by ductile folding (producing rollover folds) or by brittle failure (antithetic faults) or by a combination of both. For simplicity, only the case of brittle failure is considered in the diagram; the hypothetical gap is closed by antithetic faulting (frame C). Antithetic faults only occur where a hypothetical gap would exist (the segment of fault curvature updip from the black dot).

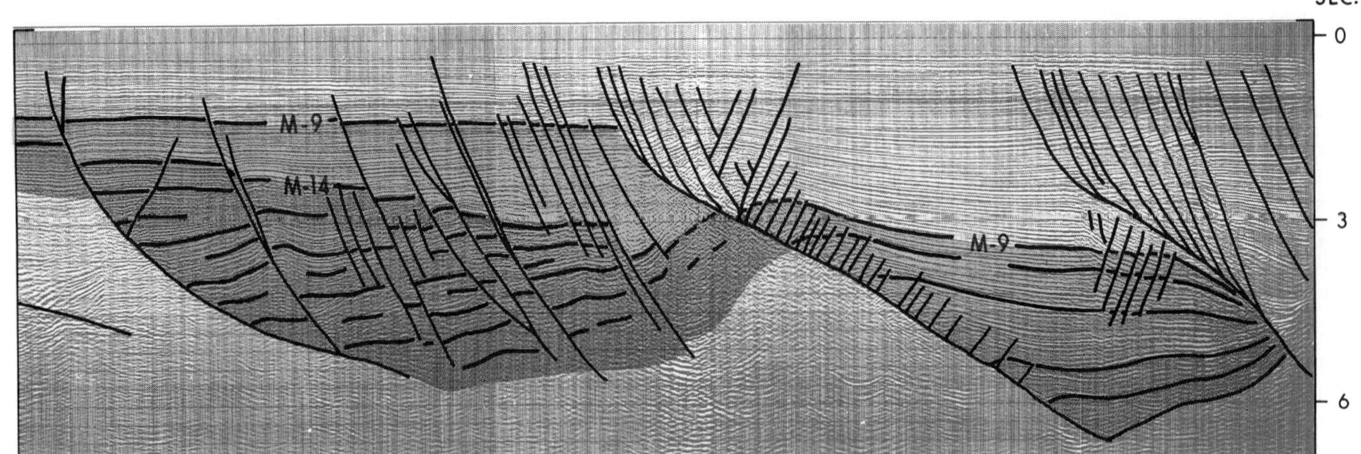

Figure 40. Seismic line through the Clemente-Tomas and Corsair systems (reduced from Plate 4). Both fault systems display two-part depositional style: each consists of an early wedge that thins basinward overlain by a later basinward-thickening stage. The Clemente-Tomas late-stage strata (middle Miocene M-9 to M-14 horizons) is coeval with Corsair's early stage (middle Miocene M-9 marker and older strata). (See Plate 4 for description of "M" terminology.)

Renewed or continuous motion along the fault surface results in another gap (frame D) and thus renewed faulting. However, only three of the four faults previously present in frame C are still active. Because the fourth (the one on the right) has been moved to a position below the hypothetical gap, it is no longer active and thus does not transect the younger strata (frame E). Two faults at the left in frame E are new and only cut the younger strata. Frames F through I show this process repeated in several stages. In each case, as older faults move below the updip "gap" region (the lower limit of which is marked by the circle), these faults become inactive. The resulting of this ongoing process is a narrow zone ("fringe") of antithetic faults that rims the master fault (I). If both folding and faulting occur, the result might resemble frame J.

Rollover folding and antithetic faulting are both restricted to the same narrow zone, as is seen in nature (Fig. 36). Frames I and J of Figure 42 do not represent endpoints; this process could extend indefinitely until the entire fault surface were fringed with antithetic faults and rollover folds. In the Corsair system, however, this process was terminated by the bottoming out of the system and the formation of a late updip graben.

The width of the zone of extensional collapse (Fig. 42; frames I and J) is very sensitive to the shape of the shallow portion of the listric fault, where the hypothetical gap is created. When the present-day shape of the Corsair fault is considered, one would expect a much wider zone of collapse than that observed at depth. A palinspastic reconstruction shows the reason (Fig. 43, taken from the reconstruction of Fig. 38 and displayed at true scale): the fault has changed shape with time. During the early stage, the fault had a more planar shape with only a small updip lip, which fits precisely the width of the observed zone of extensional collapse. After the system bottomed out, the updip fault plane steepened as it cut through younger strata. The Corsair fault was much less active in the system's late stage; continued activity was probably caused primarily by continued creep and/or differential compaction in contrast to earlier rapid extension and subsidence (compare with Fig. 41).

Summary reconstructions. Using the Corsair PREP reconstruction (Fig.37) and a more regional PREP reconstruction discussed below as guides, a smoothed, and also more interpretive, reconstruction has been constructed that better illustrates the development of this area (Fig. 44). Some limitations to the interpretation and reconstruction should be mentioned. The cross-hatched area in frame A of Figure 44 shows areas where adequate seismic data are lacking, and where geology has been inferred. Reconstructions of these deep areas are thus not as well constrained as in shallower zones. This interpreted reconstruction, while not a unique geometric solution, nevertheless demonstrates the necessity of a deep mobile material beneath these developing fault systems. We infer that this mobile material is at least partially salt because: (1) salt is clearly present in the dome included in the section; (2) the reconstruction of the

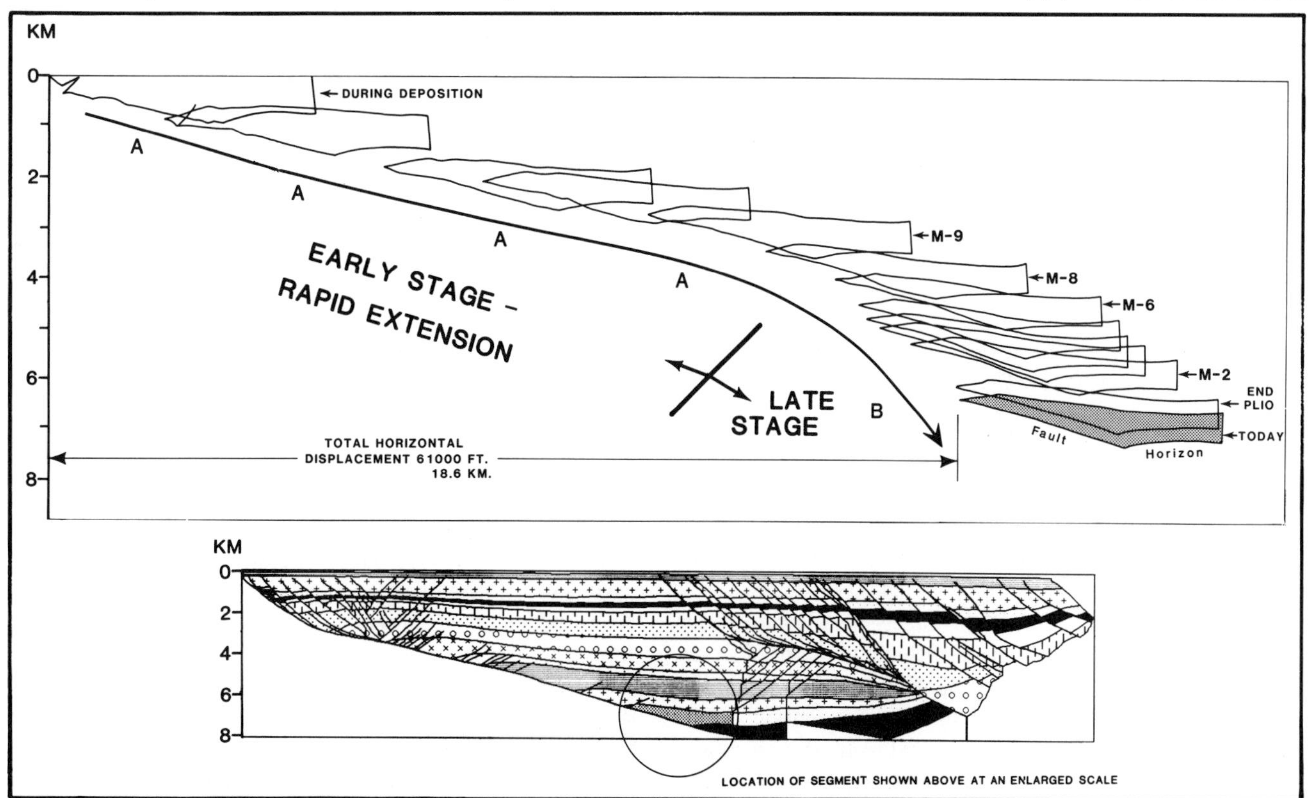

Figure 41. Movement history of a traced segment from the palinspastic reconstruction of the Corsair system, relative to the updip terminus of the fault. The history is based on the reconstruction shown in Figure 37.

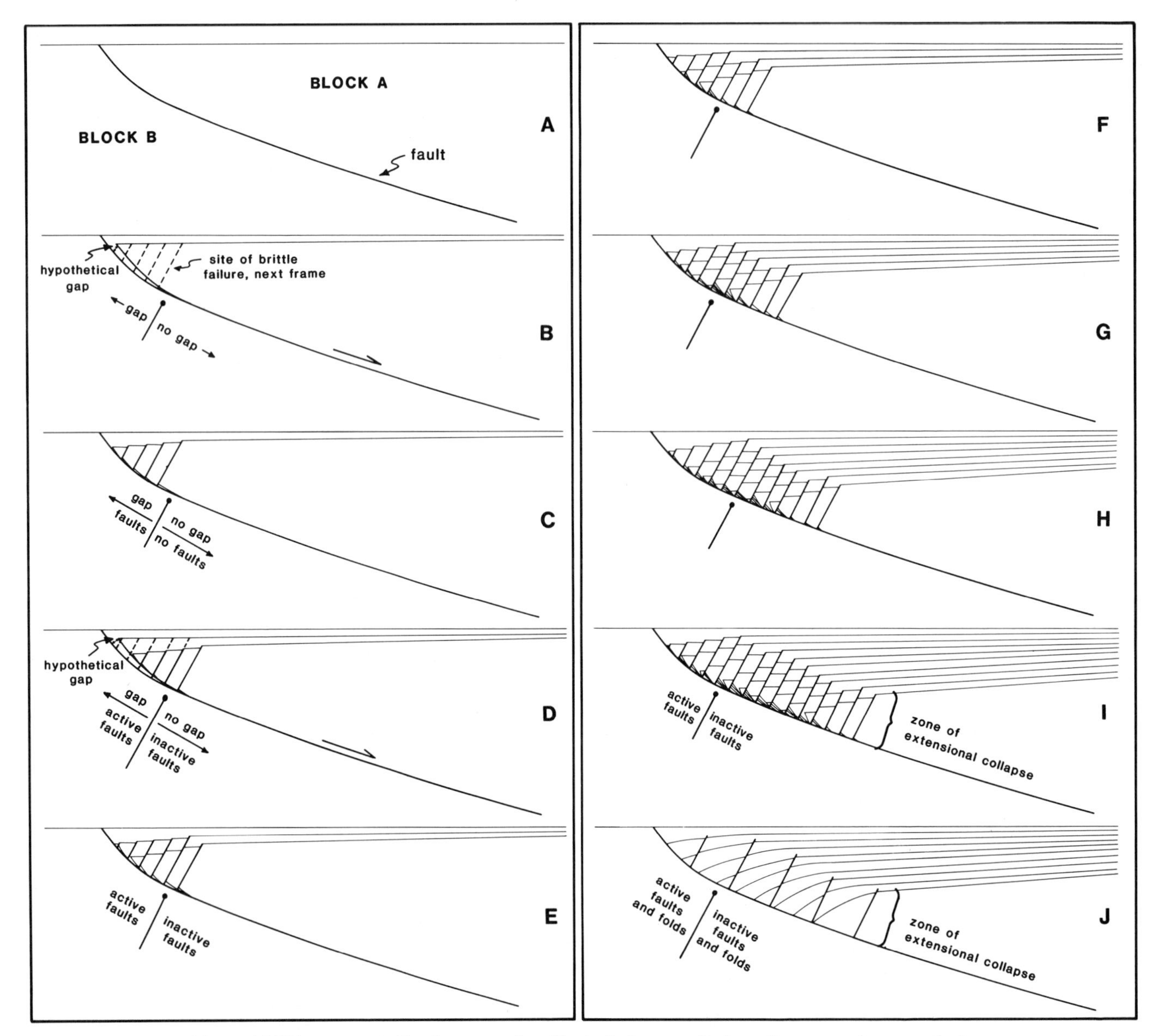

Figure 42. Diagrammatic development of antithetic faults on a listric surface, assuming completely brittle behavior. The last frame substitutes most brittle collapse structures with ductile ones (rollover folds). See text for explanation.

dome ties this salt to the "mobile material" in the reconstruction; and finally, (3) abundant shallow salt masses exist downdip in the upper slope.

This summary reconstruction highlights the role salt appears to play in the development of the tremendous amount of stratal expansion across the Corsair fault. Space for thickened strata is interpreted to have been created by lateral extension of the system, seemingly on mobile salt (see next section), as well as a more vertical component of local salt displacement (as indicated by the last frame).

Offshore Texas systems: Regional interpretation. The more regional palinspastic reconstruction of the shelf and uppermost slope portion of the cross section of Plate 4, shown in Figure 45, demonstrates that the Corsair and other fault systems make up a continuum of basinward-stepping events. The reconstruction is displayed at 5× vertical exaggeration to emphasize vertical subsidence. Rather than infer deep geology, a heavy line has been drawn at the base of reasonably good seismic data. This base of data is reconstructed along with overlying strata and faults (a fairly constant dip for the slope through time has been assumed); the last frame shows a summary of this base of data as reconstructed in the previous five frames. It seems clear that room for these fault systems and associated strata is largely provided by displacement of mobile material at depth beneath the

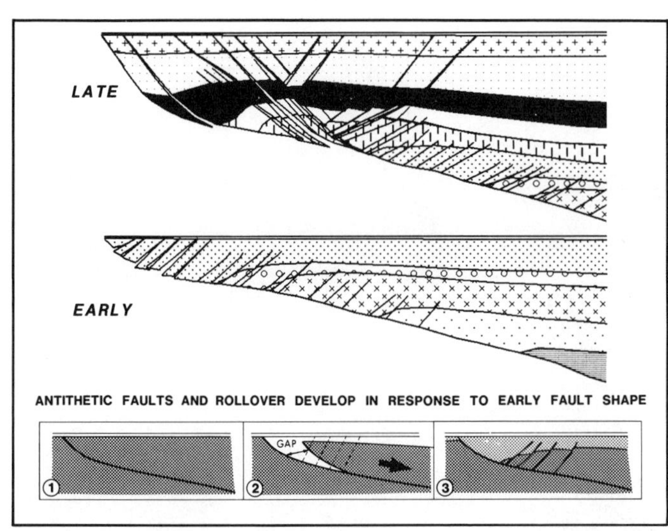

Figure 43. Comparison of early- and late-stage fault shapes, Corsair system. A full palinspastic reconstruction is shown in Figure 38. No vertical exaggeration. The earlier period was marked by a distinctly more shallow lip on the updip fault surface, resulting in the relatively narrow zone of extensional collapse observed.

slope rather than by simple progradation into deep water or purely by deep crustal subsidence induced by loading (subsidence is too localized).

Inasmuch as the Perdido fold belt has been ruled out as a site for large amounts of Miocene and younger compression, and because even the observed amount of Oligocene(?) compression here is small, space to accommodate many kilometers of updip Miocene extension does not appear to be dominantly provided by stratal compression at the base of the slope. The movement (via gravity spreading) of the mobile material to create the space for these developing fault systems must, therefore, be occurring mostly beneath the middle and lower slope at the times represented in the reconstruction. The existence of abundant salt in the present middle and lower slope (see frame 5 and Plate 4) would suggest that salt makes up part, if not most, of this mobile material, which accommodated most of the updip extension. Such a tentative interpretation is schematically shown in Figure 46, which is based on the 1:1 "frame" section (i.e., not interpreted below available seismic and well data) of Plate 4. We hasten to point out, however, that there is a relative lack of deep seismic control beneath the structurally complex and salt-rich middle and lower slope. For this reason, the possibility of a component of Mexican Ridges–style folding accompanying salt flow in the middle slope cannot be ruled out.

Whereas the bottoms of the Mexia-Talco through Lower Wilcox onshore growth-fault systems (discussed below) appear to terminate at the Jurassic Louann Salt level, the offshore systems discussed previously seem to terminate at shallower structural levels (Figs. 44, 46). The large, mostly Miocene, lateral component of extension displayed by the Corsair and Wanda systems may have been taken up largely by movement of salt in complex allochthonous flows beneath the middle slope or along a Neogene Sigsbee Escarpment overriding abyssal strata at the base of the slope.

The downdip Perdido fold belt, which formed mainly in Oligocene(?) time, appears to be detached on salt at the autochthonous Jurassic level (Blickwede and Queffelec, 1988). Thus, it is not unreasonable to assume that in Late Jurassic time, Louann Salt originally underlay much of the Texas onshore and offshore region between the Mexia-Talco system and the base of the present continental slope (Fig. 46).

Onshore Texas systems: Description and interpretation. Several important onshore Texas growth-fault systems (Wilcox, Vicksburg, and Frio) lie in the region between: (1) the peripheral growth-fault trends (Mexia-Talco fault zone, Karnes trough, and Jurassic Cotton Valley) that developed over thin autochthonous salt, and (2) the large, offshore, Corsair-like systems probably also related to salt deformation. The question to be discussed is whether salt has also played any role in the development of these intervening offshore Texas growth-fault systems.

The base of the lower Eocene Wilcox faults in central Texas (Plate 4) was not observed on available seismic data, but the base of Jurassic salt seen immediately updip projects basinward beneath these zones. Structural style, including large amounts of expanded section, is reminiscent of offshore growth-fault systems, and a similar origin involving mobile substrate (salt?) is suggested. In south Texas, where the base of the Wilcox fault system is clearly discernible on seismic data (Fig. 47), the faults terminate against Louann Salt, much like the peripheral fault zones updip. The main mobile substrate here required in restoring this system, therefore, is probably salt rather than shale.

The Oligocene Vicksburg and Monte Cristo fault systems of south Texas (Fig. 48) are very low-angle systems with a detachment surface resting upon Eocene Jackson shale in its updip portion (Erxleben and Carnahan, 1983). The Vicksburg strata here have moved basinward upon this shale-based detachment surface. Is this an early Tertiary gravity glide feature or is it the result of more deeply rooted gravity spreading, accommodated by either downdip folding of strata or the displacement of mobile salt? Unfortunately, the deep data either beneath or downdip from this system required to answer this question are not available. Although a simple slide origin is possible, analogies with younger systems suggest that a gravity spreading mechanism is more plausible.

Comparison of "Texas" and "Louisiana" styles

At the beginning of this chapter, a strong contrast was noted between "Texas style"—long, seaward-dipping listric growth faults associated with very few shallow salt structures—and "Louisiana style"—faults that are shorter, more arcuate, intimately associated with abundant salt domes, and dip in various directions. The general lack of shallow salt in the linear growth-fault belts of south-central Texas has often been interpreted as

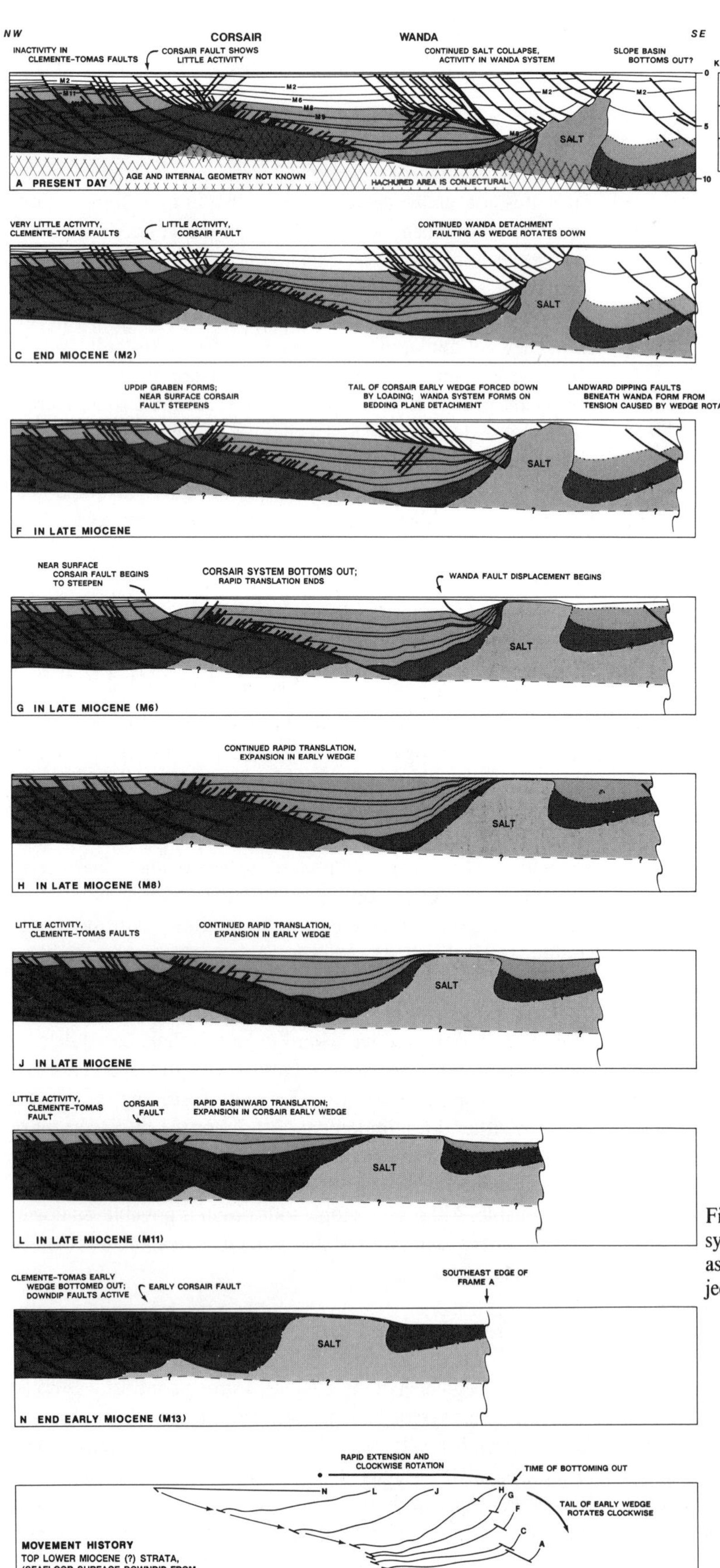

Figure 44. Speculative summary reconstruction of the Corsair system made using reconstructions of Figures 37 and 45. Inasmuch as interpretation in cross-hatched area is purely conjectural, the reconstruction is not unique.

evidence that these structures have a shale-based gravity-slide origin, presumably without salt involvement (e.g., Halbouty, 1967; R. G. Martin, 1978; Bruce, 1973; 1983; Jackson and Galloway, 1984; Humphris, 1984). However, deep seismic data and palinspastic evidence suggest that mobile salt has been present beneath much of coastal and offshore Texas, and has strongly influenced structural development. If both styles contain the effects of deformation on mobile salt, what accounts for the profound differences between "Texas" and "Louisiana" styles?

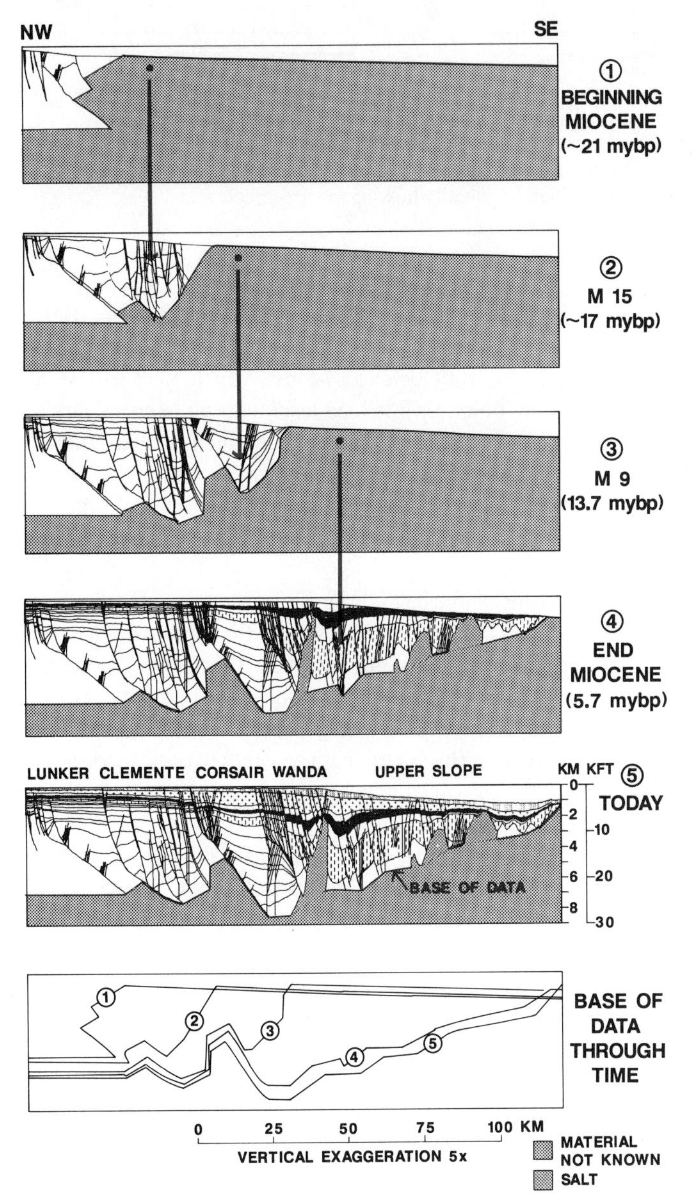

Figure 45. Miocene to Recent palinspastic reconstruction of part of regional cross section (Plate 4) through the Texas shelf and upper slope constructed using computer program PREP. Heavy red line represents an arbitrarily chosen horizon at base of reasonably good seismic data on frame 5 (today). Frames 1 through 4 show this horizon's location at earlier times, assuming a fairly constant dip of bathymetric slope through time. The last frame traces this arbitrary horizon from frames 1 through 5 and shows an eastwardly prograding pattern of rapid local subsidence.

One of several possible factors may be the way a gravity-spreading system—especially one containing salt—responds to sedimentary loading. Behaving geologically as a fluid, salt is easily displaced by differential loads. If regional depositional systems are markedly different, then their loading characteristics should result in dissimilar structural styles above the salt.

A compilation from published sources of depositional environments in parts of Texas and Louisiana for four Tertiary intervals is shown in Figure 49. Two main types of environments, alluvial-deltaic and strand plain–barrier island, dominated the Gulf region during these time periods. Note that the bulk of the Texas coast in Tertiary time, especially that central portion of the Texas coast lying along the San Marcos arch, was dominated by the same sort of long, linear, barrier island–type deposition that is seen on the present-day coast. A major exception was during early Eocene Wilcox deposition when deltas spanned the arch (Edwards, 1981; Fisher and McGowen, 1967). In Louisiana, east Texas and far south Texas, in contrast, alluvial-deltaic systems have long been predominant.

A careful comparison of the depositional environments shown in Figure 49 with the tectonic map (Fig. 2) shows a nearly perfect correspondence of the post-Wilcox Tertiary depositional systems with structural style. Deltaic systems deliver their products to the shelf and slope in rapid point- and line-shaped loads that are ever-shifting with changing drainage patterns. Such a system will cause a very uneven loading of salt. This results in complex structural patterns and somewhat inefficient regional displacement of salt, with much salt remaining in interbasin salt domes; hence, the correspondence of salt dome provinces with deltaic systems.

On the other hand, long, regular, strike-oriented, strand plain–barrier island depositional systems supply a more evenly distributed and systematically deposited load to the shelf and slope and result in equally long, regular, linear structures, which will either more efficiently displace salt (much less depositional shifting) and result in few to no shallow salt structures, or mask more complicated deep salt structures by burial with thick, relatively even layers of strata. The apparent absence of shallow salt in much of the offshore Texas shelf probably attests more to the efficiency of the lateral basinward displacement of salt, or to this masking process, than to any inferred absence of original salt. To the degree that gravity spreading by downdip folding also played a role in the development of some of the "Texas style" faults, these same effects (long, linear fault systems) would still result.

SUMMARY

The structural features of Gulf Coast Texas and Louisiana, although strikingly different, may share a common origin: both styles are believed to have been profoundly influenced at depth by mobile salt. On the Louisiana slope, regional seismic data show an enormous allochthonous mass of salt, in places as much as 8 km thick, which has been slowly but progressively overriding

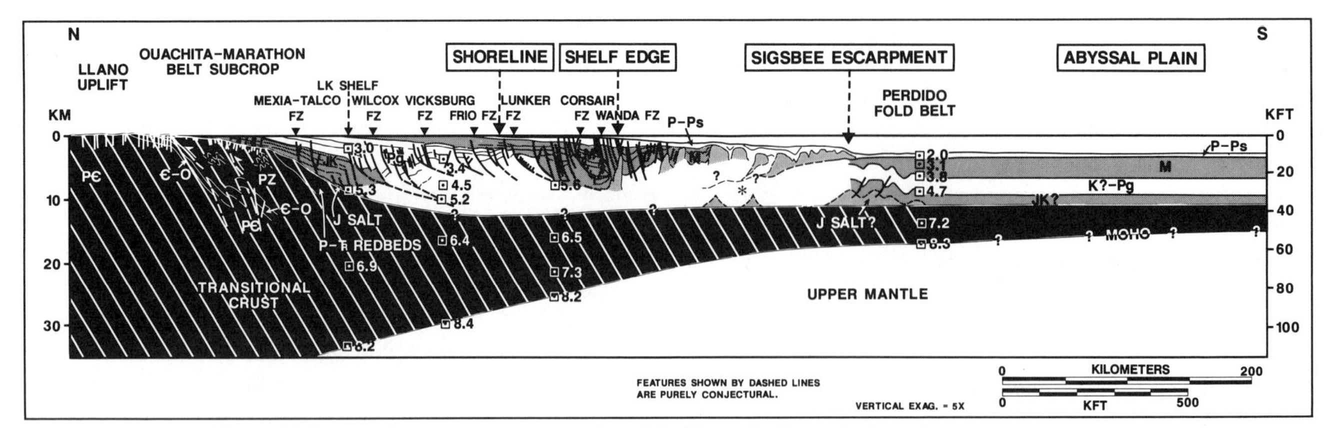

Figure 46. Interpretive summary cross section of the Texas Gulf margin. Location shown on Figure 1. Constructed from data displayed in Figure 21. Vertical exaggeration = 5×. All dashed surfaces and salt features are highly conjectural and are not supported by seismic control. Asterisk (*) indicates that some shallow salt features may root vertically to Jurassic levels rather than to laterally flowing masses; much uncertainty still exists for the deep structure of this area.

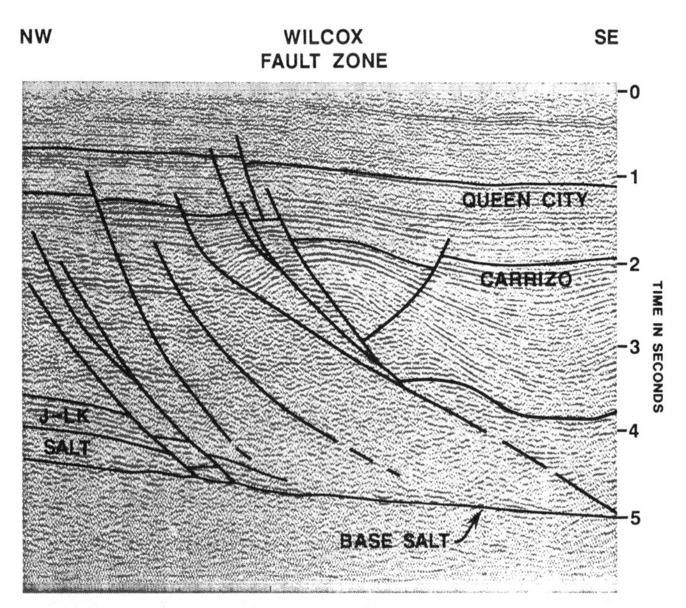

Figure 47. Upper Wilcox fault zone, south Texas onshore, showing termination of fault systems into probable Jurassic Louann Salt horizon. (Seismic data courtesy of Seismic Exchange Inc.)

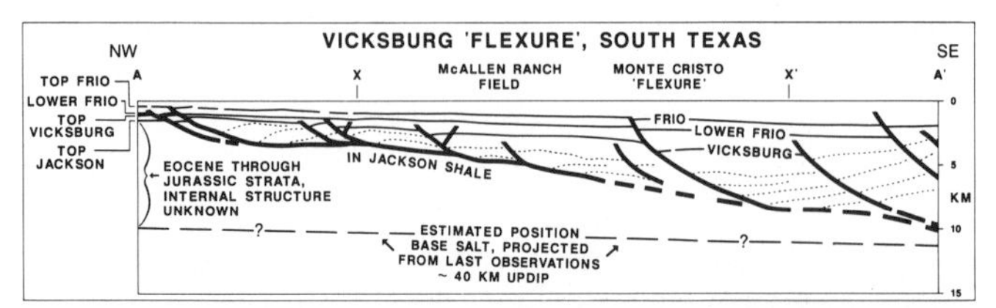

Figure 48. Schematic structural cross section across the Vicksburg and Monte Cristo growth-fault system, Hidalgo and Starr counties, south Texas. No vertical exaggeration. Portion from X to X′ modified from Winker and Edwards (1983). Base-salt horizon has been linearly projected (estimated) from the last control 40 km updip.

abyssal plain sediments since at least early Tertiary time, driven and displaced by sedimentation on the slope. This sedimentation is predominantly from deltaic systems, which load salt in an uneven, shifting point- or line-load fashion, producing a complex set of arcuate faults and mini-basins, with much remnant salt left behind. Some salt domes, on reconstruction, can be shown to originate from flat-topped, thick, extensive slope salt masses, which progressive down-building has transformed into narrow domes.

Mini-basins on the central portion of the Louisiana slope are ringed by arcuate faults, and originate by the rapid subsidence of deep-water sediments subsiding into very thick salt. Thick Plio-Pleistocene basins of the middle slope rest in some areas on probably late Eocene–early Oligocene(?) strata beneath the Sigsbee salt nappe; the hiatus between these strata records the time interval during which allochthonous salt passed through the present-day middle slope.

Structures in much of the Texas Gulf Coast consist predominantly of long, listric, basinward-dipping growth faults with little associated shallow salt in coastal and offshore shelf areas. The updip Mexia-Talco, Karnes trough, and Cotton Valley fault systems show relatively little displacement, and terminate at depth against autochthonous Jurassic Louann Salt. The Paleogene Wilcox fault system in south Texas also terminates at depth against salt. Reconstructions of offshore systems strongly suggest an origin by lateral and vertical displacement of allochthonous salt. The Corsair system, in particular, shows a two-part structural history that is difficult to explain except in terms of a half-turtle salt-displacement type of history.

Major Miocene and younger extension on many of the offshore Texas fault systems post-dates the development of the deep-water Perdido fold belt at the base of the slope; these apparently salt-cored folds thus do not appear to be the direct compressional toe-folds of at least the Neogene updip growth-fault systems. In addition, amounts of shortening in this fold belt

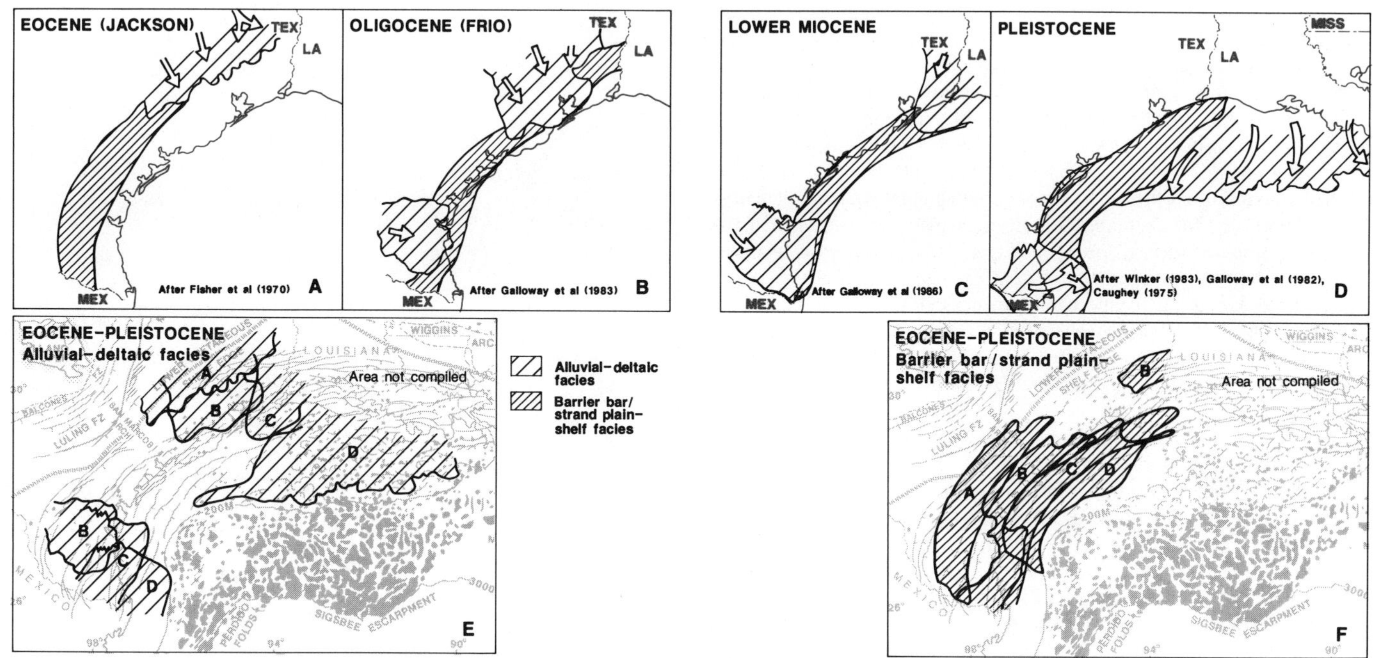

Figure 49 (A through D): Tertiary paleogeography at four time intervals, Texas coastal region, based on interpretations of Fisher and others, 1970 (Eocene); Galloway and others, 1982 (Oligocene); Galloway and others, 1986 (lower Miocene); Winker and Edwards, 1983; Galloway and others, 1982; and Caughey, 1975 (Pleistocene). An exception to the above patterns occurred during Eocene Wilcox time (not shown) when deltas spanned much of the Texas coastal region (e.g., Edwards, 1981; Fisher and McGowen, 1967). (E) Summation of alluvial and deltaic areas (A through D) superimposed on screened tectonic map of Figure 2. (F) Summation of barrier island and strand plain environments (A through D) superimposed on screened tectonic map of Figure 2.

are quite small relative to amounts of extension in any of the Tertiary growth-fault systems. Although much remains to be learned about the complex geology of the Texas slope, growth-fault stratal expansion and accompanying extension seem, by palinspastic reconstruction, to be accommodated mostly by regional-scale salt displacement and flow beneath the continental slope.

The long, linear trends of the middle Texas coastal fault systems are in keeping with the long, linear, strand plain–barrier island depositional systems that loaded the salt in this region through most of Tertiary time. The relative absence of shallow salt in this province may speak more to the efficiency of such long, regular depositional loads in either fully displacing or masking deep salt than to any absence of significant salt.

APPENDIX

In the preceding discussions, use is made of a computer graphics program named PREP, which we developed in 1979–80 to assist in making complex structural reconstructions. Briefly described, the program takes digitized seismic data, converts it to depth, divides the section into fault blocks of various times of activity, strips off sequential layers, decompacts strata, and restores to inferred paleobathymetry. This program was designed primarily as a graphics aid in assisting many of the lengthy mechanical tasks of making hand reconstructions; it was not designed to produce "finished" interpreted reconstructions or to serve as a process-oriented modeling device. Nonetheless, these machine-made reconstructions are quite satisfactory for most purposes and allow a more detailed, sequential (and decompacted) view of structural development than otherwise would be possible given normal time constraints of interpretive work.

From the outset, the idea was to develop a limited set of algorithms to perform most of the things a geologist would do with paper and scissors in making a reconstruction "by hand," as well as perform several tasks either too tedious (numerous sequential reconstructions at closely spaced time intervals) or computationally intensive (e.g., decompaction of strata, time-to-depth conversion, and scale manipulations) to be easily done. Such labor intensive tasks to do a geometrically "proper" analysis discourage all but the most committed to such work, and often the unfortunate result is a cartoon reconstruction, usually not to scale, which is of little value for the purpose of structural analysis. The program was not, however, designed to model the mechanics of rock deformation (e.g., unraveling concentric folding), and thus works best where the effects of severe bending and/or folding are minimal. Fortunately, most extensional systems fit this restriction reasonably well. An additional restriction is common to all two-dimensional reconstructions: motion must have been parallel to the plane of the cross section.

The basic reconstruction routine operates as follows (Fig. 50): *Frame A*—A time seismic section is digitized and converted to depth. A bookkeeping scheme used during digitization allows the characterization of discrete fault blocks, and also describes the times at which the faults become inactive (e.g., two small faults in frame A were not active during deposition of units 1 and 2). Where faults terminate at depth within stratal units (i.e., not against other faults), a vertical line is dropped from the fault terminus to artificially create a discrete block (see examples in Fig. 37). *Frame B*—Next, the dip of the first horizon to be restored is calculated for each fault block. *Frame C*—Each block is then rotated by the dip amount. *Frame D*—The restored horizon is flattened to remove small amounts of curvature, and the overlying unit is stripped off. *Frame E*—Corrections for decompaction are then made by calculating uplift amounts from the surface down (lithologies and decompaction functions are entered during digitization). *Frame F*—Once this process is completed for all blocks, the blocks are reassembled. This sequence is repeated for each successively deeper horizon until the sequential reconstruction is complete. At that time, paleobathymetric data may be entered, and the reconstruction fitted to a bathymetric surface (see Figs. 37 and 38).

The process is very simple and of course has its drawbacks. Gaps and overlaps (e.g., frame F of Fig. 37) are left by the process, but the resolution of these geometric problems is often the essence of the exercise of the interpreter. Such gaps can form by: (1) the rather rigid way the reconstruction process is performed (in frame F, some bending at the left end of the fault system has probably occurred in nature during deformation); (2) over- or under-decompaction; (3) slight errors in rotation amount; and most importantly, (4) errors in interpretation and correlation. The reconstruction poses the question, "Which one?" Corrections can then be made by either editing the section or by constructing a final interpretation on tracing paper over the PREP section, correcting small geometry problems (Fig. 44).

Although these routines are very simple, PREP has proven a very useful preliminary tool in Gulf Coast structural analysis. The ability to quickly view the approximate sequential development of a system provides insights that are not always obvious, and the geometric questions raised by the reconstruction process cause a more rigorous inspection of the basic seismic interpretation than might otherwise occur.

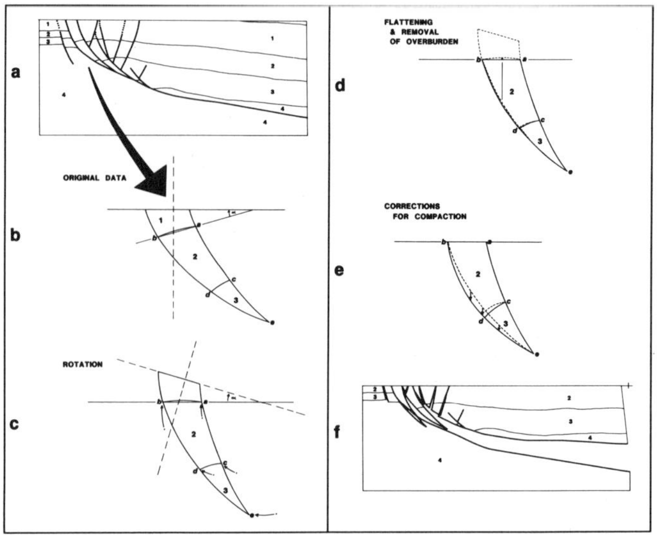

Figure 50. Schematic illustrations showing basic aspects of PREP logic.

REFERENCES CITED

Amery, G. B., 1969, Structure of Sigsbee scarp, Gulf of Mexico: American Association of Petroleum Geologists Bulletin, v. 53, p. 2480–2482.

——, 1978, Structure of the continental slope, northern Gulf of Mexico: American Association of Petroleum Geologists Studies in Geology, no. 7, p. 141–154.

Anderson, T. H., and Schmidt, V. A., 1983, The evolution of Middle America and the Gulf of Mexico–Caribbean region during Mesozoic time: Geological Society of America Bulletin, v. 94, p. 941–966.

Antoine, J. W., Martin, R. G., Pyle, T. E., and Bryant, W. R., 1974, Continental margins of the Gulf of Mexico, *in* Burke, C. A., and Drake, C. L., eds., The geology of continental margins: New York, Springer-Verlag, p. 683–694.

Baldwin, B., and Butler, C. O., 1985, Compaction Curves: American Association of Petroleum Geologists Bulletin, v. 69, p. 622–626.

Ball, M. M., and Harrison, C.G.A., 1969, Origin of the Gulf and Caribbean and implications regarding ocean ridge extension, migration, and shear: Gulf Coast Association of Geological Societies Transactions, v. 19, p. 287–294.

Bally, A. W., 1981, Thoughts on the tectonics of folded belts, *in* McClay, K. R., and Price, N. J., eds., Thrust and nappe tectonics: Geological Society of London Special Publication 9, p. 13–32.

Barton, D. C., 1933, Mechanics of formation of salt domes, with special reference to Gulf Coast salt domes of Texas and Louisiana: American Association of Petroleum Geologists Bulletin, v. 17, no. 9, p. 1025–1083.

Bebout, D. G., and Loucks, R. G., eds., 1977, Cretaceous carbonates of Texas and Mexico; Applications to subsurface exploration: University of Texas at Austin, Bureau of Economic Geology Report of Investigations, no. 89, 332 p.

Bebout, D. G., Loucks, R. G., and Gregory, A. R., 1978, Frio sandstone reservoirs in the deep subsurface along the Texas Gulf Coast: University of Texas at Austin, Bureau of Economic Geology Report of Investigations, no. 91, 92 p.

Berg, R. R., Marshall, W. D., and Shoemaker, P. W., 1979, Structural and depositional history, McAllen Ranch Field, Hidalgo County, Texas: Gulf Coast Association of Geological Societies Transactions, v. 29, p. 24–28.

Berryhill, H. L., Jr., Suter, J. R., and Hardin, N. S., 1987, Late Quaternary facies and structure, northern Gulf of Mexico: American Association of Petroleum Geologists Studies in Geology, no. 23, 289 p.

Bishop, W. F., 1973, Late Jurassic contemporaneous faults in north Louisiana and south Arkansas: American Association of Petroleum Geologists Bulletin, v. 57, p. 858–877.

Blickwede, J. J., and Queffelec, T. A., 1988, Perdido foldbelt; A new deep-water frontier in western Gulf of Mexico [abs.]: American Association of Petroleum Geologists Bulletin, v. 72, p. 163.

Bornhauser, M., 1958, Gulf Coast tectonics: American Association of Petroleum Geologists Bulletin, v. 42, p. 339–370.

Bouma, A. H., and Coleman, J. M., 1986, Intraslope basin deposits and potential relation to the continental shelf, northern Gulf of Mexico: Gulf Coast Association of Geological Societies Transactions, v. 36, p. 419–428.

Bruce, C. H., 1973, Pressured shale and related sediment deformation mechanisms for development of regional contemporaneous faults: American Association of Petroleum Geologists Bulletin, v. 57, p. 878–886.

——, 1983, Shale tectonics, Texas coastal area growth faults, *in* Bally, A. W., ed., Seismic expression of structural styles: American Association of Petroleum Geologists Studies in Geology, no. 15, p. 2.3.1–7.

Bryant, W. R., Antoine, J. W., Ewing, M., and Jones, B. R., 1968, Structure of the Mexicoan continental shelf and slope, Gulf of Mexico: American Association of Petroleum Geologists Bulletin, v. 52, p. 1204–1228.

Buffler, R. T., 1983, Structure and stratigraphy of the Sigsbee salt dome area, deep south-central Gulf of Mexico, *in* Bally, A. W., ed., Seismic expression of structural styles: American Association of Petroleum Geologists Studies in Geology, no. 15, v. 2, p. 2.3.2–56.

Buffler, R. T., Shaub, F. J., Watkins, J. S., and Worzel, J. L., 1979, Anatomy of the Mexican Ridges, southwestern Gulf of Mexico, *in* Watkins, J. S., Montadert, L., and Dickerson, P. W., eds., Geological and geophysical investigations of continental margins: American Association of Petroleum Geologists Memoir 29, p. 319–327.

Buffler, R. T., Schaub, F. J., Huerta, R., and Ibrahim, A. K., 1980, A model for the early evolution of the Gulf of Mexico Basin; Proceedings 26th International Geological Congress, Geology of continental margins symposium, Paris, July 1980: Oceanologica Acta, p. 129–136.

Cagle, J. W., and Khan, M. A., 1983, Smackover-Norphlet stratigraphy, south Wiggins Arch, Mississippi and Alabama: Gulf Coast Association of Geological Societies Transactions, v. 33, p. 23–29.

Carver, R. E., 1968, Differential compaction as a cause of regional contemporaneous faults: American Association of Petroleum Geologists Bulletin, v. 53, p. 414–419.

Caughey, C. A., 1975, Pleistocene depositional trends host valuable Gulf oil reserves: Oil and Gas Journal, v. 73, p. 90–94 and 240–242.

Chowns, T. M., and Williams, C. T., 1983, Pre-Cretaceous rocks beneath the Georgia coastal plain; Regional implications: U.S. Geological Survey Professional Paper 1313–L, 42 p.

Christensen, A. F., 1983, An example of a major syndepositional listric fault, *in* Bally, A. W., ed., Seismic expression of structural styles: American Association of Petroleum Geologists Studies in Geology, no. 15, p. 2.3.1–36–40.

Cloos, E., 1968, Experimental analysis of Gulf Coast fracture patterns: American Association of Petroleum Geologists Bulletin, v. 52, p. 420–444.

Collins, S. E., 1980, Jurassic Cotton Valley and Smackover reservoir trends, east Texas, north Louisiana, and south Arkansas: American Association of Petroleum Geologists Bulletin, v. 64, p. 1004–1013.

Cornet, B., and Traverse, A., 1975, Palynological contribution to the chronology and stratigraphy of the Hartford basin in Connecticut and Massachusetts: Geoscience and Man, v. 11, p. 1–33.

Cram, I. H., 1961, A crustal structure refraction survey in south Texas: Geophysics, v. 26, p. 560–573.

Crans, W., and Mandl, G., 1980, On the theory of growth faulting; Part II (a), Genesis of the unit: Journal of Petroleum Geology, v. 3, p. 209–236.

Crans, W., Mandl, G., and Haremboure, J., 1980, On the theory of growth faulting; A geochemical delta model based on gravity sliding: Journal of Petroleum Geology, v. 2, p. 265–307.

Curtis, D. M., 1970, Miocene deltaic sedimentation, Louisiana Gulf Coast, *in* Morgan, J. P., ed., Deltaic sedimentation, modern and ancient: Society of Economic Paleontologists and Mineralogists Special Publication 15, p. 293–308.

Curtis, D. M., and Picou, E. B., Jr., 1978, Gulf Coast Cenozoic; A model for the application of stratigraphic concepts to exploration on passive margins: Gulf Coast Association of Geological Societies Transactions, v. 28, p. 103–120.

Dickinson, W. R., and Coney, P. J., 1980, Plate tectonic constraints on the origin of the Gulf of Mexico, *in* Pilger, R. H., Jr., ed., The origin of the Gulf of Mexico and the early opening of the central Atlantic Ocean: Baton Rouge, Louisiana State University, 103 p.

Dietz, R. S., and Holden, J. C., 1970, Reconstruction of Pangaea; Breakup and dispersion of continents, Permian to present: Journal of Geophysical Research, v. 75, p. 4939–4956.

Dooley, R. E., and Wampler, J. M., 1983, Potassium-argon relations in the base dikes of Georgia; The influence of excess ^{40}Ar on the geochronology of early Mesozoic igneous and tectonic events: U.S. Geological Survey Professional Paper 1313–M, 24 p.

Dorman, J., Worzel, J. L., and Leyden, R. J., 1972, Crustal section from seismic refraction measurements near Victoria, Texas: Geophysics, v. 37, p. 325–336.

Dunbar, J. A., and Sawyer, D. S., 1988, Continental rifting at pre-existing lithospheric weaknesses: Nature, v. 333, no. 6172, p. 450–452.

Dupre, W. R., 1987, An introduction to the Cenozoic geologic history of the Texas Gulf Coast: Houston Geological Society Course Notes, 107 p.

Edwards, M. B., 1981, Upper Wilcox Rosita delta system of south Texas; Growth faulted shelf-edge deltas: American Association of Petroleum Geologists Bulletin, v. 65, p. 54–73.

Ellis, P. G., and McClay, K. R., 1988, Listric extensional fault systems; Results of analogue model experiments: Basin Research, v. 1, p. 55–70.

Erxleben, A. W., and Carnahan, G. C., 1983, Slick ranch area, Starr County, Texas, *in* Bally, A. W., ed., Seismic expression of structural styles: American Association of Petroleum Geologists Studies in Geology, no. 15, p. 2.3.1–22.

Ewing, J., Antoine, J., and Ewing, M., 1960, Geophysical measurements in the western Caribbean Sea and in the Gulf of Mexico: Journal of Geophysical Research, v. 67, p. 2509–2527.

Fisher, W. L., and McGowen, J. H., 1967, Depositional systems in the Wilcox Group of Texas and their relationship to occurrences of oil and gas: Gulf Coast Association of Geological Societies Transactions, v. 17, p. 105–125.

Fisher, W. L., Galloway, W. E., Proctor, C. V., Jr., and others, 1970, Depositional systems in the Jackson group of Texas: Gulf Coast Association of Geological Societies Transactions, v. 20, p. 234–261.

Flawn, P. T., Goldstein, A., Jr., King, P. B., and Weaver, C. E., 1961, The Ouachita system: University of Texas Publication 6120, 401 p.

Foote, R. Q., and Martin, R. G., 1981, Petroleum geology of the Gulf of Mexico maritime boundary assessment area, *in* Powers, R. B., ed., Geologic framework, petroleum geology, petroleum resource estimates, mineral and geothermal resources, geologic hazards and deep water drilling technology in the maritime boundary region in the Gulf of Mexico: U.S. Geological Survey Open-File Report 81–265, p. 68–79.

Forgotson, J. M., and Forgotson, J. M., Jr., 1976, Definition of Gilmer limestone, upper Jurassic Formation, northeastern Texas: American Association of Petroleum Geologists Bulletin, v. 60, p. 1119–1123.

Forrest, M. C., 1986, Deepwater Gulf of Mexico exploration geology, hydrocarbons, and economics: Gulf Coast Association of Geologica Societies Transactions, v. 36, p. xlv–xlvii.

Galloway, W. E., 1986, Growth faults and fault-related structures of prograding terrigenous clastic continental margins: Gulf Coast Association of Geological Societies Transactions, v. 36, p. 121–128.

Galloway, W. E., Hobday, D. K., and Magara, K., 1982, Frio formation of Texas Gulf coastal plain; Depositional systems, structural framework, and hydrocarbon distribution: American Association of Petroleum Geologists Bulletin, v. 66, p. 649–688.

Galloway, W. E., Ewing, T. E., Garrett, C. M., Tyler, N., and Bebout, D. G., 1983, Atlas of major Texas oil reservoirs: University of Texas at Austin Bureau of Economic Geology, p. 54–55.

Galloway, W. E., Jirik, L. A., Morton, R. A., and DuBar, J. R., 1986, Lower Miocene (Fleming) depositional episode of the Texas coastal plain and continental shelf; Structural framework, facies, and hydrocarbon resources: University of Texas at Austin Bureau of Economic Geology Report of Investigation 150, 50 p.

Garrison, L. E., and Martin, R. G., Jr., 1973, Geologic structures in the Gulf of Mexico Basin: U.S. Geological Survey Professional Paper 773, 85 p.

—— , 1967, Salt domes; Gulf region, United States and Mexico: Houston, Texas, Gulf Publication Company, 425 p.

Halbouty, M. T., and Halbouty, J. J., 1982, Relationships between East Texas field region and Sabine uplift in Texas: Association of Petroleum Geologists Bulletin, v. 66, p. 1042–1054.

Hamberg, L. R., 1983, Seismic profiles and a stratigraphic trap, *in* Bally, A. W., Seismic expression of structural styles: American Association of Petroleum Geologists Studies in Geology, no. 15, p. 1.2.2.15–18.

Hardin, F. R., and Hardin, G. C., Jr., 1961, Contemporaneous normal faults of Gulf Coast and their relation to flexures: American Association of Petroleum Geologists Bulletin, v. 45, p. 238–248.

Harding, P. T., and Lowell, J. D., 1979, Structural styles, their plate-tectonic habitats, and hydrocarbon traps in petroleum provinces: American Association of Petroleum Geologists Bulletin, v. 63, p. 1016–1058.

Hazzard, R. T., Spooner, W. C., and Blanpied, 1947, Notes on the stratigraphy of the formations that underlie the Smackover Limestone in south Arkansas, northeast Texas, and northern Louisiana: Shreveport Geological Society 1945 Reference Report, v. 2, p. 483–503.

Holcomb, C. W., 1971, Hydrocarbon potential of Gulf series of western Gulf basin, *in* Future petroleum provinces of the United States; Their geology and potential: American Association of Petroleum Geologists Memoir 15, v. 2, p. 887–900.

Honea, J. W., 1956, Sam Fordyce–Vanderbilt fault system of southwest Texas:

Gulf Coast Association of Geological Societies Transactions, v. 6, p. 51–54.
Hoyt, W. V., 1959, Erosional channel in the middle Wilcox near Yoakum, Lavaca County, Texas: Gulf Coast Association of Geological Societies Transactions, v. 9, p. 41–50.

Hughes, D. J., 1968, Salt tectonics as related to several Smackover fields along the northeast rim of the Gulf of Mexico basin: Gulf Coast Association of Geological Societies Transactions, v. 18, p. 320–333.

Humphris, C. C., Jr., 1978, Salt movement on continental slope, northern Gulf of Mexico, *in* Bouma, A. H., Moore, G. T., and Coleman, J. M., eds., Framework, facies, and oil-trapping characteristics of the upper continental margin: Association of Petroleum Geologists Studies in Geology, no. 7, p. 69–86.

—— , 1979, Salt movement in continental slope, northern Gulf of Mexico: American Association of Petroleum Geologists Bulletin, v. 63, p. 782–798.

—— , 1984, Interrelations of Tertiary deposition, growth faulting, and salt movement, northern Gulf of Mexico [abs.]: Economic Paleontologists and Mineralogists, Fifth Annual Research Conference Program and Abstracts, p. 50–51.

—— , 1985, Relationship of structural development and Cenozoic sedimentation, northern Gulf of Mexico [abs.]: American Association of Petroleum Geologists Bulletin, v. 69, no. 3, p. 268.

Imlay, R. W., 1980, Jurassic paleobiogeography of the conterminous United States in its continental setting: U.S. Geological Survey Professional Paper 1062, 134 p.

Indest, D. J., and McPherson, J. G., 1985, Depositional systems in the Olmos formation and their relationship to volcanic highs and hydrocarbon emplacements, Zavala County, Texas, *in* Perkins, B. F., and Martin, G. B., eds., Habitat of oil and gas in the Gulf Coast; Proceedings Fourth Annual Research Conference: Gulf Coast Section, Society of Economic Paleontologists and Mineralogists Foundation, 328 p.

Jackson, M.P.A., and Galloway, W. E., 1984, Structural and depositional styles of Gulf Coast Tertiary continental margins; Application to hydrocarbon exploration: American Association of Petroleum Geologists Continuing Education Course Note Series, no. 25, 226 p.

Jackson, M.P.A., and Harris, D. W., 1981, Seismic stratigraphy and salt mobilization along the northwestern margin of the East Texas Basin, *in* Kreitler, C. W., and others, eds., Geology and Geohydrology of the East Texas Basin: University of Texas at Austin Bureau of Economic Geology, p. 28–32.

Jackson, M.P.A., and Seni, S. J., 1983, Geometry and evolution of salt structures in a marginal rift basin in the Gulf of Mexico, east Texas: Geology, v. 11, p. 131–135.

—— , 1984, Suitability of salt domes in the East Texas Basin for nuclear waste isolation; Final summary of geologic and hydrogeologic research (1978 to 1983): University of Texas at Austin Bureau of Economic Geology Geological Circular 84–1, 128 p.

Jackson, M.P.A., Talbot, C. J., and Cornelius, R. R., 1988, Centrifuge modeling of the effects of aggradation and progradation on syndepositional salt structures: University of Texas at Austin Bureau of Economic Geology Report of Investigations no. 173, 93 p.

Johnson, H. A., and Bredeson, D. H., 1971, Structural development of some shallow salt domes in Louisiana Miocene productive belt: American Association of Petroleum Geologists Bulletin, v. 55, no. 2, p. 204–226.

Johnson, O. H., 1958, The Monroe Uplift: Gulf Coast Association of Geological Societies Transactions, v. 8, p. 24–26.

Kidwell, A. L., 1951, Mesozoic igneous activity in the northern Gulf Coastal Plain: Gulf Coast Association of Geological Societies Transactions, v. 1, p. 182–199.

King, P. B., 1975, The Ouachita and Appalachian orogenic belts, *in* Stehli, F. G., and Nairn, A., eds., The ocean basins and margins; V. 3, Gulf of Mexico and Caribbean: New York, Plenum Publishing Corp., p. 201–241.

Klitgord, K. D., and Schouten, H., 1986, Plate kinematics of the central Atlantic, *in* Vogt, P. R., and Tucholke, B. E., eds., The western North Atlantic region: Boulder, Colorado, Geological Society of America, The Geology of North America, v. M, p. 351–378.

Ladd, J. W., Buffler, R. T., Watkins, J. S., and Worzel, J. L., 1976, Deep seismic reflection results from the Gulf of Mexico: Geology, v. 4, p. 365–368.

Lehner, P., 1969, Salt tectonics and Pleistocene stratigraphy on continental slope of northern Gulf of Mexico: American Association of Petroleum Geologists Bulletin, v. 53, p. 2431–2479.

Lemoine, M., ed., 1978, Geologic Atlas of Alpine Europe: New York, Elsevier, 584 p.

Mancini, E. A., Mink, R. M., Bearden, B. L., and Wilkerson, R. P., 1985, Norphlet Formation (Upper Jurassic) of southwestern and offshore Alabama; Environments of deposition and petroleum geology: American Association of Petroleum Geologists Bulletin, v. 69, p. 881–898.

Mandl, G., and Crans, W., 1981, Gravitational glidings in deltas, *in* McClay, K. R., and Price, N. J., Thrust and nappe tectonics: Geological Society of London Special Publication 9, p. 41–54.

Mann, C. J., and Thomas, W. A., 1964, Cotton Valley Group (Jurassic) nomenclature, Louisiana and Arkansas: Gulf Coast Association of Geological Societies Transactions, v. 31, p. 143–152.

Manspeizer, W., 1982, Triassic–Liassic basins and climate of the Atlantic passive margins: Geologische Rundschau, v. 71, p. 895–917.

Martin, G. B., 1978, Paleoecology and porosity trends of abnormally high pressured sands and shales: Gulf Coast Association of Geological Societies Transactions, v. 28, p. 313–322.

Martin, R. G., Jr., 1978, Northern and eastern Gulf of Mexico continental margin; Stratigraphic and structural framework, *in* Bouma, A. H., Moore, G. T., and Coleman, J. M., eds., Framework, facies, and oil-trapping characteristics of the upper continental margin: American Association of Petroleum Geologists Studies in Geology, no. 7, p. 21–42.

—— , 1980, Distribution of salt structures, Gulf of Mexico; Map and descriptive text: U.S. Geological Survey Map MF–1213.

—— , 1984, Diapiric trends in the deep-water Gulf basin: Fifth Annual Research Conference, Program and Abstracts, Gulf Coast Section, Society of Economic Paleontologists and Mineralogists, p. 60–62.

Martin, R. G., Jr., and Case, J. E., 1975, Geophysical studies in the Gulf of Mexico, *in* Nairn, A.E.M., and Stehli, F. G., eds., Ocean basins and margins; v. 3, The Gulf of Mexico and the Caribbean: New York, Plenum Press, p. 65–106.

McBride, J. H., and Nelson, K. D., 1988, Integration of COCORP deep reflection and magnetic anomaly analysis in the southeastern United States; Implications for origin of the Brunswick and East Coast magnetic anomalies: Geological Society of America Bulletin, v. 100, p. 436–445.

McGookey, D. P., 1975, Gulf Coast Cenozoic sediments and structure; An excellent example of extra-continental sedimentation: Gulf Coast Association of Geological Societies Transactions, v. 25, p. 104–120.

McGowen, M. K., and Harris, D. W., 1984, Cotton Valley (Upper Jurassic) and Hosston (Lower Cretaceous) depositional systems and their influence on salt tectonics in the East Texas Basin, *in* Ventress, P. S., and others, eds., The Jurassic of the Gulf Rim: Gulf Coast Section Society of Economic Paleontologists and Mineralogists Foundation, Proceedings Third Annual Research Conference, p. 213–249.

Mixon, R. B., Murray, G. E., and Diaz, G. T., 1959, Age and correlation of Huizachal group (Mesozoic), State of Tamaulipas, Mexico: American Association of Petroleum Geologists Bulletin, v. 43, p. 757–771.

Moore, G. W., and del Castillo, L., 1974, Tectonic evolution of the southern Gulf of Mexico: Geological Society of America Bulletin, v. 85, p. 607–618.

Murray, G. E., 1964, Geology of the Atlantic and Gulf Coastal Province of North America: New York, Harper and Bros., 692 p.

Nicholas, R. L., and Rozendal, R. A., 1975, Subsurface positive elements within Ouachita foldbelt in Texas and their relation to Paleozoic cratonic margin: American Association of Petroleum Geologists Bulletin, v. 59, no. 2, p. 193–216.

Ocamb, R. D., 1961, Growth faults in south Louisiana: Gulf Coast Association of Geological Societies Transactions, v. 11, p. 139–173.

Oliver, W. B., 1971, Depositional systems in the Woodbine Formation, northeast Texas: University of Texas at Austin, Bureau of Economic Geology Report of Investigations, no. 23, 28 p.

Pearcy, J. R., and Ray, P. K., 1986, The production trends of the Gulf of Mexico:

Gulf Coast Association of Geological Societies Transactions, v. 36, p. 263–273.

Perrier, R., and Quiblier, J., 1974, Thickness changes in sedimentary layers during compaction history; Methods of quantitative evaluation: American Association of Petroleum Geologists Bulletin, p. 507–520.

Pew, E., 1982, Seismic structural analysis of deformation in the southern Mexican Ridges [M.A. thesis]: University of Texas at Austin, 102 p.

Pilger, R. H., Jr., 1978, A closed Gulf of Mexico, pre-Atlantic ocean plate reconstruction and the early rift history of the Gulf and North Atlantic: Gulf Coast Association of Geological Societies Transactions, v. 28, p. 385–393.

Pindell, J., 1985, Alleghenian reconstruction and the subsequent evolution of the Gulf of Mexico, Bahamas, and proto-Caribbean Sea: Tectonics, v. 4, p. 1–39.

Pindell, J., and Dewey, J. F., 1982, Permo–Triassic reconstruction of western Pangea and the evolution of the Gulf–Caribbean region: Tectonics, v. 1, p. 179–211.

Quarles, M., Jr., 1953, Salt ridge hypothesis on the origin of Texas Gulf Coast type of faulting: American Association of Petroleum Geologists Bulletin, v. 37, p. 489–508.

Ramberg, H., 1981, Gravity deformation and the earth's crust in theory, experiments, and geological application, 2nd ed.: London, Academic Press, 452 p.

Ross, M. I., and Scotese, C. R., 1988, A hierarchical tectonic model of the Gulf of Mexico and Caribbean region: Tectonophysics, v. 155, p. 139–168.

Salvador, A., 1987, Late Triassic–Jurassic paleogeography and origin of the Gulf of Mexico Basin: American Association of Petroleum Geologists Bulletin, v. 71, p. 419–451.

Salvador, A., and Green, A. R., 1980, Opening of the Caribbean Tethys, *in* Geology of Alpine chains born of the Tethys; 26th International Geological Congress, Colloquium C5: Bureau des Rescherches Geologiques et Minieres Memoire 115, p. 224–229.

Sassen, R., and Moore, C. H., 1988, Framework of hydrocarbon generation and destruction in the eastern Smackover trend: American Association of Petroleum Geologists Bulletin, v. 72, p. 649–663.

Schaub, E. J., Buffler, R. T., and Parsons, J. G., 1984, Seismic stratigraphic framework of the deep Gulf of Mexico basin: American Association of Petroleum Geologists Bulletin, v. 68, p. 1790–1802.

Scott, K. R., Hayes, W. E., and Fietz, R. P., 1961, Geology of the Eagle Mills Formation: Gulf Coast Association of Geological Societies Transactions, v. 11, p. 1–14.

Seglund, J. A., 1974, Collapse-fault systems of Louisiana Gulf Coast: American Association of Petroleum Geologists Bulletin, v. 58, no. 12, p. 2389–2397.

Seni, S. J., and Jackson, M.P.A., 1983, Evolution of salt structures, east Texas diapir province: American Association of Petroleum Geologists Bulletin, v. 67, no. 8, p. 1219–1274.

Siemers, C. T., 1978, Submarine fan deposition of the Woodbine–Eagleford interval (Upper Cretaceous), Tyler County, Texas: Gulf Coast Association of Geological Societies Transactions, v. 28, p. 493–533.

Smith, G. W., 1985, Geology of the deep Tuscaloosa (Upper Cretaceous) gas trend in Louisiana, *in* Perkins, B. F., and Martin, G. B., Habitat of oil and gas in the Gulf Coast; Proceedings Fourth Annual Research Conference: Gulf Coast Section, Society of Economic Paleontologists and Mineralogists Foundation, 328 p.

Spindler, W. M., 1977, Structure and stratigraphy of a small Plio–Pleistocene depocenter, Louisiana continental shelf: Gulf Coast Association of Geological Societies Transactions, v. 27, p. 180–196.

Stuart, C. J., and Caughey, C. A., 1977, Seismic facies and sedimentology of terrigenous Pleistocene deposits in northwest and central Gulf of Mexico, *in* Payton, C. E., ed., Seismic stratigraphy; Applications to hydrocarbon exploration: American Association of Petroleum Geologists Memoir 26, p. 249–275.

Swanson, M. T., 1986, Preexisting fault control for Mesozoic basin formation in eastern North America: Geology, v. 14, p. 419–422.

Thomas, W. A., 1976, Evolution of the Ouachita–Appalachian continental margin: Journal of Geology, v. 84, p. 323–342.

Todd, R. G., and Mitchum, R. M., Jr., 1977, Seismic stratigraphy and global changes of sea level; Part 8, Identification of Upper Triassic, Jurassic, and Lower Cretaceous seismic sequences in Gulf of Mexico and offshore West Africa, *in* Payton, C. E., ed., Seismic stratigraphy; Applications to hydrocarbon exploration: American Association of Petroleum Geologists Memoir 26, p. 145–163.

van Houten, F. B., 1977, Triassic–Liassic deposits of Morocco and eastern North America; A comparison: American Association of Petroleum Geologists Bulletin, v. 61, p. 79–99.

Vernon, R. C., 1971, Possible future potential of pre-Jurassic Western Gulf Basin, *in* Cram, I. H., ed., Future petroleum provinces of the United States; Their geology and potential: American Association of Petroleum Geologists Memoir 15, v. 2, p. 954–979.

Vogler, H. A., and Robison, B. A., 1987, Exploration for deep geopressured gas—Corsair trend, offshore Texas: American Association of Petroleum Geologists Bulletin, v. 71, p. 777–787.

Walper, J. L., 1981, Geological evolution of the Gulf of Mexico–Caribbean region, *in* Kerr, J. W., and Ferguson, A. J., eds., Geology of the North Atlantic Borderlands: Canadian Society of Petroleum Geologists Memoir 7, p. 503–525.

Walper, J. L., Henk, F. H., Loudeon, E. J., and Raschilla, S. N., 1979, Sedimentation on a trailing plate margin; The northern Gulf of Mexico: Gulf Coast Association of Geological Societies Transactions, v. 29, p. 188–201.

Walthall, B. H., and Walper, J. L., 1967, Peripheral gulf rifting in southeast Texas: American Association of Petroleum Geologists Bulletin, v. 51, p. 102–110.

White, G. W., 1980, Permian–Triassic continental reconstruction of the Gulf of Mexico–Caribbean area: Nature, v. 283, p. 823–826.

White, G. W., and Burke, K., 1980, Outline of the tectonic evolution of the Gulf of Mexico and the Caribbean region: Houston Geological Society Bulletin, v. 22, p. 8–13.

Wilhelm, O., and Ewing, M., 1972, Geology and history of the Gulf of Mexico: Geological Society of America Bulletin, v. 83, p. 575–600.

Wilson, J. T., 1966, Did the Atlantic close and then reopen?: Nature, v. 211, p. 676–681.

Winker, C. D., 1982, Cenozoic shelf margins, northwestern Gulf of Mexico: Gulf Coast Association of Geological Societies Transactions, p. 427–448.

Winker, C. D., and Buffler, R. T., 1988, Paleogeographic evolution of early deep-water Gulf of Mexico and margins, Jurassic to middle Cretaceous (Comanchian): American Association of Petroleum Geologists Bulletin, v. 72, p. 318–346.

Winker, C. D., and Edwards, M. B., 1983, Unstable progradational clastic shelf margins: Society of Economic Paleontologists and Mineralogists Special Publication 33, p. 139–157.

Wood, D. H., and Giles, A. B., 1982, Hydrocarbon accumulation patterns in the East Texas salt dome province: University of Texas at Austin, Bureau of Economic Geology Geological Circular 82–6, 36 p.

Wood, M. L., and Walper, J. L., 1974, The evolution of the Interior Mesozoic Basin and the Gulf of Mexico: Gulf Coast Association of Geological Societies Transactions, v. 24, p. 31–41.

Woodbury, H. O., Murray, I. B., Jr., Pickford, P. J., and Akers, W. H., 1973, Pliocene and Pleistocene depocenters, outer continental shelf, Louisiana and Texas: American Association of Petroleum Geologists Bulletin, v. 57, p. 2428–2439.

Woods, R. D., and Addington, J. W., 1973, Pre-Jurassic geologic framework northern Gulf Basin: Gulf Coast Association of Geological Societies Transactions, v. 23, p. 92–108.

Zartman, R. E., 1977, Geochronology of some alkalic rock provinces in the eastern and central United States: Annual Reviews Earth Sciences, v. 5, p. 257–286.

Zietz, I., 1982, Composite magnetic anomaly map of the United States, Part A; Conterminous United States: U.S. Geological Survey Geophysical Investigations Map GP–954–A, 2 sheets, scale 1:2,500,000.

Manuscript Accepted by the Society December 2, 1988

ACKNOWLEDGMENTS

The authors wish to thank Shell Oil Company for permission to publish this chapter, and to acknowledge the ideas, concepts, and suggestions provided by numerous Shell geologists, including F. A. Diegel, D. C. Schuster, S. C. Reeve, E. J. La Flure, R. L. Nicholas, C. S. Cameron, and C. D. Winker, all of whom helped to improve the manuscript by their critical review. We would like additionally to thank M.P.A. Jackson and A. Salvador for their helpful reviews, and also U. S. Allen, C. J. Ando, J. M. Beall, A. R. Christensen, C. L. Conrad, R. M. Coughlin, V. K. Cung, M. P. Deshowitz, G. Encisco, S. A. Goetsch, D. M. Gray, J. F. Karlo, G. M. Larberg, C. F. Lobo, P. T. Lucas, E. B. Picou, Jr., C. C. Roripaugh, Jr., A. D. Scardina, J. L. Shepard, R. C. Shoup, D. M. Van der Stoep, and M. Virnig for their technical input, and E. White, C. H. Robinson, and F. Rawlins for their assistance with the graphics. We also thank Grant Norpac, Inc., Seismic Exchange Inc., Teledyne Exploration, and the University of Texas Marine Seismic Institute for permission to publish portions of seismic data.

Printed in U.S.A.

The Geology of North America
Vol. A, The Geology of North America—An overview
The Geological Society of America, 1989

Chapter 8

Phanerozoic evolution of the North American Cordillera; United States and Canada

John S. Oldow, Albert W. Bally, Hans G. Avé Lallemant, and William P. Leeman
Department of Geology and Geophysics, Rice University, Houston, Texas 77251

INTRODUCTION

Early explorers and geology

The rediscovery of America by the Genovese Christopher Columbus and the conquest of Mexico by the Spaniards was followed by a more gradual, but equally relentless, occupation of North America by the French and the British. The last phase of this process involved the discovery and exploration of the western Cordillera of North America. Fur traders Anthony Henday (1754) and the La Verendrye brothers (1743) were the first non-Indians to sight the western Cordillera, while James Cook (1778) and Vitus Bering (1728, 1741) were the first to explore the coasts of the northern Pacific beyond a California that was already discovered and subdued by the Spanish.

There followed many expeditions that were driven by the search for gold and the fur trade as well as political and missionary interests. Most spectacular perhaps was the first crossing of the Canadian Cordillera by the Scot, Alexander MacKenzie, who reached the Pacific near Bella Coola, British Columbia in 1793. In his footsteps, the expeditions of Simon Fraser (1807), David Thompson (1807–1812), and others led to the geographic reconnaissance of the Cordillera of the northwestern United States and Canada. Lewis and Clark (1804–1805), who traversed the northwestern U.S. Cordillera, were the first who, while obviously involved in a politically motivated expedition, had an important charge to also make scientific observations.

Thus, the western Cordillera had first to be "discovered" through the arduous efforts of many early explorers before any significant geological studies could be undertaken. The first geological map of North America, published by Jean Etienne Guettard in 1752 in his "Mémoire dans lequel on compare le Canada à la Suisse," does not even show the existence of the western Cordillera, just as McClure in 1817 still had to limit his geological map to the eastern United States.

It should not come as a surprise, as pointed out by *E. Lopez-Ramos (1983),* that the first Cordilleran geological observations were concerned with the geology of Mexico. In 1723, Brother Juan de Torquemada in his "Viente y uno libros Vibrales y Monarchía Indiana" already discusses mines, volcanoes, earthquakes, and mineral waters of Mexico. In the period from 1724 to 1730, we find discussions of Pedro de Alarcón concerning earthquakes in Mexico. Note also that the first North American mining school, the Colegio de Minería, was founded in Mexico in 1792. It was the predecessor of today's Facultad de Ingenieriá of Mexico. But at last it was the great German naturalist Alexander von Humboldt who, in his "Ensayo político sobre el reino de la Nueva España" in 1804 and the "Carte générale du royaume de la nouvelle Espagne" in 1811, provided a first overview of the Cordillera of Mexico and today's southwestern United States.

Our chapter deals only with the U.S. and Canadian Cordillera. For additional information, we refer to the chapter on the geology of Mexico (de Cserna, this volume). Furthermore, for convenience, we will refer to the U.S. and Canadian Cordillera simply as the Cordillera.

In the Cordillera, serious geological work began in California following the discovery of gold at Sutter's Mill in 1848 and silver in the Comstock Lode of Nevada in 1859. J. B. Trask's report "On the geology of the Sierra Nevada or California Range" and the establishment in 1860 of a Geological Survey in California by Josia Dwight Whitney were the initial milestones. During the mid-century, the early U.S. railroad surveys were accompanied by geologists like J. Marcou and J. L. Leconte. In Canada, J. Hector played a similar role as "medicine man" and geologist of the Palliser expedition. However, systematic Cordilleran geological exploration will forever remain associated with the great national expeditions of the United States. These include F. V. Hayden's surveys of the territories between 1869 and 1878, C. R. King's geological survey of the 40th parallel (1867–1877), J. W. Powell's U.S. geological and geographical survey of the Rocky Mountain region (1874–1877), and Wheeler's geographical surveys west of the 100th Meridian (1869–1879). Instigated by J. W. Powell and recommended by a report of the National Academy of Science, all these survey activities

Oldow, J. S., Bally, A. W., Avé Lallemant, H. G., and Leeman, W. P., 1989, Phanerozoic evolution of the North American Cordillera; United States and Canada, *in* Bally, A. W., and Palmer, A. R., eds., The Geology of North America—An overview: Boulder, Colorado, Geological Society of America, The Geology of North America, v. A.

were consolidated in the year 1878 into the U.S. Geological Survey. In Canada, where a Geological Survey had existed since 1842, the first major Cordilleran surveys were undertaken by A.R.C. Selwyn, G. M. Dawson, and R. G. McConnell (1871–1888). Perhaps the last effort in the spirit of the great expeditions was associated with boundary surveys that were undertaken and reported by *R. A. Daly (1912),* for the 49th parallel.

The Cordillera before plate tectonics

To write about the evolution of geological and geophysical thoughts on the Cordillera prior to the advent of plate tectonics is a challenge that is well beyond the scope of this chapter. We have to limit ourselves to a few brief remarks. For the U.S. Cordillera, essentially descriptive syntheses were done by *Blackwelder (1912)* and *Eardley (1962).* In Canada as in the United States, quite justifiably, the main concern was with extensive surface mapping and the recording of geological observations. In Canada, an early synthesis of the tectonics of the Cordillera of British Columbia was published by *White (1959)* and expanded in an overview of Cordilleran geology by *Ziegler (1969),* which was based mostly on reconnaissance work done by industry geologists. A comprehensive synthesis of the Canadian Cordillera was given by Douglas and others (1970), while *Gilluly (1963, 1967)* provided similar overviews for the U.S. Cordillera.

Undoubtedly the most spectacular synthesis of the geology of the Cordillera is the 1:5,000,000 Tectonic Map of North America by King (1969), a map that incorporated much information from the Tectonic map of Canada by *Stockwell and others (1967),* the Geological Map of Mexico by *Salas and others (1960),* and *de Cserna's (1961)* Tectonic Map of Mexico. All four maps preceded the development of modern plate tectonics, and thus they mark the end of the era that laid the foundation for most modern work on the Cordillera.

The guiding principles of King's Tectonic Map included the geosynclinal classification of Kay (1951) with its emphasis on the differentiation between miogeosynclinal and eugeosynclinal fold belt segments, and the development of successor basins (see also, *Churkin, 1974*). Thus, foreland folded belt tectonics were justifiably differentiated from the interior and more westerly deformed eugeosynclinal zones. Much of this is reviewed by King in his classic *The evolution of North America* (1977; earlier edition, 1959). In this chapter we will use interchangeably the terms miogeosyncline and Paleozoic passive margins (for additional discussion, see Bally, this volume). The terms eugeosyncline or eugeocline will be avoided because they have lost their meaning.

Cordilleran plate tectonics

The concept of plate tectonics brought about fundamental changes in the perspectives of Cordilleran tectonics. Earlier, and in contrast to the European and South African earth science community, the North American geophysical and geological establishment had roundly rejected continental drift. However, a reversal of opinion occurred when, in the mid-1960s, oceanographers, geophysicists, and particularly, seismologists joined forces to lay the foundation of modern plate tectonics. The immense scale and scope of plate tectonics initially made it difficult for many Cordilleran geologists to reconcile their field observations with plate tectonics. After all, mountains were obviously characterized by intense ductile folding, much penetrative deformation, and complex metamorphic and igneous phenomena. Thus, orogenic systems presented themselves as anything but the leading edges of "torsionally rigid" plates! However, some important developments did help to set the stage for the application of plate tectonic concepts to the Cordillera, and showed ways to arrive at broad simplifications of the complex surface geology:

(1) In California, the great importance of strike-slip faulting was dramatized by Hill and Dibblee's (1953) seminal paper and further summarized in 1962 by Crowell. These observations led to *J. T. Wilson's (1965)* postulate that the San Andreas fault was a major transform boundary and eventually to Atwater's (1970) plate tectonic model for the West Coast.

(2) In Canada, following the pioneering work by *Link (1949)* and *Douglas (1950),* petroleum geologists began applying regional reflection seismic profiling to the exploration of folded belts. Publications by *Fox (1959), Shaw (1963),* and Bally and others (1966) documented for the first time that the whole foreland fold belt was underlain by a gently westward-dipping Precambrian basement homocline that was presumed to extend well under the central portion of the Cordillera. Therefore, the complex surface was underlain by a very simple basement geology. These observations eventually led to the widespread use of balanced cross sections (*Dahlstrom, 1969*) and to models describing the evolution of foreland basins (*Price and Mountjoy, 1970*; Price, 1981; Beaumont, 1981).

(3) The acceptance of low-angle (i.e., listric) normal faulting that was locally controlled by pre-existing thrust faulting, grew out of *Longwell's (1945)* work in Nevada. It was followed in Canada by the first seismic-reflection documentation for low-angle normal faulting (Bally and others, 1966). These observations were amplified by detailed mapping within extended terranes (*Anderson, 1971*; Proffett, 1977) and led to the many modern lithospheric stretching models for the Basin and Range region (Eaton, 1982; Wernicke and Burchfiel, 1982; Davis, 1983).

(4) Additional logistic and methodological advances contributed much to firmly establish modern interpretations of the Cordillera. Helicopter transport for geological field mapping was pioneered in the 1950s by the Geological Survey of Canada and Canadian petroleum companies, and led to extensive reconnaissance surveys of hitherto almost inaccessible areas of the Canadian Cordillera and Alaska by the Geological Survey of Canada and the U.S. Geological Survey. Introduction of satellite photography and modern remote sensing techniques complemented more traditional photogeologic techniques. The dramatic progress in radiometric dating (for summaries see Armstrong and others, 1977; Armstrong, 1988) had an enormous impact on

models for Cordilleran tectonics. The widespread application of geophysical techniques to solve Cordilleran problems started with regional gravity and magnetic surveys and continued with intensified application of refraction and wide-angle reflection techniques, which was spearheaded by the U.S. Geological Survey and a number of academic groups (e.g., *Pakiser, 1963; Prodehl, 1970*). The increased sophistication of paleomagnetic methods led to the recognition of large-scale displacements of vast tracts of the Cordillera and allowed characterization of regions that underwent complex tilt and rotational histories (e.g., *Packer and Stone, 1972*; *Beck and Cox, 1979*; Beck, 1980; Irving and others, 1985). The extension of industrial seismic-reflection applications to the exploration of the continental crust under the leadership of Cornell's COCORP group (for references see *Barazangi and Brown, 1986a, 1986b*) and its lineal descendant, Lithoprobe of Canada, awakened the research community to the importance of the depth dimension in tectonic processes. Finally, the increased sophistication and applicability of structural geological methods has focused attention on the need to understand the kinematic history of regions; particularly when tectonic reconstructions are attempted.

With plate tectonics, the rapid development of modern geophysical and geochemical methods, and multi-disciplinary programs, we saw the emergence of a series of new overviews. Among them we cite Hamilton and Myers (1966), Burchfiel and Davis (1972, 1975), Monger and others (1972), and Monger and Price (1979) as landmark syntheses of the Cordillera in a plate tectonic framework. These early plate tectonic models, however, were largely two dimensional. Little attention was given the possibility of substantial transcurrent motion. The widespread deformation of the Cordillera was also largely considered to be the product of relatively short-lived "orogenic" events. The relationship of regional structures and motion of lithospheric plates initially was obscure.

Oblique convergence

Many authors interpreted the widespread shortening seen throughout the Cordillera as the result of normal plate convergence (e.g., *Dickinson, 1971,* Burchfiel and Davis, 1972) or perhaps due to the collision of exotic components with the leading edge of the continental margin (e.g. *Schweickert and Cowan, 1975*). No doubt both mechanisms play an important role. In addition, it appears that the development of structures within specific compressional belts is strongly influenced by the morphology of a given plate boundary.

The recognition and definition of suspect terranes along the North American borderland again profoundly modified earlier views (Coney and others, 1980; Monger and others, 1982; Howell, 1985). At first glance, the proliferation of various terranes is rather confusing to the uninitiated. (There are approximately 200 terranes for the Cordillera!) Nevertheless, the terrane concept encourages specific identification of tectonic units and does help to focus on very real differences that may be expected by the superposition in time and space of lateral displacements and purely compressional phenomena.

With the recent advances in understanding the kinematics of continental accretion and the subsurface geometry of terranes, our perception of active margin tectonics has changed. Originally, some authors visualized terranes as lithospheric microplates that collided with the continental margin (e.g., *Dewey and Bird, 1970*). The existence of younger (post-docking) overlap successions and the lack of younger deformed marine sediments were argued to be prima facie evidence against any substantial displacement after accretion (Monger and others, 1982; *Csejtey and others, 1982*).

Large latitudinal shifts of substantial parts of the Cordillera have become obvious from various lines of evidence. The magnitudes of the latitudinal displacements, however, are often fraught with discrepancies between data sets. As pointed out by Price and Carmichael (1986), compressional and strike-slip kinematics of the Canadian Cordillera based on field mapping contrast with the increasing body of paleomagnetic data that require much larger latitudinal transport of many terranes during and after docking. Nevertheless, existence of large latitudinal shifts appears to be real; estimates are based on:

(1) paleomagnetic observations (e.g., Beck, 1976, 1980; *Beck and others, 1981a, 1981b*; Irving and others, *1980,* 1985; Stone and others, 1982; *Armstrong and others, 1985*; *Hagstrum and others, 1985, 1986*; Stone and McWilliams, 1989);

(2) stratigraphic and biostratigraphic data (*Jones and others, 1977*; *Tipper, 1981, 1984*; Taylor and others, 1984; Silberling, 1985), and;

(3) the development of a new generation of plate tectonic reconstructions (Engebretson and others, 1985; Debiche and others, 1987).

Transfer of material to the leading edge of the continent by relatively thick overthrust units (e.g., thrust sheets and/or accretionary wedges) is compatible with the development of contractional orogens. However, the implications of terrane accretion on overall volumetric balances of the continental lithosphere are commonly overlooked. The problem is two-fold:

(1) The displacement of terranes along the axis of the convergent boundary represents significant mass transfer in and out of the cross-sectional plane of a contractional belt. Thus, coeval longitudinal and compressional displacements require geometric and kinematic elucidation.

(2) Shortening in orogenic belts creates significant space problems that focus on the fate of the continental and/or transitional lithosphere, which was originally underlying regional decollements. Bally's (1975) A-type subduction attempts to call attention to this problem.

Thus, it would appear that there is an urgent need for three-dimensional reconstructions of the Cordillera through geologic time. This need is obvious if: (1) the accretionary wedge–overthrust nature of subduction zones that involve the oceanic lithosphere (Benioff or B-subduction) is accepted; (2) one recognizes the necessity of disposing of the continental or transitional

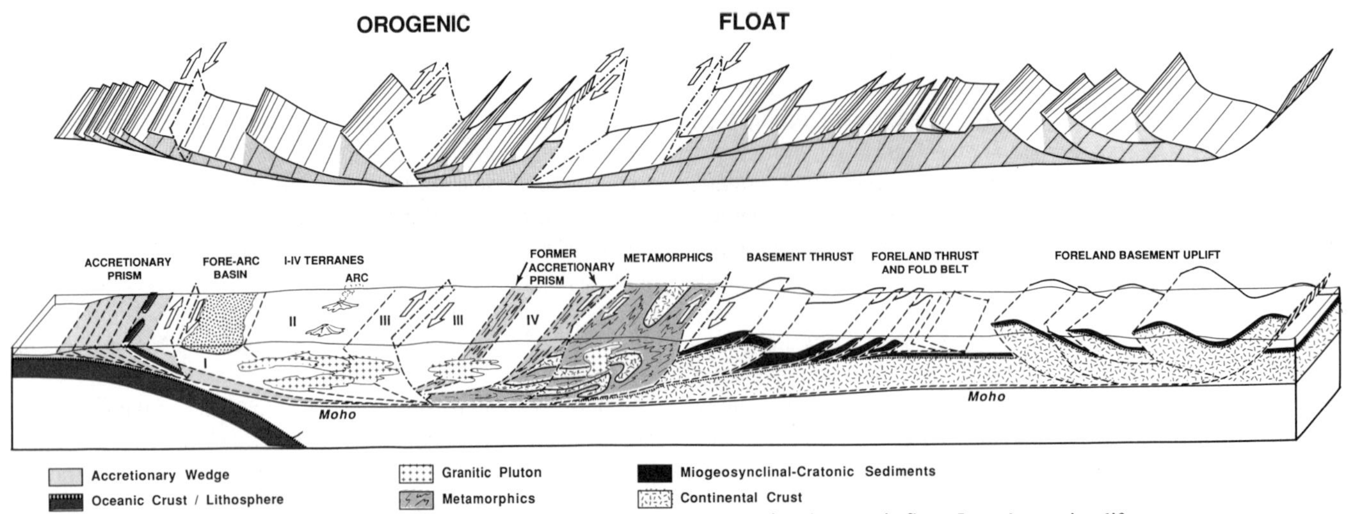

Figure 1. Conceptual diagram of a Cordilleran-type transpressional orogenic float. In order to simplify the diagram, syn- or post-orogenic extension is not considered here. The top diagram shows major decoupling systems stripped of the rock units involved in the deformation. From a deep decoupling zone at the base of the crust emanates a hierarchy of compressional decoupling levels within the basement, at the base of and within the sediments. Segments bound by strike-slip faults moved from out of the plane of the section into the plane of the section. From left to right: an accretionary wedge, involving deep-sea sediments and oceanic crust (ophiolites); several accreted terranes and former accretionary prisms (I–IV); a metamorphic core of dynamothermally reworked slices of transitional crust of the former North American passive margin; an interior basement thrust sheet (often a basement duplex); decollement foreland fold belt; and basement-involved foreland uplifts and basins. The last two zones would typically include foredeep sediments (for graphic simplicity not shown on this diagram) deposited on top of the miogeosynclinal-cratonic platform sequence. Units of the foreland belt shown on this diagram may be restored into the area now occupied by terranes transported from out of the plane of the section. In this particular section, a lithospheric root is not necessarily required (see Fig. 19). On the other hand, in the absence of units transported from out of the plane of section (i.e., U.S. Cordillera and continental-collision fold belts), the formation of the lithospheric root seems to be inescapable. Subsequent elimination of cold lithospheric roots may lead to uplift in fold belts. The concept of the orogenic float implies that fold belts represent sediments and crustal sheets separated mechanically from the underlying lithosphere. Whether the lower crust and upper mantle are partially involved in the orogenic float remains to be resolved.

lithosphere beneath the regional decollement during the shortening of crustal elements and sediments (Ampferer or A-subduction); and (3) the paleomagnetic and paleontological evidence for long-distance longitudinal transfer along the Cordilleran orogen is accepted.

It is our judgement that the Cordilleran orogen is best viewed as an orogenic float, a term we borrow from Laubscher (1977), who has fleetingly proposed it in a somewhat different and perhaps less sweeping context. In essence, the orogenic float is simply the product of the mechanical separation of sediments and crustal units from the underlying continental and oceanic lithosphere (Fig. 1). Major basal decoupling systems thus separate the very complex structures of the orogenic float from more simple lithospheric roots.

Recognition of the orogenic float helps in the conceptualization of continental tectonism in the context of plate motions. The mechanics by which relative plate motions are transmitted as displacements into forearc, arc, and back-arc regions are barely understood. It has been commonly held (*Armstrong, 1974*; Burchfiel and Davis, 1975) that the magmatic arc represents a thermally weakened region incapable of transmitting shear stresses (*Smith, 1981*). Thus, thrust displacements in the back-arc have been argued to be the product of compressional stresses oriented perpendicular to the axis of the arc. However, the displacement of suspect terranes throughout the western Cordillera is difficult to reconcile with models invoking simple arc-normal thrusting. Large tracts of the interior of the Canadian Cordillera, lying inboard of the Coast Plutonic complex, have moved tens of degrees of latitude (e.g., Irving and others, 1985) while shortening farther east was directed toward the continent (Bally and others, 1966; Price, 1981; Gabrielse, 1985; Eisbacher, 1985). In the western United States, a major transpressional fault system and associated back-arc thrust belt lying to the east of the Sierra Nevada saw tectonic transport in a direction subparallel to the axis of the coeval magmatic arc (Oldow, 1983, 1984a). Clearly the magmatic arc does not serve as an effective barrier to the transmission of shear in the continental lithosphere.

The resolution of oblique convergence into components parallel and normal to the plate boundary is well established in many fore-arc regions throughout the world (*Moore and Karig,*

1980; Walcott, 1978; *Hamilton, 1979*) and has been used to explain the longitudinal transport of terranes along continental margins (Fitch, 1972; Beck, 1976; Jarrard, 1986; Avé Lallemant and Oldow, 1988). Contractional structures and coeval strike-slip systems are spatially segregated in most cases, but are products of one displacement field (Figs. 1 and 2).

The effect of oblique convergence on back-arc regions is not well understood, because the geometry of detachments that transfer inter-plate displacements from the plate boundary to back-arc regions through the magmatic arc is not known. However, large-scale strike-slip faults, such as the Tintina in the Canadian Cordillera (Fig. 3), demonstrably were active during thrusting in the Rocky Mountain belt to the east (Gabrielse, 1985; Eisbacher, 1985). Simple balancing considerations of the relative displacement of the two systems require that they share a common basal decollement. The implication is that the surface position of the strike-slip fault migrated eastward over the subdetachment basement during the progressive shortening in the foreland. The two fault systems are the resolved components of one regional displacement field, not unlike that found in fore-arc regions.

We propose that oblique plate convergence is the driving force for the synchronous development of contractional and strike-slip fault systems throughout the active margin. We further propose that the displacements are transmitted by mid- to deep-crustal or conceivably upper-mantle detachments, which link the fault systems within the orogens and the plate boundary.

We relate these concepts to the development of the North American Cordillera. Constraints for the proposed model are outlined in the next sections.

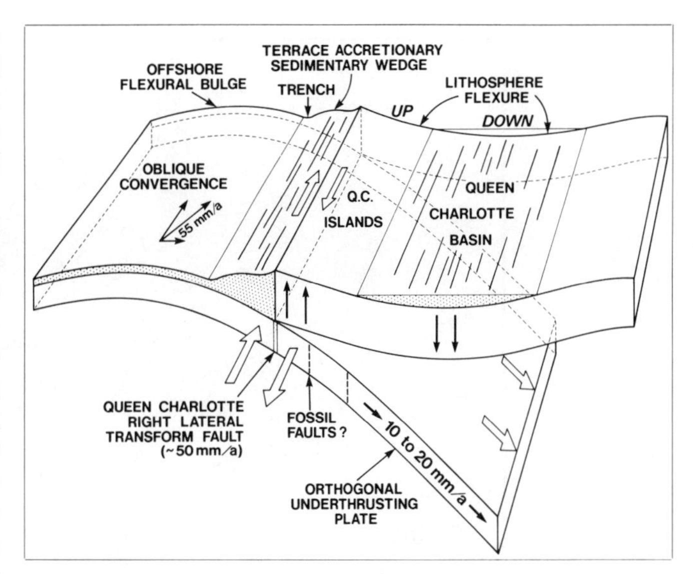

Figure 2. An example of oblique convergence on a continental margin located offshore British Columbia (from Yorath and Hyndman, 1983). Oblique convergence is resolved into dip-slip and strike-slip components. The western Queen Charlotte Islands and the adjacent Queen Charlotte basin is depressed by lithospheric flexure.

Basis for regional synthesis

In addition to traditional surface mapping, paleontology and stratigraphy, modern terrane analysis, paleomagnetic measurements, radiometric dating, and geochemical studies of igneous rocks, today's Cordilleran synthesis involves kinematic analysis of strike-slip, overthrust, and listric normal fault regimes, the interpretation of seismic-reflection profiles, and the construction of regional balanced cross sections. Ideally, kinematic reconstructions of complex transpressional systems ought to result in three-dimensional reconstructions.

In contractional belts, viable estimates of regional shortening can only be determined from balanced cross sections. Papers on balanced cross sections (e.g., *Dahlstrom, 1970; Boyer and Elliott, 1982*) emphasize techniques, but unfortunately say little about inherent uncertainties that relate to the nature of the geological and geophysical data. Even with regional seismic-reflection control, amounts of shortening derived from balanced sections are, at best, crude approximations that are dependent primarily on seismic-velocity assumptions and assumptions about the often unknown stratigraphic base of the sedimentary sequence that is being deformed (e.g., *Bally and others, 1988*). Nevertheless, within the obvious constraints of a method that is limited to flexural-slip folding, balanced sections do lead one to conclude that the external fold belt of the Cordillera is underlain by a deep basal decollement, which hugs the top of the underlying Precambrian craton and splays upward and across the sedimentary layers.

The assumption that all thrusts and folds ultimately emanate from regional basal decollement zones located at the bottom of the sedimentary section and/or within the continental crust (Fig. 1), casts a new light on the concept of an orogenic phase. The concept of orogeny, as a discrete event in time, is well entrenched in the geological literature and, in many instances, has controlled the perception of regional deformation. This bias is slowly yielding to new studies of the structural history of foreland regions of fold belts, but the impact of the foreland studies on the interpretation of the structural history of the interiors of contractional orogens is limited. Nevertheless, timing studies in the foreland region of fold belts have important implications for the entire orogen.

Stille (1924) originally visualized distinct orogenic phases that were separated by phases of tectonic quiescence. As *Gilluly (1973)* pointed out, Stille's concept is incompatible with the notion of perennially ongoing plate tectonics. To be sure, velocities of plate motion may well vary, but in essence we are dealing with a continuous process of folding and thrusting that, much of the time, uses the same regional decollement zone. Applied to fold belts, where the deformation typically proceeds from the inside to the outside and from the top to the bottom of the fold belt, this means that a displacement of a few kilometers at the leading edge of the thrust system will always be carried along the full length of the basal decollement (Bally, 1981, 1984; Oldow and others,

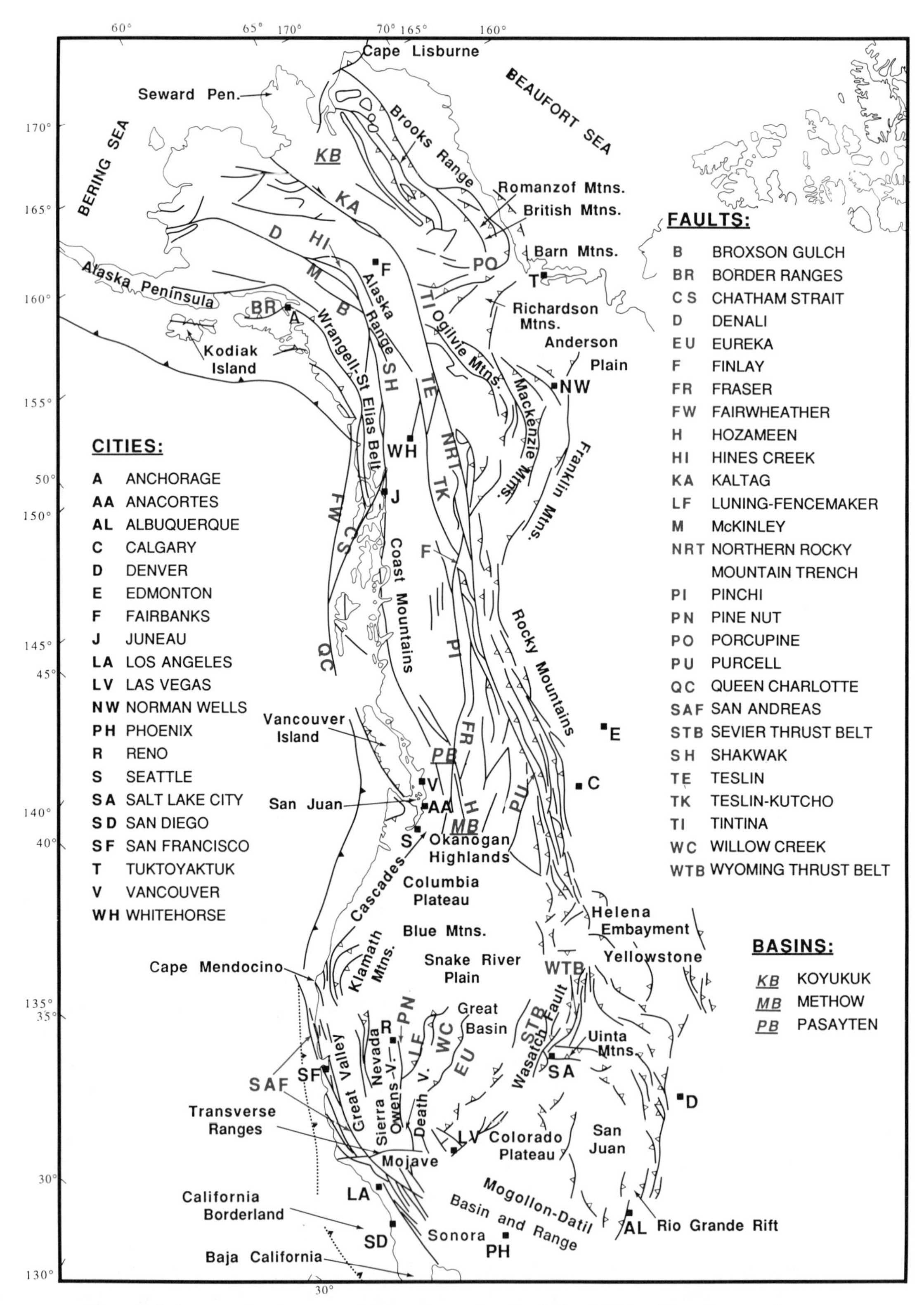

Figure 3. Index map showing geographic locations and major faults. Additional locations are shown on: Figure 9 (western conterminous United States); Figure 12 (northern Alaska and northwestern Canada); Figure 13 (southern Rocky Mountains); Figure 20 (Canada basin and adjacent continental margins); Figure 21 (Pacific Northwest basins); Figure 22 (faults in California); Figure 23 (Tertiary basins in California); Figure 29 (Cenozoic volcanic fields); and Figure 30 (Cenozoic extension provinces). For the location of sedimentary basins in the foreland see Bally, this volume.

1987a). Studies in other fold belts (e.g., Apennines; *Bally and others, 1985*) also suggest that motion on families of thrust faults overlap considerably. Older generation thrust faults generally have a period of synchronous displacement with younger, more frontal faults (Harrison and Bally, 1988).

Here we single out three important points in the progressive development of thrust belts:

(1) "In-sequence" as well as so-called "out-of-sequence" thrusting, constrained only on simple surface geological observations, cannot be reliably used as indicators of the regional progression of deformation. Such a progression can be established solely by looking at the sequential development of thrusts as they pierce a single stratigraphic reference level (see Bally and others, 1966, Fig. 6). In other words, without adequate supplementary seismic-reflection data and detailed kinematic analysis of related structures, the sequencing of thrust complexes cannot be properly evaluated by surface data alone. Of course, this difficulty has long been known to Alpine geologists and leads to the original concept of nappe envelopment, which is the overthrusting (or wrapping) of shallow thrust sheets by a previously underlying thrust unit.

(2) Stratigraphic onlap on, or plutonic intrusion of, a single fold or fault zone dates only the specific feature, not the entire fold belt. Progressive deformation in fold and thrust belts occurs over tens of millions of years, and to adequately establish the chronological history, stratigraphic analysis, regional isotopic dating, and uplift modeling must be employed.

(3) A clear understanding of the direction of tectonic transport in fold and thrust belts is indispensable in reconstruction efforts. Simple estimates based primarily on stratigraphic and facies arguments are not adequate. Transport directions, determined by the application of detailed kinematic analysis of structures are needed.

Using this type of reasoning, we have used timing relations in the foreland regions of the Cordillera fold and thrust belt as a fundamental ingredient in our reconstructions. Kinematic relations within the interior of the contractional orogen are more complex than those of the foreland and commonly include large-scale transcurrent displacements.

Possibly the most decisive controversy surrounding attempts to reconstruct the Cordillera involves estimates of the magnitude of transcurrent motion. The controversy arises from incompatibilities in displacement estimates derived from paleomagnetic, paleontological, and geological data sets. The resolution of these apparent incompatibilities is one of the fundamental problems to be addressed in the Cordillera. Most of the "problem" stems from the paleomagnetic data, which imply large displacements of vast tracts of the Cordilleran collage. As we discuss at some length later, it is our position that the paleomagnetic data must either be reconciled with geologic and paleontologic constraints or discarded out-of-hand. Because the body of carefully acquired paleomagnetic data is very large and contains a high degree of internal consistency, we accept it in the following reconstructions as a primary constraint for first-order displacement estimates in the Cordillera.

Organization of this chapter

With the overwhelming increase in new publications about the Cordillera, it is becoming increasingly difficult to gain an overview. In this chapter, problems are further compounded by our desire to give everybody fair credit for their work, a desire that is mitigated by the burden to keep this chapter relatively short. We decided to list mostly recent key references, a large number of which are contained in symposia and related collections of articles. Additional references that are in italics are listed in the expanded microfiche list of references. Instead of citing papers in extenso, we often elected to preferentially cite more recent references where additional relevant background references may be found. We ask for understanding and forgiveness from many authors who rightly expect to be cited, but are not.

Our synthesis is a team effort and, like most papers of this type, represents a form of selective journalism that leaves out some aspects while emphasizing others. Some of our concepts may appear to be new, and not adequately tested. Our main intent is to provide food for further discussion, as we all know that we are not yet close to the "truth" about the Cordillera. We are also acutely aware that many other well-founded perspectives about the Cordillera exist. Some of these will be detailed in volumes G-1 and G-2 of this series (*Plafker and others, 1989*; Gabrielse and Yorath, 1989). Whenever possible we tried to allude to existing controversy, but in this chapter, space does not permit giving alternative views "equal time."

In preparing this chapter, we had to make some tricky choices. We decided to limit stratigraphic comments to the bare essentials. For additional details, the reader is referred to Douglas and others, (1970), Cook and Bally (1975), Curtis (1975), *Stewart and others (1977b),* Howell and McDougall (1978), Armentrout and others (1979), Ernst (1981, 1988a), Flores and Kaplan (1985), Peterson (1986), Ingersoll and Ernst (1987), Tailleur and Weimer (1987), and the all-important COSUNA correlation charts (not cited individually, but see Appendix B, this volume). Some of the basic stratigraphic problems are discussed in "North American Phanerozoic basins" (Bally, this volume).

At first, we were tempted to organize this chapter in a reconstruction mode that would start with the presumably better-known mid- and late Cenozoic tectonics, then proceed to the more ambiguous early Paleogene and Mesozoic evolution, and subsequently to the much more puzzling Paleozoic past of the western Cordillera. Such a procedure would permit the reader to gradually subtract younger tectonics to uncover older tectonics and thus reveal earlier phases of structural evolution. We abandoned this plan because in it the sequencing of Cordilleran evolution is reversed, and the least known, older phases appear almost as an afterthought. We decided that the reader may prefer to study the Cordillera in a forward mode.

We also include within this Cordilleran chapter some comments concerning the Colorado Plateau, because we feel they are best presented within a Cordilleran context, but we focus mainly on the Tertiary evolution of the Plateau. Similarly our short summary of the geologic evolution of California is made within the context of the Tertiary history of the Cordillera.

For a general index map of geographic locations and faults, see Figure 3. Additional locations are shown on Figures 9, 12, 13, 20, 21, 22, 23, 29, and 30.

STRATIGRAPHIC FRAMEWORK

Introduction

The North American Cordillera records a complex stratigraphic and structural history. The stratigraphic relations of many units of the Cordillera are obscured by Phanerozoic deformation, which disrupted the original distribution of North American rocks. Such deformation involves the accretion of suspect terranes, large-scale overthrusting, transcurrent displacements, and in many regions, crustal extension. The kinematics of many of these deformational events is not known, and thus, the relations among rocks of various, originally coherent, units is not understood.

Recognition of the allochthoneity of many of the lithotectonic assemblages composing the Cordilleran collage (*Helwig, 1974*) led to a first-order division of the Cordilleran stratigraphy into an eastern, unequivocally North American stratigraphic domain on the one hand, and a number of more westerly assemblages of "suspect" origin (Coney and others, 1980). Suspect terranes include many structural units whose displacement history is not adequately understood.

In the following, we will briefly summarize major stratigraphic relations for the region stretching from western Alaska to the United States–Mexico border. For additional information on the North American stratigraphy of the Cordillera, the reader is referred to the chapter on North American Phanerozoic basins (Bally, this volume).

Elements of North American stratigraphy

In the eastern Cordillera, 15 to 20-km-thick middle Proterozoic sequences discordantly overlie a crystalline Precambrian basement. Traditionally, these sequences were seen as former passive margin sequences, but recently some authors have questioned this assumption and suggest that we may be dealing with a very large cratonic basin. Nevertheless, the Cordilleran miogeosyncline acquired its full identity only during the late Proterozoic, and ended in the Paleozoic. The overlying Mesozoic to Paleocene foredeep (exogeosyncline) sequences reflect the emergence of the Cordilleran folded belt.

In Cordilleran outcrops, Phanerozoic sedimentary sequences are all deformed, with the notable exception of the Colorado Plateau. Typically, they are involved in the overthrust units of the Brooks Range and Ogilvie, Mackenzie, and Rocky Mountains foreland fold and thrust belt, as well as in the Basin and Range extensional province of the western United States (Fig. 3). As we move farther west, the North American affinity of stratigraphic sequences becomes more difficult to establish because relationships are obscured by large-scale tectonic transport and by the related juxtaposition of North American units and suspect terranes, which took place during Paleozoic, Mesozoic, and Cenozoic time.

We start our stratigraphic overview with the eastern Canadian Cordillera, one of the best-studied segments of this fold belt (Fig. 4). From Canada we will go southward into the conterminous United States where the stratigraphy is like that of Canada. Finally, we will move back north to Alaska where foreland fold belt stratigraphy differs substantially from that of the Canada–U.S. Cordillera.

In the eastern Canadian Cordillera, a middle Proterozoic (1.7 to 1.5 Ga) sedimentary wedge discordantly overlies a crystalline basement that extends from the Canadian Shield westward and beneath the Rocky and Mackenzie Mountains. Remobilized rocks of the Precambrian basement occur sporadically within the interior Cordillera (*Parrish, 1989*). Ages of about 2.0 to 2.5 Ga have been reported from the Monashee Mountains of southeast British Columbia (Monger and Berg, 1987). Note, however, that other interior Cordilleran metamorphic complexes yield Paleozoic ages (refer to Fig. 8), and most of them are overprinted by Mesozoic and Tertiary radiometric ages that suggest uplift and/or remobilization.

Aitken and McMechan (1989) differentiate a lower, 15- to 20-km-thick, Belt-Purcell-Wernecke unit of shallow marine clastic, carbonate, and volcanic rocks, and correlate it directly with coeval sequences exposed in the northwest of the Canadian Shield (see also Hoffman, this volume). In the Mackenzie Mountains, younger (1.2 to 0.78 Ga) clastics belonging to the 4-km-thick Mackenzie Mountains assemblage overlie the preceding unit. Still, following *Aitken and McMechan (1989)* and also *Gabrielse and Campbell (1989),* we find that in the eastern Cordillera, all middle Proterozoic units are overlain with discordant, occasionally angular, contacts by the late Proterozoic (0.78 to 0.57 Ga) Windermere Supergroup, which has a typical thickness exceeding 3 km. Throughout the Windermere, clastics dominate. Rift-related basalts occur at the base of the succession, but perhaps the most characteristic feature of the Windermere is the occurrence of diamictites.

The Windermere Group marks the inception of the traditional Cordilleran miogeosyncline. Windermere isopachs parallel the strike of the Rocky Mountains and the Mackenzie Mountains. The contact of the Windermere rocks with the base of the Paleozoic section is either gradational or only mildly disconformable. However, farther east underneath the Cretaceous foredeep of the Cordillera, and on the Canadian Shield, the Paleozoic rests directly on crystalline Precambrian.

Widespread carbonate shelves characterize the Cambrian to Lower Devonian (Fig. 5) of the Mackenzie and Rocky Mountains (*Fritz and others, 1989*; *Fritz, 1989*; *Cecile and Norford, 1989, Morrow and Geldsetzer, 1989*). Carbonate shelf margins occur farther west, and they parallel the overall strike of the Rocky Mountains and the Mackenzie Mountains. It is important

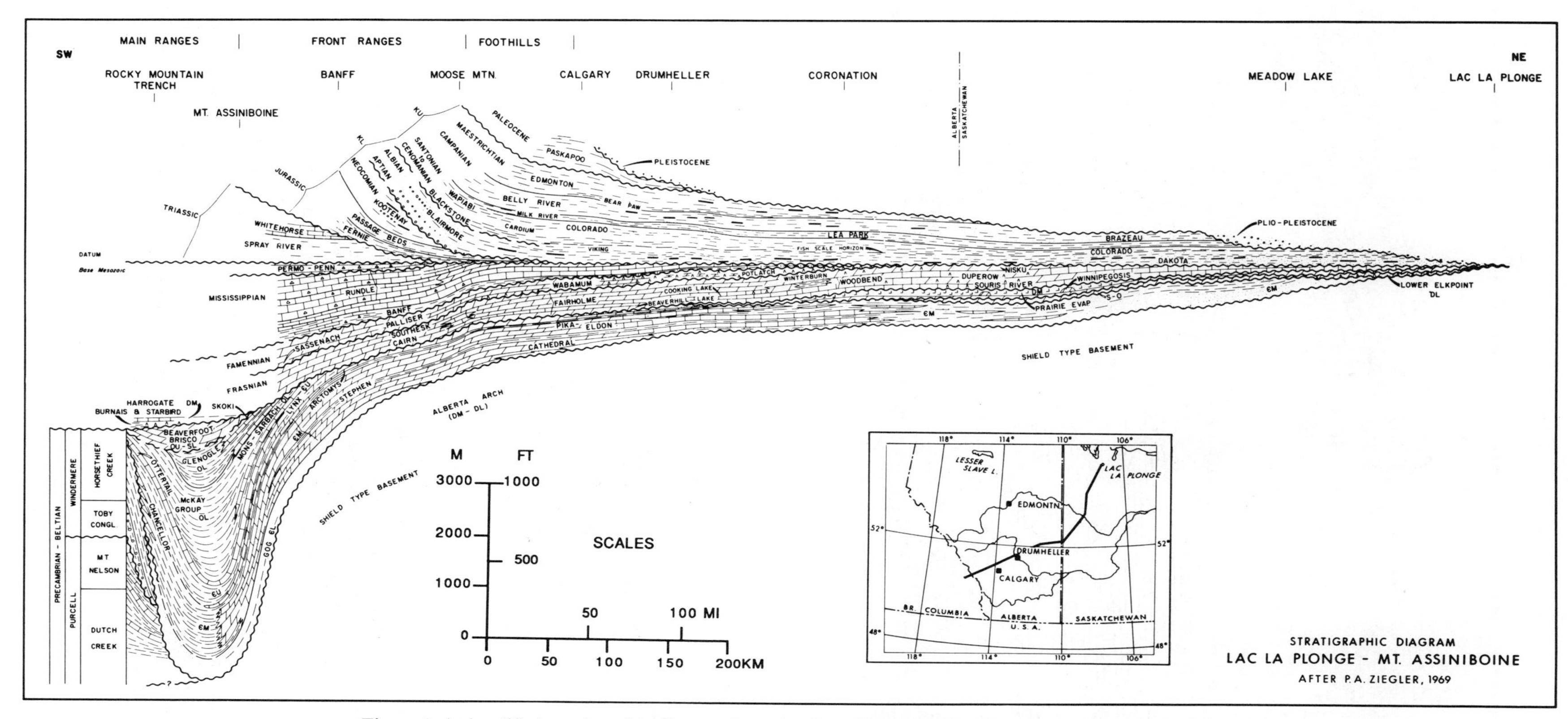

Figure 4. A simplified stratigraphic diagram from the Canadian Shield into the Rocky Mountains. Note the dramatic expansion of the stratigraphic section as the miogeosynclinal sequence is encountered west of the Front Ranges. The Mesozoic-Cenozoic boundary is the datum of the section. Also note the post-Mississippian to pre-Aptian wedge of multiple unconformities and the westward expansion of the Cretaceous foredeep sequence (from *Ziegler, 1969*).

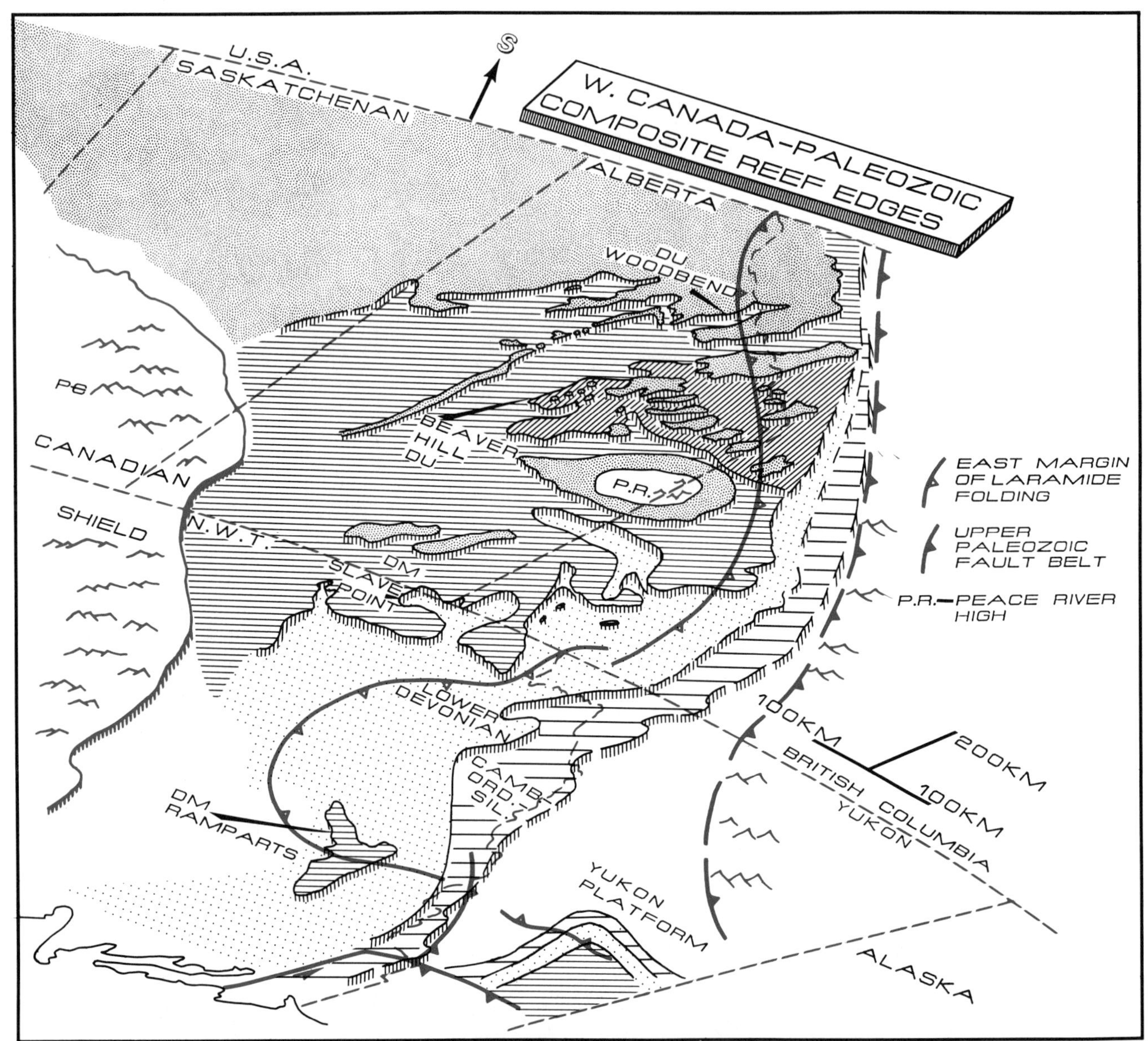

Figure 5. This somewhat unusual perspective looks southward from a point above the intersection of the United States–Canada border with the northern Arctic coast. The stratigraphy has been stripped to the level exposing most major Paleozoic carbonate shelf margins. Note that the major composite Cambrian-Ordovician-Silurian shelf margins follow a Rocky Mountain strike and outline a former passive-margin shelf. In contrast, the Mackenzie Mountains range front deviates from the strike of the Paleozoic shelf margin. The Devonian reef complexes and carbonate shelf margins trend more cratonward (i.e., they are overall transgressive). Particularly in Alberta, the Devonian reef complexes have a strike that is oblique to the structural grain of the Rocky Mountains. Thus, over the region, radical facies changes are clearly not parallel to structural trends. This observation invalidates traditional concepts of presumed coincidence of isopic facies zones with structural zones. It also questions the accepted definition of a "terrane" as a structural unit that is characterized primarily by its own stratigraphy. On the other hand, stratigraphic and facies changes along the strike of a contractional orogen are responsible for differences in decollement styles in a laterally continuous fold belt (modified from a diagram by *Bassett and Stout, 1968*).

to note, however, that the Early and Middle Devonian reefal carbonate trends in the Alberta Rockies do not parallel the strike of the Rocky Mountain fold belt (Fig. 5). In fact, they are quite discordant to the structural grain, as are most subsequent facies and isopach trends. Toward the north in the Mackenzie Mountains and in the western part of the Rocky Mountain foreland fold belt, Upper Devonian to Mississippian clastics attest to a northern sedimentary source in the Innuitian fold belt and also a westerly source in the interior Cordillera (*Gordey and others, 1989*), which we relate to the inception of the mid-Paleozoic Antler belt. The eastern margin of the mid-Paleozoic Antler foredeep is rimmed by prograding crinoidal carbonate sequences of Mississippian age.

Permo-Triassic and Jurassic isopachs are significantly modified by their erosional subcrops below the pre-Cretaceous unconformity (Fig. 6). During Permo-Triassic to Jurassic time, major siliciclastic sources occur on the craton to the east. The Permian to Jurassic sequences are split by many unconformities that form a characteristic "wedge of multiple unconformities" (Bally and others, 1966), and suggest loading by allochthonous units to the west.

The Upper Jurassic to Eocene sequences of the Canadian Rocky Mountains and its foredeep (e.g., the Alberta basin) are dominated by westerly clastic sources that record the unroofing of the rising Cordillera. Farther west, Mesozoic sediments are mostly absent because the area was actively deformed and uplifted from Middle Jurassic to Eocene times. There, radiometric K/Ar and Rb/Sr ages reflect the uplift history of the metamorphic core of the Cordillera.

Northward, the stratigraphy of the Ogilvie Mountains is similar to that of the Mackenzie Mountains, but the pre-Cretaceous hiatus of the MacKenzies is larger. In the Ogilvies, Carboniferous and Permian strata are preserved between the Upper Devonian and the pre-Cretaceous unconformities. Except for the southernmost portion, Carboniferous and Permian strata are missing in the Mackenzie Mountains.

Going south into the conterminous United States, the stratigraphy is quite similar to that of Canada. The trend of the miogeosyncline changes from northwesterly in Canada to southwesterly across the Great Basin and into the Mojave Desert of California. The upper Proterozoic section reaches thicknesses greater than 4 km, particularly in the northern part of the U.S. Cordillera, and the Paleozoic is up to 12 km thick. Precambrian units are rarely exposed in the southern part of the Cordillera, except for the big basement uplifts of the southern Rocky Mountains (Plate 5A). The Precambrian basement and Proterozoic sediments also are exposed in the Grand Canyon, Death Valley, and Mojave Desert region.

The Paleozoic miogeosynclinal section of the Great Basin may be broadly divided into two sequences of Cambrian through Devonian, and Carboniferous through Permian age. Cratonal sequences (see discussion in Bally, this volume) may be followed into the miogeosyncline and further subdivided. Our simplified twofold division of the Paleozoic reflects a fundamental change in sedimentary patterns that is related to the mid-Paleozoic Antler orogeny (see below).

In the Paleozoic platform succession of the southern Rocky Mountains, unconformity-bound cratonic sequences are easily defined. A major break in sedimentation occurred during Pennsylvanian-Permian development of the Ancestral Rocky Mountains.

The foreland fold belt of the conterminous United States extends across the Great Basin to the eastern flank of the Sierra Nevada magmatic complex. The Great Basin is particularly important because it contains the only segment of the Paleozoic

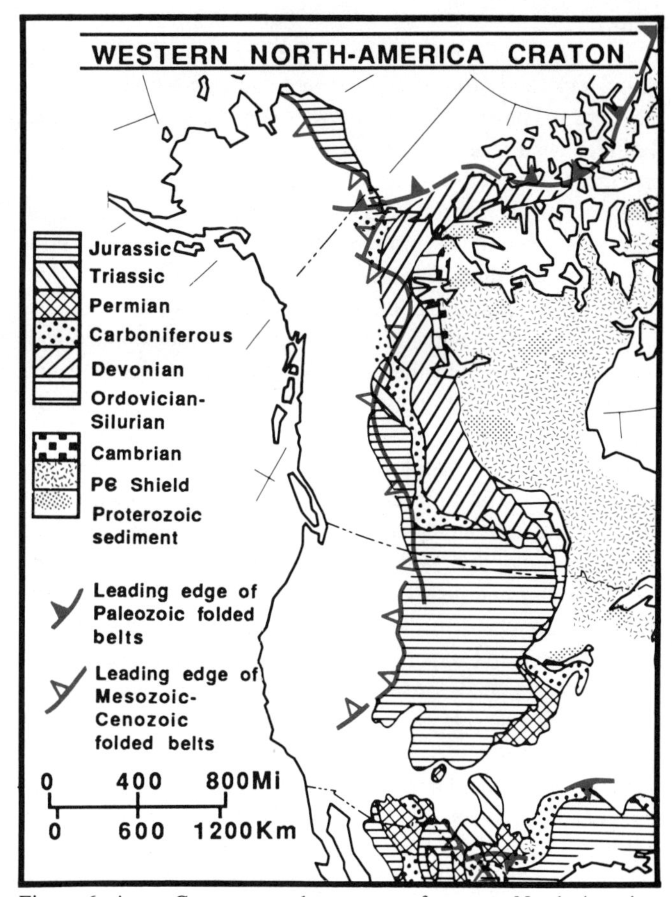

Figure 6. A pre-Cretaceous subcrop map of western North America. This map illustrates stratigraphic changes along the strike of the Cordilleran foreland (compare with Fig. 5). Note the dramatic change in subcrop strike in southern Alberta (i.e., north of the United States–Canada border). The foreland of the southern Rocky Mountains of the United States has a substantially different pre-Cretaceous stratigraphic evolution than the foreland of the Canadian Rocky Mountains and the Mackenzie Mountains. In Canada, narrow subcrop bands of upper Mesozoic and the lower Paleozoic units may be related to the docking of major terranes in the adjacent Cordillera. Most of the structures of the Canadian Rocky Mountains strike at a low angle to the subcrop belts; whereas those in the Mackenzie Mountains cut across subcrop patterns. In contrast, the U.S. Cordillera foreland has a wide Jurassic subcrop belt, which follows patterns established during the Pennsylvanian (Bally, this volume). Note also the areal coincidence of the occurrence of Laramide basement-involved uplifts in the southern Rocky Mountains with the wide subcrop belt.

miogeosyncline in which the pre-Mesozoic western shelf margin is relatively well preserved. Elsewhere in the Cordillera, the western margin of the miogeosyncline is much more obscured by later deformation. The western part of the Great Basin exposes the Roberts Mountains and Golconda allochthons (Plate 5A; refer to Fig. 9), emplaced in the mid-Paleozoic and Permo-Triassic, respectively. The relationship of the allochthons to North America is the focus of substantial debate, which is addressed later in this chapter. That they are part of North America during the Mesozoic, however, is not a major source of contention, and correspondingly, they and the Mesozoic rocks deposited upon them are included as units of unquestioned North American affinity.

The Mesozoic section of the U.S. Cordillera is dominated by clastic rocks and carbonates associated with deposition following the Permo-Triassic Sonoma orogeny. In the northwest Great Basin, in what is commonly referred to as the Mesozoic marine province (*Speed, 1978*; Oldow, 1984a), thick sequences of shelfal carbonate and clastic rocks accumulated around a U-shaped axial depression open to the north in which deep-marine clastic turbidites were deposited. The marine environments constitute a successor basin constructed on the western part of the Sonoma orogenic belt. During the Mesozoic, this basin was supplied with volcanic detritus from the Sierra Nevada arc on the west and continentally derived debris from the east. The largely marine succession was bound on the south and eastern margins by topographically positive regions (*Speed, 1978*; Oldow, 1984a) that separated the basin from the more continental and shallow marine conditions that characterized much of southern Nevada, Utah, Colorado, and western New Mexico (*Stanley and others, 1971*; *Stewart and others, 1972a, 1972b*). Few upper Mesozoic rocks are preserved in the western Great Basin. Deposition of Upper Jurassic to Cretaceous units is dominated by the clastics of the Rocky Mountain foredeep to the east.

A northeasterly trending band of mid-Tertiary to recent volcanic rocks of the Snake River Plain obscures pre-Tertiary relations between the Great Basin and western Idaho. Further complicating matters, the stratigraphy of Paleozoic units in much of Idaho is poorly understood due to an extensive cover of Tertiary units of the Challis volcanic field and due to the structural complexity of the region surrounding the Idaho batholith.

Returning north to Alaska and the Yukon and Northwest Territories, the Phanerozoic rocks exposed in the Brooks Range and the British, Barn, and northern Richardson Mountains are considered to be of North American origin (Jones and others, 1987; Monger and Berg, 1987; Wheeler and others, 1988). The stratigraphy, although not as well understood as that in the Ogilvie Mountains of northwestern Canada, is closely related to that of the Canadian Arctic (Trettin, this volume) and is divided into four stratigraphic sequences: (1) the Precambrian Inuvikian sequence, (2) the late Precambrian through Devonian Franklinian sequence, (3) the Carboniferous through Cretaceous Ellesmerian sequence, and (4) the Cretaceous through Cenozoic Brookian sequence (Norris and Yorath, 1981).

The pre-Carboniferous stratigraphy of the region is poorly understood due largely to a general lack of age control, unresolved superposition relations of Devonian and late Mesozoic to Cenozoic structures, and varying degrees of mid-Paleozoic and Mesozoic metamorphic recrystallization. Precambrian rocks of the Inuvikian sequence (Norris and Yorath, 1981) constitute a complex and poorly understood assemblage of carbonates, chert, clastics, and mafic to intermediate volcanics apparently deposited in miogeosynclinal and deep-marine basinal environments (*Moore and others, 1987*). The Precambrian rocks are at least locally overlain by upper Precambrian and lower Paleozoic units with angular unconformity. In the western exposures of the northeastern Brooks Range, a 1.5-km-thick Precambrian assemblage of interbedded volcanic rocks, sandstone, and argillite passing upward into dolomite is overlain unconformably by shallow marine carbonates of upper Precambrian to Devonian age. Whether the unconformity is related to a contractional event or possibly represents a breakup unconformity associated with rifting, is not known, however. Elsewhere, in the eastern part of the northeastern Brooks Range and the western British Mountains (an area straddling the Alaska-Yukon border), Upper Cambrian and older(?) volcanic rocks interbedded with carbonates (*Dutro and others, 1972*; *Reiser and others, 1980*) are interpreted by Norris (1985) to overlie unconformably a phyllitic unit containing lenses of carbonate and graywacke. This interpretation is questioned by *Moore (1987),* who suggests that the contact may be tectonic.

The lower Paleozoic and uppermost Precambrian(?) Franklinian sequence is best exposed in the northeastern Brooks Range and the British, Barn, and Richardson Mountains. In these areas, it is composed of interbedded carbonates, clastics, and volcanic rocks. Like the underlying Precambrian sequence, the internal stratigraphy is poorly understood (*Brosgé and Dutro, 1973*). In the southern and central Brooks Range, lower Paleozoic and possibly Precambrian rocks dominate, but were strongly deformed and recrystallized during late Mesozoic and Cenozoic Brookian tectonism.

Rocks of the Franklinian sequence are overlain unconformably by upper Paleozoic units of the basal Ellesmerian sequence, consisting of a northerly transgressive clastic and carbonate succession of Carboniferous age. The carbonates are overlain by clastic rocks apparently shed from a northern highland. The uppermost part of the sequence records the inception of a southerly source region that was active together with the northerly source region during the Late Jurassic and signifies the initial uplift of the Brooks Range to the south (*Detterman, 1973*; *Richards, 1974*; *Molenaar, 1981a*; Grantz and May, 1983; see also Bally, this volume, Fig. 6).

Until the Early Cretaceous, sediments were derived from both the northern and southern source regions, but upper Neocomian and younger sediments of the Brookian sequence seem to be entirely derived from a southern source area (*Molenaar, 1981a, 1981b*). The succession is interpreted (*Molenaar, 1983*) to represent a foredeep succession formed in response to the progressive development of the Brooks Range fold and thrust belt to the south. *Molenaar (1983)* convincingly argues that they represent deepwater onlap and prograding downlap successions migrating northward during the Cretaceous and Cenozoic.

Readers who want to familiarize themselves further with the stratigraphy of the Cordillera, may consult the chapter on Phanerozoic basins (Bally, this volume), which includes some of the key references.

Accretionary stratigraphy

The stratigraphic relations in the interior and western portions of the Cordillera are substantially more complex than those in the regions adjacent to the continental foreland. Large tracts composed of suspect terranes were added during the Paleozoic and Mesozoic. The major episodes of accretion took place during the mid-Paleozoic (Antler orogeny), the late Paleozoic to early Mesozoic (Sonoma orogeny), and during the middle and late Mesozoic. We will limit ourselves to major stratigraphic successions in the context of their accretionary history and relationship to the North American continent. We will discuss only the large terranes; smaller terranes will be mentioned where necessary.

Displaced terranes in the Canadian Cordillera (Plate 5A) can be grouped into three major assemblages (Monger and Berg, 1987): (1) an eastern assemblage of terranes, with clear North American affinity, consisting mainly of the Cassiar and Kootenay terranes and the more enigmatic Yukon-Tanana and Monashee terranes; (2) Superterrane I, consisting mainly of the Slide Mountain, Quesnellia, Cache Creek, and Stikinia terranes, and; (3) Superterrane II, in the coastal region of western Canada, composed primarily of the Alexander terrane and Wrangellia (Monger and others, 1982).

Canadian terranes with North American affinity

The terrane division of the Canadian Cordillera by Monger and Berg (1987) has recently been modified by Wheeler and others (1988). We will attempt to summarize the general relations in broad terms here, but for specifics the interested reader is referred to the previously cited works.

In the north, a belt of displaced rocks of North American affinity, composed of the Yukon-Tanana and Cassiar terranes, bounds the western margin of the North American stratigraphic province (Plate 5A). The Yukon-Tanana terrane of Monger and Berg (1987) has been divided into two structural units, an upper package correlated with the Kootenay terrane exposed in southern British Columbia and a lower unit assigned to the newly defined Neslin terrane (Wheeler and others, 1988). Although the division of the Yukon-Tanana terrane has merit, it is not used here because we must simplify regional relations and we wish to maintain consistency with exposures of the same rocks to the west in Alaska where the segregation has not been made.

In the northern Canadian Cordillera, the Yukon-Tanana lies to the west of the Cassiar terrane and extends from the Alaskan border to northern British Columbia. The Cassiar terrane (Monger and Berg, 1987 as modified by Wheeler and others, 1988) extends from southern Yukon Territory to southern British Columbia, where it is bound by the Kootenay terrane on the south and west (Wheeler and others, 1988). In the northern Canadian Cordillera, the Cassiar and Yukon-Tanana terranes are overthrust by the upper Paleozoic rocks of the Slide Mountain terrane, which was emplaced in the Late Triassic or Early Jurassic in the region near the Alaska border. In the south, the Kootenay terrane, which is locally underlain by duplexes of the Monashee terrane, occupies the same structural position as the Cassiar and Yukon-Tanana terranes farther north and lies between the superjacent Slide Mountain and rocks of ancestral North America. In the south, the Slide Mountain terrane apparently was emplaced later than in the north, during the early Middle Jurassic. The Slide Mountain terrane and overlying Mesozoic volcanic rocks of Quesnellia (Monger and others, 1982) form part of Superterrane I, which underlies much of the western interior of British Columbia and the southern Yukon.

As described by Monger and Berg (1987), the Cassiar terrane consists of sedimentary rocks ranging in age from late Precambrian to Devonian and of clear North American affinity. The rocks are generally similar to platformal successions of the Rocky Mountains to the east, and the Silurian and Devonian assemblages are condensed sections of carbonate and clean sandstone. A transitional facies of graptolitic units of Ordovician and Silurian age occurs and is similar to facies in the western Rockies.

To the south and west of the Cassiar terrane in central British Columbia, rocks originally assigned to the Barkerville and Kootenay terranes by Monger and Berg (1987) have been combined as the Kootenay terrane by Wheeler and others (1988). In the north, the rocks compose a structurally complex stack of possible Proterozoic to late Paleozoic metasedimentary and metaigneous rocks (Barkerville terrane). The rocks are highly deformed and have experienced variable degrees of metamorphism from greenschist to amphibolite facies (Monger and Berg, 1987).

To the south, the metamorphic rocks assigned to the Kootenay terrane structurally overlie the Monashee terrane. The Monashee comprises high-grade metamorphic rocks older than 2.0 Ga that have a stratigraphy and age not found elsewhere in the Canadian Cordillera (Monger and Berg, 1987). A gneiss complex as old as 2.5 Ga underlies a strongly deformed and metamorphosed sequence of clastic and carbonate rocks intruded by 2.0 Ga gneissic bodies. The Monashee rocks are assigned to a separate terrane primarily because they differ in age from the Hudsonian basement underlying the Alberta plains to the east, and because they have a highly deformed lower Proterozoic sedimentary sequence not found elsewhere in the Canadian Cordillera. The Monashee and overlying metamorphic rocks (Kootenay terrane) experienced intense Jurassic deformation and apparently represent part of an exhumed mid-crustal duplex (Brown and others, 1986). A mid-Jurassic pluton stitches the tectonic contact between the Monashee and the overlying Kootenay terrane.

To the south and east, the metasediments of the Kootenay terrane are readily correlatable with North American lower Paleozoic units that overlie the Proterozoic of the western Purcell Mountains. This relationship is depicted in sections C and D of Plate 7. The Kootenay terrane consists of lower Paleozoic shales, grits, mafic volcanics, and carbonates (Lardeau Group and underlying Lower Cambrian Badshot Formation). The units compose a miogeosynclinal succession structurally overlain by rocks of a coeval deepwater facies, which together experienced locally intense deformation, plutonism, and low-grade metamorphism probably in the Late Devonian (Wheeler and Gabrielse, 1972; Monger and Berg, 1987; *Gehrels and Smith, 1987*). Clastic and volcanic successions of late Paleozoic age (Milford Group) overlie the older units with angular unconformity. To the west, the upper Paleozoic overlap succession passes from a nearshore transgressional facies into a tholeiitic volcanic facies and then into chert-argillite, which may represent facies equivalents of the deeper-water sequence of the Slide Mountain terrane (Monger and Berg, 1987). The upper Paleozoic rocks were imbricated and intruded by diorite before deposition of Triassic basinal rocks (Slocan Group).

Polydeformed high-grade metamorphic rocks lying west of the Cassiar terrane in northern British Columbia form the Yukon-Tanana terrane. The structurally lower part of the terrane (Neslin) is composed of Devonian, Mississippian, and Permian granitoids, quartzite, quartz-mica schist and marble of a probable continental margin assemblage, and graphitic schist and quartzite of a probable offshore, lower Paleozoic assemblage (J. O. Wheeler, written communication, 1988). The upper part of the Yukon-Tanana terrane (correlated with the Kootenay) is composed of Mississippian to Upper Triassic metamorphic rocks. The Yukon-Tanana was amalgamated by the Early Jurassic, as indicated by a pluton that crosscuts the structural boundary between the upper (Kootenay) and lower (Neslin) sheets. The lower Yukon-Tanana terrane is involved in at least two episodes of deformation. Deformations in the mid- to late Paleozoic and Mesozoic are recognized; the earlier postdating Devonian granitoid plutons (Mortensen and Jilsen, 1985; *Dusel-Bacon and Aleinikoff, 1985*); the other is Jurassic and Cretaceous in age (Tempelman-Kluit, *1976*; 1979). Mesozoic metasedimentary and metavolcanic rocks of the upper Yukon-Tanana terrane achieved peak metamorphic conditions in the Late Triassic to Early Jurassic.

Superterrane I

West of the North American terranes lies Quesnellia, which is composed of early Mesozoic volcanic rocks of arc affinity overlying the Slide Mountain terrane (Monger and Berg, 1987). Although not shown on the accompanying tectonic map (Plate 5A), Quesnellia is separated to the west from Stikinia, an upper Paleozoic to lower Mesozoic volcanic arc terrane, by the oceanic mélange of the Cache Creek terrane (Fig. 7). The intervening Cache Creek terrane contains enigmatic Tethyan faunas, a source of considerable debate in tectonic reconstructions, but is demonstrably tied to Stikinia to the west and to Quesnellia to the east by cross-cutting Early Jurassic plutons (Monger and Berg, 1987; Wheeler and McFeely, 1987). Quesnellia and the Slide Mountain terrane are tied by overlap assemblages of Late Triassic to Middle Jurassic age (Monger and others, 1982). The two arc assemblages (Quesnellia and Stikinia) and oceanic mélange (Cache Creek terrane) are tied to the terranes of North American affinities by cross-cutting plutons of Middle Jurassic age (Monger and others, 1982; *Armstrong and others, 1985*; Monger and Berg, 1987).

Superterrane II

Wrangellia forms a linear belt extending north from Vancouver Island to south-central Alaska. It is composed of Carboniferous to Permian volcanics and carbonates overlain by lower Mesozoic volcanics, volcaniclastic rocks, and deep-water sediments (Monger and Berg, 1987; Jones and others, 1987). Rocks of the Peninsular terrane of southern Alaska are similar and consist of Permian carbonates overlain by lower Mesozoic carbonate, sedimentary, and volcanic rocks intruded by Middle Jurassic plutons (Jones and others, 1987). The units are distinguished mainly by pronounced differences in their lower Mesozoic sections.

The Alexander terrane lies east of Wrangellia in southeastern Alaska and westernmost Canada. It preserves a remarkably complete record from the late Proterozoic through the Middle(?) Jurassic (Gehrels and Saleeby, 1987) and is dissimilar to other successions of western North America. The Alexander terrane is divided into three subterranes that may have had separate histories until the Permian. Proterozoic(?)–Cambrian units preserved locally consist of metabasite and metacarbonates deformed and metamorphosed in the Middle Cambrian to Early Ordovician. Younger units consist of a Middle Ordovician through Permian clastic, carbonate, chert, and mafic volcanic succession that in many areas is essentially undeformed. Elsewhere, a Middle Ordovician through Early Silurian volcano-plutonic complex and associated clastic and carbonate rocks were deformed, metamorphosed, and uplifted in Middle Silurian to Early Devonian time to be overlain by an Early to Middle Devonian clastic and volcanic sequence. Upper Triassic volcanic rocks, consisting of a lower succession of rhyolites and an upper sequence of basalts, and associated clastics and carbonates unconformably overlie units of Devonian to Permian age and may represent a rift complex (Gehrels and Saleeby, 1987). The youngest rocks of the Alexander terrane belong to a Middle(?) Jurassic granite complex.

The stratigraphic and structural contrast of the Alexander terrane with other parts of North America led Gehrels and Saleeby (1987) to postulate an exotic origin for the rocks and a possible derivation from eastern Australia; an interpretation that is disputed by *Savage (1987).* Upper Jurassic to mid-Cretaceous sedimentary rocks overlap the Alexander and adjacent terranes, and Pennsylvanian and Cretaceous plutons intrude the contact

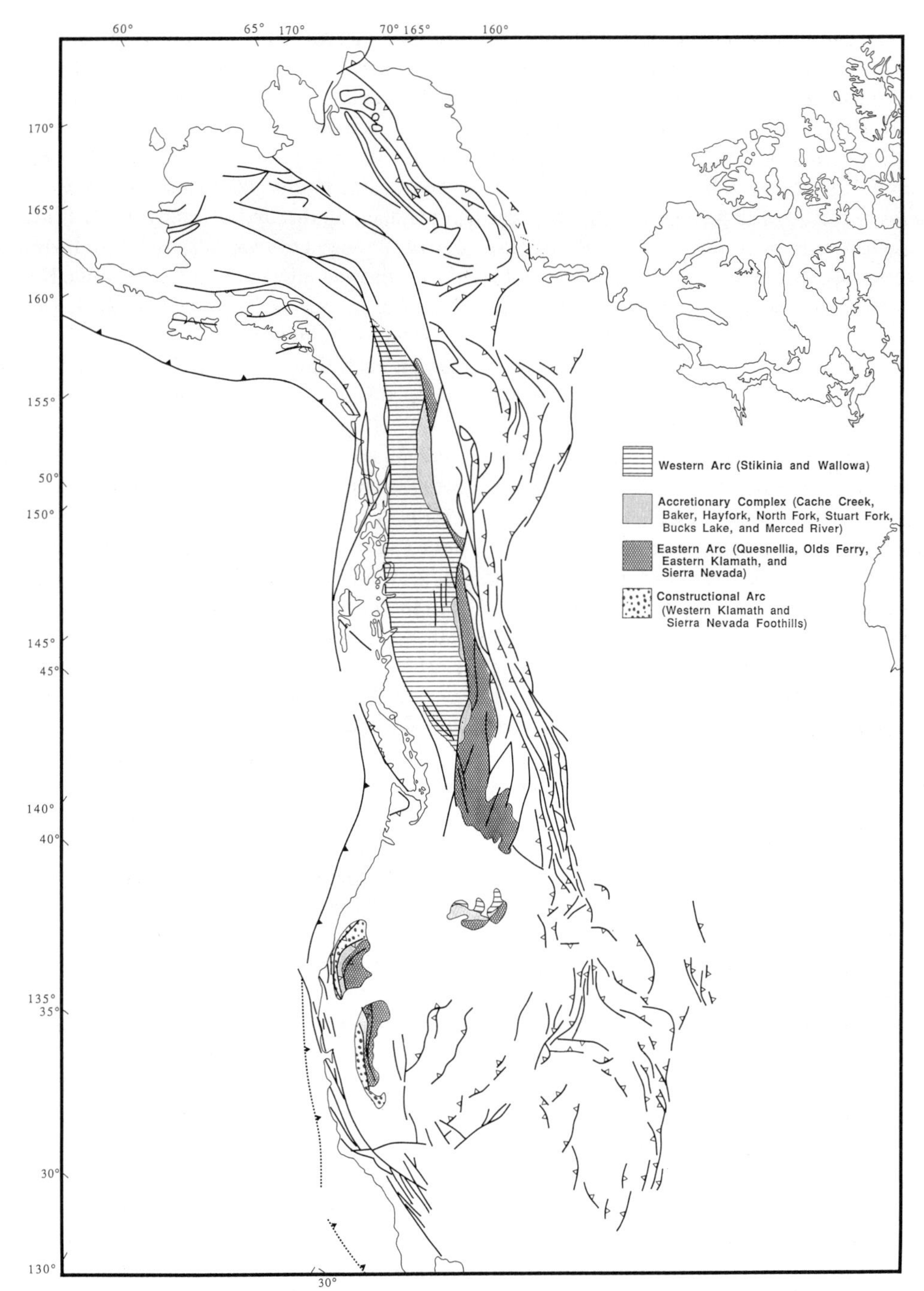

Figure 7. Generalized map of Mesozoic magmatic arc and associated accretionary prism units in the Canadian Cordillera and the western conterminous United States. An eastern volcanic arc assemblage (Quesnellia, Olds Ferry, eastern Klamath, and eastern Sierra Nevada) formed the western margin of the Cordillera during the early Mesozoic. In Canada and as far south as the west-central Nevada, the arc complex ostensibly overlies oceanic lithosphere and was flanked on the east by a marginal basin. In the southern U.S. Cordillera the arc was built on North American continental crust and was bordered on the east by subaerial to shallow-marine depositional environments. Outboard of the eastern arc assemblage, a late Paleozoic to early Mesozoic accretionary complex (Cache Creek, Baker, Hayfork, North Fork, Stuart Fork, Bucks Lake, and Merced River terranes) contains carbonate blocks with Tethyan faunas. Stretching from Canada to northeastern Oregon, an outer arc assemblage composed of late Paleozoic to Jurassic rocks (Stikinia and Wallowa) collided with the western Cordillera during the Early Jurassic in Canada and during the Late Jurassic in northeastern Oregon. In the western Klamath Mountains and the Sierra Nevada foothills, early Mesozoic volcanic and clastic rocks represent part of a constructional arc system built on the accretionary complex.

(*Mackevett and others, 1986*; Gardner and others, 1988; Gehrels and Saleeby, 1987; Monger and Berg, 1987), tying the terranes together no later than the late Mesozoic, and apparently in the mid-Paleozoic. The amalgamated terrane is bound to the rocks of Stikinia-Quesnellia (Superterrane I of Monger and others, 1982) by Cretaceous intrusives of the Coast Plutonic complex.

Thus, on the basis of cross-cutting plutons, it is clear that the entire width of the southern Canadian Cordillera is tied to North America in the late Mesozoic. This is not to say, however, that the units have not experienced a subsequent history of substantial lateral displacement.

Alaskan terranes

Stratigraphic relations are more obscure in Alaska. The relation between Arctic-derived North American units exposed in the Brooks Range and those to the south is not well established. The structurally highest sheets in the Brooks Range are ophiolitic rocks of the Angayucham and Tozitna terranes (Jones and others, 1987), which represent exotic elements emplaced in the mid- to Late Jurassic (*Wirth and others, 1986*; *Mayfield and others, 1983*). The ophiolitic rocks also structurally overlie metamorphic rocks of the Ruby terrane on the southern flank of the Koyukuk basin (Fig. 3: Plate 5A). The relation of the metamorphic rocks of the Ruby terrane and North America is equivocal, but strong similarities exist with the metamorphic rocks composing much of the southern Brooks Range.

Several smaller terranes containing complexly deformed sedimentary rocks and units of ophiolitic affinity are exposed throughout Alaska. The relation of these terranes to the large ophiolite sheets of central Alaska is not known, but we speculate that they are related and are mainly remnants of a widespread allochthon. Mesozoic volcanic and sedimentary rocks of arc affinity are commonly associated with the ophiolitic and metamorphic terranes in western and central Alaska. The bases of these volcanic successions are not exposed, but the rocks may directly overlie the ophiolitic assemblages. The amalgamation history of the various terranes of central and western Alaska is poorly understood, but they certainly were joined at least by the late Mesozoic (e.g., mid- to Late Jurassic) because they are overlapped by Cretaceous sediments and intruded by Cretaceous plutons (Jones and others, 1987).

West of the high-grade metamorphics of the Yukon-Tanana terrane in central Alaska are isolated exposures of sedimentary and metasedimentary rocks of the Nixon Fork terrane. The Nixon Fork contains Ordovician reefal and platformal carbonates depositionally overlying a Precambrian basement composed of metasedimentary and metavolcanic rocks (Jones and others, 1987). Devonian carbonates of the Nixon Fork have paleomagnetic pole positions consistent with stable North America (*Vance-Plumley and others, 1984; Plumley, 1984*), suggesting little or no latitudinal displacement. This apparent lack of displacement with respect to North America poses an unresolved enigma, however, because lower Paleozoic carbonates within the Nixon Fork contain an unusually rich Middle Cambrian faunal assemblage of clear Siberian affinity (A. R. Palmer, written communication, 1988). The older units are overlain by Permian to Triassic clastics and Cretaceous sediments.

To the south, Alaska is dominated by rocks of the Southern Alaska Superterrane (*Panuska and Stone, 1985*), which comprises the Wrangellia, Alexander, Peninsular, Chugach, and Prince William terranes. Wrangellia and Alexander terranes are the northern continuation of Superterrane II in western Canada. The Chugach terrane lies seaward of the Peninsular and Wrangellia terranes in southern Alaska and is bound on its northern margin by the Border Ranges fault. The Chugach is an accretionary prism composed of Jurassic to Upper Cretaceous flysch, blocks of upper Paleozoic carbonates, and mafic volcanic and plutonic rocks representing slabs of sea floor. Late Jurassic plutons apparently postdate local blueschist metamorphism and locally have been reset during an Early Cretaceous thermal event (*Pavlis, 1982*). Activity on the Border Ranges fault is dominated by seaward-directed thrusting that carried parts of Wrangellia and the Peninsular terrane over the Chugach in the Early Cretaceous. Subsequent strike-slip activity has probably occurred, but the timing and magnitude of displacements are unclear.

Outboard of the Chugach terrane lie deformed Paleocene and Eocene argillite and graywacke interleaved with sheets of basalt and basaltic dikes (*Tysdal and Case, 1979*; *Helwig and Emmet, 1981*). The structurally complex succession forms the Prince William terrane, which like the Chugach terrane, is a convergent margin accretionary prism. The contorted rocks of the Prince William terrane are intruded by Paleogene and Neogene plutons (*Tysdal and Case, 1979*).

Terranes of the conterminous United States

The relations among accretionary terranes of the conterminous United States and those in Canada are not well defined. Hints of relations between the rocks exposed in southern Canada and their equivalents in northern Washington with those of the Blue Mountains block of northeastern Oregon and western Idaho and the units of the Sierran-Klamath arc, and possibly more importantly with units of the Mesozoic marine province of northwestern Nevada (North American units), are tantalizing but inconclusive. Much of the problem stems from the widespread Cenozoic volcanics of the Columbia Plateau, which cover the critical intervening region (Plate 5A). As will become clear in later sections of this chapter, however, we think that much of the "confusion" in the structural and stratigraphic relations between the northern and southern parts of the U.S. Cordillera is not a simple artifact of inadequate exposure but rather is the product of a zone of tectonic juxtaposition.

As pointed out by Cowan and Bruhn (1989), mid-Cretaceous plutonic rocks intruding North American units of northeastern Washington and northern Idaho and their possible equivalents in the Okanogan highlands (north-central Washington) are probably the northern extension of the Sierran-Idaho arc complex. Thus, they represent a plausible north-south link along the Cordilleran borderland. On the other hand, while the metamorphic and plutonic rocks of the northern Cascades and associated deep-marine basinal, volcanic, and volcanogenic units composing the westerly directed thrust imbricates of the San Juan Islands are tied to units in British Columbia, they are not easily correlated directly with units in the southwestern U.S. Cordillera.

Nonetheless, there are some important features that appear to be correlative from Canada to northeastern Oregon. As in Canada, there are two lower to mid-Mesozoic volcanic arc terranes separated by a belt of upper Paleozoic to lower Mesozoic mélange in northeastern Oregon. We are in accord with Saleeby and others (1989) in correlating the eastern arc assemblage (Olds Ferry terrane) of the Blue Mountains block (Fig. 7) with Quesnellia in Canada. Although the western arc assemblage of northeastern Oregon (Wallowa terrane) is commonly correlated with Wrangellia, we subscribe to the interpretation (*Mortimer, 1986*; Avé Lallemant, 1989) that it represents the southern extension of Stikinia.

Similarities in the structural history of the arc complexes in northeastern Oregon with those of the northern Sierra Nevada and the less well-documented Klamath Mountains (Oldow and others, 1984) suggest that the Triassic to Lower Jurassic volcanic rocks of the eastern assemblage are correlatives of the arc complex in the Sierra Nevada and the eastern Klamath Mountains. The western arc terrane (Stikine correlative) exposed in eastern Oregon apparently was not developed to the south in the Klamath Mountains and Sierra Nevada. Upper Triassic and Middle Jurassic volcanics in the western foothills of the Sierra Nevada and the western Klamath Mountains (Rattlesnake Creek and western Hayfork terranes) are part of the eastern arc assemblage and were built out over their own accretionary complexes (Saleeby, 1981; Saleeby and others, 1982; Wright, 1982).

Where developed, the two arcs (Stikinia and Quesnellia) are separated by mélanges consisting of chert/argillite, ophiolitic fragments, and occasional blocks of blueschist. Where the two arcs were not developed, the inner, or eastern, arc is bound on the oceanward side by the lateral equivalent of the intervening mélange exposed farther north. The mélange occurs in the Sierra Nevada (Calaveras Formation), in the western Klamath Mountains (Hayfork, North Fork, and Stuart Fork terranes), and in eastern Oregon (Baker terrane). These mélanges generally are correlated with the Cache Creek assemblage of British Columbia.

In the mid- to Late Jurassic, ophiolitic complexes formed within the Sierran-Klamath volcanic arc. Intra-arc spreading was parallel (*Harper and others, 1985*) to the axis of the magmatic belt and formed the Josephine, Smartsville, and Coast Range ophiolites in California.

Outboard of the Sierran arc in the Early Cretaceous, a forearc ridge created a moat that formed the receptacle for in excess of 15 km of clastic sediments. The deeper and more westerly portions of this Great Valley basin were filled with turbidites while easterly coastal units onlap onto the eastern "Sierran" basement. During the Late Cretaceous, the basin was filled with deltaic prograding systems (Ingersoll, *1978,* 1979). On its western side, the Great Valley sequence overlies the lower Upper Jurassic Coast Range ophiolite. In Washington and southern British Columbia, the Methow-Tyaughton trough may have been deposited in a comparable setting as the Great Valley sequence, but here relations are less well understood.

Partly coeval with the Great Valley sequence is the Franciscan complex, which is a broad west-vergent fold and thrust belt related to subduction. The complex can be divided into three northwest-trending belts: eastern, central, and coastal (Blake and others, 1988).

The eastern Franciscan belt consists mainly of schist, metavolcanic rocks, meta-chert, argillite, metagraywacke, and serpentinite. Late Jurassic to mid-Cretaceous fossils have been found in the units that underwent blueschist metamorphism between 143 and 92 Ma. The metamorphic grade increases from west to east.

The central Franciscan belt is a tectonic mélange consisting of blocks of sedimentary, volcanic, ultramafic, and metamorphic rocks in a matrix of argillite, graywacke, and tuff ranging from Late Jurassic to mid-Cretaceous age. The metamorphic age of eclogite and amphibolite knockers is 150 to 165 Ma (Mattinson, 1988). Limestone blocks within the mélange have paleomagnetic inclinations suggesting that they formed at great distances to the south (*Alvarez and others, 1980*; *Tarduno and others, 1986*).

The coastal Franciscan is composed of basaltic volcanics, clastic rocks (often arkosic), and limestone; the rocks are of Late Cretaceous to Miocene age. Medium-grade blueschist knockers occur in chaotic formations, but generally the rocks are of low-metamorphic (lawsonite, prehnite) grade (Blake and others, 1988).

Metamorphic ages of Franciscan high P/T rocks vary considerably between 165 and 70 Ma (Mattinson, 1988). However, two main groups of ages emerge: the ages of eclogite and amphibolite knockers in the central belt range from 165 to 150 Ma; the ages of blueschists are generally between 130 and 90 Ma. Based on a thermal evolution model, *Cloos (1985)* proposed that these two age groups may be the result of a prolonged period of subduction. Blake and others (1988) suggest that the Early Cretaceous subduction was the result of normal lithospheric plate convergence that continued until about 90 Ma and that subsequent subduction became right-oblique, causing the eastern and central Franciscan belts to migrate northward on the order of 1,500 to 2,000 km (*Page and Engebretson, 1984*). At about 50 Ma, normal convergence apparently was reestablished and the coastal Franciscan belt was accreted (Blake and others, 1988).

West and farther south of the San Andreas fault, the Patton terrane of the western California Borderland may be a southern equivalent of the coastal accretionary complex of northern California. In that context, it should be noted that the base of the continental slope is marked by a large regional overthrust that separates a subducted oceanic Pacific plate from an essentially inactive accretionary wedge that forms the basement of much of offshore California. That accretionary wedge is composed of older graywackes, serpentinites, cherts, and some blueschists, as well as Upper Cretaceous graywackes. In other words, it represents a far southern equivalent of the central and coastal accretionary belts of northern California, which later was offset dextrally by the Paleogene proto–San Andreas fault system. The accretionary process presumably slowed prior to 25 Ma, before the inception of the modern San Andreas fault, but transpressional effects of that system permit us to recognize mid-Miocene to perhaps early Pliocene reactivation at the foot of this accretionary prism.

PROTEROZOIC TO TRIASSIC TECTONIC EVOLUTION OF THE NORTH AMERICAN CORDILLERA

Cordilleran basement and the Proterozoic

We have sketched the main Precambrian and the late Paleozoic tectonic features of the North American segment of the Cordillera on a single map (Fig. 8). The intent is to illustrate that the North American part of the Mesozoic–Cenozoic Cordillera is adjacent to different kinds of basement and is discordantly superposed on older structural elements.

South of the 60th parallel (i.e., the Yukon–British Columbia boundary), the Cordillera is underlain by the extension of various Precambrian basement provinces as shown by Hoffman (this volume). Note that there is a pronounced strike discordance between the Precambrian structural trends of the craton and those of the Cordillera. Consequently, often-invoked "reactivations" of preexisting Precambrian structures have only limited scope within the context of the structural evolution of the Cordillera.

South of the 60th parallel there is a reasonable correlation between an inferred eastern zero isopach of the Proterozoic sedimentary basin and the strike of the Cordillera. Exceptions are associated with the tectonically inverted (for reference on inversion see *Bally and Oldow, 1983*; Bally, 1984; *Bally and others, 1985*), east-west–trending Little Belt Mountains and Uinta extensional basins. Note that all Cordilleran outcrops are very much allochthonous, and therefore, the position of the eastern Proterozoic basin edge can only be guessed. It is not clearly visible on any seismic-reflection profiles (e.g., Bally and others, 1966).

North of the 60th parallel in the Northwest Territories, the eastern margin of the middle Proterozoic basin strikes into the foreland and is exposed in the northwestern Canadian Shield. Seismic reflection profiles reveal great thicknesses of only mildly deformed Proterozoic strata in the Anderson Plain of the Northwest Territories. Thus, the structural decollement style of the Mackenzie Mountains certainly is due to the involvement of the thick Proterozoic wedge (Plate 7, section B), but on the other hand, the Proterozoic basin margin is in overall discordance with the arcuate trend of the Mackenzie Mountains. The Mackenzie arc perhaps mirrors the isopachs of the combined Windermere-Paleozoic sedimentary basin.

Hoffman (this volume) discusses the tectonics of the Proterozoic of the Cordillera in depth. A few major points are made here. The history of middle and late Proterozoic tectonics is the subject of much creative speculation. First, there is the need to explain the origin of the great middle Proterozoic (Belt-Purcell) basin that extends from the United States to the Mackenzie Mountains and into the northwestern Canadian Shield. Some authors visualize a rifting event around 1,450 Ma (Burchfiel and Davis, 1975; Dickinson, 1977). Considering that the base of the middle Proterozoic Cordilleran basin may be as old as 1,700 Ma, there is a lot of flexibility for the selection of hypothetical rifting ages.

Until recently, there was a popular consensus favoring a passive margin setting for the Cordilleran middle Proterozoic. Recent work in Montana and Idaho (e.g., Winston, 1986), however, suggests that the middle Proterozoic Belt Supergroup may have been deposited in a huge intracratonic basin. A westerly clastic source has been established, and furthermore, east-west–trending normal growth faults are associated with the Helena (or Belt) embayment or rift system in Montana. The most important is the east-west–striking Perry fault, which is associated with the deposition of thick syn-rift conglomerates. As elsewhere in the Cordillera (e.g., the Uinta Mountains) these east-west–trending extensional structures tend to influence the formation of lateral thrust ramps during Mesozoic overthrusting, which in turn influence the segmentation of Cenozoic extensional basins (Winston, 1986). The change of perspective from a passive margin origin to a cratonic origin for the middle Proterozoic basin of the Cordillera, leads to a search for analogues. We feel that the very large, Mesozoic West Siberia basin may be suitable (*Bally and Snelson, 1980*).

Assuming a very large middle Proterozoic cratonic basin, we must inquire about the fate of the western half of the craton which, presumably, departed prior to or during early Windermere time (about 800 Ma). *Sears and Price (1978)* speculated on this problem by suggesting that western North America and Siberia were connected prior to 1,500 Ma. Obviously, according to the cratonic model, rifting and subsequent separation of any continent from western North America would have to occur quite a bit later, in and around the beginning of the Windermere sequence (about 800 Ma).

Thus begins the search for a younger rifting event that is superposed on the middle Proterozoic cratonic basin and that would initiate the Windermere-Paleozoic cycle. *Stewart (1972)* suggested a pre-Windermere rifting episode at about 850 to 750 Ma (see also Burchfiel and Davis, 1975; Monger and Price, 1979). In the Ogilvie and Mackenzie Mountains of northern Yukon, the Windermere unconformably overlies Beltian strata that were deformed during the compressional Raklan orogeny (see Hoffman, this volume). There, evidence for a subsequent rifting episode associated with the Windermere series is found in coarse clastics, evaporites, and 750 to 770 Ma volcanics (*Gabrielse and Campbell, 1989*). Farther south in the Canadian Rocky Mountains, *Devlin and Bond (1989)* report a Sm-Nd model age of about 762 Ma for possible rift-associated basalts at the base of the Windermere. All evidence points toward an epi-

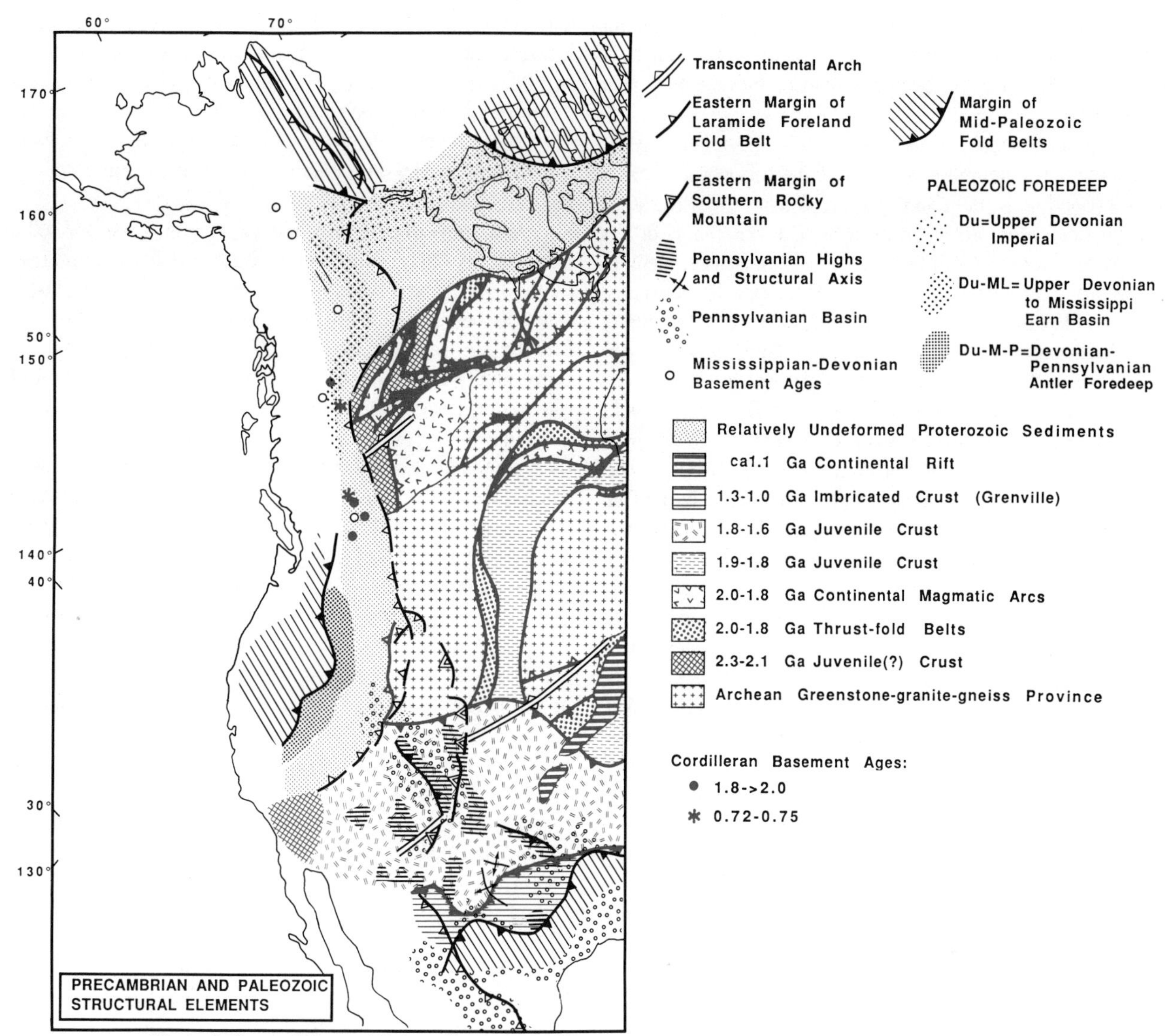

Figure 8. Precambrian and Paleozoic elements of the western Cordillera. In red, Precambrian basement patterns (after Hoffman, this volume) are discordantly cut by the zero edge of the overlying and relatively undeformed Proterozoic sediments. South of the 60th parallel, the strike of the Cordillera roughly parallels the zero edge. Exceptions are obvious failed-arm half-graben systems like the Uinta Mountains and the Little Belt Mountains. North of the 60th parallel, the Proterozoic zero edge strikes to the northeast and toward the Canadian Shield. Thus, the Mackenzie Mountains and the frontal Franklin Mountains involve the deformation of thick Proterozoic sequences (also see Plate 7, section B).

sodic rifting history for the Windermere that eventually leads to the post-rift subsidence phase of the Cordilleran miogeosyncline.

Bond and others (1984a, 1984b) studied the tectonic subsidence history of the late Proterozoic and Paleozoic of the Canadian Cordillera using sophisticated reconstructions that allow for the decompaction of sediments. They suggest a history of thermal contraction following a crustal stretching event with a breakup age of the Cordilleran passive margin between 625 and 555 Ma (i.e., substantially later than inception of the Windermere sequence). According to Bond and his colleagues, the Cordilleran breakup coincides with coeval events associated with the breakup phase of the Appalachian miogeosyncline.

Briefly referring to northern Alaska, Figure 8 shows that in northernmost Yukon, and in the Brooks Range and Alaska North Slope portion of the Cordillera, the basement is no longer the Precambrian craton of North America. Instead, it is the subsurface extension of the Innuitian fold belt. This is discussed later within the context of the Ellesmerian orogeny.

Early to mid-Paleozoic continental margins of western North America

The Cordilleran miogeosyncline, initiated during the late Proterozoic to Early Cambrian, was dominated by carbonate deposition from the Middle Cambrian to the Middle Devonian, with carbonate shelf-margin trends subparallel to the Cordillera (Fig. 5). An important question is how long the continental margin of western North America maintained its individuality as a passive margin.

Traditional models (e.g., *Churkin, 1974*) postulate a western volcanic arc throughout much of the Paleozoic and the Mesozoic, corresponding to the eugeosyncline that was paired with a miogeosyncline. More recent studies now assign much of the geology of the western Cordillera of Canada to suspect terranes that were rafted into the area during the Mesozoic. The existence of a lower Paleozoic arc and continentally derived sediments of an ocean basin in the eastern Klamath Mountains and the northern Sierra Nevada may represent the only vestige of an early Paleozoic western margin of North America. Even these rocks have been interpreted in various ways. They have been thought to be part of a fringing arc system (Burchfiel and Davis, 1972, 1975), and alternatively they have been considered part of an exotic terrane that collided with the North American passive margin in mid-Paleozoic (*Schweickert and Snyder, 1981*) or Permo-Triassic (Speed, 1979) time.

There appears little doubt, however, that an island-arc system eventually developed into a two-sided mid- to upper Paleozoic orogen (Burchfiel and Davis, 1972, 1975) situated to the west of the upper Proterozoic–Cambrian passive margin. Any western island arc that would separate the miogeosyncline from the paleo-Pacific ocean would cause the former passive margin (miogeosyncline) to become the east flank of a mid-Paleozoic back-arc system (see Dickinson, 1977).

Such a hypothetical back-arc system would differ substantially from the present-day West Pacific back-arc systems, which are all superposed on pre-existing peneplaned island-arc systems and not on long-lived passive margins like that of the early Paleozoic Cordillera. Typically, the complex late Paleogene to Neogene evolution of West Pacific back-arc basins involves complex transtensional and transpressional tectonics, including often spectacular inversion tectonics. Tertiary West Pacific back-arc basins are also typically much smaller, more localized, and appear to have a much shorter life expectancy (*Bally and Snelson, 1980*; *Letouzay and Sage, 1988*) than the much more continuous Paleozoic passive margin of western North America.

Thus, it may be concluded that a Cordilleran passive margin existed from the late Proterozoic into the early Paleozoic. Later, during the Ordovician and Silurian, island-arc systems formed in the west, and during the mid-Paleozoic collided with North America as discussed in the following paragraphs.

Mid-Paleozoic continental margin tectonism

During the mid-Paleozoic, both the Cordilleran and Arctic margins of North America were involved in major episodes of shortening. Within the resolution of available age control, the east-west–trending Ellesmerian orogenic belt of the Arctic and the northwesterly trending Antler belt of the Cordillera appear to be roughly coeval, with deformation in the Arctic being somewhat older (Fig. 8). Both resulted in continent-directed thrust belts with locally well-developed foredeep successions containing Devono-Carboniferous sediments. In Alaska and in the Yukon and Northwest Territories of Canada, evidence of both the Ellesmerian and Antler contractional belts exists. Relations are obscured by severe Mesozoic deformation, but it appears that Alaska and northwestern Canada were situated at a "corner" of the mid-Paleozoic continental margin.

Ellesmerian orogeny. The Ellesmerian orogenic belt in the Canadian Arctic Archipelago is described by Trettin (this volume). It can be divided into four approximately east-west–trending belts, which are, from north to south: (1) a middle Proterozoic to Upper Silurian accreted terrane (Pearya); (2) a Cambrian to Devonian belt consisting of volcanic rocks and marine to nonmarine sediments; (3) a belt of Cambrian to Devonian deep-marine deposits, and; (4) a Cambrian to Devonian belt of shelf sediments transitional to the Arctic platform lying to the south. During the Late Devonian, these belts were shortened and thrust southward with the accompanying development of a widespread foredeep. The Upper Devonian clastics of the foredeep, which are deformed in the frontal parts of the thrust belt (Harrison and Bally, 1988), overlie the Arctic platform to the south where they and the underlying units are not deformed. In Alaska and northern Yukon, paleotransport directions in the sediments of the clastic wedge are toward the southwest (Nilsen, 1981; *Churkin and Trexler, 1980*), and distal parts of the succession (Imperial Formation) are found as far south as the Richardson and Ogilvie Mountains.

Late Devonian structures are recognized in the Romanzof Mountains of the northeastern Brooks Range (*Reed, 1968*; *Sable, 1977*; *Reiser and others, 1971, 1980*; Oldow and others, 1987b) and in the British and Richardson Mountains in northwestern Canada (Norris and Yorath, 1981; *Avé Lallemant and Oldow, 1987*). The deformation is locally accompanied by metamorphism, and Late Devonian post-tectonic(?) granites intrude the deformed rocks. In the Romanzof, British, and Richardson Mountains, strong evidence exists that the Late Devonian structures are south vergent (*Bell, 1974*; Oldow and others, 1987b; *Avé Lallemant and Oldow, 1987*) and locally involve rocks of the Devonian clastic wedge (Imperial Formation) shed southerly during Ellesmerian tectonism.

The present-day distribution of lower Paleozoic rocks involved in the Ellesmerian orogeny is controversial. The controversy hinges on different interpretations for the Mesozoic evolution of the Canada basin in the present Arctic Ocean. The Canada basin commonly is postulated to be the product of oroclinal rotation of northern Alaska away from the Canadian Arctic Islands (e.g., *Tailleur, 1973*; Grantz and May, 1983). As discussed elsewhere in this chapter, we disagree and argue that the Brooks Range and British Mountains have probably been displaced southward along a left-lateral transform fault parallel to the Canadian Arctic continental margin.

Antler orogeny. Evidence for the Antler orogeny is primarily derived from Nevada and California (e.g., *Roberts and others, 1958*; *Johnson and Pendergast, 1981*). Elsewhere in the Cordillera, sporadic evidence exists that Late Devonian to Early Mississippian tectonism occurred in rocks of British Columbia, Yukon Territory, and Alaska (Gordey and others, 1987; *Gehrels and Smith, 1987*).

It appears that in the early Paleozoic, the southwestern flank of North America was a northeast-southwest–trending passive margin. In the Early Devonian, and possibly as early as the Ordovician, an off-shore volcanic arc appeared. On the basis of the distribution of Paleozoic units preserved in the western Great Basin and California, four depositional belts are identified. They are, from northwest to southeast: a volcanic arc, a marginal basin containing volcanic detritus and abundant deep-marine clastics and chert, a miogeosyncline dominated by carbonates, and a continental platform.

The island arc is mainly represented by Middle Devonian and Lower Mississippian rhyolite, dacite, andesite, and granitic plutons exposed in the Sierra Nevada foothills (e.g., Schweickert, 1981; *D'Allura and others, 1977*; Hanson and others, 1988; *Saleeby and others, 1987a*) and in the eastern Klamath Mountains (Irwin, 1985). The constructional arc rests on a lower Paleozoic deformed basement composed of the Cambrian–Silurian Shoo Fly complex in the northern Sierra Nevada (Schweickert, 1981; Merguerian and Schweickert, 1987) and the Central Metamorphic belt of the Klamath Mountains (Irwin, *1981,* 1985). The Shoo Fly complex is composed of highly deformed deep-marine rocks that contain continentally derived components of the same age as those in the Antler basin to the east (*Bond and DeVay, 1980*; Schweickert, 1981). The Central Metamorphic belt of the Klamath Mountains contains rocks of oceanic and island-arc affinity as well as continentally derived clastics. The lithology of the lower Paleozoic basement in the Klamath Mountains and northern Sierra Nevada appears to link the regions with the North American margin before the onset of Antler tectonism. The polarity of the fringing arc is unknown, although the existence of Devonian metamorphic rocks in the Central Metamorphic belt of the Klamath Mountains lying to the west of the volcanic arc has been interpreted to indicate eastward subduction (Burchfiel and Davis, 1972).

East of the volcanic arc, the Antler basin was floored by oceanic crust and accumulated radiolarian chert and argillite interbedded with clastics derived from the continental margin and volcaniclastic sediments derived from the arc. In eastern Nevada, Utah, and eastern Idaho, the back-arc environment gave way to a shelf area, in which mostly carbonates and siliciclastic sediments were deposited. This belt changed toward the southeast into the platformal environment of cratonic North America.

During Late Devonian to Early Mississippian times, the contents of the Antler basin were deformed and thrust to the east over coeval miogeosynclinal units. The loading of the Roberts Mountains allochthon (*Speed and Sleep, 1982*) on the continental shelf developed the Antler foredeep, which was filled with terrigenous clastics and carbonates of Carboniferous age (Fig. 9). Whether the Early and Middle Devonian ages of metamorphism (*Irwin, 1981*) in the Klamath Mountains are related to regular accretionary deformational processes or indicate the initiation of this contraction is unknown. Volcanism waned in the Carboniferous, and the arc was inactive during the Pennsylvanian.

In Canada, evidence for Antler-age deformation is found in the Kootenay and Yukon-Tanana terranes, the latter extending into Alaska (Monger and Berg, 1987). The Kootenay terrane in southeastern British Columbia and northeastern Washington consists of Proterozoic to Middle Cambrian miogeosynclinal rocks and lower Paleozoic deep-marine basinal rocks. They were deformed and metamorphosed probably during Late Devonian time (Monger and Berg, 1987), during which basinal rocks are thought to have been thrust easterly over coeval platformal successions (Wheeler and Gabrielse, 1972; *Gehrels and Smith, 1987*). Ordovician and Devonian plutons (*Okulitch, 1985*) may represent part of the plumbing system of a mid-Paleozoic magmatic arc. The deformed rocks are unconformably overlain by sediments and volcanics of Late Mississipian and Pennsylvanian age (Milford Group). Western or distal facies of the Milford Group are overlain in turn by Permian tholeiitic volcanics of the Kaslo Group (*Read and Wheeler, 1976*; Monger and Berg, 1987).

The Yukon-Tanana terrane in northern British Columbia, Yukon Territory, and Alaska consists of a heterogeneous sequence of metamorphic and plutonic rocks. The protolith of the metamorphic rocks may be of Paleozoic and Precambrian age (Tempelman-Kluit, 1979; Mortensen and Jilsen, 1985; *Dusel-Bacon and Aleinikoff, 1985*), and zircons in metamorphic granitic rocks indicate a Proterozoic (2.1 to 2.3 Ga) source and an Early Mississippian (380 to 340 Ma) intrusive age (Aleinikoff and others, 1986).

East of the Yukon-Tanana terrane in Yukon Territory and in eastern British Columbia, clastic wedges formed in the Late Devonian to Middle Mississippian and were derived from the west, presumably from the chert-dominated outer part of the Selwyn basin (Gordey and others, 1987). These basins contain chert conglomerate, chert-quartz sandstones, and mudstone (Gordey and others, 1987) interpreted as having formed either by extension or transpression, possibly in the foreland of a contractional orogen.

In addition to the evidence of Late Devonian and Early Mississippian tectonism recorded in the Yukon-Tanana terrane of central Alaska, a major belt of Devonian plutons occurs in the Schist belt of the southern Brooks Range (*Dillon and others, 1987*). The plutons, which now are orthogneisses, were deformed together with the country rocks during Mesozoic and Cenozoic Brookian tectonism (*Gottschalk, 1987*; Oldow and others, 1987a) obscuring possible earlier mid-Paleozoic structures. The plutons have commonly been associated with age-equivalent Devonian granitoids and pre-Carboniferous structures exposed in the Romanzof and British Mountains to the east. This correlation has its origins in the present-day close proximity of the units now residing in the Brooks Range fold and thrust belt. What has not been recognized until recently is the magnitude of late Mesozoic and Cenozoic shortening resulting from Brookian tectonism. Reconstruction of the central Brooks Range based on balanced cross

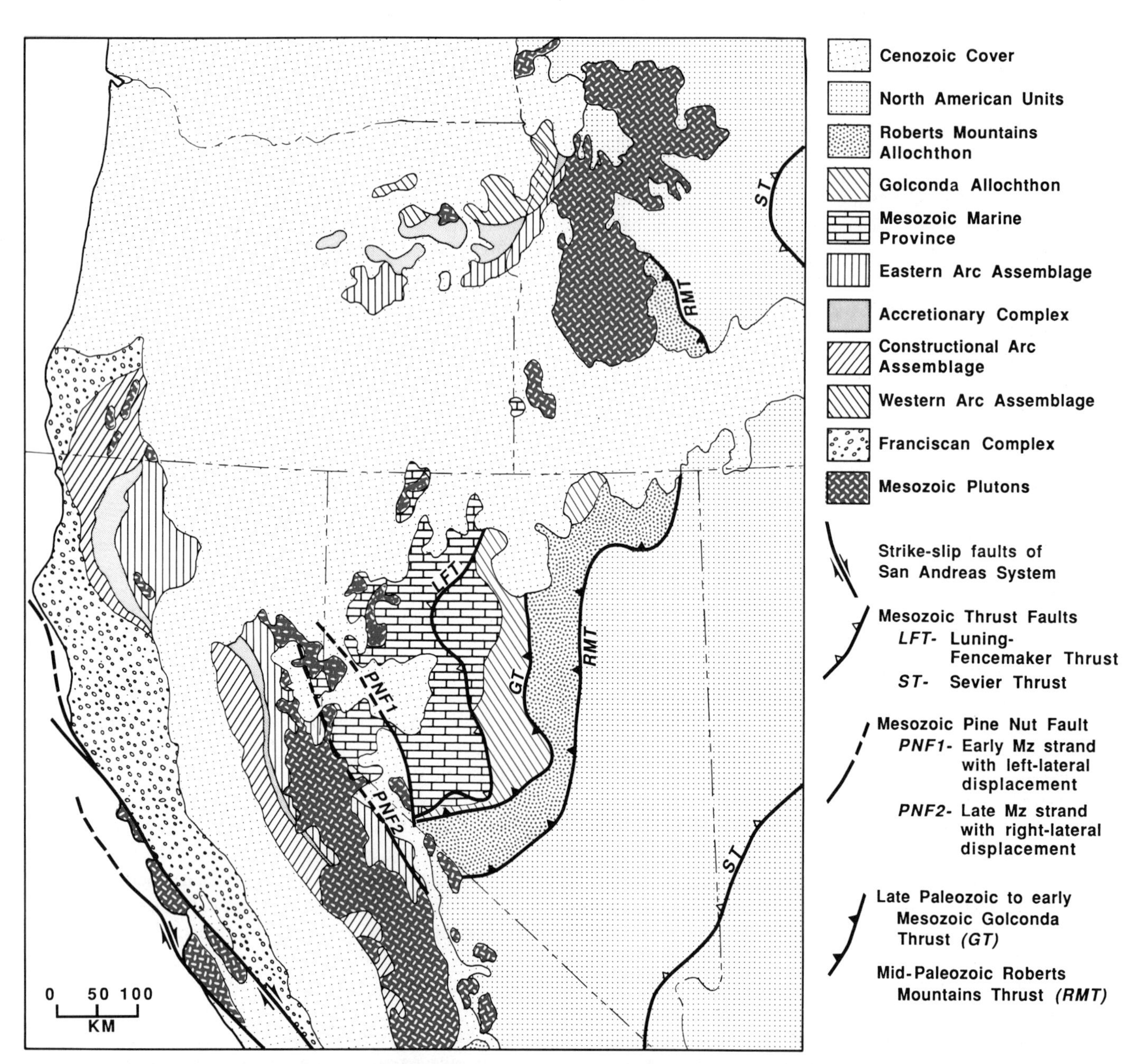

Figure 9. Generalized geologic map (modified from Silberling and others, 1987) illustrating the distribution of the mid-Paleozoic Roberts Mountains allochthon and the Permo-Triassic Golconda allochthon in the western Great Basin. Major Jura-Cretaceous structures shown include the Luning-Fencemaker and Sevier thrust belts and the Pine Nut transpressional fault system. The frontal trace of the thin-skinned Sevier thrust belt more or less follows the hingeline of the Cordillera miogeosyncline. The frontal trace of the Luning-Fencemaker thrust belt mimics the $^{87}Sr/^{86}Sr = 0.706$ isopleth in the western Great Basin. The Luning-Fencemaker thrust juxtaposes allochthonous basinal units with partially coeval platformal assemblages in the northern part of the Mesozoic marine province and carries basinal and platformal successions over partially age-equivalent, subaerial to shallow-marine units in the south. The western boundary of the Luning-Fencemaker thrust belt is marked by the eastern strand of the Pine Nut fault system (PNF1), which separates coeval rocks of the Mesozoic marine province into structural domains, one with superposed structures of the Luning-Fencemaker thrust belt to the east and the other with structures of Sierra Nevada affinity to the west. Left-lateral displacement of several hundred kilometers (>500) along the Pine Nut fault system (PNF1) accompanied northwest-southeast shortening in the Luning-Fencemaker thrust belt. After the mid-Cretaceous, right-lateral displacement on a western strand of the Pine Nut fault system (PNF2) transported the Sierra Nevada northward (>700 m km; Frei and others, 1984) leaving behind some southerly displaced units of the Mesozoic marine province.

sections (Oldow and others, 1987a) indicates that the original position of the Schist belt and its Devonian plutons lies at least 500 km to the south of its location today. The implication is that the magmatic and possibly the mid-Paleozoic structural history of the southern Brooks Range is more closely allied with that of the Yukon-Tanana terrane and, thus, is part of the Cordilleran trend.

This possibility bears strongly on the generally accepted interpretation of the tectonic setting of a widespread Upper Devonian clastic wedge exposed in the Brooks Range. The Devonian clastics have been used as a link between Ellesmerian tectonism and mid-Paleozoic history of the Brooks Range. In the Canadian Arctic Archipelago, Upper Devonian clastics are demonstrably related to the Ellesmerian orogenic belt and can be traced to the Richardson Mountains of the Yukon and Northwest Territories. We contend that the Upper Devonian clastics of the Brooks Range, although largely coeval with those of the Ellesmerian foredeep, are not related to the Arctic contractional belt. Although paleocurrent directions are similar (Nilsen, 1981), the sediments of the Brooks Range (Endicott Group) are generally much coarser grained than those in Canada, and they are not involved in Ellesmerian deformation like those in the northern Richardson Mountains. The Devonian clastics of the Brooks Range appear to be related to deposition along a passive margin, possibly accompanied by substantial extension (*Handschy, 1988*), and may represent the shelfal expression of subsidence and possible rifting associated with the formation of the basin that accumulated the ophiolitic rocks of the Angayucham and related terranes.

Late Paleozoic intra-plate tectonics

The Ancestral Rocky Mountains represent the youngest wholly Paleozoic structural event influencing the tectonic evolution of the western Cordillera. Some recent summaries have been published by *Mallory (1972a)* and Kluth (1986). Figure 8 illustrates the tectonic position of the Ancestral Rocky Mountains.

The late Paleozoic uplifts and basins of the southern Rocky Mountains have been severely overprinted by the Laramide deformation. Thus, much of the evidence for the Ancestral Rocky Mountains is derived from stratigraphic studies. More specifically, thick wedges of coarse arkosic sediments that were shed from adjacent basement uplifts have been mapped.

Eardley (1962) already related the Ancestral Rocky Mountains to deformation in the foreland of the coeval Ouachita Mountains. The main uplifts are the Pennsylvanian Uncompaghre and Front Range uplifts of New Mexico and Colorado. These have been reactivated in a modified form during the Laramide deformation of the southern Rocky Mountains (Plate 5A). The Wichita Mountains of the Ouachita foreland and the adjacent Anadarko basin offer a reasonable analog for Pennsylvanian Rocky Mountain tectonics without the Laramide overprint.

The Ancestral Rocky Mountains and its associated basins strike approximately at right angles to the northeast-striking pre–Upper Devonian Transcontinental Arch. *Eardley's (1962)* Late Devonian geological map and the pre–Upper Devonian subcrop map of Cook and Bally (1975) suggest an overall left-lateral displacement of the axis of the Transcontinental Arch along a shear zone that extends from the northeast flank of the Wichita Mountains, along the southwest flank of the Uncompaghre uplift to the approximate area of the Pennsylvanian Oquirrh basin, of Salt Lake City (see Bally, this volume; Plate 10-D). Budnik (1986) reviews all the evidence favoring a left-lateral shear along the hypothetical Wichita megashear. A pre–Middle Devonian subcrop map leads Budnik to infer a left-lateral offset of about 120 km. According to the same author, the megashear may be due to the collision of Africa with North America. *Kluth and Coney (1981),* Kluth (1986), and *Stevenson and Baars (1986)* described some of the symptomatic pull-apart and compressional structures of this essentially transpressional system, but the detailed kinematics of the zone of distributed shear remain to be worked out.

The Paradox basin (e.g., *Stevenson and Baars, 1986*) offers an example of normal faulting of Late Mississippian–Early Pennsylvanian age and has a history suggesting initial pull-apart followed by the deposition of over 3 km of carbonate-evaporite cycles and overlying clastics, which are coeval with conglomerates derived from the adjacent Uncompaghre uplift in the northeast. A Late Pennsylvanian compressional phase further uplifted the adjacent basement high and also folded the evaporites and overlying Pennsylvanian clastics into elongate "salt anticlines." The salt anticlines are unconformably overlain by Mesozoic clastics and were, in turn, reactivated during Laramide deformation.

As Kluth (1986) has emphasized, the Ancestral Rocky Mountains formed during a Pennsylvanian and Early Permian interlude between the Antler and Sonoma orogenies. It is best to relate their origin to transpressional tectonics in the foreland of the Ouachita-Marathon fold belt, which in turn may be related to a poorly understood upper Paleozoic continental collision between North and South America.

Late Paleozoic–Early Mesozoic continental margin tectonics

The paleogeography of western Nevada and California during the Permian and Early Triassic underwent a dramatic reorganization. Deposition patterns changed from those consistent with passive-margin conditions to an active-margin setting. Deformation during the Permo-Triassic Sonoma orogeny consists of emplacement of the regionally extensive Golconda allochthon in western Nevada (*Silberling and Roberts, 1962*; Silberling, 1975), the truncation of the northeast-southwest–trending continental margin and associated transcurrent faulting in the Mojave Desert region (Walker, 1988), and the formation of a new active margin. Some indications exist that age-equivalent deformation may have occurred in northeastern Oregon and southern British Columbia, but no clear evidence has been found for coeval tectonism in Alaska.

In the Great Basin region, upper Paleozoic rocks composed of argillite, sandstones, volcanic, and volcaniclastic rocks constitute the upper plate of the regionally extensive Golconda thrust (Fig. 9) and structurally overlie age-equivalent carbonates and clastics of the underlying autochthon (*Silberling and Roberts, 1962*; Silberling, 1975). Even though the rocks are relatively well preserved, the depositional setting of the Havallah basin, from which the constituents of the Golconda allochthon are thought to be derived, is controversial. The Havallah sequence may have formed on an Atlantic-type passive margin (Speed, *1977,* 1979; Speed and others, 1988) or in a marginal basin (Burchfiel and Davis, 1972, 1975; Miller and others, 1989) lying inboard of a fringing arc system. Evidence uniquely supporting either of the contending models has not been forthcoming from work in the Great Basin and may not exist.

Havallah deposition began in the Early Mississippian and is characterized by sediments derived from the Antler thrust belt to the east and an andesitic source to the west (Miller and others, 1989). The allochthon contains abundant Upper Mississippian basaltic pillow lava, possibly related to rifting (Miller and others, 1989), and radiolarian chert; it notably lacks Upper Mississippian and Pennsylvanian sedimentary rocks with a clear volcanic arc provenance. The conspicuous absence of arc-derived clastics indicates that any arc terranes lying along the continental margin at that time were physically separated from the margin. In the Pennsylvanian and Permian, carbonate turbidites derived from the east were shed from the continent into the basin. During the Early Permian, basaltic volcanism accompanied continued subsidence and deposition of sediments derived from the continent to the east. In the Late Permian, abundant arc-derived debris was shed into the Havallah basin, and along the southern margin of the basin, continental shelf and arc-derived sediments interfinger (*Speed, 1977*). The sediments within the allochthon are compatible with either of the two major contending paleogeographic models.

Age-equivalent rocks on the continental margin to the east record a history of basaltic volcanism, limestone deposition accompanied by pelitic sequences, and turbidites overlapping the earlier tectonic highlands of the Antler orogenic belt (*Little, 1987*). In the Pennsylvanian, carbonate shelf conditions were reinstated, but substantial differences in thickness of units suggest that the region was unstable and possibly was affected by faulting that continued into the Permian. The Pennsylvanian through the Permian was dominated by transgressive marine sequences. In the Middle to Late Permian, phosphatic sediments were deposited in subsiding shelfal basins, or the foreland and shelf of the allochthon.

Possibly the most important constraints for the late Paleozoic tectonic development of the southern Cordillera are preserved in the rocks of the Sierra Nevada and Klamath Mountains. During the Carboniferous, deposition was dominated by epiclastic sediments and minor volcanic rocks in the eastern Klamath Mountains and by the deposition of radiolarian chert in the northern Sierra Nevada. Substantial volcanism did not commence until the Early Permian when a northeast-southwest–trending volcanic arc formed, generally on top of older, Devonian to Lower Mississippian rocks. The arc consists of rhyolites, andesites, and related plutons in the Klamath Mountains (Irwin, *1981,* 1985), andesite in the Sierra Nevada foothills (*D'Allura and others, 1977*; Schweickert, 1981), and andesite and basaltic andesite in the marine province of northwestern Nevada (Speed, *1977,* 1979).

West of the volcanic arc occurs a belt of complexly deformed rocks of Cache Creek affinity. Although most of the assemblage is of Triassic age, it contains Permian limestone knockers, some of which have exclusively Tethyan faunas; whereas others have exclusively northeast Pacific (McCloud-type) faunas with a North American affinity. The assemblage is generally interpreted as a late Paleozoic and early Mesozoic accretionary complex (Wright, 1982).

The main result of the Sonoma orogeny was that the Havallah basin was (partially?) closed and the volcanic-basinal rocks of the Golconda allochthon were thrust toward the east, across the continental shelf. The timing and kinematics of the Sonoma orogeny are poorly constrained and leave ample room for controversy. Speed (*1977,* 1979) argued that the Permian volcanic arc was east facing, and thus, that the Golconda thrust was synthetic to the subduction zone. He speculated that the island arc was exotic and part of the microplate Sonomia. However, Lower Permian fossils in the McCloud limestone, which underlies the Permian arc in the Klamath Mountains, are different from Tethyan fossils in Permian limestone blocks contained in the Cache Creek type mélange west of the Permian arc. The McCloud-like fossils have been found in thrust blocks and/or olistoliths in north-central Nevada and in central Oregon (*Ketner and Wardlaw, 1981*; *Wardlaw and others, 1982*); their close relationship with andesitic volcanic and volcaniclastic rocks suggests an origin very different from the "oceanic" Cache Creek terrane. The existence of exotic Tethyan rocks west of the Permian volcanic arc suggests that the arc was west-facing (Miller, 1987). The record of essentially continuous volcanism in the late Paleozoic, with the Permian arc built on top of the Devonian Antler arc, was used by Burchfiel and Davis (1972, 1981) as an argument in favor of a west-facing arc.

The age of the Sonoma orogeny is also controversial. Speed (*1977,* 1979) suggested a late Early Triassic (post-Spathian) age on the basis of involved structural, sedimentological, and stratigraphic arguments concerning interfingered shelfal and arc-derived clastic and carbonate rocks exposed in west-central Nevada (Candelaria Hills; *Speed, 1984*). However, if deformation and tectonic juxtaposition of the units resulted from late Mesozoic thrusting, as suggested by *Oldow (1984b),* these rocks cannot constrain the timing of the Sonoma orogeny. In the type locality of the Sonoma orogeny, siliceous volcanic rocks unconformably overlie deformed and imbricated rocks of the Golconda allochthon. The volcanic rocks and overlying carbonate and clastic rocks have yielded fossils as old as Spathian age (Silberling, 1975; Nichols and Silberling, 1977). An older age (pre-Spathian) for the Sonoma orogeny is consistent with the structural history of rocks of the late Mesozoic Luning-Fencemaker thrust belt lying above the Golconda allochthon. Rocks in the Luning-Fencemaker thrust belt locally have yielded Early Triassic (Spathian) conodonts (Oldow, unpublished data) but did not experience deformation until after deposition of Lower to Middle(?) Jurassic units in extensional half-grabens (*Oldow and Bartel, 1987*). In all, the best age constraints for the Sonoma orogeny in western Nevada appear to point to a Late Permian or earliest Early Triassic event.

An older age for the Sonoma orogeny in Nevada is more easily reconciled with the Permian age of active margin tectonism in the Mojave Desert region and associated deposition of turbidites (*Stone and Stevens, 1988*; *Stevens and Stone, 1988*) in basins associated with transcurrent faults. Late Permian igneous activity was followed by deformation of the rocks in the Mojave region and subsequent overlap by Spathian-age units (Walker, 1988). As pointed out by Walker (1988), the facies trends within the overlap succession differ from those of the underlying rocks and follow the northwest-southeast orientation of the Mesozoic arc.

The lower to mid-Paleozoic northeast-southwest–trending tectonic and lithologic belts in Nevada and California are truncated along a northwest-southeast–trending structure. The precise location of this structure has been placed variously along the western edge of the Sierra Nevada (Schweickert, *1976,* 1981; *Saleeby, 1977*; Saleeby and others, 1989) and within or immediately behind the plutonic complex (*Davis and others, 1978*; Burchfiel and Davis, 1981). As discussed by Saleeby and others (1989), the best candidate for the site of truncation appears to be the Sierra Nevada foothills suture zone. Large transcurrent displacements in eastern California (*Stone and Stevens, 1988*; *Stevens and Stone, 1988*) and in the Mojave Desert (Walker, 1988) probably are related structures and formed in a broad zone of distributed shear. On the basis of lithologic similarities in the miogeoclinal rocks of southern California and those exposed in northwestern Mexico (Burchfiel and Davis, 1981), and the apparent sinistral offset of the Antler orogenic belt rocks in eastern California (Walker, 1988), it has been proposed that the truncation was caused by a left-lateral transform fault system. The truncation of the margin appears to have been completed by the early Early Triassic (e.g., Walker, 1988), and even though timing and kinematic relations are tantalizing, its relation to the Sonoma orogeny is not clear.

Earlier we suggested that the Sierran-Klamath volcanic arc may be correlated with Quesnellia in British Columbia and the Olds Ferry (Huntington) volcanic arc in eastern Oregon. We envision an essentially continuous arc system stretching along the western Cordillera. The Olds Ferry arc consists of Middle and Upper Triassic andesites and is believed to be built on mid- and upper Paleozoic rocks of the John Day inlier in central Oregon, in which Lower Permian keratophyres overlie Permian limestone of McCloud fossil affinity (*Wardlaw and others, 1982*). The absence of Upper Permian and Lower Triassic rocks may indicate the existence of a hiatus related to the Sonoma orogeny.

The Wallowa (Seven Devils) arc of eastern Oregon and western Idaho consists of Permian and Middle and Upper Triassic volcanic rocks. The Permian rocks are clearly arc related (*Vallier and Batiza, 1978*), indicating that the second fringing arc, so well developed in the Mesozoic, was already active in the Permian, comparable to Stikinia in British Columbia.

The Late Permian to Early Triassic Sonoma orogeny resulted in continentward thrusting and the collapse of a marginal basin in the southern Cordillera. Whether the subduction was oblique or not is not known with certainty. If left-lateral truncation in the Mojave region was related to the Sonoma orogeny, however, sinistral oblique convergence is probable.

In Canada, rocks of the Kootenay terrane record evidence of Sonoman tectonism. Permian rocks of the Kaslo Group are imbricated and intruded by diorite before being unconformably overlain by conglomerates forming the base of the sequence that contains Carnian fossils higher up in the Slocan Group (*Klepacki and Wheeler, 1985*). Elsewhere, in part of the Slide Mountain terrane (Sylvester allochthon), Permian granite and diorite cut some early structures that were further imbricated and emplaced onto North America in the Mesozoic (*Harms, 1986*). The rocks of the Milford (Carboniferous) and Kaslo (Permian) are interpreted as being deposited in a marginal basin setting (J. O. Wheeler, written communication, 1988) similar to that proposed for the Havallah basin by Burchfiel and Davis (1972, 1975) and Miller and others (1989).

In Alaska, upper Paleozoic and lower Mesozoic rocks lithologically similar to those of the Havallah basin compose the Angayucham and Tozitna terranes. The Angayucham and Tozitna terranes in the Brooks Range structurally overlie metamorphosed rocks of North American affinity. Unlike their counterparts in the Canadian Cordillera and the western Great Basin, they do not demonstrably contain structures formed before the mid-Mesozoic.

The Golconda, Slide Mountain, and Angayucham-Tozitna terranes constitute parts of vast "ophiolitic" allochthons structurally overlying rocks of North America (Plate 5A). The Slide Mountain terrane of the Canadian Cordillera was emplaced after the Late Triassic and before the Early Jurassic (Monger and Berg, 1987), substantially later than the emplacement of the Golconda allochthon in Nevada. In Alaska, the Angayucham-Tozitna terrane, containing cherts, basalts, gabbros, and locally ultramafic rocks, with ages ranging from Early Carboniferous to Late Triassic and possible Early Jurassic (Jones and others, 1987), were tectonically emplaced in the Middle to Late Jurassic. It is possible that the apparent decrease in age of emplacement of late Paleozoic deep-marine sedimentary and igneous rocks is the product of diachronous deformation progressing northward along the coast.

MESOZOIC AND EARLY CENOZOIC TRANSPRESSION AND TERRANE ACCRETION

Introduction

The Triassic to Paleocene evolution of the Cordillera involves the docking and overthrusting of rafted terranes and Triassic to Paleocene left- and right-lateral transpression. Thus, strike-slip fault systems displace previously overthrust terranes, accretionary wedges, and foreland fold belts.

A critical component in deciphering the tectonic evolution of active margins is establishing the structural architecture of regional detachments. The definition of sub-horizontal decollement (decoupling) levels, however, is often problematic. The tectonic significance of large strike-slip systems is equally problematic. Particularly with regard to the depth of strike-slip systems, we ask: Are most continental strike-slip faults decoupled within the upper or middle crust, or do they represent true lithospheric boundaries? Thus, there is a need to establish the existence of a hierarchy of low-angle or flat decollement levels (i.e., shear zones) within the sedimentary cover, the middle and lower crust, and perhaps within the upper mantle and to ascertain their relationship with major transcurrent fault systems. The existence of widespread regional decollement systems inevitably poses the question of the fate of the lithosphere that was originally underlying the decoupled layers. Often the existence of lithospheric subduction zones or "cold lithospheric roots" is suggested. The assimilation of such roots into the asthenosphere could lead to thermal expansion and uplift of the folded belt. In other words, the high topographic elevation of orogenic belts may be due to the elimination of transpressional lithospheric roots.

The general principle of transfer of material to the leading edge of continents by the emplacement of structural sheets is compatible with the development of transpressional orogens along active margins. Nevertheless, the implications of terrane accretion on continental lithospheric volume balances in the North American Cordillera is commonly overlooked and includes three important aspects:

(1) The longitudinal displacement of terranes along the strike of a convergent boundary represents significant out-of-the-cross-section transfer of material in the contracted region. The geometric and kinematic relation between longitudinal displacements and coeval shortening within active margins must be considered.

(2) When palinspastic restorations are attempted, significant space problems relate to the position and nature of the sub-detachment lithosphere during contraction (A-type subduction; Bally, 1975).

(3) The late Paleogene–Neogene transtension of the Cordillera is also associated with the formation of a new Neogene Moho that obliterates all evidence of pre-Neogene lithospheric tectonics and consequently opens the way for unbridled modeling.

Tectonic belts

Our lithotectonic maps (Plates 5 and 6) emphasize the distribution of related terranes. By the middle of the Cretaceous a number of these terranes were assembled, but they were located much farther to the south. The map omits most details of post–late Oligocene transpressional and transtensional structures. Nevertheless, our map (Plate 5A) sketches the outer boundary of the B-subduction–related accretionary wedge and some features associated with the San Andreas fault system.

The stratigraphic division of the Cordillera into unequivocal North American units and those that are displaced facilitates the recognition of major tectonic belts. The North American units compose an eastern tectonic belt; whereas the displaced rocks form what we have termed a transpressional complex. The locations of major late Mesozoic and Cenozoic strike-slip systems of the Cordillera are not controlled by pre-existing terrane boundaries, as they cut obliquely across many terranes. We use these known or inferred strike-slip boundaries to subdivide the Cordillera from east to west into four tectonic belts (Fig. 10).

The first is the Foreland fold belt, which in the south, can be divided into two elements: the southern Rocky Mountains, including the Colorado Plateau; and the Sevier belt, which extends to the north and merges with the Canada and Alaska decollement fold belt (A-subduction). The Foreland fold belt corresponds more or less to the traditional deformed miogeosynclinal folded belt. In other words, we are dealing with unquestioned North American rocks.

The remaining three belts make up the Transpressional complex. They have undergone varying degrees of displacement: (1) The Central belt has strong North American affinities and commonly contains what appears to be remobilized metamorphic North American basement; (2) the Columbia belt includes the amalgamated Superterranes I and II of southern British Columbia, and; (3) the Coastal belt includes much of the amalgamated terranes (Superterrane II and the South Alaska superterrane) exposed in the coastal region of northwestern Canada and southern Alaska (Fig. 10).

Structure and kinematics of the Foreland fold belt

The Foreland fold belt extends for a length exceeding 5,000 km, from Cape Lisburne, Alaska, to Las Vegas, Nevada, and El Paso, Texas, and continues on into Mexico. It includes the Brooks Range, and the Romanzof Mountains (northeastern Brooks Range) of Alaska; the British, Ogilvie and Richardson Mountains of northern Yukon; the Mackenzie Mountains of the Northwest Territories; the Rocky Mountains of British Columbia, Alberta, Montana, Wyoming, Utah, and New Mexico; and the Great Basin of Utah and Nevada. Seismic-reflection profiles from Alaska (Oldow and others, 1987a), Alberta (Bally and others, 1966; *Gordy and others, 1975*; *P. B. Jones, 1982*; *F. A. Cook, 1986*), and Wyoming (Royse and others, 1975; *Williams and Dixon, 1985*) give clear evidence that in all cases the Foreland fold belt is extensively underlain by a basement homocline dipping gently toward the interior of the orogen.

In Alaska and in northern Yukon, metamorphic and deformed Proterozoic and lower Paleozoic sediments constitute the basement (Ellesmerian basement), which becomes involved in overthrusting in the Romanzof and British Mountains. In the Doonerak window of the central Brooks Range (refer to Fig. 12), a pre-Carboniferous sedimentary-volcanic sequence that may be

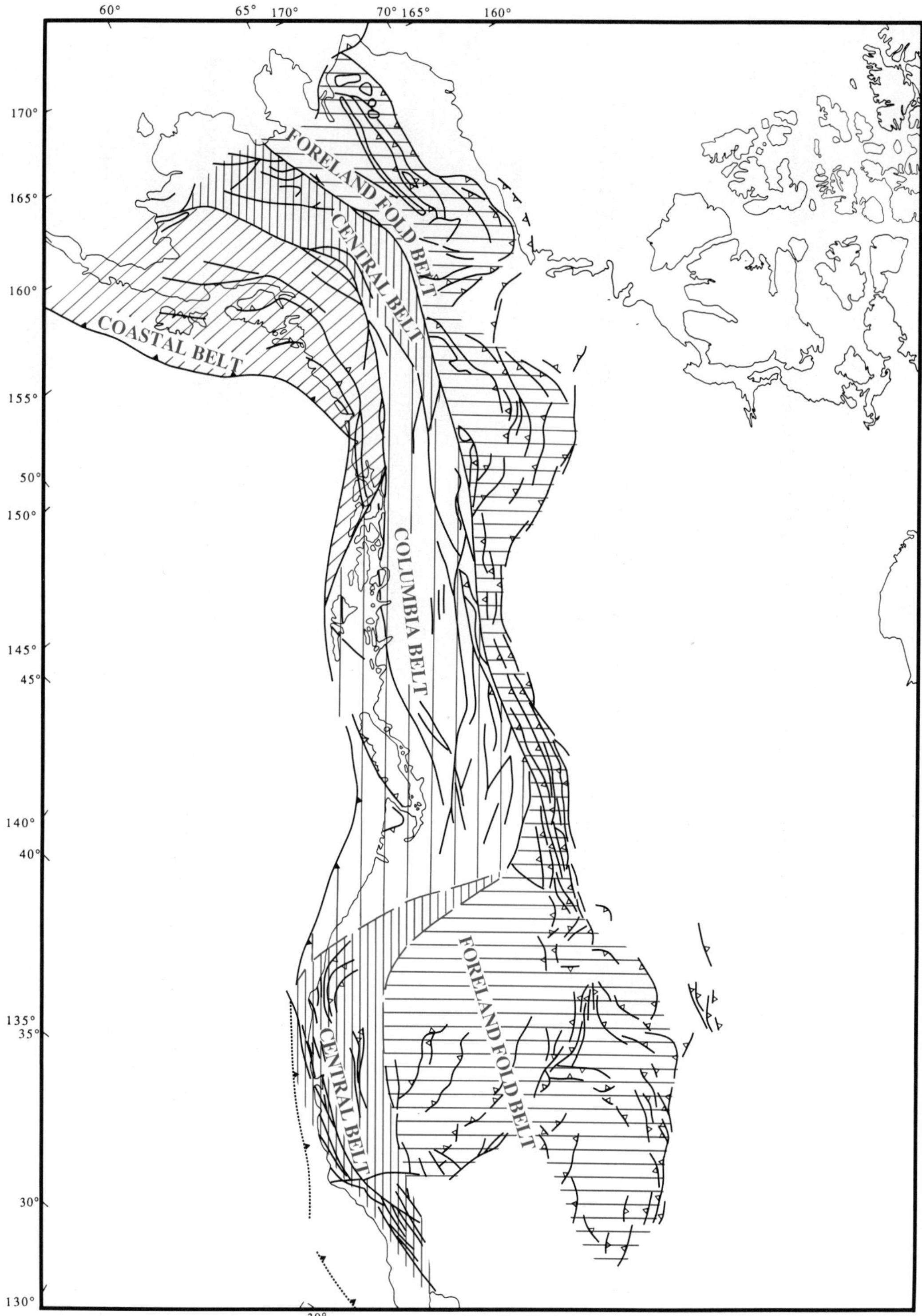

Figure 10. Map of the tectonic belts of the North American Cordillera. The Foreland belt contains North American units that have not experienced significant transcurrent displacements. The Central, Columbia, and Coastal belts have experienced large transcurrent displacement during the Mesozoic and Cenozoic. They are segregated on the basis of paleomagnetically inferred magnitudes of displacement. Note that the tectonic belts do not correspond to terrane boundaries.

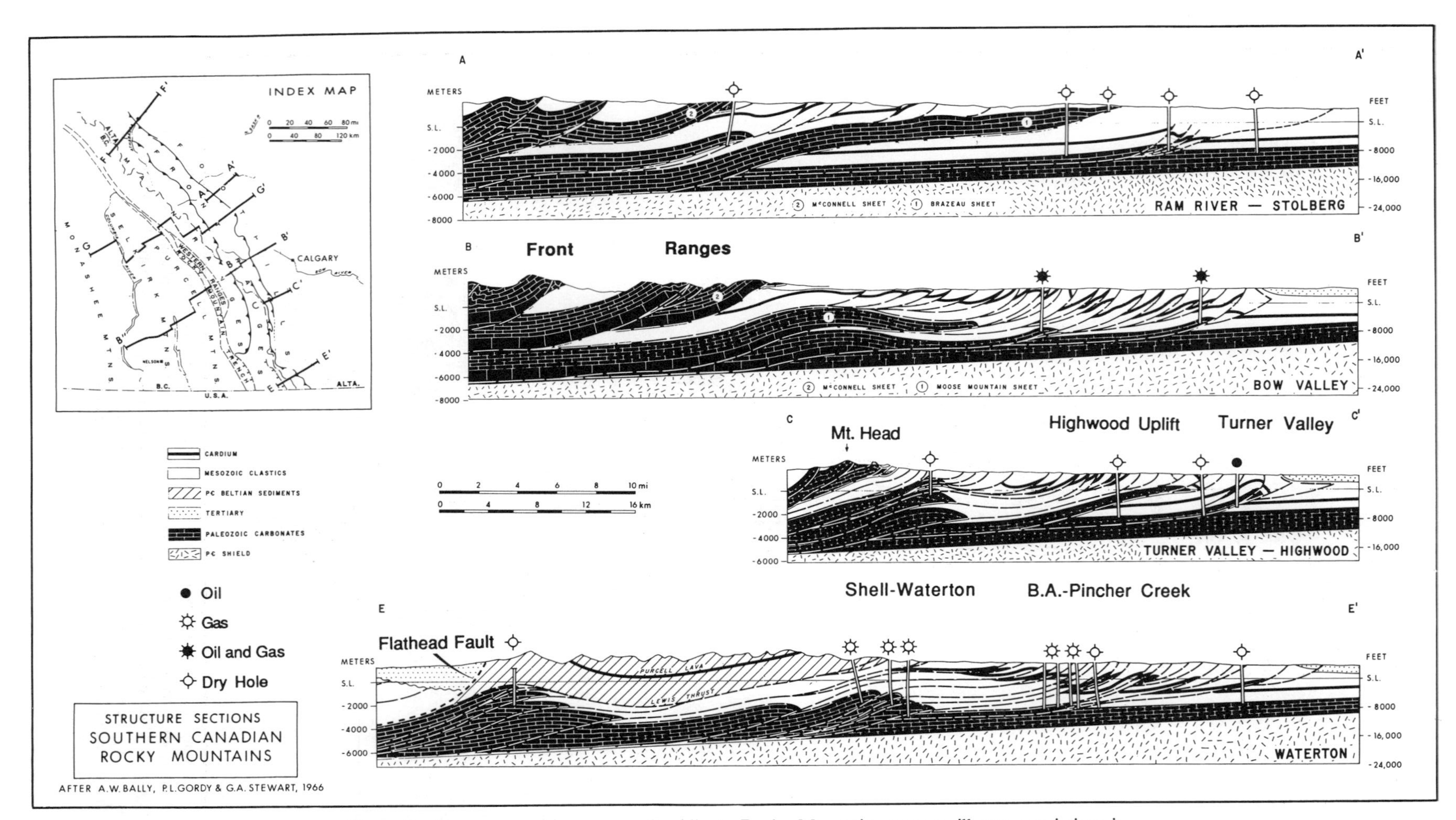

Figure 11. Four cross sections across the Alberta Rocky Mountains serve to illustrate variations in structural style along strike. Section A shows contraction utilizing two major decoupling levels in the Paleozoic section; sections B and C illustrate the effect of additional decoupling levels in Mesozoic units; and section D depicts activity on an additional decoupling level at the base of the Beltian sequence composing the Lewis overthrust.

regarded as "basement" was not involved in Ellesmerian contraction but is incorporated into the Mesozoic belt as a large-scale duplex. From the central Yukon to Nevada, we believe the basement underlying the decollement folded belt consists of mostly crystalline Precambrian rocks.

Much has been written about decollement tectonics in the eastern Cordillera. In the context of this summary, we focus on a few aspects. Plate 7 and Figure 11 show a comparison of some typical profiles across the Cordillera. We also refer the reader to the fine set of balanced cross sections across Alberta and British Columbia that were published by Price (1981), *Price and Fermor (1985),* and *Thompson (1981).* Mudge (1982) published sections across the Montana folded belt, and Royse and others (1975) and *Dixon (1982)* published sections across Wyoming.

Shortening estimates. Minimum shortening estimates for the Rocky Mountains of southern Canada and the northern United States, based on balanced cross sections (Bally and others, 1966; Bally, 1984; Dahlstrom, 1970; *Price and Mountjoy, 1970*; Price, 1981), range from 100 to 200 km. Shortening within the Wyoming-Utah foreland fold belt is well constrained by balanced cross sections derived from surface and subsurface data. Estimates of post–mid-Cretaceous shortening are on the order of 100 to 150 km (Royse and others, 1975; Villien and Kligfield, 1986).

The amount of Jurassic and Cretaceous shortening in the hinterland underlying the Basin and Range province, on the other hand, is poorly constrained because the original basement configuration is unknown. In the Luning-Fencemaker thrust belt of northwestern Nevada, shortening during the Late Jurassic to mid-Cretaceous is on the order of several hundred kilometers (Oldow, 1983, 1984a; Oldow and others, 1984). The magnitude of shortening within intervening areas of central Nevada (Eureka thrust belt) is controversial (compare Fig. 22-15 of Speed and others, 1988, with Fig. 23-11 of Snoke and Miller, 1988, and our Plate 5B, section D), but it is probably quite large.

The belt of Late Cretaceous and Early Tertiary contraction west of the Colorado Plateau extends southeasterly from Las Vegas through western and south-central Arizona. In much of Arizona, evidence of regional shortening is obscured by large-scale Tertiary extension structures (e.g., Armstrong, 1982; Reynolds and others, 1988). Nevertheless, in southeastern Arizona, Late Cretaceous and Tertiary thrusts and folds are preserved in widespread Paleozoic and Mesozoic supracrustal rocks (*Davis, 1979*; *Drewes, 1978*). Farther west, in south-central Arizona, dynamothermal metamorphism accompanied late Mesozoic and early Tertiary contraction (Reynolds and others, 1988).

Evidence of Jurassic to Early Cretaceous shortening, so prevalent in the hinterland of the western Great Basin to the north, is lacking in the southwestern Basin and Range. In southeastern California and southwestern Arizona, early Mesozoic metamorphism is reported as associated with plutonism but not accompanied by any significant thrusting (Reynolds and others, 1988). This apparent along-strike inconsistency in the amount of Jura-Cretaceous shortening in the U.S. Cordillera, between the Great Basin and southern Basin and Range, poses a serious problem for regional reconstructions. If the difference in shortening is real, and this appears to be the case, a major structure must separate the Mojave Desert region from the western end (near Las Vegas) of the Jura-Cretaceous thrust belt of the Sevier hinterland. The nature of this hypothetical structure is unknown, but conceivably it is some type of transform that was active during the mid- to Late Jurassic through the Early Cretaceous. It is plausible that a southern extension of the transpressional Pine Nut fault system preserved in west-central Nevada (Oldow, 1983, 1984) finds its way into this region. The southern path of such a structure is not understood and may not extend through the Owens Valley as originally speculated (Oldow, 1984). The Jura-Cretaceous fault probably has been modified by subsequent deformation and does not have a simple trace. Part of the fault may lie within the Sierra Nevada (*Schweickert and Lahren, 1987*), but its passage through the Las Vegas region is unconstrained at present.

Turning our attention to the north, estimates of shortening in the foreland thrust belt exposed in the Mackenzie Mountains are about 50 km (*Gordey, 1981*; *Cook, 1989*). The estimated contraction within the interior of the thrust belt, exposed in the Selwyn Mountains, is on the order of 150 km (*Gordey and Thompson, 1989*; *Cook, 1989*). All of these estimates are minimum values because they do not include shortening by internal strain.

At least 500 km of shortening is estimated in the central Brooks Range from balanced cross sections (Oldow and others, 1987a). The estimates do not include shortening related to the imbrication and emplacement of the ophiolitic succession forming the highest structural sheets of the mountain chain nor the contraction in the volcanic and metamorphic rocks flanking and underlying the Koyukuk Basin to the south (Fig. 12).

Even within the limits of accuracy for balanced cross sections, there is an obvious jump in the amount of shortening in the Brooks Range when compared to the northern Cordilleran foreland fold belt of Canada. As is discussed at length below, we argue that this difference is real and a direct consequence of the resolution of boundary-normal and boundary-parallel components of motion around a bend in the active margin of North America.

Longitudinal variations in structural style. Aside from the variability of the degree of shortening, there is also the variability in decollement styles that can be studied along the Cordillera. Basically, these stylistic variations are due to changes in ductility contrasts within the sedimentary sequence that is being deformed (i.e, the distribution and frequency of incompetent beds). Below are some examples:

(1) North of Norman Wells in the northeastern Mackenzie Mountains, the style of deformation is strongly influenced by the presence of Cambrian saline evaporites such that structures change their vergence along the strike of a single anticline (*Cook and Aitken, 1973*; *Cook, 1983, 1989*);

(2) Over most of the eastern Mackenzie Mountains there seems to be only one major decollement level somewhere near

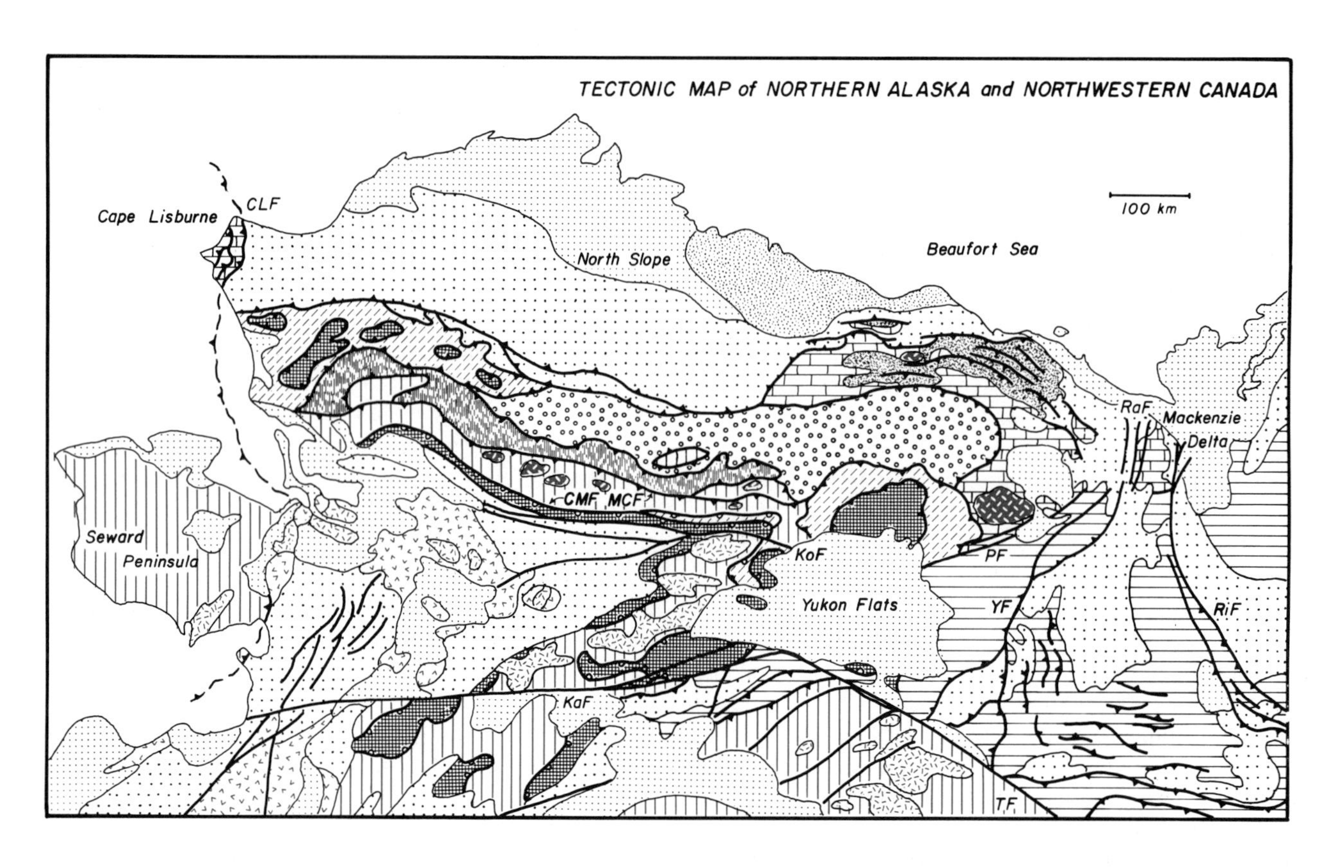
TECTONIC MAP of NORTHERN ALASKA and NORTHWESTERN CANADA
100 km
Cape Lisburne
CLF
North Slope
Beaufort Sea
RaF
Mackenzie
Delta
CMF MCF
KoF
PF
Seward
Peninsula
Yukon Flats
YF
RiF
KaF
TF

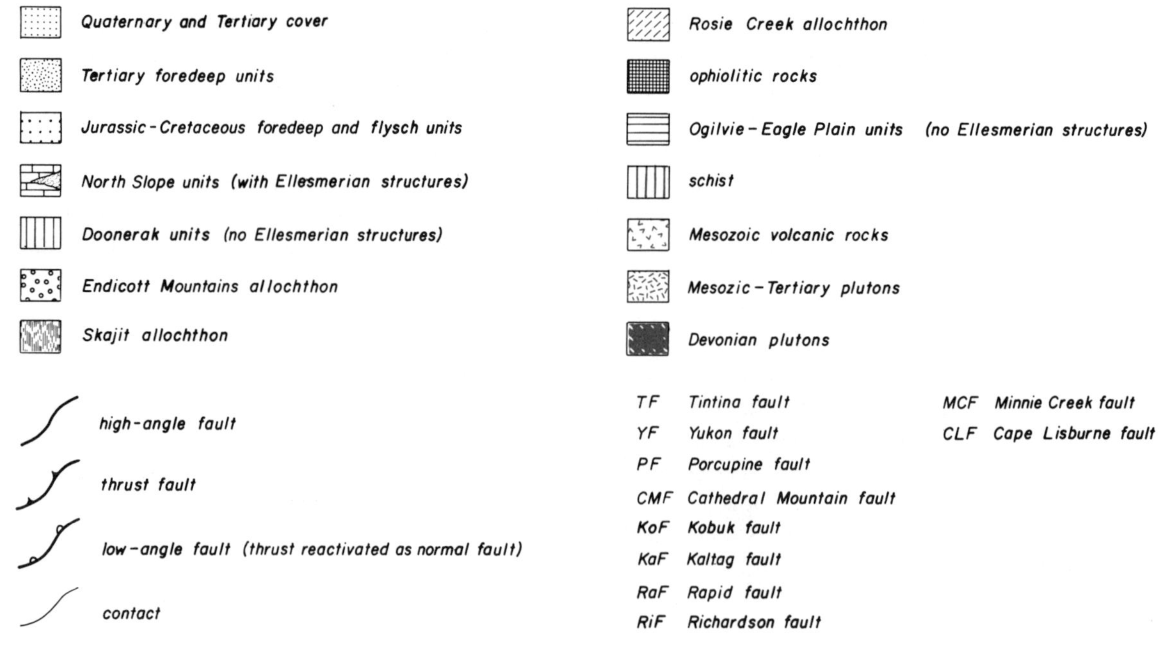
Quaternary and Tertiary cover
Tertiary foredeep units
Jurassic-Cretaceous foredeep and flysch units
North Slope units (with Ellesmerian structures)
Doonerak units (no Ellesmerian structures)
Endicott Mountains allochthon
Skajit allochthon
Rosie Creek allochthon
ophiolitic rocks
Ogilvie-Eagle Plain units (no Ellesmerian structures)
schist
Mesozoic volcanic rocks
Mesozic-Tertiary plutons
Devonian plutons
high-angle fault
thrust fault
low-angle fault (thrust reactivated as normal fault)
contact
TF Tintina fault
YF Yukon fault
PF Porcupine fault
CMF Cathedral Mountain fault
KoF Kobuk fault
KaF Kaltag fault
RaF Rapid fault
RiF Richardson fault
MCF Minnie Creek fault
CLF Cape Lisburne fault

Figure 12. Tectonic map of northern Alaska and northwestern Canada. Major structures of the region consist of the north-directed Brooks Range fold and thrust belt, the Tintina-Kaltag transcurrent fault system (TF and KaF), the Porcupine shear zone (PF), the Yukon thrust belt (YF), the Richardson fault system (RiF), and the Cape Lisburne thrust system (CLF). The Porcupine shear zone (PF) marks a major tectonic boundary and separates Proterozoic to Mesozoic units to the north and south with different structural histories. In the north, Proterozoic to Middle Devonian rocks are deformed in south-directed Ellesmerian structures of Late Devonian age that are crosscut by post-kinematic Devonian plutons. The lower Paleozoic and Proterozoic sequence is deformed together with upper Paleozoic through Cenozoic rocks in superposed north-directed Brookian structures. South of the Porcupine shear zone (PF), Proterozoic through early Tertiary units are deformed in north- and east-vergent structures that developed during protracted contraction beginning in the Late Jurassic to Early Cretaceous and continuing into the Eocene. No mid-Paleozoic Ellesmerian structures are recognized south of the Porcupine fault zone. The only indication of Ellesmerian deformation is the existence of distal sediments of a mid-Paleozoic clastic wedge derived from the north. The Richardson fault system (RiF) also marks a major tectonic boundary and separates rocks deformed in "Laramide" structures to the west from undeformed units of the North American craton to the east. Late Mesozoic to early Tertiary displacement on the Richardson fault consisted of easterly directed thrusting and dextral strike-slip. The northern part of the Richardson fault apparently nucleated on an earlier structure, where it separates lower Paleozoic and Proterozoic units involved in Ellesmerian deformation to the west from undeformed Cambro-Devonian rocks to the east. The Brooks Range fold and thrust belt is composed of seven major structural elements. The North Slope of Arctic Alaska is underlain by a late Mesozoic to Cenozoic foredeep succession formed in response to northerly thrusting of the Brooks Range fold belt. The foredeep succession locally is overthrust by older units of the fold belt but generally resides in the upper plate of a regionally extensive triangle-zone (for reference to triangle-zone see Price, 1981). In the northeastern Brooks Range, pre-foredeep units of the North Slope (Proterozoic through Mesozoic) were thrust north during the early and late Tertiary, and recent seismicity suggests continued activity today. In the central Brooks Range, lower Paleozoic and Precambrian(?) clastic and volcanic rocks form the lower plates of the Doonerak duplex but differ structurally from coeval units in the northeastern Brooks Range by having no penetrative Ellesmerian structures. The Doonerak duplex is thought to have formed synchronously with the structures of the northeastern Brooks Range and is connected by an oblique ramp, whose surface expression is marked by the northeasterly trending boundary between the northeastern Brooks and the foredeep units of the North Slope. The frontal portion of the thrust belt is overlain by the mid-Paleozoic clastic and subordinate carbonate rocks of the Endicott Mountains allochthon. The Endicott Mountains allochthon is structurally overlain by lower Paleozoic to Precambrian(?) metasedimentary and metavolcanic rocks of the Skajit allochthon, slightly metamorphosed Paleozoic and Mesozoic clastic and carbonate rocks of the Rosie Creek allochthon, and high-grade metamorphic rocks of the Schist belt. The structurally highest thrust sheets in the Brooks Range are composed of upper Paleozoic to lower Mesozoic ophiolitic rocks (Angayucham and Tozitna terranes). The structure of the southern Brooks Range is complicated by a major mid-Cretaceous envelopment thrust, the Minnie Creek thrust (MCF), and roughly age-equivalent low-angle normal faults of the Cathedral Mountain fault system (CMF). In the western and central Brooks Range, the Minnie Creek thrust carries rocks of the Schist belt to the north over the southern margin of the Skajit allochthon. To the east, the Minnie Creek thrust cuts upsection and juxtaposes the Rosie Creek and Endicott Mountains allochthons. The mid-Cretaceous Cathedral Mountain fault zone disrupts the earlier contractional structures in down-to-the-south low-angle normal faults. The high-grade metamorphic rocks of the Schist belt of the Brooks Range are correlated with similar metamorphic rocks underlying central Alaska (Seward, Ruby, and Yukon-Tanana terranes). In much of central Alaska, ophiolitic rocks (Angayucham and Tozitna terranes) structurally overlie the high-grade metamorphics with a low-angle structural contact interpreted to be part of a mid-Cretaceous extensional fault system. Dextral transcurrent motion on the Tintina-Kaltag system was coeval and kinematically linked with thrusting in the Brooks Range to the north. Part of the strike-slip component of motion on the Tintina fault was necessarily transformed to thrust displacements in the Brooks Range to accommodate the change in fault trajectory to that of the Kaltag system. The Cape Lisburne thrust system (CLF) carries North Slope units exposed in the far western coastal region of northern Alaska easterly over the foredeep successions. The Cape Lisburne thrust system is interpreted to extend to the south where it carries metamorphic rocks of the Seward Peninsula eastward over the volcanic and clastic units of the Koyukak basin. The age of easterly thrusting is mid-Tertiary and may have resulted from convergence between North America and Siberia.

the base of, or within, the Proterozoic strata and a minor level associated with Cambrian evaporites. The resulting structures involve a thick Proterozoic to mid-Devonian carbonate beam that forms broad box-folds characterized by large flexure-type roll-overs (*Gordey, 1981*; and Plate 7, section B).

(3) In British Columbia, there are several decollement levels—one presumably near the base of the Proterozoic, and others at the base of a condensed Devono-Mississippian shale sequence, at the base of the Triassic, and within the Cretaceous (*Thompson, 1981*).

Implicit in the preceding examples are substantial changes in the basic stratigraphy that occur along the strike of the folded belt. It is important to realize that along the Cordilleran fold belt, stratigraphic trends do not everywhere coincide with structural trends. Nowhere is this better demonstrated than in Alberta where the fold belt diagonally cuts across the Upper Devonian reef trends (Fig. 5). Thus in southern Alberta, the Upper Devonian sequence is hardly separated by decollement levels; whereas, farther north (in the Jasper area) the basinal Devonian shales strongly influence the formation of tight folds and internal zones of flexural-slip (*Mountjoy, 1980*). Comparing three Alberta sections that are only some 80 km apart, we see profound differences in structural styles (see Fig. 11; compare with *Ollerenshaw, 1978*). We see also large differences in structural styles when comparing Wyoming with Montana, Idaho, and Alberta, and with sections across the Mackenzie Mountains and the Brooks Range (compare sections E and F on Plate 7).

To sum up, structural styles in the Cordilleran foreland fold belt directly reflect the distribution and frequency of incompetent levels, or in other words the ductility contrasts, within the Cordilleran passive margin and the overlying foredeep sequence. Typically, evaporites and shale sequences are preferred decollement levels. These often correspond to eustatic lowstands (for the evaporites) and maximum transgressional and associated downlap surfaces (for the shales) associated with eustatic highstands.

Because stratigraphic-facies trends and structural trends cross each other at considerable angles, definitions of structural units based on stratigraphy are not realistic, even in the relatively simple setting of a foreland fold belt. The reader may perhaps consider that the much more complex definition of terranes in the interior Cordillera based on their intrinsic stratigraphy also may be somewhat questionable.

So far we have focused only on thin-skinned deformation limited to sediments of the foreland fold belt. A major question is how the basement becomes involved in the deformation of the foreland fold belt. Moving farther west, the Cordilleran fold belt eventually does involve metamorphic complexes such as the Yukon-Tanana, Cassiar, and Monashee terranes. These metamorphic complexes all appear to have a Precambrian protolith that underwent a complex Mesozoic and Tertiary metamorphic history. It is probable that these terranes represent parts of the distal or more seaward portions of the former passive margin of North America. Thus, the Precambrian basement of the far western Cordillera is involved in the Mesozoic and Cenozoic deformation (Brown and others, 1986; Struik, 1988), which involves large-scale shortening and substantial transcurrent displacement.

Another example of the variation in structural style is the development of basement duplex structures that deform overlying sedimentary thrust sheets (see Plate 7, sections A and E). This style of deformation is observed in the Doonerak window of the central Brooks Range and in the Precambrian Farmington basement complex north of Salt Lake City. The Doonerak duplex is genetically related to "basement-cored" foreland structures of the Romanzof Mountains (northeastern Brooks Range), which formed during the latest stage of deformation of the Arctic margin. Similarly, we view the Farmington complex as representative of Laramide basement deformation of the southern Rocky Mountains.

Southern Rocky Mountains. We now turn to the southern Rocky Mountains of Wyoming, Colorado, Utah, and New Mexico. We include in this discussion the Colorado Plateau with its monoclinal uplifts.

As early as *1906, Darton* mapped overthrusts associated with the basement uplifts of Wyoming, and for some time the nature of these uplifts has been debated. *Thom (1923)* viewed these structures as compressional wedges, and the overthrust nature of the major faults in Wyoming was lucidly discussed by *Berg (1962)*. Compressional interpretations were further modified by *Sales (1968)* and *Lowell (1974)* to include strike-slip components of displacement. An alternative school of thought viewed Wyoming basement structures as vertical uplifts. Theoretical considerations, proposed by *Sanford (1959)* and further developed by others (*Prucha and others, 1965*; Stearns, 1978; *Couples and Stearns, 1978*), led to the popular view that in essense the Wyoming structures represented vertical uplifts bounded by "upthrusts."

The discussion was resolved in favor of regional compression when industry-produced seismic-reflection profiles were published (Gries, 1983; *Stone, 1985*; Gries and Dyer, 1985). A crustal line obtained by COCORP across the Wind River Mountains clearly revealed shear zones extending well into the lower crust. The shear zones are imaged as discontinuous reflectors, which perhaps correspond to mylonites (Smithson and others, 1979; *Brewer and others, 1980*; *Sharry and others, 1986*). We conclude that the southern Rocky Mountains are compressional basement-involved structures.

Sales (1968) replicated much of what later was demonstrated on seismic-reflection profiles with some ingenious plaster model experiments. He essentially explained the southern Canadian Rocky Mountains as a compressive system that was modified by a superposed left-lateral shear couple. Brown (1987, *1989*) gives an in-depth discussion of the structural problems associated with this tectonic style of deformation. He concludes that out-of-the-basin vergence in Wyoming suggests northeast-southwest–directed contraction from 80 to 40 Ma.

Our map (Fig. 13) and the cross section (Plate 7, section G) sum up the essence of the tectonics of the southern Rocky Mountains. Simply stated, basement uplifts are bound by medium-angle

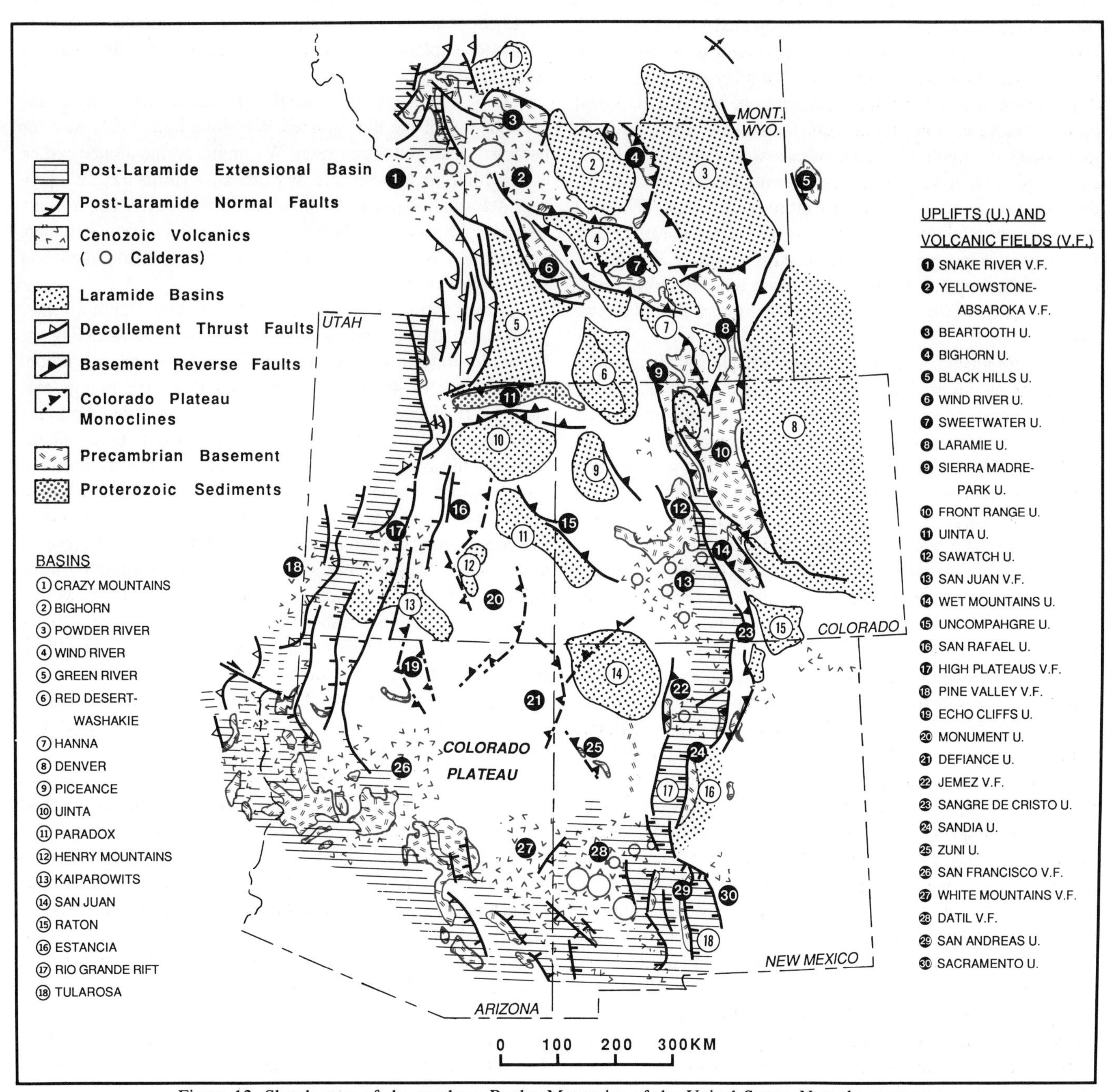

Figure 13. Sketch map of the southern Rocky Mountains of the United States. Note the contrast between thin-skinned decollements (open triangle) in the Wyoming-Wasatch thrust belts and the basement-involved thrusts (black triangle) of the Colorado-Wyoming Rocky Mountain thrust belt. Laramide basins are superposed on the Cretaceous Rocky Mountain foredeep and are filled with Paleogene sediments. The formation of post-Laramide extensional half-graben systems follows the Paleocene to Eocene individualization of the Laramide basins.

(25 to 35°) reverse faults. Basement uplifts are literally ramped up and often have subsidiary sedimentary decollement features (*Ouellette and Boucher, 1983*). Major uplifted blocks are often bound by conjugate sets of thrust faults, leading to the formation of "floating" basement wedges. In a number of cases, as the displacement across a thrust increases on one side of a basement uplift, it decreases along its conjugate fault on the other side of the same basement uplift. Conspicuous east-west–trending fault systems suggest an oblique or strike-slip component of motion, but this assertion needs to be defined more convincingly. The best examples are sections across the Uinta Mountains, east of Salt Lake City, where seismic data combined with surface and subsurface geology suggest a Paleogene inversion of a Proterozoic half-graben system (Gries, 1983; *Clement, 1983*; *Bruhn and others, 1986*).

In our judgement, the basement-cored uplifts of the southern Rocky Mountains are best explained within the context of intracrustal decoupling levels, including one major decoupling level within the middle or lower crust. While such a basal decoupling level at this time is still inferred, all geophysical data so far suggest that the mantle is not involved in the basement uplifts. No doubt better geophysical crustal resolution is required to define any hypothetical decoupling level within the lower crust.

Among the easternmost outliers of the Rocky Mountains, the most important are the Black Hills of South Dakota and the Cedar Creek and Nesson anticlines of the Williston Basin. It is important to recognize that all these features are "Laramide" anticlines; meaning they were formed during the early Paleogene and are coeval with most other basement uplifts of the southern Rocky Mountains. The Black Hills appear to be a simple domal uplift, but on closer inspection, particularly of the western flank, are characterized by elongated monoclines. These, in our view, mask deep-seated west-verging reverse faults. The work of *Clement (1986)* and *Petersen and others (1985)*, in particular, clearly shows a Paleozoic ancestry for the Cedar Creek anticline of the Williston basin. Thus, our postulated regional decollement at the base of the lower crust may well extend into the Williston Basin, about 600 km beyond the margin of the thin-skinned Montana and Wyoming foreland folded belt (see Plates 5A and 5B section D).

Some authors argue that the diversity of trends in the southern Rocky Mountains suggests that a simple southwest-northeast compression is insufficient to explain the variability in structural trends. Together with others, we feel that much of the variability in these trends may be due to "pre-existing zones of weakness." Of course, these always tend to be somewhat mysterious, but we would like to reiterate the observation that at least in parts of the southern Rocky Mountains, we know that northeast-southwest–trending basement uplifts and basins were formed during the Pennsylvanian. We can equally well relate the east-west–striking Uinta Mountains to a Proterozoic extensional system. Gries (1983) made a careful study of the age of thrusting and concomitant basin subsidence and concluded that the diversity of structural trends was due to progressive changes in the direction of compression from east-west during the Late Cretaceous, to southwest-northeast during the Paleocene, to north-south during the Eocene. The observations are convincing, but we still lack an adequate explanation for the change in the direction of compression.

Our sections (Plate 7, sections F and G) also contrast the deformation of the thin-skinned Wyoming folded belt with the basement-involved structures of Wyoming. As mentioned earlier, even within the thin-skinned Wyoming overthrust belt, a Paleocene deformation phase also involves the basement (the Farmington complex north of Salt Lake City). In essence, basement deformation is superposed and deforms earlier and shallower thin-skinned overthrusts.

Aside from the structural problem, many authors have pointed out that the southern Rocky Mountains, including the Colorado Plateau, are characterized by an unusually thick continental crust of 45 to 50 km and a rather high topographic elevation (in excess of 2 km). Following a number of authors and, more recently, Bird (*1984,* 1988), it is reasonable to think that the marine and coastal deposits of the Mesozoic suggest a crustal thickness on the order of 35 km prior to the Laramide deformation. A basement-involved shortening during Late Cretaceous–Eocene of about 15 percent could not thicken the crust from 35 km to 45 or 50 km. Following unsuccessful attempts by some authors to tie the "Laramide" deformation of the Rocky Mountains to plate activity farther west, Lipman and others (1971), Snyder and others (1976), and Dickinson and Snyder (1978) related the deformation in the southern Rockies to the flattening of a subducted oceanic slab. The region underlain by the shallow slab was limited to a sector of the Cordillera characterized by a gap in the otherwise continuous volcanic belt.

Compilation of igneous radiometric dates indeed reveals such a gap for the period of 74 to about 40 Ma in the segment that initially extended from Idaho into northern Arizona. *Lowell (1974)* argued that a subhorizontal lithospheric slab would have a low density and hence cause buoyancy of the crust (but, alas, no thickening!); Cross and Pilger (1978) suggested a heavy slab to explain substantial subsidence increases in the Upper Cretaceous foredeep sequence (but this leaves basement uplifts unexplained!). Dickinson and Snyder (1978) suggest that the shear stress between the slab and the overlying North American lithosphere may be responsible for the Laramide compression. Bird (*1984,* 1988) modeled the situation using finite-element techniques. He suggested that lower crust flow from west to east is caused by shear traction of the underlying subhorizontal subducted oceanic Farallon slab, leading to the formation of the thick crust of the southern Rocky Mountains. Subsequent steepening and westward migration of the slab hinge would leave the Rocky Mountains and the Basin and Range crust directly exposed to the inflowing hot asthenosphere, leading to thermal uplift and extension after 40 Ma (but that part of the model requires stripping of the underlying lithospheric mantle, a process that is inconsistent with isotopic data from Cenozoic volcanics, which indicate the preservation of lithospheric mantle beneath most of the Cordillera). So we conclude that none of the models so far proposed can satisfactorily explain the thick crust underlying the southern Rocky Mountains.

Sedimentary basins of the southern Rocky Mountains. The Laramide basement uplifts of the southern Rockies disrupt the Cretaceous foredeep and segment it into a number of dominantly fluvio-lacustrine basins, which all acquired their individuality during the latest Cretaceous to Eocene (Gries, 1983; Dickinson and others, 1988). The basins in the north ceased to be active depocenters in the Eocene, and those in the south in the Miocene (Dickinson and others, 1988). *Hagen and others (1985)* suggest that the Early Cretaceous to Eocene subsidence of these basins was due primarily to tectonic loading by adjacent thrust sheets. The topographic expression of this region during this time is generally thought to be relatively close to sea level. Several of the basins, in particular the Powder River, Denver, Raton, and San Juan basins (Fig. 13), are the more important "perimeter" basins (usage of Dickinson and others, 1988) with a drainage toward the Great Plains and eventually to the Gulf of Mexico (*Winker, 1982*). In a sense, they are the final expression of the former Cretaceous interior seaway.

More internal Laramide basins (i.e., Dickinson and others' ponded and axial basins) are more confined and have a drainage toward the Great Basin and eventually to the Pacific Northwest. Paleocene lake deposits outcrop in the Great Basin (*Fouch, 1979*; *Solomon and others, 1979*), and it is plausible that the distribution of these lake beds may be quite widespread in the subsurface. The tectonic origin of these internal basins remains obscure; it is not clear whether they have an extensional or compressional origin. In any event, however, these basins appear in a setting that is different from the adjacent Rocky Mountain basins.

We agree with Dickinson and others (1988) that there is a lack of a significant topographic expression related to regional contraction during the early Tertiary in the U.S. Cordillera. Unlike the topographic highs in the Andean system of South America or the Tibetan Plateau, it appears that no such topography was formed in the conterminous United States.

We have not included in our description of the "Laramide" basins additional comments on their earlier evolution. There is evidence that all southern Rocky Mountain basins went through a Paleozoic cratonic platform phase, some of them had an earlier Pennsylvanian phase tied to the ancestral Rockies, and all basins had a Cretaceous foredeep phase. The reader is referred to our earlier brief description of the ancestral Rocky Mountains and to the chapter on Phanerozoic Basins of North America (Bally, this volume). For a more complete description, refer to the spectacular *Geological Atlas of the Rocky Mountain Region* (Mallory, 1972) and to Peterson (1986) and Baars and others (1988).

Dating deformation in the Cordilleran foreland fold belt. The progressive deformation of Rocky Mountain decollement systems is often rather loosely bracketed. Perhaps the best studies have been made in the Wyoming Rocky Mountains where *Armstrong and Oriel (1965)* and Royse and others (1975) and, more recently, Wiltschko and Dorr (1983) made a careful evaluation of stratigraphic data that involve onlap relations on thrust sheets, and the influx and distribution of coarse clastics.

All these authors agree that there is an overall progression in thrust displacement from west to east. There is some debate as to the beginning of the thrusting in Wyoming, which *Armstrong and Oriel (1965)* originally viewed as part of a progression that started with the Paleozoic Antler orogeny. Royse and others (1975) as well as Wiltschko and Dorr (1983) visualize the initiation of thrusting in the Late Jurassic to Early Cretaceous, while *Heller and others (1986)* propose a mid-Cretaceous start. Subsequently, deformation progressed eastward, although perhaps at different rates, until the early Eocene. Only the later compressional phases involved the basement of the southern Rocky Mountains. The earliest weak indications for foreland basement uplift are in the uppermost Cretaceous, with most of the deformation occurring during the Paleocene and Eocene. Brown (1987, *1989*) suggested that the Laramide basement deformation began in the west during the Campanian and moved northeastward with maximum rates of deformation in the Wind River Mountains during Maastrichtian time and the Bighorn Range to the east during Paleocene and Eocene time.

Many authors would like to rigorously separate a pre–Late Cretaceous Sevier orogeny (*Armstrong, 1968*) from a Late Cretaceous–early Tertiary Laramide orogeny. We doubt that a distinct pre–Upper Cretaceous hiatus in the kinematic progression can be reliably established. If by "Laramide" one means a Late Cretaceous to Eocene structural regime, then much of the Canadian Rockies and the Sierra Madre Oriental of Mexico is "Laramide." If, instead, one prefers to limit the term to a basement-involved structural style, then the term should not be applied outside the southern Rocky Mountains. There is terminological confusion, but there is little doubt that thin-skinned deformation in Wyoming, Montana, Alberta, and Mexico for a great part is coeval with basement deformation in the southern Rockies. Consequently, whatever the model chosen to explain the special situation of the southern Rockies, one has to provide a reason for the absence of coeval basement-involved thrust faulting in the foreland of the Canadian Cordillera and the Mexican Cordillera.

Elsewhere along the foreland fold belt, the age of deformation is not nearly as well constrained as in Wyoming. Farther south in the Wasatch (Utah) segment, east-directed thrusting may be tracked across the foreland by synorogenic sediments of mid-Cretaceous to late Paleocene age (Villien and Kligfield, 1986). In the western hinterland of the fold belt, the Great Basin, thrusting involves Proterozoic and younger rocks and began as early as the mid- to Late Jurassic (*Allmendinger and Jordan, 1981*; Miller and others, 1988). In the central part of the Basin and Range, mid- to Late Jurassic thrusting is recognized in the Eureka thrust belt (Speed and others, 1988), but unlike the regions to the east, the vergence of structures in this belt is to the west or west-northwest (Miller and others, 1988; Snoke and Miller, 1988). Farther west, in the region immediately east of the Sierra Nevada, mid- to Late Jurassic to mid-Cretaceous thrusting formed the

Luning-Fencemaker belt, which is characterized by southeasterly tectonic transport (Oldow, 1983, 1984). Thus, the hinterland of the Sevier thrust system was active from the mid-Jurassic to the mid-Cretaceous in belts of opposed vergence. Note also that transport directions are not parallel. Rather, they record a progressive change from southeast in the Luning-Fencemaker belt, to west or northwest in the Eureka belt of central Nevada, to essentially east in the Wyoming-Utah thrust belt. It is conceivable that the change in transport direction in the thrust belts may be related to changes in the relative plate motion between North America and the Pacific basin.

Going farther north in the Alberta and British Columbia Rockies, the development of the foredeep reflects a beginning of the deformation in the mid–Late Jurassic (Bally and others, 1966; *Price and Mountjoy, 1970*; *Porter and others, 1982*). A substantial amount, probably greater than 40 percent, of a total of 150 to 200 km of the shortening is Cenozoic in age. Paleocene strata are involved in the deformation of the Alberta foothills. Thus, based on a rather crude resolution, we conclude that the Canadian Rocky Mountains were formed between mid-Jurassic and Eocene times.

Thrusting in the Mackenzie and Ogilvie Mountains occurred first in the interior fold belt during Late Jurassic to Early Cretaceous; prior to the intrusion of mid-Cretaceous, post-kinematic granitoids (*Gordey and Thompson, 1989*; *Cook, 1989*). However, as in the southern Rocky Mountains, deformation continued into the Eocene in the eastern region of the Mackenzie Mountains (*Cook, 1989*).

In the Brooks Range of northern Alaska, ophiolitic rocks of the highest allochthon were emplaced in the Middle to Late Jurassic (*Wirth and others, 1986*; *Mayfield and others, 1983*). The schists of the southern Brooks Range and related rocks of the Seward Peninsula underwent a complex metamorphic history, with thermal peaks in the Late Jurassic and mid-Cretaceous (Armstrong and others, 1986; *Gottschalk, 1987*). The metamorphic rocks south of the Koyukuk basin (the Ruby terrane of Jones and others, 1987) generally yielded mid-Cretaceous K/Ar ages, but these may only indicate uplift and cooling periods. Mid-Cretaceous granitoid plutons intrude the Ruby metamorphic rocks and are post-kinematic.

Progressive north-directed thrusting of Precambrian(?), Paleozoic, and Mesozoic rocks of the Brooks Range resulted in the filling of a Cretaceous to early Tertiary foredeep that underlies the North Slope. Thrusting continued into the Eocene and, based on relations in the Romanzof and British Mountains (*Leffingwell, 1919*; *Kelley and Molenaar, 1985*; *Leiggi and Russell, 1985*; Leiggi, 1987; Oldow and others, 1987b) and as shown on seismic-reflection profiles of the Beaufort Sea (Grantz and May, 1983), continued through the Pliocene. Recent earthquakes suggest that deformation is continuing today (Estabrook and others, 1988).

In summary, the inception of the foredeep typically occurred during the Middle to Late Jurassic, and much of the overthrusting was finished by the end of Eocene time. The one conspicuous exception is the Neogene Beaufort fold belt to the north of the British and Romanzof Mountains, which is still being deformed today. Cretaceous metamorphic dates and intrusions in the interior Cordillera date the uplift in the interior portion of the Rocky Mountains. Finally, basement-involved overthrusting of the southern Rocky Mountains occurred during Late Cretaceous–Eocene time, and is coeval in part with much of the thin-skinned deformation occurring all along the foreland fold belt.

Structure and kinematics of the Transpressional complex

The Central, Columbia, and Coastal tectonic belts of the Transpressional complex of the Cordillera have undergone large transcurrent displacements and are bound by long trace-length faults (Fig. 10). The tectonic belts are defined on the basis of their inferred displacement histories (outlined above) for the past 160 m.y. The bounding fault systems are subparallel to the axis of the Cordillera and are informally termed, from east to west, the Internal, Central, and External faults.

Central belt. In Canada, the Central belt (Fig. 10) consists mainly of the Yukon-Tanana, Slide Mountain, and Cassiar terranes. A fragment of the Quesnellia terrane (Monger and Berg, 1987) exposed east of the Teslin fault is also included in the belt. In Alaska, the belt consists of the Yukon-Tanana terrane, parts of the Nixon Fork and Ruby terranes, and part of a Jurassic arc/ophiolite assemblage (parts of the latter two are also included in the foreland fold belt). In the conterminous United States, the Central belt consists of the Blue Mountains province in Oregon, the Klamath Mountains, and the Sierra Nevada.

Mesozoic deformation in the Yukon-Tanana, Slide Mountain, and Cassiar terranes of northwestern Canada is dominated by northeasterly directed shortening. Within the Cassiar terrane, northeasterly-directed thrusting caused a cumulative shortening of between 80 and 135 km (*Tempelman-Kluit, 1989a*). The Yukon-Tanana terrane experienced intense dynamothermal metamorphism with the formation of mylonitic to blastomylonitic fabrics, which locally dip southwesterly and have a strong lineation generally trending easterly (*Tempelman-Kluit, 1989b*). The penetrative strain in the Yukon-Tanana terrane differs from the more heterogeneous strain characterized by folds and thrusts in the underlying Cassiar and overlying Slide Mountain terranes. The Slide Mountain exhibits northeasterly directed folds and thrusts and associated low-grade metamorphism. In the western part of the belt, rocks of the Yukon-Tanana and Slide Mountain terranes are deformed ductilely. As summarized in Hansen (1988), the structures are mylonites with shallow southwesterly dips and two lineations. The first lineation, where not reoriented by the later deformation, has a westerly trending, down-dip orientation and exhibits both normal and reverse senses of shear. The superposed lineation is subhorizontal and indicates dextral motion. Dynamothermal metamorphism is dated isotopically by K-Ar as between 215 to 160 Ma (*Tempelman-Kluit, 1989b*) and was completed in late Early to Middle Jurassic time (Hansen, 1988). During the mid-Jurassic to mid-Cretaceous, the rocks were imbricated and transported to the northeast (Hansen, 1988; *Tempelman-Kluit, 1989b*). Metamorphic rocks reaching amphibolite grade, and locally occurring eclogite and blueschist mineralogy, indicate high-pressure conditions dated by K-Ar and Rb-Sr as between 246 and 258 Ma (*Tempelman-Kluit, 1989b*).

The structural history of the Central belt is less well known in Alaska. The rocks of the Yukon-Tanana terrane in Alaska were deformed, metamorphosed, and intruded by granitoid plutons during the Late Triassic to Early Jurassic and mid-Cretaceous. The Late Triassic to Early Jurassic event involves thrusting caused by east-west contraction. The Cretaceous event is characterized by northeast-directed thrusting in eastern Alaska; this direction apparently changes to the north and northwest in central Alaska (e.g., *Foster and others, 1983*; *Chapman and others, 1971, 1982*), but it is not clear if the change is primary or due to later deformation.

The contact between the Yukon-Tanana and the Nixon Fork terranes is not exposed but probably represents a major tectonic boundary. Structural juxtaposition may explain the profound differences in metamorphic grade of the partially coeval rocks of the two terranes, which now lie within a few kilometers of one another. The age of structural juxtaposition is unclear, but apparently post-dates deposition of fossiliferous Cretaceous sedimentary rocks of the Nixon Fork (Jones and others, 1987).

Dynamothermal metamorphism of the Ruby terrane is remarkably similar to that of the Schist belt of the southern Brooks Range and the metamorphics of the Seward Peninsula. On this basis, we speculate that they have a related origin with peak metamorphic conditions occurring in the Late Jurassic and uplift in the mid-Cretaceous. Our proposed linkage of the metamorphic rocks is strengthened by the common structural association of ophiolitic sheets (Angayucham and Tozitna terranes) structurally overlying the Ruby and Schist belt metamorphics in interior Alaska.

Aside from the obvious significance of this proposed tie between rocks of the Central belt and those of North American affinity in the foreland fold belt (Brooks Range), there is a peculiar structural relationship that both share. In much of the southern Brooks Range, a younger-on-older and low-metamorphic-grade-over-high-metamorphic-grade structural configuration is observed. This structural geometry has been attributed to low-angle normal faulting (Gottschalk and Oldow, 1988). Estimates of metamorphic conditions in the upper and lower sheets indicate the omission of at least 10 km of structural section across the contact. The proposed faults were active in the mid-Cretaceous, more or less simultaneously with the onset of sediments in the Koyukuk basin.

Although comparable detailed structural and metamorphic studies have not been completed in the Ruby terrane of the Central belt, similar relations exist. Relatively unmetamorphosed ophiolite rocks directly overlie high-grade metamorphics. It is obvious that rocks of intermediate metamorphic grade are absent.

This structural relationship is widespread (Fig. 12) and to our knowledge has not been adequately addressed in tectonic models. In the likelihood that preliminary studies are corroborated by later work, this regional relationship can be explained by very different mechanisms involving contraction or extensional tectonism. In a contractional scenario, a structural history like that posed in the conceptual model of *Roeder (1980)* can be invoked. The model relies on out-of-sequence thrusts rooted in a shallower structural level than the regional decollement. During emplacement, the out-of-sequence thrust decapitates previously emplaced schistose rocks of the lower plate. Decapitation would result in the partial removal of structurally intervening units, juxtaposing younger low-grade metamorphic rocks over older high-grade metamorphics. Although this mechanism could produce the relations observed, many detailed field studies in the southern Cordillera have clearly demonstrated that younger-over-older and low-grade-over-high-grade structural relations are products of extensional tectonism (e.g., Crittenden and others, 1980). With this in mind, and considering the relations in the southern Brooks Range, we speculate that the widespread omission of structural section in the Central belt may be caused by extension, presumably on low-angle normal faults. Cross-cutting relations by Late Cretaceous plutons indicate that the structural juxtaposition occurred in the Early to mid-Cretaceous.

In the southern extension of the Central belt in the conterminous United States, we correlate the Wallowa, Baker, and Olds Ferry terranes of the Blue Mountains region in northeastern Oregon with the Stikinia, Cache Creek, and Quesnellia terranes in British Columbia, respectively. However, we assigned the latter to the Columbia belt, and the rocks of the Blue Mountains province to the Central belt. The primary reason for this is that the Blue Mountains have not undergone large latitudinal translation since the Late Triassic (*Hillhouse and others, 1982*), although structural data indicate that some southward displacements have occurred in Late Triassic and Early Jurassic time (Avé Lallemant and others, 1985; Avé Lallemant, 1989). Furthermore, the Blue Mountains province was juxtaposed with the North American continent in the mid-Cretaceous (Lund and Snee, 1988; Snee and others, 1989), whence Stikinia, Cache Creek, and Quesnellia of the Columbia belt started their northward trek from Baja California (Umhoefer, 1987; Avé Lallemant and Oldow, 1988).

Paleomagnetic studies (*Wilson and Cox, 1980*; *Hillhouse and others, 1982*) show that northeastern Oregon has rotated approximately 65° clockwise since the Early Cretaceous. Part of the rotation has been related to the post-Eocene extension of the Great Basin, but part may be related to collision and emplacement of the Blue Mountains province on North America. Restored, most structural elements in the Blue Mountains trend northwest-southeast, similar to coeval structures in the Klamath Mountains and the Sierra Nevada (Oldow and others, 1984). Late Triassic to Early Jurassic structures in the mélange of the Baker terrane and overlying fore-arc basin sediments (*Dickinson, 1979a*) indicate southwesterly thrusting or northeasterly subduction (after rotation is restored). Amalgamation of the three terranes occurred in latest Jurassic time: rocks of the Baker terrane and overlying Jurassic clastics were thrust eastward over the Olds

Ferry terrane (*Avé Lallemant, 1983*) and westward over the Wallowa terrane (Avé Lallemant, 1989).

In the Klamath Mountains and Sierra Nevada, Mesozoic deformation is dominated by polyphase northwesterly trending folds and associated southwesterly vergent thrust faults. Superposed structures are generally coaxial and parallel the trend of the magmatic arc system. The near coaxiality of the structures has been the source of substantial debate in deducing the number and timing of deformational events in the region. Segregation of particular phases of deformation is often difficult due to the complexity of structural relations and inadequate age control. Where the kinematic relations of plutons, ages of deformed rocks, and unconformable relations are well established, however, several episodes of Jurassic and Early Cretaceous structures are documented (Wright, 1982; Wright and Fahan, 1988; Saleeby and others, 1982; Schweickert and others, 1984, 1988; *Patterson and others, 1987*; *Tobisch and Fiske, 1976*; *Sharp, 1988*).

We assign the Franciscan complex to the Central belt as well, although parts of it may have to be reassigned ultimately to the Columbia belt (Fig. 10). Although commonly perceived as a chaotic assemblage of rocks, the Franciscan complex more nearly resembles conventional fold and thrust belts or accretionary prisms. In a way similar to that proposed by *Suppe (1973)* and *Worrall (1981)*, the Franciscan is composed of three westerly vergent allochthons each of which are composed of numerous imbricate sheets. Protolith and metamorphic ages (Blake and others, 1988; Mattinson, 1988) decrease westward and are consistent with a model of east-directed underthrusting or subduction (*Cloos, 1985*) from 165 to 90 Ma. Major dextral displacements occurred along north-northwest–striking transcurrent faults (*Alvarez and others, 1980*; *Tarduno and others, 1986*). Simultaneously, old low-angle thrust faults were reactivated as low-angle normal faults (*Jayko and others, 1987*), resulting in tectonic denudation and exposure of high P/T metamorphic rocks, possibly due to a mechanism similar to that proposed by *Platt (1986)*. At about 50 Ma, northward translation of the Franciscan complex was terminated, and normal subduction resulted until the late Neogene when the San Andreas fault system was established.

Columbia belt. The main components of the Columbia belt (Fig. 10) in Canada are the Stikinia and Quesnellia terranes, the Monashee complex, and parts (south of the Chatham Strait fault) of the Wrangellia and Alexander terranes (Superterranes I and II of Monger and others, 1982). This belt may not extend into Alaska and apparently extends into the conterminous United States only as far south as central Washington.

The Columbia belt stretches from the present plate boundary offshore of Vancouver Island eastward to its tentatively placed boundary at the western flank of the Purcell Mountains. The main structures of the Columbia belt verge westerly in the west and easterly in the east. However, oppositely vergent structures occur both in the east and west. Where timing relations are established, structures range in age from the Middle Jurassic through the Late Cretaceous into the early Tertiary. Structures in the central and eastern part of the belt are generally older than those in the vicinity of the Coast Plutonic complex in the west. Although poorly constrained, timing relations suggest that the development of structures in the Coast Plutonic complex corresponds in age to the development of the foreland fold and thrust belt. The age of deformation appears to decrease more-or-less symmetrically outward from the center of the Columbia belt.

In the east, Proterozoic to Middle Jurassic rocks are deformed in superposed northeasterly and southwesterly vergent structures associated with large-scale crustal shortening (*Simony, 1989*; *Struik and others, 1989*; *Brown, 1981*; Brown and others, 1986, *1989*; *Fyles and Hoy, 1989*). Regional structures plunge northwest and southeast, exposing rocks deformed at depths as great as 25 km. Deep structures associated with high-grade metamorphism, such as the internal nappes of the Selkirk allochthon and the Monashee complex, pass upward into more brittle regimes characterized by flexural-slip folds and thrust faults (Murphy, 1987; *Struik and others, 1989*). Shortening is interpreted as related to easterly directed crustal duplexing during the Middle Jurassic to Early Cretaceous and is estimated to be on the order of 200 km (Brown and others, 1986).

In the central Columbia belt, the intensity of deformation and associated metamorphism is greatly reduced. Rocks of Stikinia and Quesnellia rarely achieve middle greenschist facies, and structures characteristically are southwesterly vergent folds and thrusts (*Gabrielse, 1989a, 1989b*; *Woodsworth, 1989*; *Woodsworth and Monger, 1989*; *Gabrielse and Mansy, 1989*). Rocks of the Bowser basin, which constitute a clastic wedge that prograded southwesterly over Stikinia beginning in the Middle Jurassic, are deformed in northeast-vergent structures formed during the Late Cretaceous. The rocks were never deeply buried, and in the early Tertiary they were the source of clastics shed to the northeast. The northeasterly directed structures are related to the uplift of the Coast Plutonic complex. As the Coast Plutonic complex to the west is approached, structures become more ductile. Near the eastern flank of the Coast Plutonic complex, deformation is Late Cretaceous or younger (*Woodsworth, 1989*), and mylonitic rocks are thrust easterly over low-grade rocks of the central Columbia belt.

Relations within the Coast Plutonic complex are poorly understood. In the westerly parts of the complex, ductile and brittle structures verge westerly; whereas those along the eastern flank verge easterly (*Woodsworth, 1989*). In the central Coast Plutonic complex, deformation was accompanied by high-grade metamorphic conditions of approximately 8 kb and 625°C (*Crawford and Hollister, 1982*). Mid- to Late Cretaceous plutons post-date peak metamorphism (Woodsworth and others, 1983; *Woodsworth and others, 1989*).

In the metamorphic core of the Cascade Mountains, polyphase deformation is associated with structures that now are essentially vertical but which originally may have been easterly dipping thrust faults (*Lowes, 1972*; *Brown, 1988*). Deformation is probably of mid-Cretaceous to early Tertiary age (Cowan and Bruhn, 1989). Westerly directed thrusts and associated folds compose the western flank of the Cascades and may record Cretaceous closure of oceanic or marginal basins. The San Juan Islands are composed of thrust imbricates that overlie Wrangellia, which constitutes much of Vancouver Island to the west. Emplacement of these thrusts post-dates depositions of late Albian rocks but predates Upper Santonian strata, which contain clasts of the San Juan imbricates (Brandon and others, 1988; Cowan and Bruhn, 1989). To the east of the Cascades, the Tyaughton-Methow trough is composed of clastics derived from a volcanic and plutonic complex lying to the northeast. Sediments were shed from the northeast in the Jurassic through the Neocomian. In the Albian-Cenomanian, a westerly source of chert, shale, and phyllite developed. On the eastern flank of the Cascades, this change in sedimentary source region was followed by the development of easterly overturned folds and west-dipping reverse faults that are crosscut by plutons dated by K/Ar at 84 Ma (*Monger, 1989*).

Coastal belt. The Coastal belt (Fig. 10) occurs only in northern British Columbia and in Alaska. It is dominated by rocks of several terranes: Wrangellia, Alexander, Peninsular, Chugach, Prince William, Nixon Fork, and Jurassic volcanics that are included as part of our Ruby-Koyukuk succession (Plate 5A). In the western part of the Coastal belt, relations are unclear. Rocks of the Nixon Fork terrane are exposed and may be in structural contact with the Peninsular terrane (Jones and others, 1987), but the contact is obscured by intensely deformed Jurassic and Cretaceous flysch units. Jurassic volcanic and associated epiclastic rocks are also in evidence west of the Nixon Fork exposures. The Jurassic units are probably part of an arc assemblage and are included as part of the Ruby-Koyukuk assemblage. As elsewhere, the contact is covered but probably is structural with the underlying Nixon Fork and/or Peninsular terranes.

Transcurrent displacements. The existence of large-scale transcurrent motion in parts of the Cordillera is well entrenched in the literature, but substantial disagreement exists over estimates of the magnitude. It is generally accepted that rocks of the foreland fold belt have experienced little transcurrent displacement with respect to the North American craton. Rocks of the Transpressional complex, on the other hand, have experienced significant transcurrent displacements with respect to the North American foreland. The Central belt has undergone northerly displacements on the order of several hundreds of kilometers as deduced from lithologic and paleontologic data, which agree well with the results of paleomagnetic studies. The Columbia and Coastal belts have also undergone large transcurrent displacements, but displacement estimates based on geological data are substantially less, commonly by an order of magnitude, than those apparently required by the paleomagnetic data. In the following sections, we discuss the estimates of transcurrent displacement based on geological, paleontological, and paleomagnetic data.

Geologic constraints: Internal fault system. Within the Canadian Cordillera, the northern part of the Internal fault system is composed of the Tintina fault and the Northern Rocky Mountain trench. These faults have a remarkably well-defined physiographic expression that can be traced for over 1,500 km. Right-lateral displacements of 400 to 500 km were originally suggested by *Roddick (1967)* and Tempelman-Kluit (*1976,* 1979). Recently, estimates have been expanded to greater than 900 km on the basis of offsets of plutons, metamorphic terranes, and facies of coeval sedimentary rocks (Gabrielse, 1985). The onset of displacement is less well constrained than the magnitude; motion may have begun as early as the Jurassic. The best evidence, however, indicates dextral transcurrent motion from the mid-Cretaceous to the Eocene–Oligocene (Gabrielse, 1985). Recent seismic activity along the northern Tintina fault in Alaska, however, indicates that displacements, thought to be occurring at a diminished rate, have continued through the Tertiary into the Quaternary (Estabrook and others, 1988).

In Alaska, the northern extension of the Tintina fault is controversial. Variously, it has been argued to be part of the Kobuk fault system, which parallels the southern boundary of the Brooks Range, or to be continuous with and to curve into the southwesterly trending array of faults loosely referred to here as the Kaltag fault system (Fig. 12; Plate 5A). Because there appears to be a link between the southern Brooks Range and the terranes underlying and flanking the Koyukuk basin, we doubt that the structural discontinuity represented by the Kobuk fault system is sufficient to accommodate the dextral displacements recorded on the Tintina fault in Canada. Therefore, we prefer the Kaltag fault system as the primary continuation of the Tintina but do not discount the possibility that part of the motion is accommodated by the Kobuk. There is a remarkable similarity in the trace morphology of the Tintina-Kaltag system and that observed in the Denali and Border Range–Castle Mountain faults to the south. The similarity in morphology may not be coincidental and possibly reflects the position of an important lithospheric boundary.

Given that the displacement, or some substantial part of the dextral transcurrent offset, on the Tintina continues into the Kaltag system, the change in the fault trajectory requires reordering of the dip-slip and strike-slip components of motion. The Kaltag fault has a reported 110 km of right-lateral displacement since the mid-Cretaceous (*Patton and Hoare, 1965*). For compatibility with the displacement on the Tintina fault, substantially greater strike-slip motion is required for the Kaltag fault but is as yet unconfirmed. In addition, due to the bend in fault orientation, a substantial component of thrust motion is expected to be transferred to the Brooks Range thrust belt to the north.

In the conterminous United States, the western margin of the foreland fold belt is marked by the Pine Nut fault system. The Pine Nut fault is a major transpressional structure that served as the western boundary of the mid- to Late Jurassic to Early Cretaceous Luning-Fencemaker thrust belt of the western Great Basin (Oldow, 1983, 1984a) and separates the thrust belt from the Sierra Nevada province to the west. The Pine Nut fault had an early history of large (on the order of 500 to 700 km) left-lateral displacement in the Jurassic and Early Cretaceous. After emplacement of mid-Cretaceous plutons, different strands of the fault system served as the locus of northward transport of the Sierra Nevada (Frei and others, 1984; Frei, 1986), leaving behind displaced assemblages of the Mesozoic marine province (Pine Nut assemblage of Oldow, 1984a) carried south during earlier motion along the fault system.

Geologic constraints: Central fault system. Definition of the structural boundary between the Central and Columbia belts is difficult. Justification for its existence is drawn primarily from paleomagnetic data and the necessity of juxtaposing far-traveled components of the Cordillera with those that ostensibly did not experience displacements resolvable with paleomagnetic techniques.

In northern British Columbia and southwestern Yukon Territory, the Teslin fault system (sensu lato) and parts of the Pinchi fault (Fig. 3) are the best candidates for the site of large-scale displacement between the Columbia and Central belts (Eisbacher, 1985). We extend the Teslin fault to the northwest, where we infer that it merges with the Denali and with structures associated with the numerous small terranes lying to the southwest of the Yukon-Tanana terrane in Yukon Territory and eastern Alaska.

To the southeast, we propose that the Central fault system merges with the Central Rocky Mountain trench and extends into eastern British Columbia where the inferred fault is inadequately defined. The physiographic character of the Northern Rocky Mountain trench is more or less continuous with the northern Purcell fault, but the displacement history of the southern part of the system is unclear. As outlined by Price and Carmichael (1986), even minimal displacement estimates of 450 km for the Tintina fault system are difficult to carry into eastern British Columbia. The problem is greatly compounded by the 900-km displacement on the Tintina proposed by Gabrielse (1985) and is far too great to be transferred en echelon to the west by the Pinchi and Fraser faults (Fig. 3) as has been proposed by Price and Carmichael (1986). When the displacements suggested by the paleomagnetic data from the Columbia belt are included, the problem of compatibility becomes truly overwhelming. The large displacement along the Tintina fault system and the paleomagnetic requirement for great transcurrent displacement of much of the Stikinia–Cache Creek–Quesnellia terrane leads to a search for the eastern boundary of the Columbia belt. We consider three alternatives.

(1) A fault system located to the west of the Purcell Mountains plausibly has been suggested by earlier workers (Beck, 1976; Umhoefer, 1987) and lies in a region where Tertiary extension on low-angle normal faults (Parrish and others, 1988; Carr and others, 1987) may have obscured the trace of an earlier transcurrent fault system.

(2) A locus of displacement along the east side of the Purcell Mountains is also possible, where Paleozoic sections on the western flank of the Southern Rocky Mountain trench differ substantially in their thickness and number of internal unconformities from the sections located in the Rocky Mountains to the east.

(3) A final possibility is that displacement was accommodated on unrecognized fault systems west of the Monashee terrane.

In support of the first two options, it is noted that the basement ages to the east of the Southern Rocky Mountain trench (i.e., in the Alberta Plains) are on the order of 1.7 Ga, whereas the Monashee protolith to the west ranges from 2.0 to 2.5 Ga (Monger and Berg, 1987). All options need to be studied further, and additional measurements and evaluation of the paleomagnetic data on either side of the postulated fault systems have to be made.

Geologic contraints: External fault system. Characterizing the displacement history of the External fault system, which forms the eastern boundary of the Coastal belt, is less difficult than that of the Central fault system, but also is not without controversy. The most easily recognized part of the system is the arcuate Denali fault stretching through central Alaska southeasterly into Yukon Territory and northwestern British Columbia (Fig. 3). In the area just west of Skagway, Alaska, the fault appears to bifurcate into a southerly strand linked with the Chatham Strait fault and a southeasterly system along the western flank of the Coast Plutonic complex.

Estimates of displacement on the Denali system conflict both in magnitude and timing. Much of the discrepancy arises from the estimated right-lateral offset of 350 to 400 km of uppermost Cretaceous to lower Tertiary metamorphic rocks and lower Mesozoic flysch units (Lanphere, 1978; *Forbes and others, 1973, 1974*; *Turner and others, 1974*; *Eisbacher, 1976*; Nokleberg and others, 1985) along the northwesterly trending Shakwak segment of the Denali fault (Fig. 3). The displacements are thought to have occurred less than 55 m.y. ago (Lanphere, 1978) and are incompatible with coeval displacements estimated to be smaller by an order of magnitude on the McKinley segment in central Alaska (*Csejtey and others, 1982*). Part of the incompatibility in displacement, for the interval from 38 Ma to the present, can be explained by southerly directed contraction south of the McKinley strand on the Broxson Gulch thrust system (Stout and Chase, 1980).

Nevertheless, this solution does not account for 300 km of right-lateral offset on the Shakwak strand between 55 and 38 Ma. Stout and Chase (1980) suggest that unrecognized contractional structures lying to the west of the Broxson Gulch thrust system may help to alleviate the problem for the interval between 55 and 38 Ma. *Csejtey and others (1982),* however, argue that the incompatibility arises from miscorrelation of metamorphic rocks across the Denali fault system; thus removing the necessity of large right-lateral offset. The argument dismissing the metamorphic correlation is strongly contested by Nokleberg and others (1985) on the basis of their detailed studies in the region. Nevertheless, some questions still exist concerning specific correlations of metamorphic assemblages based, at least in part, on discordant amphibole and biotite K/Ar dates. The dates may actually record uplift and cooling, possibly related to fault displacements, and not the age of peak metamorphism.

The offset of Upper Jurassic and Lower Cretaceous flysch units recognized by *Eisbacher (1976)*, however, is unaffected by the arguments of *Csejtey and others (1982)* and still requires substantial transcurrent displacement. Large-scale offset of between 65 and 315 km is apparent on the Hines Creek strand of the Denali fault (Fig. 3). The displacement is constrained as being post-Devonian and pre–Late Cretaceous by the age of displaced rocks and a 95-Ma pluton that intrudes the fault zone (*Wahrhaftig and others, 1977*). It is conceivable that the offset of 300 km on the lower Mesozoic flysch unit was accommodated on the Hines Creek strand.

In addition, the compatibility problem of continuous strike-slip offset on a curved transcurrent fault system like the Denali may not have been as pronounced before 55 Ma. Paleomagnetic data from much of southern and interior Alaska indicate about 40° of counterclockwise rotation of the region since the Late Cretaceous, probably between 67 and 53 Ma (*Coe and others, 1985*).

To the west, large horizontal offsets of allochthonous terranes are reported by Jones and others (1982) and are essentially compatible with the inferred displacement history farther east. The lack of high-angle intersections between the offset markers and the fault, however, make accurate estimation of lateral displacement difficult and additional work necessary.

In southeastern Alaska, part of the displacement on the Denali fault system may be carried to the Fairweather by the Chatham Strait fault. As was pointed out by Lanphere (1978), estimates of right-lateral offset of up to 205 km have been proposed for the Chatham Strait fault, but of that only 50 to 100 km are considered to have occurred since the early or middle Tertiary (*Ovenshine and Brew, 1972*).

Lanphere (1978) postulated that much of the Denali offset extended southeasterly along the poorly defined Coast Range "megalineament" (*Brew and Ford, 1978*). Crawford and others (1987) and *Gehrels and McClelland (1988)* show that this structure is an east-dipping thrust fault that brings higher-grade metamorphic rocks into contact with lower-grade rocks to the west. Displacement on the fault is poorly understood, but it apparently represents the tectonic boundary between Superterranes I and II, which were amalgamated by the mid-Cretaceous (Monger and Berg, 1987).

Paleomagnetic constraints. The Central and Columbia belts are differentiated by their structural relations to the North American continent. Mid-Cretaceous and Cenozoic displacement of the rocks of the Central belt with respect to stable North America is estimated at 900 km of northward motion along the Tintina system (Gabrielse, 1985). Between 500 and 700 km of northward displacement is postulated for the Sierra Nevada (Frei and others, 1984; Oldow and others, 1984) along a westerly strand of the Pine Nut fault system (Oldow, 1984). Though large, the displacements are relatively minor when compared to those postulated for the Columbia belt.

Paleomagnetic data from Mesozoic rocks of Superterranes I and II of the Canadian Cordillera (Columbia belt) cannot be reconciled easily with their current location with respect to North America. Paleomagnetic inclinations from early Mesozoic rocks of Superterrane I have been interpreted, depending on whether a north- or south-pole position is assumed, to indicate a few degrees to several tens of degrees of post-depositional latitudinal shift with respect to stable North America during the last 100 m.y. (Beck, 1976, 1980; *Beck and others, 1981a, 1981b*; *Irving and others, 1980*; *Monger and Irving, 1980*; Irving and others, 1985; Stone and McWilliams, 1989). Aspects of these interpretations have been questioned recently by May and Butler (1986) on the basis of reinterpretation of the Late Triassic to Early Jurassic apparent polar wander (APW) path for North America based on a simple paleomagnetic Euler pole analysis (Gordon and others, 1984). They suggest that Late Triassic and Early Jurassic paleomagnetic data from Superterrane I were not statistically discordant with the APW path for North America, and that perhaps Superterrane I never moved latitudinally with respect to North America.

Even in light of this interpretation of the paleomagnetic data, arguments for the displacement of Superterrane I still exist. Paleomagnetic data from early Mesozoic rocks of Superterrane II (Wrangellia, Peninsular, Alexander, and Chugach) indicate substantial latitudinal shifts since the mid-Cretaceous, ranging from 20° to 40° (about 2,200 to 4,400 km) for a northern-hemisphere solution and substantially greater if a southern-hemisphere solution is used (*Stone and Packer, 1977*; Stone and others, 1982; Stone and McWilliams, 1989). Amalgamation of Superterranes I and II in the mid-Cretaceous is difficult to reconcile if Superterrane I was in its present-day position with respect to North America.

The position of Superterrane I in the Cretaceous is further constrained by numerous mid- to Upper Cretaceous plutons that indicate substantial northward displacement (up to 2,400 km) since their emplacement (Irving and others, 1985; Umhoefer, 1987; Avé Lallemant and Oldow, 1988).

The consistency of the inclination anomalies shown by numerous plutons could be explained by a systematic and regionally uniform 30° southwestward tilt, as recognized and later rejected by Irving and others (1985). Considering the areal extent over which the plutons are exposed (much of western British Columbia and western Washington), we consider it unlikely that tilts of this magnitude are the product of structural processes. Nevertheless, two mechanisms for large-scale tilting can be envisioned: one involving crustal extension and the other related to contractional tectonism and/or uplift. Development of substantial tilts in plutons and associated country rock (in excess of 65°) is well documented in parts of the western Great Basin (Proffett, 1977; Geissman and others, 1982; *Shaver and McWilliams, 1987*), where large-scale extension is observed. Large extension is recognized in central and eastern British Columbia (Parrish and others, 1988; Carr and others, 1987; Friedman and Armstrong, 1988) but not as yet in western British Columbia. Assuming a fault geometry similar to that of the western Great Basin, a 30° tilt of the plutons in British Columbia requires crustal extension of at least 75 percent. Faults necessary to accommodate this magnitude of extension are as yet unrecognized. Furthermore, regions of

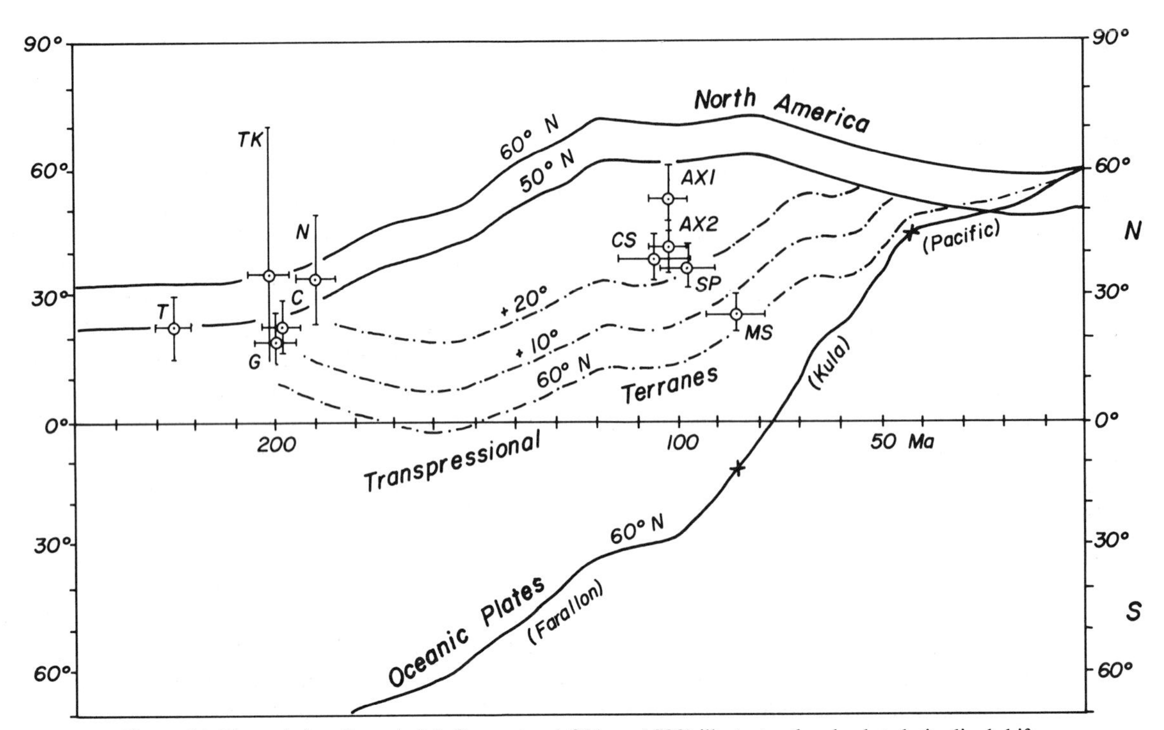

Figure 14. Figure (taken from Avé Lallemant and Oldow, 1988) illustrates the absolute latitudinal shifts from 250 Ma to Present of: (1) two sites presently at 50° and 60°N on the margin of western stable North America; (2) one site presently at 60°N,215°E situated in the Columbia belt and two points farther north, all of which were fixed with respect to North America at about 50 to 60 Ma; and (3) a site presently at 60°N,215°E situated on an oceanic plate. The North American curves are after Debiche and others (1987) from 180 Ma to Present and after May and Butler (1986) from 250 to 180 Ma. Paleomagnetic data: T, Takla Group; N, Nilkitkwa Formation; TK, Telkwa Formation; G, Guichon batholith; and C, Copper Mountain intrusions (from May and Butler, 1986); SP, Spuzzum pluton (from Irving and others, 1985); MS, Mount Stuart batholith (from *Beck and others, 1986b*; ages from *Engel and Crowder, 1971*); CS, Captain Cove pluton (from *Symons, 1977*); AX_1 and AX_2, Axelgold pluton (from *Monger and Irving, 1980*). The travel path of the transpressional terranes illustrates that, until about 200 Ma, rocks of the Columbia belt (units T, TK, N, G, and C of Superterrane I) essentially track with North America. The mid-Cretaceous plutons within the Columbia belt (units AX_1, AX_2, CS, SP, and MS of Superterranes I and II) have magnetic inclinations consistent with a mid-Cretaceous position near the latitude of Baja California. Using the calculated displacement curves for the transpressional terranes, the Columbia belt is predicted to have arrived at its present relative position with respect to stable North America at about 50 to 60 Ma.

large-scale extension generally are characterized by reversals of tilt polarity along strike. It is difficult to imagine a single extensional system that would cause the entire region, which stretches for more than 1,100 km along strike, to experience a uniform southwesterly tilt.

An alternative explanation, invoking contractional deformation, is also difficult to reconcile with known relations. If southwesterly tilts of 30° are related to hanging-wall displacements of decapitated plutons over ramps, it is difficult to understand why the plutons, which are found along the coastal ranges from 57°N to 47°N latitude, all underwent the same relative displacement. An explanation invoking regional uplift is also inadequate. The angle of tilt associated with 9 km of uplift of the Canadian Coast Mountains during the last 40 m.y. (*Parrish, 1983*) is too small by at least a factor of four.

Arguments concerning the age of magnetization acquisition by the plutons are more plausible if taken uncritically. If magnetization blocking occurred in mid-Tertiary time during uplift, any inclination anomaly associated with mid- to Upper Cretaceous plutons is essentially removed. This mechanism would also accommodate the systematic and predicted variation in magnetization inclination of several plutons from north to south (Fig. 14). Note the systematic decrease in magnetic inclination recorded by the plutons of the Columbia belt on Figure 14 (which, from north to south, are the Axelgold, Captains Cove, Spuzzum, and Mount Stuart). This explanation is unlikely, however, because K/Ar ages for the plutons are based on concordant hornblende-biotite or biotite determinations. The blocking temperatures of biotite and hornblende approximate the temperature interval over which magnetizations are blocked in nearly pure magnetite, which carries the magnetic signature of the plutons. It appears that the isotopic age determinations for the plutons are good approximations of the date of magnetization. More compelling support for a Cretaceous age of magnetization is supplied by Irving and others (1985) for the Spuzzum pluton, where Tertiary overprints (normal and reversed) occur and have been isolated and corrected in the laboratory. We agree with Irving and others (1985) that the inclination anomalies appear to be real.

Paleomagnetic data from the rocks of the Coastal belt indicate substantial northward latitudinal shift through the late Mesozoic and Tertiary (Irving and others, 1985; *Stone and Packer, 1977*; Stone and others, 1982). Early perceptions of the displacement path of the terranes envisioned migration across a broad Pacific basin and docking at or near their present locations (Stone and others, 1982; Jones and others, 1982; *Csejtey and others, 1982*). The data of Irving and others (1985) imply that docking of the amalgamated terranes of the Coastal belt with the terranes of the Columbia belt occurred at the latitude of Baja California. There is, however, no need from the paleomagnetic data to postulate that there were important longitudinal shifts of the terranes before amalgamation. Transpressional deformation related to oblique convergence can accommodate the subsequent northward migration of the entire assemblage of terranes stitched by the Coast Plutonic complex from the mid-Cretaceous to present (Debiche and others, 1987; Umhoefer, 1987; Avé Lallemant and Oldow, 1988).

Paleontological constraints. Faunal distributions of ammonites (*Nichols and Silberling, 1979*; *Tozer, 1982*; *Tipper, 1984*; Taylor and others, 1984) indicate a net northerly displacement of units of the Columbia and Coastal belts with respect to the foreland fold belt (Fig. 15). In fact, there appears to be relative displacement among rocks composing the Columbia belt, with the Tethyan to Boreal transition within Stikinia offset northward about 500 km with respect to that in Quesnellia. The best-defined offset lies with the distribution of Pliensbachian ammonites (Taylor and others, 1984).

A similar northerly displacement is recognized in the occurrence of *Monotis* in Upper Triassic strata (Silberling, 1985). The boundary between various faunal associations, consisting of different species, groups, or subgenera, does not correspond geographically with the province boundaries of the ammonites but does exhibit approximately the same degree of offset. Thus, the bivalve distribution appears to corroborate the relative displacements defined by ammonites.

The distribution of *Monotis* suggests large displacement of parts of the Coastal and Columbia belts. A distinct faunal association occurs within part of the Alexander terrane and is related to faunal occurrences along the Pacific borderland of South America. This relation suggests a southern hemisphere origin for at least this part of the Alexander terrane. This relation may suggest that Wrangellia had a southern hemisphere origin, because at least parts of Wrangellia and the Alexander terrane were amalgamated in the Late Carboniferous (*Mackevett and others, 1986*; Gardner and others, 1988).

Faunal distributions within the Columbia and Coastal belts can be reconciled with the paleomagnetic data. If the original Triassic and Early Jurassic positions of Stikinia and Quesnellia of the Columbia belt were several hundred kilometers (500 to 700) south of their current locations, the faunal boundaries would correspond to those in the foreland fold belt and still lie within the resolution of paleomagnetic data. Following amalgamation of Superterrane I in the Early to Middle Jurassic, the rocks were transported southward to the latitude of Baja California. There they were sutured with Superterrane II, which apparently arrived at the same latitude in the mid-Cretaceous from a southerly source region. Together, they were displaced to a position north of the original location of Stikinia and Quesnellia. Several hundred kilometers of net right-lateral displacement may have occurred within the Columbia belt during the northerly migration, resulting in the northerly step in the Jurassic ammonite distributions. The possibility that the offset in ammonite faunal boundaries between Stikinia and Quesnellia occurred during the original amalgamation cannot be discounted, but a corresponding right-lateral offset in an east-west–trending belt of Early Jurassic plutons that stitches Stikinia to Cache Creek and Cache Creek to Quesnellia suggests that the displacement occurred later. (The interested reader is referred to the map of the Canadian Cordillera by Wheeler and McFeeley, 1987.)

Kinematic model for transpression

Geologic constraints indicate large transcurrent displacements and coeval shortening in the foreland fold and thrust belt of the Cordillera. If paleomagnetic data are accepted, the outboard tectonic belts of the Cordillera have undergone margin-parallel displacements of several thousands of kilometers. The transcurrent displacement of the tectonic belts and coeval shortening in the foreland thrust belt appear to be related to the relative motions of North America and the plates of the Pacific basin. Here, we propose a kinematic framework relating relative plate motion and the deformation within the active margin orogenic belt of the Cordillera.

The mechanism of forearc terrane migration in response to oblique convergence has been described by Fitch (1972), Beck (1983), Jarrard (1986), and Avé Lallemant and Oldow (1988). The component of the convergence vector normal to the plate boundary (subduction zone, magmatic arc) is directly responsible for compressional strain and displacements normal to the boundary in the fore-arc, and as we propose here, in back-arc regions. The shortening involved may amount to several hundred kilometers. The component of convergence parallel to the plate boundary results in displacements parallel to one or more arc-parallel strike-slip fault zones and in fold and thrust belts. The arc-parallel displacements can be very large and may be an order of magnitude greater than the thrust displacements.

In a previous paper (Avé Lallemant and Oldow, 1988), two of us have presented a simple kinematic model for such arc-parallel migrating complexes, called "transpressional terranes." This model was proposed to explain southward migration of Cordilleran allochthonous terranes during the Triassic to mid-

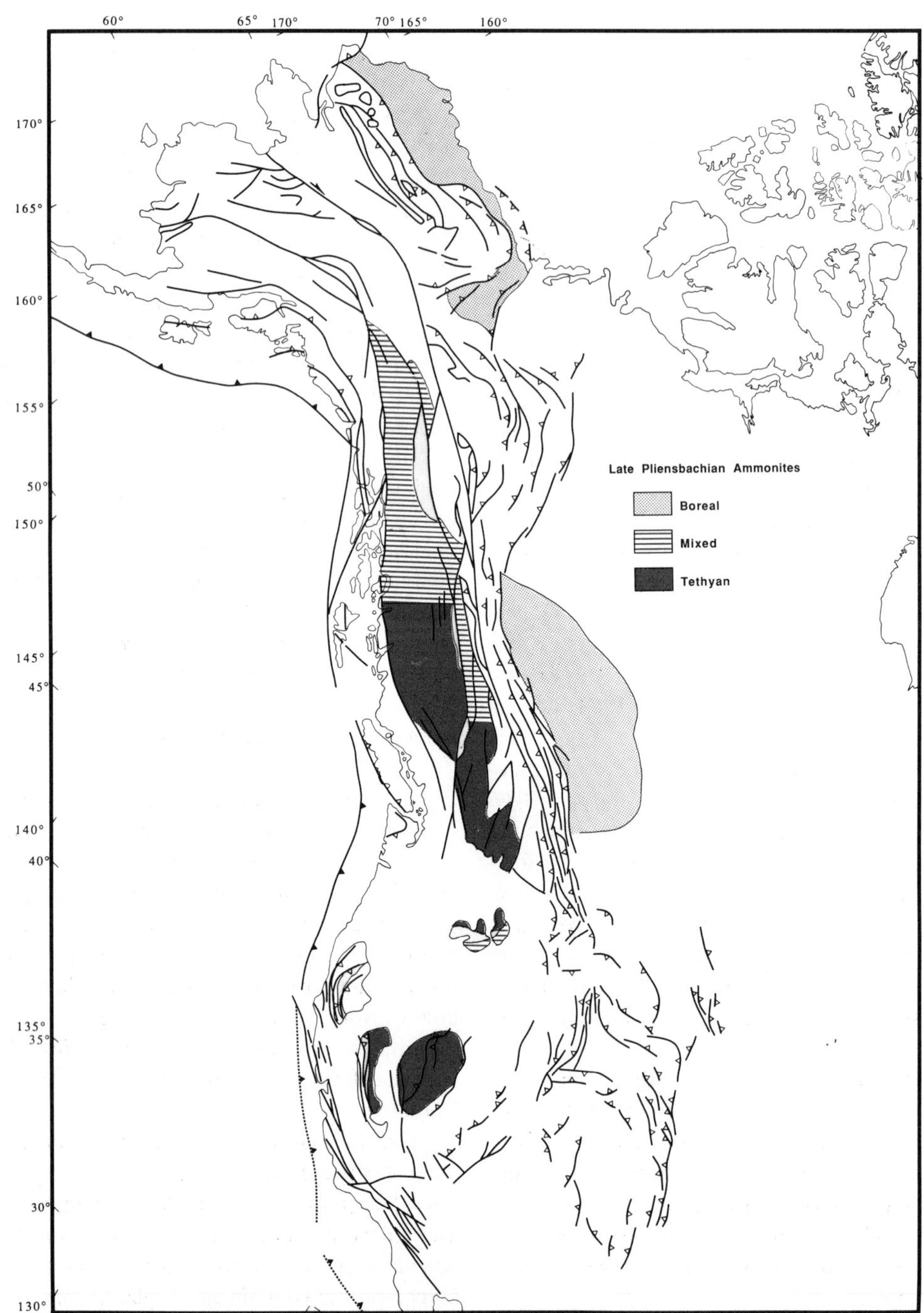

Figure 15. Map showing the generalized distribution of late Pliensbachian Ammonite faunas of Boreal, Tethyan, and mixed Boreal-Tethyan affinity in the Cordillera (Taylor and others, 1984). Transition of Boreal and Tethyan fauna in undisplaced rocks of North America occurs somewhere between the latitude of the southern Canadian Rocky Mountains and the western Great Basin. In Stikinia and Quesnellia of the Canadian Cordillera, the Tethyan to mixed Boreal-Tethyan transition is preserved in both terranes. The transition is offset by about 500 km in a right-lateral sense along the boundary of Stikinia and Quesnellia. The ammonite data and comparable distributions of the Triassic *Monotis* (Silberling, 1985) indicate a net northerly displacement of Stikinia and Quesnellia with respect to North America of 500 to 700 km. The occurrence of the Tethyan to mixed Boreal-Tethyan transition in both Stikinia and Quesnellia is compatible with the interpretation that they represent a pair of fringing arc systems and is inconsistent with alternative interpretations that they represent displaced along-strike segments of the same arc. The occurrence of a mixed Boreal-Tethyan fauna in the Olds Ferry terrane of northeastern Oregon is problematic, but tentatively is discounted because the faunal association of that terrane is based on very sparse data.

Cretaceous, caused by left-oblique convergence consistent with the plate-motion models of Engebretson and others (1985). However, this simple mechanism is not adequate to explain the Late Cretaceous to recent structural evolution of the western Cordillera. Therefore, we present here a more complicated model, which still is, no doubt, an oversimplification.

The model (Fig. 16) applies to the plate configuration at a time between 100 and 50 Ma. All three fault systems—the Denali, Teslin-Pinchi, and Tintina—were active, and arc-normal shortening occurred throughout the Cordillera, from the subduction zone to the folds and thrusts of the foreland fold belt.

In the model (Fig. 16), the North American continent (A) is kept fixed, and the oceanic plate (O) moves N20°E at a velocity (V) with respect to the continent. The subduction zone (S), Denali fault (D), Teslin-Pinchi system (TP), and Tintina fault (T) all trend N35°W. Thus, the obliquity is 35°. Only a small fraction of the displacements of the oceanic plate are transmitted across the subduction zone; this fraction is indicated as V′. The normal component V_N' is responsible for the northeasterly displacements and strains in the Coastal belt (C), Columbia belt (Co), Central belt (Ct), and foreland fold belt (F). The suture-parallel component V_T' is responsible for the northward migration of the three westerly belts.

After one unit of time at velocity V′, a point P_0 in the accretionary prism is displaced to P_1 with respect to North America (A). With respect to an internal coordinate set, P_0 is displaced to P_1'. Point Q_0, just east of the Denali fault (D), moves to Q_1' (internal coordinates); the displacement $Q_0Q_1' = P_0P_1' - E_p$, where E_p is the displacement related to internal strain (folding and thrusting) in the Coastal belt (C). Thus, the Denali fault migrates northeastward by an amount equal to Q_0Q_1'. Similarly, the Teslin-Pinchi and Tintina faults move northeastward by the amount $R_0R_1' = (Q_0Q_1' - E_q)$ and $K_0K_1 = (R_0R_1' - E_r)$, respectively, where E_q and E_r are the displacements related to the internal strain in the Columbia and Central belts, respectively. The displacement K_0K_1 is responsible for folding and thrusting in the foreland fold belt. Note that the deformation front (DF) in the foreland fold belt does not move.

The suture-parallel component of displacement V_T' is responsible for the north-northwesterly migration of the Coastal, Columbia, and Central belts. The Coastal belt is displaced to the north-northwest by an amount $P_1'P_1$, the Columbia belt by an amount $Q_1'Q_1$, and the Central belt by an amount $R_1'R_1$.

The west-southwest–east-northeast shortening and north-northwest strike-slip displacements have occurred simultaneously in the northern Cordillera. This requires (Fig. 16) that all major faults (Denali, Teslin-Pinchi, and Tintina) were displaced toward the east-northeast while strike-slip motion along them occurred.

Estimated displacements in the northern Cordillera. One of the several options for the plate motion history of the Pacific basin with respect to North America, as calculated by Engebretson and others (1985), is presented in Figure 17 for a point at 55°N, 228°E, near the Queen Charlotte Islands. The option chosen is that for a point having resided in the Farallon plate until 85 Ma; from 85 to 43 Ma it was part of the Kula plate; and from 43 Ma to the present it was part of the Pacific plate.

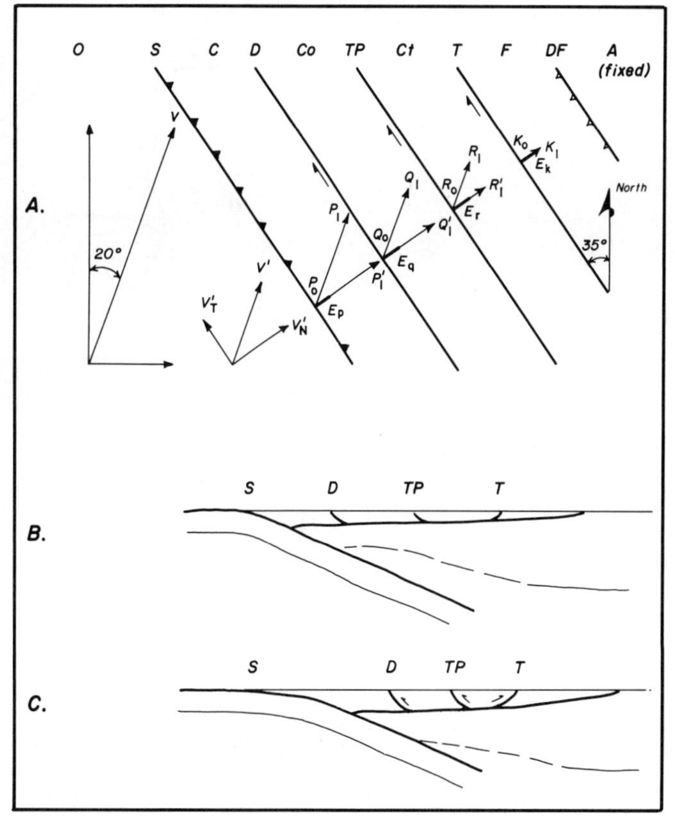

Figure 16. Model of Cordilleran terrane migration between approximately 100 and 50 Ma: A. Map, and B. and C. northeast-southwest–trending cross sections at about 100 and 50 Ma, respectively. Subduction zone (S), Coastal belt (C), Denali fault (D), Columbia belt (Co), Teslin-Pinchi fault system (TP), Central belt (Ct), Tintina fault (T), and Foreland belt (F) all trend N35°W. North America (A) is fixed. Oceanic plate (O) moves N20°E at relative velocity V; only part (V′) of the convergence vector is transmitted to the transpressional terranes: the component normal to the subduction zone (V_N') results in shortening (E_p, E_q, E_r, E_k in the Coastal, Columbia, Central, and Foreland belts, respectively; for details see text); northeast of the deformation front (DF) no deformation occurs; the tangential component (V_T') results in dextral strike-slip displacements (P_1P_1', Q_1Q_1', and R_1R_1' for the Coastal, Columbia, and Central belts, respectively; all with respect to a fixed North America). The consequence of this model is (B and C) that the three fault systems (Denali, Teslin-Pinchi, Tintina) migrate northeastward and must be connected through a common decollement zone.

From 120 to 100 Ma, the subduction was almost normal (obliquity of about 10°). From 100 to 43 Ma the convergence of the two plates was strongly right-oblique (obliquity of 35°). From 43 Ma to the present the Pacific–North American boundary is almost purely strike-slip (obliquity of 83°).

The model of Engebretson and others, (1985) predicts that the amount of displacement of the sea floor from 100 to 43 Ma is about 8,350 km (4,350 km from 100 to 66 Ma, and 4,000 km from 66 to 43 Ma). The displacement from 43 Ma to the present is about 1,900 km.

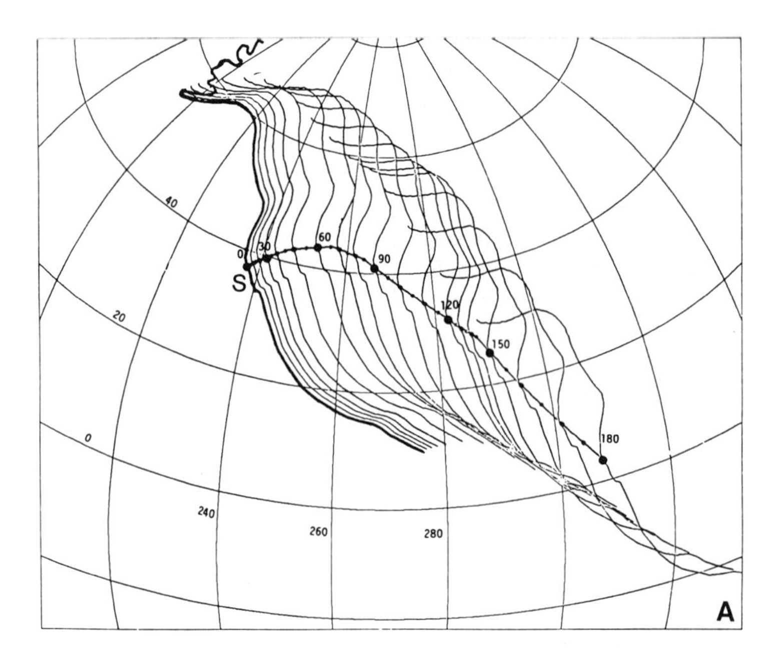

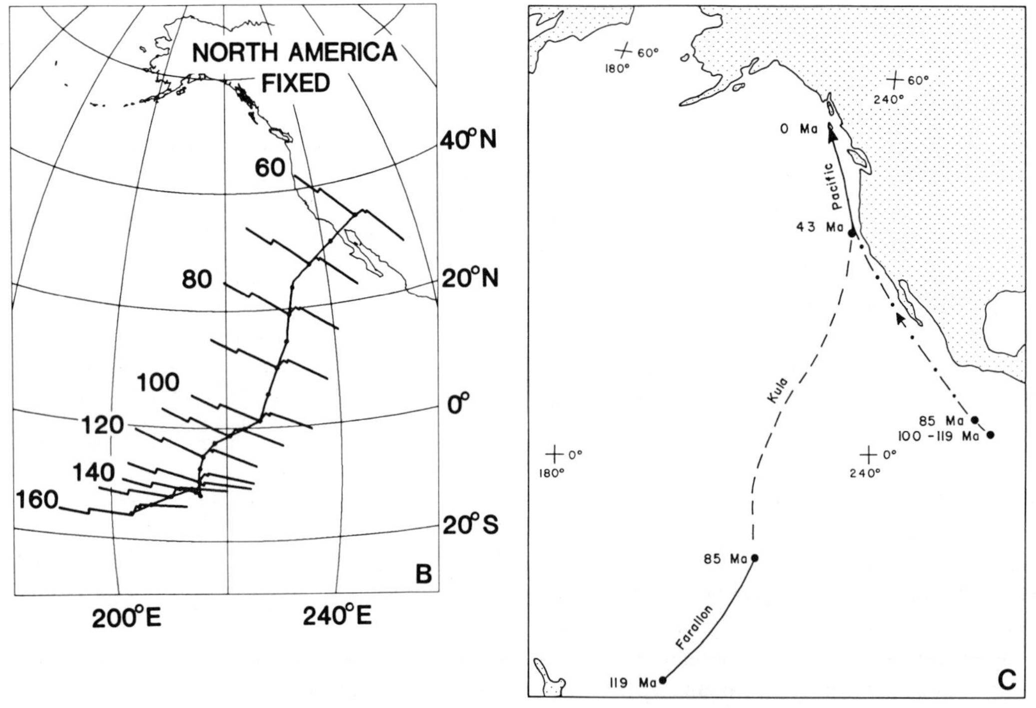

Figure 17. Maps of Pacific–North America plate convergence from 180 Ma to Present (from Engebretson and others, 1985; Avé Lallemant and Oldow, 1988). A. Motion of North America with respect to the hot spots from 180 Ma at 10-m.y. intervals. The dark line is the trajectory of a point (S) near present-day San Francisco. Small dots show positions of S at 5-m.y. intervals and large dots show positions at 30-m.y. intervals. B. Sequence of dots shows the trajectory of a point on the Farallon plate as the Farallon plate moved across the Pacific basin. This point is located on anomaly M29 (164 Ma) where the anomaly is offset by a small fracture zone. Coordinates remain fixed relative to North America. C. Map of the Pacific basin and western North America showing plate convergence from 119 Ma to present. A point presently residing on the Pacific plate near Queen Charlotte Islands moved northeasterly across the ocean from 119 to 85 Ma as part of the Farallon plate and from 85 to 43 Ma as part of the Kula plate; subsequently it moved northward with the Pacific plate. The map also shows the migration curve of a transpressional terrane (presently lying inboard of the Queen Charlotte Islands), if the entire subduction-zone parallel component of convergence were transmitted to the terrane.

If the subduction zone always had a N35°W trend, then the amount of sea floor subducted from 100 to 66 Ma is 3,400 km, from 66 to 43 Ma 3,350 km, and from 43 Ma to the present 150 km. The maximum amount of dextral strike-slip displacement is then 2,700 km from 100 to 66 Ma, 2,200 km from 66 to 43 Ma, and 1,900 km from 43 Ma to the present.

The amount of shortening in the Rocky Mountains in the interval from 100 to 43 Ma has been estimated at between 100 and 200 km (Price, 1981), and in the Brooks Range at about 500 km (Oldow and others, 1987a). No estimates are available for shortening in the Coastal, Columbia, and Central belts. Even if the shortening in these belts is large and of the same order as in the Rocky Mountain fold and thrust belt, it is clear that the subducting plate was not strongly coupled to the upper plate, because the width of sea floor subducted is almost 7,000 km. Strike-slip displacement along the Tintina between 100 and 43 Ma has been estimated at 900 km (Gabrielse, 1985) and that along the Denali at 300 km (Lanphere, 1978). These are minimum estimates. With the numerous splays of the two fault systems it would not be surprising if the total offset is on the order of 2,500 km instead of 1,200 km. The total possible offset derived from the model of Engebretson and others (1985) is 4,900 km.

Displacements along the Denali from 43 Ma to the present have been estimated as 100 km (Stout and Chase, 1980). The Tintina has not been as active in the post-Eocene as before, but certain splays like the Hozameen fault (*Ray, 1986*) were active, and the Tintina fault in Alaska is seismically active at present (Estabrook and others, 1988). To accommodate late Cenozoic displacements in the Brooks Range, a displacement of about 200 km is needed along the Tintina fault system. The total displacements are only a small fraction of the theoretical displacement (1,900 km).

It is interesting to note that the amount of axis-parallel displacements in the Cordillera is about 25 percent at a minimum and probably more like 50 percent of the amount of displacement between the Pacific basin and North American plates, as based on the model of Engebretson and others (1985); however, the amount of shortening in the Cordillera may only be about 10 percent of the total amount of sea floor subducted. This may indicate that much more shortening, in particular internal strain, has occurred, but it has not yet been documented. Typically, shortening estimates based on balanced sections are conservative. Alternatively, it may indicate that transmittal of the tangential displacements is more efficient than transmission of normal displacements.

Complications of a curved boundary. The kinematic model as presented in Figure 16 is only an approximation of the history of Cordilleran transpression. The model clearly is too simple. If, for example, the orientation of the subduction zone changes, major strain and displacement heterogeneities occur. The N35°W trend of the subduction zone in British Columbia must have changed to a N70°W trend in Alaska. A simplified model of such a configuration is presented in Figure 18A. In this model, we move the Central belt as a coherent body in a direction N20°E at a velocity V′ (from t_0 to t_1) in order to illustrate the consequence of a curved boundary on the structure of the foreland fold and thrust belt. In the southeastern region, the normal component V_N' causes displacement by thrusting in the foreland. At the same time, the Central belt moves toward the N35°W at V_T'. In the northwestern region, the convergence is normal. The amount of displacement in the foreland fold and thrust belt is equivalent to V′. A dextral transpressional fault (T) may develop, and a dramatic reduction in shortening or even extension may occur in the transitional area (B). The transpressional fault zone and area of reduced contraction only occurs above the decollement and does not influence the basement. The effect of a bend in the continental margin and the resultant displacement field outlined above, nicely accommodates the morphology of the transition from the Ogilvie Mountains to the eastern Brooks Range in northwestern Canada.

The model shown in Figure 18B is similar to the one in Figure 18A, but with the additional complication of a component of tangential displacement (V_T'') along the N70°W–trending segment of the Tintina-Kaltag fault system. As in the previous model (Fig. 18A), A_0, B_0, C_0, D_0, H_0, and K_0 move in a straightforward fashion to A_1, B_1, C_1, D_1, H_1, and K_1, respectively. Note that the magnitudes of the normal components of convergence (V_N', V_N'') are the same as the displacement vectors in the thrust belts; for simplicity we did not include internal strain in any of the belts.

The behavior of points E_0, T_0, and G_0 is different from the previous model. Point E_0 moves toward N20°E until it arrives at E′. At this point the travel path of point E is intersected by the travel path of the kink in the Tintina-Kaltag fault system. Subsequently, this point moves toward N55°E as it is pushed by the N35°W–trending sector of the Central belt and Tintina-Kaltag fault. Point F_0 does not move until the Tintina-Kaltag kink arrives at point E′. Thereafter, F_0 moves to F_1. Point G_0 moves to G′ as E_0 moves to E′. At this point, G has stopped moving. The model predicts that in the rocks in the thrust segment, which includes point F_1 (Ogilvie Mountains), a relatively large amount of shear strain has to occur (shear rotation of about 45° of the thrust front). The Yukon fault system (including point G′) is primarily a dextral strike-slip shear zone; although the system can be considered transpressional.

It cannot be overemphasized that even this model (Fig. 18B) is simplistic. First, the kink in the Tintina-Kaltag fault system constitutes an abrupt change of orientation; in reality, the radius of curvature is quite large. Secondly, we assumed that no internal strain occurred in the thrust belt, which clearly is unrealistic. In the third place, we assumed that thrusting is rigorously normal to the Tintina fault; this assumption is at best a good first approximation.

Tectonic implications of transpression

Development of widespread transpression in the western Cordillera appears to be a dominant feature of the Mesozoic and

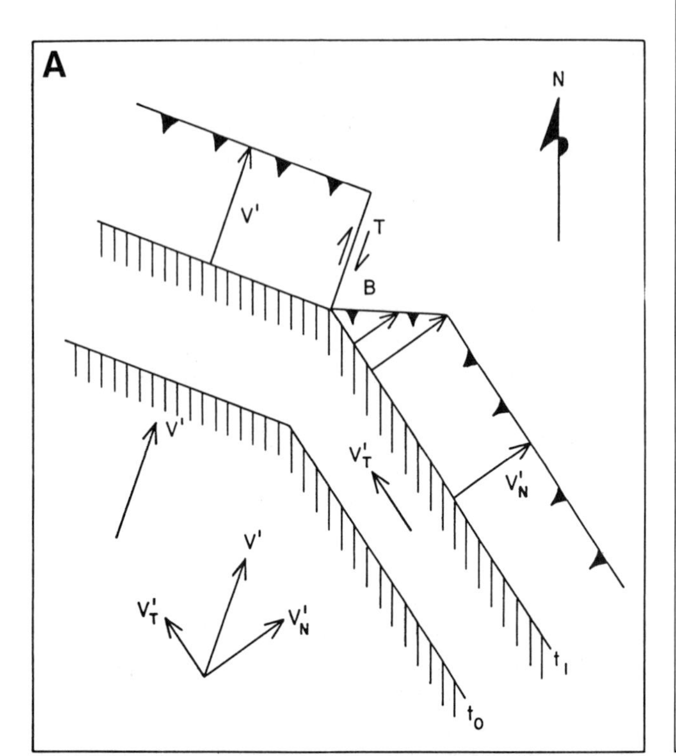

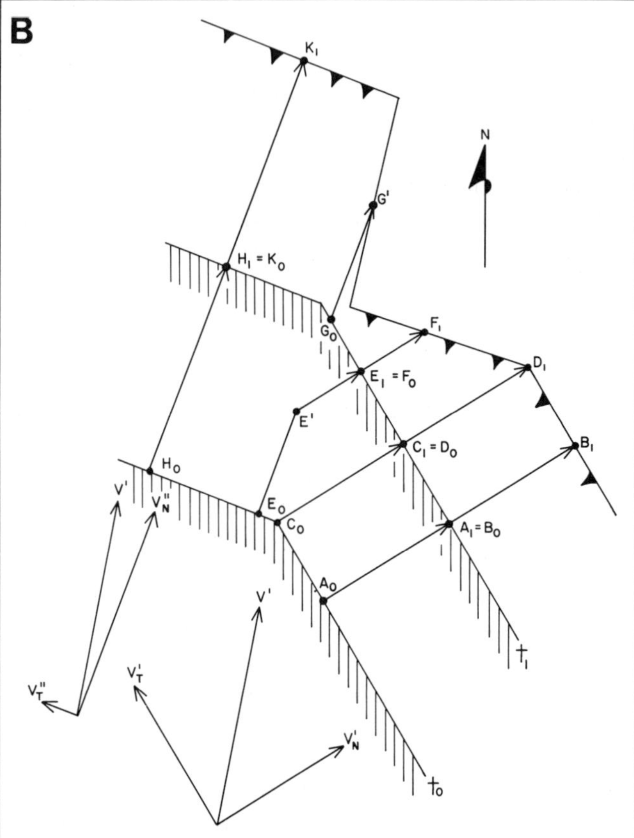

Figure 18. Models of transpression along a curved boundary, trending N35°W in the south and N70°W in the north. In the first model (A) the convergence is N20°E. Thus, in the north, the entire convergence vector (V′) is transmitted to the foreland thrust belt, but in the south, this vector is decomposed in a normal (V_N') and a transcurrent component (V_T'). This results in a N20°E-trending strike-slip fault (T) bounding the northern foreland thrust belt. Area B is not deformed during the time frame t_0-t_1. Note that thrust displacements in the south are less than in the north. In the second model (B), the convergence is toward N10°E. Thus, both the N35°W- and N70°W-trending segments undergo transpression (for details see text). Note that the terrane boundary in this figure could represent the Tintina-Kaltag fault system. The D_1B_1 and D_1F_1 thrust segments may represent the Mackenzie and Ogilvie belts, respectively. The N10°E-trending segment containing point G′ is mostly a dextral strike-slip fault with some minor thrust component and may represent the Yukon fault zone. The N70°W-trending thrust segment represents the Brooks Range fold and thrust belt.

early Tertiary history. Here, we wish to draw attention to several fundamental points and their implications for plate margin tectonism. First, the transcurrent and thrust faults in the back-arc regions of the orogen are interpreted to share a common decollement. Coeval displacement on foreland thrusts and large transcurrent faults calls for the development of a shared basal detachment to maintain compatibility during motion. In our reconstruction (Plates 5 and 6), we connect the back-arc transpressional system to the plate boundary by deep detachment through the magmatic arc region, resulting in a single regional decollement underlying the entire orogenic belt (Fig. 1). The actual morphology of the deep decollement is unknown, and our construction is speculative. Nevertheless, the existence of a through-going decollement of some form is needed to transfer displacements from the plate boundary to the back-arc transpressional system.

The basal decollements in the accompanying sections (Plates 5 and 6) are depicted at lower crustal depths. Justification for this stems from depth conversions of geobarometric data from highly deformed rocks of hinterland thrusts of the southern Canadian Rockies (*Brown and Journeay, 1987*) and the southern Brooks Range of Alaska (*Gottschalk, 1987*; Gottschalk and Oldow, 1988). Similar and greater depths of decollement surfaces are found in the Appalachians (*Cook and others, 1979, 1982*) and are postulated to overlie lithospheric roots in the Alps (*Laubscher, 1974, 1983*; Panza and others, 1980).

We visualize transcurrent faults, such as the Tintina and Denali, as inclined structures rather than the more conventional expression as vertical structures. Some evidence for this interpretation is seen in seismic-reflection data acquired in the U.S. Geological Survey TACT program in Alaska. Reflection data across the Denali fault show the existence at depth of a moderately north-dipping fault that projects through a zone of no data to the surface position of the Denali (*Fisher and others, 1986*). Although a direct link between the surface expression of the Denali and the seismically imaged fault in the subsurface cannot be made, strike-slip displacements transformed from the northwest- to southwest-trending strands of the Denali system require substantial thrust motion on the southwest-trending faults. It is unlikely that a fault with a substantial thrust component would be vertical. Elsewhere, in the Transverse Ranges of California, the existence of subhorizontal detachments associated with transpressive displacements have been proposed (Yeats, 1983; Namson and Davis, 1988a) and illustrate the detached nature of transcurrent faults.

An important feature of the reconstructions to follow is the timing history of displacement on throughgoing decollements and the inferred decapitation of plutons at depth, particularly those associated with subduction-related magmatic processes. Restoration of foreland thrust belts, where deformation has continued after emplacement of post-kinematic plutons in the hinterland regions, implies that the hinterland plutons are detached at depth. Thus, even though the plutons commonly are younger than the structures in the rocks they intrude, hinterland plutons are allochthonous and have ridden piggy-back during foreland thrusting. This relation has two important implications, outlined below.

The allochthoneity of plutons is important to the spatial and temporal migration of magmatic belts at active margins. The shift of the position of magmatic belts in response to changes in the characteristics of the downgoing slab is well established during the Tertiary in the western United States (*Stewart and others, 1977b*; Dickinson, 1979b). In regions where large-scale back-arc thrusts formed during arc-magmatism, however, the effects of thrusting must be included in assessing the significance of the apparent displacement of the magmatic system.

This relationship probably is best expressed in Alaska, where a progressive decrease in the age of plutonism from the mid-Mesozoic in the interior region to the Cretaceous-Tertiary of central and coastal parts of the region are clearly recorded (*Beikman, 1980*). Models relying on different rates of plate convergence (*Wallace and Engebretson, 1984*), steepening of the downgoing slab, or the roll-back and southerly migration of the active site of subduction are plausible, but considering the magnitude of transpressional displacements within the lithospheric section of Alaska, cannot be solely responsible. With displacement of large thrust sheets during arc magmatism, the actual site of plate convergence, located by the subdecollement boundary of continental and oceanic lithosphere, is not required to move and, thus, behaves as a relatively fixed source of magmatism. The apparent migration of the plutonic belts of Alaska is due to displacement of the allochthonous crustal section on a deep decollement. Thus, the age of plutonism appears to migrate oceanward with respect to the crustal section.

The second implication of pluton decapitation focuses on the significance of post-kinematic plutons in dating regional tectonism. Only in the case where a fault is actually crosscut by a pluton is motion demonstrably bracketed. With recognition of so-called "out-of-sequence" thrusts (e.g., Oldow and others, 1987a; *Geiser and Boyer, 1987*) as relatively common features of progressive deformation in fold and thrust belts, plutons that post-date folds and metamorphism associated with contractional tectonism may not date the last episode of motion on thrust systems in a particular area.

Another fundamental consideration of the reconstructions (Plates 5 and 6) is the role of the lithosphere in active margin tectonism. The base of the lithosphere in our sections is the inferred thermal boundary approximated by the 1200°C isotherm (*Pollack and Chapman, 1977*), which is about 300 km for old continental regions and about 80 km for mature oceanic plates. The thickness of the upper-plate lithosphere in a subducting margin is difficult to establish. Thermal re-equilibration and rise of the asthenosphere in the region of arc magmatism is expected but poorly constrained. In addition, due to mass redistribution within the lithosphere, the time in which equilibration is achieved is not clear. Based on the age of lithospheric thinning of the Basin and Range province and the formation of the Neogene Moho (Gans, 1987), reequilibration probably is on the order of tens of millions of years.

The inherent uncertainty about the lower lithospheric boundary poses a significant problem for mass-balance considerations beneath transpressional orogens. Estimation of the mass balance of the material above the basal decollement is a relatively straightforward three-dimensional problem. The amount of material shortened in the line of the contractional section and the material transferred out of the section by transcurrent faulting must have sufficient subdetachment "basement" upon which to rest after restoration. Resolution of the distribution of subdetachment lithosphere during regional transpression, however, potentially faces severe space problems (Fig. 19).

The potential for subdetachment space problems arises from the magnitude of shortening associated with back-arc thrusting and the position of the subduction boundary through time. In the case of Alaska, where large volumes of material were added above the regional decollement by oblique displacements, the position of the subduction zone is not required to move during the shortening in the back-arc region. Thus, shortening above the regional detachment is compensated by the addition of material to the system, and the subdetachment lithosphere is more-or-less balanced.

If, on the other hand, convergence occurs as in the western conterminous United States, where the arc system resides on supracrustal rocks of known North American origin, substantial space problems are encountered. Back-arc shortening above the basal decollement is accommodated by folds, faults, and internal strain. As the thrust front migrates continentward, the position of the magmatic belt, at least the portion above the basal decollement, moves continentward as well. In regions like southern California and southern Nevada, where North American miogeosynclinal rocks occur all the way to the plate boundary,

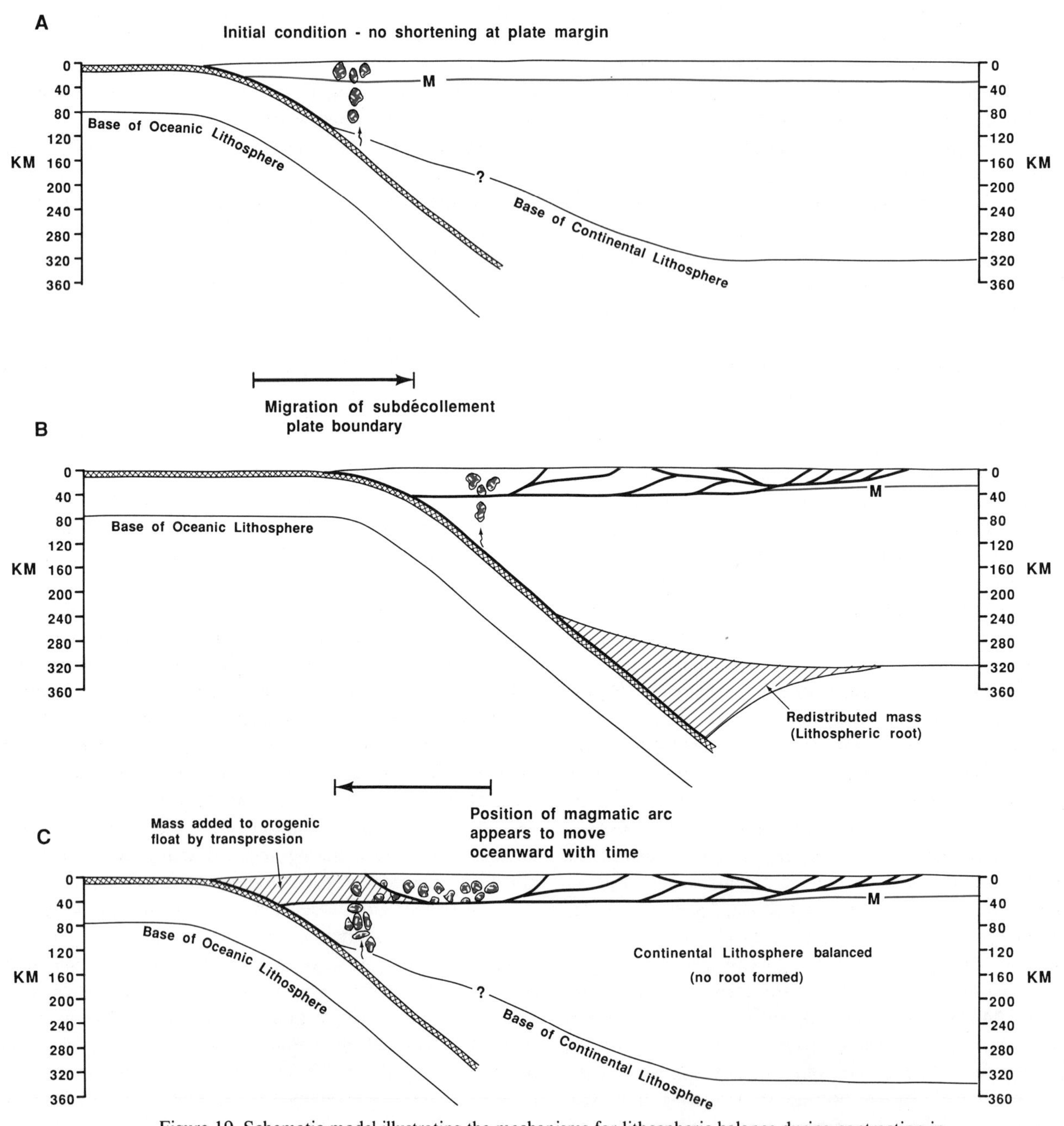

Figure 19. Schematic model illustrating the mechanisms for lithospheric balance during contraction in the orogenic float. A: Initial condition of a convergent plate boundary without regional contraction. B: Large-scale shortening and formation of an orogenic float without the addition of terranes to the leading edge of the upper continental plate (e.g., comparable with the Mesozoic and early Cenozoic history of the southern U.S. Cordillera). Shortening of the sedimentary and crustal units overlying the basal decollement requires comparable shortening in the subdecollement lithosphere and migration of the subdecollement plate boundary (to the right). Area balance requirements call for the development of a lithospheric root. C: Shortening of the sedimentary and crustal units originally overlying the continental lithosphere is compensated by the addition of terranes to the leading edge of the upper plate. The position of the subdecollement plate boundary does not move; hence there is no necessity to form a lithospheric root.

shortening above the decollement and concomitant continentward migration of the trench results in an apparent volume loss in subdecollement continental lithosphere. The subdecollement position of the leading edge of the North American continental lithosphere must move together with the trench, resulting in thickening of the continental lithosphere and formation of a large root that resides beneath the contractional orogen (Fig. 19). The rate of thermal re-equilibration and transformation of lithosphere to asthenosphere may be outpaced by mass transfer during shortening and result in transient preservation of the root. It is also conceivable that the subdecollement continental lithosphere may be tectonically removed during the subduction process as a means of preserving mass balance.

Based on our estimates, a correspondence seems to exist in regions of the North American Cordillera between the formation of a subdetachment mass excess during contraction and the subsequent development of Basin and Range extensional structures, suggesting a cause-effect relationship. The dynamic effect of mass excess in the continental lithosphere may have a substantial impact on the tectonics of the continental margin.

Opening of the Canada basin

Before we present our reconstruction, it is important to discuss the role of the Canada basin in the history of the northern Cordillera. The Mesozoic evolution of the Canada basin (Fig. 20) is critical for establishing a link between the histories of the North American Cordilleran and Arctic tectonic belts. The mode of formation of the basin, particularly as it relates to the evolution of the Arctic continental borderland of North America, is unclear, however.

Aside from the pioneering regional studies of the U.S. and Canadian Geological Surveys, only limited detailed work has been done in the region. As a result, the complex geology of the Arctic margin is imperfectly known, and its evolution is poorly constrained. Plausible models of the evolution of the Canada basin fall into two general categories: (1) those calling upon counterclockwise oroclinal rotation of northern Alaska away from the Canadian Arctic Islands about a pole in the Mackenzie delta region, and (2) those calling upon a major left-lateral transform system to accommodate the southerly migration of northern Alaska and the opening of the Canada basin. In both families of models, the Mackenzie delta region plays a central role. The region serves either as the site of the pole of rotation or as the area in which the inferred transform fault system, paralleling the western margin of the Canadian Arctic Islands, comes onland.

Canada basin. The Canada basin occupies the deepest part of the Amerasian basin, which floors the Arctic Ocean (Fig. 20), and it is underlain by oceanic crust. For details, refer to Nairn and others (1981) and Trettin (this volume). Physiographically, the abyssal plain of the basin achieves a depth of 4.0 km (Grantz and May, 1983) and has sedimentary accumulation in excess of 2.0 km (*Hall, 1973*) and possibly as thick as 4.0 to 4.5 km (*Grantz and others, 1979*). The depth to the crystalline crust (6.0 to 8.5 km) is typical of old oceanic lithosphere. Direct evidence of an oceanic crust is derived from seismic studies of surface waves (*Oliver and others, 1955*; *Hunkins, 1963*) and seismic refraction (*Mair and Lyons, 1981*).

The age and spreading history of the oceanic lithosphere flooring the basin is equivocal and has contributed substantially to debates about the evolution of Arctic North America. Initially, it was unclear whether the oceanic crust formed in place, related to some rifting process (e.g., *Carey, 1958*; Grantz and May, 1983; *Nilsen and others, 1982*; Hubbard and others, 1987; *Crane, 1987*) or if it represented a fragment of older Pacific basin lithosphere rafted into the region (*Churkin and Trexler, 1980*). Part of the ambiguity has been resolved by seismic-reflection profiles of the Alaska margin (Grantz and May, 1983; *Grantz and others, 1979*), which illustrate that the boundary is characterized by passive margin extensional structures involving down-to-the-basin growth faults. Based on correlation of uncalibrated seismic reflectors, rifting is thought to have initiated in the mid- to Late Jurassic (Grantz and May, 1983; *Vogt and others, 1982*) with subsequent drifting in the Early to mid-Cretaceous (*Sweeney, 1985*).

Direct evidence for the age of rifting and sea-floor spreading does not exist. Aerial magnetic studies (*Vogt and others, 1982*) of the Canada basin yield equivocal results. No clear pattern exists in the magnetic polarity distribution from which "stripes" of typical sea floor can be defined. It is unclear whether the lack of coherent stripes is real or apparent. It is possible that the amorphous pattern is the result of cloaking by thick accumulations of marine sediments. Alternatively, it may be the product of sea-floor spreading during the Cretaceous magnetic quiet interval, or possibly it may be characteristic of this particular tectonic setting.

Continental margin. The non-uniqueness of the geophysical data from the Canada basin has led most workers to seek answers from reconstructions of the tectonic history of the Alaskan and Canadian continental margins. Outlined below are some of the major regional structural relations that must be accommodated by any successful model for the opening of the Canada basin. The Richardson fault system forming the eastern flank of the north-south–trending Richardson Mountains in the Mackenzie delta region (Fig. 12) marks a fundamental boundary in the spatial distribution of both the Mesozoic and Cenozoic deformation and mid-Paleozoic structures. We use this boundary to divide the Alaska, Yukon, and Mackenzie delta region into western and eastern structural domains.

Western fold belt domain. In the western domain (Romanzof, British, Barn, and Richardson Mountains; Fig. 3), Mesozoic and Cenozoic structures consist of major north- and northeast-directed thrusts and associated northerly and easterly trending folds (*Reed, 1968*; *Sable, 1977*; *Dyke, 1971, 1974, 1975*; *Norris and Hopkins, 1977*; Norris, 1985; Oldow and others, 1987b). Deformation may be the product of two major phases of Albian and Maastrichtian age (*Norris and Hopkins, 1977*) with minor post-Paleocene uplift; although we suspect that deformation was essentially continuous within the age brackets. Continuity of deformation is also suggested by the steady development of the North Slope Cretaceous–Tertiary foredeep (Molenaar and others, 1987).

An earlier episode of deformation is recognized by the presence of a mid-Paleozoic unconformity and the existence of more phases of structures in the lower Paleozoic and Precambrian rocks than are found in the overlying successions (*Reed, 1968*; Oldow and other, 1987b). The upper age limit of the mid-Paleozoic deformation is constrained by the involvement of rocks as young as Middle Devonian (*Avé Lallemant and Oldow, 1987*) and from regional stratigraphic relations (*Bell, 1974*). The age of the lower assemblage increases to the north, and the onlapping succession decreases in age to the south. In the north, Silurian and older rocks are overlain with angular unconformity by Carboniferous shales and carbonates (*Norris, 1972*). Farther to the south, rocks as young as Middle Devonian are overlain unconformably by Upper Devonian and Lower Carboniferous units of a south-directed clastic wedge (*Norris, 1968*). In the Ogilvie Mountains and farther south, no Devonian unconformity is recognized (*Bamber and Waterhouse, 1971*).

Eastern cratonic domain. East of the Richardson Mountains, Cambrian through Middle Devonian rocks consist of a lower carbonate platform sequence containing minor clastics. The Cambro-Devonian sequence contains several internal disconformities and overlies Proterozoic rocks. The lower carbonate sequence is overlain disconformably by Devonian rocks of a major south-directed clastic wedge (*Pugh, 1983*). Both Paleozoic successions are overlain disconformably by a major clastic wedge of Albian age. This younger clastic wedge is westerly directed and formed in response to the fold and thrust belt in the western structural domain. Although disconformities exist in the section, the Paleozoic and Mesozoic rocks are not deformed and are essentially flat-lying. This relation is critical in light of the abrupt juxtaposition of these rocks with the deformed sequences across the Richardson fault system (Fig. 12). The eastern domain is part of the cratonic platform of North America (see Bally, this volume) and it has stratigraphic relations essentially the same as in the Canadian Arctic Islands where, however, the rocks were involved in the mid-Paleozoic Ellesmerian fold and thrust belt.

Western Canadian Arctic Islands. The sedimentary rocks of the western Canadian Arctic record an important south-to-north increase in structural complexity. The sedimentary sequence of

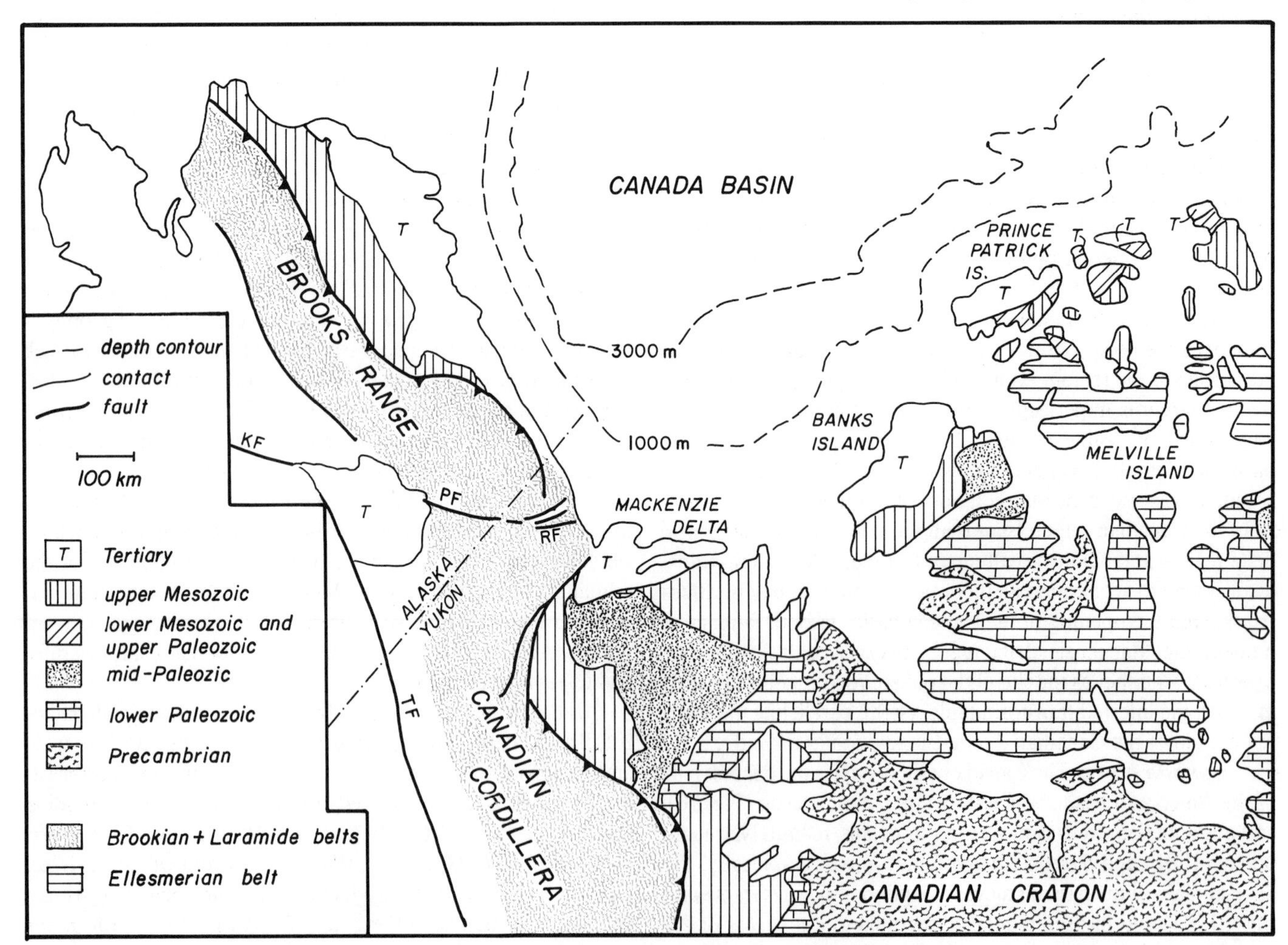

Figure 20. Generalized geologic map of the Canada basin and Alaskan and Canadian continental margins.

Banks Island (Fig. 20) dips homoclinally to the northwest where it projects beneath Cenozoic clastics of the continental margin (*Miall, 1975, 1976a, 1976b*; Norris and Yorath, 1981; Kerr, 1981; Trettin, this volume). The exposed stratigraphic relations are an extension of and are like those briefly outlined above for the eastern structural domain, with the exception that Jurassic and Lower Cretaceous marine clastics are exposed beneath the mid-Cretaceous unconformity. Comparable sediments, if deposited in the area to the south, were removed by erosion before deposition of the Albian clastic wedge. No evidence exists on the surface or in the subsurface to indicate involvement in mid-Paleozoic or late Mesozoic folding and faulting (*Miall, 1975*; Norris and Yorath, 1981; Kerr, 1981).

Relations on Melville and Prince Patrick Islands (Fig. 20), on the other hand, are quite different. A south-directed mid-Paleozoic fold and thrust belt (Innuitian belt) is exposed (*Tozer and Thorsteinsson, 1964*; Kerr, 1981; *Fox, 1985*; Harrison and Bally, 1988; *Harrison and others, 1988*) and is part of the Ellesmerian fold and thrust belt of the Canadian Arctic. Lower Carboniferous rocks overlie folded Devonian and older rocks and are themselves gently warped in folds discordant with the earlier structures. Carboniferous units were deposited in extensional half-grabens superposed on the earlier south-directed fold and thrust belt and were subsequently inverted prior to Permian deposition (*Harrison and others, 1986*). Unlike their correlatives farther south, rocks of Melville Island are not involved in Mesozoic shortening.

Comparison of opening models. The oroclinal opening of the Canada basin is the most popular concept. In this model, both continental boundaries with the Arctic Ocean are passive margins. Grantz and May (1983) indeed have shown that the Alaska continental margin is a rifted passive margin. Whether the Canadian Arctic margin was originally a passive margin is debatable, and possibly is not resolvable. Earlier structural relations have been strongly modified by later right-lateral displacements on the spatially coincident northeastern extent of the Rapid fault system (Fig. 12 and 20). The oroclinal model is commonly cited as best fitting regional stratigraphic relations (Grantz and May, 1983) in which facies patterns in Arctic Canada and northern Alaska are said to represent mirror images about their respective coastlines. Our assessment of the regional stratigraphy leads us to the conclusion that the relations are far from unique and do not yield a compelling argument for or against the oroclinal model.

Paleomagnetic studies would be the most straightforward means of testing the oroclinal model, but results are inconclusive. Most studies have been thwarted by a Cretaceous thermal or geochemical event (*Van Alstine, 1986*) that has reset the older paleomagnetic signatures. In others (*Halgedahl and Jarrard, 1987*), questionable tilt corrections and steep (80°) magnetic inclinations have conspired to make results unreliable.

Structural arguments in favor of the oroclinal model have centered on the Brooks Range fold and thrust belt, and to a lesser degree on structures in the Mackenzie delta region. Mull (1982), like others (*Tailleur, 1973*; Norris, 1985), attempted to directly link the development of the Brooks Range fold and thrust belt with the opening of the Canada basin. In support of this hypothesis, the magnitude of north-directed thrusting in the Brooks Range was proposed to systematically decrease from west to east as the inferred pole of rotation in the Mackenzie delta was approached (Mull, 1982). Structural studies in the central and eastern Brooks Range (Oldow and others, 1987a, 1987b) and balanced cross sections in the central Brooks Range (Oldow and others, 1987a) do not support this contention. Rather, shortening is found to be essentially constant from west to east.

Mid-Paleozoic structures in Devonian to Precambrian rocks of the eastern Brooks Range and the British and Richardson Mountains of northwestern Canada (Fig. 12) were originally thought to be north-vergent and were contrasted with age-equivalent structures in the Canadian Arctic Islands. Devonian structures of the Ellesmerian belt are demonstrably related to a south-directed fold and thrust belt overriding the Arctic platform to the south. Restoration of northern Alaska by oroclinal rotation was invoked to bring the facing of the structural belts into better correspondence.

Kinematic analyses of mid-Paleozoic structures in the eastern Brooks Range and the British and Richardson Mountains (Oldow and others, 1987b; *Avé Lallemant and Oldow, 1987*) indicate that mid-Paleozoic structures in this region are south-vergent. These results are consistent with regional relations, which indicate a systematic decrease in metamorphic grade of lower Paleozoic and Precambrian rocks from north to south in the British and Richardson Mountains (*Bell, 1974*).

In the Mackenzie delta region, the northerly striking Richardson fault system represents a fundamental boundary between rocks involved in "Laramide" deformation on the west and essentially flat-lying rocks to the east. The fault system also juxtaposes Devonian and older rocks with different structural histories. West of the Richardson fault system, the lower Paleozoic rocks are deformed in late Devonian structures; whereas to the east, Devonian clastics and Cambro-Ordovician carbonates are part of undeformed cratonic North America.

A similar boundary is recognized for the southern extent of Devonian structures and more or less follows the southwesterly flowing Porcupine River (Porcupine Shear zone). Although strongly modified by later post-Jurassic tectonism, a clear break between rocks involved in Devonian structures on the north and coeval units not involved in Paleozoic tectonism to the south is evident. A major break in regional stratigraphic relations corresponds to the structural discontinuity.

Restoration of the Devonian thrust front preserved in the Richardson Mountains (west of the Richardson fault) with the projection of the Devonian front in Melville and Prince Patrick Islands (*Bally, 1976*; Dutro, 1981) near the Canadian margin results in approximately 1,200 km of displacement. The onland continuation of the proposed transform is more difficult to locate precisely due to extensive thrusting in the region west of the Mackenzie delta after the opening of Canada basin. Although a southern continuation of the transform along the Richardson fault system into the Mackenzie fold belt cannot be discounted, our preferred projection extends southwesterly through the Porcupine River region in a manner similar to that proposed by Nilsen (1981).

Reconstruction of the Mesozoic Cordillera

Major elements of the accretionary history of the Cordillera are outlined in the maps and sections in Plates 5 and 6. The maps represent progressive restoration of displacements of the primary structural units of the Cordillera, from the present configuration to that in the mid-Eocene (45 Ma), the Paleocene-Cretaceous (65 Ma), and the mid-Cretaceous (100 to 120 Ma). Four sections are depicted for each time frame and illustrate known or inferred structural relations at depth. Less specific reconstructions are made for the Early Cretaceous and mid-Jurassic, the Early Jurassic to Late Triassic, and the mid-Triassic to Late Permian. For these time intervals no cross sections are attempted.

Present configuration. The map on Plate 5A, discussed in some detail in an earlier section, illustrates the major tectonic units that we have differentiated in the North American Cordillera. The boundaries of the tectonic belts are depicted in Figure 10. Four sections illustrate our interpretation of the depth relations and focus on the position of the Moho and postulated deep crustal decollements, the relation of the decollements with the plate boundary, and the base of the lithosphere. The lithosphere in sections A, B, and C all achieve a maximum depth of 300 km under old continental regions. In the Alaskan section (A), the lithosphere is shown to thin toward both the Pacific and Arctic ocean margins. In sections B and C through Canada, the lithosphere thins toward the Pacific. In the northern section (B) the thinning of the lithosphere is interpreted to represent the effects of Precambrian(?) rifting. In section C, part of the thinned lithosphere may be attributed to extensional thinning of late Tertiary age.

In section D, through the Basin and Range province, the lithosphere and Moho are thinned in response to large-scale extension. Comparison of this section with the earlier time frames illustrates the possible effect of thermal and/or mechanical re-equilibration in changing the lithosphere morphology. It is doubtful that sufficient extension occurred in the late Cenozoic to completely restore the thickened crust and lithosphere of earlier time frames to the calculated depths of today. Part of the reduction in lithospheric thickness may be the result of thermal transformation and/or tectonic removal.

Mid-Eocene (45 Ma). The mid-Eocene restoration (Plate 5B) results in a configuration that differs only slightly from that of today. The major difference stems from removal of approximately 75 km of shortening in the frontal part of the Brooks Range of Arctic Alaska (Oldow and others, 1987a, 1987b). Restoration of the Brooks Range front requires recovery of right-lateral motion on the Porcupine shear zone and approximately 200 km of compensation along the Tintina fault system.

Recovery of 200 km of right-lateral motion on the Tintina is not confirmed by geologic relations, but is allowable in the northern part of the fault system where the fault is still seismically active (Estabrook and others, 1988). Restoration of 200 km of dextral slip is problematic if the offset is carried south to the Northern Rocky Mountain trench. We postulate that the displacement steps westerly in a manner similar to that proposed by Price and Carmichael (1986). The best candidate for the displacement is the Finlay fault system (Fig. 3), interpreted to offset the Pinchi-Takla and Kutcho-Teslin faults of northern British Columbia (Gabrielse, 1985). We propose that the offset is transferred to the south through the northern Fraser fault to the Hozameen fault zone where displacements have occurred since 38 Ma (*Ray, 1986*).

Farther west, restoration of about 100 km of right-lateral displacement on the Shakwak segment of the Denali fault system and the Chatham Strait fault is required. This displacement is accommodated in the manner proposed by Stout and Chase (1980). About 40 km of right-lateral motion is removed from the McKinley strand of the Denali fault, and about 55 km of shortening is recovered from the Broxson Gulch thrust system.

In all, the mid-Eocene configuration results in minor southerly displacement of part of the Canadian and Alaskan Cordillera. The displacements are best illustrated in section A through Alaska where the Denali and Kaltag-Tintina fault systems migrate southerly as the frontal portion of the Brooks Range is restored. It is important to remember that the greatest part of the restored displacement occurs in a direction perpendicular to the section.

In sections B and C in Canada, all displacements are essentially normal to the plane of the section, and as such they illustrate little difference between the present-day and mid-Eocene configurations. Section B is modified from a section through the Mackenzie Mountains foreland by *Gordey (1981)* (Plate 7, section B) and through the western tectonic belts to the Pacific coast by *Gabrielse and Taylor (1982).* We have illustrated a Moho depth of about 40 km, which is consistent with depths in the regions to the east. The region apparently has not been affected by substantial extensional tectonism. In section C, we have not restored any Tertiary extension because the magnitude is probably relatively small and difficult to illustrate at the scale of the diagram. The depth of the Moho is restored to below the inferred position of the contractional decollement because it may have been modified by early Tertiary extension related to the development of the Monashee complex to the south (Parrish and others, 1988; Carr and others, 1987).

A substantial difference exists between the present morphology and that of the mid-Eocene in section D through the western United States. We have restored approximately 200 km of late Cenozoic extension and reconstructed a hypothetical subsurface structure for the Sevier hinterland. The major elements of this section are the basal detachment linking displacements in the Laramide uplift structures of Wyoming with those in the Sevier foreland via deep decollements beneath central and western Nevada. Reconstruction of the Sevier foreland is reasonably well constrained from surface and subsurface data (Royse and others, 1975; Bally, 1984). The proposed existence of the mid-crustal duplex underlying central and eastern Nevada is invoked to explain the reversal in vergence of the Eureka thrust (Snoke and Miller, 1988; Miller and others, 1988) and Willow Creek thrust (Speed and others, 1988) during mid- to late Mesozoic deformation. In support of this interpretation is the general lack of high-grade metamorphic rocks in the thrusts west of the Sevier belt. With few local exceptions (*Chan, 1988*), rocks of western and central Nevada do not reach grades higher than lower greenschist facies. Thus, in order to accommodate the easterly directed thrusts of the Sevier foreland and the lack of exposed deeper crustal units like those found in the Shuswap of southern British Columbia (Brown and others, 1986; *Brown and Journeay, 1987*) in the hinterland of the Sevier belt, we invoke a large mid-crustal duplex. We also restore the Moho to depths consistent with the observed depth below the Sierra Nevada. We argue, as have Coney and Harms (1984) before, that a crustal root existed beneath what ultimately became the Basin and Range province. This should not be confused with our interpretation of a lithospheric root, however, invoked to accommodate subdecollement shortening in the continental lithosphere.

Cretaceous-Paleocene (65 Ma). As is readily apparent from Plate 6A, substantial changes in the inferred margin configuration occur between the mid-Eocene and the Cretaceous-Paleocene. Large-scale migration of the Coastal and Columbia belts is depicted, and an additional 250 km of right-lateral motion along the Tintina fault is restored for a total of 450 km. Farther south in the western United States, approximately 250 km of right-lateral motion is restored along the Pine Nut fault system east of the Sierra Nevada and Klamath Mountains. Pre-Tertiary rocks of northeastern Oregon are inferred to lie to the east of the northern projection of the Pine Nut fault, because they are sutured with the continental margin in the vicinity of the Idaho batholith at about 120 Ma (Snee and others, 1989: Lund and Snee, 1988).

In the Brooks Range, 165 km of north-directed thrusting is restored for a total of 235 km. The eastern extension of the frontal Brooks Range restores to a position suggesting that the frontal thrusts of the Brooks Range merge with the eastern part of the Yukon thrust of northwestern Canada. Note that the reconstructed geometry of the Brooks Range and Ogilvie-MacKenzie thrust belts are similar to the geometry predicted in the displacement compatibility model for resolved thrust and strike-slip components around a curved boundary (Fig. 18A and B).

Within the MacKenzie Mountains, an estimated total of 75 km is restored in the frontal portion of the thrust belt. The magnitude of displacement is poorly constrained and exceeds the amount of shortening attributed to the foreland (*Gordey, 1981*; *Gordey and Thompson, 1989*). However, the estimate is comparable to inferred shortening to the north in the MacKenzie and Ogilvie Mountains in published sections by *Vann and others (1986).*

We restored 150 km of east-directed thrusting in the Rocky Mountains of southern Canada and the northern United States. This displacement is close to the total minimum estimates determined by Price (1981) and Bally and others (1966) for the mid-Cretaceous to present. In this region, we invoke a greater amount of shortening than reported in the literature for this and the next interval in order to reduce the severity of the bend in the continental margin depicted in Plates 6A and 6B. The existence of the bend appears to be real and is supported by the trend of the Paleozoic miogeosynclinal section of the western United States. Its existence, however, is problematic for the reconstruction in that it requires substantial distortion of the outboard tectonic belts during southerly restoration. Our attempt to effectively straighten the continental margin by restoration of a large amount of shortening in the foreland fold belt is not unreasonable considering the lack of knowledge of the projected position of the basal detachment of the Rocky Mountain belt in this hinterland region and uncertainties in the thickness of the Proterozoic units.

Farther south, in the Sevier and Laramide belts, we restore 75 km of shortening. Restoration is accommodated both on east- and west-directed thrusts of the foreland region. We have taken the estimated shortening in this foreland region (Royse and others, 1975; Bally, 1984) at face value and have not increased the magnitude.

In Canada and Alaska, restoration of 450 km on the Tintina fault system requires recovery of about 350 km of right-lateral offset from the Kaltag-Tintina fault of Alaska because of the change in orientation of the fault system. An additional 135 km of south-directed shortening is recovered from inferred thrusts between the Ruby-Koyukuk assemblage and the Nixon Fork and Yukon-Tanana terranes of the Central belt. The amount of south-directed thrust displacement predicted is dependent on the amount of estimated north-directed thrusting accommodated in the Brooks Range for the same period. The antiparallel thrusts represent components of a single system and must balance with the strike-slip motion of the Kaltag and Tintina faults.

Recovery of 1,200 km of right-lateral displacement is proposed for the Central fault system separating the Columbia and Central belts. For the same time interval, little or no displacement is postulated for the External fault system. As discussed at some length earlier, it is unlikely that substantial motion occurred on either the McKinley or Hines Creek strands of the Denali fault between 50 and 95 Ma. Thus, we speculate that the Coastal and Columbia belts experienced little differential motion between the Cretaceous-Paleocene and mid-Eocene. Our estimate of 1,200 km of right-lateral displacement of the Central fault system is based on the following reasoning. First, paleolatitude-time curves (Stone and others, 1982; Stone and McWilliams, 1989) suggest an essentially monotonic progression of the coastal terranes northward through the early Tertiary. This scenario is compatible with the plate models of Engebretson and others (1985) and Debiche and others (1987), and without any data to the contrary, we accept the relation as an acceptable first approximation. This estimate appears to be reasonable considering the paleomagnetic data of Irving and others (1985), indicating that rocks of the

Columbia belt were at the latitude of Baja California in the mid-Cretaceous (2,400 km south).

It is likely that substantial southerly restoration of components of the Franciscan complex of California is necessary. We do not have sufficient data, however, to differentiate which parts of the accretionary complex were attached to California or lay farther to the south. We illustrate the possibility of substantial displacement diagrammatically in the reconstruction.

All four sections illustrate the migration of the thrust fronts in the foreland regions and the spatial displacement of the major transcurrent faults. Large displacements of units out of the section are shown; removal of the units composing the Central belt from the section in Alaska is the most dramatic. Displacements out of the plane of the section are responsible for the substantial increase in cross-sectional width of the Ruby-Koyukuk assemblage in Alaska. Section D depicts a reduction in the proposed sub-detachment lithospheric root beneath the orogenic belt compatible with the amount of restored shortening above the decollement.

Mid-Cretaceous (100–120 Ma). The mid-Cretaceous restoration (Plate 6B) is drawn to illustrate the plate-margin configuration immediately after the docking of the amalgamated Wrangellia, Alexander, Peninsular, and Chugach terranes with Superterrane I at relatively low latitudes (Baja California). The position of Superterrane I is interpreted to lie immediately outboard of the continental margin of the western United States without an intervening seaway. Justification for the proximity of the tectonic belts arises primarily from the lack of deformed marine sediments of appropriate age in the proposed displacement zones. The possibility that part of the Franciscan complex was emplaced along the California borderland at this time, however, may suggest that a narrow oceanic belt, open to the south, existed in the southern part of the reconstructed margin.

An additional 150 km of thrusting (for a total of 385 km) is restored in the Brooks Range. The frontal thrust of the Brooks Range is approximately aligned with the reconstructed position of the Tintina fault in northwestern Canada. The Porcupine shear zone, or at least that part of the fault system active during the late Mesozoic and Cenozoic, ceases to exist. We have included the proposed trace of an earlier left-lateral transform active during the opening of the Canada Basin in the Late Jurassic and Early Cretaceous (Avé Lallemant and Oldow, 1988).

Within Canada, 75 km of shortening is restored in the Mackenzie Mountains (for a total of 150 km). Large-scale shortening in the Selwyn and the southern Ogilvie Mountains occurred in the Late Jurassic and Early Cretaceous and may be related to the early history of thrusting in the Brooks Range. In the Brooks Range, thrusting before the mid-Cretaceous was related to the emplacement of Jurassic volcanic arc rocks and late Paleozoic to Jurassic ophiolotic assemblages.

Farther south, in the Rocky Mountains, 150 km of shortening is restored, for a total of 300 km. In the Sevier foreland, 75 km is restored with the complete removal of the Laramide foreland uplifts. Additional shortening in the hinterland of the Sevier belt probably occurred in eastern and central Nevada, but the age of deformation and the amount of shortening is not sufficiently well constrained to warrant inclusion in this reconstruction.

Along the Interior fault system, in Alaska and Canada, an additional 450 km of displacement is removed to restore the estimated 900 km displacement on the Tintina system (Gabrielse, 1985). This restores the continuity of the rocks of the Cassiar and Yukon-Tanana terranes with units residing east of the Tintina fault of today. The fragment of the Yukon-Tanana terrane reported as a thrust sheet in the Selwyn Mountains lies inboard of the northern flank of the Yukon-Tanana now exposed in central Alaska. We speculate that during Late Jurassic and Early Cretaceous contractional deformation in this region, the northern Tintina fault system may not have existed, at least as a major transcurrent structure. To the south, the reconstruction places part of the northern Cassiar terrane outboard of the Proterozoic rocks of the Purcell Mountains.

The southern continuation of the Interior fault system, the Pine Nut fault, accommodates an additional 250 km of displacement for a total of 500 km. Justification for this or greater magnitudes of offset arises from two lines of evidence. In the first, paleomagnetic data from plutons of the Sierra Nevada yield inclination anomalies suggestive of northward displacements of about 700 km since emplacement in the mid-Cretaceous (Frei and others, 1984). The data are consistent with displacements necessary to cause the observed right-lateral step in the initial strontium ratio 0.706 isopleth for Mesozoic rocks in the Sierra Nevada and Great Basin (*Kistler and Peterman, 1978a, 1978b*; Kistler, 1978). They are also consistent with estimates of Late Jurassic and Early Cretaceous left-lateral displacements on the Pine Nut fault based on structural and stratigraphic arguments (Oldow, 1984; Oldow and others, 1984).

Within the Central belt of Alaska, the inferred structural continuity of the Ruby-Koyukuk assemblage is restored. We assert that the entire assemblage of Jurassic volcanic arc, ophiolitic, and metamorphic rocks was emplaced as an internally complex but relatively coherent structural unit during collapse of a marginal basin in the Late Jurassic and Early Cretaceous. We further speculate that the eastern extent of this allochthon is marked by the reconstructed location of the deformed Jurassic-Cretaceous flysch units marking the boundary between the Ruby-Koyukuk province and the Nixon Fork terrane.

The Nixon Fork terrane is restored to a position north and outboard of the Selwyn Mountains. This is consistent with paleomagnetic studies of Devonian carbonates in the Nixon Fork (*Vance-Plumley and others, 1984; Plumley, 1984*), which indicate that there is no evidence of substantial latitudinal displacement with respect to stable North America. The reconstructed position is well within the resolution of paleomagnetically determined displacements.

A large displacement of 1,200 km (2,400 km total) is restored along the Central fault system, bringing the Columbia belt to a position outboard of Baja California and into compatibility with the paleomagnetic data of Irving and others (1985). Restoration of the Columbia belt may be accompanied by comparably large southerly displacements of parts of the Franciscan complex to more southerly latitudes. The arrival and docking of the components of the Columbia belt along the Coastal "megalineament" occurred during this interval. The nature of the tectonic boundary is poorly understood, but local studies (Crawford and others, 1987) indicate that the boundary separates high-grade rocks of the eastern block from lower grade rocks in the west. Development of strong ductile stretching lineations in the fault zone and the metamorphic juxtaposition suggest a large component of thrusting.

Restoration of the Coastal belt by displacement along the Exterior fault system is based on paleomagnetic data (Stone and McWilliams, 1989). For the most part, the Coastal belt consists of the same units as the outer part of the Columbia belt and differs primarily in that the present-day paleomagnetic inclination anomalies of the units indicate approximately 30 to 40° of northward transport; wheras those of the Columbia belt suggest displacements of about 20°. The implication is that the Exterior fault system accommodated from 3,000 to 3,500 km of right-lateral displacement in the late Mesozoic and Cenozoic. An implication of the reconstruction is that the original shape of the Superterrane II during and immediately after docking was less elongate and more equant.

Sections A, B, and C are typified by relatively narrow orogenic belts near the plate margin. The proximity of the back-arc fold and thrust belts to the plate boundary is particularly helpful for the Alaskan section (A) in explaining the obduction of the volcanic-ophiolitic rocks now residing as the structurally highest sheets in the Brooks Range. In this reconstruction, the ophiolites represent parts of large sheets that have been carried north piggyback in the Brooks Range and underthrust by terranes inserted from along the plate boundary to the southeast.

Section D illustrates the space problem of the subdetachment lithosphere with the arrival and docking of Superterrane II to the Columbia belt. As restored, we have the Columbia belt riding on the Farallon oceanic plate without a deep lithosphere of its own. This configuration is based on a previous model of transpressional terrane displacement (Avé Lallemant and Oldow, 1988) in which the Columbia belt had an origin in western Canada and was displaced southward to the mid-Cretaceous position during the Late Jurassic and Early Cretaceous. As is developed elsewhere (Avé Lallemant and Oldow, 1988), relative and absolute plate-motion trajectories between the Pacific basin and North America allowed the southerly displacement of the terranes during the mid-Mesozoic and possibly earlier.

With the docking of Superterrane II to the Columbia belt, the lithosphere of Superterrane II is either subducted or incorporated into the leading edge of the continental lithosphere of North America. If the Superterrane II lithosphere is removed by subduction processes, the removal must occur after amalgamation, because post-emplacement plutons of the Coast Plutonic complex require magmatic sources in the subjacent lithosphere at depths of about 150 km. If the lower part of the lithosphere of Superterrane II was stripped off immediately upon collision with the Columbia belt, the downgoing oceanic slab would have a shallow dip, and the predicted site of arc-related magmatism would lie well to the east of the tectonic boundary.

We illustrate the effect of transferring the Superterrane II lithosphere to the leading edge of North America by augmenting a pre-existing subdetachment root. The pre-existing root is the product of earlier Jurassic and Early Cretaceous shortening in the region east of the Sierra Nevadan arc complex. The effect of the earlier mass balance problem below the regional decollement is mitigated somewhat by the original morphology of the continental lithosphere, which presumably was thinned during Late Proterozoic rifting of the miogeosyncline.

Early Cretaceous to Mid-Jurassic. The Early Cretaceous and mid-Jurassic reconstructions (Plate 6C and 6D) depict the inferred distribution of tectonic belts before large-scale southerly migration of transpressional terranes. Sections are not constructed for this and all remaining reconstructions because we lack reliable constraints. Thus, the following reconstructions illustrate our conception of fundamental aspects of the North American Cordillera but do not address specific details.

The Early Cretaceous reconstruction represents an intermediate stage between the southern migration of the Canadian Cordilleran arc assemblages and their original, pre-displaced position in the Middle to Late Jurassic. One of the major elements of this illustration is the left-lateral transform system (Nilsen, 1981) that we postulate for the opening of the Canada basin. Also shown are the final stages of emplacement of the Angayucham terrane on the southern Alaskan continental margin. Most of the shortening of the metasedimentary rocks of the Brooks Range is restored, and the thrust front shown represents the leading edge of the proto–Brooks Range orogenic belt. Rocks of the near offshore and continental margin of southern Alaska are thought to be imbricated and buried beneath the ophiolitic sheet and to form parts of the southern Brooks Range Schist belt and the Ruby and Seward terranes. In Canada, the Yukon-Tanana and related terranes to the south are found in the same tectonic setting and are reconstructed to the west of their current location by removing thrust displacements from more frontal thrusts of the orogen. It is important to note that our view of the amount of displacement during this and later stages of contraction is unclear. The positions of the Stikinia-Quesnellia arcs in the Columbia belt are largely restored from their southern migration and lie near, but to the south of, their present-day locations. Additional contraction is restored in the western Great Basin, as is some left-lateral motion on the Pine Nut fault system behind the Sierran-Klamath arc system. The boundary between the Canadian contractual belt and that of the fold belt in the conterminous United States is poorly understood.

During the mid-Jurassic most large-scale displacements are restored. In Canada, Stikinia and Quesnellia are restored to a position 500 to 700 km south of their current location, with their southern margins extending to the relative latitude of Idaho. The inferred 500-km right-lateral displacement of Stikinia with respect to Quesnellia (Taylor and others, 1984) is restored such that Pliensbachian ammonite associations are aligned and consistent with the ammonite transition from Tethyan to Boreal in the foreland fold belt. The Monashee and northern Kootenay (Barkerville) terranes are restored to a position nearly coincident with their present-day latitude, but they lie outboard of the Cassiar, southern Kootenay, and southern Slide Mountain terranes. East-directed thrusts are found throughout the Canadian Cordillera and are responsible for substantial shortening.

The Canada basin is closed by restoration of motion along a late Mesozoic left-lateral transform fault system. The Nixon Fork terrane lying in eastern Alaska and northwestern Canada in the mid-Cretaceous reconstruction is moved to the northeast into a foreland position with respect to the Selwyn Mountains thrust belt. Ophiolitic rocks (e.g., Angayucham, Tozitna, and Innoka terranes) and overlying Mesozoic volcanic arc assemblages (Koyukuk and Togiak terranes) are thrust to the north toward the southern Alaskan borderland during the closure of a wide marginal basin.

The Sierran-Klamath arc system is restored to a position approximately 500 km north of that in the previous time frame, yet still about 300 km south of the present-day location. The rotation of the Blue Mountains block of northeastern Oregon is restored about a pole in the northern Klamath Mountains. The region at the latitude of Idaho is the complex juncture of the southern extent of Stikinia-Quesnellia of Canada, the Sierran-Klamath arc, and the double arc system of northeastern Oregon. Northerly displacement for the restoration of the Sierra Nevada–Klamath arc is accommodated along the Pine Nut Fault system. To the east, the Luning-Fencemaker and Sevier thrust systems merge to the southwest with the Pine Nut fault system and do not extend into the southern Sierran arc of the Mojave desert.

The North American Cordillera is represented as a single active margin in the Late Jurassic with an essentially laterally continuous back-arc thrust system directed toward the continent. The mid- to Late Jurassic marks the inception of large-scale southerly migration of transpressional terranes and the onset of opening of the Canada basin. Transpressional displacements along the continental borderland and the morphology of the continental margin strongly affected the axis of contraction in the associated thrust belt in the back-arc region. Close to the plate margin, particularly in the western conterminous United States, shortening was subparallel to the plate boundary. The transport direction apparently is in response to southerly transcurrent displacement on the Pine Nut fault system and to the westerly deflection of the miogeocline.

During the Middle to Early Jurassic, the sense of transcurrent displacement along the Cordilleran margin is not well constrained. A few local studies, such as the work of Hansen (1988) in the western Yukon-Tanana of the Central belt in northwestern Canada, however, indicate dextral transpression of late Early to Middle Jurassic age. Elsewhere, in the western Great Basin, mid-Jurassic mylonites that formed in an ancestral Pine Nut fault system suggest pre–170 Ma right-lateral transpression (*Oldow and Gelber, 1987*; Avé Lallemant and Oldow, 1988). Similarly, dextral displacements are proposed for parts of the Sierra Nevada foothills during the Early(?) to mid–Middle Jurassic (J. B. Saleeby, written communication, 1988). As pointed out by Avé Lallemant and Oldow (1988), there is ample evidence for left-lateral transpression from 245 to 120 Ma, but there is a strong possibility that sinistral transpression was interrupted by dextral motion during this interval.

Early Jurassic to Late Triassic. The Early Jurassic and Late Triassic (Plate 6E and 6F) records the amalgamation of the double-arc system (Stikinia and Quesnellia) of the Canadian Cordillera. Rocks of Stikinia and Cache Creek, and Cache Creek and Quesnellia, are stitched by Early Jurassic plutons and thus were juxtaposed in the earliest Jurassic or possibly in the latest Triassic. Major tectonic activity appears to have been restricted to western Canada, with the onset of the emplacement of the Slide Mountain terrane. Less widespread deformation apparently occurred within the arc system of the conterminous United States. Deformation within arc assemblages of Alaska may have occurred but is not supported by direct evidence.

Emplacement of the Slide Mountain terrane as a widespread allochthon stretching from the Selwyn Mountains in the north to southern British Columbia is interpreted to represent closure of a marginal basin. The age of early thrusting is constrained as post–Late Triassic and pre–Middle Jurassic and may represent the onset of more or less continuous contraction in the Canadian Cordillera. No comparable deformation is recorded in Alaska or in the conterminous United States, where deposition in marginal basin systems continued into the Early Jurassic (Oldow, 1984).

We have reconstructed the central Cordillera during the Late Triassic as a double arc system bound on the east by a narrow marginal basin. In our view, both arcs have a westerly polarity. In Canada, the eastern arc represents Quesnellia and the western arc Stikinia, with the Cache Creek terrane as an intervening accretionary complex associated with Quesnellia. The southern extension of the double-arc system is found within the Mesozoic exposures of northeastern Oregon. Amalgamation of the arc terranes in Oregon apparently occurred in the Late Jurassic and was later than the pre–Early Jurassic docking in Canada.

The rocks with Tethyan faunas in the Cache Creek and related terranes to the south lying inboard of Stikinia are probably off-scraped sediments derived from a remnant of a Pacific basin plate trapped between the North American convergent margin (Quesnellia) and a constructional fringing arc (Stikinia) that evolved in the late Paleozoic to early Mesozoic. The latitudinal position of Stikinia with respect to North America is broadly constrained by the ammonite and bivalve faunas (Taylor and others, 1984; *Tozer, 1982; Tipper, 1981, 1984*; Silberling, 1985) and corresponds to that of Quesnellia. The implication is that Stikinia and Quesnellia are not parts of the same arc system that was subsequently doubled by late Mesozoic tectonism (*Wernicke and Klepacki, 1988*), but rather they formed as a double arc system slightly south of their current location in the Canadian Cordillera.

Mid-Triassic to Late Permian. Broad aspects of the late Early Triassic to mid-Triassic history (Plate 6G and 6H) of the Cordillera margin appear to be quite simple. The entire margin is flanked on the west by a west-facing magmatic arc system. The arc assemblage apparently was constructed on oceanic lithosphere from Alaska, through Canada, and into the western conterminous United States. The southern extent of the arc overlies North American continental lithosphere as the western edge of the Paleozoic miogeosyncline is encountered in the southern Sierra Nevada and Mojave Desert regions. Inland of the southern part of the arc, volcanics were shed easterly and interfinger with continental sediments. Farther north, in the western Great Basin, the southern extent of a long marginal basin that apparently flanked the entire Cordillera from Alaska to Nevada is encountered. The southern part of the marine enclave, in what is commonly referred to as the Mesozoic marine province of the western Great Basin, is a successor basin to the earlier Sonoma orogeny. The origin of the successor basin is unclear and may be the result of thermal contraction of the older orogenic belt or, alternatively, the product of rifting in a purely extensional or possibly transtensional regime. The width of the marginal basin apparently was quite variable from south to north. Considering the timing of the onset of deformation in western British Columbia, it is possible that the Canadian Cordillera was underlain by a narrow segment of the marine system. We envision a widening of the marginal basin in Alaska as a means of delaying emplacement of the ophiolitic rocks of the Angayucham and Tozitna (and other) terranes until the Middle to Late Jurassic.

The continental configuration in the Late Permian to early Early Triassic is similar to that of succeeding time frames, with the exception that upper Paleozoic rocks of the Havallah basin are thrust eastward onto coeval platformal successions in the western Great Basin; a similar situation apparently occurs in the Kootenay terrane of southern British Columbia. Possibly during or slightly before the Sonoma deformation, truncation of the western extension of the Paleozoic miogeosyncline occurred in the Mojave Desert region. Based on preliminary studies of the stratigraphy of Sonora, Mexico, part of the miogeoclinal succession may have been transported southeasterly during the truncation event. If true, this suggests tectonism in a sinistral transpressive regime. Clear evidence of age-equivalent deformation elsewhere in the Cordillera is not recognized as yet, and we illustrate the margin as dominated by a fringing arc system.

Summary. Based on previous work (e.g., Beck, 1976, 1980; Irving and others, 1985; Umhoefer, 1987; Avé Lallemant and Oldow, 1988) and our restorations, we envision the Mesozoic to Recent history of the Cordillera active margin as characterized by large-scale distributed shear with a smaller component of boundary-normal shortening. The displacement history is dominated by southerly migration of transpressional terranes of the Cordilleran borderland in the early Mesozoic, possibly interrupted by an interval of dextral motion, followed by northerly displacement of the terranes in the late Mesozoic and Tertiary.

The early Mesozoic margin consisted of a westerly facing double-arc system that impinged upon the continental margin in the Late Triassic to Early Jurassic, resulting in diachronous closure of a marine marginal basin system stretching from the western conterminous United States through Canada into Alaska. The collision of the inner fringing arc with the North American margin (Slide Mountain terrane emplacement) apparently occurred first in the Canadian Cordillera, suggesting that the marginal basin was not as wide as in areas to the south and north. The impetus for collapse of the marginal basin may have been related to the collision of the outer arc (Stikinia) with the inner arc (Quesnellia).

In the Late Jurassic, oblique plate convergence resulted in the southerly migration of many terranes of the Canadian Cordillera as parts of the Columbia belt. The amalgamated Stikinia-Quesnellia arc moved south outboard of the Sierran-Klamath arc system to a position at the latitude of Baja California. There, Superterrane II was incorporated into the Columbia belt during the mid-Cretaceous. Docking of the terranes either occurred during or was followed by a change in plate motion resulting in right-oblique convergence, which drove the fringing assemblages north.

During the northward migration of the assemblages, the transcurrent component of motion was apparently attentuated in a stepwise fashion with distance inboard of the plate boundary. The Coastal belt records the largest northward displacement of about 40° of latitude (3,500 to 4,500 km). This displacement was taken up on the External fault system and resulted in the dismemberment of Superterrane II.

The Columbia belt migrated north about 20° (2,000 to 2,500 km) with displacements accommodated on the Central fault system. The western part of the Columbia belt, composed of the Wrangellia and Alexander terranes, did not move as far north as their counterparts in the Coastal belt now lying to the north. The eastern portion of the Columbia belt, that part containing the Stikinia and Quesnellia terranes, was returned to the vicinity of its original location after an early Mesozoic displacement to the latitude of Baja California. Paleomagnetic data from Triassic and Jurassic rocks of the Stikinia and Quesnellia terranes do not show a statistically significant displacement with respect to stable North America (Gordon and others, 1984; May and Butler, 1986), indicating that they currently lie within about 500 to 700 km of their original location. The distribution of ammonites and bivalves in the Stikinia and Quesnellia terranes, however, indicates a net northerly displacement with respect to North American faunal assemblages in the foreland fold belt (*Tozer, 1982; Tipper, 1981, 1984*; Taylor and others, 1984; Silberling, 1985). This suggests that the post–mid-Cretaceous northerly motion overcompensated for the earlier south-directed displacement.

Displacement of the Central belt is substantially less than that of the outboard assemblages. In Canada, about 900 km of right-lateral transcurrent motion is taken up on the northern segment of the Interior fault system (Tintina sensu lato). We estimate about 600 to 700 km of right-lateral offset on the continuation of the Tintina fault in Alaska, the Kaltag system. The southern part of the Interior fault system in the western conterminous United States, the Pine Nut fault system, accommodates about 500 to 700 km of right-lateral displacement. The Sierra Nevada and Klamath Mountains, lying outboard of the Pine Nut system, have a net northerly displacement with respect to their inferred positions in the earliest Mesozoic. Northward displacement since the mid-Cretaceous was greater than previous southerly motion in the early Mesozoic.

During progressive northward displacement of the tectonic belts, shortening of 150 to 500 km occurred in the foreland fold belt. The degree of contraction accumulated in the outer tectonic belts for the most part is unknown, but probably is substantial. The amount of shortening within the foreland fold belt is largely controlled by the orientation of the plate boundary and its relationship to relative plate motion. In the Cordillera, stretching from southern California to the Canada-Alaska border, where relative plate motions had large components of boundary-parallel motion, shortening in the foreland fold belt was about 150 to 300 km. In Alaska, where the boundary was oriented at a higher angle to the direction of relative plate motion, over 500 km of shortening is accommodated in the foreland fold belt. An additional 150 to 200 km of south-directed thrusting is estimated in the Central and Coastal belts of Alaska.

CENOZOIC TECTONISM AND VOLCANISM IN THE CORDILLERA

Introduction

Following the pre-Cenozoic accretionary history described above, the pre-Tertiary basement of present-day North America was largely established. A few relatively small allochthonous terranes were amalgamated with North America during the Cenozoic, but these are more notable for their apparent influence on continental deformation and magmatic styles than for the amount of new real estate added to the collage. Continued subduction produced arc magmatism all along the western margin in the early Cenozoic; this activity became more localized after North America overrode the East Pacific Rise and the San Andreas strike-slip zone was developed (Atwater, 1970; Fig. 21). Subsequently, transcurrent and extensional tectonics have strongly influenced Cordilleran magmatic styles, particularly in Neogene time.

Gilluly (1963) and Hamilton and Myers (1966) provided prescient overviews of major tectonic features of the western United States, and Hamilton (1969) and Atwater (1970) were prominent among the first to relate Cenozoic tectonism explicitly to the then relatively new concepts of plate tectonics. Lipman and others (1971), and *Christiansen and Lipman (1972)* provided the first detailed regional overviews relating magmatic activity to convergence between oceanic plates and the western margin of North America, specifically linking the histories of plate interaction and volcanism in the continental interior. Since then, numerous contributions have led to refinements to our understanding of relations between on-land geology and the plate tectonic framework (e.g., *Armstrong, 1974; Elston, 1976, 1984*; Snyder and others, 1976; *Coney and Reynolds, 1977*; Souther, 1977; *Minster and Jordan, 1978; Coney, 1978; Molnar and Atwater, 1978*; Cross and Pilger, 1978; *Keith, 1978, 1982; Pilger and Henyey, 1979*; Dickinson, 1979; Lipman, 1980; *Ewing, 1980; Barrash and Venkatakrishnan, 1982; Glazner and Bartley, 1984*; Engebretson and others, 1985).

In addition, in the past two decades new data have been published: (1) distribution, chronology, and compositions of igneous rocks compiled in useful map form (Stewart and Carlson, 1978; R. B. Smith and Luedke, 1984 and references therein); (2) regional geophysics—heat flow, crustal structure, seismic properties of the crust, seismicity, gravity, and magnetic fields (e.g., R. B. Smith, 1978; Smithson and others, 1979; Eaton, 1982; *Simpson and others, 1986*; Allmendinger and others, 1987); and (3) regional state of crustal stress and its variation with time and space (Zoback and others, 1981). Paleomagnetic studies have demonstrated significant rotational and translational deformation of tectonic blocks within many parts of the Cordillera, and particularly in response to transform or strike-slip deformation along the western margin (e.g., *Magill and others, 1981; Beck, 1984; Wells and others, 1984; Beck and others, 1986*; Frei, 1986).

Heterogeneously distributed extension characterizes many parts of the continental interior in the form of high-angle normal, strike-slip, and low-angle normal faults (e.g., *Davis, 1980*; Eaton, 1982; Coney and Harms, 1984; Hamilton, 1988). Areas affected by low-angle normal faulting commonly involve significant extension accompanied by uplift of deep crust, and are apparently compensated by plutonic underplating of the crust (e.g., Gans, 1987). Geochemical constraints, and especially isotopic data, bear on the distribution of crustal provinces (e.g., Bennett and DePaolo, 1987; Wooden and others, 1988), and the relative roles of lithospheric and asthenospheric mantle in magma production (e.g., *Zartman, 1974*; Leeman, 1970, 1982a; Armstrong and others, 1977; Farmer and DePaolo, 1983; *Hart, 1985; Carlson and Hart, 1987; Perry and others, 1987*; Ormerod and others, 1988; Fitton and others, 1989).

In the following sections, we review these topics in more depth to give some flavor of the current understanding of Cordilleran Cenozoic geology. For additional details we refer the reader to the references cited above and to other contributions to *The Geology of North America,* particularly Christiansen and Yeats' (1989) summary of the Cenozoic geologic history of the Cordilleran western United States.

Tectonic provinces

Until the Eocene, almost all of the western North American margin was in compression, causing thrusting and margin-parallel transcurrent faulting. Following strong right-oblique convergence during the late Mesozoic through the early Oligocene, the East Pacific Rise impinged upon the North American borderland, resulting in the development of a transform boundary.

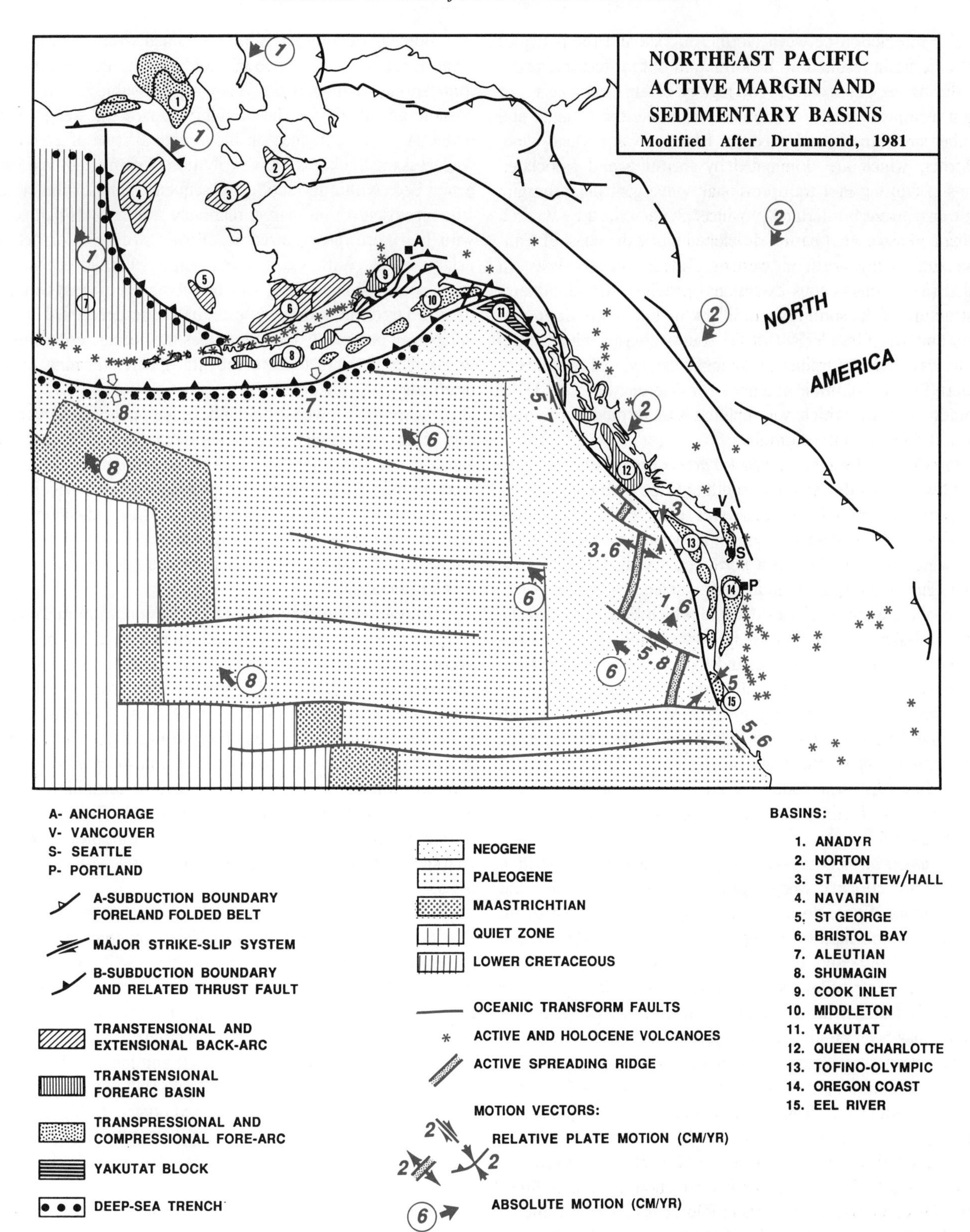

Figure 21. Tectonic and index map of sedimentary basins of the Pacific Northwest. Ocean basins are shown in red. Plate convergence rates are taken from *Drummond (1981)*. Of all the sedimentary basins shown on the map, only the Cook Inlet has significant hydrocarbon accumulations; minor accumulations occur also in the Anadyr basin.

The interaction between North America and the plates of the Pacific basin resulted in the formation of four tectonic provinces during the Cenozoic: (1) two regions of late Cenozoic active margin tectonism, one in Alaska and northwestern Canada and the other stretching from Vancouver Island to Cape Mendocino, California, which are dominated by thrusting and associated strike-slip faulting in a transpressional convergent plate margin; (2) a transcurrent borderland province, characterized by wrench faulting and associated basins, developed along the coast of California and to the north in western Canada and southeastern Alaska; (3) a conspicuous extensional province that dominates the structure of the southern Cordillera, including the Basin and Range and Rio Grande Rift of the southwestern United States and the less obvious Omineca-Okanogan extensional complex of southern British Columbia and northern Washington; and (4) the Colorado Plateau, which was uplifted and formed a coherent structural domain in the Cordillera.

Pacific Northwest and Alaska active margins. The Pacific Northwest from the Aleutians south to Cape Mendocino, California, can best be divided into several sectors (Fig. 21): (1) the Gulf of Alaska–Aleutian arc system, associated with the Pacific plate, which is subducted in a northwesterly direction; (2) the Queen Charlotte transform fault, which extends from the northern end of the Juan de Fuca ridge and which bifurcates into the Gulf of Alaska accretionary wedge system and the Shakwak-Denali strike-slip fault onshore; and (3) the Cascade Island arc system, which extends onshore from the projection of the north end of the Juan de Fuca ridge to Cape Mendocino and which corresponds to a transpressional system sandwiched between the southwest-moving North American plate and the more north-moving Juan de Fuca plate. For an overview of the western North American Tertiary basins and structures, we refer to Scholl and others (1987).

Comment on accretionary wedges. Much has been written about the accretionary wedges of the northeastern Pacific and their formation. Space does not permit the review of all pertinent literature, but informative reviews have been published by *Scholl and others (1980)* and *Cowan (1985).* An outstanding set of seismic-reflection profiles across many of the accretionary wedges offshore of Alaska, British Columbia, and the conterminous United States, has been published by von Huene (1986).

Accretionary wedges are homologous to the foreland folded belts such as that of Alberta, Canada. In one case, oceanic lithosphere is subducted, leading sometimes to decoupled and imbricated oceanic crust (e.g., Olympic Mountains), and perhaps more characteristically to imbricated sediments. This structural style is related to Benioff-type or B-subduction of oceanic lithosphere. This contrasts with foreland fold belts (Plates 5A and 7) where frontal decoupling is often limited to the sediments, and where additional decoupling involves parts of the continental crust itself. Often implicit in this tectonic style is the subduction of limited amounts of the underlying continental lithosphere; it is referred to as Ampferer or A-subduction (Bally, 1975; see also Fig. 1).

Both subduction types are associated with classical decollement tectonics. But active-margin, accretionary wedges have some special characteristics. They are not subjected to subaerial erosion, and therefore, the original taper of the wedge remains intact. A major influence on the structural style of accretionary wedges is the thickness and distribution of competent and incompetent beds within the subducted sequence. Thus, submarine fan sequences deform into large, relatively simple folds that contrast with the more disorganized to chaotic structures of deformed pelagic oozes. With a rough and perhaps faulted oceanic basement, some sediments may well be subducted to great depths, but by and large, the sediments eventually are decoupled from the underlying basement, and sometimes the oceanic crust and mantle itself is decoupled from the lithosphere, forming ophiolite imbricates.

Accretionary wedges often have high pore pressures at shallow depths, as was suggested earlier by the drilling results offshore Vancouver Island (Shouldice, 1971; *von Huene and Lee, 1982*). Accretionary wedges also often contain hydrates, which are visible as sea-floor–parallel reflectors on seismic-reflection profiles. Hydrates lead to unstable slope conditions on the sea floor, often expressed as a seismically transparent sediment apron that covers much of the slope.

All these elements influence the formation of mélange. Accretionary wedges replicate decollement principles, but specific decollement styles are modified by the high pore pressures and near-surface hydrates. High pore pressures lead to the flow of shales, shale diapirs, and mud volcanoes, but also to hydrofracturing of indurated sediments as observed in clastics and carbonates in outcropping mélange sequences (*Letouzay and Sage, 1988*). Hydrates, on the other hand, may lead to unstable slopes and associated gliding and slumping phenomena. Thus, accretionary wedge mélanges form in a setting that combines decollement tectonics in a high pore pressure environment with surficial gliding and slumping.

Gulf of Alaska–Aleutian Island arc system. The Gulf of Alaska has had a long history of plate convergence. The Cretaceous Kula plate (*Cooper and others, 1987*) was subducted underneath the Okhotsk-Chukotsk volcanic arc of easternmost Siberia and the northern Peninsular terrane in Alaska. To the north of this ancestral arc, several Tertiary transtensional backarc basins formed on the Bering shelf and include the economically prospective Navarin, St. Matthew-Hall, and Norton basins (*Fisher and others, 1982*; *Marlow and others, 1987*). The Upper Cretaceous to Tertiary Anadyr Basin of Siberia, according to *Marlow and others (1987),* is a forearc basin associated with the East Siberian volcanic arc.

The formation of the Aleutian arc to the south of the Cretaceous ancestral arc began in Eocene time, when a fragment of the Cretaceous oceanic Kula plate with its cover of Cretaceous to Tertiary sediments (Aleutian basin) was captured. The sediments of the Aleutian basin thicken toward the northern accretionary zone of the Peninsular terrane. The Aleutian arc is a composite volcanic complex that formed 55 to 50 m.y. ago during three distinct phases: (1) early to middle Eocene, (2) Oligocene to Miocene, and (3) Pliocene to Quaternary (*Scholl and others, 1987b*). Minor fore-arc basins of transtensional character separate the volcanic complex from an accretionary wedge, which is particularly well displayed on seismic-reflection profiles.

Farther to the east, the continuation of the Tertiary Aleutian volcanic arc complex is built on the Mesozoic Peninsular terrane, which along its truncated southern boundary is thrust across the Upper Cretaceous to Paleogene accretionary wedge of the Chugach and Prince William terranes. Superposed on that accretionary wedge are additional small Tertiary forearc basins of presumably transtensional origin (*Bruns and others, 1987*; *von Huene and others, 1987*). The economically most important one is the oil-bearing Cook Inlet basin (*Magoon and Claypool, 1981*; *Fisher and others, 1987*), which is characterized by large Neogene inversion anticlines.

Where the Aleutian arc system intersects the Queen Charlotte–Fairweather transform fault system, interesting structures have developed (*Plafker, 1987*). The Aleutian thrust is the southernmost boundary of the accretionary wedge that parallels the Aleutian deep-sea trench. Neogene accretionary thrusting and folding extends into the eastern half of the Gulf of Alaska shelf and onshore, where east-west–trending folds are interrupted by a few northwesterly trending thrust faults. Thus, the forearc region that lies in front of the Chugach–St. Elias Mountains of southern Alaska is essentially a Neogene folded belt that is "underthrust" on the east by the much less deformed Yakutat terrane. The Oligocene-Neogene Yakutat basin overlies the Yutatat terrane of a Mesozoic "continental crust" to the east and a Paleogene oceanic crust to the west (*Plafker, 1987*). At least the eastern segment of the Yakutat terrane, according to Plafker, has been rafted from over 600 km farther south along the Queen Charlotte–Fairweather fault system. *Bruns (1983)* even postulated rafting distances in excess of 2,000 km.

Queen Charlotte transform. The Alexander Archipelago, of southernmost Alaska, and the Queen Charlotte Islands are underlain by the combined Alexander-Wrangellia terranes that have been dissected by a number of dextral strike-slip fault systems. The westernmost, the Queen Charlotte–Fairweather fault system is, in essence, a transform fault that connects the Juan de Fuca spreading ridge with the Aleutian subduction zone. The Queen Charlotte fault is mildly transpressional (*Yorath, 1987*; Yorath and Hyndman, 1983).

To the east of the Queen Charlotte Islands is the large Neogene Queen Charlotte basin, which on seismic-reflection profiles, appears to be characterized by transtensional faulting. The southern half of the basin is covered by widespread basaltic volcanics that may be underlain by a considerable thickness of Neogene sediments. The overall tectonic setting of the basin bears some similarity to the Salton basin in California, and there is evidence that the basin is underlain by attenuated crust (Yorath and Hyndman, 1983).

Cascade fore-arc. The active margin sector that extends from the Juan de Fuca ridge to the Mendocino transform fault is part of the Cascade volcanic arc system, with its active volcanos in the northwestern United States and some extinct volcanos in British Columbia. Volcanism in the Cascades began at about 44 to 38 Ma.

The Canadian segment includes Vancouver Island, a fragment of the old Wrangellia terrane, which, as shown by recent crustal surveys, is thrust over the eastern, probably imbricated, extension of the oceanic Juan de Fuca plate (see, Clowes and others, 1987; *Yorath, 1987*). Drilling in the Tofino Basin offshore of western Vancouver Island has penetrated Neogene mélange complexes and encountered very shallow, high pore pressures, suggesting a genetic relationship between pore pressure and mélange (Shouldice, 1971). The Tofino basin itself is characterized by elongated compressional anticlines that often are cored by chaotic, overpressured Miocene rocks. The same drilling program also penetrated Tertiary basalts, which on the basis of aeromagnetics, are linked to the Paleogene basalts of the Olympic Mountains to the south.

Coastal Washington, Oregon, and northern California and the offshore regions can be viewed as a Tertiary accretionary wedge and forearc basin complex. In the Olympic Mountains of western Washington (Snavely, 1987), Paleocene and Eocene alkalic basalts and thick pillow lavas overthrust younger, mostly Neogene mélange sequences. A number of models have been postulated for the formation of the basalts. For example, *Snavely and others (1980)* suggested accretion of a seamount-bearing oceanic plate, and more recently, Snavely (1987) suggested an oceanic pull-apart setting comparable to the Gulf of California–Salton trough basin. The pull-apart basins apparently experienced small (350 km) northward translation based on paleomagnetic studies of Eocene basalts. Eocene clastics are deposited both on the allochthonous basalts of western Washington and on coastal areas of the Klamath Mountains to the south, clearly indicating that these oceanic terranes were accreted to the North American continent by the Eocene.

On the inner continental shelf, there are a number of small Neogene forearc basins that are superposed on a folded Eocene accretionary complex (Fig. 21). Toward the outer shelf, the Eocene accretionary complex overthrusts a younger Neogene accretionary wedge to the west. Northerly trending anticlines in the offshore are typically elongate and often cored by mobile shales. The anticlines are generally interpreted as diapiric structures, and seismic-reflection profiles show obvious stratigraphic convergences that reflect growth of these compressional features. Occasional allochthonous shale flows are sandwiched between clastics on the flanks of these anticlines.

The continental slope corresponds to the leading edge of the accretionary wedge, which is still active today. While the dominant vergence of the structures is to the west, seismic-reflection data show that some structures have a clear vergence toward the continent (*Seely, 1977*; Snavely, 1987). These structures are analogous to the "triangle zone" or "wedging" structures that have long been known from foreland fold belts such as the Alberta foothills (Price, 1981).

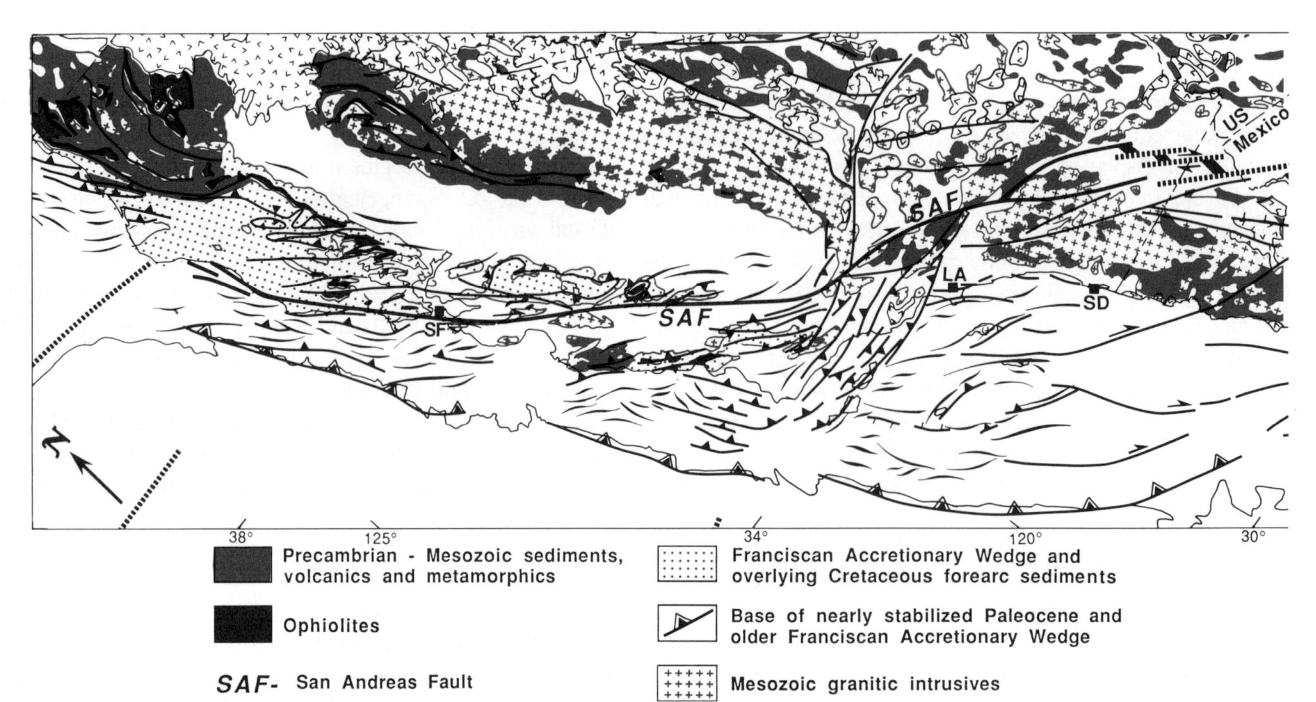

Figure 22. Simplified geologic map of California and Baja California. Note the widespread occurrence of folds and thrust faults associated with the San Andreas fault (SAF).

The Eel River basin offshore of northern California is important because of its size and economic potential. It is another dominantly compressional fore-arc basin that is overlying an accretionary wedge facing the Gorda plate. It contains more than 3 km of upper Cenozoic, dominantly marine sediments (*Clarke, 1987*). The northeast flank of the basin is a strike-slip fault, which emphasizes the transpressional character of the basin.

Transcurrent tectonics of California. California offers a splendid example of Tertiary strike-slip tectonics (Fig. 22) that affects a complex Mesozoic substratum composed of fore-arc, arc, and accretionary prism terranes. For additional geographic locations and fault names the reader should refer to Figure 26. For locations of basins, refer to Figure 23. Figure 24 shows a simplified distribution of California basement provinces.

During the Paleogene, an oblique-slip regime controlled the formation of successor basins that were superposed on a Cretaceous fore-arc basin (Fig. 23). In the late Paleogene the dextral San Andreas strike-slip system was initiated (about 29 Ma), and it is clear that numerous Tertiary basins are temporally associated with Neogene displacement along the fault. Deformation of these basins by late Neogene thrust faulting and folding is associated with a transpressional belt in central and northern California.

The San Andreas fault is one of California's most outstanding geologic features. Its length is in excess of 1,000 km and it has a cumulative right-lateral slip of greater than 320 km. *Hill (1981)* reports G. K. Gilbert's early measurements of right-lateral offset associated with the 1906 earthquake. Until the mid-1920s, however, it was widely accepted that the principal movement along the fault was dip-slip. *Vickery (1925)* and *Noble (1926)* were the first to propose substantial cumulative strike-slip displacement, but the real breakthrough came with Hill and Dibblee (1953) who postulated more than 560 km of dextral slip. Crowell (1962) summed up most of the pre-plate tectonic data on the displacement along the San Andreas fault. For additional background see Sylvester (1984, 1988).

Proto–San Andreas fault system. The Jurassic-Cretaceous history of California left a record of complex accretionary tectonism involving first sinistral and later dextral plate convergence, an associated Cretaceous forearc basin, and the presently exhumed Jurassic and Cretaceous arc system of the Sierra Nevada and Peninsular Range. This arc–forearc–accretionary wedge system was fragmented during: (1) the Late Cretaceous–Paleocene (proto–San Andreas fault), and (2) the mid- and late Paleogene and Neogene (San Andreas fault system).

Paleomagnetic data suggest that during the Late Cretaceous the Salinia terrane was located some 2,600 km south of its present location. After the Paleocene, oblique dextral subduction of the Farallon plate beneath North America was responsible for about 1,500 km of northward displacement of Salinia along the proto–San Andreas fault (*Kanter and Debiche, 1985*). Poorly dated, probably Lower Cretaceous, volcanics in outcrops near Point Arena, north of San Francisco, may have originated even farther south (*Kanter and Debiche, 1985*) and may have undergone northward migration of about 2,900 km between 90 and 48 Ma.

The proto–San Andreas system formed as the result of oblique subduction of the Farallon plate, and in the Late Cretaceous to Paleocene by subduction of the Kula plate (Enge-

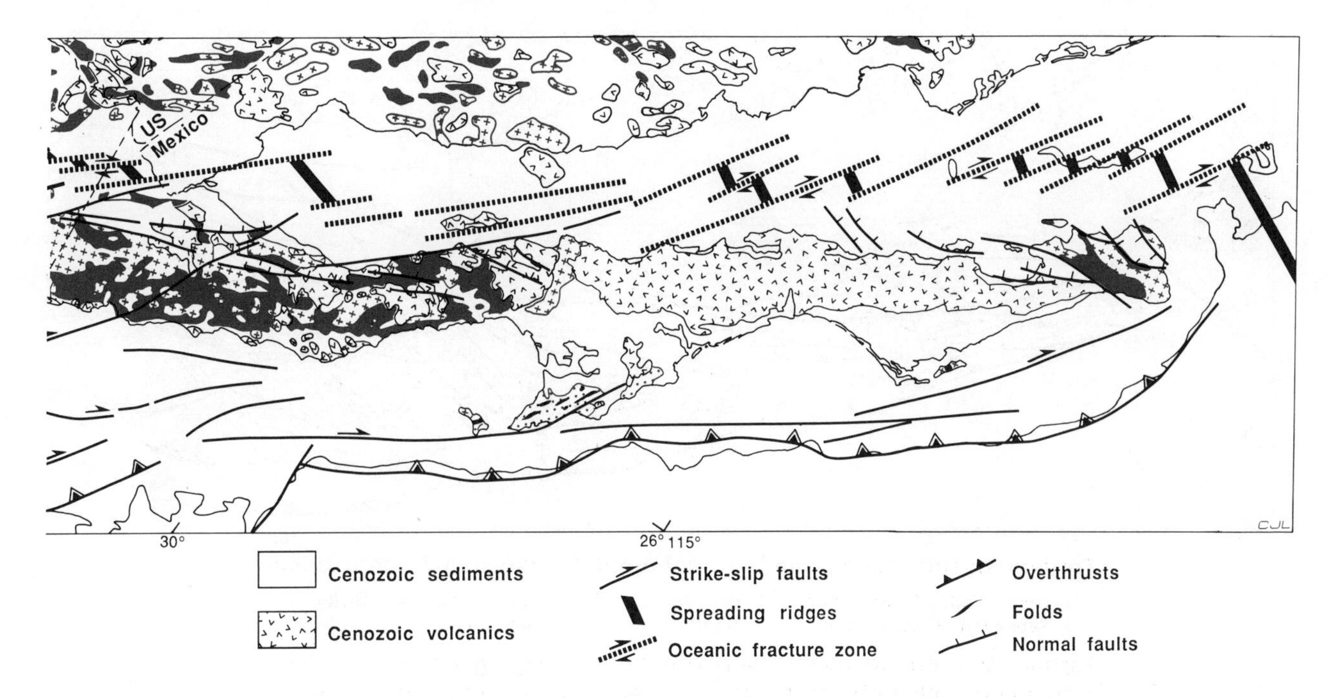

bretson and others, 1985; Beck, 1986). Much later, about 4 Ma, the Salinian block and an attached accretionary wedge began to travel with the Pacific plate because of propagation of the East Pacific rise into the continental margin at the mouth of the Gulf of California. A sliver (Baja California) was rifted from the continent and, together with part of coastal California, is now moving northward relative to the North American craton. Long distance rafting of the Salinian unit and its associated accretionary wedge poses the inevitable question concerning the original location of the Paleogene sedimentary basins of California (*Nilsen and Clark, 1975*; Nilsen 1987). An essential aspect of this question is that the Cretaceous Great Valley basin has been truncated by the San Andreas fault, and its rafted southern half has not been identified as yet farther north.

It is useful to separate the Paleogene sequences deposited in the Great Valley basin, which maintained its continuity with the adjacent Klamath-Sierran basement, from those that occur in numerous basins southwest of the San Andreas fault. The basins southwest of the San Andreas were formed in a mobile environment associated with a fore-arc region. During the Paleogene, they were swiftly rafted toward the north and subsequently segmented and further deformed by Neogene transtensional and transpressional events.

In general, Paleogene sediments were supplied from uplifted Mesozoic granites and metamorphics to the east and deposited in troughs that more or less coincide with the earlier Cretaceous fore-arc basins. During the Eocene, a faulted arch (the Stockton arch; Nilsen, 1987) separated the northern Great Valley from the southern San Joaquin basin. During the early Eocene, sediment influx from the adjacent Salinian block lying to the west is observed for the first time. Sediments accumulated in the form of two deep-sea fans deposited across the fault system into the San Joaquin basin. Today the San Andreas fault offsets these fans by about 315 km (*Clarke and Nilsen, 1973*).

During this time, a series of borderland basins formed, including the predecessors of today's Santa Maria and Ventura–Santa Barbara basins. The mechanics of the formation of these basins remain obscure. Either a transtensional pull-apart origin or a transpressional origin is possible for these basins.

Oligocene oblique subduction of the Farallon plate continued in northern California, and perhaps at slower rates at the base of the central California accretionary wedge. During the Oligocene, marine conditions continued in the San Joaquin–Sacramento basins, but most of the Salinian borderland is characterized by continental deposits. According to Nilsen (1987) restoration of Neogene displacements suggests a single basin that connects many basins of the Salinian block with the Oligocene sequences of the Transverse Ranges. The Paleogene and older accretionary prism that formed offshore of California was essentially stabilized by the end of the Paleogene. Only mild reactivation occurred during the Neogene (Figs. 24 and 25B).

San Andreas fault and the transverse ranges. During the late Oligocene and early Miocene, widespread magmatism occurred along the Cordilleran continental margin. Subduction was terminated along this segment of the coast by the early Miocene upon the arrival of the Pacific-Farallon spreading ridge and the birth of the San Andreas strike-slip fault in central California. The associated widespread individualization of several Neogene sedimentary basins was followed by extensive folding, thrust faulting, and inversion tectonics. All this suggests considerable transtension and transpression.

To gain a perspective on the overall Neogene displacements in California, displacement estimates, as recently compiled by Nilsen (1987), are listed on Figure 26. Nilsen points out that the

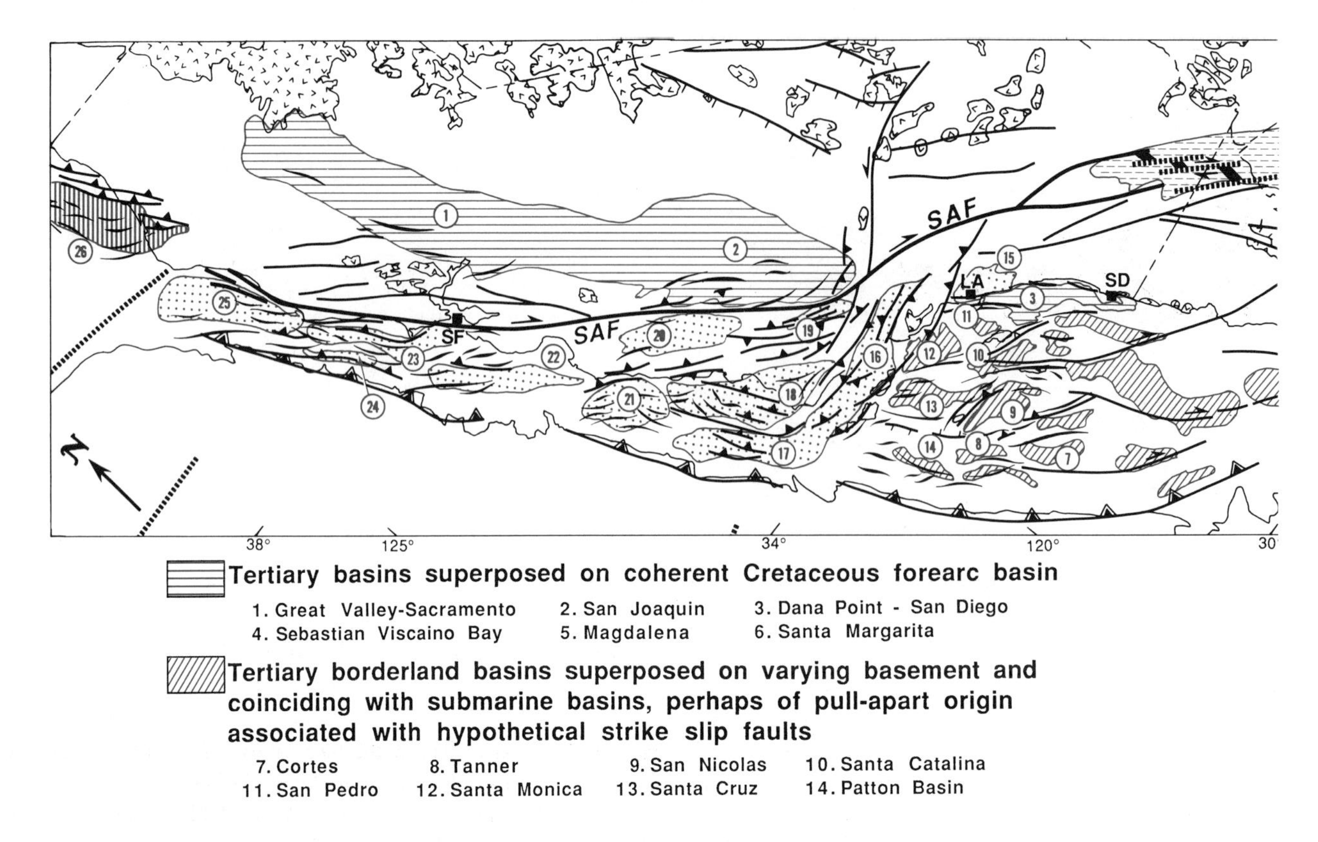

Figure 23. Map showing the location and types of sedimentary basins of California and Baja California. SAF: San Andreas fault.

cumulative right-lateral Neogene displacement along faults associated with the San Andreas amounts to about 1,000 km, and that cumulative left-lateral displacements add up to about 150 km. Of course, the displacements that have been proposed by different authors have large uncertainties. As Crowell (1962) pointed out, the accuracy of strike-slip displacement estimates is dependent on the acceptability of long-distance correlations of like geology on either side of a fault. Even with the uncertainties, the amounts of Neogene displacements listed in Figure 26 are generally accepted, and if anything, larger estimates of strike-slip displacement may be anticipated from future studies.

Tectonic styles associated with strike-slip faulting have been addressed by *Wilcox and others (1973), Dibblee (1977), Harding (1974, 1976),* and *Sylvester and Smith (1976).* The main emphasis of these studies is on simple shear tectonics, en echelon folding (e.g., *Dibblee, 1977*), and the formation of both contractional and extensional flower structures. Recently, a growing number of studies show the widespread occurrence of thrust faults and associated folds, particularly in central California (between San Francisco and Los Angeles).

Across the Transverse Ranges and the Ventura basin, Yeats (1981, 1983) documents a considerable amount of Plio-Pleistocene thrust faulting. The shortening is tied to a speculative mid-crustal decollement level that can also be inferred from seismic studies of *Hadley and Kanamori (1975).* The Ventura basin is overthrust from both the south and north. The northern overthrust system continues westward to form the northern margin of the Santa Barbara basin. To the north, in the Wheeler Ridge area and across the left-lateral Garlock fault, north-verging overthrusts have been known for some time. Thus, the Transverse Ranges appear as a floating allochthon that overlies a deep lithospheric root (Namson and Davis, 1988a). Seismic tomographic studies (*Humphreys and others, 1984*) suggest a high-velocity anomaly extending to about 250 km depth, which is interpreted as a lithospheric root (see also, *Bird and Rosenstock, 1984*). Perhaps thermal uplift associated with the incipient elimination of that root is responsible for the rapid uplift of the Transverse Ranges.

Northward underthrusting of the lithosphere beneath the Transverse Ranges also must be related to paleomagnetic data reported by Luyendyk and Hornafius (1987) and their colleagues. Data from Tertiary volcanics imply Neogene clockwise rotation on the order of 70 to 90°, affecting the northern Channel Islands and the Santa Ynez Range to the north. An early phase of about 50 to 60° of rotation occurred during the middle Miocene, and another 20 to 30° occurred during the late Miocene to Quaternary. The implication is that, prior to the rotation, the domain of the future Transverse Range had a north-south orientation.

Luyendyk and Hornafius (1987) propose a simple shear model involving a number of rotating prismatic borderland fault blocks of the Transverse Ranges. Structural geologists may find it difficult to reconcile this model and its regular prismatic blocks with the reality of widespread surface and subsurface folds and

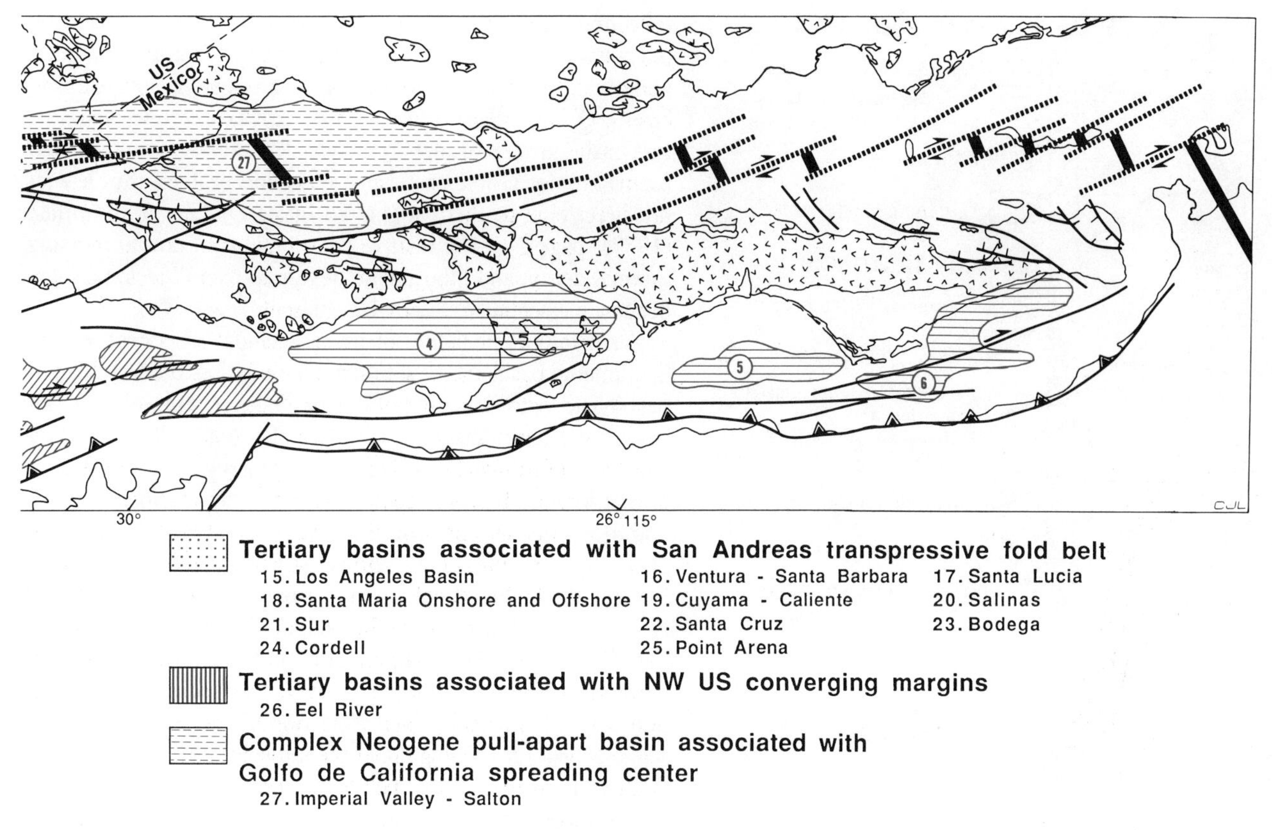

thrust faults, and possibly more importantly with the absence of direct observations supporting deep-seated extensional structures. In agreement with Namson and Davis (1988a), we prefer to combine, in a single model, rotation and overthrusting with transpression, beginning during the middle Miocene and culminating during the Plio-Pleistocene. Such a process can also be related to the origin of the Los Angeles, Ventura–Santa Barbara, Cuyama, and Santa Maria basins (Fig. 23).

Farther north, in a transect that extends from the San Joaquin Valley to the offshore Santa Maria basin, the studies of Crouch and Bachman (1984), Namson and Davis (1988b), and *Meltzer (1988)* also suggest widespread Neogene compression that is superposed on the Paleogene strike-slip tectonics of the Salinia block (Fig. 24) and, to the west, the adjacent rafted Franciscan collage (the Sur Obispo terrane). Like *Suppe's (1973)* explanation for earlier deformation in northern California, Namson and Davis (1988a) treat central California essentially as a folded belt with a well-developed decollement structure, blind thrusts, backthrusting, etc. The proposed amount of shortening is relatively small, but nevertheless poses the problem of a lithospheric root, which Namson and Davis show as a distributively thickened lithosphere. On the other hand, a lithospheric root could also be a subducted slab that would not necessarily have to lie below the San Andreas fault itself.

The perception of widespread compression is further strengthened by borehole studies undertaken by *Mount and Suppe (1987)* who suggest that displacement along the San Andreas fault itself may be nearly frictionless. The transpressional tectonics in the area apparently are characterized by a low-stress strike-slip component and high-stress compressive component. An important element of this idea is that it may serve as a modern analog to the processes that involve Paleogene and earlier terrane rafting due to oblique convergence.

The San Andreas fault system thus had a conspicuous transpressional component leading to the formation of decollement fold belts that may overlie a lithospheric root; the major strike-slip faults themselves separate segments of the fold belts with overall opposite vergence (Figs. 24 and 25). This tentative conclusion emphasizes the need to substantially improve seismic-reflection and refraction techniques to obtain better resolution for any flat decoupling levels that may occur within California's middle and lower crusts. In particular, greater detail is needed for the structure of the lower crust and upper mantle structure immediately adjacent to the San Andreas fault.

Sedimentary basins. Figure 23 shows the distribution and a broad breakdown of the different kinds of basins that are characteristic of California. Dickinson and others (1987a) have analyzed most of the important basins in California using conventional backstripping methods; their work provides a first overview of residual subsidence that may be due to tectonic factors. Dickinson and others (1987a) point out that basin reconstructions are seriously hampered by paleontological problems such as diachroneity of benthic faunas, imprecision of paleobathymetry based on the paleoecology of foraminiferal associations, and difficulty of compiling reliable stratigraphic columns in the near-absence of good quality published regional seismic-

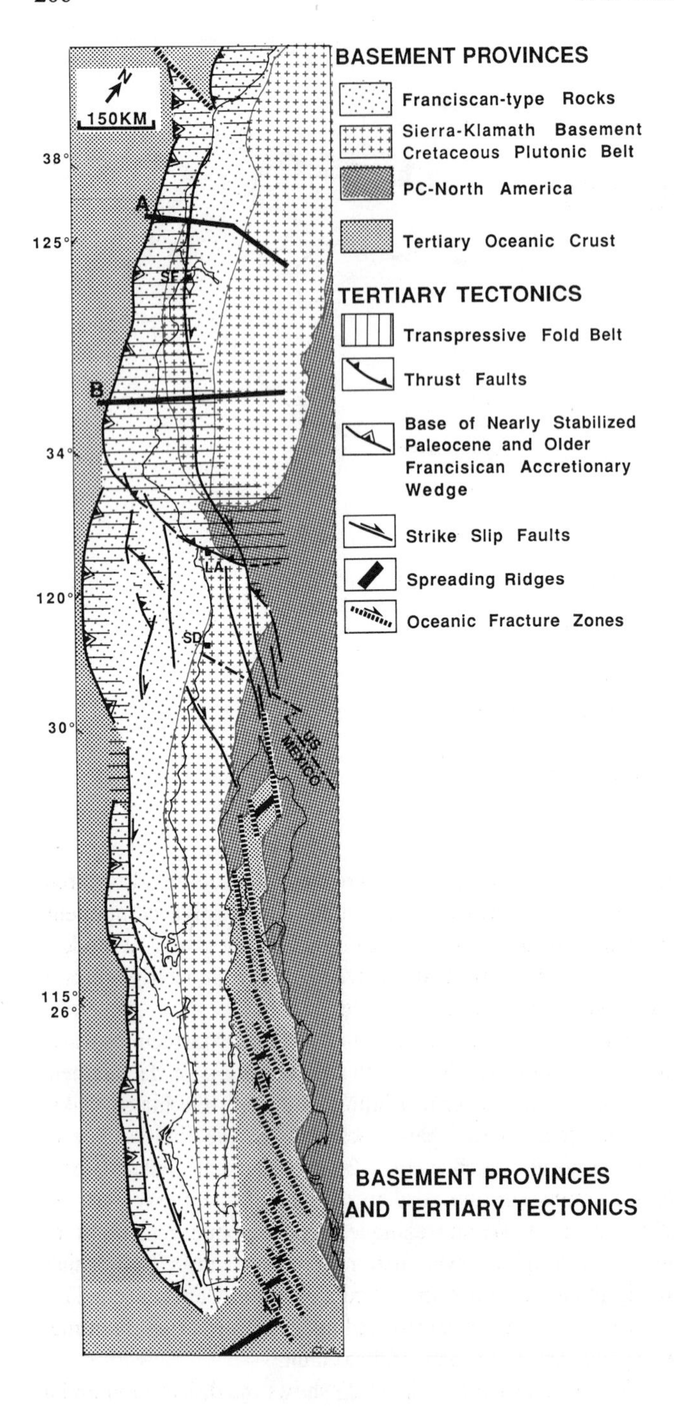

Figure 24. Simplified basement map and the distribution of Tertiary transpressive folds. Franciscan-type rocks represent accretionary wedge complexes that contain Jurassic to Paleocene strata. The Sierra Nevada–Klamath basement represents older units that are intruded by Mesozoic plutons. Note that the Precambrian craton of North America extends almost to the Pacific coast.

reflection data. So far, published reflection-seismic data show only a relatively bland, westward-dipping "Sierran" basement underlying most of the Sacramento–San Joaquin and Cuyama basins. On the other hand, the important Los Angeles and Ventura basins are seismically "bottomless" because the bases of these basins are not visible on seismic-reflection profiles; thus leaving no direct clue to their origin. To quote Dickinson and others (1987a, page 2), "The relative contributions of crustal thinning, thermal decay, and lithospheric flexure to overall tectonic subsidence are essentially unknown at present."

An important family of basins includes the Great Valley–Sacramento basin and its southern continuation, the San Joaquin basin. The tectonic setting of this basin as a Cretaceous fore-arc basin has been discussed earlier (see also Ingersoll *1978*, 1979, *1982b*). Unfortunately, we lack convincing models for the formation of fore-arc basins in general. Often a transtensional origin is appealing, but seismic-reflection data in the Great Valley show only minor amounts of extensional basement faulting. During the Eocene, the faulted Stockton arch separated the Great Valley in two segments, the northern Sacramento basin and the southern San Joaquin. The San Joaquin is dominated by marine sedimentation throughout most of the Tertiary, with sediment accumulation rates dramatically increasing during the Neogene, which suggests flexural bending under the influence of the adjacent San Andreas transpressive fold belt to the west.

A second group of basins is located west of the San Andreas fault and is superposed mostly on Franciscan-type basement or small slivers of Sierran-type basement of the Salinian block (Fig. 24). These "basement" elements, in addition to Neogene strike-slip rafting, underwent large Paleocene and earlier northward displacement; thus they originated at a latitude somewhere offshore of central Mexico.

The most important of the basins west of the San Andreas fault is the Los Angeles basin, which has been extensively studied because, in terms of barrels per sediment volume, it is one of the richest petroleum-bearing basins of the world. It is also the only petroleum-bearing basin located south of the Transverse Ranges. Dickinson and others (1987a) suggest the existence of an earlier lower to middle Miocene fault system that was located offshore in the borderland. The proposed fault system was active during most of the clockwise rotation of the Transverse Ranges, as proposed by *Luyendyk and others (1980)* and Luyendyk and Hornafius (1987). From the upper Miocene on, the San Andreas fault stepped inland and east of the Los Angeles basin (*Yerkes and others, 1965*). An analysis of the basin by *Mayer (1987)* shows a dramatic increase in subsidence rates during the lower and middle Miocene (i.e., from 21 to 10 Ma). Luyendyk and Hornafius (1987) explain the opening of the Los Angeles basin and the neighboring offshore Santa Cruz and Catalina basins as the result of the same rotation that was responsible for the clockwise swing of the Transverse Ranges. Mid-Miocene volcanism indeed reinforces the notion of an extensional origin. Yet north of the basin, in the much-rotated Transverse Ranges, compressional structures are quite evident, and if some of the speculations of Yeats (1981,

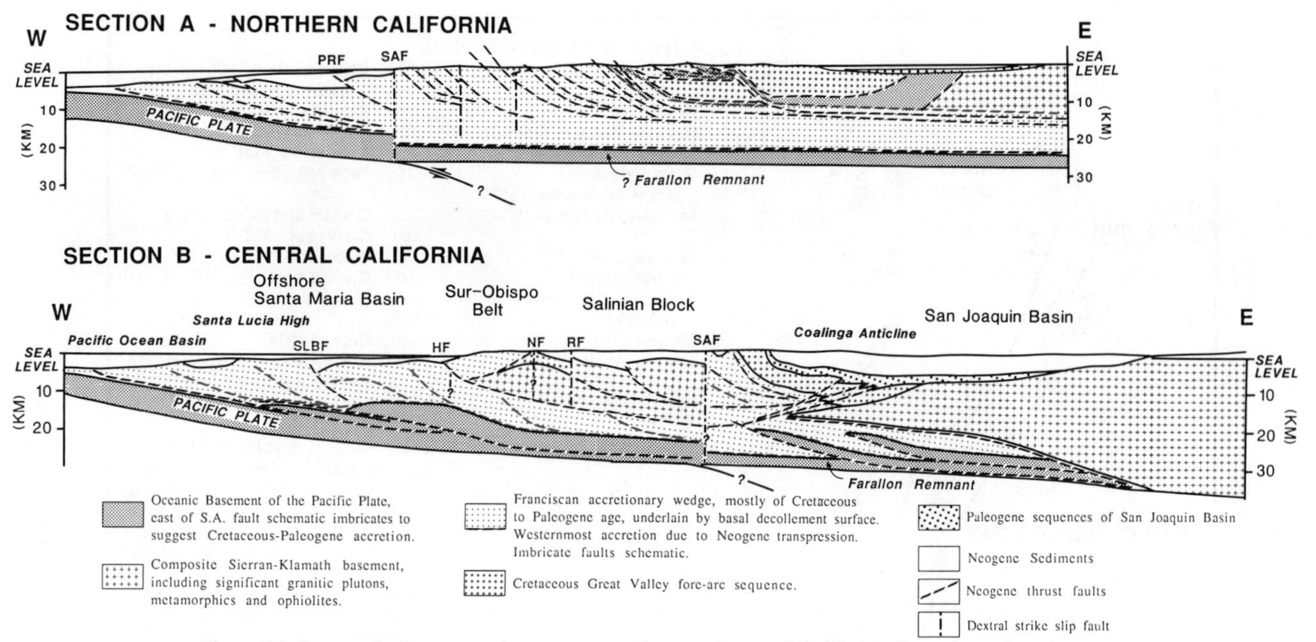

Figure 25. Two typical cross sections across northern and central California. Locations of sections are indicated on Figure 24. Section A is based on but modified from *Suppe (1979).* Section B is based on but modified from *Meltzer (1988).* Symbols: PRF, Point Reyes fault; SAF, San Andreas fault; SLBF, Santa Lucia bank fault; HF, Hosgri fault; NF, Nacimiento fault; RF, Rincon fault.

1983) and the cross sections of Namson and Davis (1988b) are accepted, a good case for a shallow-depth decollement can be made. Here, as elsewhere in California, there are no dramatic displays of normal faults associated with the inception of the basin, even though the models of *Mayer (1987)* suggest that stretching by a factor of 2 to 4 (a thinning by 50 to 70 percent) would suffice to explain the approximately 3 km of Plio-Pleistocene tectonic subsidence in the center of the basin.

This brings up some fundamental questions concerning pull-apart basins in California. Crowell (*1974a, 1974b,* 1987), perhaps more than anybody else, has combined careful mapping with careful reasoning to propose what is now the classical pull-apart basin model. He was particularly successful in showing how sedimentation along the flanks of these basins, with lateral clastic influx from point sources on the upthrown margin of the basin, would lead to dextrally shingled depocenters within the basin itself. While the pull-apart model itself is accepted by most, it is unfortunate that we lack direct seismic-reflection evidence for a stretched basin floor. Such evidence would presumably display conspicuous listric normal faults at the appropriate angles to the strike-slip flanks of the basin.

As mentioned before, seismic penetration so far does not seem adequate to resolve this question. It would seem most plausible to expect a fairly simple pull-apart origin for structures directly associated with opening of the Gulf of California. The same origin may be anticipated for some of the Tertiary borderland basins shown on the map of Figure 23. The application of pull-apart models to the basins that appear to be associated with a transpressive fold belt is perhaps more questionable. Most of these basins are characterized by subsequent compressional folds and thrust faults, which suggests that they may be transpressional flexural basins, which we would like to call "push-together" basins. As Namson and Davis (1988a, 1988b) pointed out, and as was emphasized earlier by Yeats (1983), compressional structures associated with these basins are best resolved as parts of regional decollement systems with at least some of the strike-slip faults floating over a deeper decollement level. Note also that all the basins shown in this class typically overlie the highly mobile and more ductile Franciscan-type basement (Figs. 23 and 24) or else the very narrow Salinia block. Of particular importance is that, at least on some seismic-reflection profiles, there is evidence for minor Neogene deformation at the toe of the so-called stabilized accretionary wedge of the central California slope (Fig. 25B, after *Meltzer, 1988*).

However, compromise models can be visualized. Petroleum geologists familiar with inversion tectonics have noted that on seismic sections in California many structures show thinning of the deeper strata, revealing the possible existence of pre-existing half-grabens. A particularly striking example has been offered by Meltzer (Fig. 27) from the offshore Santa Maria basin.

Despite the plethora of models, additional deep crustal observations are needed to understand the origin of California's basins. Fortunately the discovery of huge volumes of petroleum did not have to wait for a complete understanding; in fact, it is the exploration activity itself that has contributed most to the mapping and understanding of California basins.

Sequence stratigraphy of California. Sequence stratigraphy in California, as elsewhere, has had an enormous impact on the

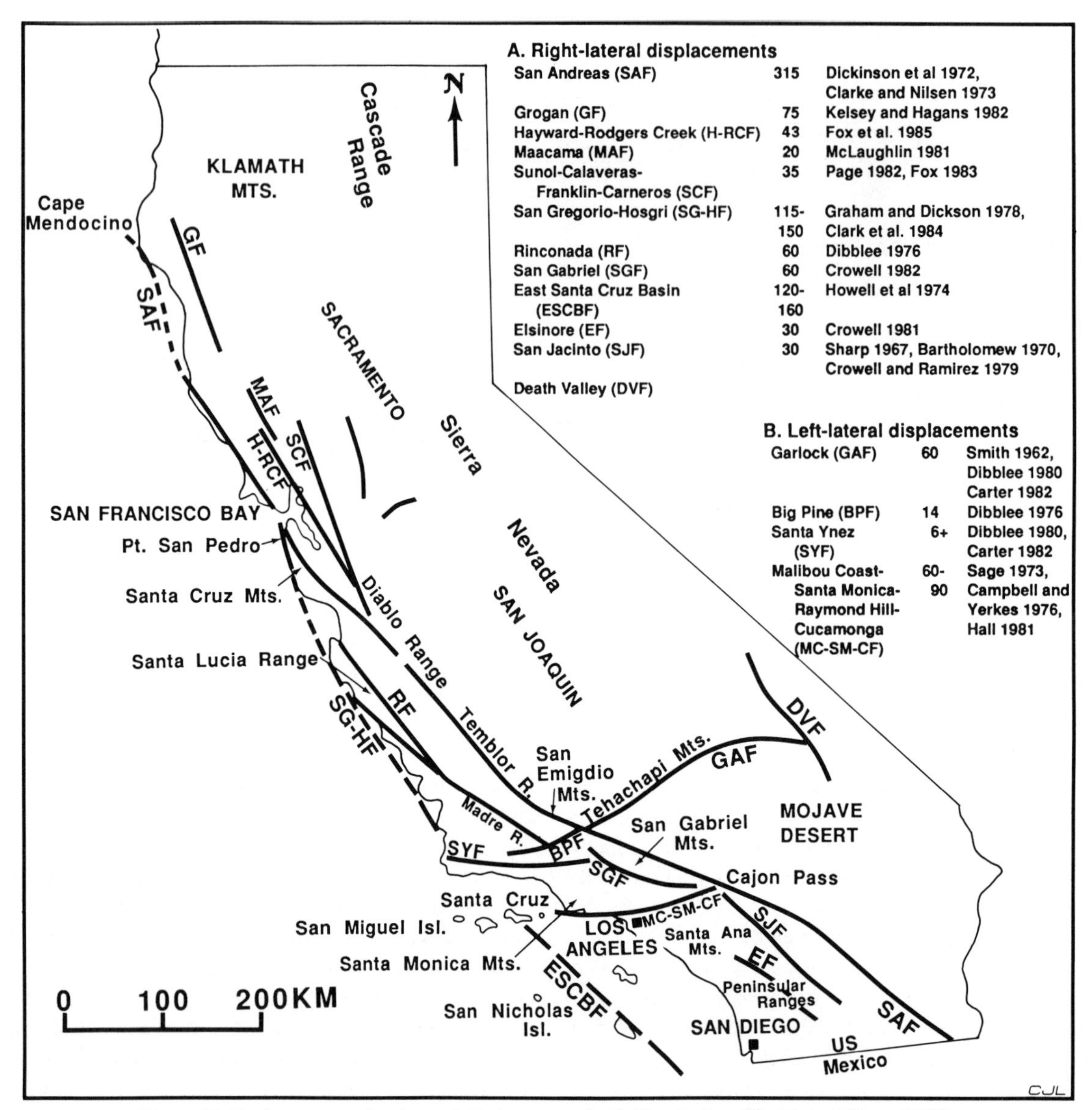

Figure 26. Fault names and estimated displacements in California (modified from Nilsen, 1987).

interpretation of the regional stratigraphy. By the late 1950s, California petroleum geologists had already tried to simplify a stratigraphy that was burdened with many local formation names and complex correlation problems. A solution was found with the recognition of Cenozoic depositional cycles that were correlatable along the whole Pacific Coast of North America. Because of its economic usefulness, however, not much of this work was published, but a few examples are mentioned (top of Fig. 28, modified from *Abbott, 1985*; Vail 1987). A fundamental problem with sequence stratigraphy correlations in California is highlighted by a discussion by May and Warme (1987) that emphasizes the mid-cycle position of turbiditic fan deposits. This interpretation contrasts dramatically with that of Vail (1987) and *Vail and others (1987),* who point out that most deep-sea fans fill in low-stand wedges that are intimately associated with sequence boundaries (see also *Shanmugan and others, 1985*). Figure 28 compares a traditional California sequence concept (*Abbott, 1985*) with the interpretation proposed by P. Vail for such a cycle (Vail, written communication, 1988).

Perhaps more important is the fundamental question of whether the California sequence stratigraphy reflects tectonic synchroneity of growing structures or the imprint of eustatic sea-level changes. A simple comparison of the COSUNA charts of California (*Bishop and Davis, 1984*; see Appendix B) with the cycle chart published by *Haq and others (1987*; also in Vail, 1987) easily demonstrates that there are numerous California-wide unconformities that can be reconciled with the sequence boundaries derived from global seismic stratigraphic correlations. California would appear to be an ideal laboratory, because the tectonic history has been described in terms of plate tectonic

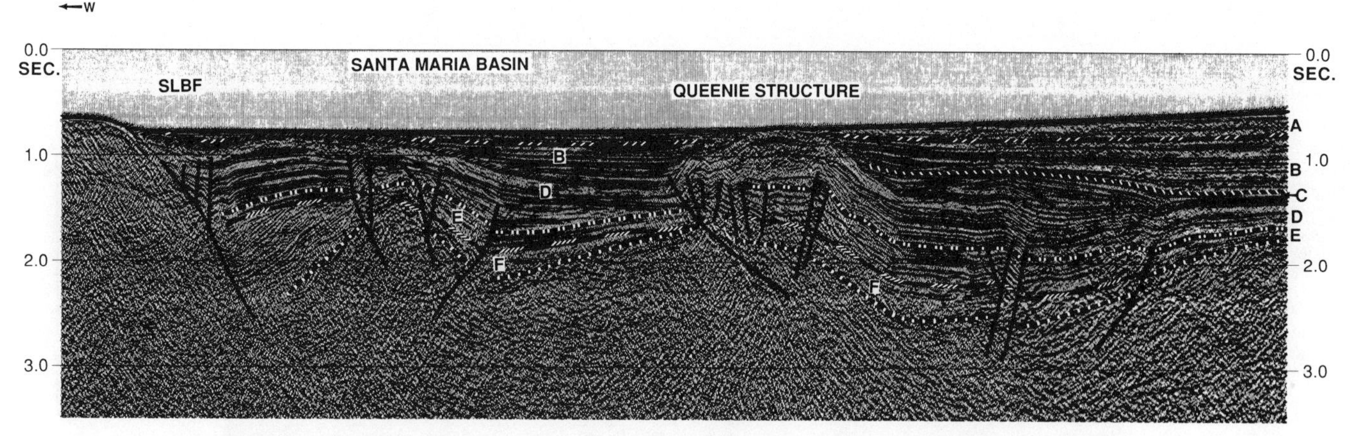

Figure 27. An example of an inversion structure from the offshore Santa Maria basin (from *Meltzer, 1988*). This is part of an east–west seismic profile located east of the Santa Lucia bank fault. The vertical scale is in time, and the maximum sediment thickness shown is about 4 km. Intervals from the top to bottom are: Plio-Pleistocene (A); lower Pliocene (B); upper Miocene (C); middle and upper Miocene Monterey Formation (D); and lower Miocene (E and F). Note the asymmetrical structure in the western part of the line and the geometry of intervals F to C over the Queenie structure. The asymmetrical thickening of stratigraphic units is characteristic of half-graben structures. The two anticlines shown on the profile are due to the inversion of the half-graben systems. The inversion of the Queenie structure began during the upper Miocene and was presumably terminated during the Pleistocene. The western structure was inverted during the lower Pliocene. Note how both the extensional and inverted structures enhance sequence-boundary unconformities (see also *McIntosh and others, 1989*).

regimes (*Page and Engebretson, 1984*). Unfortunately, the start and finish of tectonic regimes is not defined with the same precision as that which is claimed by *Vail and others (1987)* for their world-wide cycles. In fact, taken at face value, intervals of plate tectonic regime transition often include more than one third-order sequence boundary!

Particularly in the context of California geology, we prefer Vail's working hypothesis (*Vail and others, 1987*), which states that local tectonism often enhances the expression of sequence boundaries. Thus, sequence boundaries (i.e., unconformities) that are superposed on growing anticlines would simply accentuate the convergence on the flanks of such continuously growing structures. As already shown by *Harding (1976)* for the southern San Joaquin basin, anticlines grew since the beginning of the upper Miocene, over a time interval that includes more than eight significant global sequence boundaries of *Vail and others (1987)*. Thus, California may offer the ideal setting to study in detail the respective roles of tectonism and eustasy in the formation of sequence boundaries. Such an evaluation, however, would entail a complete re-evaluation of the paleontological control of all sequences, a clarification of the position of deep-sea fans within California sequences, and a study of structural growth as shown by surface mapping and seismic-reflection profiles in California.

Extensional province. The tectonic history of the extensional province of the southern Cordillera has received much attention over the last decade. The setting of Tertiary extensional tectonics and the location of major volcanic fields is shown on Figure 29. Notwithstanding the great progress in unraveling the complex structural history of the region, a clear and comprehensive understanding of its tectonic evolution still does not exist. Nevertheless, several loosely defined structural domains are identified (Fig. 30), each characterized by differences in direction, magnitude, style, and/or age of extension.

In southern British Columbia and northern Washington, substantial crustal extension is recognized in the Omineca-Okanogan domain. The southern margin of this area and its relation, if any, to the well-known Great Basin structural domain is obscured by the voluminous basalts of the Columbia River Plateau. The Great Basin, composing the northern part of the Basin and Range province, stretches from southern Idaho to southern Nevada and is flanked by the Sierra Nevada and Colorado Plateau to the west and east, respectively.

The transition from the Great Basin to the Sonoran Desert domain, which composes the southern part of the Basin and Range, is marked by the relative close proximity of the Colorado Plateau and Sierra Nevada. The boundary region lacks abundant Tertiary volcanic rocks and is characterized by an east-west–trending belt of pre-Tertiary outcrops that marks part of the Paleozoic miogeosynclinal hingeline. A substantial gravity gradient of 90 mgal (*Eaton and others, 1978*; Eaton, 1979) is associated with the transition zone and ostensibly marks a significant crustal boundary. The Sonoran Desert domain encompasses southeastern California and extends to eastern Arizona and New Mexico, where it merges with a domain that encompasses the Rio Grande rift system.

Major uncertainties remain about the Cenozoic structural history of the region. The duration and rates of extension of major extensional events, for the most part, are poorly constrained. The direction of extension is one of the more well-established relations in most areas, but the reasons for changes in the extension direc-

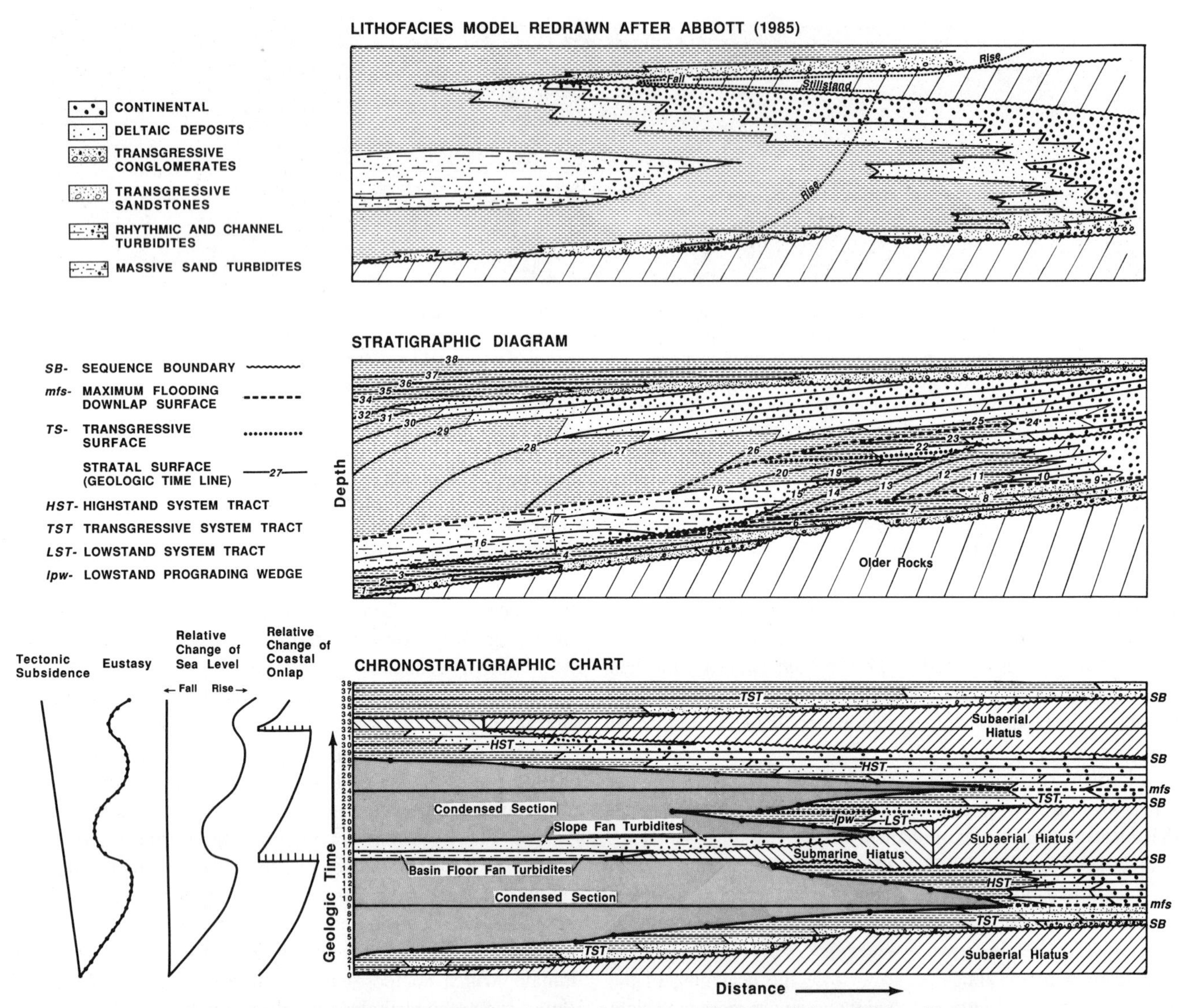

Figure 28. A comparison of a "typical" California sequence diagram (*Abbott, 1985*) with recent interpretations as illustrated by Vail for this chapter (written communication). In the "typical" version, the turbidites are coeval with a rising sea level. In Vail's recent interpretation, low stands are responsible for basin floor and slope fan turbidites. Hiatuses are due to low stands and have subaerial and submarine segments. Shales of transgressive system tracts and high-stand system tracts downlap and thin into condensed sequences. The chronostratigraphic chart at the bottom of the figure shows the distribution of facies and sequence with respect to time. The conceptual diagram to the left of the chart schematically illustrates, from right to left, the relationship of linear tectonic subsidence and eustasy to relative change of sea level and coastal onlap. For further detail, see Vail (1987) and *Vail and others (1987).* Most Tertiary third-order cycles recognized by *Haq and others (1987)* and Vail (1987) also can be observed in California. Nevertheless, additional detailed work with seismic-reflection profiles and surface and subsurface stratigraphy is required to adequately document this concept.

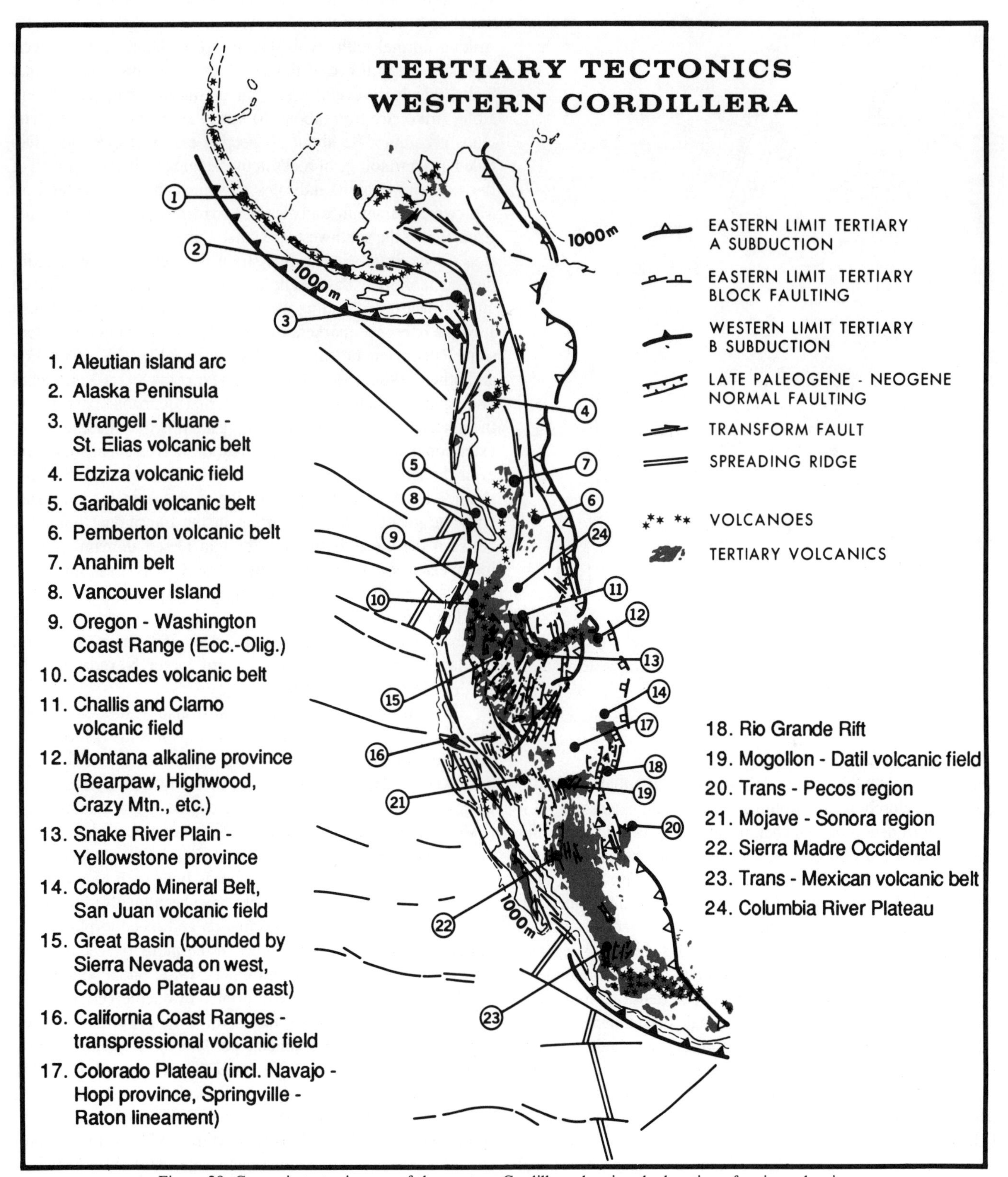

Figure 29. Cenozoic tectonic map of the western Cordillera showing the location of major volcanic centers.

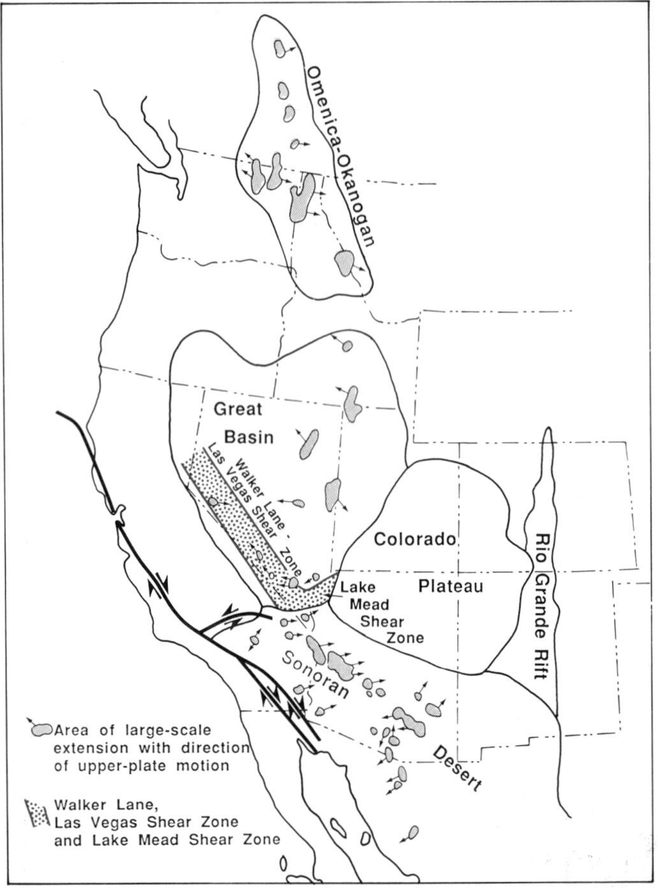

Figure 30. Map of Cenozoic extensional provinces in the western United States and southwestern Canada.

tion are poorly understood. Episodes of substantial volcanism seem to be closely related to times of significant extension, but it is difficult to determine whether magmatism preceded and facilitated major extension or whether large-scale extension created conduits for extrusion of vast amounts of volcanics. Earlier contractional deformation may have exerted significant control on the development of subsequent extensional tectonism. The geometry and evolution of extensional fault systems are debated; do the master decollements in extensional terranes originate at high angles and flatten during progressive extension, or are they formed at shallow angles? Some low-angle detachments are kinematically related to large-scale transcurrent fault systems, further complicating the Cenozoic picture. Even with all these uncertainties, some relations appear to be relatively well established. The history of the structural domains is summarized below.

Omineca-Okanogan. Recognition of major extensional structures in the southern Omineca crystalline belt of British Columbia and the Okanogan of northern Washington (e.g., Carr and others, 1987; Parrish and others, 1988) permit the complex structure of the region to be unraveled. Although it is not clear whether the origin of many ductile structures is related to contractional or extensional tectonism, the existence of major, northerly striking normal faults with shallow to moderate east and west dips is well established. Estimates of displacements on the normal faults, which in several cases can be traced for up to 100 km along strike, are from about 20 km to as much as 40 km. The faults accommodate about 30 percent east-west extension. Detailed geochronology of rocks in the hanging wall and footwall of the extensional faults indicates movement between 58 and 52 Ma, which is significantly earlier than motion on extensional structures in the southwestern United States.

Great Basin. Extensional strain is heterogeneously distributed in the Great Basin. The northerly trending Sierra Nevada and northeasterly trending western flank of the Colorado Plateau serve as reference markers to establish the magnitude of extension. Paleomagnetic studies (*Hannan and Verosub, 1980*; Frei and others, 1984; Frei, 1986) indicate that the Sierra Nevada has undergone no significant rotation during Cenozoic extension in the adjacent Great Basin. The implication is that the amount of extensional displacement in the Great Basin is essentially constant even though the extensional domain widens substantially from south to north. Thus, the partitioning of extensional strain varies, with the greatest strain occurring in the transitional boundary between the Great Basin and Sonoran Desert domain. A minimum extension of 190 km for the Great Basin is constrained by a transect through the Las Vegas region with upper bounds set at 250 km (Wernicke and others, 1988). In reconstructions calling for extension substantially greater than 250 km, a significant overlap occurs between the southern Sierra Nevada and the southwestern Colorado Plateau.

Within the Great Basin, several structural subdomains are recognized (Fig. 30). Perhaps the best known is the belt of metamorphic core complexes exposed in northeastern Nevada, northwestern Utah, and southeastern Idaho. All of these complexes are characterized to varying degrees by a metamorphic lower plate overlain by a brittlely deformed upper plate. Dynamothermal metamorphism of the lower plate successions is commonly complex and often records two or three events. In several areas, the lower plate rocks have been involved in one or two episodes of Mesozoic deformation and metamorphism, one in the Late Jurassic and the other in the mid-Cretaceous (*Armstrong, 1968, 1972*; Miller and others, 1988; Snoke and Miller, 1988). The lower plates are overprinted by ductile Tertiary structures, commonly mylonites, that involve the lower-plate successions, which commonly contain pre-kinematic granitoid intrusives dated between 45 and 20 Ma (*Dallmeyer and others, 1986*). The estimates of extension within individual metamorphic core complexes generally are in the range of 200 to 500 percent (e.g., Miller and others, 1983; Snoke and Miller, 1988), with a tectonic transport direction of the upper plate either N60°W or S60°E.

Where well exposed, as in the East Humboldt Range and Ruby Mountains, the mylonites associated with Tertiary displacements form a relatively thin zone of deformation concentrated near the top of the lower metamorphic plate. The ductile

Tertiary structures gradually diminish with depth (on the order of a few kilometers) leaving earlier ductile structures related to Mesozoic contraction well preserved.

The onset of extension in the northeastern Great Basin is not well dated. Extension may have begun, at least locally, as early as the Late Cretaceous (Snoke and Miller, 1988) and may be related to foreland thrusting in the Sevier and Laramide belts to the east. However, the best estimate of the inception of regional extension is the early Oligocene (35 to 30 Ma). This age is based on the inferred relationship between volcanism and faulting and on the existence of Tertiary sediments thought to be deposited in extensional basins. These sediments include coarse conglomerates and, in some cases, huge slide blocks (Snoke and Miller, 1988).

Extension is commonly considered to mark the initiation of the development of metamorphic core complexes (Snoke and Miller, 1988; Gans and others, 1989), but no direct link has been established between the early Oligocene extension and the metamorphic core complexes. Recent Ar/Ar geochronologic and paleothermobarometric studies in the Albion Range by Hodges and Sutter (K. Hodges, personal communication, 1988) indicate that a lower Oligocene pluton (35 to 32 Ma) crystallized at depths on the order of 25 to 30 km and passed through the blocking temperatures of muscovite and biotite at about 20 and 17 Ma, respectively; this suggests that the pluton was uplifted and cooled to temperatures below 350°C in the early Miocene. Thus in the Albion Range, Miocene uplift and exhumation of mid-crustal shear zones apparently occurred 10 to 15 m.y. after the inferred onset of regional extension. The question at hand is whether or not this time lag is regionally characteristic, and what are its implications for the extensional kinematics of the region.

The present-day geometry of the ductile decollements, which dip shallowly to the northwest or southeast, is reasonably clear, but there is still much controversy as to their initial dip, kinematic history, and relationship to high-angle Basin and Range faults. The original dip of the master decollement may have been steep, with subsequent shallowing of the dip during progressive extension. Alternatively, the decollement could have been formed as a relatively shallow detachment surface exhumed during extension.

Superposed on the earlier metamorphic core complexes, and found throughout the Great Basin, are younger high-angle normal faults. Seismic-reflection studies of many of the Tertiary basins (e.g., *Effimoff and Pinezich, 1987*; *Gans and others, 1985*) clearly show that they are half-grabens and that the bounding faults were active during Cenozoic sedimentation. Rotated beds of the basin fill suggest that the master faults are listric. The polarity of most of the basin-bounding faults changes along strike at ill-defined transfer fault systems that form complexly deformed zones of steeply dipping faults oriented at a high angle to the basin-bounding structures. Estimates of extension for the Tertiary basins are small (about 20 percent) compared to those of earlier episodes of extension related to the metamorphic core complexes.

In the western Great Basin, Cenozoic structures seemingly more complex than in regions farther to the east are exposed. Here, some areas have undergone wholesale crustal extension, whereas others were subjected to substantial clockwise and counterclockwise rotations. In addition, major right- and left-lateral strike-slip fault zones form well-defined tectonic belts.

The best-described extensional areas are in north-central Nevada (Yerington and San Antonio Mountains) and to the south, at the latitude of Las Vegas, in the ranges stretching from Death Valley to the Colorado Plateau (Fig. 30). With the notable exception of the Death Valley region, extension in these regions is not accompanied by exhumation of a metamorphosed lower plate. Extension is large, at least 175 to 200 percent in the Yerington district (Proffett, 1977; *Proffett and Dilles, 1984*), with magnitudes possibly as great as 500 percent recorded in the region near Las Vegas (Wernicke and others, 1988). Extension directions are not as well established as in the regions characterized by the ductile structures of the metamorphic core complexes. Based on the morphology of faults in the Yerington district and San Antonio Mountains, extension was east-west during the mid-Miocene. In the Death Valley region, extension was west-northwesterly (Wernicke and others, 1988); whereas, in the eastern part of the region, extension was west–southwesterly.

The initial orientation of the extensional faults varies from region to region. In the Yerington district, and to a lesser degree in the San Antonio Mountains, normal faults were formed at high angles to bedding. They owe their current shallow dips to large-scale extension and the successive development of superposed normal faults (Proffett, 1977). Shallowly inclined basal detachment surfaces are postulated for the extensional faults in the Las Vegas region and apparently formed with initial low dips (*Wernicke and others, 1985*).

Timing relations during the development of extensional faults only locally are well defined in the western Great Basin. However, vast regions have not been studied at other than a reconnaissance level, and detailed mapping and geochronology are needed to better constrain regional relations. In the Yerington district, detailed minerals-exploration work resulted in remarkably well-established timing relations. Large-scale extension began at about 19 Ma, with most rapid displacement occurring in the interval from 17 to 13 Ma. The period of rapid extension, which accomplished on the order of 40 to 60° of tilt of both the pre-Tertiary basement (Geissman and others, 1982) and the Tertiary cover, was followed in the post–mid-Miocene by at most an additional 30° of tilt. Elsewhere, details of the extensional history are less well known. In the Death Valley region, major extension occurred during the last 14 m.y., and in the region east of Las Vegas, extension was greatest in the interval from 15 to 11 Ma (Wernicke and others, 1988).

In the Great Basin, highly extended areas form core complexes (with or without metamorphosed lower plates) bound by regions of relatively little extension. Unlike the across-strike change in the amount of extension, the along-strike juxtaposition of highly extended regions with those experiencing relatively little extension is not easily reconciled with current fault models. Clearly, some transfer or accommodation structure is required and is reconcilable with the observed antiparallel, upper-plate transport directions in core complexes of a given region. High-angle accommodation fault systems exposed in southeastern California (*Dokka, 1986*) and northern Arizona (*Faulds and others, 1989*) transfer antiparallel displacements and juxtapose extended and relatively unextended domains. In much of the Great Basin, comparable high-angle structures are not observed in association with the longitudinal terminations of the core complexes. In these regions, it is conceivable that accommodation zones are low-angle fault systems that transfer displacements to deeper decoupling levels.

Major strike-slip zones are recognized in the Great Basin. Left-lateral transcurrent displacement is recorded in the east-northeast–striking Lake Mead shear zone (*Anderson, 1973*; *Bohannon, 1979*). More conspicuous are the northwesterly trending Walker Lane and the Las Vegas shear zone (Fig. 30), which has experienced substantial right-lateral displacement since the mid-Miocene. Tertiary deformation in the Walker Lane and the Las Vegas shear zone is quite complex.

Within the Walker Lane and the Las Vegas shear zone, unusual but widespread structures only now are being recognized. They consist of low-angle detachment faults separating strongly tilted Tertiary units above virtually untilted pre-Tertiary basement (*Hardyman and others, 1984*; *Keller and others, 1987*; *Scott and Hofland, 1987*). The detachments are kinematically associated with strike-slip faults and are not the product of large-cale crustal extension (*Hardyman, 1978*; *Keller and others, 1987*). In most characteristics, these structures are virtually indistinguishable from Yerington-type extensional features; the only distinguishing feature is the lack of tilt of the basement. This seemingly simple criterion often is difficult to apply because the preservation of depositional contacts between the pre-Tertiary and Tertiary cover is poor. Commonly the only reliable way to establish basement tilts is a detailed paleomagnetic survey.

Paleomagnetic investigations in the Great Basin also have identified substantial areas that have experienced large-scale clockwise and counterclockwise rotations (e.g., Hudson and Geissman, 1987). These commonly are attributed to displacements of fault-bound blocks. Where studied in some detail, such as Dixie Valley in north-central Nevada, counterclockwise rotations of about 25° of late Oligocene to early Miocene tuffs occurred before extrusion of middle Miocene basalts. The significance of such rotational domains and their relation to other Cenozoic structures currently is enigmatic.

Changes in the direction of extension in the western Great Basin are indicated by regional and local studies (Zoback and others, 1981; *Ander, 1984*; *Angelier and others, 1985*). Extension occurred in a northerly to north-northeasterly direction during much of the Oligocene-Miocene (30 to 17 Ma) and was accompanied by the development of syn-volcanic half-grabens. Where preserved, the half-grabens consistently strike east-northeast and have down-to-the-north displacements of 1.5 km or greater (*Speed and Cogbill, 1979*). The direction of extension shifted to east-west and then to northwest-southeast in the mid-Miocene (17 to 15 Ma). The temporal and spatial relations of the changes in extension direction are not well constrained. It is not clear whether the change from north-northeasterly to east-west was gradual or abrupt. It is also unclear whether the transition from east-west to present-day northwest-southeast extension occurred at the same time throughout western and southern Nevada, or if it was a progressive change migrating northerly, possibly related to the passage of the Mendocino triple junction.

Extensional features in the Great Basin are superposed on the Luning-Fencemaker, Eureka, and Sevier fold belts. In Wyoming, Idaho, and Montana, listric normal faults often flatten and merge into pre-existing thrust faults. This situation contrasts with the Sonoran Desert where extensional systems are superposed on cratonic and previously little-deformed rocks.

Sonoran Desert. The Cenozoic structure of the Sonoran Desert (Fig. 30) is dominated by numerous metamorphic core complexes exposed in southeastern California and southwestern Arizona. Like the region in the northeastern Great Basin, the complexes are characterized by a metamorphic lower plate overlain by a brittlely deformed carapace. Tertiary mylonites within the lower plates range in thickness from 50 to 100 m (*Reynolds, 1982, 1985*) to greater than several kilometers (*Davis and others, 1980, 1986*). Brittle structures superposed on the lower-plate ductile features record the progressive deformation from ductile to brittle conditions during the relative upward displacement of the lower plate (Davis and Lister, 1988). Mylonites formed at mid-crustal depths in the Oligocene-Miocene (Anderson, 1988) and were subsequently uplifted and exposed by later cross-cutting shallow detachments (Davis and Lister, 1988; *Davis, 1987*). Rapid extension during the early Miocene (20 to 18 Ma), involving displacements on the low-angle detachment in excess of 40 to 45 km, has been established in southeastern California (Whipple Mountains). Associated uplift of the lower plate is remarkably fast and is about 3 to 7.2 mm/yr (*Davis, 1987*).

The age of the onset of extension is not well bracketed, but is thought to immediately predate the period of rapid uplift in the early Miocene. The extension direction in the Sonoran Desert is S60°W or N60°E, which is at a substantial angle (60°) to that of the northeastern Great Basin. Following the period of rapid extension, the Sonoran Desert has been relatively inactive since 10 Ma.

Rio Grande rift. Rifting in the Rio Grande depression (Fig. 30) began in the mid-Oligocene (32 to 27 Ma) and may have reactivated a northerly trending zone of crustal weakness inherited from early orogenic events of the late Paleozoic and late Mesozoic to early Tertiary. The onset of rifting was approximately 5 m.y. earlier in the southern part of the rift than in the north. The magnitude of extension systematically increases from the northern terminus near the Colorado-Wyoming border to the south where the expression of the rift is obscured by the eastern Basin and Range province (Sonora Desert domain) that extends south into Mexico.

The northern two-thirds of the rift is typified by en echelon half-grabens separated by steep east-west–trending transfer faults across which the half-grabens change polarity. To the south, the rift bifurcates, with one leg trending southwest into Arizona and the other south toward El Paso. Between the active legs of the rift is a triangular region that has experienced substantial extension of early Miocene and older sedimentary and volcanic units on "domino-type" faults similar to those found in the Yerington district of western Nevada (*Chamberlin, 1978*).

Extension within the rift continues today, as expressed by numerous active fault scarps cutting Pleistocene units (Chapin, 1979). During the Neogene (7 to 4 Ma) the region underwent substantial uplift (on the order of 1.1 km), thought to be related to deep-seated processes (Chapin, 1979).

Discussion. The age of major crustal extension within the Cordillera broadly decreases from north (British Columbia and Washington) to south (Basin and Range; Rio Grande rift). The significance of the age difference and degree of extension is not understood and may be the result of several factors. In the Omineca-Okanogan province, the extension started immediately after or just before the cessation of thrusting in the Canadian foreland to the east; thus, the two processes may be related. As suggested by Coney and Harms (1984) and Parrish and others (1988), extension may be directly related to crustal instability induced by thickening and thermal weakening during earlier contraction.

This explanation runs into trouble in the Basin and Range and Rio Grande rift to the south because timing relations appear to be wrong. The metamorphic core complexes of the northeastern Great Basin more or less correspond with the position of a postulated mid-crustal duplex of late Mesozoic and early Tertiary age (Plate 5B, section D). In this respect, the development of the core complexes may be nucleated by areas of thickened crust, as previously proposed by Coney and Harms (1984). Shortening in the foreland regions to the east is generally accepted as having ceased in the Eocene, earlier than the period of rapid extension in the Oligocene-Miocene. Since the age of extension is poorly constrained, however, the possibility of partial synchroneity of the two events cannot be discarded out of hand. Alternatively, either the shortening continued much longer in the southwestern United States than is currently thought or there was a substantial lag in the onset of gravitational collapse. A similar origin for the core complexes of the Sonoran Desert, however, is more problematic if the contention of *Dickinson and others (1987b),* that only minor thrusting occurred in this region during the late Mesozoic and early Tertiary, is true. Estimates of regional shortening based on balanced sections in the Sonoran Desert region, with which one could test this assertion, do not yet exist.

Considering the complex history of extension in the Basin and Range and Rio Grande rift, several processes may have contributed to the extensional history of the region. At this time, it is premature to discard the possibility that the onset of extension was related to contractional thickening of the crust and probably the continental lithosphere. More work is necessary to determine if the apparent lag is real or an artifact of inadequate age control on the beginning of extension in the Basin and Range or on the cessation of shortening in the foreland regions to the east. It also appears to be clear that extension in the Neogene cannot be attributed solely to collapse of a thickened crust; the process probably requires additional impetus derived from the transtensional deformation at the plate boundary.

There are other serious problems with the extensional history of the western Basin and Range. If our current understanding of extension direction during the mid-Miocene is correct, an apparent space problem is encountered. In the northeastern Great Basin, extension during the Miocene was along a line N60°W to S60°E, in sharp contrast with the S60°W to N60°E extension in the Sonoran Desert region. At about the same time, in the western Great Basin, the extension direction apparently was essentially east-west.

Two kinematic models can be invoked to explain this change in extension direction. In one model (Fig. 31A), the extension is caused by gravitational spreading from an elongate high in the east (A in Fig. 31A), and the extension direction everywhere is parallel to the dip direction of the high. Accommodation structures such as half-grabens (B in Fig. 31A) must form, and strike-slip displacements along the Sierra Nevada have to occur (sinistral in the north and dextral in the south). The megascopic strain ellipsoid in this case is an oblate spheroid (flattening strain). In the second model (Fig. 31B), the Sierra Nevada moves westward, perhaps due to a sinking lithosphere root and subsequent convection in the upper mantle. Alternatively, the westerly migration could be related to thermal re-equilibration of the root and associated uplift. Be that as it may, the rifted margin (MN in Fig.

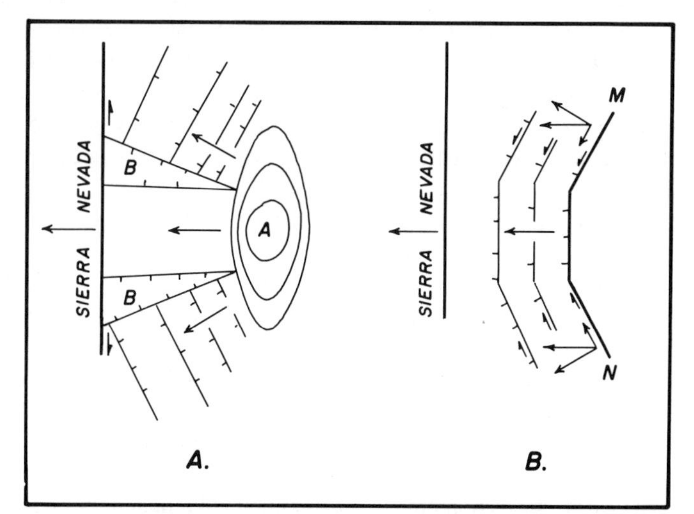

Figure 31. Models for mid-Miocene extension of the Basin and Range. In the first model (A) gravitational spreading from an elliptical high (A) results in extension in northwest, west, and southwest directions in the northern, central, and southern parts of the region, respectively. Structures accommodating the displacement may form (grabens B). In the second model (B) extension is everywhere toward the west. The extended margin (MN) is curved, perhaps as the result of older structure. If displacement vectors are decomposed in normal and transcurrent components, northeast–, north-south–, and northwest–trending normal faults in the northern, central, and southern areas, respectively, may form, giving the impression of variable extension directions.

31B) is irregular: it trends S30°W in the north, north-south in the center, and S30°E in the south, causing oblique divergence along the northern and southern segments of MN. The west-trending component causes the N60°W and S60°W extension directions in the north and south, respectively, and a tangential component causes strike-slip shear zones. Evidence to differentiate between the above scenarios is not available as yet, but hopefully will be forthcoming in the future.

Fault activity during the last 10 m.y. appears to be restricted to the Great Basin and the Rio Grande rift system, with the intervening Sonoran Desert region being inactive (Eaton, 1979). The implication is that extensional strain has stepped, en echelon, from the Great Basin to the southeast into the Rio Grande rift system. The northwest-southeast extension direction in the Great Basin during this interval is compatible with a right-lateral shear couple imparted to the western United States, and recent extension in the Rio Grand rift may be related. A scenario of this type is consistent with paleomagnetically determined, 5° clockwise rotation of the Colorado Plateau (*Bryan and Gordan, 1986, 1988*) and the lack of extension in the Sonoran Desert.

Colorado Plateau. The history of the Colorado Plateau is intimately related to that of the extensional province. Both regions experienced regional uplift of as much as 3 km after about 24 Ma (*Lucchitta, 1979*; *Young, 1979*; *Epis and others, 1980*), but unlike the Basin and Range province, the structural integrity of the Colorado Plateau as a discrete tectonic block was maintained. Surface-wave studies of the Plateau indicate that it has a 45-km-thick crust (Keller and others, 1979) characterized by elevated heat-flow values (about 70 mW/m^2; *Reiter and others, 1979*). Magnetic anomalies (Thompson and Zoback, 1979) indicate a higher conductivity than normal Precambrian continental crust, also suggesting elevated mantle temperatures. The anomalous nature of the lower crust and mantle beneath the Colorado Plateau is further supported by volcanic xenoliths, which indicate hydration effects not found in adjacent regions (Smith, 1978; *Smith and Levy, 1976; Padovani, 1977; Padovani and others, 1978*).

In the Paleogene, the elevation of much of the eastern U.S. Cordillera was substantially lower than today, and the mean elevation of the region may have been less than 1 km (for references see Dickinson and others, 1988). Small differential elevation may have existed between the Colorado Plateau and the latter may have been slightly higher. Elevation control is based largely on a widespread Miocene tuff (18.3-Ma Peach Spring tuff) whose deposition predated substantial differential uplift. Between 18 and 10 Ma, the Colorado Plateau was differentially uplifted at least 1 km with respect to the Basin and Range province. During this interval, the Colorado Plateau region was uplifted to elevations in excess of 3 to 4 km. Possibly the Great Basin region experienced similar uplift. Today, the mean elevation of the Colorado Plateau is on the order of 2 km. That of the Basin and Range varies substantially, with the elevation of valley floors generally about 1 to 1.5 km.

Both regions were extended in the early Miocene (20 to 18 Ma), with the development of block faults in the Colorado Plateau and large-scale crustal extension in the Basin and Range. An apparent regional difference is the lack of major contractional "conditioning" of the Colorado Plateau, as opposed to widespread Mesozoic and early Tertiary shortening in the Basin and Range province. This is not to say that the Colorado Plateau was not involved in Cordilleran shortening. It is obvious that during Laramide tectonism the Plateau was decoupled at some depth and was displaced easterly. Nevertheless, internal deformation was minor and apparently was not sufficient to nucleate later crustal-extension faults.

The uplift of the Colorado Plateau and Basin and Range province is part of a Cordilleran-wide phenomenon. Comparable uplift is observed throughout the northern U.S. and southern Canadian Rockies during the Oligocene. The region of uplift crudely mimics the pre-Cretaceous subcrop distribution of Jurassic successions in the Cordillera (Fig. 6) and the broad region where we propose the existence of a subdecollement lithospheric root (Plate 5A, section D). Although highly speculative, the hypothetical root conceivably resulted in lithospheric depression during the shortening phase of regional tectonism and the formation of a broad foreland moat. Following the cessation of contraction in the Eocene, thermal re-equilibration, aided by some process of physical removal of the lithospheric root, may have resulted in ensuing uplift of the entire region. Where contractional structures were well developed, large-scale crustal extension mitigated the uplift. In the Colorado Plateau, however, such structures did not exist and uplift was more fully achieved. If Miocene-Pliocene estimates of the elevation of the Colorado Plateau are correct at 3 or 4 km, an apparent reduction in the mean elevation has occurred since the high stand. This may be the result of erosion and Pliocene-Quaternary extension in the Great Basin and Rio Grande rift.

Magmatic evolution of the Cordillera

Cenozoic magmatism in the Cordillera can be rationalized in terms of general tectonic episodes that are punctuated by notable "events" marking transitions in tectonic style, particularly major accelerations of plate convergence (80 to 55 Ma), major changes in direction of plate motion (42 Ma), and changes in the nature of plate boundaries (30 Ma). Within the Cordillera, it is clear that tectonic transitions are diachronous, and in many instances only affect local areas. Our necessarily brief narrative is organized according to timing of major tectonic transitions, admittedly with a bias toward events that affected the western U.S. Cordillera, with which we are more familiar. Figure 29 identifies the tectonic and/or physiographic provinces that are most frequently mentioned here.

For convenience in following the discussion of the magmatic history, Figure 32 (from Lipman, 1980) is used to show temporal distribution of magmatic belts in the conterminous United States in a simplified plate-tectonic framework. No attempt has been made to reconstruct original configurations of magmatic and tectonic provinces, despite the fact that much of the Cordillera was

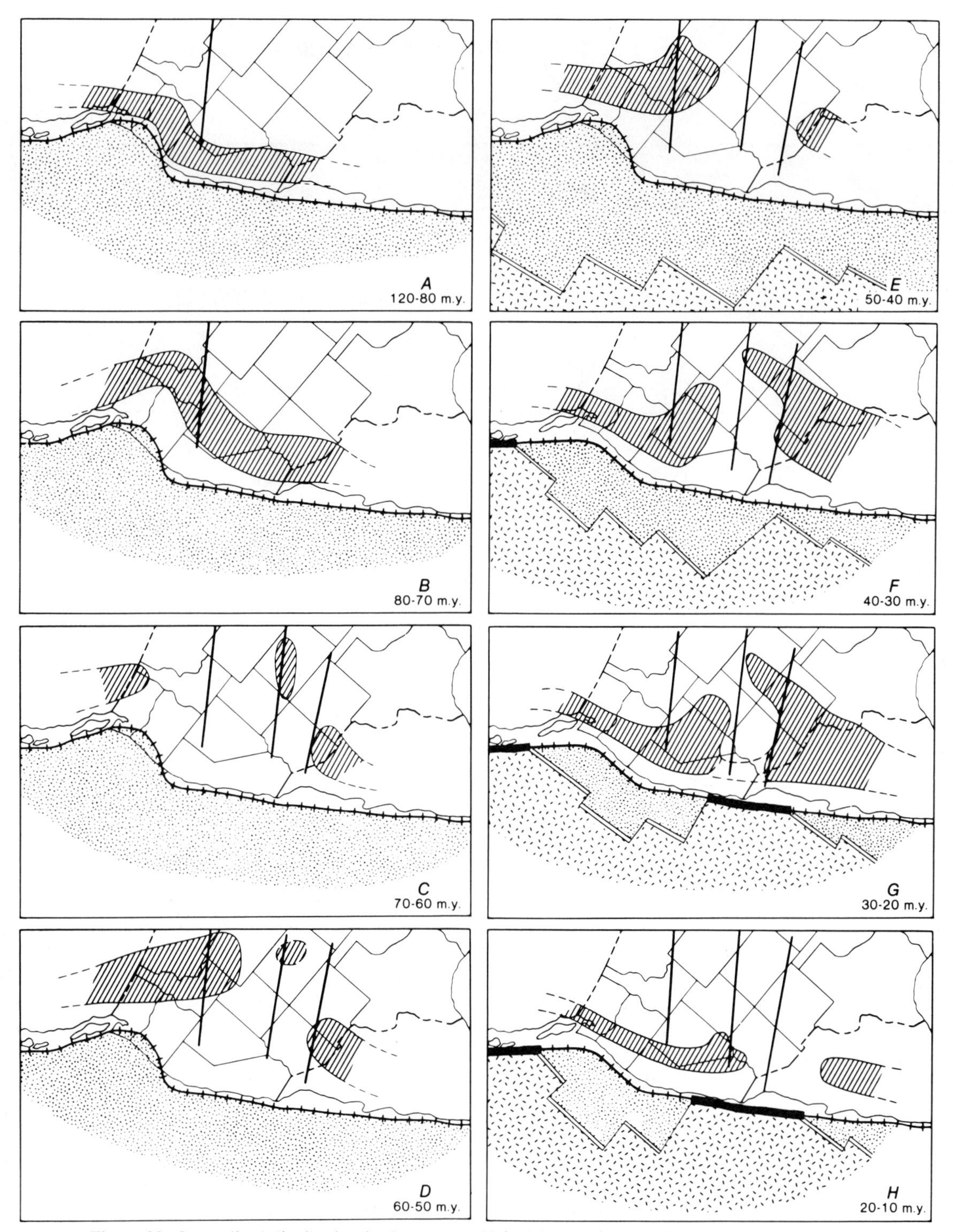

Figure 32. Generalized distribution in the western United States of predominantly andesitic volcanic suites, inferred to be related to subduction (from Lipman, 1980). North lies to the left. Ruled fields represent the distribution of active volcanism during a particular timeframe. No attempt has been made to remove effects of late Cenozoic extensional and rotational deformation. From north to south, the northeast-trending lines mark approximate traces of the Snake River–Yellowstone zone, the Colorado mineral belt, and the Springerville-Raton zone.

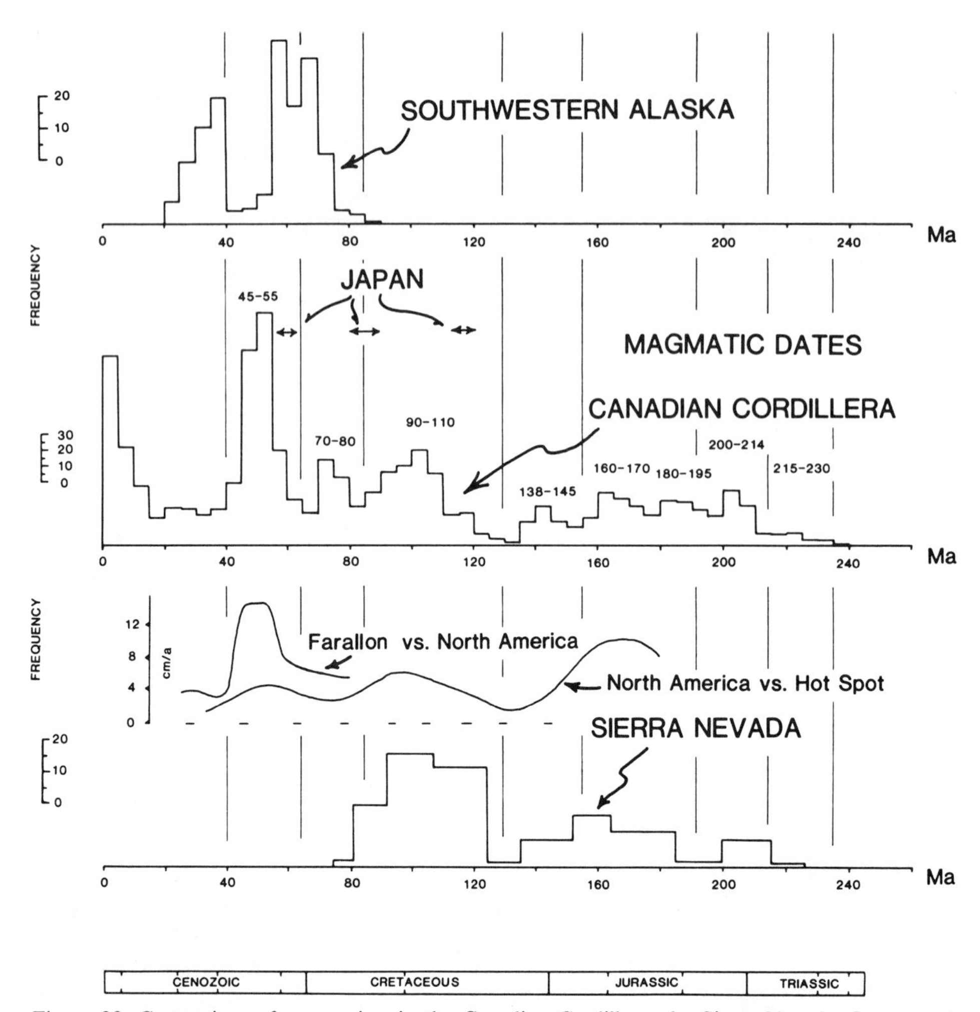

Figure 33. Comparison of magmatism in the Canadian Cordillera, the Sierra Nevada, Japan, and southwestern Alaska with Mesozoic and Cenozoic plate motions (from Armstrong, 1988).

affected by significant Cenozoic extension and strike-slip deformation.

Late Cretaceous–early Cenozoic plutonic framework. As noted in preceding sections, late Paleozoic and Mesozoic convergence along the western margin of North America left a striking magmatic record in the form of a nearly continuous plutonic belt from Mexico to the Alaskan Peninsula (Plate 5A; Fig. 32A and B). These rocks form composite batholiths (tonalitic to granitic) that represent exhumed roots of ancient volcanic arcs (Hamilton, 1969, 1988; Burchfiel and Davis, 1972, 1975). Although there are minor exceptions, ages of these igneous rocks tend to fall into discrete time intervals, marking major pulses of magmatism (Fig. 33; from Armstrong, 1988) that are widely attributed to periods of more rapid plate convergence (e.g., Hamilton, 1988). Locations of these belts also varied in distance from the margin at different times. This spatial migration presumably is caused at least in part by changes in dip of subducting oceanic plate. Care must be taken when making such an assessment, however, because of the allochthonous nature of the terranes containing the plutons.

Cretaceous plutonic and associated volcanic rocks occur as far inland as western Montana (*Meen and Eggler, 1987*), and an exhumed belt of muscovite granites is exposed in eastern Nevada and southeastern California (*Miller and Bradfish, 1980*). In the Sierra Nevada, which is a well-developed composite plutonic belt, Cretaceous plutons systematically range in age from 125 Ma to 80 to 90 Ma from west to east (*Stern and others, 1981*; Chen and Moore, 1982; Saleeby and others, 1987b). They are bound on the east by Jurassic to Triassic plutons and volcanic rocks (*Bateman and others, 1963*; *Tobisch and others, 1986*). Compositionally, the Cordilleran plutons appear to become more enriched in crustal material toward the east (*DePaolo, 1981*; Farmer and DePaolo, 1983; *Ague and Brimhall, 1988a*).

The Cretaceous Peninsular Ranges batholith in southern California and Baja California displays analogous age and compositional variations (*Silver and others, 1979*). Granitic plutons of the allochthonous Salinian block of coastal California are similar petrologically and chronologically to the Peninsular and Sierran batholiths (*Kistler and Peterman, 1978b*; *Mattinson, 1978*). The depths of crystallization of the two batholith belts differ: from 8 to 16 km (2 to 4 kb) for the Sierra Nevada and more than 24 km (>6 kb) for the Peninsular Range (*Ague and Brimhall, 1988b*). The Idaho batholith formed between 90 and 70 Ma (*Bennett, 1980*; Lund and Snee, 1988; R. Lewis, personal communication, 1988); it was essentially contemporaneous with Late Cretaceous magmatism in western Canada (Coast Plutonic complex), the Alaska Panhandle (Admiralty-Revillagigedo belts), southeast Alaska (Insular belt), and southwestern Yukon (*Hudson and others, 1979*; *Wallace and Engebretson, 1984*; Armstrong, 1988).

The present configuration of Mesozoic batholithic belts, especially in southwestern North America (Hamilton, 1988) and coastal Alaska (e.g., *Panuska, 1985*; *Stamatakos and others, 1988*), is significantly distorted due to Cenozoic and older rotations and translations. Restoration of this deformation by removal of counterclockwise rotation of the Sierra Madre Occidental (*Urrutia-Facugauchi, 1981*; *Gose and others, 1982*) and several hundred kilometers of strike-slip motion of the Salinian and Baja–Southern California batholiths (Hamilton, 1969; *Pilger and Henyey, 1979*; Beck, 1986) results in a much simpler, roughly north–south arrangement of the batholiths between Canada and Mexico.

Early Cenozoic magmatic type. Early Cenozoic magmatism was essentially a continuation of late Mesozoic activity, particularly in western Mexico (*McDowell and Clabaugh, 1979*), and followed a brief lull (70 to 55 Ma) in the regions from Canada (Coast Plutonic complex and scattered volcanic-plutonic complexes from intermontane British Columbia to the Yukon) to Idaho and western Montana (Armstrong, *1974,* 1988; *Ewing, 1980*; Hyndman, 1983). Uplift along the coastal margin in mid-Eocene time is recorded by metamorphic assemblages (e.g., *Hollister, 1982*) as well as a depositional hiatus and angular unconformities. This event closely coincided with an apparent westward shift in the locus of magmatism in British Columbia that accompanied rearrangement of plate boundaries in the Pacific Northwest.

Alaska. Southern Alaska was a region of rapid (15 to 25 cm/yr) north-northeast subduction between 80 and 45 Ma (*Rea and Duncan, 1986*). Accretion of some of the coastal terranes was in progress (*Panuska, 1985*; Page and others, 1986) during coeval magmatic activity that produced the Alaska-Aleutians batholith of the Alaska Peninsula (*Reed and Lanphere, 1973*), early to mid-Eocene tonalitic to granitic intrusions in the fore arc of the St. Elias and Gulf of Alaska region (*Hudson, 1979*), and arc volcanism in the Bering shelf region. There was a magmatic lull at approximately 63 Ma when magma chemistry changed, indicating involvement of lithosphere and crustal melting of the accretionary prism. Before the lull, magmatism was widespread, covering an area 600 by 1,200 km. The width of this magmatic province has been interpreted as representative of a shallowly dipping subduction zone (*Bergman and others, 1987*). Alternatively, thrust displacement of the crustal section over a relatively fixed magma source could also explain such a widespread magmatic province.

The proto-Aleutian arc was initiated at approximately 50 to 55 Ma, shortly following an inferred accretion event that jammed the more northerly Bering margin subduction zone and trapped Cretaceous oceanic crust of the Bering plate between the new trench and the old continental margin (*Scholl and others, 1986*).

Northern Cordillera and Great Basin. To the south, the active margin (the Challis belt of Christiansen and Yeats, 1989) was characterized by generally calc-alkalic to potassic magmatism in an extensive belt (Fig. 32D and E) ranging from near the coast (in Washington, British Columbia, and as far north as the Yukon) to eastern Oregon, southwestern Montana, and western Wyoming (early Clarno, Challis, and Absaroka fields). This type of magmatism occurred largely between 50 and 45 Ma and died out by about 43 Ma. During the same period, much of this area was uplifted and extended, most notably the Okanogan Highlands, Bitteroot Dome and similar metamorphic core complexes, and portions of the Idaho batholith (*Hyndman, 1980*; *Bennett, 1986*). Intrusives and volcanics in this belt were predominantly intermediate to silicic in composition; any mafic magmas apparently stagnated within the crust (Leeman, 1983). Sr and Nd isotopic and trace-element compositions of Challis plutonic and volcanic rocks indicate that these magmas formed largely, or in part, by crustal anatexis (*Norman and Leeman, 1988*) due to heating by mafic intrusions and/or decompression melting as the crust was elevated. A number of small, Cretaceous to Eocene, potassic, volcanic/intrusive centers—including the Bearpaw, Highwood, and Crazy Mountains, which lie in a north-south belt along the Sevier foreland in western Montana—represent partial melts of old lithospheric mantle (*Dudas and others, 1987*); however, their relation to convergent margin processes is unclear. A similar potassic center occurs as far east as the Black Hills of South Dakota.

Southern Basin and Range. Generally similar types of magmatism are present in the Paleocene-Eocene southern province (Sierra Madre Occidental belt). This belt was restricted to Mexico, west Texas, and southern New Mexico until about 45 Ma, and thereafter migrated northward into the southwestern United States through Eocene and Oligocene time (Figs. 32E and F; *Elston, 1984*; Christiansen and Yeats, 1989). The dominant magma types were intermediate to silicic, mildly potassic calc-alkaline varieties. As magmatism encroached northward, early andesitic magmatism generally gave way to progressively more silicious magmatism associated with formation of calderas and ash flow eruptions. By 40 Ma, such activity had reached as far north as central Colorado and as far northwest as south-central Arizona. Far inland from the western margin, 35 to 49 Ma alkaline rocks occurred in the Trans-Pecos region of west Texas; these rocks are compositionally similar to many oceanic island or continental rift magmas (*Barker, 1977*). *Price and Henry (1984)* consider them to have formed in a back-arc region of the active Sierra Madre Occidental magmatic arc.

Mid-Tertiary magmatism. A dramatic transition in magmatic type occurred throughout the Cordillera about 40 to 42 Ma. This event coincided with a major (global?) change in plate interactions. Convergence between the Farallon and North American plates became more orthogonal, and convergence rates decreased (*Coney, 1978*; *Carlson, 1982*; *Jurdy, 1984*; Engebretson and others, 1985). Timing of this transition corresponds to the age of the bend in the Hawaiian-Emperor seamount chain (42 Ma; *Dalrymple and Clague, 1976*), indicating a change in Pacific plate motion. Dominantly intermediate to silicic magmatism in the Cordilleran interior and associated crustal extension have been interpreted as manifestations of back-arc spreading. A common hypothesis (*Coney and Reynolds, 1977*; *Keith, 1978*; Lipman, 1980) to account for this activity involves increasing dip of subduction and subsidence of the Farallon slab in response to slower convergence.

Alaska. Northward convergence near the Aleutian arc resulted in eventual subduction of the Kula ridge, and by 40 Ma, convergence had slowed (5 to 10 cm/yr) and taken a northwesterly azimuth. This transition led to increasing obliquity of convergence with an increasing strike-slip component from east to west along the Aleutian arc (e.g., *Davies and House, 1979*). Many of the Aleutian islands formed by arc magmatism in the mid-Tertiary (by 30 Ma), but only a few of the older plutonic complexes have been studied in much detail (Marsh, 1982). Magmatic activity was apparently minor between 25 and 15 Ma, after which the modern arc was established. Throughout southeastern Alaska and coastal British Columbia, magmatic activity at this time was restricted to lamprophyre dike swarms related to extension or transtension.

Cascades arc. Duncan (1982) suggested that the Oregon-Washington Coast Range (a Paleocene to Eocene seamount chain) was accreted at approximately 40 Ma, and that this event resulted in a seaward jump in the subduction zone relative to its former position near the modern Cascade Range. At about the same time, the Pacific Northwest margin was uplifted, fore-arc sediments were folded, and Western Cascades arc volcanism was initiated. By 37 Ma, this new "arc" was distributed in a wide belt between western British Columbia and northwestern to west-central Oregon; it had extended southward to the northern Sierra Nevada and northwestern Nevada by 31 Ma, and as far as the latitude of southernmost Nevada by 17 Ma.

Great Basin. During late Eocene to Oligocene there was a "flare-up" of dominantly silicic to intermediate volcanism with production of voluminous and extensive ash flow sheets in both the northern Great Basin and in the southwestern United States. In detail, the loci of active magmatic belts and associated extensional deformation shifted with time, southward and northward respectively, from their early Cenozoic positions; gradually occupying the previously quiescent central Cordillera (Figs. 32E, F, and G). The encroaching magmatic fronts were rather sharply defined in time, although waning volcanic activity persisted locally for a short time in their wake. In the northern region, the southerly transition occurred crudely in steps as follows (in terminology of Christiansen and Yeats, 1989): (1) the 43 to 37 Ma Tuscarora belt (western Washington and Oregon through central and southern Oregon and northeastern California into northern Nevada and west-central Utah); (2) the 36 to 20 Ma John Day belt (east-central Oregon, northwestern Nevada, and southwestern Idaho); (3) the 37 to 34 Ma (northern Nevada to central Utah) and 34 to 21 Ma (west-central Nevada to south-central Utah) Sierra-Wasatch belts; and (4) the 28 to 21 Ma Tonopah belt that extended from Reno across southern Nevada to southwestern Utah (Fig. 29).

Although extension accompanied the southward migration of magmatic activity (Zoback and others, 1981), and may be associated with uplift of metamorphic core complexes in eastern Nevada and western Utah (Coney and Harms, 1984), these processes may not be precisely contemporaneous (at least in eastern Nevada; *Taylor and others, 1989*). Wide distribution of ash flow tuffs in eastern Nevada precludes the existence of significant uplift and block faulting prior to late Eocene or early Oligocene time.

Southern Basin and Range. In the southern region, the large Mogollon-Datil volcanic field (Fig. 29) was active by 39 Ma, and from 35 to 28 Ma, magmatism extended between the Rio Grande and southeastern Arizona (*Elston, 1984*). Coeval early volcanism associated with the Rio Grande Rift progressed northward into a large region of southwestern Colorado (e.g., the 31 to 23 Ma San Juan volcanic field; Lipman, 1980). Eruptive centers in this region typically produced voluminous early intermediate-composition lavas followed by dominantly silicic ash flows. Between 35 and 21 Ma, similar magmatism migrated progressively northwestward across southern Arizona to the Mojave region of southern California. *Nelson and Wood (1989)* propose that this transition may correlate with a diachronous change from compressional to extensional stress regime related to subsidence of the subducted Farallon slab (following a decrease in convergence rates at 40 Ma).

By about 20 Ma, magmatism declined to the east (west Texas) and became more silicic to the west (Mojave area). *Glazner and Bartley (1984)* show that low-angle detachment faulting and generally southwest-northeast to east-west extension likewise progressed northward with time from southern Arizona (25 Ma) through the Mojave area (20 Ma) to the Las Vegas area (between 10 and 15 Ma). The Colorado Plateau and the Laramide foreland experienced only minor magmatic activity in early Cenozoic time; compositions of these magmas were alkalic to lamproitic (e.g., Navaho province; Spanish Peaks; Fig. 29).

Late Cenozoic magmatism. A major transition in the magmatic and tectonic history of the southern Cordillera accompanied initiation of the modern San Andreas fault zone as the East Pacific rise impinged on the subduction margin at about 29 to 30 Ma (Atwater, 1970; Atwater and Molnar, 1973; *Pilger and Henyey, 1979*; *Ingersoll, 1982a*). This event resulted in development of the Mendocino and Rivera triple junctions, which have migrated north and south, respectively, along the Pacific margin (Fig. 32G and H) to their present locations. Convergence shifted from oblique transpression to a transform boundary between North America and the Pacific plate. Magmatic styles also began to change, eventually leading to decreasing overall volcanic intensity (or volume) and emergence of widespread basalt or bimodal basalt-rhyolite activity. As the transform boundary extended, subduction-related magmatism retreated. Extensive strike-slip and related deformation resulted in significant displacement of older magmatic belts and fields well into the interior Cordillera.

Alaska and Canada. Since about 15 Ma, the modern Aleutian arc exhibited renewed intensity, producing mafic to andesitic calc-alkaline magmas. In the back-arc region (e.g., Bogoslof and Pribolof Islands) and portions of western interior Alaska (e.g., Seward Peninsula) there are minor occurrences of alkalic basalt. Along the Alaska Peninsula segment of the arc, which is underlain by older and thicker sialic crust, andesitic to dacitic products are more typical. The Wrangell–Kluane–St. Elias volcanic belt in southeastern Alaska and adjacent Canada (Fig. 29) produced similar magmas between 20 Ma and the present (D. Richter, personal communication, 1988), although plate convergence was quite oblique in this sector of the Cordillera (*Stephens and others, 1984*).

Throughout most of the Canadian Cordillera, there was a mid-Tertiary magmatic lull that apparently was accompanied by a period of renewed uplift in coastal British Columbia and southeastern Alaska (*Parrish, 1983*). Miocene magmatism was represented by large outpourings of alkalic flood basalts in central British Columbia, and by smaller cinder cones and flows farther north. In late Cenozoic time, volcanism was dominated by sporadic eruptions of highly varied lavas from separate central volcanoes in British Columbia and the Yukon. The majority of late Cenozoic volcanoes in these areas fall within restricted belts (Fig. 29): a north-south–oriented belt in northwest British Columbia (including Mt. Edziza; *Souther and others, 1984*), the Garibaldi/Pemberton belts in southwest British Columbia, and the east-west–trending Anahim belt, which crosses south-central British Columbia and possibly becomes younger to the east (Souther, 1977; Bevier and others, 1979; *Berman and Armstrong, 1980*).

The Miocene Pemberton volcanic belt consists of andesite-rhyolite calc-alkaline volcanoes related to subduction of the Juan de Fuca plate between 22 and 7 Ma; cessation of volcanism coincided with a seaward jump in the locus of subduction and segmentation of that plate into the present Juan de Fuca and Explorer subplates, and also with a brief episode of volcanism on Vancouver Island (2.5 to 8 Ma Alert Bay volcanic belt). After a long hiatus (3 m.y. in the north and 20 m.y. in the south), activity resumed in the north-northwest–trending Garibaldi belt (mainly 2.5 Ma to present) in response to subduction of the Juan de Fuca and Explorer subplates. Early Garibaldi belt volcanism was mainly andesitic to dacitic; basaltic lavas erupted during the Holocene (*Green and others, 1988*).

Cascade arc. By 17 Ma, a wide (100 km) belt of andesitic calc-alkaline volcanoes extended along nearly the entire western interior of the Cordillera, with the exception of an "amagmatic gap" between the latitude of southern Nevada and northern Mexico (Figs. 32G and H). This gap had progressively narrowed since late Eocene time. Following establishment of the San Andreas transform boundary, the narrowing trend was reversed and the gap again widened, essentially tracking separation of the Mendocino and Rivera triple junctions and development of a "subduction window" or gap in the subducted plate (Snyder and others, 1976). The southern terminus of the early Cascades arc gradually retreated northward to its present position at Mount Lassen volcano. By 8 to 9 Ma, the Cascade volcanic front was relatively narrow, and the main stratovolcano centers defined an oblique trend transecting the Western Cascades belt in Oregon and Washington. *Verplanck and Duncan (1987)* demonstrated that volcanic intensity in the Oregon Cascades steadily waned with time between 30 Ma and the present, and that this trend tracked an approximately five-fold decrease in convergence rate between the Juan de Fuca (Farallon remnant) and North American plates. Basaltic lava fields and intra-arc extension are more prevalent, and regional heat flow is higher in the southern Cascades than in the segments to the north. This relation may reflect the importance of intra-arc rifting to the south where plate convergence is much more oblique (*Rogers, 1985*), but in addition, differences in the underlying crust may play a role (McBirney and White, 1982; Leeman, 1983).

Coastal province of California. Shallow upwelling of asthenospheric mantle in the wake of the Mendocino triple junction (transform-transform-trench) is thought to account for northward-propagating tectonic uplift and Oligocene (23 Ma) to Recent, intermediate to silicic volcanism in the California Coast Ranges (*Pilger and Henyey, 1979*; *Zandt and Furlong, 1982*). Mafic- to intermediate-composition magmatism in the southern California basin is similarly correlated with southward migration of the Rivera triple junction (ridge–transform–trench). *Johnson and O'Neil (1984)* have shown that Coast Range volcanic rocks have Sr and O isotopic ratios consistent with their formation by crustal anatexis; associated basalts are relatively primitive and are distinctive from subduction-related magmas in their trace-element compositions. Many of the Oligocene to Miocene western Mojave and coastal volcanic fields were fragmented by strike-slip faults. Palinspastic restoration of volcanic rocks in the northwesterly displaced blocks (Transverse and Coast Ranges, southern California Borderland, and northern Baja California) places them near autochthonous counterparts distributed from the Mojave region to Sonora (*Pilger and Henyey, 1979*).

Great Basin. As a continuation of the earlier southward volcanic migration across this region, 22- to 17-Ma potassic bimodal basalt-rhyolite centers extended in a broad basin across southernmost Nevada. A brief lull in activity was followed by renewed magmatism (14 Ma) associated with late-stage Basin and Range faulting and regional uplift. The latter magmatic pulse produced bimodal basalt-rhyolite eruptive centers, but was mainly characterized by dispersed basaltic lava fields. Over the past 10 m.y., magmatism migrated to the east and west margins of the region and encroached onto the western Colorado Plateau and the Sierra Nevada–Owens Valley areas, where much of the late Cenozoic activity is focused. Many of the younger basalts are distinct from earlier subduction-related magmas and instead resemble oceanic island basalts (OIB). The transition in composition (and presumably magma sources) is diachronous and has migrated northward with time from the Mojave-Sonora region (Ormerod and others, 1988; Fitton and others, 1989).

In the mid-Miocene (17 to 16 Ma), apparent southwest-northeast extension formed the Northern Nevada rift (*Stewart and others, 1975*), which is characterized by dike swarms, associated basalt-rhyolite volcanism, and a conspicuous elongate magnetic anomaly. This rift zone is parallel in strike with the western Snake River Plain graben and dike swarms that produced much of the Columbia River basalt. *Zoback and Thompson (1978)* suggested that these features may originally have been part of a continuous structural zone that was subsequently offset by post–10-Ma northwest-trending strike-slip faults, such as those now bounding the northwestern Basin and Range province (*Lawrence, 1976*). In any event, the Oregon and Columbia River Plateaus were inundated by extensive 14- to 17-Ma subalkaline flood basalts that represent a significant addition to the crust in this region (*Swanson and others, 1979*; *Carlson and Hart, 1987*). Nearly contemporaneous (17 to 14 Ma) large bimodal basalt-rhyolitic eruptive centers formed in the region near the Oregon, Idaho, and northern Nevada state borders.

Similar eruptive centers have since propagated northeastward to form the Snake River Plain–Yellowstone Plateau (SRP-YP) province (*Armstrong and others, 1975*). *Morgan (1972)* suggested that this province may represent the track of a hot spot that is now located beneath Yellowstone, but its origin remains uncertain (Christiansen and McKee, 1978; Leeman, 1982b). The SRP-YP province bounds the northeastern Basin and Range province and may be a zone of accommodation for differential extension on block faults to the north and south. Bimodal Neogene basalt-rhyolite magmatism associated with normal faulting characterizes the entire region from southeastern Oregon and northeastern Nevada to the Cascade Range. *MacLeod and others (1976)* observed that silicic volcanism migrated systematically toward the west across this region since 10 Ma. Although this temporal pattern seemingly mimics that of the SRP-YP, the latter is considerably more voluminous and more focused spatially. The Oregon trend more likely reflects northwestward propagation of Basin and Range–style extension across the Cascades back-arc region.

Southern Cordillera. A regime of Basin and Range–style normal faulting developed in portions of the southern Cordillera (west Texas, southern New Mexico, Arizona, and northern Mexico) beginning around 30 to 32 Ma (e.g., *Laughlin and others, 1983*; *Price and Henry, 1984*); silicic magmatism subsequently declined, whereas basaltic (or bimodal basalt-rhyolite) magmatism became more prevalent. *Nelson and Wood (1989)* note that the number, size, and distribution of caldera-forming silicic volcanic fields diminished drastically in the southern Cordillera following contact of the East Pacific rise with North America and cessation of subduction in that region. Between 29 and 20 Ma, extensive basaltic andesites and minor basalts were erupted over much of this region (Cameron and others, 1989). This period pre-dated and possibly coincided in part with dramatic extension by low-angle normal faults focused in a corridor along the lower Colorado River.

In southern New Mexico and the southern Rocky Mountains, dominantly basaltic and bimodal basalt-rhyolite magmatism started locally by 26 Ma and was widespread by 21 Ma. The modern Rio Grande rift developed since mid-Miocene time (10 to 13 Ma), and is now an active magmatic focus. As regional extension proceeded, many monogenetic basaltic fields developed across the region, commonly in close proximity to zones of normal faulting. In general, there seems to be no systematic temporal distribution except that magmatism progressively encroached onto margins of the Colorado Plateau (e.g., *Tanaka and others, 1986*), which had been nearly amagmatic throughout Cenozoic time. Some of these fields, particularly around margins of the Colorado Plateau, are associated with evolved central volcanoes (e.g., San Francisco Peaks, Mormon Mountains, Mt. Taylor, Jemez Mountains, northern Rio Grande rift) that produced "anorogenic" calc-alkaline magmas and bimodal basalt-rhyolite. Many of these are located along the Springerville-Raton lineament, which has been interpreted to be an old zone of crustal weakness (Lipman, 1980). Young basalts within the Basin and Range are dominantly alkalic and, like those in the southern Great Basin, have compositional affinities with ocean island basalts (Fitton and others, 1989).

The Gulf of California opened by sea-floor spreading as strike-slip deformation stepped inboard at 5 to 6 Ma, and Baja California began its northwestward displacement (*Karig and Jensky, 1972*). The Salton Sea basin formed in conjunction with this event. Associated magmatism in Baja California and Sonora is dominated by alkalic to tholeiitic basalts, many of which have extremely low $^{87}Sr/^{86}Sr$ ratios similar to those in mid-ocean ridge basalts (Leeman, 1982a).

Minor, but notable, basanitic (e.g., Hopi province), ultrapotassic (e.g., Sierra Nevada), or lamproitic (e.g., Leucite Hills) magmatism occurred locally in areas marginal to the main region of Cenozoic Cordilleran deformation. Their compositions generally suggest that these magmas represent low-degree partial melts of pre-existing lithospheric mantle.

Summary. For the U.S. Cordillera, several general impressions are worth noting: (1) the volumes of eruptive products (or rates of magma production) decreased with time through the Cenozoic, and the mean composition of these products became progressively more mafic; (2) the cumulative volume of late Cenozoic volcanic rocks generally increases toward the northwest, as does the volume of material erupted in local volcanic fields; (3) tholeiitic and subalkaline basalts are predominant in the northwest, whereas alkalic basalts are characteristic of the Basin and Range province; (4) silicic magmas erupted in greatest volume in the eastern Cordillera, where crustal thicknesses are greatest and, perhaps more important, where there is a cratonic basement of ancient (Archean to Proterozoic) sialic crust; and (5) most regions affected by Laramide and older crustal shortening subsequently underwent extension and regional

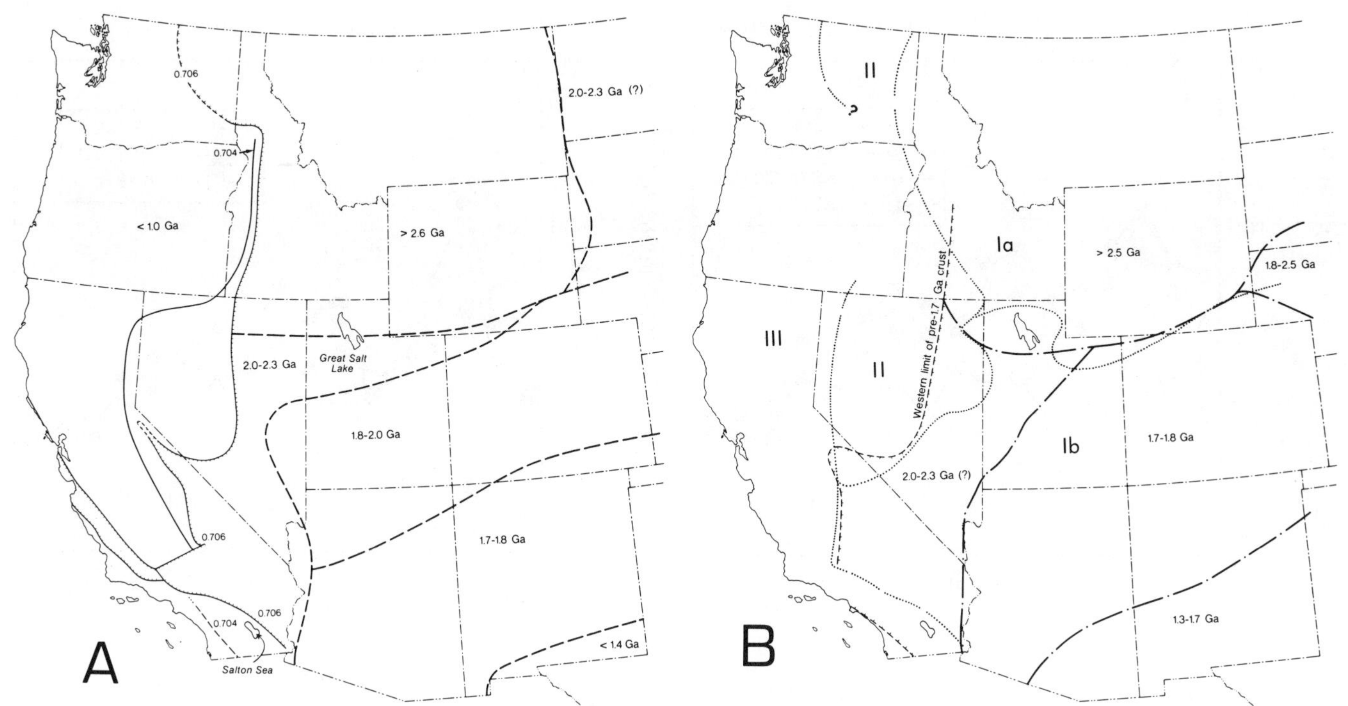

Figure 34. Maps showing basement provinces for the western conterminous United States (from Ernst, 1988b). A: Map showing isotopic and crystallization age provinces. Nd-depleted mantle model ages and strontium ($^{87}Sr/^{86}Sr$ = 0.706 and 0.704) initial ratio limits in Mesozoic and Cenozoic granitoids. Mid-Paleozoic and older basement lies inboard of the 0.706 line. B: Pb isotopic provinces and areas characterized by radiometric, chiefly Rb/Sr and U/Pb, bulk-rock ages of crystallization. Regions I, II, and III, separated by dotted lines, are typified by lead from post-Paleozoic igneous rocks occurring in regions principally of Precambrian basement, derivative sedimentary strata, and young "eugeoclinal" mixed provenance, respectively.

magmatism—elsewhere (e.g., Colorado Plateau and eastern margin of the Cordillera), magmatism was limited to dispersed small ultra-alkalic igneous centers.

Geochemical variations. The single most striking feature of Cenozoic Cordilleran magmatism (and particularly the Basin and Range province) is the prevalence and large volume of intermediate to silicic eruptive products associated with subduction-related processes prior to regional extension, and the prevalence and relatively small volume of mafic eruptive material thereafter. Leeman (1970, 1982a) and Scott and others (1971) suggested on the basis of strontium isotopic studies that the early calc-alkalic magmas represent either extensive fusion of the underlying lower(?) crust or at least contain a large proportion of such melts, and that the younger basalts represent more or less unmodified partial melts of the deeper mantle. It is implied (Leeman, 1982a, 1983) that stagnation of mantle-derived magmas within lower-density crust induced crustal melting in the first case, and that eruption of basaltic liquids was facilitated only after lithosphere density had increased (e.g., by solidification of earlier mafic intrusions, extraction of silicic magmas, and extensional thinning of the crust).

Another major observation is that late Cenozoic basaltic magmas display spatially systematic isotopic variations (Figs. 34A and B) that mimic compositional and/or age patterns in the underlying basement (Leeman, 1970, 1982a; *Zartman, 1974*; *Menzies and others, 1983*; *Hart, 1985*). A notable exception is the existence of sharp Sr, Nd, and Pb isotopic gradients in primitive basaltic magmas from a transect across the Oregon-Idaho border (*Hart, 1985*; *Leeman and Hawkesworth, 1986*; Leeman, unpublished data), roughly coincident with the $^{87}Sr/^{86}Sr$ = 0.706 isopleth defined in Mesozoic plutons (Armstrong and others, 1977; *Kistler and Peterman, 1978b*; *Fleck and Criss, 1985*). Because isotopic variations occur in late Cenozoic basalts having otherwise similar bulk compositions, it appears that the Oregon–Idaho gradient must reflect compositional variations in the mantle and not simply crustal contamination effects.

On a regional scale, young basalts erupted in transition zones marginal to the Basin and Range province, and some older (but post-extension) basalts well within the province, commonly have isotopic and trace-element compositions distinct from those of oceanic island basalts (Leeman, 1982a; Fitton and others, 1989). Because their compositional characteristics are not readily attributed to effects of crustal contamination (*Lum and others, 1989*), it appears that these basalts tapped mantle domains that are physically distinct from the asthenosphere; i.e., lithospheric mantle of differing ages (as reflected by ages of the crystalline

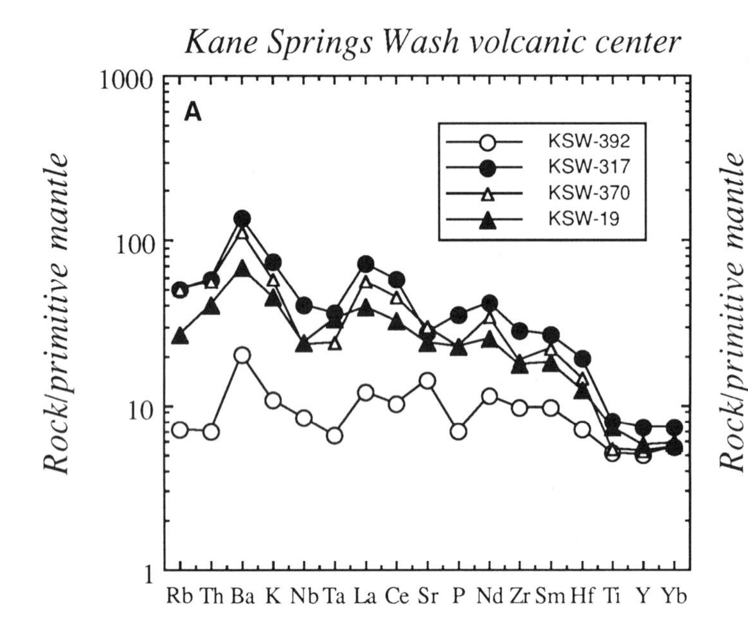

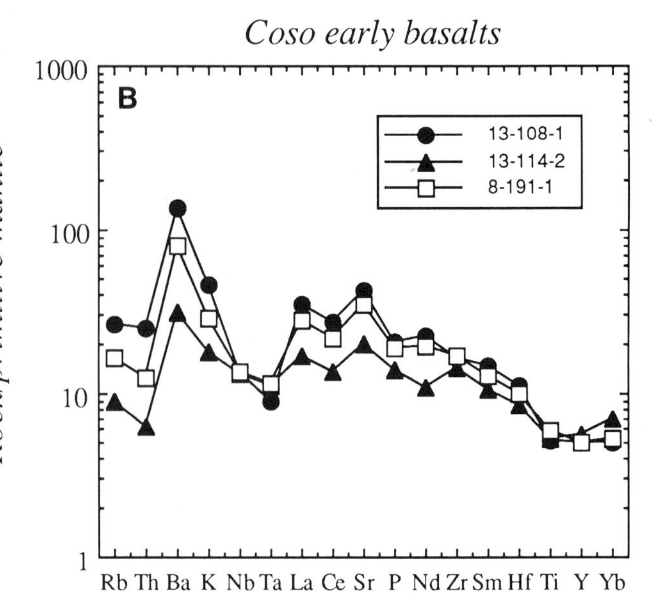

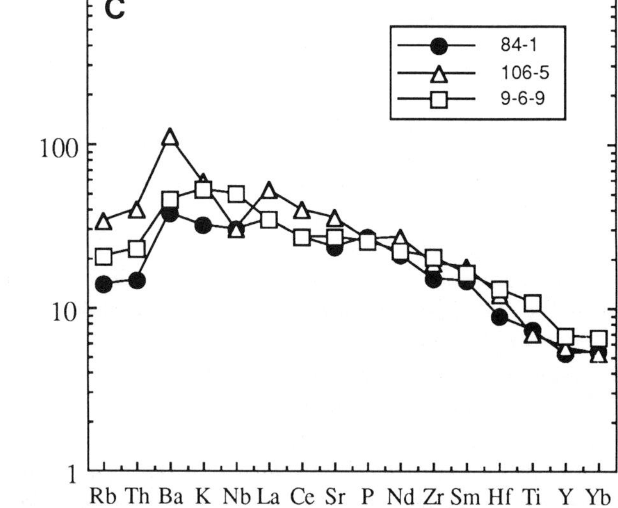

Figure 35. A: Trace element abundance profiles for mafic lavas of the 12 to 14 Ma Kane Springs Wash volcanic center (*Novak and Mahood, 1986*; Leeman unpublished data) normalized to estimated "primitive mantle" values of *Wood (1979)*. Although these basalts are related to early Basin and Range extensional tectonics and clearly postdate subduction, they display pronounced Nb-Ta depletions characteristic of most subduction-related volcanic arcs. They are believed to be formed by melting of subcontinental lithospheric mantle that was metasomatized during earlier Cordilleran subduction episodes. Trace element abundance profiles for Pliocene (early; B) and Holocene (late; C) basalts of the Coso volcanic field (*Novak and Bacon, 1986*; Leeman unpublished data), normalized as in the previous diagram. These diagrams illustrate the apparent shift in magma sources from a lithospheric mantle with vestigial "memory" of the earlier subduction episodes to "asthenospheric" mantle much like that which produces oceanic island basalts, which have smooth convex-upward profiles similar to those in the youngest Coso basalts. Similar transitions have been documented at different times for other volcanic centers in the western Great Basin (Ormerod and others, 1988).

basement; Bennett and DePaolo, 1987; Wooden and others, 1988). Even though they clearly postdated active subduction, many of these basalts have relative trace-element abundances resembling those in typical arc basalts (Fig. 35A to C). It is reasonably inferred that these magmas were derived from lithospheric mantle sources that were metasomatically overprinted with an arc signature during earlier episodes of active subduction.

In contrast, many young basaltic lavas from the Basin and Range province have strong similarities to oceanic island basalts and seem to come from similar sources, presumably the asthenosphere (Leeman, 1982a; *Menzies and others, 1983*; *Perry and others, 1987*). Thus, extension in the western United States was accompanied by temporal transitions in magma sources, eventually from lithospheric to sublithospheric domains. Ormerod and others (1988) demonstrated that such transitions are diachronous in that, at least along the western margin of the Great Basin, they have migrated northward at a rate similar to that of northward passage of the Mendocino triple junction.

An important implication of the isotopic data is the preservation of lithospheric mantle beneath most of the Cordillera. Although its thickness is uncertain and probably varies considerably over this region, lithosphere certainly extends to depths of basaltic magma production. On petrologic grounds, early post-extension basaltic magmas could have formed at depths as shallow as 60 km, and possibly deeper (Leeman, 1970). In many areas such as the Rio Grande rift and eastern Sierra front, which are characterized by active extension, high heat flow, and unusually low Pn velocities, the lithosphere-asthenosphere boundary may be substantially shallower, and partial melting of asthenosphere is suggested by the magma compositions (*Perry and others, 1987*).

CONCLUDING REMARKS

The Phanerozoic history of the Cordillera is one of transpressional and transtensional tectonism. During the Mesozoic and early Cenozoic, development of the contractional orogen along the active margin conforms to an early Mesozoic history dominated by sinistral transpression, but possibly containing intervals of dextral motion, followed in the mid-Cretaceous by dextral transpression. The broad outer margin of the Cordilleran orogen, termed the transpressional complex, is characterized by substantial contraction and wholesale transcurrent displacement of many if not most of the structural elements. Displacements in the plate margin regions differ from those of the continental flank where deformation is typified by foreland fold belts. Several structural elements of the Cordilleran orogen have experienced thousands of kilometers of displacement parallel to the plate margin. Nevertheless, most of the Cordilleran collage is composed of units originally of North American affinity. Addition of exotic components is relatively minor.

The transpressional history of the Cordillera involves remarkable transcurrent displacements along the active margin, but these earlier displacements are commonly overlooked in studies of the transform tectonics of regions such as California. The earlier history of transpression had a profound impact in forming the tectonic framework for later transtensional structures and associated basin development. The transition from transpressional to transtensional motion during the late Cenozoic contributed to the development of widespread extension in the Cordillera of the conterminous United States. The Cenozoic regional extension seems largely to have been driven by a mechanical-thermal mechanism that perhaps was related to the re-equilibration or removal of a cold lithospheric root formed beneath the conterminous U.S. Cordillera during earlier contraction.

The tectonic setting of the late Proterozoic and Paleozoic, although occasionally viewed as less complex than that of the Mesozoic, is largely unknown and enigmatic. Much of the apparent simplicity is an artifact of inadequate understanding of the pre-Mesozoic kinematic framework. Only broad tectonic relations are known. The Cordillera experienced passive-margin conditions of deposition only in the early Paleozoic after the inferred late Proterozoic break-up of the North American supercontinent. It is likely that the so-called passive margin of the Cordillera was coupled with a fringing-arc system by Ordovician time.

Certainly since the mid-Paleozoic Ellesmerian and Antler orogenic events, the configuration of the continent was permanently altered. Collision and loading of the continental margin apparently propagated from the northern Arctic margin southward along the Cordillera. Unlike the Ellesmerian thrust belt, which is characterized by a huge foreland basin, that of the Cordilleran Antler system is small and generally poorly developed. In fact, the only well-developed foredeep overlies the northeast-southwest–trending miogeosyncline preserved in the western Great Basin. Elsewhere, preservation is poor; in the Canadian Cordillera, for instance, Devono-Carboniferous clastics do not demonstrably form a foredeep succession. Possibly the general lack of a well-developed foredeep connotes little A-subduction of the continental foreland and may indicate the existence of a strong transcurrent component of motion during the mid-Paleozoic collision. Preferential development of the Antler orogenic belt and its associated foredeep along the northeasterly trending miogeosyncline of the Great Basin may suggest that tectonism was the product of sinistral transpression.

In the Pennsylvanian and Early Permian, the Cordillera experienced intraplate deformation during the formation of the Ancestral Rocky Mountains. Relations are best described as the product of transpressional tectonics in the foreland of the Ouachita Marathon fold belt formed during the poorly understood collision of North and South America.

During the latest Paleozoic and earliest Miocene, plate margin tectonism is best expressed by the Sonoma orogeny of the western conterminous United States. Comparable deformation occurred in the southern Canadian Cordillera but cannot be clearly identified in Alaska. In the Great Basin, the emplacement of basinal rocks over coeval platform units to the east marks the Sonoman event, which is not accompanied by the development of a clastic foredeep succession. Again, this may indicate a substantial component of strike-slip motion during regional deformation, a notion consistent with the apparently coeval transcurrent truncation of the southern miogeosyncline in the Mojave Desert region.

We have made several propositions concerning the architecture of the Cordilleran active margin. The structural relations discussed are not necessarily restricted to the North American Cordillera and with judicious modification may be relevant to many other orogenic belts. The major features are summarized below.

(1) The existence of a throughgoing basal detachment in the contractional orogen, at mid- to lower crustal levels or conceivably in the upper mantle, detaches the entire Cordillera from the underlying lithosphere. The upper structural sequence constitutes an "orogenic float" whose internal structure is more complex than that of the region underlying the decollement.

(2) The notion of displacement on a throughgoing detachment system connecting the frontal portion of the orogenic belt with the plate margin supplies a means to relate orogeny to relative plate motions. Within this framework, episodes of long-lived (tens of millions of years) tectonism, which characterize Cordilleran tectonic history, are easily reconciled within the time-frame of plate tectonic convergence patterns.

(3) The existence of a regional basal detachment connects transcurrent and coeval thrust belts and allows their motions to be viewed as the resolved components of a regional displacement field driven by relative plate motions.

(4) Motion on the basal decollement involves the entire orogen. Thus, late-stage displacements generally localized in foreland regions of thrust belts involve the whole deformational system. The implication is that many post-kinematic plutons in the interior of contractional belts are decapitated and carried above the basal decollement by foreland shortening.

(5) The relationship between the orientation of Cordilleran structures and the plate margin implies that the formation of structures is controlled to a large degree by plate-margin morphology. Primary structures within the Cordillera consist of long trace-length transcurrent faults and associated contractional belts. Displacements on the linked systems represent resolved components of a regional displacement field; where changes in the orientation of the plate margin occur along strike, corresponding changes in the orientation of major structures result in a repartitioning of the components of strike-slip and normal motion.

(6) The formation of the regional decollement during contraction may result in subdecollement volume problems and the development of a "lithospheric root." Shortening in an active margin, such as the Cordillera of the conterminous United States, must be compensated at depth by comparable contraction in the subdetachment lithosphere, resulting in the development of a tectonic root. On the other hand, where lateral mass transfer into the orogenic float exists (say with the addition of terranes as in much of the Canadian and Alaskan Cordillera), shortening of the indigenous rocks overlying the decollement may be compensated and cross-sectional balance preserved. Thus, no mismatch in cross-sectional area develops above and below the decollement, the system is essentially balanced, and a root is not necessary.

(7) As is apparent from the California borderland, the concept of regional detachments is not restricted to contractional orogens and is compatible with the development of transtensional and extensional regimes.

In the preceding pages, we have discussed the complex interaction of crustal elements in the evolution of the North American Cordillera. We have hinted at the role of deeper parts of the lithosphere, but the kinematic and dynamic relations of subcrustal regions and their relation to shallower tectonics is poorly understood. Therefore, we feel that the investigation of continental margin tectonism demands careful integration of surface and subsurface data, from the local to the lithospheric scale.

A first step toward this goal is to carefully constrain the displacement history in space and time of structural units exposed at the surface. Useful regional syntheses can no longer depend solely on broad stratigraphic analyses and generalized estimates of displacement in deformational belts. In addition to more classical approaches, reconstructions require detailed kinematic and geochronologic studies. Adequate kinematic investigations include modern structural analysis techniques coupled with detailed geochronological studies, both of which must be integrated with comprehensive paleomagnetic investigations.

Although kinematic analysis is a critical ingredient in the study of tectonic belts, a clear understanding of three-dimensional displacements through time cannot be determined from surface data alone. In the context of a hierarchy of subhorizontal decoupling levels, a well-defined history of motion on detachment surfaces and the corresponding development of structures is necessary. To develop appropriate regional syntheses, observations and tectonic models must be integrated at a one-to-one scale. This scale bias brings us to an important point.

Different techniques applied to a common problem have strengths and limitations that must be understood and compensated. As an example, detailed kinematic analysis of structures at outcrop scale yields important relative timing relations amongst structures and a view of the displacements involved during deformation. Expansion of these relations to wider regions by incorporation of geochronological studies is critical in establishing a framework of regional displacements. The significance of the kinematic analysis in a still-wider framework requires application of paleomagnetic work to establish an absolute reference frame. This level of sophistication, generally not attained in most regional studies, is still inadequate to fully unravel the tectonic history of a region. What is required to expand this data into the scale of regional development of contractional orogens is the documentation of the relationship between structures and displacements measured at the surface with those at depth. Some insight into this problem can be derived from incorporation of geobarometric and geothermometric constraints based on calculated estimates of the conditions of dynamothermal metamorphism. But the actual structural architecture remains inadequately constrained.

Incorporation of geophysical data, particularly that focusing on imaging crustal structure, supplies the critical link between surface studies and crustal tectonic models. Without a clear understanding of the subsurface dimension, the truly mobilistic framework in which we, as geoscientists, work cannot be appreciated. Regional tectonic analysis requires a "renaissance view" of the earth sciences, which, considering the complexity and diversity of scientific endeavors involved, demands interaction and collaboration of different disciplines.

REFERENCES CITED

(Text references in *italics* will be found only on the accompanying microfiche.)

Aleinikoff, J. N., Dusel-Bacon, C., and Foster, H. L., 1986, Geochronology of augen gneiss and related rocks, Yukon-Tanana terrane, east-central Alaska: Geological Society of America Bulletin, v. 97, p. 626–637.

Allmendinger, R. W., Hauge, T. A., Hanse, E. C., Potter, J. C., Kemper, S. L., Nelson, K. D., Knuepfer, P., and Oliver, J., 1987, Overview of the COCORP 40°N transect, western United States—The fabric of an orogenic belt: Geological Society of America Bulletin, v. 98, p. 308–319.

Anderson, L. S., 1988, Core complexes of the Mojave Sonoran Desert—Conditions of plutonism, mylonitization, and compression, *in* Ernst, W. G., ed., Metamorphism and crustal evolution of the western United States, Rubey volume 7: Englewood Cliffs, New Jersey, Prentice-Hall, p. 502–525.

Armentrout, J. M., Cole, M. R., and TerBest, H., 1979, Cenozoic paleogeography of the western United States: Pacific Section, Society of Economic Geologists and Mineralogists Pacific Coast Paleogeographic Symposium 3, 335 p.

Armstrong, R. L., 1982, Cordilleran metamorphic core complexes—from Arizona to southern Canada: Annual Reviews of Earth and Planetary Sciences, v. 10, p. 129–154.

——, 1988, Mesozoic and early Cenozoic magmatic evolution of the Canadian Cordillera, *in* Clark, S. P., Jr., Burchfiel, B. C., and Suppe, J., eds., Processes in Continental Lithosphere Deformation: Geological Society of America Special Paper 218, p. 55–92.

Armstrong, R. L., Taubeneck, W. H., and Hales, P. O., 1977, Rb-Sr and K-Ar geochronometry of Mesozoic granitic rocks and their Sr isotopic composition, Oregon, Washington, and Idaho: Geological Society of America Bulletin, v. 88, p. 397–411.

Armstrong, R. L., Harakal, J. E., Forbes, R. B., Evans, B. W., and Thurston, S. P., 1986, Rb-Sr and K-Ar study of metamorphic rocks of the Seward Peninsula and southern Brooks Range, Alaska, *in* Evans, B. W., and Brown, E. H., eds., Blueschists and eclogites: Geological Society of America Memoir 164, p. 185–203.

Atwater, T., 1970, Implications of plate tectonics for the Cenozoic tectonic evolution of western North America: Geological Society of America Bulletin, 81, p. 3513–3536.

Atwater, T., and Molnar, P., 1973, Relative motion of the Pacific and North American plates deduced from seafloor-spreading in the Atlantic, Indian, and South Pacific oceans, *in* Kovach, R. L., and Nur, A., eds., Proceedings, Conference on tectonic problems of the San Andreas fault system: Stanford, California, Stanford University Publications on Geological Science, v. 13, p. 136–148.

Avé Lallemant, H. G., 1989, Pre-Cretaceous tectonic evolution of the Blue Mountains Province, northeastern Oregon: U.S. Geological Survey Professional Paper 1438 (in press).

Avé Lallemant, H. G., and Oldow, J. S., 1988, Early Mesozoic southward migration of Cordilleran transpressional terranes: Tectonics, v. 7, p. 1057–1088.

Avé Lallemant, H. G., Schmidt, W. J., and Kraft, J. L., 1985, Major Late Triassic strike-slip displacement in the Seven Devils terrane, Oregon and Idaho—a result of left-oblique plate convergence?: Tectonophysics, v. 119, p. 299–328.

Baars, D. L., and others, 1988, Basins of the Rocky Mountain region, *in* Sloss, L. L., ed., Sedimentary cover—North American craton, U.S.: Boulder, Colorado, Geological Society of America, Geology of North America, v. D-2, p. 109–220.

Bally, A. W., 1975, A geodynamic scenario for hydrocarbon occurrences: Tokyo, 9th World Petroleum Congress, v. 2, p. 23–44.

——, 1981, Thoughts on the tectonics of folded belts, *in* McClay, K. R., and Price, N. J., eds., Thrust and nappe tectonics: Geological Society of London Special Publication 9, p. 13–32.

——, 1984, Tectogenèse et sismique reflexion: Societe Geologique de France Bulletin, p. 279–285.

Bally, A. W., Gordy, P. L., and Stewart, G. A., 1966, Structure, seismic data, and orogenic evolution of southern Canadian Rockies: Canadian Society of Petroleum Geologists Bulletin, v. 14, p. 337–381.

Beaumont, C., 1981, Foreland basins: Geophysical Journal of the Royal Astronomical Society, v. 65, p. 291–329.

Beck, M. E., Jr., 1976, Discordant paleomagnetic pole positions as evidence of regional shear in the western Cordillera of North America: American Journal of Science, v. 276, no. 6, p. 694–712.

——, 1980, Paleomagnetic record of plate-margin tectonic processes along the western edge of North America: Journal Geophysical Research, v. 85, p. 7115–7131.

——, 1983, On the mechanism of tectonic transport in zones of oblique subduction: Tectonophysics, v. 93, p. 1–11.

——, 1986, Model for late Mesozoic–early Tertiary tectonics of coastal California and western Mexico and speculations on the origin of the San Andreas fault: Tectonics, v. 5, p. 49–62.

Bennett, V. C., and DePaolo, D. J., 1987, Proterozoic crustal history of the western United States as determined by Neodymium isotopic mapping: Geological Society of America Bulletin, v. 99, p. 674–685.

Bevier, M. L., Armstrong, R. L., and Souther, J. G., 1979, Miocene peralkaline volcanism in west-central British Columbia—its temporal and plate tectonic setting: Geology, v. 7, p. 389–392.

Bird, P., 1988, Formation of the Rocky Mountains, western United States—a continuum computer model: Science, v. 239, p. 1501–1507.

Blake, M. C., Jr., Jayko, A. S., McLaughlin, R. J., and Underwood, M. B., 1988, Metamorphic and tectonic evolution of the Franciscan complex, northern California, *in* Ernst, W. G., ed., Metamorphism and crustal evolution of the western United States, Rubey volume 7: Englewood Cliffs, New Jersey, Prentice Hall, p. 1035–1060.

Brandon, M. T., Cowan, D. S., and Vance, J. S., 1988, The Late Cretaceous San Juan thrust system, San Juan Islands, Washington: Geological Society of America Special Paper 221, 88 p.

Brown, R. L., Journeay, J. M., Lane, L. S., Murphy, D. C., and Rees, C. J., 1986, Obduction, backfolding, and piggyback thrusting in the metamorphic hinterland of the southern Canadian Cordillera: Journal of Structural Geology, v. 8, p. 255–268.

Brown, W. G., 1987, Structural style of the Laramide orogeny, Wyoming foreland [Ph.D. thesis]: Fairbanks, University of Alaska, 532 p.

Budnik, R. T., 1986, Left-lateral intraplate deformation along the Ancestral Rocky Mountains—implications for late Paleozoic plate motions: Tectonophysics, v. 132, p. 195–214.

Burchfiel, B. C., and Davis, G. A., 1972, Structural framework and evolution of the southern part of the Cordilleran orogen in the United States: American Journal of Science, v. 272, no. 2, p. 97–118.

——, 1975, Nature and controls of Cordilleran orogenesis, western United States—extensions of an earlier synthesis: American Journal of Science, v. 275A, p. 363–396.

——, 1981, Triassic and Jurassic evolution of the Klamath Mountains–Sierra Nevada geologic terrane, *in* Ernst, W. G., ed., The geotectonic development of Calfornia, Rubey volume 1: Englewood Cliffs, New Jersey, Prentice-Hall, p. 50–70.

Cameron, K. L., Nimz, G. J., Kuentz, D., Niemeyer, S., and Gunn, S., 1989, The southern Cordillera basaltic andesite suite, Mexico and the USA—a link between Tertiary continental arc and flood basalt magmatism in North America: Journal of Geophysical Research, v. 94, (in press).

Carr, S. D., Parrish, R. R., and Brown, R. L., 1987, Eocene structural development of the Valhalla complex, southeastern British Columbia: Tectonics, v. 6, p. 175–196.

Chapin, C. E., 1979, Evolution of the Rio Grande rift—a summary, *in* Riecker, R. E., ed., Rio Grande rift—tectonics and magmatism: American Geophysical Union, p. 1–5.

Chen, J. H., and Moore, J. G., 1982, Uranium-lead isotopic ages from the Sierra Nevada batholith, California: Journal of Geophysical Research, v. 87, p. 4761–4784.

Christiansen, R. L., and McKee, E. H., 1978, Late Cenozoic volcanic and tectonic evolution of the Great Basin and Columbia Intermontane regions: Geological Society of America Memoir 152, p. 283–311.

Christiansen, R. L., and Yeats, E. H., 1989, Post-laramide geology of the Cordilleran region, *in* Burchfiel, B. C., Lipman, P. W., and Zoback, M. L., eds., The Cordilleran orogen; Conterminous U.S.: Boulder, Colorado, Geological Society of America, Geology of North America, v. G-3 (in press).

Clowes, R. M., Brandon, M. T., Green, A. G., Yorath, C. J., Sutherland-Brown, A., Kanasewich, E. R., and Spencer, C., 1987, Lithoprobe—southern Vancouver Island; Cenozoic subduction complex imaged by deep seismic reflections: Canadian Journal of Earth Sciences, v. 24, p. 31–51.

Coney, P. J., and Harms, T. A., 1984, Cordilleran metamorphic core complexes; Cenozoic extensional relics of Mesozoic compression: Geology, v. 12, p. 550–554.

Coney, P. J., Jones, D. L., and Monger, J.W.H., 1980, Cordilleran suspect terranes: Nature, v. 299, p. 329–333.

Cook, T. D., and Bally, A. W., 1975, Stratigraphic atlas of North and Central American: Princeton, New Jersey, Princeton University Press, 272 p.

Cowan, D. S., and Bruhn, R. L., 1989, Late Jurassic to early Late Cretaceous geology of the U.S. Cordillera, *in* Burchfiel, B. C., Lipman, P. W., and Zoback, M. L., eds., The Cordilleran orogen; Conterminous U.S.: Boulder, Colorado, Geological Society of America, Geology of North America, v. G-3 (in press).

Crawford, M. L., Hollister, L. S., and Woodsworth, G. J., 1987, Crustal deformation and regional metamorphism across a terrane boundary, Coast Plutonic complex, British Columbia: Tectonics, v. 6, p. 343–361.

Crittenden, M. D., Jr., Coney, P. J., and Davis, G. H., eds., 1980, Cordilleran metamorphic core complexes: Geological Society of America Memoir 153, 490 p.

Cross, T. A., and Pilger, R. H., Jr., 1978, Constraints on absolute motion and plate interaction inferred from Cenozoic igneous activity in the western United States: American Journal of Science, v. 278, p. 865–902.

Crouch, J. K., and Bachman, S. B., eds., 1984, Tectonics and sedimentation along the California margin: Pacific Section, Society of Economic Paleontologists and Mineralogists, Field Guide series, v. 38, 188 p.

Crowell, J. C., 1962, Displacement along the San Andreas fault, California: Geological Society of America Special Paper 71, 61 p.

—— , 1987, Late Cenozoic basins of onshore southern California—complexity is the hallmark of their tectonic history, *in* Ingersoll, R. V., and Ernst, W. G., eds., Cenozoic basin development of coastal California, Rubey volume 6: Englewood Cliffs, New Jersey, Prentice-Hall, p. 207–243.

Curtis, B. F., ed., 1975, Cenozoic history of the southern Rocky Mountains: Geological Society of America Memoir 144, 279 p.

Dahlstrom, C.D.A., 1969, Balanced cross-sections: Canadian Journal of Earth Science, v. 6, p. 743–757.

Davis, G. A., and Lister, G. S., 1988, Detachment faulting in continental extension—Perspectives from the southwestern U.S. Cordillera, *in* Clark, S. P., Jr., Burchfiel, B. C., and Suppe, J., eds., Processes in continental lithospheric deformation: Geological Society of America Special Paper 218, p. 133–160.

Davis, G. H., 1983, Shear-zone model for the origin of metamorphic core complexes: Geology, v. 11, p. 342–347.

Debiche, M. G., Cox, A., and Engebretson, D., 1987, The motion of allochthonous terranes across the North Pacific basin: Geological Society of America Special Paper 207, 49 p.

Dickinson, W. R., 1977, Paleozoic plate tectonics and the evolution of the Cordilleran continental margin, *in* Stewart, J. H., Stevens, C. H., and Fritsche, A. E., eds., Paleozoic paleogeography of the western United States: Pacific Section, Society of Economic Paleontologists and Mineralogists Pacific Coast Paleogeography Symposium 1, p. 137–155.

—— , 1979b, Cenozoic plate tectonic setting of the Cordilleran region in the United States, *in* Armentrout, J. W., Cole, M. R., and TerBest, H., eds., Cenozoic Paleogeography of the western United States: Pacific Section, Society of Economic Paleontologists and Mineralogists Pacific Coast Paleogeography Symposium 3, p. 1–13.

Dickinson, W. R., and Snyder, W. S., 1978, Plate tectonics of the Laramide orogeny: Geological Society of America Memoir 151, p. 355–366.

Dickinson, W. R., and others, 1987a, Geohistory analysis of rates of sediment accumulation and subsidence for selected California basins, *in* Ingersoll, R. V., and Ernst, W. G., eds., Cenozoic basin development of coastal California, Rubey volume 6: Englewood Cliffs, New Jersey, Prentice-Hall, p. 1–23.

Dickinson, W. R., and 6 others, 1988, Paleogeographic and paleotectonic setting of Laramide sedimentary basins in the central Rocky Mountain region: Geological Society of America Bulletin, v. 100, p. 1120–1130.

Douglas, R.J.W., and others, 1970, Geology of western Canada, *in* Douglas, R.J.W., ed., Geology and economic minerals of Canada: Geological Survey of Canada Economic Geology Report 1, 5th edition, p. 366–488.

Duncan, R. A., 1982, A captured island chain in the Coast Range of Oregon and Washington: Journal of Geophysical Research, v. 87, p. 10827–10837.

Dutro, J. T., Jr., 1981, Geology of Alaska bordering the Arctic Ocean, *in* Nairn, A.E.M., Churkin, M., Jr., and Stehli, F. G., eds., The ocean basins and margins; Volume 5, The Arctic Ocean: New York, Plenum Press, p. 21–36.

Eaton, G. P., 1979, A plate-tectonic model for late Cenozoic crustal spreading in the western United States, *in* Riecker, R. E., ed., Rio Grande rift; Tectonics and magmatism: American Geophysical Union, p. 7–32.

—— , 1982, The Basin and Range province; Origin and tectonic significance: Annual Reviews of Earth and Planetary Science, v. 10, p. 409–440.

Eisbacher, G. H., 1985, Pericollisional strike-slip faults and synorogenic basins, Canadian Cordillera, *in* Biddle, K. T., and Christie-Blick, N., eds., Strike-slip deformation, basin formation, and sedimentation: Society of Economic Paleontologists and Mineralogists Special Publication 37, p. 265–282.

Engebretson, D. C., Cox, A., and Gordon, R. G., 1985, Relative motions between oceanic and continental plates in the Pacific basin: Geological Society of America Special Paper 206, 59 p.

Ernst, W. G., ed., 1981, The geotectonic development of California, Rubey volume 1: Englewood Cliffs, New Jersey, Prentice-Hall, 706 p.

—— , ed., 1988a, Metamorphic and crustal evolution of the western United States, Rubey volume 7: Englewood Cliffs, New Jersey, Prentice-Hall, 1152 p.

—— , 1988b, Metamorphic terranes, isotopic provinces, and implications for crustal growth of the western United States: Journal of Geophysical Research, v. 93, p. 7634–7642.

Estabrook, C. H., Stone, D. B., and Davies, J. N., 1988, Seismotectonics of northern Alaska: Journal of Geophysical Research, v. 93, p. 12026–12040.

Farmer, G. L., and DePaolo, D. J., 1983, Origin of Mesozoic and Tertiary granite in the western United States and implications for pre-Mesozoic crustal structure; 1, Nd and Sr isotopic studies in the geocline of the northern Great Basin: Journal of Geophysical Research, v. 88, p. 3379–3401.

Fitch, T. J., 1972, Plate convergence, transcurrent faults, and internal deformation adjacent to southeast Asia and the western Pacific: Journal of Geophysical Research, v. 77, p. 4432–4461.

Fitton, J. G., James, D., Kempton, P. D., Ormerod, D. S., and Leeman, W. P., 1989, The role of lithospheric mantle in the generation of late Cenozoic basic magmas in the western United States: Journal of Petrology (in press).

Flores, R. M., and Kaplan, S. S., eds., 1985, Cenozoic paleogeography of the west-central U.S. Rocky Mountains: Rocky Mountain Section, Society of Economic Paleontologists and Mineralogists Paleogeography Symposium 3, 460 p.

Frei, L. S., 1986, Additional paleomagnetic results from the Sierra Nevada—further constraints on Basin and Range extension and northward displacement of western United States: Geological Society of America Bulletin, v. 97, p. 840–849.

Frei, L. S., Magill, J. R., and Cox, A., 1984, Paleomagnetic results from the central Sierra Nevada—constraints on reconstructions of the western United States: Tectonics, v. 3, p. 157–177.

Friedman, R. M., and Armstrong, R. L., 1988, Tatla Lake metamorphic complex—an Eocene metamorphic core complex on the southwestern edge of the Intermontane belt of British Columbia: Tectonics, v. 7, p. 1141–1166.

Gabrielse, H., 1985, Major dextral transcurrent displacements along the northern Rocky Mountain Trench and related lineaments in north-central British Columbia: Geological Society of America Bulletin, v. 96, p. 1–14.

Gabrielse, H., and Yorath, C. J., eds., 1989, The Cordilleran orogen: Ottawa, Geological Survey of Canada, Geology of Canda, v. 4 (also, Geological Society of America, Geology of North America, v. G-2) (in press).

Gans, P. B., 1987, An open-system two-layer crustal stretching model for the eastern Great Basin: Tectonics, v. 6, p. 1–12.

Gans, P. B., Mahood, G., and Schermer, E., 1989, Synextensional magmatism in the Basin and Range province—a case study from the eastern Great Basin: Geological Society of America Special Paper 233 (in press).

Gardner, M. C., and 8 others, 1988, Pennsylvanian pluton stitching of Wrangellia and the Alexander terrane, Wrangell Mountains, Alaska: Geology, v. 16, p. 967–971.

Gehrels, G. E., and Saleeby, J. B., 1987, Geologic framework, tectonic evolution, and displacement history of the Alexander terrane: Tectonics, v. 6, p. 151–173.

Geissman, J. W., Van der Voo, R., and Howard, K. L., Jr., 1982, A paleomagnetic study of structural deformation in the Yerington District, Nevada: American Journal of Science, v. 282, p. 1042–1109.

Gordey, S. P., Abbott, J. G., Tempelman-Kluit, D. J., and Gabrielse, H., 1987, "Antler" clastics in the Canadian Cordillera: Geology, v. 15, p. 103–107.

Gordon, R. G., Cox, A., and O'Hare, S., 1984, Paleomagnetic Eueler poles and the apparent polar wander and absolute motion of North America since the Carboniferous: Tectonics, v. 3, p. 499–537.

Gottschalk, R. R., and Oldow, J. S., 1988, Low-angle normal faults in the south-central Brooks Range fold and thrust belt, Alaska: Geology, v. 16, p. 395–399.

Grantz, A., and May, S. D., 1983, Rifting history and structural development of the continental margin north of Alaska, *in* Watkins, J. S., and Drake, C. L., eds., Studies of continental margin geology: American Assocation of Petroleum Geologists Memoir 34, p. 77–100.

Gries, R., 1983, North-south compression of Rocky Mountain foreland structures: Denver, Colorado, Rocky Mountain Association of Geologists, p. 9–32.

Gries, R. R., and Dyer, R. C., eds., Seismic exploration of the Rocky Mountain region: Denver, Colorado, Rocky Mountain Association of Geologists and the Denver Geophysical Society, 298 p.

Hamilton, W., 1969, Mesozoic California and the underflow of Pacific mantle: Geological Society of America Bulletin, v. 80, p. 2409–2430.

—— , 1988, Tectonic setting and variation with depth of some Cretaceous and Cenozoic structural and magmatic systems of the western United States, *in* Ernst, W. G., ed., Metamorphism and crustal evolution of the western United States, Rubey volume 7: Englewood Cliffs, New Jersey, Prentice-Hall, p. 1–40.

Hamilton, W., and Myers, W. B., 1966, Cenozoic tectonics of the western United States: Reviews of Geophysics, v. 4, p. 509–549.

Hansen, V. L., 1988, A model for terrane accretion—Yukon–Tanana and Slide Mountain terranes, northwest North America: Tectonics, v. 7, p. 1167–1177.

Hanson, R. E., Saleeby, J. B., and Schweickert, R. A., 1988, Composite Devonian island-arc batholith in the northern Sierra Nevada, California: Geological Society of America Bulletin, v. 88, p. 446–457.

Harrison, J. C., and Bally, A. W., 1988, Cross-section of the Parry Islands fold belt on Melville Island, Canadian Arctic islands—implication for the timing and kinematics of some thin-skinned décollement systems: Canadian Petroleum Geology Bulletin, v. 36, no. 3, p. 331–332.

Hill, M. L., and Dibblee, T. W., Jr., 1953, San Andreas, Garlock, and Big Pine faults, California: Geological Society of America Bulletin, v. 64, p. 443–458.

Howell, D. G., ed., 1985, Tectonostratigraphic terranes of the circum-Pacific region: Houston, Texas, Circum-Pacific Council for Energy and Mineral Resources Earth Science Series, no. 1, 581 p.

Howell, D. G., and McDougall, K. A., eds., 1978, Mesozoic paleogeography of the western United States: Pacific Section, Society of Economic Paleontologists and Mineralogists Pacific Coast Paleogeography Symposium 2, 547 p.

Hubbard, R. J., Edrich, S. P., and Rattey, R. P., 1987, Geological evolution and hydrocarbon habitat of the "Arctic Alaskan microplate": Marine and Petroleum Geology, v. 4, p. 1–92.

Hudson, M. R., and Geissman, J. W., 1987, Paleomagnetic and structural evidence for middle Tertiary counterclockwise block rotation in the Dixie Valley region, west-central Nevada: Geology, v. 15, p. 638–642.

Hyndman, D. W., 1983, The Idaho batholith and associated plutons, Idaho and western Montana: Geological Society of America Memoir 159, p. 213–240.

Ingersoll, R. W., 1979, Evolution of the Late Cretaceous fore-arc basin, northern California: Geological Society of America Bulletin, v. 90, part 1, p. 813–826.

Ingersoll, R. W., and Ernst, W. G., eds., 1987, Cenozoic basin development of coastal California, Rubey volume 6: Englewood Cliffs, New Jersey, Prentice-Hall, 496 p.

Irving, E., Woodsworth, G. J., Wynne, P. J., and Morrison, A., 1985, Paleomagnetic evidence for displacement from the south of the Coast Plutonic Complex, British Columbia: Canadian Journal of Earth Sciences, v. 22, p. 584–598.

Irwin, W. P., 1985, Age and tectonics of plutonic belts in accreted terranes of the Klamath Mountains, California and Oregon, *in* Howell, D. G., ed., Tectonostratigraphic terranes of the circum-Pacific region: Houston, Texas, Circum-Pacific Council for Energy and Mineral Resources, Earth Science Series no. 1, p. 187–199.

Jarrard, R. D., 1986, Terrane motion by strike-slip faulting of forearc slivers: Geology, v. 14, p. 780–783.

Jones, D. L., Silberling, N. J., Gilbert, W., and Coney, P., 1982, Character, distribution, and tectonic significance of accretionary terranes in the central Alaska Range: Journal of Geophysical Research, v. 87, p. 3709–3717.

Jones, D. L., Silberling, N. J., Coney, P. J., and Plafker, G., 1987, Lithotectonic terrane map of Alaska (West of the 141st meridian): U.S. Geological Survey Miscellaneous Field Studies Map, MF–1874–A, scale 1:2,500,000.

Kay, M., 1951, North American geosynclines: Geological Society of America Memoir 48, 143 p.

Keller, G. R., Braile, L. W., and Morgan, P., 1979, Crustal structure, geophysical models, and contemporary tectonism of the Colorado Plateau: Tectonophysics, v. 61, p. 131–147.

Kerr, J. W., 1981, Evolution of the Canadian Arctic Islands—a transition between Atlantic and Arctic Oceans, *in* Nairn, A.E.M., Churkin, M., Jr., and Stehli, F. G., eds., The Ocean Basins and Margins, volume 5, The Arctic Ocean: New York, Plenum Press, p. 105–199.

King, P. B., 1969, The tectonics of North America—a discussion to accompany the Tectonic Map of North America: U.S. Geological Survey Professional Paper 628, 94 p., scale 1:5,000,000.

—— , 1977, The evolution of North America: Princeton, New Jersey, Princeton University Press, revised edition, 197 p.

Kistler, R. W., 1978, Mesozoic paleogeography of California—a viewpoint from isotope geology, *in* Howell, D. G., and McDougall, K. A., eds., Mesozoic paleogeography of the western United States: Pacific Section, Society of Economic Paleontologists and Mineralogists Pacific Coast Paleogeography Symposium 2, p. 75–84.

Kluth, C. F., 1986, Plate tectonics of the ancestral Rocky Mountains, *in* Peterson, J. A., ed., Paleotectonics and sedimentation in the Rocky Mountain region, United States: American Association of Petroleum Geologists Memoir 41, p. 353–370.

Lanphere, M. A., 1978, Displacement history of the Denali fault system, Alaska and Canada: Canadian Journal of Earth Sciences, v. 15, p. 817–822.

Laubscher, H. P., 1977, Foreland folding—the northern foreland of the central Alps: 25th International Geological Congress Abstracts with Programs, v. 3, p. 687.

Leeman, W. P., 1970, The isotopic composition of strontium in late Cenozoic basalts from the Basin–Range province, western United States: Geochimica et Cosmochimica Acta, v. 34, p. 857–872.

—— , 1982a, Tectonic and magmatic significance of strontium isotopic variations in Cenozoic volcanic rocks from the western United States: Geological Society of America Bulletin, v. 93, p. 487–503.

—— , 1982b, Origin and development of the Snake River Plain–Yellowstone Plateau volcanic province, Idaho and Wyoming—an overview and petrologic model, *in* Bonnichsen, B., and Breckenridge, R. M., eds., Cenozoic geology of Idaho: Idaho Bureau of Mines and Geology Bulletin, v. 26, p. 155–177.

—— , 1983, The influence of crustal structure on compositions of subduction-related magmas: Journal of Volcanology and Geothermal Research, v. 18, p. 561–588.

Leiggi, P. A., 1987, Style and age of tectonism of the Sadlerochit Mountains to Franklin Mountains, Arctic National Wildlife Refuge, Alaska, *in* Tailleur, I., and Weimer, P., eds., Alaskan North Slope geology: Pacific Section, Society of Economic Paleontologists and Mineralogists and Alaska Geological Society, v. 2, p. 749–756.

Lipman, P. W., 1980, Cenozoic volcanism in the western United States—implications for continental tectonics, *in* Continental tectonics: Washington, D.C., National Academy of Sciences, p. 161–174.

Lipman, P. W., Prostka, H. J., and Christiansen, R. L., 1971, Evolving subduction zones in the western United States as interpreted from igneous rocks: Science, v. 174, p. 821–825.

Lund, K., and Snee, L. W., 1988, Metamorphism, structural development, and geology of the continent-island arc juncture in West Central Idaho, *in* Ernst, W. G., ed., Metamorphism and crustal evolution of the western United States, Rubey volume 7: Englewood Cliffs, New Jersey, Prentice-Hall, p. 296–331.

Luyendyk, B. P., and Hornafius, J. S., 1987, Neogene crustal rotations, fault slip, and basin development in southern California, *in* Ingersoll, R. V., and Ernst, W. G., eds., Cenozoic basin development of coastal California, Rubey volume 6: Englewood Cliffs, New Jersey, Prentice-Hall, p. 259–293.

Mallory, W. W., ed., 1972, Geologic Atlas of the Rocky Mountain Region: Denver, Colorado, Rocky Mountain Association of Geologists, 331 p.

Marsh, B. D., 1982, The Aleutians, *in* Thorpe, R. S., ed., Andesites—orogenic andesites and related rocks: New York, Wiley and Sons, p. 99–114.

Mattinson, J. M., 1988, Constraints on the timing of the Franciscan metamorphism—geochronological approaches and their limitations, *in* Ernst, W. G., ed., Metamorphism and crustal evolution of the western United States, Rubey volume 7: Englewood Cliffs, New Jersey, Prentice-Hall, p. 1023–1034.

May, J. A., and Warme, J. E., 1987, Synchronous depositional phases in West Coast basins—eustasy or regional tectonics?, *in* Ingersoll, R. V., and Ernst, W. G., eds., Cenozoic basin development of coastal California, Rubey volume 6: Englewood Cliffs, New Jersey, Prentice-Hall, p. 24–46.

May, S. R., and Butler, R. F., 1986, North American Jurassic apparent polar wander—implications for plate motions, paleogeography and Cordilleran tectonics: Journal of Geophysical Research, v. 91, p. 1519–1544.

McBirney, A. R., and White, C. M., 1982, The Cascade province, *in* Thorpe, R. S., ed., Andesites—orogenic andesites and related rocks: New York, Wiley and Sons, p. 115–135.

Merguerian, C., and Schweichert, R. A., 1987, Paleozoic gneissic granitoids in the Shoo Fly complex, central Sierra Nevada, California: Geological Society of America Bulletin, v. 99, p. 699–717.

Miller, E. L., Gans, P. B., and Garing, J., 1983, The Snake Range décollement—an exhumed mid-Tertiary brittle-ductile transition: Tectonics, v. 2, p. 239–263.

Miller, E. L., Gans, P. B., Wright, J. E., and Sutter, J. F., 1988, Metamorphic history of the east-central Basin and Range Province—Tectonic setting and relationship to magmatism, *in* Ernst, W. G., ed., Metamorphism and crustal evolution of the western United States, Rubey volume 7: Englewood Cliffs, New Jersey, Prentice-Hall, p. 649–682.

Miller, E. L., and 4 others, 1989, Latest Devonian to Permian and Triassic time, *in* Burchfiel, B. C., Lipman, P. W., and Zoback, M. L., eds., The Cordilleran Orogen—conterminous U.S.: Boulder, Colorado, Geological Society of America, The Geology of North America, v. G-3 (in press).

Miller, M. M., 1987, Dispersed remnants of a northeast Pacific fringing arc; Upper Paleozoic terranes of Permian McCloud faunal affinity: Tectonics, v. 6, p. 807–830.

Molenaar, C. M., Bird, K. J., and Kirk, A. A., 1987, Cretaceous and Tertiary stratigraphy of northeastern Alaska, *in* Tailleur, I., and Weimer, P., eds., Alaskan North Slope Geology: Pacific Section, Society of Economic Paleontologists and Mineralogists and Alaska Geological Society, v. 1, p. 513–528.

Monger, J.W.H., and Berg, H. C., 1987, Lithotectonic terrane map of western Canada and southeastern Alaska: U.S. Geological Survey Miscellaneous Field Studies Map MF–1874–B, scale 1:2,500,000.

Monger, J.W.H., and Price, R. A., 1979, Geodynamic evolution of the Canadian Cordillera—progress and problems: Canadian Journal of Earth Sciences, v. 16, p. 770–791.

Monger, J.W.H., Souther, J. G., and Gabrielse, H., 1972, Evolution of the Canadian Cordillera—a plate-tectonic model: American Journal of Science, v. 272, p. 577–602.

Monger, J.W.H., Price, R. A., and Tempelman-Kluit, D. J., 1982, Tectonic accretion and the origin of the two major metamorphic and plutonic welts in the Canadian Cordillera: Geology, v. 10, p. 70–75.

Mortensen, J. K., and Jilsen, G. A., 1985, Evolution of the Yukon–Tanana terrane—evidence from southeastern Yukon Territory: Geology, v. 13, p. 806–810.

Mudge, M. R., 1982, A resume of the structural geology of the northern disturbed belt, northwestern Montana, *in* Powers, R. B., ed., Geologic studies of the Cordilleran thrust belt: Rocky Mountain Association of Geologists, v. 1, p. 91–122.

Mull, C. G., 1982, Tectonic evolution and structural style of the Brooks Range, Alaska—an illustrated summary, *in* Powers, R. B., ed., Geologic studies of the Cordilleran thrust belt: Rocky Mountain Association of Geologists, v. 1, p. 1–46.

Murphy, D. C., 1987, Supracrustal/infrastructure transition, east-central Cariboo Mountains, British Columbia—geometry, kinematic, and tectonic implications: Journal of Structural Geology, v. 9, p. 13–29.

Nairn, A.E.M., Churkin, M., Jr., and Stehli, F. G., eds., 1981, The Ocean Basins and Margins, volume 5, The Arctic Ocean: New York, Plenum Press, 672 p.

Namson, J. S., and Davis, T. L., 1988a, Structural transect of the western Transverse Ranges, California—implications for lithospheric kinematics and seismic risk evaluation: Geology, v. 16, p. 675–679.

—— , 1988b, Seismically active fold and thrust belt in the San Joaquin Valley, central California: Geological Society of America Bulletin, v. 100, p. 257–273.

Nichols, K. M., and Silberling, N. J., 1977, Stratigraphy and depositional history of the Star Peak Group (Triassic), northwestern Nevada: Geological Society of America Special Paper 178, 73 p.

Nilsen, T. H., 1981, Upper Devonian and Lower Mississippian red beds, Brooks Range, Alaska, *in* Miall, A. D., ed., Sedimentation and tectonics in alluvial basins: Geological Association of Canada Special Paper 23, p. 187–219.

—— , 1987, Paleogene tectonics and sedimentation of coastal California, *in* Ingersoll, R. V., and Ernst, W. G., eds., Cenozoic basin development of coastal California, Rubey volume 6: Englewood Cliffs, New Jersey, Prentice-Hall, p. 81–123.

Nokleberg, W. J., Jones, D. L., and Silberling, N. J., 1985, Origin and tectonic evolution of the MacLaren and Wrangellia terranes, eastern Alaska Range, Alaska: Geological Society of America Bulletin, v. 96, p. 1251–1270.

Norris, D. K., 1985, Eastern Cordilleran fold belt of northern Canada—its structural geometry and hydrocarbon potential: American Association of Petroleum Geologists Bulletin, v. 69, p. 788–808.

Norris, D. K., and Yorath, C. J., 1981, The North American plate from the Arctic Archipelago to the Romanzoff Mountains, *in* Nairn, A.E.M., Churkin, M., Jr., and Stehli, F. G., eds., The Ocean Basins and Margins, volume 5, The Arctic Ocean: New York, Plenum Press, p. 37–103.

Oldow, J. S., 1983, Tectonic implications of a late Mesozoic fold and thrust belt in northwestern Nevada: Geology, v. 11, p. 542–546.

—— , 1984, Evolution of a Late Mesozoic backarc fold and thrust belt, northwestern Great Basin, U.S.A., *in* Carson, R. L., and Kobayashi, K., eds.,

Geodynamics of backarc regions: Tectonophysics, v. 102, p. 245–274.

Oldow, J. S., Avé Lallemant, H. G., and Schmidt, W. J., 1984, Kinematics of plate convergence deduced from Mesozoic structures in the western Cordillera: Tectonics, v. 3, p. 201–227.

Oldow, J. S., and 7 others, 1987a, Balanced cross sections through the central Brooks Range and North Slope, Arctic Alaska: American Association of Petroleum Geologists, 19 p. and 8 plates.

Oldow, J. S., Avé Lallemant, H. G., Julian, F. E., and Seidensticker, C. M., 1987b, Ellesmerian(?) and Brookian deformation in the Franklin Mountains, northeastern Brooks Range, Alaska, and its bearing on the origin of the Canada Basin: Geology, v. 15, p. 37–41.

Ormerod, D. S., Hawkesworth, C. J., Rogers, N. W., Leeman, W. P., and Menzies, M. A., 1988, Tectonic and magmatic transitions in the western Great Basin: Nature, v. 33, p. 349–353.

Page, R. A., and 6 others, 1986, Accretion and subduction tectonics in the Chugach Mountains and Copper River Basin, Alaska—initial results of the Trans-Alaska Crustal Transect: Geology, v. 14, p. 501–505.

Panza, G. F., Calcagnile, G., Scandone, P., and Mueller, J., 1980, La struttura profonda dell'area Mediterranea: Scienze, no. 141, p. 276–285.

Parrish, R. R., Carr, S. D., and Parkinson, D. L., 1988, Eocene extensional tectonics and geochronology of the southern Omineca belt, British Columbia and Washington: Tectonics, v. 7, p. 182–212.

Peterson, J. A., ed., 1986, Paleotectonics and sedimentation in the Rocky Mountain Region, United States: American Association of Petroleum Geologists Memoir 41, 693 p.

Price, R. A., 1981, The Cordilleran foreland thrust and fold belt in the southern Canadian Rocky Mountains, *in* McClay, K. R., and Price, N. J., eds., Thrust and nappe tectonics: The Geological Society of London Special Publication 9, p. 427–448.

Price, R. A., and Carmichael, D. M., 1986, Geometric test for Late Cretaceous–Paleogene intracontinental transform faulting in the Canadian Cordillera: Geology, v. 14, p. 468–471.

Proffett, J. M., Jr., 1977, Cenozoic geology of the Yerington District, Nevada, and implications for the nature and origin of Basin and Range faulting: Geological Society of America Bulletin, v. 88, p. 247–266.

Reynolds, S. J., Richard, S. M., Haxel, G. B., Tosdal, R. M., and Laubach, S. E., 1988, Geologic setting of Mesozoic and Cenozoic metamorphism in Arizona, *in* Ernst, W. G., Metamorphism and crustal evolution of the western United States, Rubey volume 7: Englewood Cliffs, New Jersey, Prentice-Hall, p. 466–501.

Royse, F., Jr., Warner, M. A., and Reese, D. L., 975, Thrust belt of Wyoming, Idaho, and northern Utah—structural geometry and related problems, *in* Bolyard, D. W., ed., Symposium on deep drilling frontiers in central Rocky Mountains: Rocky Mountain Geological Association, p. 41–54.

Saleeby, J. B., 1981, Ocean floor accretion and volcano-plutonic arc evolution of the Mesozoic Sierra Nevada, *in* Ernst, W. G., ed., The geotectonic development of California, Rubey volume 1: Englewood Cliffs, New Jersey, Prentice-Hall, p. 132–181.

Saleeby, J. B., Harper, G. D., Snoke, A. W., and Sharp, W. D., 1982, Time relations and structural-stratigraphic patterns in ophiolite accretion, west-central Klamath Mountains, California: Journal of Geophysical Research, v. 87, p. 3831–3848.

Saleeby, J. B., Sams, D. B., and Kistler, R. W., 1987b, U/Pb zircon, strontium, and oxygen isotopic and geochronological study of the southernmost Sierra Nevada batholith, California: Journal of Geophysical Research, v. 92, p. 10443–10466.

Saleeby, J. B., and 7 others, 1989, Early Mesozoic tectonic evolution of the western U.S. Cordillera, *in* Burchfiel, B. C., Lipman, P. W., and Zoback, M. L., eds., The Cordilleran orogen; Conterminous U.S.: Boulder, Colorado, Geological Society of America, Geology of North America, v. G-3 (in press).

Scholl, D. W., Grantz, A., and Vedder, J., eds., 1987, Geology and resource potential of the continental margin of western North America and adjacent ocean basins—Beaufort Sea to Baja California: Houston, Texas, Circum-Pacific Council for Energy and Mineral Resources, Earth Science Series 6, 799 p.

Schweickert, R. A., 1981, Tectonic evolution of the Sierra Nevada Range, *in* Ernst, W. G., ed., The geotectonic development of California, Rubey volume 1: Englewood Cliffs, New Jersey, Prentice-Hall, p. 87–131.

Schweickert, R. A., Bogen, N. L., Girty, G. H., Hanson, R. E., and Merguerian, C., 1984, Timing and structural expression of the Nevadan orogeny, Sierra Nevada, California: Geological Society of America Bulletin, v. 95, p. 967–979.

Schweickert, R. A., Bogen, N. L., and Merguerian, C., 1988, Deformational and metamorphic history of Paleozoic and Mesozoic basement terranes in the western Sierra Nevada metamorphic belt, *in* Ernst, W. G., ed., Metamorphism and crustal evolution of the western United States, Rubey volume 7: Englewood Cliffs, New Jersey, Prentice-Hall, p. 789–822.

Scott, R. B., Nesbitt, R. W., Dasch, E. J., and Armstrong, R. L., 1971, A strontium isotope evolution model for Cenozoic magma genesis, eastern Great Basin, U.S.A.: Bulletin Volcanologique, v. 35, p. 1–26.

Shouldice, D., 1971, Geology of the western Canadian continental shelf: Canadian Petroleum Geology Bulletin, v. 19, p. 405–436.

Silberling, N. J., 1975, Age relationships of the Golconda Thrust fault, Sonoma Range, north-central Nevada: Geological Society of America Special Paper 163, 28 p.

——, 1985, Biogeographic significance of the Upper Triassic bivalve, *Monotis,* in circum-Pacific accreted terranes, *in* Howell, D. G., ed., Tectonostratigraphic terranes of the circum-Pacific region: Houston, Texas, Circum-Pacific Council for Energy and Mineral Resources, Earth Science Series p. 63–70.

Silberling, N. J., Jones, D. L., Blake, M. C., Jr., and Howell, D. G., 1987, Lithotectonic terrane map of the western conterminous United States: U.S. Geological Survey Miscellaneous Field Studies Map MF–1874–C, scale 1:2,500,000.

Smith, R. B., 1978, Seismicity, crustal structure, and intraplate tectonics of the interior of the western Cordillera, *in* Smith, R. B., and Eaton, G. P., eds., Cenozoic tectonics and regional geophysics of the western Cordillera: Geological Society of America Memoir 152, p. 111–144.

Smith, R. B., and Luedke, R. G., 1984, Potentially active volcanic lineaments and loci in the western conterminous United States, *in* Explosive volcanism—inception, evolution, hazards: Washington, D.C., National Academy of Sciences, p. 47–66.

Smithson, S. B., Brewer, J. A., Kaufman, S., Oliver, J. E., and Hurich, C. A., 1979, Structure of the Laramide Wind River uplift, Wyoming, from COCORP deep reflection data and gravity data: Journal of Geophysical Research, v. 84, p. 5955–5972.

Snavely, P. D., Jr., 1987, Tertiary geologic framework, neotectonics, and petroleum potential of the Oregon–Washington continental margin, *in* Scholl, D. W., Grantz, A., and Vedder, J. G., eds., Geology and resource potential of the continenal margin of western North America and adjacent ocean basins: Circum-Pacific Council for Energy and Mineral Resources, Earth Science Series 6, p. 337–352.

Snee, L. W., Lund, K., Sutter, J. F., Balcer, D. E., and Evans, K., 1989, An $^{40}Ar/^{39}Ar$ chronicle of the tectonic development of the Salmon River suture zone, western Idaho: U.S. Geological Survey Professional Paper 1438 (in press).

Snoke, A. W., and Miller, D. M., 1988, Metamorphic and tectonic history of the northeastern Great Basin, *in* Ernst, G. W., ed., Metamorphic and crustal evolution of the western United States, Rubey volume 7: Englewood Cliffs, New Jersey, Prentice-Hall, p. 606–648.

Snyder, W. S., Dickinson, W. R., and Silberman, M. L., 1976, Tectonic implications of space-time patterns of Cenozoic magmatism in the western United States: Earth and Planetary Science Letters, v. 32, p. 91–106.

Souther, J. G., 1977, Volcanism and tectonic environments in the Canadian Cordillera—a second look, *in* Barragar, W.R.A., Coleman, L. C., and Hall, J. M., eds., Volcanic regimes in Canada: Geological Association of Canada Special Paper 16, p. 3–24.

Speed, R. C., 1979, Collided Paleozoic microplate in the western United States: Journal of Geology, v. 87, p. 279–252.

Speed, R. C., Elison, E. M., and Heck, F. R., 1988, Phanerozoic evolution of the Great Basin, *in* Ernst, W. G., Metamorphism and crustal evolution of the western United States, Rubey volume 7: Englewood Cliffs, New Jersey, Prentice-Hall, p. 572–600.

Stearns, D. W., 1978, Faulting and forced folding in the Rocky Mountain foreland, *in* Matthews, V., III, ed., Laramide folding associated with basement block faulting in the western United States: Geological Society of America Memoir 151, p. 1–36.

Stewart, J. H., and Carlson, J. E., 1978, Generalized maps showing distribution, lithology, and age of Cenozoic igneous rocks in the western United States, *in* Smith, R. B., and Eaton, G. P., eds., Cenozoic tectonics and regional geophysics of the Western Cordillera: Geological Society of America Memoir 152, p. 263–264.

Stewart, J. H., Stevens, C. H., and Fritsche, A. E., eds., 1977a, Paleozoic Paleogeography of the western United States: Pacific Section, Society of Economic Paleontologists and Mineralogists Pacific Coast Paleogeography Symposium 1, 502 p.

Stone, D. B., and McWilliams, M., 1988, Paleomagnetic evidence for relative terrane motion in western North America, *in* Ben-Avraham, Z., ed., Evolution of the Pacific Ocean margin: Oxford Monographs on Geology and Geophysics 8, 320 p.

Stone, D. B., Panuska, B. C., and Packer, D. R., 1982, Paleolatitudes versus time for southern Alaska: Journal of Geophysical Research, v. 87, p. 3697–3708.

Stout, J. H., and Chase, C. G., 1980, Plate kinematics of the Denali fault system: Canadian Journal of Earth Sciences, v. 17, p. 1527–1537.

Struik, L. C., 1988, Crustal evolution of the eastern Canadian Cordillera: Tectonics, v. 7, p. 727–748.

Sylvester, A. G., compiler, 1984, Wrench fault tectonics: American Association of Petroleum Geologists Reprint Series no. 28, 374 p.

—— , 1988, Strike-slip faults: Geological Society of America Bulletin, v. 100, p. 1666–1703.

Taylor, D. G., Callomon, J. H., Smith, R., Tipper, H. W., and Westermann, G.E.G., 1984, Jurassic ammonite biogeography of western North America, *in* Westermann, G.E.G., ed., Jurassic-Cretaceous biochronology and paleogeography of North America: Geological Association of Canada Special Paper 27, p. 121–142.

Tempelman-Kluit, D. J., 1979, Transported cataclasite, ophiolite and granodiorite in Yukon—evidence for arc-continent collision: Geological Survey of Canada Special Paper 79–13, 27 p.

Thompson, G. A., and Zoback, M. L., 1979, Regional geophysics of the Colorado Plateau: Tectonophysics, v. 61, p. 149–181.

Umhoefer, P. J., 1987, Northward translation of "Baja British Columbia" along Late Cretaceous to Paleocene margin of western North America: Tectonics, v. 6, p. 377–394.

Vail, P. R., 1987, Seismic stratigraphy interpretation using sequence stratigraphy, *in* Bally, A. W., ed., Atlas of seismic stratigraphy: American Association of Petroleum Geologists Studies in Geology 27, p. 11–14.

Villien, A., and Kligfield, R. M., 1986, Thrusting and synorogenic sedimentation in central Utah, *in* Peterson, J. A., ed., Paleotectonics and sedimentation in the Rocky Mountain Region, United States: American Association of Petroleum Geologists Memoir 41, p. 353–370.

von Huene, R., ed., 1986, Seismic images of modern convergent margins tectonic structure: American Association of Petroleum Geologists Studies in Geology 26, 60 p.

Walcott, R. I., 1978, Geodetic strains and large earthquakes in the axial tectonic belt of North Island, New Zealand: Journal of Geophysical Research, v. 83, p. 4419–4429.

Walker, J. D., 1988, Permian and Triassic rocks of the Mojave desert and their implications for timing and mechanisms of continental truncation: Tectonics, v. 7, p. 685–709.

Wernicke, B., and Burchfiel, B. C., 1982, Modes of extensional tectonics: Journal of Structural Geology, v. 4, p. 105–115.

Wernicke, B., Axen, G. J., and Snow, J. K., 1988, Basin and Range extensional tectonics at the latitude of Las Vegas, Nevada: Geological Society of America Bulletin, v. 100, p. 1738–1757.

Wheeler, J. O., and Gabrilese, H., 1972, The Cordilleran structural province, *in* Price, R. A., and Douglas, R.J.W., eds., Variations in tectonic styles in Canada: Geological Association of Canada Special Paper 11, p. 1–81.

Wheeler, J. O., and McFeely, P., 1987, Tectonic assemblage map of the Canadian Cordillera and adjacent parts of the United States of America: Geological Survey of Canada Open-File 1565, scale 1:2,000,000.

Wheeler, J. O., Brookfield, A. J., Gabrielse, H., Monger, J.W.H., Tipper, H. W., and Woodsworth, G. J., 1988, Terrane map of the Canadian Cordillera: Geological Survey of Canada Open-File 1894, scale 1:2,000,000.

Wiltschko, D. V., and Dorr, J. A., 1983, Timing of deformation in Overthrust belt and foreland of Idaho, Wyoming and Utah: American Association of Petroleum Geologists Bulletin, v. 67, p. 1304–1322.

Winston, D., 1986, Sedimentation and tectonics of the Middle Proterozoic Belt basin and their influence on Phanerozoic compression and extension in western Montana and northern Idaho, *in* Peterson, J. A., ed., Paleotectonics and sedimentation in the Rocky Mountain region, United States: American Association of Petroleum Geologists Memoir 41, p. 3–20.

Wooden, J. L., Stacey, J. S., Doe, B. R., Howard, K. A., and Miller, D. M., 1988, Pb isotopic evidence for the formation of Proterozoic crust in the southwestern United States, *in* Ernst, W. G., ed., Metamorphism and crustal evolution of the western United States, Rubey volume 7: Englewood Cliffs, New Jersey, Prentice-Hall, p. 69–86.

Woodsworth, G. J., Loveridge, W. D., Parrish, R. R., and Sullivan, R. W., 1983, Uranium-lead dates from the Central Gneiss complex and Ecstall pluton, Prince Rupert map area, British Columbia: Canadian Journal of Earth Sciences, v. 20, p. 1475–1483.

Wright, J. E., 1982, Permo-Triassic accretionary subduction complex, southwestern Klamath Mountains, north California: Journal of Geophysical Research, v. 87, p. 3805–3818.

Wright, J. E., and Fahan, M. R., 1988, An expanded view of Jurassic orogenesis in the western U.S. Cordillera—Middle Jurassic (pre-Nevadan) regional metamorphism and thrust faulting within an active arc environment, Klamath, Mountains, California: Geological Society of America Bulletin, v. 100, p. 859–876.

Yeats, R. S., 1981, Quaternary flake tectonics of the California Transverse Ranges: Geology, v. 9, p. 16–20.

—— , 1983, Large-scale Quaternary detachments in Ventura basin, southern California: Journal of Geophysical Research, v. 88, p. 569–583.

Yorath, C. J., and Hyndman, R. D., 1983, Subsidence and thermal history of Queen Charlotte Basin: Canadian Journal of Earth Science, v. 20, p. 135–159.

Zoback, M. L., Anderson, R. E., and Thompson, G. A., 1981, Cenozoic evolution of the state of stress and style of tectonism of the Basin and Range province of the western United States: Philosophical Transactions of the Royal Society of London, v. 300, p. 407–434.

MANUSCRIPT ACCEPTED BY THE SOCIETY JANUARY 12, 1989

ACKNOWLEDGMENTS

We would like to thank our colleagues, D. S. Cowan, H. Gabrielse, J. W. Geissman, E. L. Miller, B. M. Page, J. B. Saleeby, R. A. Schweickert, W. D. Sharp, N. J. Silberling, D. B. Stone, and J. O. Wheeler for undertaking the arduous task of reviewing an early edition of this manuscript. We especially thank Chingju Liu for drafting most of the figures and plates. We wish to thank E. Irving for the words of encouragement concerning some of the concepts presented here. Finally, we acknowledge funding of our research by the National Science Foundation, the Department of Energy, and the United States Geological Survey in Arctic Alaska and Canada, southern Alaska, northeastern Oregon, Washington, the Snake River Plain, and the western Great Basin. We are also grateful for funding supplied by various petroleum companies: Amoco, Arco, Chevron, Conoco, Exxon, Gulf Oil, and Standard Oil.

Printed in U.S.A.

The Geology of North America
Vol. A, The Geology of North America—An overview
The Geological Society of America, 1989

Chapter 9

An outline of the geology of Mexico

Zoltan de Cserna
Instituto de Geología, Universidad Nacional Autónoma de México, Cuidad Universitaria, Coyoacán, 04510 México, D.F., México

INTRODUCTION

This chapter provides a brief introduction to the geology of Mexico for members of the international geological community unfamiliar with the geology of the southern border region of the North American continent and adjacent parts of northern Central America. The main geologic features are presented by morphotectonic provinces, including the adjacent sea floor, accompanied by relevant references, primarily in English. Since most of the geological information is of reconnaissance nature, regional interpretations necessarily involve speculations and resulting controversial issues. These have been avoided, for their objective presentation would have exceeded the predetermined number of pages for this chapter.

The first geological map of Mexico was prepared by the staff of Comisión Geológica Nacional, the starting organization of the Mexican Geological Survey, under the direction of Antonio del Castillo (1889a); the explanatory text constitutes the first geological synthesis of the country, the *Bosquejo geológico de México,* and was published with the participation and coordinating efforts of Aguilera (1896). The pioneer descriptions of the geology of the Yucatán Peninsula (*Heilprin, 1891; Sapper, 1896*), Chiapas and Tabasco (*Böse, 1905*) and northern Central America (*Sapper, 1899*) allowed the presentation of a regional tectonic synthesis during the 8th International Geographical Congress in Washington, D.C. (Sapper, 1905). On the occasion of the 10th session of the IGC, held in Mexico in 1906, a set of 31 field trip guidebooks was edited, presenting the country's geology in a very objective way. The so-called Bailey Willis geological map of North America was distributed to the participants, although it was published formally by the U.S. Geological Survey (Willis, 1912), while *Aguilera (1906)* presented an overview on the tectonics and volcanism in Mexico. The first description of the physiography of Mexico according to physiographic provinces is credited to *Thayer (1916)*; the first book on the geology of Mexico, which was published in Berlin, is credited to *Freudenberg (1921).* Böse (1923) wrote a landmark paper on the recognition of older terranes beneath the deformed Mesozoic rocks in northern Mexico and their role in the paleogeography and subsequent deformation, while the first synthesis of the country's Mesozoic stratigraphy is a masterpiece by Burckhardt (1930). *Flores (1931)* published the geologic map of the Baja California Peninsula with an explanatory text. Schuchert's (1935) book on the geology of the Antillean–Caribbean region contains an extraordinary wealth of information on Mexico's geology. The synthesis of the physiography of Mexico by Ordóñez (1936) can be considered to be the first, more realistic attempt to recognize physiographic provinces in the country. The excellent volume on the geology and biology of the San Carlos Mountains in Tamaulipas (*Kellum, 1937*) not only presents invaluable information on results of the University of Michigan expedition, but marks the beginning of outstanding geological, especially stratigraphical and paleontological, work in northern Mexico (see Imlay, 1938, for references). That work was also sponsored in part by the Geological Society of America, as was the regional geological work of R. E. King (1939) in Sonora, which still serves as a basic reference source on that part of Mexico. In 1936, Muir presented what was learned about the geology of Mexico's first commercially producing hydrocarbon province, the Tampico region, during the first three decades of this century.

The first modern geological map of a large segment of the Sierra Madre Oriental in east-central Mexico, together with the description of its geology, is the work of *Heim (1940).* In 1942, P. B. King published his modern tectonic synthesis and a tectonic map of northern Mexico. A few years later, as a result of a cooperative project between the U.S. Geological Survey and Instituto de Geología, of Universidad Nacional Autónoma de México (UNAM), the first modern geological map of Mexico was published covering the area from the U.S.–Mexico border to latitude 20°N (*P. B. King, 1947*). During the war years, Imlay (*1943a,* 1943b, and 1944) updated the Jurassic and Cretaceous stratigraphic information for Mexico and adapted it to North American stratigraphic usage. Toward the end of that decade, an outstanding monograph by Beal (1948) appeared on the geology of the Baja California Peninsula and, one year later, this time in Mexico City, a second book on the geology of Mexico was published (*Garfias and Chapin, 1949*). The last two papers of that decade were produced by geologists of Petróleos Mexicanos (PEMEX). Alvarez (1949) presented a tectonic synthesis of Mexico that is based in good measure on unpublished reports in the files of PEMEX, particularly on a report by D. Trumpy; meanwhile *G. P. Salas* (*1949*) published the results of his field work in

de Cserna, Z., 1989, An outline of the geology of Mexico, *in* Bally, A. W., and Palmer, A. R., eds., The Geology of North America—An overview: Boulder, Colorado, Geological Society of America, The Geology of North America, v. A.

south-central Mexico, which appeared in the first volume of the bulletin of the then recently founded Asociación Mexicana de Geólogos Petroleros.

During the beginning of this century, geological work got underway with great impetus in anticipation of the 10th session of the IGC. Just so, after 50 years and 10 sessions, a considerable amount of geological work was done in the country before the 20th session of the IGC was held in Mexico in 1956. The first modern geological map covering all of Mexico (*Hernández-Sánchez Mejorada, 1956*), as well as a series of guidebooks, were prepared for the 32 field trips. In addition, several monographs of regional scope were published, including *Barnetche and Illing (1956)* on the Tamabra Limestone of the Poza Rica oilfield; *Edwards* (*1956*) on early Tertiary red conglomerates of central Mexico; *González-Reyna (1956a)* on mineral deposits of Chihuahua; and de Cserna (1956) on the tectonics of the Sierra Madre Oriental between Torreón and Monterrey.

Several papers that appeared during the 1950s deserve particular mention, because of their importance in a regional geologic context. These are on the geology of northeastern Guerrero and the Mesozoic and Cenozoic sediments of the Gulf Coastal Plain (*Guzmán,* 1950, *1952*); the distribution of mineral deposits (González-Reyna, 1956b) and metallogenetic provinces of Mexico (*Behre, 1957*); Mexican petroleum geology (*Benavides-García, 1956*); the seismicity of the country (*Figueroa-Abarca, 1956*); gravity, regional geology, and crustal structure in Mexico (Woollard and Monges-Caldera, 1956); the tectonics of northeastern Mexico (Humphrey, 1956); the geology of southern Baja California (*Mina-Uhink, 1957*) and Chihuahua (*Ramírez-Montes and Acevedo-Cruz, 1957*); and the tectonics of southern Mexico (de Cserna, 1958). The first landform map, prepared from aerial photographs, was published by Raisz (1959).

In the following decade, important contributions were published on the geology of Mexico: a new edition of the geologic map of Mexico, sponsored by the Comité de la Carta Geológica de México (*Hernández-Sánchez Mejorada, 1960*); a synthesis on the spatial and time relations of orogenies in Mexico (*de Cserna, 1960*); and the tectonic map of Mexico (de Cserna, 1961). The Instituto de Geología, UNAM, edited the monograph of *Fries (1960)* on the geology of south-central Mexico, while *Hamilton (1961)* wrote an important paper on the origin of the Gulf of California. At this time a major synthesis on the geology of the Gulf Coastal Province of North America was published (Murray, 1961), which includes a great deal of information on the geology of Mexico.

In 1962, the publication of geological quadrangle maps with explanatory text was started by the Instituto de Geología, UNAM. They form the 1:100,000 scale series of Carta Geológica de México and, by 1988, a total of 20 quadrangles was published (Fig. 1). *Alvarez (1962)* published his views on the pre-Tertiary orogenies in Mexico, and in the following year, a tectonic synthesis of the country was presented by Guzmán and de Cserna (1963). Marine geological investigations by U.S. scientists in the early 1960s resulted in better understanding of the bathymetry and structure of the Middle America Trench (Fisher, 1961), the Gulf of California (van Andel and Shor, 1964), and the continental shelf and slope of the Gulf of Mexico (Bryant and others, 1968). An important monograph was also published on the Baja California Peninsula (*Gierloff-Emden, 1964*), which contains geological and geomorphological information. De Cserna (1965) presented the results of his studies on the Sierra Madre del Sur and showed the truncated nature of the southern coast of Mexico, as well as the oblique nature of subduction along the Middle America Trench (de Cserna, 1967). In the Mexican National Report on Volcanology to the International Union of Geodesy and Geophysics (*Mooser and Maldonado-Koerdell, 1967*), an overview on the Trans-Mexico volcanic belt was given.

The Geological Society of America, for the first time, held its annual meeting in Mexico City in 1968. Although the overall conditions prevented the publication of an important volume on the geology of Mexico, a new edition of the geological map of Mexico did appear (Hernández-Sánchez Mejorada, 1968). The tectonic map of North America (P. B. King, 1968, 1969), published in that year, depicts remarkably well the tectonic makeup of Mexico in relation to the rest of the continent. The excellent paper by Molnar and Sykes (1969) planted a seed of suspicion in the minds of those who are engaged in tectonic research in Mexico; i.e., what is the real neotectonic makeup, especially of southern Mexico? A summary of the available information on the Paleozoic rocks of the country was published by López-Ramos (1969).

At the beginning of the 1970s, two syntheses were published on the Precambrian of Mexico (*de Cserna, 1970a, 1971a*), a third on the Paleozoic orogenic belt of eastern Mexico (*de Cserna, 1971b*), a fourth on the age and evolution of salt basins in southeastern Mexico (Viniegra-Osorio, 1971), and a fifth on the Mesozoic of northern Mexico (de Cserna, 1970b). In two of these publications, the early Mesozoic segmentation of Mexico was shown along WNW-ESE–trending left-lateral faults or frac-

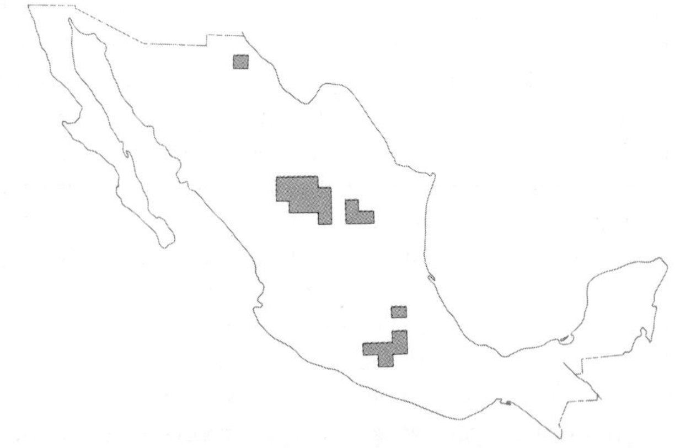

Figure 1. Outline map of Mexico, showing areas covered by the 1:100,000-scale series of geological maps and explanatory texts, published by Instituto de Geología, UNAM. It should be noted that the entire State of Sinaloa is also covered by geological maps of the same scale, but these have no individual explanatory texts and, as a result, have not been distributed in the same series.

ture zones. Among the publications of this epoch, the symposium volume in honor of R. K. DeFord on the Chihuahua tectonic belt (*Seewald and Sundeen, 1970*), and the paper on the Lower Cretaceous stratigraphy of northern Coahuila (Smith, 1970) deserve special mention. Other important publications are the paper by *Baker (1971),* which was originally written during the 1920s, on the Sierra Madre Oriental; the very valuable contribution of *Carrillo-Bravo (1971)* toward the understanding of the geology of the mid-Cretaceous Valles–San Luis Potosí platform; the fine geological map and monograph on northern Baja California by R. G. Gastil and others (1971, 1975); the good overview of the tectonics of the Trans-Mexico volcanic belt by Mooser (1972); the excellent paper on the plate-tectonic history of the mouth of the Gulf of California (Larson, 1972); and a paper on the geologic setting of southern Mexico in the context of the evolution of the Caribbean Plate (Malfait and Dinkelman, 1972).

In 1974, López-Ramos began to publish his lecture notes on the geology of Mexico as books (*López-Ramos, 1974, 1979a, 1979b*); these contain a great deal of previously unpublished material, principally from PEMEX, on the geology of the country. In the following year, Salas (1975) made available his views and map of the metallogenic provinces of Mexico, while the writer's overview of the geology of the country, originally written in 1971, was published in the *Encyclopedia of world regional geology* (*de Cserna, 1975*). In that same year appeared the *Stratigraphic atlas of North and Central America* (Cook and Bally, 1975), which contains an extraordinary wealth of information on Mexico.

Toward the end of the 1960s and during the 1970s, graduate students from France came to Mexico to fulfill their military service through doctoral research. The first results of this enterprise are credited to *Tardy (1975),* who presented a reinterpretation of the Sierra Madre Oriental in northeastern Mexico in terms of a huge nappe, involving tectonic transport over large distances, and later, his geotectonic synthesis of northern Mexico *(Tardy, 1977).*

During the early 1970s, the Mexican government's mapping agency, which changed its name several times and at present is called Instituto Nacional de Estadística, Geografía e Informática (INEGI), started the publication of geological maps on the scales of 1:50,000, 1:250,000, and 1:1,000,000. While these maps do not conform strictly with geological maps in the conventional North American sense, they do provide a good first approximation of the geologic makeup of a given area or region. Of these three series of maps, the 1:1,000,000 series now covers the entire country (Anonymous, 1981). The coverage of the 1:250,000 and 1:50,000 series is shown in Figures 2 and 3, respectively. In 1976 this agency published a 1:2,000,000–scale lineament map of the country (*Guerra-Peña, 1976*). On the occasion of the 3rd session of the Latin-American Geological Congress, held in Acapulco, a new edition of the geological map of Mexico was released for distribution (López-Ramos, 1976). In that year, Mossman and Viniegra (1976) portrayed beautifully the overthrusts in the Córdoba region of eastern Mexico.

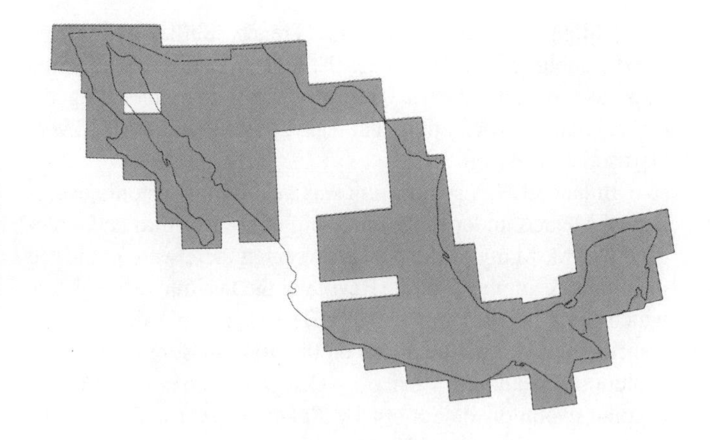

Figure 2. Outline map of Mexico, showing areas covered by the 1:250,000-scale series of geological maps, published by Instituto Nacional de Estadística, Geografía e Informática.

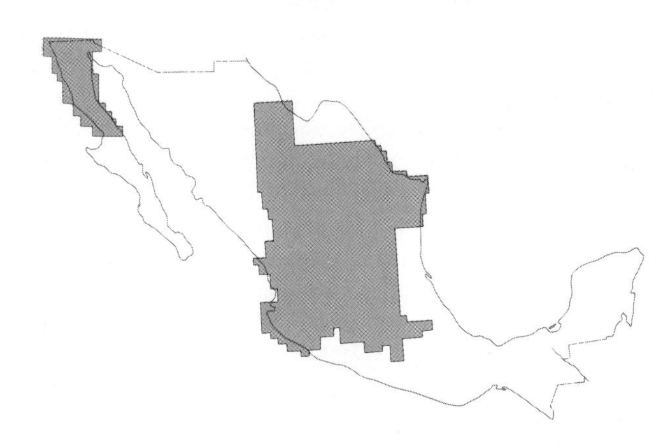

Figure 3. Outline map of Mexico, showing areas covered by the 1:50,000-scale series of geological maps, published by Instituto Nacional de Estadística, Geografía e Informática.

The results of research carried out in the Sierra Madre Occidental by faculty members and graduate students from the University of Texas at Austin started to appear in print during the early 1970s, providing realistic bases for the geologic evolution of this important region of Mexico (*Clabaugh, 1972; McDowell and Keizer, 1977; Swanson and others 1978;* McDowell and Clabaugh, 1979). In 1976, this writer published a synthesis of the geotectonic framework of Mexico in relation to the mineral deposits of the country (*de Cserna, 1976a*). The following year the fine volume on the geology of the Puebla-Tlaxcala region appeared, accompanied by an excellent map (von Erffa and others, 1977) containing the geological results of an interdisciplinary research project sponsored by the Deutsche Forschungsgemeinschaft. *Demant (1978)* published his paper on the Trans-Mexico volcanic belt, and Karig and others (1978) presented geophysical evidence for late Cenozoic subduction and truncation of the continent along the Middle America Trench. Buffler and others (1979) published an analysis of the fold belt on the continental slope of the southwestern Gulf of Mexico, complementing the earlier studies carried out in that region (Bryant and others, 1968; Garrison and Martin, 1973).

In late 1979, a symposium was held on the tectonic evolution of Mexico under the sponsorship of the Instituto de Geología, UNAM. Many of the papers presented there were published in volume 5, number 2 of the Revista of the Instituto de Geología, which came off the press in 1984. The papers included original contributions or interpretations on the pre-Mississippian tectonic evolution of southern Mexico by Ortega-Gutiérrez (1981a); the tectonic evolution of Sonora by *Roldán-Quintana (1981)*; the tectonic evolution of southeastern Mexico by *Carfantan (1981)*; and the Mesozoic of Mexico by *López-Ramos (1981).*

In the early 1980s, two important papers appeared that provide a large amount of information on the Mesozoic stratigraphy and petroleum geology of southeastern Mexico. The paper by Bishop (1980) splendidly integrates the geology of southeastern Mexico with that of Guatemala and Honduras; the paper by Viniegra-Osorio (1981) emphasizes the Cretaceous carbonate bank of Yucatán.

In 1978, 1980, and 1982, the Instituto de Geología, UNAM, prepared three field trip guidebooks for the conventions of Sociedad Geológica Mexicana. The first one deals with the geology of the middle parts of the Balsas River basin (*Del Arenal, 1978*), the second with the upper parts of the same river basin (*Instituto de Geología, 1980*), and the third with the geology of the Zimapán and surrounding region in the states of Hidalgo and Querétaro (*Alcayde and de Cserna, 1982*).

This writer had been intrigued for some time by the neotectonic makeup of the coastal region of the Gulf of Mexico, especially since the publication of papers by Bryant and others (1968), Molnar and Sykes (1969), Stoiber and Carr (1973), *Moore and Del Castillo (1974),* Hanus and Vanek (1977–1978), and Buffler and others (1979), and by the northeast quadrant of the plate-tectonic map of the Circum-Pacific region (Drummond, 1981). As a result, I published a tectonic analysis on the southwestern margin of the Gulf of Mexico in terms of truncation of the continental shelf and slope and active convergence (de Cserna, 1981).

Although *Bodenlos (1956)* made a fine reconnaissance map along the highway between Tamazunchale and Zimapán for the 20th session of the IGC, modern structural investigation of the Sierra Madre Oriental in east-central Mexico began only in 1979; the first results of this work were published by *Suter (1980,* 1984) and *Carillo and Suter (1982).* Ortega-Gutiérrez (1981b) published his synthesis on the metamorphic belts of southern Mexico, and Nixon (1982) published his excellent paper on the relation of Quaternary volcanism of central Mexico to the seismicity and structure of the subducted lithosphere. In that same year, *Clark and others (1982)* published an interesting paper on subduction-related volcanic arcs and Cenozoic mineral deposits in Mexico. As an explanatory text for the 1:1,000,000-scale geologic map of Mexico, the Coordinación General de los Servicios Nacionales de Estadística, Geografía e Informática published a handy volume on the geology of Mexico (Anonymous, 1982).

As a result of their investigations of tectono-stratigraphic terranes, *Campa and Coney (1983)* published a paper on the distribution of Mexican mineral deposits and a tectonic model for Mexico. A lithotectonic terrane map of Mexico was also prepared by *Coney and Campa (1984)* and published jointly by the Instituto Mexicano del Petróleo (IMP) and INEGI (*González-Herbert and others, 1986*). In the Mesozoic volume of *Phanerozoic Geology of the World,* Young (1983) contributed an excellent chapter on the Mesozoic stratigraphy and paleogeography of Mexico. Also, *Carfantan (1983)* published a synthesis on the Mesozoic and Cenozoic geodynamic evolution of southern Mexico, and *Salvador (1987)* published a synthesis on the origin of the Gulf of Mexico basin.

In light of the exploratory work carried out by PEMEX during a decade of big discoveries and production, in 1984 the Schlumberger Company, operating in Mexico, sponsored a volume on formation evaluation in Mexico. In it an important synthesis of the petroleum geology of Mexico is presented by Santiago-Acevedo and others (1984). The following year, two papers were published on the Sierra Madre Oriental—one on the Monterrey region by Padilla y Sánchez (1985) and one on the Saltillo region by Quintero-Legorreta and Aranda-García (1985), both of which present evidence for thrusting in the tectonic development of this cordillera. In 1986, a synthesis by *Morán-Zenteno* on the tectonic evolution of Mexico and a paper by *Padilla y Sánchez (1986)* on the role of post-Paleozoic tectonics in the evolution of the Gulf of Mexico appeared. It is perhaps noteworthy to mention the simultaneous publication of two papers during early 1988. One calls for a latest Proterozoic and Paleozoic southern margin of North America at latitude 28°N (Stewart, 1988); the other considers an alternative whereby Proterozoic and Paleozoic metamorphic rocks of southern Mexico, on the basis of Sm-Nd data, may represent the continuation of the Cordilleran or Appalachian–Caledonian orogenic belts (Ruiz and others, 1988).

PRINCIPAL MORPHOTECTONIC PROVINCES

Figure 4 provides a grid for locating most of the principal geographic features referred to in the text. A scheme of morphotectonic provinces, in a way comparable to the one used by *Harrington (1956)* for South America, was employed in an earlier paper to serve as a frame for the presentation of the tectonic history of Mexico (Guzmán and de Cserna, 1963). At a distance of a quarter of a century, there has been considerable progress in the geological sciences and also in our knowledge of the geology of Mexico. Consequently, the divisions recognized 25 years ago are somewhat modified, and the current views of this writer are shown in Figure 5. To be able to follow more easily the description of each principal morphotectonic province, a highly generalized geologic map of Mexico is presented in Figure 6; Figure 7 shows the country's principal tectonic features.

Submarine regions

Pacific Ocean floor. The western and southern Pacific coasts of Mexico have a total length of about 3,000 km. Along these coasts, the adjacent ocean floor is formed by the Pacific, Rivera, and Cocos Plates (Fig. 7), and by the northern truncated end of the East Pacific Rise. Stretches of continental shelf, exceeding 30 to 40 km in width but generally not wider than 100 km, are present north of the Vizcaíno Peninsula (Fig. 4:2; G-3) on the west coast of Baja California and north of Bahía de Magdalena (Fig. 4: 2; J-5) southeast of the Isthmus of Tehuantepec (26; R-24 and 25).

West of longitude 105°W, the sea floor is at an average depth of about 3,500 m and is formed by the Pacific Plate. It is characterized by abundant seamounts, the Baja California seamount province (Menard, 1955), and there are about 35 islands within this region (*Tamayo, 1949*). About one-third of these islands are located near the west coast of the Baja California Peninsula. The islands comprise blocks of metamorphic and sedimentary rocks, identical or similar to those found on the adjacent land (*Hanna, 1927*; Beal, 1948; *Sedlock, 1988*), and constitute topographic highs of the submerged "continental borderland" of *Shepard and Emery (1941).* All other islands and the seamounts in this region are of volcanic origin; the most recent volcanic activity is recorded from San Benedicto Island of the Revillagigedo Archipelago (Fig. 6) with the birth of Bárcena Volcano in 1952 (*Richards, 1959*).

The present northeastern boundary of the Pacific Plate with the North America Plate is formed by a series of en echelon transform faults along the Gulf of California (*Vine, 1966; Sykes, 1968*), developed since the Baja California Peninsula began to separate from the North America Plate about 4 Ma (Larson, 1972). At the mouth of the Gulf, the displaced segment of the East Pacific Rise and the Rivera Fracture Zone form the Pacific–Rivera plate boundary (Fig. 7). The East Pacific Rise (*Menard, 1960*), which trends NNW at longitude 105°W, forms the

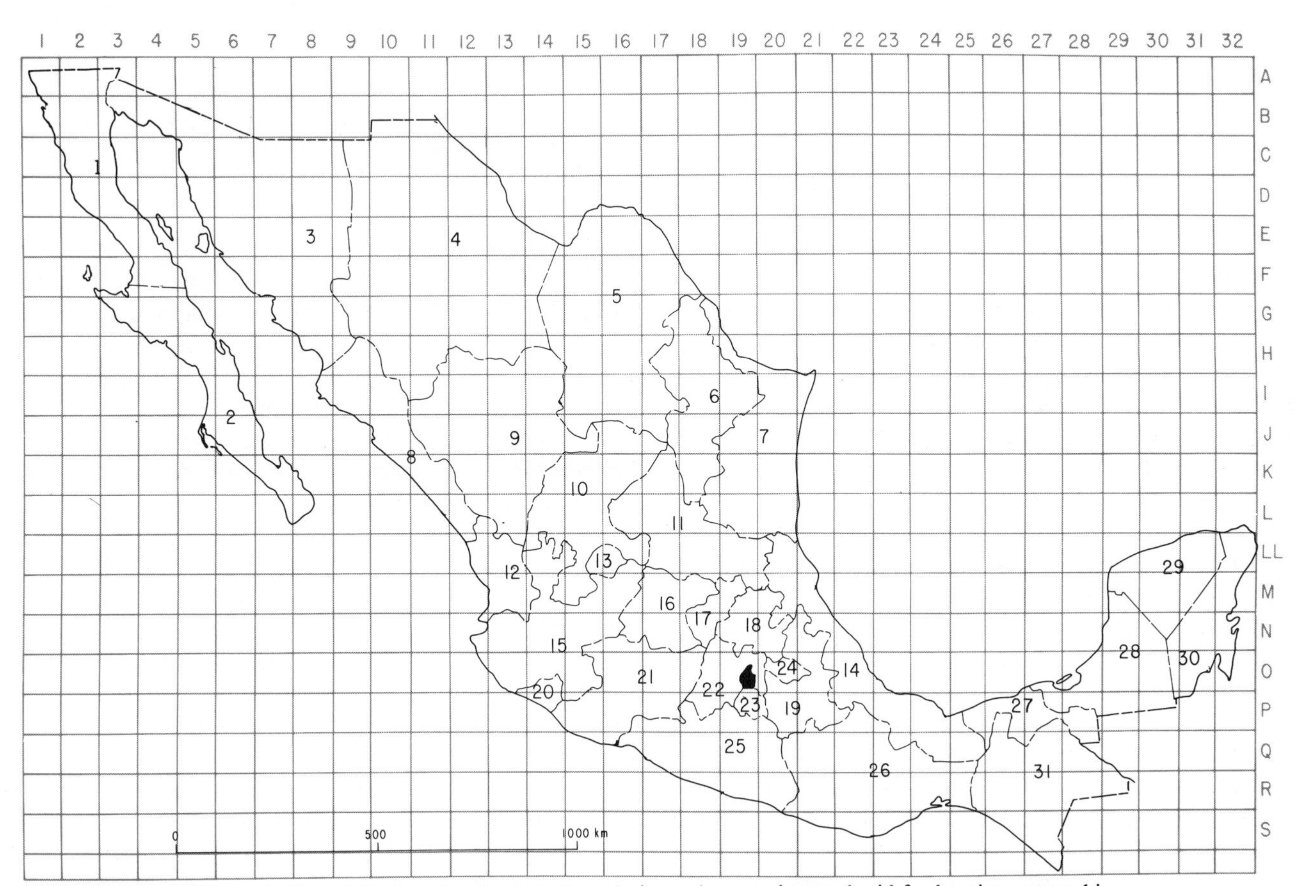

Figure 4. Map of Mexico showing state boundaries and a superimposed grid for locating geographic features mentioned in the text. Used parenthetically in the text, the first number identifies the respective state, the letter that follows refers to the ordinate, and the number after the hyphen refers to the abcissa. 1, Baja California Norte; 2, Baja California Sur; 3, Sonora; 4, Chihuahua; 5, Coahuila; 6, Nuevo León; 7, Tamaulipas; 8, Sinaloa; 9, Durango; 10, Zacatecas; 11, San Luis Potosí; 12, Nayarit; 13, Aguascalientes; 14, Veracruz; 15, Jalisco; 16, Guanajuato; 17, Querétaro; 18, Hidalgo; 19, Puebla; 20, Colima; 21, Michoacán; 22, México; 23, Morelos; 24, Tlaxcala; 25, Guerrero; 26, Oaxaca; 27, Tabasco; 28, Campeche; 29, Yucatán; 30, Quintana Roo; 31, Chiapas. The Federal District (Distrito Federal) is in black.

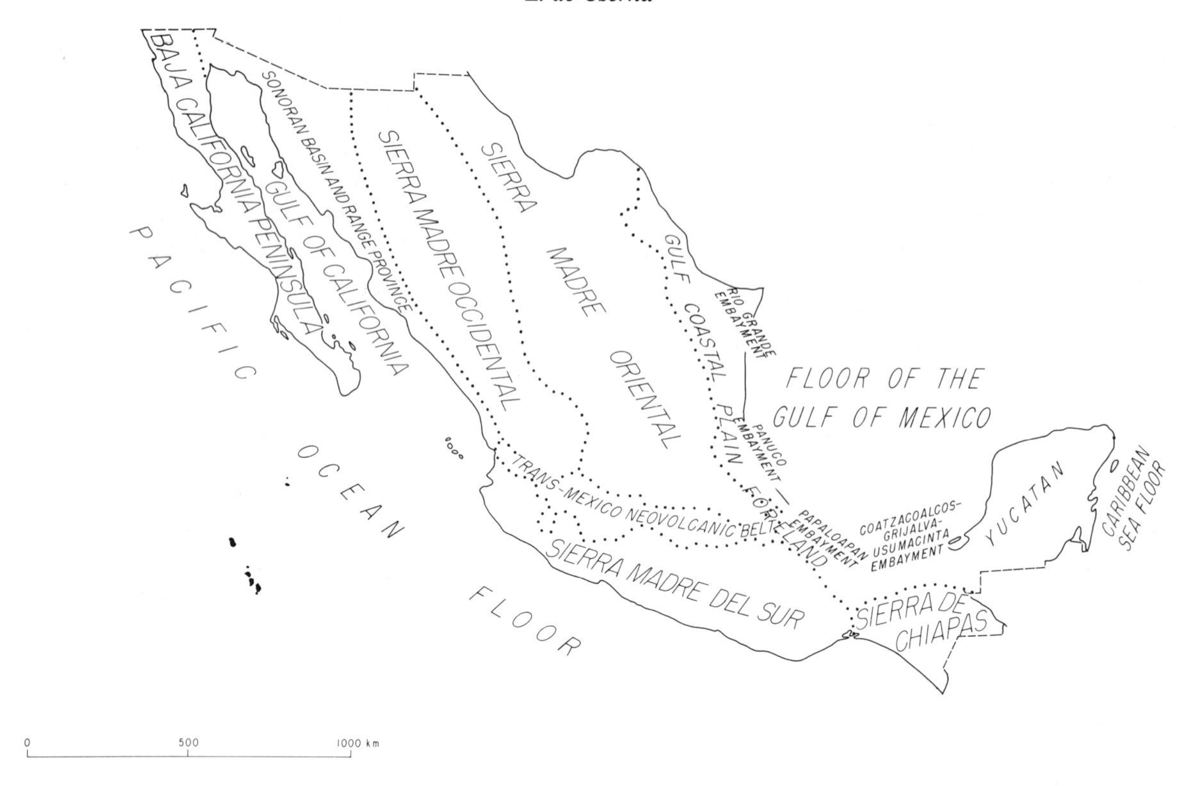

Figure 5. Map showing the principal morphotectonic provinces of Mexico.

boundary between the Pacific Plate and the Cocos Plate to the east (Nixon, 1982).

Two major trans-Pacific fracture zones terminate within the Pacific Plate in this region (Fig. 7). The Molokai Fracture Zone ends in front of Cedros Island, just northwest of the Vizcaíno Peninsula, whereas the Clarion Fracture Zone terminates in the area of the Revillagigedo Archipelago (*Menard, 1955*; Drummond, 1981).

The East Pacific Rise is at an average depth of about 3,000 m. It is truncated in the north by the Rivera Fracture Zone and its northern segment is left-laterally displaced to the mouth of the Gulf of California (Larson, 1972). Near latitude 15°N, the East Pacific Rise is again displaced left-laterally by the Orozco Fracture Zone (*Menard, 1966*). Sea-floor spreading, at a rate of 9 cm/yr, is currently active along the East Pacific Rise north of the Orozco Fracture Zone, with motion vectors oriented roughly east-west (Drummond, 1981).

The floor of the Pacific Ocean east of the East Pacific Rise is formed by the Cocos Plate, which descends gently to a depth of about 3,500 m as it approaches the edge of the Middle America Trench and the NE-SW–trending Tehuantepec Fracture Zone, which is directly to the east. East of the Tehuantepec Fracture Zone, the sea floor is characterized by a series of troughs, oriented NE-SW, or by irregular small basins reaching depths of around 4,000 m.

The north-northeastern margin of the Cocos Plate is marked by the Middle America Trench. This is the most prominent submarine topographic feature of the Pacific Ocean floor; its deepest parts, west-northwest of the Tehuantepec Fracture Zone, reach 5,000 m, whereas to the east-southeast of the ridge they reach 6,000 m (Fisher, 1961). Along the north-northeastern slope of this trench runs the trace of the Continental Thrust (de Cserna, 1961), whose upper plate, roughly between the longitudes of Manzanillo and Tehuantepec, is formed by the North America Plate; toward the east-southeast the upper plate is formed by the Caribbean Plate. The active convergence between the Cocos Plate and the two aforementioned plates between longitudes 92° and 105°W varies from 6 to 7 cm/yr, with motion vectors oriented N35° to 45°E (Molnar and Sykes, 1969; *Minster and Jordan, 1978*). Northwestward from longitude 105°W, the Middle America Trench extends to the vicinity of Marías Islands. These islands are on the North America Plate, while the trench forms the boundary with the presently only slightly active prolongation of the Continental Thrust, between the North America and Rivera Plates (Larson, 1972).

The last portion of the Pacific Ocean floor adjacent to Mexico is formed by the Rivera Plate (Atwater, 1970), located SSE of the mouth of the Gulf of California. Its boundaries in the northeast with the North America Plate are formed by the Tamayo Fracture Zone and the Continental Thrust. In the northwest and southwest, its boundaries with the Pacific Plate are formed by the displaced segment of the East Pacific Rise and the Rivera Fracture Zone, respectively. The southeastern boundary is formed by a transform fault that extends northeastward from the truncated northern end of the East Pacific Rise at longitude 105°W; at the Middle America Trench it forms, together with the Continental

Thrust, the North America–Rivera–Cocos triple junction (Nixon, 1982). The sea floor over the Rivera Plate deepens gently from the west-lying displaced segment of the East Pacific Rise, whose crestal region is about 2,800 m deep, toward the east-southeast where the edge of the Middle America Trench is outlined by the 3,600-m depth contour. There are numerous abyssal hills over the western half of the Rivera Plate that are elongated in a north-northeasterly direction, while over its eastern half these features, together with some basins, are oriented roughly in a northwesterly direction. Active spreading along the displaced segment of the East Pacific Rise, which forms the northwestern boundary of the Rivera Plate, produces plate motion at a rate of 6 cm/yr, with a motion vector oriented S22°E (Drummond, 1981). During the last 2 m.y., this plate has been accreting to the North America Plate at the estimated rate of convergence of 2 cm/yr (Nixon, 1982).

The oldest oceanic crust in the Pacific Ocean floor morphotectonic province is in the Cocos Plate adjacent to the Continental Thrust in the region southeast of the Tehuantepec Fracture Zone, generally referred to as the Guatemala Basin. In this region, the NW-trending magnetic lineations range in age from 28 to 24 Ma (*Lynn and Lewis, 1976*; Nixon, 1982), which indicate a late Oligocene age. The northeast-trending Tehuantepec Fracture Zone is a structural discontinuity, apparently of right-lateral displacement, which juxtaposes middle Miocene (16 to 12 Ma) rocks of the Cocos Plate of the region that lies to the west-northwest of the upper Oligocene rocks of the Guatemala Basin. The oceanic crust elsewhere in the Cocos Plate of this region is of late Miocene–Pliocene age (Drummond, 1981; *Lynn and Lewis, 1976*; Nixon, 1982).

The roughly north-south–trending magnetic lineations within the Pacific Plate of this region indicate that north of the Molokai Fracture Zone, the oceanic crust represents mostly the Miocene, while toward the south, extending to the Clarion Fracture Zone, both the Miocene and Pliocene (Drummond, 1981) are represented.

The Rivera Plate, which is a small remnant of the Farallon Plate, has a complex history. Magnetic lineations, trending north-northeast, indicate that the oceanic crust ranges in age from late Miocene (10 to 8 Ma) to Holocene (Larson, 1972).

Gulf of California. The Gulf of California, known also as the Vermilion Sea or Sea of Cortés, is about 1,200 km long and oriented NW–SE. Its southwestern shores are formed by the Baja California Peninsula, and its northeastern shores by the Sonora and Sinaloa coasts of mainland Mexico. The head of the Gulf is formed by the delta of the Colorado River, although the morphologic and structural characteristics of the Gulf extend northwestward, as evidenced by the presence of Salada Lagoon and, farther northwest, by the Salton Sea. The width of this complex structural trough generally varies from 120 to 170 km, although at latitude 28°30′N it is only about 85 km, and at its mouth it is little over 200 km.

The submarine topography is complex, for it contains nine closed basins, which in the southern parts of the Gulf, vary in depth between 3,200 and 4,000 m (*Rusnak and others, 1964*). These basins in the northern one-third of the Gulf, north of about 28°30′N, are located right next to the Baja California Peninsula. In this northern region, the gulf floor is smooth and bowl shaped, has an alluvial sedimentary cover about 5,000 m thick, and the water depth over the largest part is less than 200 m. In the central and southern thirds of the Gulf, the basins are axial depressions with long axes oriented about N50°W; that is, slightly to the west of the axis of the Gulf. In general, there are well-developed shelves adjoining the coast of the mainland, built largely by sediments supplied by the major rivers that drain the Sierra Madre Occidental. On the west side of the Gulf, there is practically no shelf, but instead there are narrow benches cut in rocky cliffs. Thus, the bottom morphology of the Gulf follows the topography of the adjacent land areas, and as a result, there are lowlands with moderate slopes, and highlands with steep slopes.

The rugged, although to a certain extent aligned, nature of the floor of the Gulf, together with the presence of about 110 islands (*Tamayo, 1949*) mostly formed by rocks similar or identical to those that crop out in the Baja California Peninsula or in mainland Mexico (Beal, 1948; *Anderson, 1950*), indeed indicate a tectonic origin for the Gulf. Most of the islands are formed by granitic or Tertiary volcanic rocks that, in several localities, are covered unconformably by remnants of marine Pliocene sediments, indicating that their separation from the adjacent landmasses occurred very recently. On the other hand, some of the volcanic islands—such as Isla Tortuga in the central part of the Gulf at latitude 27°26′N, which appears to be a Quaternary volcano possibly related to the Tres Vírgenes volcanic center north of Santa Rosalía (Fig. 4:2; G-5) on the peninsula, or the numerous volcanic seamounts on the floor of the southern Gulf (*Rusnak and others, 1964*)—tend to indicate that tectonism that affected the Gulf was locally accompanied by volcanic activity.

Shepard (1950), Hamilton (1961), and *Rusnak and others (1964),* on the basis of submarine topography, some geophysical evidence of the presence of the M-discontinuity at a depth of only 6 km beneath the Gulf floor, and in light of the greater than 500 km right-lateral displacement along the San Andreas fault of California, which continues into the Gulf, advanced a model whereby the Baja California Peninsula was rifted away from mainland Mexico as a result of displacement along and across the San Andreas fault; the Gulf of California reflects the presence of right-lateral strike-slip faults in en échelon arrangements, trending about 30° to the west of the axis of the Gulf, which is associated with complementary orthogonal tension faults. As more information became available and ideas about plate tectonics progressively evolved, the above model was somewhat modified. In this context, *Wilson (1965)* called for the role of a transform fault, while *Vine (1966)* and *Sykes (1968)* considered the earlier suggested en échelon strike-slip faults to be transform faults. Thus, the Gulf currently is considered to be the result of sea-floor spreading and transform faulting. While the presently available geophysical information as to the separation of the Baja California Peninsula from mainland Mexico, and also from the

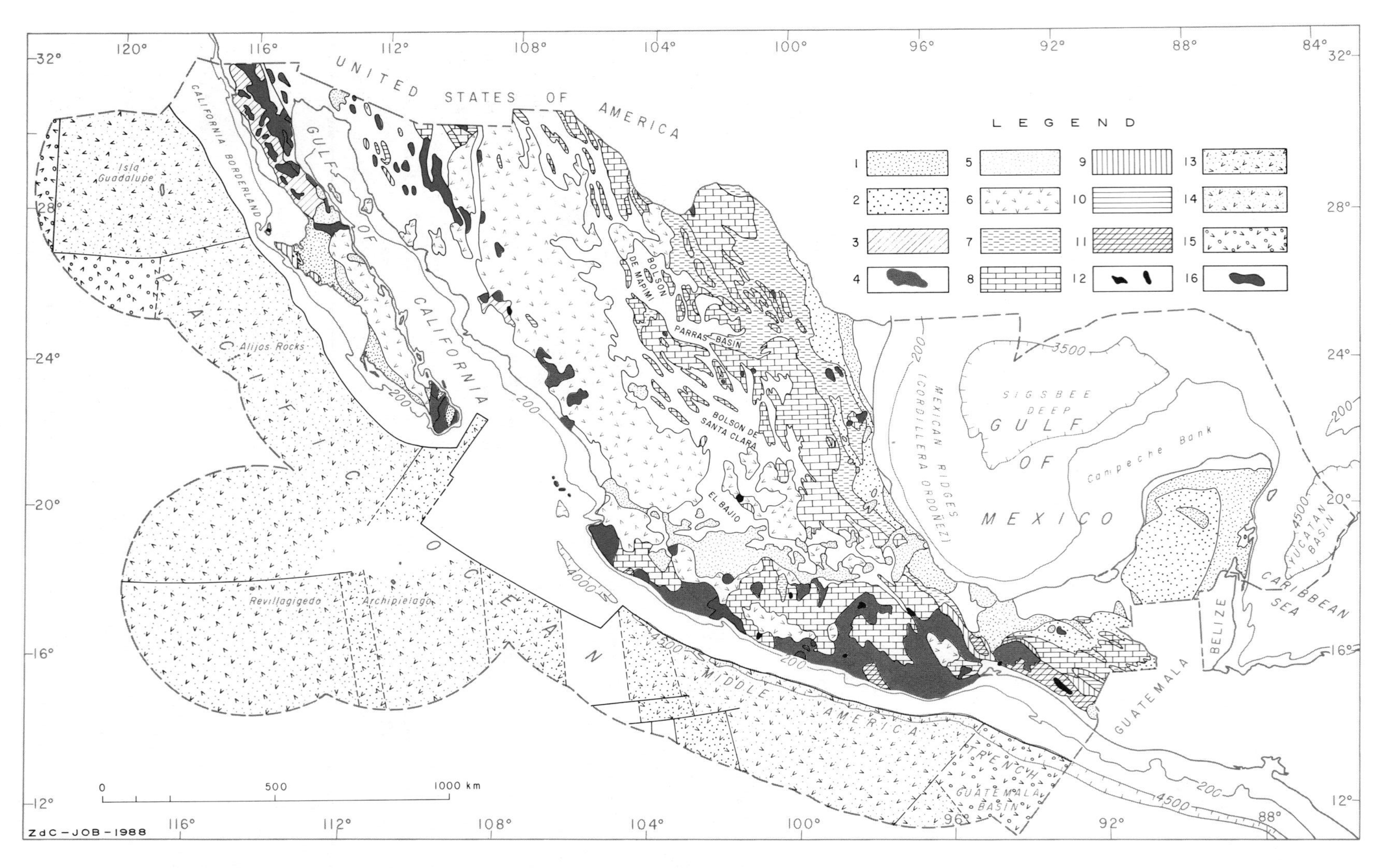

Figure 6. Simplified geological map of Mexico, including adjacent marine areas in the Pacific Ocean. The map is based on information adapted from the *North American Geologic Map Committee (1965),* López-Ramos (1976), *Lynn and Lewis (1976),* Anonymous (1981), Drummond (1981), and Nixon (1982). Blank areas on the continent correspond to Plio-Quaternary terrestrial clastic and coastal deposits. In oceanic areas blank areas correspond to the active spreading ridge; Rivera Plate; the continental shelf and slope along the Middle America trench; and floors of the Gulf of Mexico, Gulf of California, and Caribbean Sea. 1, Neogene marine deposits; 2, Paleogene marine deposits; 3, Upper Jurassic–Lower Cretaceous variably deformed and metamorphosed eugeoclinal deposits; 4, Precambrian and Paleozoic metamorphics and associated minor plutonic bodies; 5, Plio-Quaternary volcanics; 6, Tertiary volcanics; 7, Upper Cretaceous–Paleocene clastic wedge; 8, Upper Jurassic–Lower Cretaceous miogeoclinal deposits; 9, Upper Triassic–Lower Jurassic redbeds and eugeoclinal deposits; 10, Paleozoic marine deposits; 11, Paleozoic intrusives; 12, Ophiolites in Cedros Island, Vizcaíno Peninsula, Santa Margarita Island, and in northern Sinaloa; elsewhere, ultrabasic intrusives and serpentinites; 13, Pliocene oceanic crust; 14, Miocene oceanic crust; 15, Oligocene oceanic crust; 16, Upper Cretaceous to Tertiary granitoid intrusives. Because of limitations imposed by the map scale, the areas of pre-Upper Jurassic to Lower Cretaceous miogeoclinal deposits of Miquihuana, Aramberri, and the Huizachal and Huayacocotla anticlinoria are not shown.

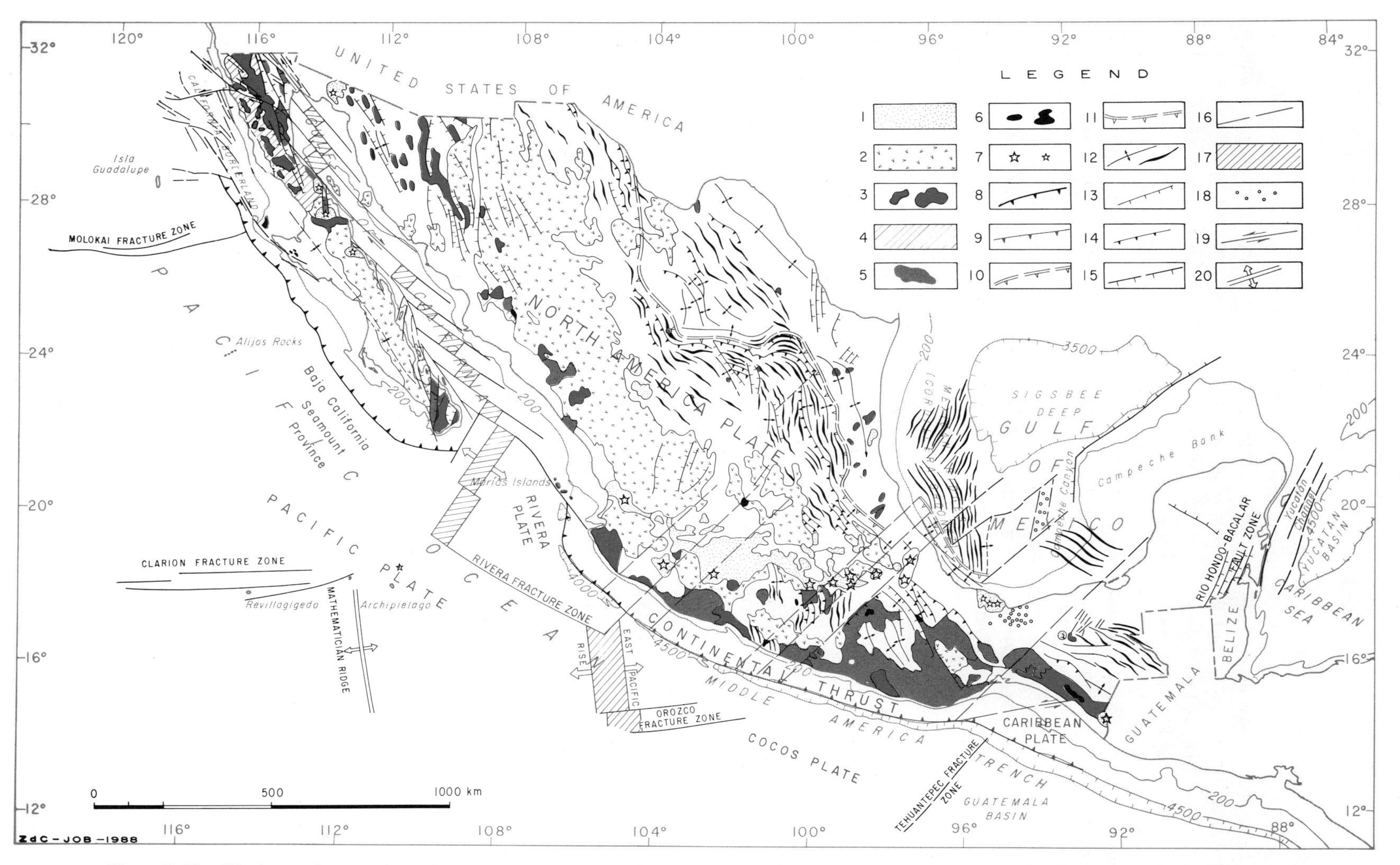

Figure 7. Simplified tectonic map of Mexico, including adjacent marine areas. The map is based on the current interpretation of the writer, and includes information adapted from de Cserna (1961), P. B. King (1968), Garrison and Martin (1973), *Moore and Del Castillo (1974),* Drummond (1981), and Meneses de Gyves (1980). 1, Quaternary volcanics; 2, Tertiary volcanics; 3, Granitoid stock and batholith; 4, Mesozoic metamorphics; 5, Precambrian and/or Paleozoic metamorphics and associated intrusives; 6, Ophiolite in Cedros Island, Vizcaíno Peninsula, and Santa Margarita Island—all on the Pacific side off Baja California Peninsula; elsewhere, it includes ultrabasic rocks and serpentinites; 7, Major and minor Quaternary volcanoes; 8, Inactive B (Benioff)-type subduction front; 9, Active B-type subduction front; 10, Inactive A (Ampferer)-type subduction front; 11, Active A-type subduction front; 12, Axes of folds involving basement or only sedimentary cover; 13, Fault, showing the downthrown block; 14, Thrust—the triangles are on the upper plate; 15, Fault in marine areas, inferred from bathymetric and/or geophysical evidence; 16, Seismically active shear-zone; 17, Active oceanic spreading ridge or center; 18, Salt domes; 19, Major active transcurrent fault, showing directions of relative displacement; 20, Inactive former spreading ridge.

North America Plate, is conclusive only for the past 4 m.y. (Larson, 1972), conventional stratigraphic information indicates that the "proto-Gulf" was already formed during the late Miocene (*Durham and Allison, 1960*).

The floor of the Gulf of Mexico. The Mexican Gulf Coast, between the mouth of Río Grande (or Río Bravo) and the northeastern tip of the Yucatán Peninsula, is approximately 2,000 km long. The adjacent continental shelf at the latitude of the mouth of Río Grande is about 75 km wide and it gradually narrows to about 25 km at latitude 20°N. Although it widens again between this point and the volcanic massif of The Tuxtlas (Fig. 4:14; P-24), its full proportions are only attained eastward, with widths ranging from 60 km in front of Coatzacoalcos at the northern end of the Isthmus of Tehuantepec, to close to 280 km in front of the northern coast of the Yucatán Peninsula. The surface of the shelf has some low relief, due either to the presence of small fault scarps, small reef developments, possibly salt intrusions, or to low sea levels during the Pleistocene that produced terrace-like features (*Uchupi, 1967*; Garrison and Martin, 1973; Perry, 1984).

Along the roughly N-S–trending east coast of Mexico, the continental shelf is bordered by a continental slope, which extends to an average depth of approximately 3,000 m and varies in width from about 70 km in front of the mouth of the Río Grande, to about 200 km at latitude 23°N, and to about 130 km northeast of the port of Veracruz (Fig. 4:14; 0-23). This important stretch of the continental slope of the Gulf is quite different from the adjacent continental shelf, which is practically devoid of relief; it is the site of a roughly N-S–trending fold and thrust belt (Fig. 7) referred to by Bryant and others (1968) as the Mexican Ridges. This submarine foldbelt, the Ordóñez Cordillera of de Cserna (1981), is 570 km long (Garrison and Martin, 1973) and extends northward from the volcanic massif of The Tuxtlas to latitude 24°N; it may extend another 200 km north-northeastward, on the basis of bathymetric configuration presented by Perry (1984). The foldbelt is about 40 to 70 km wide, and the folds have wavelengths of approximately 10 km with a topographic relief reaching 500 to 700 m (Buffler and others, 1979). There are numerous thrusts with seaward transport. The sediments involved in the deformation have a thickness of approximately 4,000 to 5,000 m; they are silty clays and fine-grained turbidites and represent the lower Tertiary–Holocene. A variety of mechanisms have been proposed to account for the origin of this fold and thrust belt, ranging from gravity sliding and related growth-fault systems, to tectonic compression acting in an east-west direction and originating in a deeper crustal level beneath Mexico. In both cases, the deformation occurred above a décollement horizon, which might have been salt or clay and might also form the cores of the anticlines (Bryant and others, 1968; *Antoine, 1972*; Garrison and Martin, 1973; *Moore and Del Castillo, 1974*; Buffler and others, 1979).

While the information regarding the northern termination of the foldbelt is unclear, toward the southern end, tectonic truncation is interpreted, whereby the continental shelf overrides in a northeasterly direction the N-S–trending folds and related structures of the continental slope between latitudes 18°45′ and 20°30′N (de Cserna, 1981). In view of these overall structural relations of the continental slope off eastern Mexico, the gross picture is indicative of an active continental margin where A-type subduction may be underway (Bally, 1981; Bally and others, 1985) along the southern one-quarter of its length, a process which is also suggested, if not necessarily supported, by seismic activity (Molnar and Sykes, 1969; Hanus and Vanek, 1977–1978).

The continental slope east of longitude 95°W and west of the N-S–trending escarpment of the Campeche Bank (Banco de Campeche) is considered to be underlain by salt. This stretch of the continental slope between the edge of the continental shelf and the 1,000-m depth contour is characterized by the presence of a series of NW-SE–trending ridges and valleys in front of the coast of Tabasco, while farther north between the 1,000-m depth contour and the base of the continental slope, it is characterized by a great number of irregular-shaped knolls (Perry, 1984). Earlier marine geological and geophysical studies showed conclusively that the knolls are salt diapirs, either as salt domes or salt stocks of different shapes related to faults and folds, some of which have relief as great as 1,500 m; the alignment of these knolls was considered to be northeasterly, following possibly deep-seated ridges (Garrison and Martin, 1973). Relatively recent oil and gas developments in this offshore region revealed that while the northeasterly trend of the knolls might indeed be the case in the area north-northwest of the 1,000-m depth contour, toward the southeast the structures are NW-SE–trending folds, asymmetric or overturned to the northeast, which are modified by thrusts and normal faults, and extend southeastward beneath the continental shelf. Along some of these complex structures, such as in the Cantarell Field, the salt was squeezed in as a diapir, implying the emplacement of the salt as a result of lateral compression rather than by the weight of the overlying sedimentary sequence. The deformed sequence represents the Upper Jurassic–Miocene and has a maximum thickness of about 5,000 m. The overlying Pliocene–Holocene deposits are silty clays and turbiditic sands and silts whose thickness ranges from approximately 200 to 600 m (Meneses de Gyves, 1981; Santiago-Acevedo and others, 1984).

The northeasterly trend of the knolls, detected over the continental slope north of the 1,000-m depth contour, requires a tectonic explanation with respect to the NW-SE trend of the structures just outlined. Perhaps a NE-SW–trending segmentation of the Gulf of Mexico indeed exists, comparable to that proposed by *Mooser (1975)* for the subducted Cocos Plate, or else the alignment of the salt domes (N35°E), as shown by Garrison and Martin (1973, p. 16, Fig. 6), could represent the expression of en échelon fracturing related to a left-lateral fault that may merge with the fault of the Campeche Escarpment (Fig. 7). This structural model would be quite similar to the one shown by Dengo and Bohnenberger (1969) for the Chamelecón fault zone of Honduras in relation with the Motagua fault. In this context, the folds and thrusts beneath the Pliocene–Holocene cover of the continental shelf and upper continental slope in front of the Tabasco coast, which are oriented NW-SE, could also represent en échelon folds related to a similar major NE-SW–trending left-lateral fault that would extend from the northern part of The Tuxtlas volcanic massif to the western edge of the Campeche Bank.

East of Campeche Canyon, the continental margin is represented by a broad continental shelf, the Campeche Bank, which is the northern submerged extension of the Yucatán platform. The continental slope around this bank is the narrowest and steepest (20°) on the west along Campeche Canyon, and moderately narrow (10 to 45 km) and steep (12°) on the northwest, facing the Sigsbee Plain; both are possibly controlled by major faults (Drummond, 1981). The slope on the northeast is rather complex. Here the upper slope between the 200- and 3,000-m depth contours is about 100 km wide and has an average slope angle at about 5°, while the lower slope, which is extremely narrow and about 200 m high, is very steep (34°). The Campeche Bank is formed essentially of carbonate rock of biogenic or chemical origin with intervening horizons of evaporites that are in a flat-lying position. The thickness of this sequence is slightly more than 3,400 m, and it represents the middle Cretaceous–Holocene. Part of a Lower Cretaceous reef trend is exposed close to the base of the northeastern continental slope facing the West Florida Escarpment. This may be connected to the prolific oil- and gas-producing Lower Cretaceous reef trends toward the southwest in Tabasco.

Adjacent to the continental slope, forming the central part of the Gulf of Mexico, is the Sigsbee Plain or Sigsbee Deep, which is properly outlined by the 3,500-m depth contour, but whose deepest part is about 3,700 m (Garrison and Martin, 1973). It is a flat sea floor developed on practically horizontal stratified turbidites and pelagic oozes of Pliocene–Holocene age. Occasional knolls close to the central part of this submarine plain, which are believed to be the expressions of deep-seated salt domes, have a submarine topographic relief between 100 and 200 m.

The Yucatán Channel constitutes a narrow seaway that separates northeastern Yucatán from southwestern Cuba and, at the same time, allows communication between the Gulf of Mexico and the Caribbean Sea. The channel is oriented NE-SW and has a sill depth of 2,000 m, located practically midway between Cape San Antonio, Cuba, and Cozumel Island, Mexico. It is a tectonically controlled submarine feature that resulted from the interactions of the major intraplate frontal thrust of Cuba and the eastern Yucatán marginal faults (Drummond, 1981) whose expression on land may be the Río Hondo–Bacalar fault zone in Mexico (*Alvarez, 1954*). The Yucatán side of the channel is characterized by a series of ridges that parallel the coast and then turn northeast toward Cuba. These ridges are considered to be fault-controlled and trapped upper Tertiary–Quaternary sediments on top of lower Tertiary and Cretaceous carbonates. Phyllite and marble samples dredged just below the sill of the Yucatán Channel from about 2,500 m depth yielded a calculated K-Ar minimum age of 92.5 Ma; however, the evidence for possible systematic loss of argon suggests that these rocks were more likely produced by older metamorphism, perhaps during mid-Mesozoic time (*Vedder and others, 1973*).

Caribbean Sea floor. The east coast of the Yucatán Peninsula, south of the Yucatán Channel, adjoins the Caribbean Sea. A continental shelf to a depth of 200 m is only a few kilometers wide, and the continental slope in this region descends to a depth of about 4,000 m. This slope has a step-like profile, produced by down-to-the-east displacement by the eastern Yucatán marginal faults. There are two NNE-elongated islands in the northern parts of the upper slope—Isla Mujeres and Cozumel—and in the southern part there are about 25 cays (keys) and banks (*Tamayo, 1949*). The slope is formed by Cretaceous and Tertiary carbonates that are flanked by Quaternary sediments due to the damming effect of the fault-produced ridges. Phyllite fragments were dredged about 100 km to the east-southeast of Cozumel Island from a depth of nearly 3,000 m; their geochronological characteristics are similar to those mentioned in connection with the dredged samples from the Yucatán Channel (*Vedder and others, 1973*).

The deepest part of the Caribbean Sea within the Exclusive Economic Zone recognized by Mexico corresponds to the Yucatán Basin, which has a flat floor at an approximate depth of 4,500 m (Perry, 1984).

Continental regions

The dynamics of the sea floor surrounding mainland Mexico, now and during the relatively recent geologic past, exerted a profound influence on the shaping of the morphology of the country. The active nature of the continental margin along the Pacific resulted in the uplifting and related vigorous erosion of the western and southern parts of Mexico, thereby creating large outcrop areas of deeper levels of the upper crust formed by metamorphic and plutonic rocks. In contrast with the Pacific side of the country, the continental margin along the Gulf of Mexico has been generally considered a gradually emergent passive margin, over which sedimentation took place during the Cenozoic Era. Although there are local exceptions to this very broad generalization, the principal morphotectonic provinces recognized in mainland Mexico do reflect this broad framework.

Baja California Peninsula. The westernmost principal morphotectonic province of mainland Mexico is the Baja California Peninsula. This stretch of land, oriented north-northwest, extends from the Transverse Ranges of California to Cape San Lucas, a distance of about 1,450 km. The Mexican portion of this length, between the international boundary and Cape San Lucas, is 1,300 km. It is bounded on the west by the Pacific Ocean and on the east by the Gulf of California. Adjacent to the peninsula on the west and extending southeastward to about latitude 29°N, is the submerged "California Borderland," whereas on the east is a complex structural depression whose floor lies beneath sea level and deepens toward the southeast. This structural depression north of the international boundary is occupied by the Salton Sea or Sink, and parts of Imperial Valley, and toward the south by Laguna Salada and the Gulf of California. The delta of the Colorado River separates the inundated part of this structural though underlying the Gulf of California from its landlocked northern portion and provides a "land bridge" between mainland Mexico and the peninsula.

The peninsula from north to south is divisible into three morphotectonic subprovinces. The northern one extends southward from the international boundary practically to the southern limits of the state of Baja California Norte and is referred to as the Peninsular Ranges. The subprovince to the south of latitude 28°N and north of the Isthmus of La Paz is formed by a horizontal or very gently westward inclined and dissected volcanic plateau, the Sierra de La Giganta, which is flanked on the west by younger Tertiary sediments and Plio-Quaternary volcanics. The southernmost subprovince, referred to as the Southern Cape region, is a granitic and metamorphic terrain, to a certain extent geologically similar to the Peninsular Ranges, but different because of its lower elevations and desert landscape.

The following brief description of the highlights of the geology of the peninsula is taken from the excellent works of Beal (1948), *Mina-Uhink (1957),* and R. G. Gastil and others (1975), unless otherwise stated.

In the eastern half of the Peninsular Ranges and adjacent Colorado delta in the north, the oldest identifiable rocks of the peninsula are distributed in 27 discontinuous outcrop areas. These rocks are more or less metamorphosed sandstones, shales, limestones, and basic volcanic rocks. From less metamorphosed sections, there are fossils ranging in age from Precambrian to Triassic (*Gastil and Miller, 1984*).

The next younger sequence of rocks in the northern subprovince is rather widespread in the western half where it consists of several thousand meters of metasedimentary and metavolcanic rocks of Aptian–Albian (middle Cretaceous) age. The rocks are andesitic pillow lavas, pyroclastics, and epiclastic volcanics with intervals of limestone, which are deformed and metamorphosed. The fauna obtained from these rocks, now known as the Alisitos Formation (*Santillán and Barrera, 1930*), allowed *Böse and Wittich (1913)* to date stratigraphically the emplacement of the granitic rocks of this region as Turonian (Late Cretaceous), since the overlying Upper Cretaceous sediments, the Rosario Formation, are unmetamorphosed and contain a Senonian fauna. Modern high-precision radiometric dating of the granitic rocks in this subprovince, however, indicates ages ranging from 119 to 102 Ma in the western half, to 95 Ma in the eastern half (*Silver and others, 1969; Banks and Silver, 1969*), suggesting that some of these plutons were emplaced contemporaneously with the Alisitos volcanic activity. 387 separate plutons have been mapped in the Peninsular Ranges, and 250 of these have been properly identified as to rock composition. It is noteworthy that of the 250 plutons identified, 118 are tonalites and quartz diorites, 87 granodiorites, and 34 gabbro and diorites. Of the remaining 11 plutons, only 5 are granites and 6 adamellites. The total outcrop area of the plutonic rocks is calculated as about 28,000 km^2, which is close to 40 percent of the surface area of Baja California Norte.

The post-batholithic marine sedimentary deposits are in a narrow discontinuous belt along the west coast of the peninsula and accumulated in response to the uplift of the batholithic terrane. These are molasse deposits of Late Cretaceous and early Tertiary age. The continental molasse deposits of this age are preserved beneath younger volcanics to the northwest and southwest of San Felipe (Fig. 4: 1; C-3), respectively, and toward the southern limits of the subprovince. It is probably a fair assumption that the Tertiary volcanics, in a certain way equivalents of the Miocene Comondú volcanics of the Sierra de La Giganta farther south, covered larger areas in the past than their present outcrop areas in the Peninsular Ranges. Faulting and attendant sinking not only facilitated the preservation of these volcanic rocks and the underlying continental molasse deposits, but was instrumental in localizing the Plio-Quaternary volcanism in this region.

Pliocene marine deposits have a very restricted distribution along short stretches adjacent to the coasts of the Pacific Ocean and the Gulf of California; the largest areas underlain by marine Quaternary strata are along the coast of the Gulf of California to the north of San Felipe, and on the Pacific side in the region of San Quintín (Fig. 4: 1; C-2).

The northern subprovince was affected by deformation, regional metamorphism, and batholithic emplacement toward the end of the Early Cretaceous, and subjected to uplift and erosion during the Late Cretaceous and early Tertiary. Volcanic activity and probably some faulting during the Miocene, and continued faulting since the Pliocene with attendant volcanic activity, constitute the tectonic processes that controlled the geomorphic development of this subprovince. As a result, through this northern part of the peninsula, from west to east, the following geomorphic regions or units are recognized: Pacific coastal, coastal mountain, highland plateaus, highland valleys, and Gulf of California. The most characteristic features of these geomorphic regions are: (1) elevated late Pliocene and Pleistocene marine terraces, in the Pacific coastal region; (2) perhaps the most rugged topography of this entire subprovince, in the coastal mountain region; (3) Late Cretaceous and early Tertiary erosion surfaces that are tilted west-southwestward and whose northeastern parts, near the main gulf escarpment, form the highest topographic elevations of the entire peninsula (3,095 m, summit of La Providencia, Sierra de San Pedro Mártir; Fig. 4: 1; D-2) and also form the highland plateaus region; and (4) the more or less isolated mountains with the intervening valleys and/or basins, reflecting west-dipping antithetic faults and eastward-tilted blocks along the relatively narrow strip between the main gulf escarpment on the west, and the shore of the Gulf of California on the east, including in the north the western parts of the Colorado delta (Fig. 4:1; B-3). Along the coast of the Gulf, elevated marine terraces of Plio-Pleistocene age are also widespread; in fact, these were observed and described from the area of San Luis Gonzaga ca. 1750 with a logical geological explanation by the missionary *del Barco (1973, p. 145–151)*, considerably earlier than *Darwin (1899)* made his observations along the southern coast of Chile.

The highland plateaus of the Peninsular Ranges subprovince gradually lose their elevation toward the south, where they are replaced by gently inclined (west-southwestward) and highly dissected plateaus and mesas of the Sierra de La Giganta subprovince. These landforms, with intervening canyons, form a rather desolate landscape, in which the highest elevations [Cerro de La Bandera, 1,585 m (Fig. 4:2; G-5); Cerro de La Giganta, 1,785 m (Fig. 4: 2; I-6)] are in the eastern one-half, or eastern one-third, of the peninsula and the drainage divide is but a few kilometers from the shores of the Gulf of California. This volcanic terrane is about 500 km long and extends southward to the Isthmus of La Paz (Fig. 4:2; K-7). The western slopes of Sierra de La Giganta constitute a tableland that extends practically to the Pacific Coast at latitude 26°N for a stretch of about 50 km. This complex mountain range has an average width between 30 and 50 km.

West of the Sierra de La Giganta proper, there are two major roughly N-S–elongate plains with extensive sand dune development; one between latitudes 26°45′ and 28°30′N (Llano del Berrendo, Desierto de Vizcaíno, and Llano de Santa Clara) and the other between latitudes 24°15′ and 26°00′N (Llano de Magdalena). These plains are bordered farther to the west either by complex mountain ranges, such as on the Vizcaíno Peninsula (Fig. 4: 2; G-3), or by islands of granitic and metamorphic rocks, such as Isla Santa Margarita (Fig. 4: 2; J-6) and related small islands. Both the plains and the mountains indicate gross geologic relations similar—though not properly understood as of today—to those that exist to the west of the highland plateaus of the Peninsular Ranges subprovince, namely the coastal mountains, the Pacific Coastal, and California Borderland regions.

The oldest rocks in the Sierra de La Giganta morphotectonic subprovince crop out in the southeastern part of the Vizcaíno Peninsula. These *Halobia*-bearing dolomitic limestones, interbedded with chert, pillow lavas, breccias, and volcanic sandstones, make up a sequence of about 2,400 m (San Hipólito Formation) considered to be of Norian age (Late Triassic) (*Finch and others, 1979*). These may be part of an ophiolitic basement. In the Sierra de San Andrés, which is in the central part of the Vizcaíno Peninsula, and in the mountains that extend to the northwest, Upper Triassic ophiolitic basement is exposed that is partially disrupted (*T. E. Moore, 1979*). Farther toward the northwest, on Cedros Island, *Kilmer (1979)* mapped the pre-Bajocian (Middle Jurassic) Choyal Formation, which is also an ophiolite complex and is overlain by the 2,300-m-thick Bajocian–Callovian Gran Cañón Formation, made up of radiolarian chert, siltstone, sandstone, conglomerate, tuff, and pillowed greenstones. This formation, in turn, is overlain unconformably by the Kimmeridgian(?) Coloradito Formation, ranging in thickness from 150 to 600 m, and composed of megabreccia, interbedded shale, sandstone, and conglomerate. The conformably(?) overlying Tithonian–lower Neocomian Eugenia Formation, about 100 to 150 m thick in Cedros Island but with thicknesses of more than 2,000 m in the mountains of the Viczaíno Peninsula, consists of conglomerate, graywacke, and andesitic flows.

There is a distinct break in the stratigraphic record in this part of the subprovince between the middle Neocomian (Lower Cretaceous) and the Campanian (Late Cretaceous). Structural relations observed in key areas and backed by radiometric dating indicate that isoclinal folding and thrusting, accompanied by blueschist metamorphism, occurred and was in turn followed by thrusting and normal faulting. The metamorphism was subduction related, and its peak occurred in late Early Cretaceous time (*Sedlock, 1988*).

Outcrops of Upper Cretaceous molasse, the Valle Formation, are found extensively in the mountains of the Vizcaíno Peninsula. As a result of oil and gas exploration by PEMEX, the presence of this formation in the subsurface has also been adequately established through geophysical work and subsequent wildcats. There is a major synclinal structure that underlies the plains formed between the Sierra de La Giganta on the east, and the Vizcaíno Peninsula on the west, as well as the Llano de Magdalena, between the Sierra de La Giganta and Isla Santa Margarita. This major elongated structure is the Baja California syncline and is considered to be an approximately 600-km-long structure that served as a sedimentary basin for the Upper Cretaceous and lower Tertiary deposits. There are several faults along the flanks of this structure—probably listric normal faults (or growth faults)—as well as minor undulations in the accumulated strata. The Valle Formation consists of about 3,000 m of sandstones and shales, and the unconformably overlying Malarrino Formation, which is Paleocene, is a chiefly conglomeratic unit about 150 m thick that transgresses from the east and pinches out toward the west. The latest unit directly related to the accumulation of this structure is the Eocene Bateque or Tepetate Formation, also about 3,000 m thick, which consists of shales and sandstones with minor amounts of calcareous siltstones and limestones in the upper part.

Another major break in sedimentation followed Eocene deposition, since there is no record of Oligocene deposits in the region. The lower and middle Miocene shales and sandstones, with some interbedded limestones, contain tuffaceous beds and diatomaceous shales, as well as phosphorites, and range in thickness from 100 to 800 m. This sequence rests unconformably over the older Tertiary rocks, and its principal outcrop area is along the ENE margin of the Llano de Magdalena. These marine sedimentary clastics, in turn, are overlain—in a few areas conformably, and elsewhere unconformably—by the 150- to 1,300-m-thick upper Miocene volcanic sequence, known as the Comondú Formation or Comondú Group. This group consists of lavas, agglomerates, tuffs, and lahars predominantly of andesitic and basaltic composition. In addition, the presence of water-laid epiclastic rocks has been reported also, as well as rocks of rhyolitic and dacitic composition (*Wilson and Rocha-Moreno, 1955*). The rocks of the Comondú Formation are covered unconformably by marine sandstones and shales included in the Pliocene Salada Formation, whose maximum thickness is around 650 m. The major outcrop area of this formation is also along the ENE margin of the Llano de Magdalena, although it has been identified at a few localities along the coast of the Gulf of California.

The Sierra de La Giganta morphotectonic subprovince loses its elevation gradually toward the southeast and is practically at sea level at the Isthmus of La Paz, where the peninsula is only about 45 km wide. Southeast of the isthmus, the Southern Cape region is formed by a large granitic massif, the Sierra de Victoria, that reaches elevations slightly over 2,000 m. This massif is flanked by metamorphic rocks and overlying thin Miocene volcanics and Pliocene marine sedimentary rocks. The crystalline terrain has certain similarities to those of the Peninsular Ranges subprovince in the north, but differs in its ruggedness, reflecting deeper dissection.

The oldest rocks of the subprovince form a sequence of slate-phyllite-schist-gneiss-migmatite, with both andalusite and cordierite-sillimanite, intruded by a syntectonic gabbroic pluton with noritic and dioritic to granodioritic phases (*Ortega-Gutiérrez, 1982*). The presence of this metamorphic complex was recognized, although not properly understood, by *del Castillo (1889b).* Although no radiometric ages are available for this metamorphic-plutonic complex, in view of its geological–petrological characteristics and the presence of Paleozoic fossiliferous and also metamorphic rocks both in the eastern one-half of the Peninsular Ranges subprovince and in the adjacent state of Sinaloa (after restoring the peninsula to its pre-spreading position), this writer considers a late Paleozoic age appropriate for this complex. The major batholith (Sierra de Victoria) of granitic to tonalitic composition was emplaced during the Late Cretaceous, apparently without significant contact metamorphism. The deeply unroofed plutonic mass was covered by rhyolitic pyroclastic flows, quite unlike the Comondú volcanics, and affected by faulting. Low-lying areas became flooded during the Pliocene, and marine clastics were deposited. Thus, the Southern Cape region is essentially a major horst with related minor faults.

The pre-batholithic rocks in the Peninsular Ranges subprovince are highly folded with a dominant northwesterly trend. While this trend more or less parallels the axis of this portion of the peninsula, it also circles or wraps around many of the plutonic bodies. At about 28°30′N, the outcrop areas of the Alisitos Formation and the structural trend in these, as well as the granitic bodies, gradually swing eastward, toward the Gulf of California. South of here, the Alisitos volcanic rocks have not been identified on the peninsula, even in the subsurface, with the exception of a diorite pluton near Loreto (*Ritter, 1895*), south of Santa Rosalía (Fig. 4:2; H-6), and the Triassic and Jurassic ophiolites and associated highly deformed and metamorphosed sediments and volcanics of the Vizcaíno Peninsula. The Upper Cretaceous and lower Tertiary molasse deposits that accumulated in the Baja California syncline do show some degree of folding. The folds interpreted in the subsurface from geophysical information and drilling appear to this writer to be effects of transpeninsular transcurrent faulting east of the Vizcaíno Peninsula, while under the Llano de Magdalena they appear to be gravity induced, for they more or less parallel the general axis of the great synclinal basin. On the geologic map of Beal (1948), a 300-km-long anticlinal structure is shown in the Comondú volcanics, paralleling the coast of the Gulf southeast of Santa Rosalía, with its axis practically along the coast. This structure could be the southern expression of the main gulf escarpment, identified in the Peninsular Ranges subprovince.

The dominant geologic structures of the Baja California Peninsula are faults. Many high-angle faults have been mapped in the Peninsular Ranges subprovince in a belt bordering the Gulf. This belt is an active zone, where the individual faults have lengths between 15 and 20 km, and follow a northerly or north-northwesterly trend. In the region north of San Felipe (Fig. 4: 1; C-3) and Ensenada (Fig. 4: 1, B-1), two important right-lateral faults, or fault systems, have been identified. These extend from the main gulf escarpment to the Pacific Coast. The southern one is the Agua Blanca fault (*Allen and others, 1960*), and the northern one is the San Miguel–Vallecitos fault.

By observing the distribution of the Plio-Quaternary basaltic (or basaltic andesite) volcanics over the peninsula, the best known of which is the Tres Vírgenes volcanic field (Fig. 4: 2; G-5) northwest of Santa Rosalía (*Demant, 1981a*), one cannot fail to notice certain alignments. The volcanic cones show numerous N-S or NW-SE trends, while the alluvium-filled valleys between San Luis Gonzaga (Fig. 4: 1; D-3) and latitude 28°00′N are oriented N-S. The published gravity data allow the drawing of several NW-SE–oriented lines across the peninsula, which are undoubtedly transcurrent faults of right-lateral displacement. While some investigators may be skeptical about the presence of transpeninsular transcurrent faults or shear zones, this writer visualizes several of these across the peninsula, which not only explains the origin of several stretches of the morphology of the Pacific Coast, the southwestward tilting of major blocks, and the great geologic contrast along both sides of latitude 28°00′N, but also the N-S–trending alluvial valleys as en echelon grabens and, or course, the location of the Plio-Quaternary volcanic cones (*Sawlan, 1981*).

The Southern Cape region subprovince is a major structural block that appears to be out of place. It is bounded on the west by the N-S–trending La Paz fault, on the northeast off shore by the Tamayo Fracture Zone, and on the southeast by a series of high-angle faults (*Normark and Curray, 1968*).

Sonoran Basin and Range province. This province extends south-southeastward from the Arizona–Sonora segment of the international boundary to latitude 21°N. On the west-southwest, it reaches the coast of the Gulf of California, and on the east-northeast it is bounded by the volcanic plateaus of the Sierra Madre Occidental. Between the international boundary and the latitude of Guaymas (28°N) (Fig. 4: 3; E-6), the region is characterized by NNW-trending mountain ranges that are separated by valleys. These valleys become broader westward, and in the northwest there is a large desert region, the Altar Desert, with moving sand dunes, which emphasize the Inselberg aspect to many of the isolated mountain ranges. West of longitude 110°W this region is very similar to the Basin and Range province of the southwestern United States.

Southeast of Guaymas, the province corresponds to the rather narrow coastal plain of the Gulf of California and the adjacent foothill belt of the Sierra Madre Occidental, where erosion has stripped the Tertiary volcanic cover from the underlying Mesozoic and Paleozoic rocks. The major rivers in this region drain the Sierra Madre Occidental. Along certain stretches of this coastal plain they have built their deltas, and as a result, several contributed to the local widening of the coastal plain. Perhaps the most important is the delta of Río Fuerte in northern Sinaloa (Fig. 4: 8; I-8) where the delta itself is protected by the volcanic center of Topolobampo. South of Mazatlán (Fig. 4: 8; L-11) the prograding coastal plain adjacent to the lower course of Río Grande de Santiago is impressive. It is reflected in the structure of the continental terrace in this area (*Curray and Moore, 1964*).

The oldest rocks that crop out in Mexico are found in this morphotectonic province. They consist of muscovite-quartz schists, quartzites, and biotite-quartzofeldspathic gneisses that are cut by 1,750 to 1,710 Ma calc-alkaline intrusives. These rocks are exposed in the Caborca region where upper amphibolite facies, layered quartzofeldspathic and amphibolitic gneisses are also present, whose deformation and metamorphism are dated at 1,660 Ma (*Anderson and Silver, 1978a*). In northeastern Sonora, severely deformed eugeoclinal rocks, metamorphosed to greenschist facies about 1,650 Ma and later intruded by anorogenic quartz monzonite plutons (1,475 to 1,425 Ma), constitute the basement of the Paleozoic sedimentary sequence in this part of the province (*Anderson and Silver, 1977*). Rare small plutons of micrographic granite, which are the youngest Precambrian igneous rocks (1,100 Ma) in northern Sonora, are also present. In the El Fuerte region, near the border between Sonora and Sinaloa, the pre-Carboniferous felsic and mafic gneisses (*de Cserna and Kent, 1961; Mullan, 1978*) may represent part of the Precambrian basement. While the structural complexities of the gneisses do not allow inferences as to regional trends, the older Precambrian suite in northwestern Sonora and the younger in northeastern Sonora are parts of northeasterly-trending orogenic belts that are apparently disrupted by the Middle Jurassic or younger NW-SE–trending Mojave-Sonora Megashear (*Anderson and Silver, 1979*).

The Precambrian crystalline terrain of the Caborca region is overlain by a 4,128-m-thick sequence of latest Precambrian (younger than 1,100 Ma) quartzite and dolomite with a few intervals of limestone, shale, and conglomerate, which in turn, passes into the *Olenellus*-bearing Lower Cambrian (Cooper and Arellano, 1952; *Anderson and others, 1980;* Stewart and others, 1984). These deposits record the beginning of deposition in the Cordilleran miogeocline in Mexico. In this region, the Lower and Middle Cambrian strata are 1,272 m thick and formed by quartzite, dolomite, limestone, and sandstone. In an isolated outcrop area, there is a 420-m-thick sequence of limestone of possible Late Ordovician and Silurian age, and west of Caborca in the area of El Antimonio, 280 m of Upper Devonian limestone and dolomite are overlain by about 50 m of Lower Mississippian cherty limestone. The highest Paleozoic unit in this area is the Middle Permian, which consists of 660 m of clastics at the base, and clean limestone upward in the section. The stratigraphic information in the northwestern part of this province thus indicates that there was continuous marine shelf sedimentation from latest Precambrian to at least Middle Cambrian time. This seems to have been followed by a break; sedimentation was resumed toward the end of the Ordovician and could have continued into the Silurian. Another break occurred sometime between the Silurian and Late Devonian, since sedimentation apparently proceeded during Late Devonian and Early Mississippian. The third major break in sedimentation took place during Middle Mississippian–Early Permian times, before the deposition of Middle Permian strata (*Cooper and Arellano, 1946; Arellano, 1956; Easton, 1958; Fries, 1962a*). The isolated nature of the mountain ranges, where the Paleozoic rocks crop out, makes piecing together the real meaning of the stratigraphic record rather difficult. While the published information indicates that the Paleozoic sequence in northwestern Sonora is about 2,700 m thick, *Poole and Madrid (1986)* reported this sequence to be 7,000 m thick, and they believe it to be parautochthonous.

In the northeastern parts of this province, the Paleozoic sedimentary sequence is about 1 km thick; its base is younger (i.e., late Cambrian instead of late Proterozoic, as in the Caborca area) and shows clearly that it accumulated on the border of the craton (*Velasco, 1966*).

In the central and eastern parts of Sonora, about 50 m of massive limestone with Richmond fauna (Upper Ordovician) overlie dark limestone, siliceous shale, and quartzite; the age of this lower sequence is unknown, but could be Early Ordovician (R. E. King, 1939). *Poole and Madrid (1986)* consider these rocks, together with others, including the Permian, to be allochthonous continental rise or marginal ocean basin deposits.

Toward the south-southeast, extending to the vicinity of Mazatlán (Fig. 4:8; L-11), the oldest rocks are Carboniferous shale, chert, and quartzite, with occasional thin limestone horizons. This sequence is exposed in the El Fuerte region as well as north of Mazatlán, has a minimum thickness of about 800 m, and shows the effects of varying degrees of contact metamorphism (*Carrillo-Martínez, 1971; Mullan, 1978*).

Upper Triassic continental and locally coal-bearing clastic deposits, which are about 1,400 m thick, are practically confined to the Sonoran portion of this province, with principal outcrop areas east of the longitude of Hermosillo (Fig. 4:3; E-6; R. E. King, 1939; *Alencaster, 1961*). Toward the west, in the Sierra del Alamo (or the El Antimonio area) west-southwest of Caborca, Upper Triassic rocks rest on Middle Permian rocks without perceptible angular relations. These rocks form a 1,300-m-thick sequence and are coastal plain deposits, transitional laterally into marine accumulations and vertically into marine Lower Jurassic (*White and Guiza, 1950; González-Léon, 1979*).

The Lower Jurassic strata in the Sierra del Alamo are Hettangian and Sinemurian, with a thickness of about 2,000 m. The sequence is formed by marine clastics, and its top is beveled by an erosion surface. In the Sierra de Santa Rosa (Fig. 4: 3; D-6), southeast of Caborca, Lower Jurassic rocks are 1,600 m thick (*Hardy, 1981*). The lower 900 m of these strata are quite similar to those that crop out in the Sierra del Alamo, while the remaining upper 700 m are chiefly volcaniclastic rocks.

The unit that overlies this Lower Jurassic sequence is a subaerial 860-m-thick volcanic and volcaniclastic unit whose base is formed by a 70-m-thick conglomerate. The overlying unit can be either Jurassic or Cretaceous. The rocks of the Sierra de Santa Rosa have been mapped as an allochthonous sequence on top of a Precambrian crystalline basement, and the sequence in itself contains several thrusts indicating tectonic transport toward the east.

No information is available as yet regarding the presence and distribution of Middle Jurassic rocks in this morphotectonic province except north of latitude 29°N in Sonora. Northern Sonora is crossed by a NW-SE–trending belt of Middle Jurassic shearing, brecciation, folding, thrusting and associated voluminous quartz porphyry, attributed to the site of the Mojave-Sonora Megashear (*Anderson and Silver, 1979*).

So far, Upper Jurassic rocks in this province have only been identified in Sonora, in the Santa Ana–Magdalena area (longitude 110°W and latitude 30°35′N). From here, *Rangin (1977)* reported a 600-m-thick sequence of marine limestones, andesitic flows, volcanic fragmentals, and black and red shales with late Oxfordian ammonites.

Rocks that are known with reasonable assurance to be Cretaceous are found in this province east of longitude 110°W, and their scattered outcrops extend from the international boundary to latitude 25°N in Sinaloa. In general, most of these Cretaceous rocks are of late Aptian–Albian age, although Upper Cretaceous rocks do crop out in the Cabullona area (Fig. 4: 3; C-8; *Taliaferro, 1933*) near the northeast corner of Sonora.

The Lower Cretaceous sequence generally consists of a conglomerate unit at its base, followed by interbedded sandstone, siltstone, and mudstone, which in turn, are overlain by limestone that has local rudistid reef developments. The exposed stratigraphic sections are practically nowhere complete. Near the Arizona–Sonora border, roughly between longitudes 109° and 111°W, projected information from southern Arizona suggests thicknesses ranging from 1,800 to 2,500 m for the Lower Cretaceous rocks (Hayes, 1970a). There is a definite westward change in facies; the rocks are calcareous and fossiliferous in the east, while toward the west clastic sediments thicken and become volcanic with abundant flows and volcaniclastics. In central Sonora as well as in western Sonora, the Lower Cretaceous is chiefly volcanic with occasional limestone horizons. These relations are documented by R. E. King (1939), and more recently by *Gastil and Krummenacher (1974)* in Sonora, and by Hayes (1970b) in southern Arizona and New Mexico. In southern Sonora and northern Sinaloa the Lower Cretaceous rocks are also volcanics, chiefly andesitic, and contain occasional limestone horizons that, at places, carry Albian and/or Cenomanian(?) rudists or oysters (*Bonneau, 1969*): these rocks show the effects of varying degrees of metamorphism.

The Lower Cretaceous sequence is affected by folding and thrusting with tectonic transport toward the northwest in the eastern parts of this province (*Roldán-Quintana and González-León, 1979*). These structures apparently originated prior to the deposition of the Upper Cretaceous Campanian molasse sediments of the Cabullona area. Folding and thrusting with westward tectonic transport was documented earlier from east-central Sonora by R. E. King (1939), but the age limits of the lower Baucarit Formation at that time were not adequately established.

Numerous granitic plutons are emplaced throughout this province, ranging in age from Late Cretaceous to Tertiary. There is a tendency for these granitic plutons to become younger from the west to the east, a relation that was observed by *Lindgren (1933)* and de Cserna (1970b) for the Cordilleran region, and confirmed in Sonora by *Anderson and Silver (1974)* and southern Sinaloa by Henry (1975 *in* McDowell and Clabaugh, 1979). In the context of this magmatic activity, two metamorphic core complexes have been identified to date in the northern part of this province, one in the Santa Ana–Magdalena region (*G. A. Salas, 1968; Anderson and others, 1980*), and the other at Mazatán, located about 70 km east of Hermosillo, on the eastern border region of this province (*Davis and others, 1981*).

After the accumulation of Upper Cretaceous molasse sediments and associated volcanics (*Taliaferro, 1933*), another period of deformation is recorded in the eastern parts of this province consisting of folding and thrusting, this time toward the southeast, which concluded before the outpouring of andesitic continental volcanics during the early Tertiary (*Roldán-Quintana and González-León, 1979*). This andesitic volcanism was interrupted by a period of erosion and then resumed during the middle Tertiary with a rhyolitic character, as evidenced by the extensive ignimbrite sheets whose remnants are present in many places in this province.

Deep fracturing of the northern part of this province during the later Miocene and Pliocene reflects the Basin and Range tectonics of southwestern North America. In Sonora, this resulted in NNW–oriented block mountains and adjacent valleys, controlled by high-angle faults. The deep fracturing facilitated the ascent of basaltic magma, and the accumulation of clastic material eroded from the elevated mountain blocks in the subsiding fault blocks. The Quaternary volcanic features, located in the western parts of this province, are undoubtedly related to faulting that originated from the tectonic framework of the opening of the Gulf of California. The Pinacates volcanic field, for example, located east of Sonoyta on the Arizona–Sonora border in the northwest corner of Sonora, is formed by basaltic flows and includes about 10 craters, which are diatremes subsequently affected by collapse (*Jahns, 1959*).

Sierra Madre Occidental. The limits of this morphotectonic province are drawn somewhat arbitrarily. The northern limit is practically at the international boundary between longitudes 108° and 110°W, although it is quite possible that the

Tertiary volcanic rocks of southwestern Arizona and adjacent New Mexico once were parts of a continuous volcanic cover that now extends south of the international boundary. The western and southwestern boundaries of this province are coextensive with the eastern and northeastern limits of the Sonoran Basin and Range province. In the south, an arbitrary boundary is drawn at the Lerma–Río Grande de Santiago River and the lavas and pyroclastics of the Plio-Quaternary Trans-Mexico neovolcanic belt. Although there are large erosional remnants of Tertiary volcanic rocks in the region south of the Trans-Mexico neovolcanic belt, the overall geologic configuration of this southern region, the Sierra Madre del Sur, is quite different from the Sierra Madre Occidental to the north. Because the late Tertiary–Quaternary morphologic development of the Sierra Madre del Sur is the result of the tectonic and magmatic frameworks related to subduction processes along the Middle America Trench, these remnants of Tertiary volcanic rocks are included here in this southern morphotectonic province, rather than extending the Sierra Madre Occidental southward beyond latitude 20°N. The eastern and northeastern margins of the Sierra Madre Occidental are certainly transitional features; these are drawn where the Tertiary volcanics give way to limestone fold mountains, modified by Basin and Range tectonics-created, continental, clastic-filled valleys and basins that form the western part of the Sierra Madre Oriental morphotectonic province. Although this east-northeastern boundary could be represented by a NNW–oriented line, there are two eastward-extending dissected prongs of the Sierra Madre Occidental; one in Chihuahua that reaches the vicinity of the Big Bend country of the Río Grande, and another in San Luis Potosí and Guanajuato, extending practically to the western limits of the closely folded frontal portion of the Sierra Madre Oriental (*Labarthe-Hernández and others, 1982*).

The geology of the Sierra Madre Occidental, as a whole, is very poorly known, due in good part to the lack of easy access. There is one railway line that crosses the province [Chihuahua City (Fig. 4: 4; E-11) to Topolombampo (Fig. 4: 8; I-8)], and one paved highway (Durango City to Mazatlán). The published geological information until about the late 1960s came from early explorations and local geological studies (*Weed, 1902; Hovey, 1907;* R. E. King, 1939; *Córdoba, 1963*). Our present understanding of the geology between Durango City (Fig. 4: 9; K-13) and Mazatlán results from systematic work started in about 1968 by faculty members and students of the University of Texas at Austin; this can be extrapolated to a large part of the province (*McDowell and Keizer, 1977;* McDowell and Clabaugh, 1979). Along the railway line between Chihuahua City and Topolobampo, a geologic section prepared in connection with studies of the mineral deposits of that region was published by *Clark (1976).*

The Sierra Madre Occidental is a linear volcanic plateau elongated in a NNW direction. It is about 1,200 km long, and its width varies between 200 and 300 km; its average altitude is close to 2,000 m above sea level, although occasional summits reach 3,000 m, and west of Guanaceví it reaches to 3,348 m (latitude 26°N and longitude 106°30′W). It is a very broad anticlinal uplift with gently dipping eastern flanks and more steeply dipping western flanks. The entire structure is cut by numerous longitudinal faults. In the east, where the adjacent faulted fold mountains and intervening valleys and basins are at general elevations between 1,500 and 2,000 m, the down-drops are minor. In the west, the down-drop is impressive, not only because of larger vertical displacements along the faults, but also because of the lower elevation of the adjacent Sinaloa portion of the Sonoran Basin and Range province, which is only about 250 m and reaches sea level over a distance of 70 km or less.

Most drainage of this province is toward the west into the Gulf of California; exceptions are two major rivers on which dams have been constructed. One of them is the Río Conchos in Chihuahua, a tributary of the Río Grande, and the other is the Río Nazas in Durango, which empties its waters into the Laguna de Mayrán, an interior drainage basin near Torreón (Fig. 4:5; I-15). The west-draining streams have excavated spectacular barrancas with relief and beauty comparable to those of the Grand Canyon of the Colorado River.

In this province, *McDowell and Keizer (1977)* distinguished a "lower volcanic complex," formed by batholithic intrusives and associated extrusive rocks whose ages range from about 100 to 45 Ma, and an "upper volcanic supergroup," formed mostly by ignimbrites, caldera complexes, and small amounts of mafic lavas with ages confined to the interval between 34 and 27 Ma.

The extrusive rocks of the lower volcanic complex rest unconformably on a deeply eroded terrain of Precambrian, Paleozoic, and Mesozoic metamorphic and plutonic rocks, and remnants of some sedimentary rock. The dominant rock is andesite, although there are some interlayered rhyolitic ignimbrites. Water-laid pyroclastic material, as well as agglomerates and tuffs, are found at many places in this sequence, which is about 1,000 to 1,400 m thick (McDowell and Clabaugh, 1979). The plutonic rocks generally intrude the lower volcanic complex. A characteristic feature of these rocks is their intense alteration and the presence of mineral deposits, in contrast with the overlying upper volcanic supergroup.

A nearly 10 m.y. gap in the volcanic activity in this region allowed the terrain formed by the lower volcanic complex to be faulted, tilted, and deeply dissected, before the products of renewed volcanic activity covered the region. The upper volcanic supergroup unconformably covers the lower volcanic complex and comprises mostly rhyolitic and rhyodacitic ignimbrites, forming perhaps the largest continuous ignimbrite expanse in the world. Some mafic lava flows are found near the top of the ignimbrite sequence, which is about 600 to 800 m thick. Numerous rhyolite domes and calderas have been identified in this sequence. The Chupaderos Caldera at Durango City houses what was at one time Mexico's most important commercial iron ore deposit (*Swanson and others, 1978*).

Of the two eastward-extending prongs of the Sierra Madre Occidental, only one—in Chihuahua—has been studied in detail. Although in both prongs the sequence rests on folded Cretaceous limestone and flysch, and the rocks are felsic ignimbrites with some intermediate lava flows, information as to the chemistry of the rocks is only available for the Chihuahua prong. This information indicates that, while the rocks in the Sierra Madre Occidental are calc-alkalic, and in the Trans-Pecos Texas region alkalic (*Barker, 1977*), in the Chihuahua prong they are intermediate in chemistry between these two regions (Campbell, 1977 *in* McDowell and Clabaugh, 1979). *Barker (1977)* attributed the alkalic rocks of Trans-Pecos Texas to mantle diapirism and associated crustal rifting, and concluded that if this process was related to plate convergence, then the increase in alkalinity inland could be the consequence of subduction. In this context, Figure 8 illustrates the magma distribution and its chemistry in time and distance from the subduction front in the Pacific, in relation to the geo-dynamic processes.

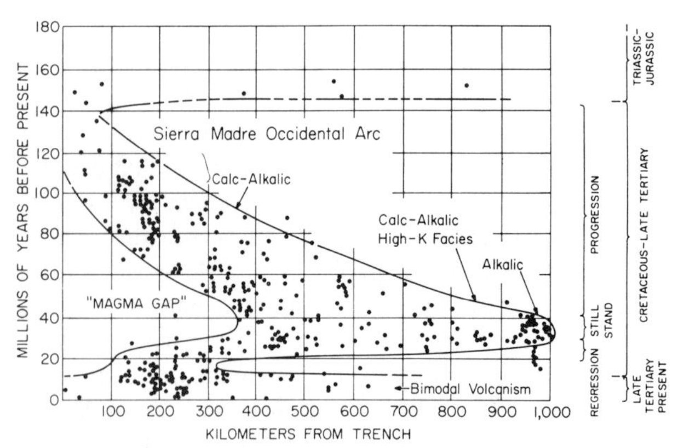

Figure 8. Magma distribution and its chemistry in time and distance from the subduction front in the Pacific, in relation to geodynamic processes. From *Clark and others (1982).*

Although the volcanic activity that produced the bulk of the upper volcanic supergroup ceased about 27 Ma, locally there is evidence for eruptive activity as recently as 23 Ma, which corresponds roughly to the Oligocene-Miocene boundary. These time relations have implications regarding the timing of the uplift of the Sierra Madre Occidental and the Sierra Madre Oriental to the east, and their subsequent geomorphologic development. It appears now as if the process of uplift resulted from the combination of Basin and Range tectonics and opening of the Gulf of California. This hypothesis would imply that after the cessation of the volcanic activity a period of peneplanation took place, and uplift began probably only toward the end of the Miocene with the onset of block faulting.

Sierra Madre Oriental. This morphotectonic province extends south from the international boundary between longitudes 101° and 108°W, to approximately latitude 20°N. Its western limits are transitional to the main Sierra Madre Occidental; in the east it extends to the western margin of the low-lying Mexican portion of the Gulf Coastal Plain. Basically, this region is formed by a complexly folded and thrusted sequence of Mesozoic carbonates and some interbedded shale, overlain by flysch, into which locally post-tectonic granitoid stocks are emplaced. Although details of deformational style in this province vary as a function of the anisotropy created by facies and thickness variations of the deformed sequence, its overall character is very similar. A notable feature, however, is the gradual increase from east to west of the width of the valleys, and even basins, between the anticlinal mountains, reflecting the effects of superimposed late Tertiary block faulting and related alluviation.

This province is elongated in a north-northwesterly direction. It has an average length of about 1,500 km, and its width varies from 200 km in Chihuahua to between 400 and 500 km farther south. The average elevation is about 1,500 to 1,600 m above sea level, although at Torreón it is only about 850 m. In the eastern frontal portion of this province, the mountains reach close to 3,000 m; Cerro del Potosí (Fig. 4: 6; J-18), south of Monterrey, is 3,713 m high. A considerable part of this province in the north is drained by the Río Grande through its tributary the Río Conchos, while the frontal eastern belt is drained by several streams that empty their waters into the Gulf of Mexico. Through headward erosion, these streams have gradually reached the transitional boundary between this frontal belt with the western highlands. Local relief in the frontal eastern belt varies from 1,000 to 2,000 m, on the average, while in the highlands it is between 350 and 750 m.

The dominating structures of this province are folds that in many places are modified by thrusts and later normal faults. These structures are formed principally in Lower Cretaceous carbonate and Upper Cretaceous flysch, although Upper Jurassic sandstones, shales, and some carbonates of the lower parts of the deformed sequence are occasionally exposed. These relations indicate that the deformation affected primarily the upper interval of the supracrustal sequence. However, the exposure of pre–Upper Jurassic rocks at about 20 localities in the province implies local involvement of this basement in the deformation. In these exposures, Precambrian metamorphic rocks crop out only at three, lower Paleozoic at two, upper Paleozoic at about ten, and lower Mesozoic at about five or six. Under these circumstances, piecing together the pre–Upper Jurassic stratigraphy and geologic evolution of the region necessarily is a highly speculative task. Although several endeavors of this sort have been published in the past, the resulting models mostly contributed in an important way to stimulation of geological research.

The Precambrian rocks in northeastern Chihuahua (Fig. 4: 4; E-13; *Mauger and others, 1983; Quintero-Legorreta and Guerrero-García, 1985; Dyer, 1986*), west of Ciudad Victoria in southwestern Tamaulipas (Fig. 4: 7; K-18; *Fries and others, 1962; Ortega-Gutiérrez, 1978a*), and in the core of the Huayacocotla anticlinorium in northeastern Hidalgo (Fig. 4: 18; M-20; *von Kuegelgen, 1958; Fries and Rincón-Orta, 1965*) consist of schists, amphibolites, gabbroid-anorthositic orthogneisses, quartz-ofeldspathic paragneisses, and marbles with abundant garnet. Their radiometric ages, obtained by different methods, indicate an average 1 Ga age, which corresponds to the Grenvillian and consequently makes them part of a younger orogenic belt than the Precambrian crystalline rocks of northwestern Mexico.

Pre-Carboniferous Paleozoic strata in this province have been identified in surface outcrops at Placer de Guadalupe–Sierra de Carrizalillo (Fig. 4: 4; F-13) in northeastern Chihuahua (*Bridges, 1964; Dyer, 1986*), and in the core of the Huizachal-Peregrina anticlinorium west of Ciudad Victoria (Fig. 4: 7; K-18) in southwestern Tamaulipas (Carrillo-Bravo, 1961). At Placer de Guadalupe, where the base is not exposed, these rocks are shaly limestones and dolomites with a thickness of 550 m, representing Ordovician to Devonian sedimentation over a shallow carbonate shelf. In the adjacent Sierra de Carrizalillo, the Precambrian crystalline rocks are overlain by a 200-m-thick unit of Cambro-Ordovician quartzites and glauconitic sandstones, which are followed by 450 m of limestone and silty and cherty limestone. This 450-m sequence might be equivalent to the Ordovician to Devonian section of the Placer de Guadalupe area. West of Ciudad Victoria, the lower Paleozoic sequence is 218 m thick and represents the Ordovician(?) to Devonian interval. It consists of conglomerate, limestone, and shale, with numerous faults within the sequence; the base is not exposed clearly, since the Silurian portion is stated to be resting on "gneissoid rock" (Carrillo-Bravo, 1961, p. 11). Recently, this sequence was interpreted to be formed by gravity-flow deposits (Stewart, 1988).

Upper Paleozoic strata (Carboniferous–Permian) in the Sierra de Palomas, in the northwestern corner of Sierra Madre Oriental, consist of about 2,400 m of Mississippian, Pennsylvanian, and Permian (basal Leonardian) limestones and dolomites, accumulated on the northeastern flank of the Pedregosa Basin (*Díaz-González and Navarro-Galindo, 1964*). At Placer de Guadalupe, the Mississippian–lowermost Permian section is 415 m thick and formed by silty limestone in the lower part, and by clean limestone in the remainder of this interval. The overlying 1,100 m of Permian strata consist of siltstone and conglomerate, and contain a rhyolite flow and a reef (*Bridges, 1964*). In the Sierra del Cuervo (Fig. 4: 4; E-11), just northwest of Chihuahua City, 1,000 m or more of a highly deformed flysch (or flysch-like) sequence, including some lenses of limestone with upper Wolfcampian fusulinids (*Flawn and Díaz-González, 1959*), is exposed. Farther south in the Las Delicias area of Coahuila (Fig. 4: 5; I-16), north-northeast of Torreón, outcropping upper Paleozoic rocks with an aggregate thickness of about 3,700 m represent the Pennsylvanian(?) and the entire Permian; this sequence is folded and thrusted with vergence toward the west and consists of interbedded sandstone, graywacke, shale, limestone, and lava flows of basic and intermediate composition (R. E. King, 1944). West of Ciudad Victoria in southwestern Tamaulipas, the Mississippian (Keokuk) through Permian (Wolfcampian) section is about 1,500 m thick, and between the Mississippian and Pennsylvanian there is an angular unconformity. These Mississippian through Permian rocks consist of sandstone, dark gray shale, sandy limestone, and flysch (Carrillo-Bravo, 1961). The southern outcrop area of dated upper Paleozoic rocks in this province is in the core of the Huayacocotla anticlinorium(Fig. 4: 18; M-20) where a nearly 1,000-m-thick turbidite sequence, whose lower part is marine Lower Permian, rests on Precambrian gneiss (*Martínez-Pérez, 1962*). Elsewhere in this province, as in the Caopas area of northern Zacatecas (Fig. 4:10; K-16), at Zacatecas City (Fig. 4: 10; L-15), or in the Sierra de Catorce (Fig. 4: 11; K-17) in northern San Luis Potosí, the late Paleozoic age of the rocks has not been conclusively established.

Upper Triassic continental red beds and volcanics, ranging in exposed thickness from 450 to 2,000 m and dated reasonably well, are in the area just west of Torreón (*Pantoja-Alor, 1972*), in the Sierra de Catorce (*Mixon, 1963*), in the area of Galeana (Fig. 4: 6; J-18) Nuevo León (*Michalzik, 1988*), west of Ciudad Victoria (Carrillo-Bravo, 1961), and in the core of the Huayacocotla anticlinorium (Carrillo-Bravo, 1965). These continental deposits at Charcas, just southwest of the Sierra de Catorce, intertongue westward with about 250 m of fossiliferous marine Upper Triassic graywackes, which in turn are interbedded with spilitic pillow lavas at Zacatecas City (*Burckhardt and Scalia, 1906; Martínez-Pérez, 1972*). North of Zacatecas City, in the outskirts of Fresnillo, folded basaltic pillow lavas, considered to be identical to those at Zacatecas City, are unconformably overlain by fossiliferous basal Cretaceous shales and graywackes (*de Cserna, 1976b*), while in the Caopas area to the northeast, a schist that is a rhyolite metaignimbrite has ages between 220 and 156 Ma, with the corresponding analytical uncertainties (*Fries and Rincón-Orta, 1965*), These metavolcanic rocks may have formed in the west and been transported tectonically to their present area (de Cserna, 1970b), or else they developed in the Caopas region, as did also schists in the Sierra de Catorce (*Mixon, 1963*). In the Sierra de Guanajuato (Fig. 4: 16; M-17), which is southeast of Zacatecas, basaltic pillow lavas, graywackes, and some limestones, all deformed by folding and thrusting, are overlain unconformably by Lower Cretaceous (Aptian-Albian) limestones (Quintero-Legorreta, personal communication, 1988). For more than 100 years, these rocks have been correlated with the sedimentary and volcanic rocks of Zacatecas (*Burkart, 1836*), which are Upper Triassic. The southernmost outcrop area of Upper Triassic rocks in this province is in the Huayacoctla anticlinorium, where about 2,000 m of continental clastics are unconformably overlain by 1,000 m of Sinemurian–Pliensbachian(?) marine dark shales, sandstone, and some coal (Burckhardt, 1930; Carrillo-Bravo, 1965); the fauna of this sequence is considered to be characteristic of the Pacific Coast region of North America (Imlay, 1980).

Early Mesozoic rocks in the Sierra Madre Oriental that are exposed south of latitude 26°N are continental clastics in the east, whereas toward the west these are replaced by marine sediments and volcanics. This situation is not apparent in the northern part of this province and not in the neighboring parts of the United States. Near Reno, Nevada, marine sediments and volcanics of early Mesozoic age, similar but not entirely identical to those of this province, were recently splendidly deciphered (*Dilles and Wright, 1988*). Indeed there are similarities between the pre–Upper Jurassic basement of this province, especially in light of recent findings in the Santa María del Oro district (Fig. 4: 9; J-12), located on the western boundary of this province at latitude 26°N (*Aranda-García and others, 1988*) and the Reno,

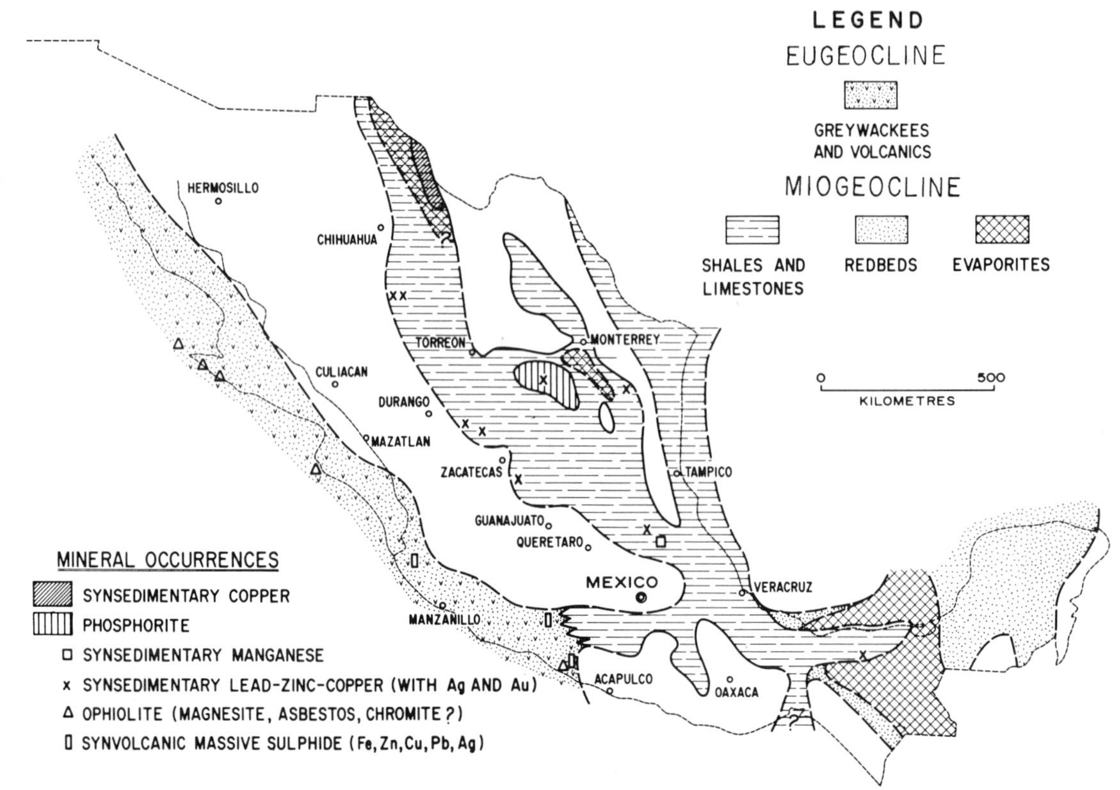

Figure 9. Late Jurassic–Neocomian sedimentary framework of Mexico, showing mineral occurrences considered to be intimately related to the different lithofacies of this age. Modified from *de Cserna (1976a).*

Nevada, region. The Late Triassic and/or Early Jurassic volcanic activity in the western one-half to two-thirds of this province must have been related to Pacific subduction, which implies that the Mexican part of the North America Plate was also moving to the west. Thus, it is not considered here to be very probable to account for the graben development in the eastern part of this province—where the continental clastics are deposited—in terms of a rim-basin (*Michalzik, 1988*), primarily because this theory does not consider the tectono-sedimentary framework of the early Mesozoic in south-central Mexico. I intended to resolve the apparent absence of the Upper Triassic and/or Lower Jurassic rocks in Sierra Madre Oriental north of latitude 26°N with the Torreon-Monterrey Fracture Zone (de Cserna, 1970b); unfortunately, its timing at that time was inadequately known. Now it would be more appropriate to consider the left-lateral movements during the Middle Jurassic, after the deformation of the Upper Triassic–Lower Jurassic sequence, but probably prior to the deposition of the Bajocian-Bathonian continental clastics and intertonguing marine deposits in south-central Mexico as the cause.

Depending on the surface relief of the terrain toward the end of the Middle Jurassic, the marine transgression beginning with the Callovian flooded only the low-lying areas, whereas coastal plain sedimentation took place elsewhere. At places, coastal barriers formed that allowed the accumulation of marine evaporites in the region north and south of Monterrey (Fig. 4:6; J-18); these reach 1,500 m or more in thickness (*Wall and others, 1961*). The transgression became more extensive during the Oxfordian and continued more or less with the same pattern during the first half of the Early Cretaceous (Fig. 9). The Upper Jurassic and pre–upper Aptian (Lower Cretaceous) sequence varies in average thickness from 1,400 to 2,400 m; it is formed principally by limestone and some shale, with sandstone at the base or adjacent to the positive areas. The basin of accumulation of this sequence was referred to as the Mexican geosyncline (Imlay, 1938), and the positive area in the north that extended as a prong from Texas into mostly western Coahuila, as the Coahuila Peninsula (Böse, 1923; Kellum and others, 1936). The eastern margin of this peninsula was formed by the Sabinas Gulf (Humphrey, 1956; Longoria, 1984) of the Mexican geosyncline, and beyond that in the east, another narrow prong extended southward practically to the vicinity of Tampico, known as the Tamaulipas Peninsula (*Imlay, 1943a*). In addition to these major positive paleogeographic elements, there were several islands in southern Nuevo León and San Luis Potosí. Toward the end of the Neocomian, as transgression progressed, the Coahuila Peninsula and the Tamaulipas Peninsula became islands, and the islands in the south became considerably reduced in size. At the same time, a spectacular reef development started that lasted during the Barremian in the region, extending roughly from Parras east to Monterrey and from there on toward the north-northeast.

Carbonate deposition halted toward the end of the Aptian as

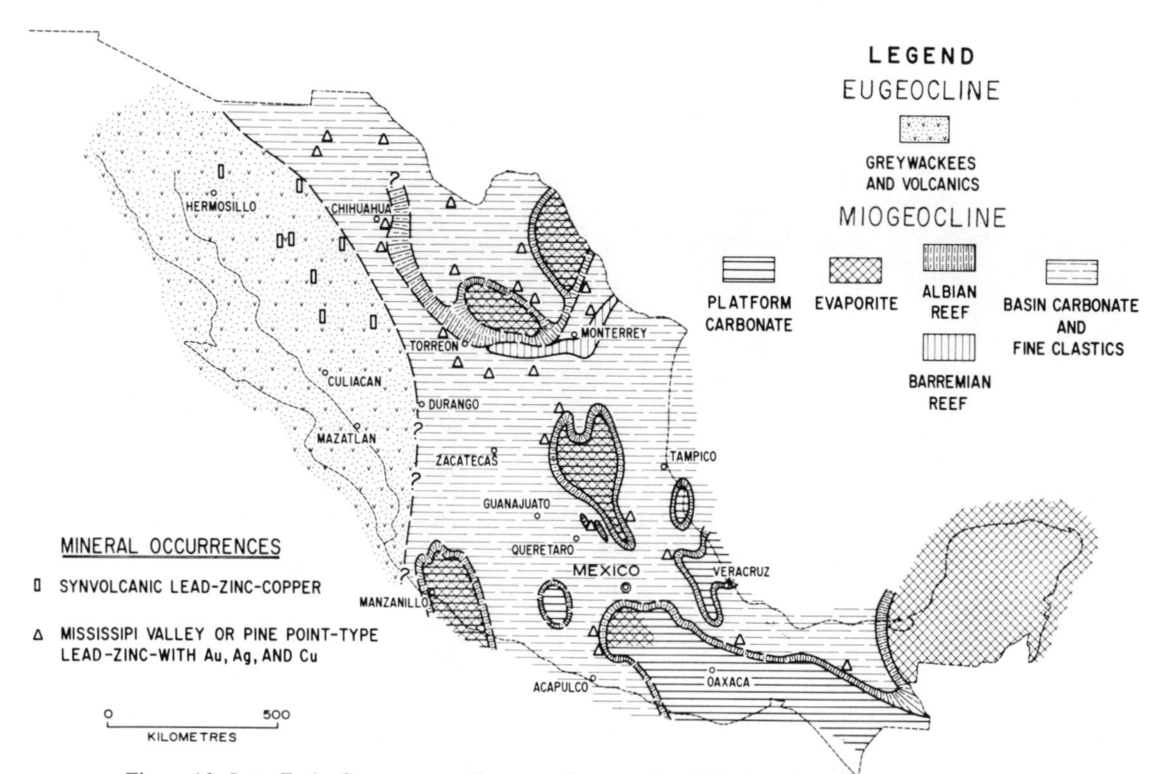

Figure 10. Late Early Cretaceous sedimentary framework of Mexico, showing platform areas, reef trends, and mineral occurrences considered to be intimately related to the different lithofacies of this age. The boundary between eugeoclinal and miogeoclinal deposits in the south is slightly farther east than is shown on this map. Modified from *de Cserna (1976a).*

there was an important influx of terrigenous material into the sea during the latest Aptian (Young, 1983). With further gradual increase in sea level, rudistid reef complexes developed on and over the margins of the positive areas. These areas became converted into platforms or banks, and first evaporites and later limestones were deposited (Smith 1970; *Carrillo-Bravo,* 1971). Away form the reef-encircled platforms, basin-facies limestones accumulated. This pattern of sedimentation lasted until the end of the Albian or at some places until the end of the early Cenomanian (Fig. 10). Tectonic instability of much of this province is reflected by local erosion surfaces and even karst development in many areas; Turonian (Upper Cretaceous) deposits indistinctly cover lower Cenomanian or even middle Albian limestones. The proper recognition of these relations requires careful detailed field work, which unfortunately, covers only a very limited part of Mexico. The aggregate average thickness of the upper Aptian–lower Cenomanian sequence in this province ranges from about 500 m to 1,000 m.

The Upper Cretaceous deposits, in general terms, constitute an upward-coarsening and eastward-overlapping clastic wedge. While this entire sequence was considered to be a flysch deposit (*de Cserna, 1960*), detailed local studies demonstrated that the sequence contains the products of two orogenic pulses, one during the Coniacian and the other during the Maastrichtian, that resulted in two pairs of flysch and molasse, and that the Maastrichtian couple overlapped farther to the east than the Coniacian (*McBride and others, 1974;* Young, 1983, Fig. 15). In the eastern parts of this province, this clastic wedge is as young as Paleocene. The general pattern of the withdrawal of the Late Cretaceous sea is shown in Figure 11.

Folding and thrusting with an active component from the west-southwest affected the entire province. Its exact timing is tenuous, because it is contingent on the age of the youngest rocks involved in the deformation. Earlier dating of this deformation was based on the relations between the youngest deformed marine fossiliferous sediments and the oldest overlying undeformed marine fossiliferous sediments. Because such relations are found only in the eastern marginal areas of Sierra Madre Oriental, the early Eocene age for this deformation (*Böse and Cavins, 1927*) is no longer meaningful for the central and western parts of the province. It is probably a fair assumption, in light of the documented deformation and its timing in the Baja California Peninsula, and the progressively younger emplacement of granitic rocks from west to east during the Late Cretaceous, that deformation within this province was also advancing with time from the west to the east. The Coniacian flysch-molasse couple could reflect the first phase of the orogenic process that must have occurred in the western parts of the province. This resulted in anticlinoria and synclinoria, observed in the basinal facies Lower Cretaceous rocks, that reflect involvement of the basement in the deformation (*de Cserna, 1976b*). About 150 km to the northeast of the west-southwest margin of this province, the folding and

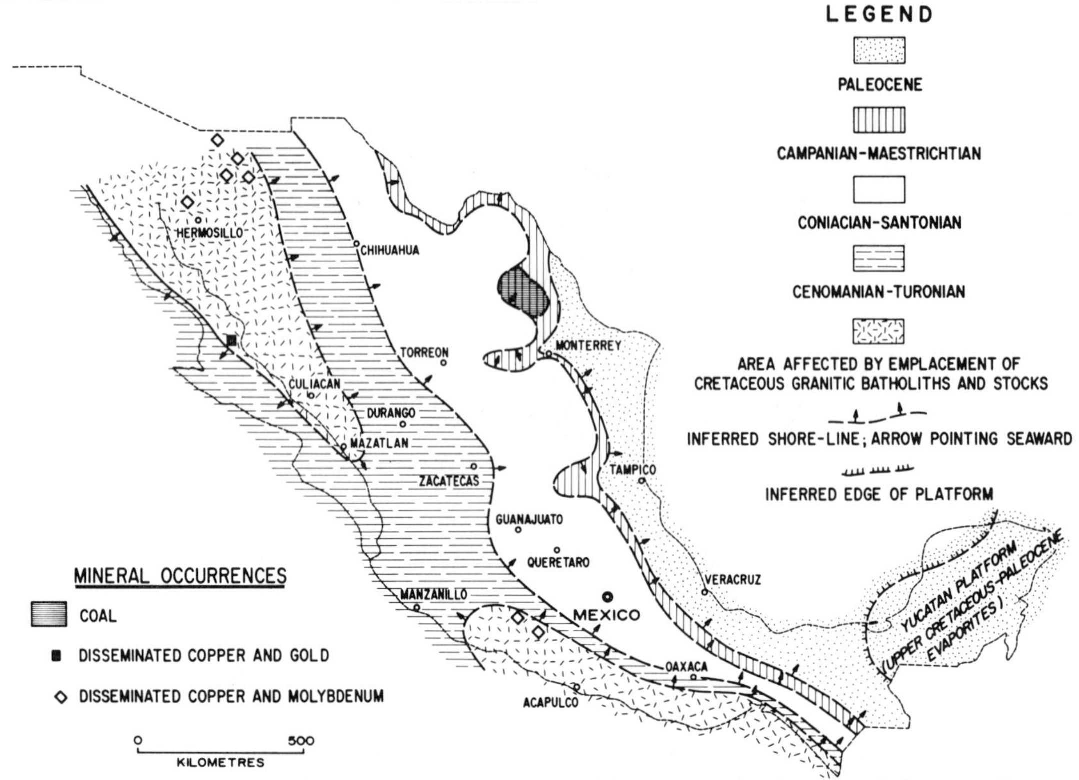

Figure 11. Late Cretaceous–Paleocene paleogeography of Mexico, showing the progressively eastward-shifting shoreline with time. From *de Cserna (1976a).*

thrusting appears to be post-Santonian, and from there toward the east-northeast, these deformations are early Eocene. The thickness of the sedimentary sequence involved in the deformation also increases to the east because of the presence of Upper Jurassic to pre-upper Aptian strata beneath the upper Lower Cretaceous. Thus, the greater thickness and the presence of platform-facies limestones as well as Upper Jurassic and Albian evaporites produced a structural style in the eastern one-half of this province radically different from the west. In this eastern region, reconstruction of the folds necessarily calls for décollement, and the basement appears to be involved in the deformation only in a few areas. While the presence of thrusts was recognized and properly documented long ago in several areas in this province, their integration into a model comparable with those of the southern Canadian Rocky Mountains (Bally and others, 1966; Price, 1981) or the Swiss Jura Mountains (Laubscher, 1986) is just beginning.

Although the attempt to integrate the folds and thrusts into an overall pattern within the Sierra Madre Oriental in the region of Torreón–Monterrey–San Luis Potosí can be credited to *Tardy and others (1975),* several geologists undertook more detailed study of key areas to establish sound bases for modern regional interpretations. In this context, the fine work carried out in the Sierra de Juárez in northern Chihuahua (Fig. 4:4; B-11), just across from El Paso, Texas (Lovejoy, 1980); northwest of Ojinaga (Fig. 4:4; D-13) in northeastern Chihuahua (*Gries and Haenggi, 1970*); in the Saltillo-Monterrey region (Fig. 4:5; I-17 and 6; I-18) (Padilla y Sánchez, 1985; Quintero-Legorreta and Aranda-García, 1985); and in the region of Xilitla-Jacala (Fig. 4:11; LL-19 and 18; M-20) in east-central Mexico (Suter, 1984, 1987) deserves special mention. Figure 12 illustrates the tectonic styles observed and interpreted in some of these regions. Because of lack of adequate mapping, stratigraphic, drilling, and geophysical information, it is difficult to construct balanced cross sections (*Dahlstrom, 1969*) that could allow meaningful interpretations.

The period of folding and thrusting in the entire province was followed by the emplacement of high-level granitic, monzonitic, and granodioritic stocks toward the end of the Eocene. Although these intrusives are widely distributed in the western two-thirds of the Sierra Madre Oriental, only very few have been localized in the eastern frontal belt. The intrusives produced some important skarn mineralization in the limestones and set the stage for hydrothermal activity and mineral deposition. During the late Eocene–Oligocene, continued uplift and peneplanation took place, accompanied by block faulting. In the subsiding (or orphaned) blocks, the clastics eroded from the folded structures accumulated mostly as a result of drainage blocking. Some basic magmatic activity accompanied this block faulting and in some of these subsiding blocks even continental evaporites formed. The products of the Miocene volcanic activity of the Sierra Madre Occidental covered some of the western parts of this province, independently of the two eastward-extending prongs mentioned

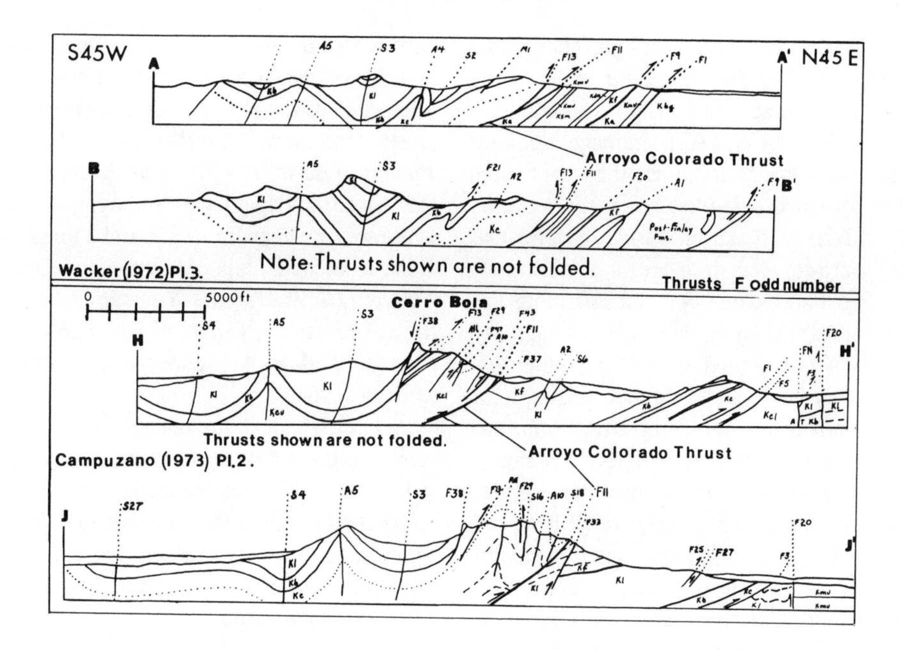

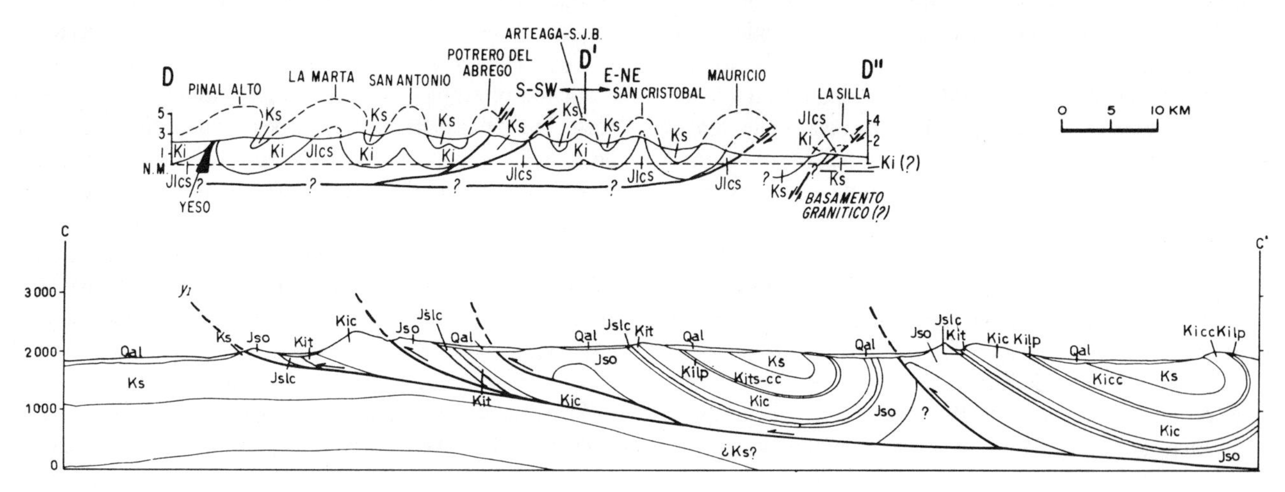

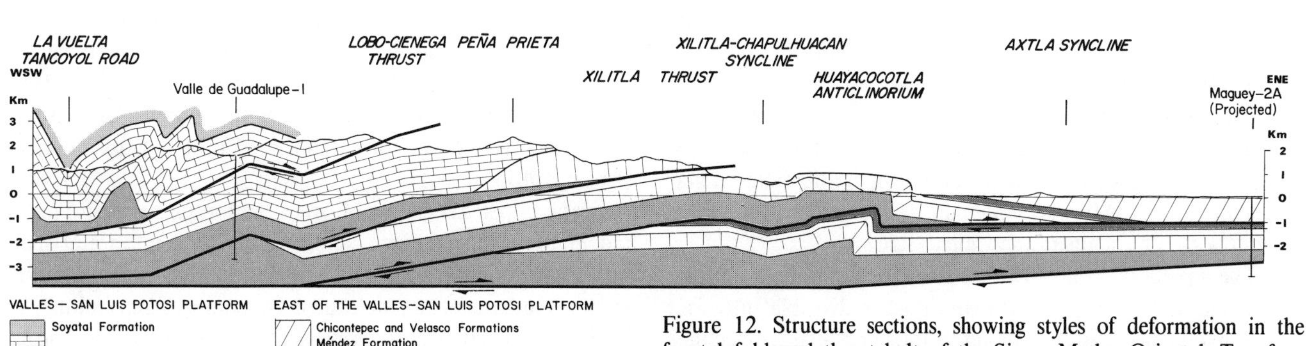

Figure 12. Structure sections, showing styles of deformation in the frontal fold and thrust belt of the Sierra Madre Oriental. Top four sections are across the Sierra de Juárez, just SW of El Paso, Texas (Nodeland, 1980 *in* Lovejoy, 1980). Fifth section from the top has an ENE–WSW orientation and is located south of Monterrey (Padilla y Sánchez, 1985). The sixth section is oriented NNE (left)–SSW (right) and is located south of Saltillo (Quintero-Legorreta and Aranda-García, 1985). The seventh section is in east-central Mexico, and it is a speculative area-balanced section from Tamazunchale southwestward (Suter, 1987).

earlier in this chapter. Widespread block faulting (Basin and Range tectonics) accompanied the Pliocene uplift of the entire province as well as of the Sierra Madre Occidental. This created a "rain shadow" from both the west and east, drainage blocking, and alluviation. This last process was accentuated by the formation of a volcanic dam oriented east-west across the country between latitudes 18° and 20°N. It started during the Pliocene, which interrupted the south-flowing drainage of the southern parts of the province. The Plio-Quaternary block faulting and alluviation was also accompanied by basaltic volcanic activity, producing mostly lava flows of limited extent, and numerous explosion craters. These explosion craters and their related magmatic material contain abundant xenoliths that provide important information on lower-crustal and upper-mantle levels (Aranda-Gómez and Ortega-Gutiérrez, 1987). While some of the eruption centers for the basaltic activity are clearly related to the NNW–oriented Basin and Range faults, it appears as if the explosion craters are along a NE oriented shear or fracture zone.

While the frontal portion of this fold and thrust belt extends beyond the southern limits of this morphotectonic province as far as the Isthmus of Tehuantepec, the southern continuation of its western parts is reflected only by erosional remnants. Its connection to the north-northwest with the Cordilleran foreland fold and thrust belt of Nevada through Arizona has been suggested by Drewes (1978), although such interpretation poses some difficulties. Inasmuch as fold and thrust belts, in one way or another, are related or coextensive with sedimentary basins, and the late Mesozoic Mexican basin barely reached southwestern Arizona, perhaps the continuation of the Sierra Madre Oriental toward the north-northwest should be sought through a complex transcurrent fault system or shear zone.

Gulf Coastal Plain foreland and Yucatán. This morphotectonic province is adjacent to the eastern edge of the Sierra Madre Oriental, barely flanks the eastern termination of the Trans-Mexico neovolcanic belt, is east of the Sierra Madre del Sur, and lies north and northeast of the Sierra de Chiapas (Fig. 5). This region represents the breakdown of the foreland of the Late Cretaceous–early Tertiary east- and northeastward-directed folding and thrusting north of The Tuxtlas volcanic massif, and the burial and build-up of the present coastal plain by the products of erosion of the west, southwest, and south-lying fold and thrust belt. In the north, a considerable amount of clastic material was supplied by the Río Grande, whose upper course also drains parts of the Rocky Mountains of the United States.

The coastal plain between the Río Grande in the north and the Laguna del Carmen in the southeast is divisible into four paleoembayments that correspond to four principal depocenters of major rivers. The Yucatán Peninsula actually is a platform area, similar in many respects to the Florida Peninsula of the United States.

Practically all geological work carried out during the present century in this morphotectonic province in one way or another was related to oil and gas exploration, with the exception of some petrological and volcanological studies. Among the basic reference works the following can be cited: *Böse and Cavins (1927),* and *Kane and Gierhardt (1935)* for the northern region here referred to as the Río Grande Embayment; *Kellum (1937),* Muir (1936), and *Barker and Blow (1976)* for the Pánuco Embayment; *Viniegra-Osorio (1950),* and Mossman and Viniegra-Osorio (1976) for the Papaloapan Embayment; *Calderón-García (1951), Contreras-Velázquez (1958),* and Viniegra-Osorio (1981) for the Coatzacoalcos-Grijalva-Usumacinta Embayment; and *López-Ramos (1979b)* for the Yucatán Peninsula. The regional syntheses include the papers of Guzmán (1952), *Benavides-García (1956),* Santiago-Acevedo and others (1984), and the book of Murray (1961).

The basement for the upper Eocene and younger, chiefly clastic, sequence is formed by deformed Mesozoic–Paleocene sediments, truncated somewhat by an erosion surface. These rocks are practically the same as those that form the Sierra Madre Oriental to the west. The deformation recorded in these rocks in the subsurface is considerably milder than that of the Sierra Madre Oriental, since the folds are mostly open anticlines and synclines, and thrusting was detected only in a narrow belt adjacent to the Sierra Madre front, which during the Paleocene was a foredeep. The oldest rocks penetrated by drilling consist of Paleozoic metamorphics, which, at places, are overlain by Permian flysch. The deformed and semi-eroded Paleozoic rocks in many places are overlain by Triassic red beds or are intruded by Triassic granitic rocks. Marine Lower Jurassic and Middle Jurassic continental clastics complete the pre–Late Jurassic, or pre–Lower Cretaceous stratigraphic record (*López-Ramos, 1972*). However, east of The Tuxtlas volcanic massif, and extending to Laguna del Carmen, the oldest sedimentary rocks penetrated beneath the Coatzacoalcos-Grijalva-Usumacinta Embayment are Middle Jurassic salt and anhydrite (Viniegra-Osorio, 1971). Throughout the region, during the Late Jurassic and Early Cretaceous, there were islands and platforms, just as in the Sierra Madre Oriental morphotectonic province. As a result, neither the deposition of the Upper Jurassic, nor the facies of the Lower Cretaceous are uniform beneath the coastal plain. Among the most significant platform developments and associated reef complexes are the Tuxpan Platform south of Tampico (Bonet, 1952), whose western margin is the site of the famous Golden Lane (*Barnetche and Illing, 1956*) and the Yucatán Bank (Viniegra-Osorio, 1981).

The upper Eocene to Miocene, and at places even Pliocene and Pleistocene, sequence is formed by sandstones and shales, with some conglomerates and limestones. Most of these deposits are undisturbed, or are deformed by compaction, faulting, and folding produced as drag along faults. However, in the northern parts of the Isthmus of Tehuantepec, numerous salt domes are emplaced into the Tertiary sequence, producing doming and associated faulting. It appears that in this region the initial ascent of the salt was controlled by faulting, which helped to penetrate the Cretaceous limestones. East of the isthmus and extending to Laguna del Carmen, the Tertiary sediments are folded, or must be folded and thrusted with a northwesterly trend and cut by a series of northeast-trending faults where the recently important oil- and gas-producing areas of Comalcalco, Reforma, and Macuspana are located. The Tertiary sequence in the Gulf Coastal Plain varies in maximum thickness from about 10,000 m in the Río Grande Embayment, to 2,000 m in the Pánuco Embayment, and 5,000 m in the Papaloapan Embayment. In the Coatzacoalcos-Grijalva-Usumacinta Embayment, the depocenter only developed after the deformation of the lower Miocene and older Tertiary sediments, and as a result, the Plio-Quaternary deposits attain a maximum thickness of only about 500 m.

Although the Yucatán Peninsula is considered to be a stable platform, the available published subsurface information tends to indicate that it was affected by tilting and faulting during its post-Paleozoic history. A deeply eroded Paleozoic orogenic belt, represented in this region by schists and granitic intrusives and overlain by Carboniferous shales and sandstones, was a part of the Gulf Shield, which toward the end of the Triassic was subject to faulting with the development of a graben system. One major graben in which red beds accumulated developed across the northern part of the peninsula with an ENE orientation (*López-Ramos, 1973*). During the Early Cretaceous, in the southern part of the peninsula and extending south into Guatemala, evaporite accumulation took place, while in the northern part, at least in the region of Mérida (Fig. 4:29; LL-30), andesitic volcanic activity took place. Over the remainder of the region, limestone deposition of thicknesses as great as 2,000 m is recorded. The overlying Upper Cretaceous is made up of interbedded limestone, dolomite, and anhydrite with a thickness of approximately 1,200 m, and the overlying Paleocene is beveled by an erosion surface over which Eocene limestone was deposited. The peninsula was slightly uparched through its central part with a gentle north-northeasterly plunge; as a result, the Oligocene, but more completely the Miocene, encircled this uplift. These deposits are marls and limestones with an aggregate thickness of about 2,000 m.

A notable feature of the Gulf Coastal Plain is the presence of 28 to 7 Ma alkalic intrusive rocks in the Sierra de San Carlos (Fig. 4: 7; J-19) and the southern parts of the Sierra de Tamaulipas (*Cantagrel and Robin, 1979*); and numerous basaltic volcanic rocks in the form of flows, volcanic necks, and dikes. The first producing commercial oil well in Mexico was drilled in 1904 next to a volcanic neck, where the contact metamorphic effects that reduced the porosity in the sedimentary rock created a trap for oil accumulation (*DeGoyler, 1932*). Recently, Robin (1982) considered this region, including the The Tuxtlas volcanic massif, to be an alkalic magmatic province, possibly related to the alkalic province of the Trans-Pecos Texas region, or to the Río Grande Rift. Within the context of magmatic rocks in this region, the presence of the largest known positive gravity anomaly in Mexico (70 mgal) in the area of The Tuxtlas volcanic massif deserves special mention. It implies the existence of ultrabasic rocks beneath the surface lava flows (Woollard and Monges-Caldera, 1956).

Commercial oil and gas production (Santiago-Acevedo and others, 1984) in the northern parts of the Río Grande Embayment is from lower and middle Tertiary coastal sands, modified frequently by down-to-basin faults. In the Pánuco Embayment, the traps are basement highs covered by overlapping Upper Jurassic strata, anticlinal structures and reef trends in the Lower Cretaceous, and the Chicontepec paleo-channel, a large "shoestring sand" of early Tertiary age. An overthrust belt-type production area exists in the western parts of the Papaloapan Embayment where Lower Cretaceous–middle Paleocene strata are within thrust slices buried by upper Eocene and younger Tertiary sediments. In the eastern part of the Coatzacoalcos-Grijalva-Usumacinta Embayment, oil and sulfur production is associated with salt domes within Tertiary sediments; in the Villahermosa region it is associated with folded and thrusted Upper Jurassic to Upper Cretaceous carbonates.

Sierra Madre del Sur. This region is a sort of window that allows one to observe the rocks and the geomorphology that might be under Mexico north of latitude 19°N, had the Trans-Mexico neovolcanic belt not formed during Plio-Quaternary time. This province is bounded on the south by the Pacific Ocean between Bahía de Banderas at Puerto Vallarta (Fig. 4: 15; N-12) and the Isthmus of Tehuantepec, on the north by the Trans-Mexico neovolcanic belt, and on the northeast by a stretch of the Gulf Coastal Plain. The morphology of this vast region has been governed by subduction processes along the Middle America Trench since the end of the Miocene (*Watkins and others, 1982*) that resulted in the truncation of the continent along the southern coast of Mexico (de Cserna, 1965), uplift documented by the presence of onshore marine Cenozoic strata (*Durham and others, 1981*), and generation of magma and adequate tectonic conditions to form the natural dam across Mexico, which is the Trans-Mexico neovolcanic belt.

Aside from reduced areas of coastal plain along the Pacific, which appear to be coincident with the traces of major NE-SW–trending faults where they meet the coast and the mouths of major rivers, practically the entire province is maturely dissected. The most prominent topographic feature is the segmented coastal cordillera, generally referred to as the Sierra Madre del Sur, which extends from Bahía de Banderas east-southeastward for a distance of about 900 km. Its morphologic continuity is interrupted at longitude 98°W, as it is displaced 100 km toward the south, and from there it continues to Tehuantepec (Fig. 4: 26; R-24). Most of the highest elevations along this cordillera are between 2,600 and 3,000 m, although its highest peak reaches 4,342 m at 96°W and 16°10′N.

The major river system, the Balsas River, and its principal tributary the Tepalcatepec River, have a general course parallel to the coast and about 100 km inland. The first- and second-order tributaries of these rivers either descend from the north-lying Trans-Mexico neovolcanic belt or from the south-lying Sierra Madre del Sur and integrate the region known as the Balsas Basin, whose central parts have elevations ranging from 300 to 800 m above sea level. Between longitudes 99° and 98°W, there is a gradual transition eastward from the Balsas Basin to the Puebla-Oaxaca uplands, where average summit highs are around

3,000 m. Still farther to the east, this upland region is replaced by the Sierra de Juárez, which is a NNW–trending belt about 70 to 100 km wide that forms the boundary between this province and the adjacent Gulf Coastal Plain. Most of the Puebla-Oaxaca upland is drained to the Pacific, whereas the Sierra de Juárez drains to the Gulf of Mexico.

This complex morphologic region has a very complex geology that, as a whole, is poorly understood. The oldest rocks, the Oaxacan Complex, are exposed in the eastern parts of this province, roughly between longitudes 96°40′ and 97°30′W. They are 1-Ga Precambrian granulites formed by quartzofeldspathic orthogneisses, charnockites, paragneisses, marble, calc-silicates and meta-anorthosites (*Anderson and Silver, 1971; Bloomfield and Ortega-Gutiérrez, 1975*), which developed from a continental rift sequence (*Ortega-Gutiérrez, 1984*). These rocks are very similar petrologically and geochronologically to the Precambrian rocks exposed in the cores of the Huayacocotla and Huizachal-Peregrina anticlinoria of the Sierra Madre Oriental and, at the same time, to the Grenville Precambrian rocks of eastern North America.

Almost 500 m.y. passed before the next geologic event became registered in the eastern parts of the Sierra Madre del Sur. The deeply eroded Precambrian terrain became unconformably covered by 200 m or more of shale and arkosic sandstone whose basal part contains calcarenites. This Tremadocian stratigraphic unit contains trilobites similar to those of Argentina; the closest relatives in North America are found in southern Nova Scotia (Pantoja-Alor and Robison, 1967; *Robison and Pantoja-Alor, 1968; Keppie, 1977*). The Tremadocian rocks are exposed in northwestern Oaxaca State, where they are unconformably overlain by a 600-m-thick sequence of shale, sandstone, and some limestone that represents the Middle Mississippian to Middle Pennsylvanian (*Pantoja-Alor, 1970*). These later Paleozoic rocks form part of the western flank of a roughly N-S–trending anticline, which developed and was considerably eroded prior to the deposition of the overlying Lower Cretaceous sediments.

Adjacent to the Precambrian terrain on the west, and extending roughly between longitudes 97°30′ and 99°00′W, is a region partially covered by Mesozoic and younger deposits, which are underlain by a 15-km-thick package of rocks consisting of slate, schist, migmatite, granite, ultramylonite, gabbro, eclogite, and tectonized ophiolite and referred to as the Acatlán Complex (*Ortega-Gutiérrez, 1978b,* 1981b). In the east, this complex has a west-dipping tectonic contact with the structurally underlying Precambrian rocks. This is considered by Ortega-Gutiérrez (1981b) to be a suture zone. On the west, the contact relations have not been established yet. Detailed petrographic and structural studies show that these metamorphic rocks form a lower parautochthonous plate originally consisting of clastic sediments and volcanics, and an upper autochthonous plate of ophiolite, granitoids, and clastics. The minimum distance of tectonic transport is calculated to be 200 km. Although the vergence of major structures is indicative of a westward direction, the distribution of the eclogitic rocks suggests that the root zone of the thrust sheet was located in the west (Ortega-Gutiérrez, 1981a). Four phases of pre-Carboniferous deformation and at least four metamorphic events are recorded in the Acatlán Complex: one was high pressure and low to moderate temperature during the Middle Ordovician; another was high temperature and medium pressure during the Early Devonian. The geologic events recorded in the rocks of the Acatlán Complex are considered indicative of a Wilson Cycle and certainly show affinities with the Appalachian-Caledonian orogenic belt. On the basis of radiometric ages and a cystoid, the Acatlán Complex represents a time span between the Cambrian and the Devonian.

In the region south of Tehuacán in Puebla (Fig. 4: 19; P-21), the Precambrian rocks, as well as the Acatlán Complex, are overlain unconformably by about 600 m of deltaic and carbonaceous clastics carrying Pennsylvanian plants (*Silva-Pineda, 1970*). About 140 km southwest of this locality, in the Olinalá area of Guerrero, the basement is overlain by 635 m of littoral to near-shore marine clastic rocks, including a limestone interval about 100 m thick. Based on paleontological evidence this sequence ranges in age from Pennsylvanian(?) to Late Permian, and the fauna is similar to the Permian fauna of northwestern Mexico (*Corona-Esquivel, 1981*). In the "three corners area" where the states of Guerrero, Puebla, and Oaxaca join, *Enciso de la Vega (1988)* recently reported an approximately 250-m-thick Permian (Leonardian) section formed by conglomerate, shale, and sandstone with some limestone and gypsum, which overlies unconformably the Acatlán Complex. These relations indicate that during the late Paleozoic, the Precambrian and lower Paleozoic metamorphic terranes of the eastern part of the Sierra Madre del Sur morphotectonic province were gradually overlapped and that the sedimentation was continental in the east and became marine toward the west-southwest.

The pre-Mesozoic basement of this province west of longitude 99°W is mapped only in a few areas, and the interpretations as to its age and geotectonic setting are highly controversial. These rocks are exposed at Taxco (Fig. 4: 25; P-18) and west of it, forming the core of a major uplift, southwest of Chilpancingo, and in the southern foothills of the Sierra Madre del Sur proper, extending to about longitude 101°W.

In the Taxco region, which is about 100 km northwest of the nearest outcrop area of the Acatlán Complex, the basement rocks are chlorite schists, slates, quartzites, and metatuffs, all of which developed from a eugeoclinal assemblage of pelitic and volcanic rocks (*Fries, 1960; de Cserna and Fries, 1981; Elías-Herrera, 1981*) The general trend of foliation is northerly, and three periods of deformation are recorded in these rocks. They are unconformably overlain by about 1,300 m of dark slates with some interbedded quartzites; a highly recrystallized 20-m-thick, sandy limestone interval forms the top of this unit (*Díaz-García, 1980*). The unit has some lithologic similarity with the Pennsylvanian(?) to Permian strata on top of the Acatlán Complex in the Olinalá area.

Southwest of Chilpancingo in the upper part of the Papagayo River valley (at 99°45′ and 17°25′), biotite schists are exposed. These developed from argillaceous and somewhat arkosic sediments, experiencing first almandine-amphibolite facies metamorphism and later retrogression to the epidote-amphibolite facies (*Klesse, 1968*). The general foliation trend in this area is northerly, and the schists are overlain unconformably by 400 m of phyllite and quartzite, containing a stratiform massive sulfide ore body. These rocks developed from a tuffaceous shale and sandstone sequence that also contained two peridotite sills. The age of this upper unit is unknown, but is suspected to be Paleozoic.

The southern outcrop areas of the basement in this general region are along the lower course of the Papagayo River, along the Mexico City–Acapulco highway, and west-northwestward from Acapulco extending to the vicinity of Petatlán. The basement rocks of this region originally were described by the writer (de Cserna, 1965) as biotite schists, biotite gneisses, and some marble, which developed through amphibolite-facies metamorphism from a sequence of shales, sandstones, and some impure limestones.

In these southern outcrop areas the metamorphic basement rocks not only contain a few observed syntectonic, but also many post-tectonic, granitoid intrusives; deformed and undeformed pegmatites; and younger doleritic dikes. *Halpern and others (1974)* concluded that these rocks probably represent the roots of an ancient volcanic arc. In the western border region of these southern outcrop areas of the basement near Petatlán (Fig. 4: 25; R-18), andesitic and basaltic tuffs about 350 m thick, intruded by a gabbro sill and a leucomonzonite dike, all metamorphosed into the greenschist facies, form northwest-trending folds modified by thrusting from the southwest; they yielded Early Pennsylvanian radiometric ages (*de Cserna and others, 1978a*). This deformed sequence also contains a huge peridotite sill and massive sulfide ore bodies. The sequence is similar but, because it contains primarily volcanic material, not identical to the rocks that rest on the biotite schist basement southwest of Chilpancingo (Fig. 4: 25; Q-19).

The age of the basement complex and the overlying pre-Mesozoic rocks, with the exception of the last locality mentioned above and a syntectonic granitoid just north of Acapulco (Fig. 4: 25; R-19) (*Guerrero-García and others, 1978*), is not established in spite of many efforts. It appears that it developed from a Paleozoic and possibly very early Mesozoic eugeoclinal belt trending roughly northwest, which was penetratively deformed on several occasions along various stretches along its length, and intruded. Perhaps the last of such events occurred in Callovian time in the Acapulco region and can be related to the Middle Jurassic magmatic arc recognized by *Anderson and Silver (1978b)* in Sonora (*Guerrero-García and others, 1978*).

The geology of the Sierra Madre del Sur morphotectonic province west of longitude 102°W is largely unknown, except for parts of Colima. Reconnaissance information indicates, however, that in the Arteaga (Fig. 4: 21; P-16) area of southeastern Michoacán, and in the region south-southwest of Puerto Vallarta, coarse-grained feldspathic biotite schist and gneiss of possible pre–Early Cretaceous or pre–Late Jurassic age crop out (*Gastil and others, 1975*). At Cihuatlán (Fig. 4: 15; O-13), near the Pacific Coast at longitude 104°40′W, a granitic intrusive yielded a Late Mississippian apparent age (*Fries, 1962b*). This entire region is intruded by granitoid stocks and batholiths, some of which are decidedly of Late Cretaceous age because they cut Lower Cretaceous fossiliferous rocks; others may be Middle Jurassic or Paleozoic.

A line extending SE from Tehuacán, Puebla, through Oaxaca City (Fig. 4: 26; R-22) and from there to the Isthmus of Tehuantepec, marks roughly the east-northeastern boundary of the Precambrian granulitic basement. The belt between this line and the Gulf Coastal Plain represents the south-southeastward continuation of the frontal fold and thrust belt of the Sierra Madre Oriental. Between latitudes 17° and 18°N, this belt is known as the Sierra de Juárez. Here, the oldest rocks are biotite schists that at places show retrogression into chlorite schist. These rocks form parts of WSW–dipping thrust slices with tectonic transport toward the east-northeast. This writer tentatively correlated these rocks with the metamorphic rocks of the area of Teziutlán, Puebla (Fig. 4: 19, N-21), at the southeastern exposed end of the Huayacocotla anticlinorium, and those, in turn, with the latest Precambrian or early Paleozoic metamorphic rocks of the southern Appalachians (*de Cserna, 1976a*).

The oldest paleontologically dated Mesozoic rocks in this province are found in the border area of Puebla and Oaxaca states southeast of Tehuacán, where a black, impure, Lower Jurassic sequence about 1 km thick overlies the northern prolongation of the latest Precambrian(?) or early Paleozoic(?) schist basement of the Sierra de Juárez (*Echanove-Echanove, 1963*). Toward the southwest, in the region where the states of Puebla, Oaxaca, and Guerrero join, the oldest paleontologically dated rocks are Middle Jurassic (Bajocian); they form the lowest marine tongue of a 400-m-thick continental clastic sequence whose marine connection either to the Pacific or the Tethys is not established satisfactorily on geological or paleontological grounds. These Middle Jurassic rocks unconformably overlie a 200-m-thick sequence formed by continental clastics containing coal, which may be of Early Jurassic or Late Triassic age (Burckhardt, 1930); in turn, these rocks rest on the metamorphic basement of early Paleozoic age (Acatlán Complex). This entire package of lower Mesozoic rocks becomes continental toward the north-northwest and has a transitional contact with the overlying marine Upper Jurassic. Toward the west and southwest, it increases in thickness to about 1,000 to 1,500 m and contains andesitic to rhyolitic volcanics also; west of longitude 99°30′W the sequence becomes marine and the volcanics are chiefly andesitic pillow lavas and related volcaniclastics and graywackes showing incipient or low greenschist-facies metamorphism (*Klesse, 1968; de Cserna and Fries, 1981*). Similar volcanics occur in the Arteaga region of Michoacán (102°20′W and 18°20′N), where these are the host rocks of gold-bearing quartz veins.

The Upper Jurassic–Lower Cretaceous sequence in this province is quite similar to that of the Sierra Madre Oriental morphotectonic province. There are westward facies changes from predominantly carbonate sequences in the east, to volcaniclastic and volcanic sequences in the west. The Upper Jurassic strata unconformably overlie the lower Mesozoic or older rocks, whereas their contact is transitional with the Middle Jurassic.

The Lower Cretaceous deposits, particularly the Albian–Cenomanian, have several platform developments. Their facies change from miogeoclinal to eugeoclinal at about longitude 100°W (*de Cserna and others, 1978b*), and curiously, within the eugeoclinal assemblage a carbonate platform development is recorded in southwestern Michoacán and adjacent Colima (*Vivar, 1926; Palmer, 1928*). Near the mouth of the Balsas River, from a Middle Jurassic(?)–Lower Cretaceous(?), partly marine continental sequence, dinosaur footprints were described recently (*Ferrusquía-Villafranca and others, 1978*).

Although Upper Cretaceous and some older granitic stocks are widely distributed in this province, their presence appears to be more prominent in the coastal cordillera. In southern Michoacán and adjacent regions there are numerous iron deposits associated with the Lower Cretaceous volcanics and volcaniclastics in contact with the Cretaceous intrusives; in fact, Mexico's first steel mill was put into operation in Coalcomán (Fig. 4: 21; P-15), Michoacán, during the first years of the past century (*Bargalló, 1955*).

The Late Cretaceous–early Eocene deformation that affected this province was practically identical to the one observed in the Sierra Madre Oriental morphotectonic province. The major difference, however, is in the fairly good exposure of the basement in the Sierra Madre del Sur, which permits recognition of the numerous basement folds in this region. In addition, while in the northern part of the Sierra de Juárez the deformation during the early Eocene produced an impressive imbricate structure of thrust sheets with eastward transport in the supracrustal rocks (Mossman and Viniegra, 1976; *González-Alvarado, 1976*), in the southern part these structures clearly involved the metamorphic basement also. These relations indicate that in the construction of balanced cross sections across the Sierra Madre Oriental, where mostly supracrustal rocks are exposed, the structure of the basement must also be taken into consideration.

The Late Cretaceous sedimentary framework in this province is also very similar to that of the Sierra Madre Oriental, characterized by a progressively east-shifting shoreline. The Upper Cretaceous deposits form a flysch sequence whose outcrop areas are practically confined to the region east of longitude 100°W.

Early Tertiary deposition consisted of continental clastics that are preserved in fault-controlled basins, while middle Tertiary volcanic activity of andesitic composition, whose geotectonic setting is not understood at present, is practically confined to the north-central part of Oaxaca (*Ferrusquía-Villafranca, 1976*).

Sierra de Chiapas. This morphotectonic province extends east of the Isthmus of Tehuantepec and south of the Coatzacoalcos-Grijalva-Usumacinta Embayment of the Gulf Coastal Plain. In the southwest it extends to the Pacific Coast. The topography of this region has a general northwest-trending grain in its northeastern half, and a northeast-trending grain in its southwestern half. The Pacific Coastal Plain, whose average width is about 20 km, widens at Tehuantepec to about 50 km, and at Tapachula, which is at the international boundary with Guatemala, to about 40 km. This coastal plain is primarily built by the rivers that descend southwestward from the coastal cordillera, the Chiapas Massif, whose average elevation is about 1,500 m. This cordillera forms the divide between the Pacific and Gulf of Mexico drainage of this province. Northeast of this cordillera, the drainage follows a general northwesterly course, controlled by the main structural trend in the Mesozoic and Tertiary deposits. The Mesozoic deposits are adjacent to the coastal cordillera in the northeast and they form the northwest-elongated and fault-controlled Central Depression of Chiapas, as well as the northeast-lying Chiapas Highlands. Elevations within the Central Depression are less than 800 m above sea level, while the Chiapas Highlands are over 2,000 m, and at San Cristóbal de las Casas (92°40′W and 16°40′N), the highest peak reaches 3,004 m. The principal streams that drain this province to the Gulf of Mexico are the Grijalva River, which flows along the Central Depression, and the Usumacinta River, which forms a stretch of the international boundary with Guatemala in the northeast. The Grijalva River with its four hydroelectric plants generates a substantial amount of Mexico's electric power. North and northeast of the Chiapas Highlands is the Sierra de Chiapas proper, formed by a series of elongated mountain ranges and parallel valleys, having a northwest trend that curves northward. The average elevation of this region is about 1,000 m.

The oldest rocks of this province are in the Chiapas Massif, which is a pre-Permian Paleozoic, probably Devonian, batholith, emplaced in upper Precambrian(?) or lower Paleozoic(?) metamorphic rocks that appear to be the southeastern displaced continuation of the metamorphic rocks of the southern parts of the Sierra de Juárez (Viniegra-Osorio, 1971). Thus, the oldest rocks adjacent to the Gulf Coastal Plain just northwest of the isthmus of Tehuantepec also form the oldest rocks adjacent to the narrow Pacific Coastal Plain southeast of the isthmus. Obviously, there is a major truncation of the Sierra Madre del Sur between Puerto Angel (Fig. 4:26, S-22) and Tehuantepec (Fig. 4: 26; R-24), which the writer interprets to be due to a left-lateral transcurrent fault or shear zone across the isthmus, with a northeasterly trend.

The northeast flank of the deeply eroded batholith is overlain on the southeast by 2,700 m of black slates and ferruginous sandstones, which might be either Carboniferous or Lower Permian. These are in fault contact with 1,127 m of Permian (Wolfcampian-Leonardian) shales and limestones. These upper Paleozoic rocks form a northwest-trending anticline and an adjacent syncline (*Thompson and Miller, 1944*; *Gutiérrez-Gil, 1956*).

The oldest Mesozoic rocks in Chiapas are continental red beds that for a long time were believed to be of Late Triassic age. Recent studies show, however, that these deposits underlie or interfinger with fossiliferous Upper Jurassic and basal Cretaceous marine deposits (Blair, 1988). These rocks were deposited over block-faulted portions of the Chiapas Massif. They had periodic marine communication, and reach thicknesses of about 800 m. The deposits are overlain unconformably by 2,400 to 3,400 m of Cretaceous (Barremian(?) to Turonian) platform limestones (*Castro-Mora and others, 1975*; *D. R. Steele, 1985*; *Waite, 1985*), which are unconformably overlain by about 700 m of yellow and red limey sandstones and interbedded limestones of Campanian–Maastrichtian age (*Chubb, 1959*).

The deposition in the beginning of the Tertiary took place without interruption from the Late Cretaceous. The Paleocene to lower Miocene strata in central Chiapas have an aggregate thickness of about 12,000 m, and consist of shale, sandstone, and limestone (*Frost and Langenheim, 1974*). In this sedimentary record there appears to be no break prior to the end of the early Miocene, and therefore, the existence of an early Tertiary compressive deformation in this province is highly questionable to this writer.

The Mesozoic and Tertiary sedimentary rocks of this province are folded and thrusted with a northwesterly trend. The folds are asymmetric toward the southwest, and the low-angle thrusts with southwestward transport are accompanied by tear faults with northeasterly orientation. A notable feature is the crowding of the folds as one approaches the Chiapas Massif from the northeast (*Gutiérrez-Gil, 1956*). From these structural features the writer concludes that active compression during the deformation proceeded from the northeast toward the southwest, and that the Chiapas Massif acted as a foreland. This deformation took place after the early Miocene; Laramide events are evidenced only by sea-level oscillations during the middle and late Cenomanian and the Turonian, as recorded in the Sierra Madre Limestone (*D. R. Steele, 1985*), and by the hiatus during the Coniacian-Santonian (*Chubb, 1959*). The folded and thrusted Mesozoic–lower Miocene sequence was partially eroded and covered locally by undeformed Plio-Pleistocene deposits, which thus bracket the age of this compressive deformation. WNW–trending high-angle faults are considered to be responsible for the development of the Central Depression, although it is claimed that some of these faults have lateral displacements also.

Post-Paleozoic magmatic activity is evidenced by the presence of a few granitic stocks of Late Triassic–Early Jurassic age (Damon, 1975 *in* G. P. Salas, 1975), whose emplacement was probably related to the break-up of the Gulf Shield, and by a few Miocene granitoids in the Chiapas Massif. Quaternary volcanic activity of andesitic composition is recorded by the Tacaná Volcano, just north of Tapachula on the international boundary with Guatemala, and in the area of San Cristóbal de las Casas (Fig. 4:31; R-27; *Böse, 1905*). Tacaná is a composite stratovolcano with an altitude of 4,100 m (Fig. 4:31; S-27), located on the Caribbean Plate about 30 km south of its boundary with the North America Plate, which here is the Polochic fault zone (*Muehlberger and Ritchie, 1975*; *Burkart, 1983*); it presently has fumarolic activity. The volcano El Chichón or Chichonal (Fig. 4:31; Q-26) (*Müllerried, 1932*), whose existence was discovered by geologists only in 1928, had disastrous eruptions in 1982 (Duffield and others, 1984); it is located near the northern margin of this province (93°10′W and 17°20′N).

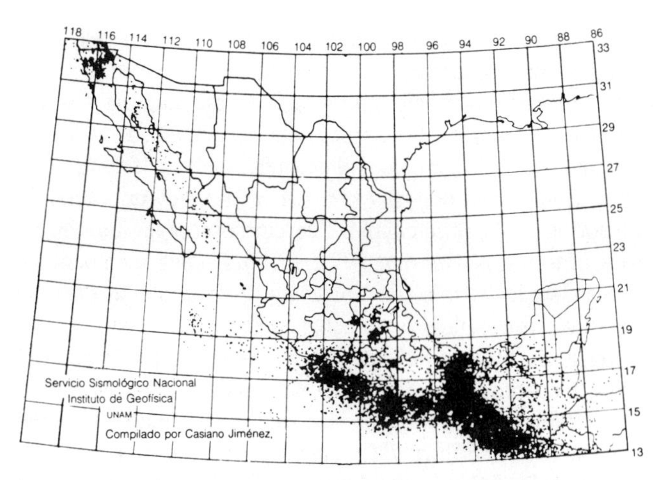

Figure 13. Computer-generated map, showing the locations of epicenters of earthquakes that occurred in Mexico between 1974 and 1983. Data compiled by C. Jiménez, Servicio Sismológico Nacional, Instituto de Geofísica, UNAM.

While the north-lying Gulf Coastal Plain apparently continues without interruption from west to east across the northern part of the Isthmus of Tehuantepec, the geologic relations between the Sierra Madre del Sur and the Sierra de Chiapas morphotectonic provinces are radically different. The inferred presence of a transcurrent fault or shear zone between them is strengthened by the intense earthquake activity in this area, indicating the active nature of the boundary between North and Central America (Fig. 13).

Trans-Mexico neovolcanic belt. This province extends across Mexico from the Pacific Coast at Nayarit, to near the coast of the Gulf of Mexico, roughly between latitudes 19° and 20°N. Actually, this belt follows an east-west orientation between longitudes 97° and 102°30′W, but beyond that to the Pacific Coast the direction is northwesterly. It is about 900 km long and about 100 km wide, although northwestward from Guadalajara (Fig. 4:15; N-15) it narrows to about 60 km. Morphologically, it is a broad, west-sloping volcanic plateau, formed by polygenetic stratovolcanoes, monogenetic volcanoes and cinder cones, caldera complexes, and explosion craters or Maaren, with associated lava flows and pyroclastic deposits. Some half-dozen of the stratovolcanoes form the highest elevations of the country, and four of those have permanent snow; the Volcán Pico de Orizaba (Fig. 4: 14; O-21) is the highest peak in Mexico (5,675 m). The average elevation of this plateau is about 2,300 m in the eastern part, about 1,600 m in the central part, and about 1,000 m in the western part. Earlier descriptions of some of the major volcanoes, calderas, and explosion craters are contained in the guidebooks of the 10th session of the IGC, 1906.

Modern volcanological studies in this province started with the birth of Volcán Paricutín (Fig. 4:21; O-16) in 1943. These are published as *Geologic investigations in the Paricutín area, Mexico*

(U.S. Geological Survey Bulletin 965). Starting in the early 1950s, Mooser pioneered in the mapping of the entire province, using aerial photo-mosaics and whatever base maps he was able to obtain. His regional mapping was accompanied by limited sampling, and petrographic and chemical studies (*Mooser, 1961, 1968*; *Mooser and others, 1958*; *Gunn and Mooser, 1970*); he also addressed the problem of the development of this province in terms of tectonics (*Mooser,* 1972, *1975*). Faculty members and graduate students from the University of California at Berkeley undertook volcanological research in the western parts of this province, including Volcán Colima (Luhr and Carmichael, 1980), Ceboruco (Nelson, 1980), the Guadalajara region (Mahood, 1980; *Gilbert and others, 1985*), the Tepic region (Fig. 4:12; M-13) (*Nelson and Carmichael, 1984*), and the Jorullo (Fig. 4: 21; P-17) (*Luhr and Carmichael, 1985*). The geodynamic framework of this region was addressed by Luhr and coworkers (1985). For the central parts of the province, including the regions of Michoacán and Guanajuato, Hasenaka and Carmichael (1985), and *Connor (1987)* made important contributions; for the Volcán Nevado de Toluca (Fig. 4: 22; O-19) and the monogenetic volcano field of that region, contributions were made by Bloomfield (1975) and Bloomfield and Valastro (1974). In the region surrounding Mexico City, *Negendank (1972), Mooser and others (1974),* and *W. K. Steele (1985)* presented petrological and paleomagnetic information, while Robin (1982, 1984) presented volcanological information for the Popocatepetl, Orizaba, and Nevado de Toluca volcanoes. The overall tectonic and geodynamic scenario of the evolution of the province was treated by Stoiber and Carr (1973), *Demant (1978, 1981b),* Nixon (1982), and more recently, by Nixon and others (1987).

From the presently available information, it appears that the Trans-Mexico neovolcanic belt began to form in its central parts during late Miocene or early Pliocene time with the eruption of calc-alkaline lavas, but by early Quaternary time the volcanic activity had gradually migrated toward the southern parts of the province. The Quaternary volcanic arc that is formed principally by calc-alkaline andesite and dacite, also contains reduced areas of rhyodacites and even rhyolites. The magma generation was intimately related to the subduction processes of the Rivera and Cocos Plates. The presence of potassium-rich lamphrophyres in the Colima region of the western part of this province is attributed to the development of the Colima graben, which bisects the Sierra Madre del Sur, as a result of an incipient eastward-spreading-ridge jump and the early formation of a transform boundary that separates the Cocos and Rivera Plates. The monogenetic volcano fields, which occupy large areas within this province, are formed by basalts (or basaltic andesites, chemically) and are interpreted to have originated from the mantle during subduction without much contamination.

While the subduction process along the Middle America Trench was, and still is, responsible for magma generation at depth, the ascent of magma to the surface is attributed by this writer to tectonic control. Reconnaissance studies indicate the presence of several major northeast-oriented shear zones across southern Mexico (Fig. 7), evidenced by faults and lineaments, as well as by the alignment of Quaternary volcanoes; and some of these are even active, as deduced from the location of epicenters of shallow earthquakes. These shear zones extend to the subduction zone, and since the convergence is oblique in front of central Mexico, the shear zones are interpreted to be left-lateral.

SELECTED REFERENCES*

Aguilera, J. G., ed., 1896, Bosquejo geológico de México: Instituto Geológico de México, Boletinles 4, 5, and 6, 270 p.

Alvarez, M., Jr., 1949, Tectonics of Mexico: American Association of Petroleum Geologists Bulletin, v. 33, p. 1319–1335.

Anonymous, 1981, Atlas nacional del medio fisico: Mexico, D. F., Secretaría de Programación y Presupuesto, 224 p.

——, 1982, Geología de la República Mexicana: México, D. F., Coordinación General de los Servicios Nacionales de Estadística, Geografía e Informática, 82 p.

Aranda-Gómez, J. J., and Ortega-Gutiérrez, F., 1987, Mantle xenoliths in Mexico, *in* Nixon, P. H., ed., Mantle xenoliths: New York, John Wiley and Sons, p. 75–84.

Bally, A. W., 1981, Thoughts on the tectonics of folded belts, *in* McClay, H. R. and Price, N. J., eds., Thrust and nappe tectonics: London, Geological Society of London, p. 13–32.

Bally, A. W., Gordy, P. L., and Stewart, G. A., 1966, Structure, seismic data, and orogenic evolution of southern Canadian Rockies: Bulletin of Canadian Petroleum Geology, v. 14, p. 337–381.

Bally, A. W., Catalano, R., and Oldow, J. S., 1985, Elementi di tettonica regionale: Bologna, Pitagora Editrice, 276 p.

Beal, C. H., 1948, Reconnaissance of the geology and oil possibilities of Baja California, Mexico: Geological Society of America Memoir 31, 138 p.

*A full listing of references, including those shown in italics in the text, is on a microfiche accompanying this volume.

Bishop, W. F., 1980, Petroleum geology of northern Central America: Journal of Petroleum Geology, v. 3, p. 3–59.

Blair, T. C., 1988, Mixed siliciclastic-carbonate marine and continental syn-rift sedimentation, Upper Jurassic–lowermost Cretaceous Todos Santos and San Ricardo Formations, western Chiapas, Mexico: Journal of Sedimentary Petrology, v. 58, p. 623–636.

Bloomfield, K., 1975, A late Quaternary monogenetic volcano field in central Mexico: Geologische Rundschau, v. 66, p. 476–497.

Bloomfield, K., and Valastro, S., 1974, Late Pleistocene eruptive history of Nevado de Toluca, central Mexico: Geological Society of America Bulletin, v. 85, p. 901–906.

Bonet, F., 1952, La facies urgoniana del Cretácico medio de la región de Tampico: Boletín de la Asociación Mexicana de Geólogos Petroleros, v. 4, p. 153–262.

Böse, E., 1923, Vestiges of an ancient continent in northeast Mexico: American Journal of Science, v. 6, p. 127–136, 196–214, and 310–337.

Bryant, W. R., Antoine, J., Ewing, M., and Jones, B., 1968, Structure of Mexican continental shelf and slope, Gulf of Mexico: American Association of Petroleum Geologists Bulletin, v. 52, p. 1204–1228.

Buffler, R. T., Shaub, F. J., Watkins, J. S., and Worzel, J. L., 1979, Anatomy of the Mexican Ridges Foldbelt, southwestern Gulf of Mexico, *in* Watkins, J. S., Montadert, L., and Dickerson, P. W., eds., Geological and geophysical investigations of continental margins: American Association of Petroleum Geologists Memoir 29, p. 319–327.

Burckhardt, C., 1930, Etude synthétique sur le Mésozoïque mexicain: Mémoires de la Société Paléontologique Suisse, v. 49–50, 280 p.

Carrillo-Bravo, J., 1961, Geología del Anticlinorio Huizachal–Peregrina al N-W de Ciudad Victoria, Tamps.: Boletín de la Asociación Mexicana de Geólogos

Petroleros, v. 13, p. 1–98.
—— , 1965, Estudio geológico de una parte del Anticlinorio de Huayacocotla: Boletín de la Asociación Mexicana de Geólogos Petroleros, v. 17, p. 73–96.
Cook, T. D., and Bally, A. W., eds., 1975, Stratigraphic atlas of North and Central America: Princeton, New Jersey, Princeton University Press, 272 p.
Cooper, G. A., 1952, Introduction and stratigraphy, *in* Cambrian stratigraphy and paleontology near Caborca, northwestern Sonora, Mexico: Smithsonian Miscellaneous Collections, v. 119, no. 1, p. 1–26.
de Cserna, Z., 1956, Tectónica de la Sierra Madre Oriental de México, entre Torreón y Monterrey: México, D. F., 20th Congreso Geologico Internacional, Monograph, 87 p.
—— , 1958, Notes on the tectonics of southern Mexico, *in* Weeks, L. G., ed., Habitat of oil: American Association of Petroleum Geologists, p. 523–532.
—— , 1961, compiler, Tectonic map of Mexico: Geological Society of America, scale 1:2,500,000.
—— , 1965, Reconocimiento geológico en la Sierra Madre del Sur de Mexico, entre Chilpancingo y Acapulco, Estado de Guerrero: Instituto de Geología, UNAM, Boletín 62, 76 p.
—— , 1967 (1969), Tectonic framework of southern Mexico and its bearing on the problem of continental drift: Boletín de la Sociedad Geológica Mexicana, v. 30, p. 159–168.
—— , 1970 (1971), Mesozoic sedimentation, magmatic activity, and deformation in northern Mexico, *in* Seewald, K., and Sundeen, D., eds., The geologic framework of the Chihuahua Tectonic Belt: West Texas Geological Society, p. 99–117.
—— , 1981 (1984), Margen continental de colisión activo en la parte suroccidental del Golfo de México: Instituto de Geología, UNAM, Revista v. 5, p. 255–261.
del Castillo, A., 1889a, Bosquejo de una carta geológica de la República Mexicana: México, D. F., Comisión Geológica, scale 1:3,000,000.
Dengo, G., and Bohnenberger, O., 1969, Structural development of northern Central America, *in* McBirney, A. R., ed., Tectonic relations of northern Central America and the western Caribbean—the Bonacca Expedition: American Association of Petroleum Geologists Memoir 11, pt. 2, p. 203–220.
Drewes, H., 1978, The Cordilleran orogenic belt between Nevada and Chihuahua: Geological Society of America Bulletin, v. 89, p. 641–657.
Drummond, K. J., ed., 1981, Plate tectonic map of the Circum-Pacific region, northeast quadrant: American Association of Petroleum Geologists, scale 1:10,000,000.
Duffield, W. A., Tilling, R. I., and Canul, R. F., 1984, Geology of El Chichon Volcano, Chiapas, Mexico: Journal of Volcanology and Geothermal Research, v. 20, p. 117–132.
Erffa, A. von, Hilger, W., Knoblich, K., and Weyl, R., 1977, Geologie des Hochbeckens von Puebla–Tlaxcala und seiner Umgebung: Wiesbaden, Franz Steiner, 133 p., and geologic map, scale 1:200,000.
Fisher, R. L., 1961, Middle America Trench; Topography and structure: Geological Society of America Bulletin, v. 72, p. 703–720.
Garrison, L. E., and Martin, R. G., Jr., 1973, Geological structures in the Gulf of Mexico basin: U.S. Geological Survey Professional Paper 773, 85 p.
Gastil, R. G., Phillips, R. P., and Allison, E. C., compilers, 1971, Reconnaissance geologic map of the State of Baja California: Geological Society of America Map and Chart Series MC-3, scale 1:250,000.
—— , 1975, Reconnaissance geology of the State of Baja California: Geological Society of America Memoir 140, 170 p.
González-Reyna, J., 1956, Riqueza minera y yacimientos minerales de México: México, D. F., Banco de México, S. A., 497 p. (Distributed also as 20th International Geological Congress Monograph.)
Guzman, E. J., 1952, Volumes of Mesozoic and Cenozoic sediments in Mexican Gulf Coastal Plain: Geological Society of America Bulletin, v. 63, p. 1201–1220.
Guzman, E. J., and Cserna, Z. de, 1963, Tectonic history of Mexico, *in* Childs, O. E., and Beebe, B. W., eds., Backbone of the Americas: American Association of Petroleum Geologists Memoir 2, p. 113–129.
Hanuš, V., and Vanek, J., 1978, Subduction of the Cocos Plate and deep active fracture zones of Mexico: Geofisica Internacional (Mexico), v. 17, p. 14–53.
Hasenaka, T., and Carmichael, I.S.E., 1985, The cinder cones of Michoacán–Guanajuato, central Mexico—their age, volume and distribution, and magma discharge rate: Journal of Volcanology and Geothermal Research, v. 25, p. 105–124.
Hayes, P. T., 1970a, Mesozoic stratigraphy of the Mule and Huachuca Mountains, Arizona: U.S. Geological Survey Professional Paper 658–A, p. A1–A28.
—— , 1970b, Cretaceous paleogeography of southeastern Arizona and adjacent areas: U.S. Geological Survey Professional Paper 658–B, p. B1–B42.
Hernández-Sánchez Mejorada, S., ed., 1968, Carta geológica de la República Mexicana: México, D. F., Comité de la Carta Geológica de México, scale 1:2,000,000.
Humphrey, W. E., 1956, Tectonic framework of northeastern Mexico: Gulf Coast Association of Geological Societies Transactions, v. 6, p. 25–35.
Imlay, R. W., 1938, Studies of the Mexican geosyncline: Geological Society of America Bulletin, v. 49, p. 1651–1694.
—— , 1943b, Jurassic formations of Gulf region: American Association of Petroleum Geologists Bulletin, v. 27, p. 1407–1533.
—— , 1944, Cretaceous formations in Central America and Mexico: American Association of Petroleum Geologists Bulletin, v. 28, p. 1077–1195.
—— , 1980, Jurassic paleobiogeography of the conterminous United States in its continental setting: U.S. Geological Survey Professional Paper 1062, 134 p.
Karig, D. E., Cardwell, R. K., Moore, G. F., and Moore, D. G., 1978, Late Cenozoic subduction and continental-margin truncation along the northern Middle America Trench: Geological Society of America Bulletin, v. 89, p. 265–276.
Kellum, L. B., Imlay, R. W., and Kane, W. G., 1936, Evolution of the Coahuila Peninsula, Mexico, Part 1, Relation of structures, stratigraphy, and igneous activity to an early continental margin: Geological Society of America Bulletin, v. 47, p. 969–1008.
King, P. B., 1942, Tectonics of northern Mexico: Washington, D.C., 8th American Scientific Congress, Proceedings, v. 4, p. 395–398.
—— , compiler, 1968, Tectonic map of North America: U.S. Geological Survey, scale 1:5,000,000.
—— , 1969, The tectonics of North America—a discussion to accompany the Tectonic Map of North America, scale 1:5,000,000: U.S. Geological Survey Professional Paper 628, 95 p.
King, R. E., 1939, Geologic reconnaissance in northern Sierra Madre Occidental of Mexico: Geological Society of America Bulletin, v. 50, p. 1624–1722.
—— , 1944, Part 1. Geology, *in* King, R. E., and others, eds., Geology and paleontology of the Permian area northwest of Las Delicias, southwestern Coahuila, Mexico: Geological Society of America Special Paper 52, p. 3–33.
Larson, R. L., 1972, Bathymetry, magnetic anomalies, and plate-tectonic history of the mouth of the Gulf of California: Geological Society of America Bulletin, v. 83, p. 3345–3360.
Laubscher, H. P., 1986, The eastern Jura, relations between thin-skinned and basement tectonics, local and regional: Geologische Rundschau, v. 75, p. 535–553.
Longoria, J. F., 1984, Stratigraphic studies in the Jurassic of northeastern Mexico; evidence of the origin of the Sabinas basin: Society of Economic Paleontologists and Mineralogists, Gulf Coast Section, 3rd Annual Research Conference Proceedings, p. 171–193.
López-Ramos, E., 1969, Marine Paleozoic rocks of Mexico: American Association of Petroleum Geologists Bulletin, v. 53, p. 2399–2417.
—— , 1976, ed., Carta geológica de la República Mexicana: México, D. F., Comité del la Carta Geológica de Mexico, scale 1:2,000,000.
Lovejoy, E.M.P., ed., 1980, Sierra de Juárez, Chihuahua, Mexico, structure and stratigraphy: El Paso, Texas, El Paso Geological Society, 59 p.
Luhr, J. F., and Carmichael, I.S.E., 1980, The Colima Volcanic Complex, Mexico; I., Post-caldera andesites from Volcán Colima: Contributions to Mineralogy and Petrology, v. 71, p. 343–372.
Luhr, J. F., Nelson, S. A., Allan, J. F., and Carmichael, I.S.E., 1985, Active rifting in southwestern Mexico, manifestations of an incipient eastward spreading-

ridge jump: Geology, v. 13, p. 54–57.
Mahood, G. A., 1980, Geological evolution of a Pleistocene rhyolitic center, Sierra La Primavera, Jalisco, Mexico: Journal of Volcanology and Geothermal Research, v. 8, p. 199–230.
Malfait, B. T., and Dinkleman, M. G., 1972, Circum-Caribbean tectonic and igneous activity and the evolution of the Caribbean Plate: Geological Society of America Bulletin, v. 83, p. 251–272.
McDowell, F. W., and Clabaugh, S. E., 1979, Ignimbrites of the Sierra Madre Occidental and their relation to the tectonic history of western Mexico: Geological Society of America Special Paper 180, p. 113–124.
Meneses de Gyves, J., 1980 (1981), Geología de la Sonda de Campache: Boletín de la Asociación Mexicana de Geólogos Petroleros, v. 32, p. 1–26.
Molnar, P., and Sykes, L. R., 1969, Tectonics of the Caribbean and Middle America regions from focal mechanisms and seismicity: Geological Society of America Bulletin, v. 80, p. 1639–1684.
Mooser, F., 1972, The Mexican volcanic belt, structure and tectonics: Geofisica Internacional (Mexico), v. 12, n. 2, p. 55–70.
Mossman, R. W., and Viniegra-Osorio, F., 1976, Complex fault structures in Veracruz province of Mexico: American Association of Petroleum Geologists Bulletin, v. 85, p. 379–388.
Muir, J. M., 1936, Geology of the Tampico region, Mexico: American Association of Petroleum Geologists, 280 p.
Murray, G. E., 1961, Geology of the Atlantic and Gulf coastal province of North America: New York, Harper and Brothers, 692 p.
Nelson, S. A., 1980, Geology and petrology of Volcán Ceboruco, Nayarit, Mexico: Geological Society of America Bulletin, v. 91, p. 2290–2431.
Nixon, G. T., 1982, The relationship between Quarternary volcanism in central Mexico and the seismicity and structure of subducted ocean lithosphere: Geological Society of America Bulletin, v. 93, p. 514–523.
Nixon, G. T., Demant, A., Armstrong, R. L., and Harakal, J. E., 1987, K-Ar and geologic data bearing on the age and evolution of the Trans-Mexican Volcanic Belt: Geofisica Internacional (Mexico), v. 26, p. 109–158.
Ordóñez, E., 1936, Principal physiographic provinces of Mexico: American Association of Petroleum Geologists Bulletin, v. 20, p. 1277–1307.
Ortega-Gutiérrez, F., 1981a (1984), La evolución tectónica premisisipica del sur de México: Instituto de Geología, UNAM, Revista, v. 2, p. 112–131.
—— , 1981b, Metamorphic belts of southern Mexico and their tectonic significance: Geofísica Internacional (México), v. 20, p. 177–202.
Padilla y Sánchez, R. J., 1985, Las estructuras de la Curvatura de Monterrey, Estados de Coahuila, Nuevo León, Zacatecas y San Luis Potosí: Instituto de Geología, UNAM, Revista, v. 6, p. 1–20.
Pantoja-Alor, J., and Robison, R. A., 1967, Paleozoic sedimentary rocks in Oaxaca, Mexico: Science, v. 157, p. 1033–1035.
Perry, R. K., 1984, Bathymetry of the Gulf of Mexico and the Caribbean Sea: American Association of Petroleum Geologists, scale 1:3,289,263 at 20°N latitude.
Price, R. A., 1981, The Cordilleran foreland thrust and fold belt in the southern Canadian Rocky Mountains, *in* McClay, H. R., and Price, N.J., eds., Thrust and nappe tectonics: Geological Society of London, p. 427–448.
Quintero-Legorreta, O., and Aranda-García, M., 1985, Relaciones estructurales entre el Anticlinorio de Parras y el Anticlinorio de Arteaga (Sierra Madre Oriental), en la región de Agua Nueva, Cohuila: Instituto de Geología, UNAM, Revista, v. 6, p. 21–36.
Raisz, E., 1959, Landforms of Mexico: Cambridge, Massachusetts, scale: 1:3,000,000.
Robin, C., 1982, Relations volcanologie-magmatologie-géodynamique, application au passage entre volcanismes alcalin et andestique dans le sud mexicain (Axe Trans-Mexican et Province Alcaline Orientale): Annales Scientifiques de l'Université de Clermont-Ferrand II. no. 70, fascicule 31, 503 p.
—— , 1984, Le volcan Popocatepetl (Mexique); structure, evolution, pétrologique et risques: Bulletin Volcanologique, v. 47, p. 1–23.
Ruiz, J., Patchett, P. J., and Ortega-Gutiérrez, F., 1988, Proterozoic and Phanerozoic basement terranes of Mexico from Nd isotopic studies: Geological Society of America Bulletin, v. 100, p. 274–281.
Salas, G. P., 1975, Carta y provincias metalogenéticas de la República Mexicana: Consejo de Recursos Minerales (México), Publication 21-E, 242 p. (The metallogenetic chart was published in 1976 as "Contribution of Mexico to the Metallogenetic chart of North America" in the Geological Society of America Map and Chart Series as MC-13, scale 1:2,000,000).
Santiago-Acavedo, J., Carrillo-Bravo, J., and Martell-Andrade, B., 1984, Geología petrolera de México, *in* Marmisolle-Daguerre, D., and others, eds., Evaluación de formaciones en México: Mexico, D. F., Schlumberger, p. 1.1–1.36.
Sapper, K., 1905, Grundzüge des Gebirgsbaus von Mittelamerika: Washington, D.C., 8th International Geographical Congress, Report, p. 231–238.
Schuchert, C., 1935, Historical geology of the Antillean–Caribbean region, or the lands bordering the Gulf of Mexico and the Caribbean Sea: New York, Wiley and Sons, 811 p.
Smith, C. I., 1970, Lower Cretaceous stratigraphy, northern Coahuila, Mexico: University of Texas, Bureau of Economic Geology, Report of Investigations 65, 101 p.
Stewart, J. H., 1988, Latest Proterozoic and Paleozoic southern margin of North America and the accretion of Mexico: Geology, v. 16, p. 186–189.
Stewart, J. H., McMenamin, M., and Morales-Ramírez, J. M., 1984, Upper Proterozoic and Cambrian rocks in the Caborca region, Sonora, Mexico; physical stratigraphy, biostratigraphy, paleocurrent studies and regional relations: U.S. Geological Survey Professional Paper 1309, 36 p.
Stoiber, R. E., and Carr, M. J., 1973, Quaternary volcanic and tectonic segmentation of Central America: Bulletin Volcanologique, v. 37, p. 304–325.
Suter, M., 1984, Cordilleran deformation along the eastern edge of the Valles–San Luis Potosí carbonate platform, Sierra Madre Oriental fold-thrust belt, east-central Mexico: Geological Society of America Bulletin, v. 95, p. 1387–1397.
—— , 1987, Structural traverse across the Sierra Madre Oriental fold-thrust belt in east-central Mexico: Geological Society of America Bulletin, v. 98, p. 249–264.
Van Andel, T. H., and Shor, G. G., Jr., eds., 1964, Marine geology of the Gulf of California; A symposium: American Association of Petroleum Geologists Memoir 3, 408 p.
Viniegra-Osorio, F., 1971, Age and evolution of salt basins of southeastern Mexico: American Association of Petroleum Geologists Bulletin, v. 55, p. 478–494.
—— , 1981, Great carbonate bank of Yucatán, southern Mexico: Journal of Petroleum Geology, v. 3, p. 247–278.
Willis, B., 1912, Index to the stratigraphy of North America, by Bailey Willis, accompanied by a geologic map of North America, *in* Willis, B., and Stose, G. W., eds., U.S. Geological Survey Professional Paper 71, 894 p., scale 1:5,000,000.
Woollard, G. P., and Monges-Caldera, J., 1956, Gravedad, geología regional y estructura cortical en México: Instituto de Geofísica, UNAM, Anales, v. 2, p. 60–112.
Young, K., 1983, Mexico, *in* The Phanerozoic geology of the World, II, The Mesozoic B: Amsterdam, Elsevier, p. 61–88.

MANUSCRIPT ACCEPTED BY THE SOCIETY DECEMBER 23, 1988

ACKNOWLEDGMENTS

A substantial part of this paper was prepared while I was on sabbatical from Universidad Nacional Autónoma de México, and the rest at Instituto de Geología, UNAM, in Mexico City. The draft of the final version of the manuscript was corrected for English and style by Mrs. M. Alcayde, typed by Mrs. E. Gutiérrez, and the list of cited references checked and assembled by Miss C. de Luna. Illustrations, other than those already published, were drafted by S. J. Osorio-Betancourt and E. Gutiérrez-Navarrete. E. Monroy-Soto kindly prepared the negatives for printing. To all these persons, who are members of the Instituto de Geología, UNAM, I am greatly indebted.

Printed in U.S.A.

The Geology of North America
Vol. A, The Geology of North America—An overview
The Geological Society of America, 1989

Chapter 10

The northeast Pacific Ocean and Hawaii

Edward L. Winterer
Scripps Institution of Oceanography, University of California at San Diego, La Jolla, California 92093
Tanya M. Atwater
Department of Geological Sciences, University of California, Santa Barbara, California 92106
Robert W. Decker
4087 Silver Bar Road, Mariposa, California 95338

INTRODUCTION

This chapter highlights salient aspects of the geology of the northeast Pacific basin and its interactions with the rim of North America. We include all the Pacific from the equator northward to the Aleutians, and from the North American continental margin westward to longitude 165°E—an area about twice that of North America. The treatment is thus necessarily summary; for a more complete and balanced coverage, and for more complete lists of the works that have contributed to our knowledge of the northeast Pacific region, see Winterer and others (1989).

There has been a veritable explosion of knowledge about the northeast Pacific in the 25 years since the appearance of Menard's (1964) *Marine Geology of the Pacific.* Since then, the major features of the magnetic anomaly pattern have been mapped, and can be interpreted in the framework of plate tectonics; an extensive web of seismic reflection lines and cores from a network of about 150 deep-sea drill holes provides the data and samples for dating, correlating and interpreting the oceanic sedimentary cover, the constitution of the oceanic crust, and the tectonics of the continental margins. New swathmapping techniques and near-bottom observations and sampling using deep-towed instruments and manned submersibles have opened a window into the processes of crustal accretion and hydrothermal activity along active spreading centers, and modern instrumentation has provided a rich new data base for interpretation of active volcanism in Hawaii.

To synthesize the new findings, we have organized this chapter into two topical sections and one geographic section; primary responsibility for each section is as follows: Tectonics (Atwater), Sediments (Winterer), and Hawaii (Decker). The sections necessarily overlap, and many worthy topics are treated in only the most cursory fashion.

TECTONICS OF THE NORTHEAST PACIFIC REGION

T. M. Atwater

INTRODUCTION

At present, the north Pacific is dominated by the huge Pacific plate (Fig. 1). However, the evidence embedded in this plate (Fig. 2) shows that this configuration is a recent development. In early Cenozoic and Mesozoic time, the north Pacific basin was rich in plates and spreading systems that have mostly been subducted or disrupted against the Pacific margin of North America (Atwater, 1989).

The configuration of the boundaries between major oceanic plates in the north Pacific and their inferred relations to the North American continent are shown in a series of diagrams (Fig. 3). Important steps in this evolving mosaic are described in the following sections, starting with the history of the oceanic plates, and then going on to ocean-continent interactions.

The primary data bases used to decipher the existence and evolution of these systems are maps of topography and of magnetic anomaly isochrons of the ocean floor. New compilations of these data bases are presented in Mammerickx (1989) and Atwater and Severinghaus (1989). The primary difference between previous interpretations and those presented in the new tectonics map is the liberal use of propagating rift traces (pseudofaults and shear zones) wherever they are suggested by the data. The seafloor magnetic isochrons are dated by comparing them to the polarity reversal time scales of Kent and Gradstein (1985) and Berggren and others (1985), and dates from these scales are used.

Winterer, E. L., Atwater, T. M., and Decker, R. W., 1989, The northeast Pacific Ocean and Hawaii, *in* Bally, A. W., and Palmer, A. R., eds., The Geology of North America—An overview: Boulder, Colorado, Geological Society of America, The Geology of North America, v. A.

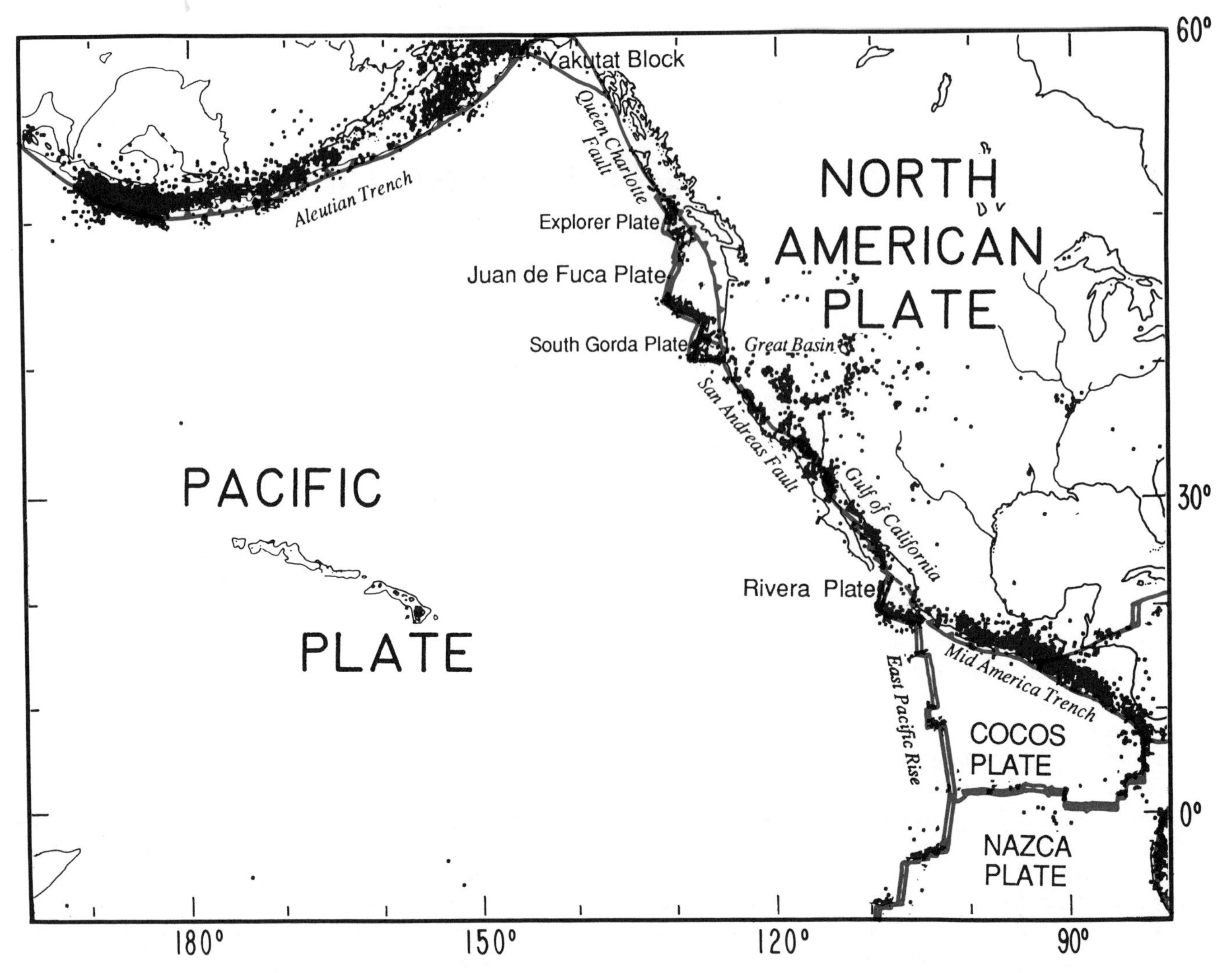

Figure 1. Seismicity and present-day plate boundaries in the northeast Pacific and western North America (from Atwater, 1989).

MESOZOIC SPREADING PATTERNS

The earliest decipherable record of oceanic crustal patterns in the North Pacific comes from the M-series magnetic anomalies, formed from Middle Jurassic to mid-Cretaceous time (about 160–118 Ma). The anomalies form three distinct sets: (a) the Phoenix, (b) Hawaiian, and (c) Japanese lineations (Fig. 4). They record the growth of the Pacific plate in three directions from a central core by spreading from axes between the Pacific plate and the Phoenix, Farallon, and Izanagi plates. Although the Farallon-Pacific spreading history is plainly readable in the magnetic lineations, this history cannot be confidently used to reconstruct interactions between the Farallon plate and North American continent: other plates, now subducted or incorporated in the continent, may have existed in between. Nonetheless, it is from this early configuration that the later Cretaceous and Cenozoic plate arrangements evolved.

After the M-series reversals, between about 118 and 84 Ma, the earth's magnetic field became stable with continuous normal polarity: the Cretaceous quiet period. Little can be deduced about Pacific spreading history during this time. Comparisons of the isochron patterns formed before and after show that major reorganizations occurred then on all the spreading systems. On the southern flank, the spreading center somehow moved from the Phoenix group at the equator to the Pacific-Antarctic spreading center at 40°S. On the east, spreading between the Pacific and Farallon plates included major reorganizations, drastically changing the lengths of the fracture zone offsets and creating the anomalous topography of the Hess rise and Emperor trough (Fig. 5). On the northern side, the Izanagi plate moved to the north-northwest to an unknown fate, and another northern plate, the Kula plate, was created near the end of the quiet period. It seems that the Kula plate originated as a piece of the northern Pacific or Farallon plate that progressively broke away from west to east along the Chinook trough (Mammerickx and Sharman, 1988).

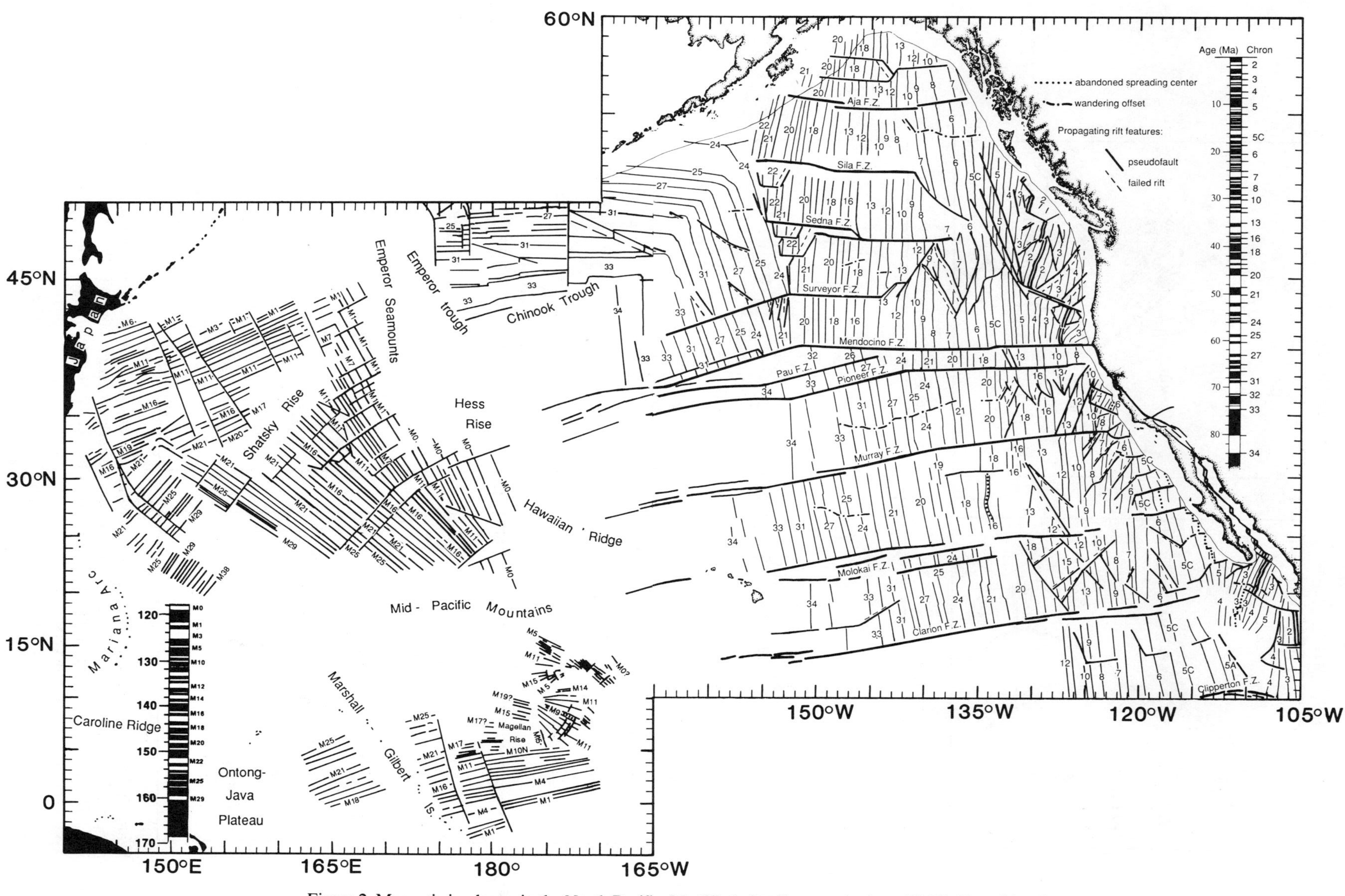

Figure 2. Magnetic isochrons in the North Pacific. Modified after Sager and others (1988), Tamaki and Larson (1988), Atwater and Severinghaus (1989), and Atwater (1989). Magnetic polarity reversal time scale after Berggren and others (1985) and Kent and Gradstein (1985).

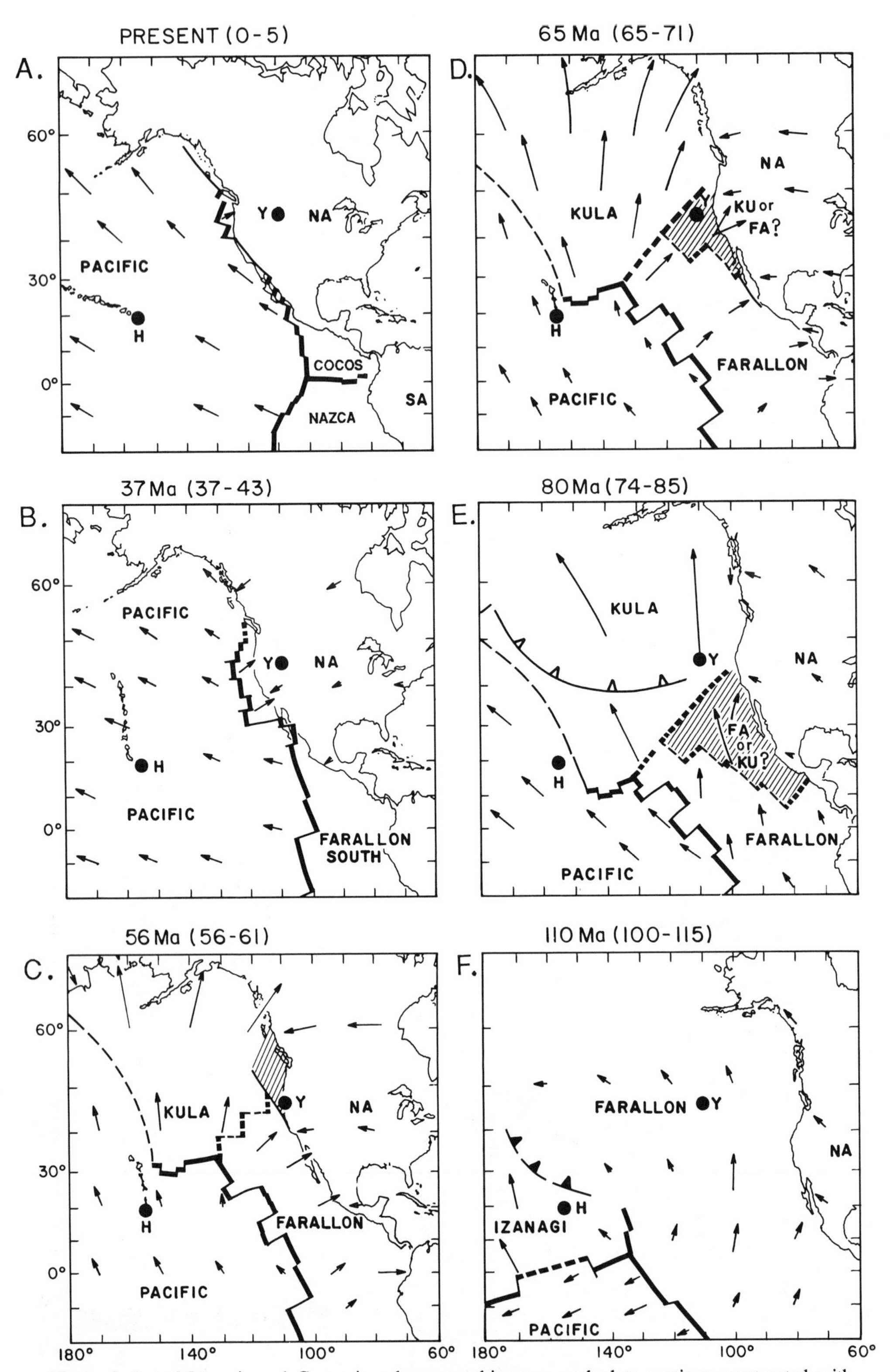

Figure 3. Late Mesozoic and Cenozoic paleogeographic maps and plate motions constructed with respect to hot spots (from Atwater, 1989—modified after Engebretson and others, 1985). Shaded areas in C, D, and E indicate range of possible locations for the Kula-Farallon spreading center. Y = Yellowstone hot spot, H = hot spot.

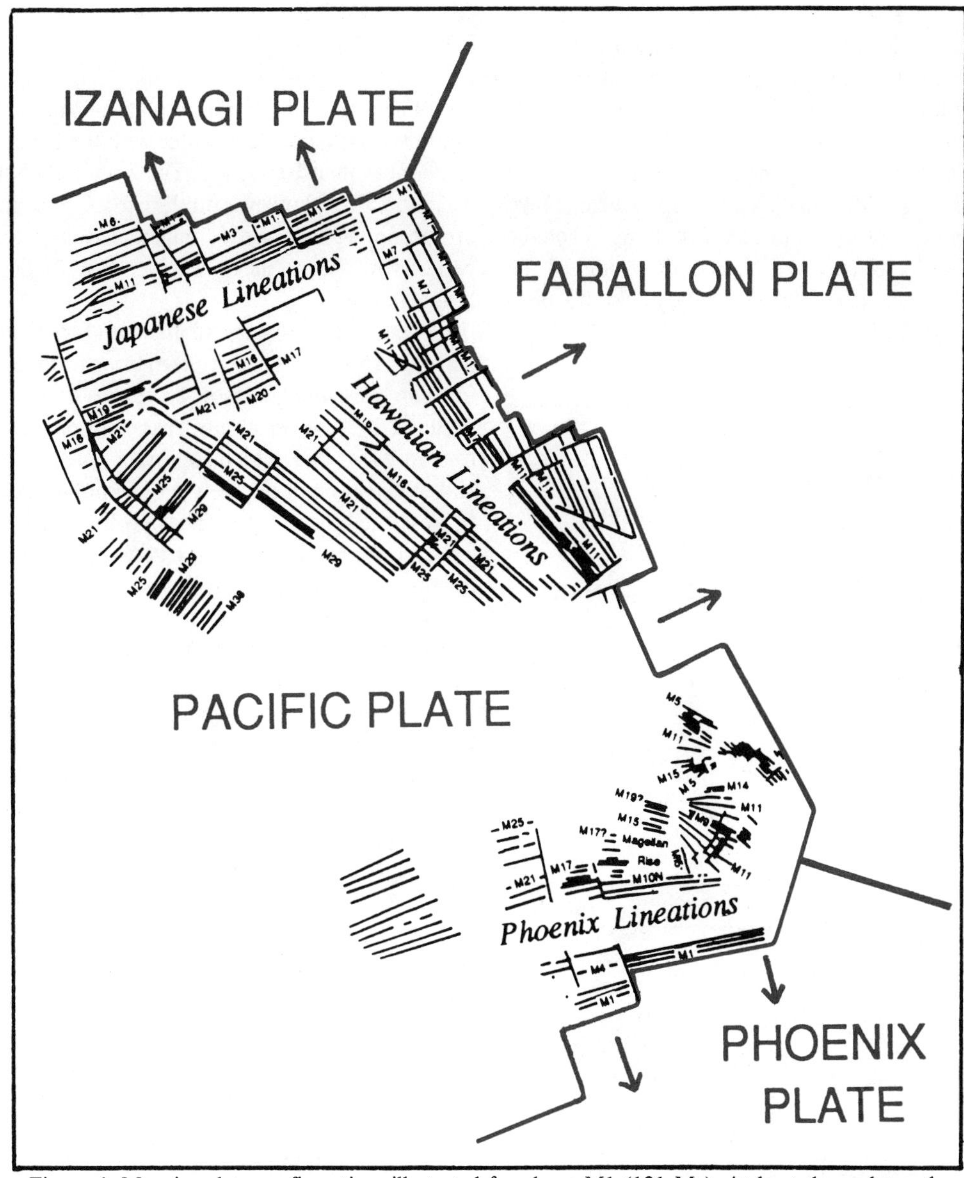

Figure 4. M-series plate configuration, illustrated for chron M1 (121 Ma). At least three plates, the Izanagi, Farallon, and Phoenix plates, were moving away from the small Pacific plate and from one another along at least 5 spreading centers.

HISTORY OF THE KULA PLATE

The history of the Kula plate is important because of its fast northward motions. Adding the Kula-Pacific spreading rate to the already fast northward motion of the Pacific plate, the Kula would have been moving northward at speeds up to 170 mm/yr with respect to the hot spots. These fast northward motions are often invoked by North American paleomagnetists and geologists looking for a mechanism for the quick northward transport of terranes across the Pacific basin and/or along the rim of North America.

Unfortunately, our record of Pacific-Kula spreading is incomplete. The east-west–trending magnetic anomalies south of the Aleutian trench in Figure 5B were formed by the northward spreading of the Kula plate away from the Pacific plate between about 85 and 58 Ma. Subduction has destroyed the younger record, leaving only two small sections of younger sea floor at the northwest and northeast ends of the pattern. Data in both regions indicate a major change at anomaly 24 (56 Ma), but there is disagreement as to the nature of the change. Patterns in the northwestern section are interpreted by Lonsdale (1988) to show that, with respect to the Pacific plate, the Kula plate slowed down and veered left at 56 Ma, then stalled at 43 Ma. In the northeastern section, the anomaly pattern at 24r has variously been interpreted as a drastic speed up, a ridge jump, or as a cessation of spreading. Each of these scenarios has its own different ramifications for larger plate motion questions.

Another frustrating aspect of the Kula plate story is our total lack of knowledge of the location of the Kula-Farallon spreading center and its intersection with North America. Because only the Pacific plate record has been saved, we have no direct sea-floor evidence concerning the shape and location of this plate boundary. The predicted plate tectonic regime along the rim of North America is, of course, very different depending upon which plate, Kula or Farallon (or perhaps some other), lay offshore. When the possible extremes are considered for the configuration of the Kula-Farallon boundary, much of the west coast of North America falls within the region of ambiguity.

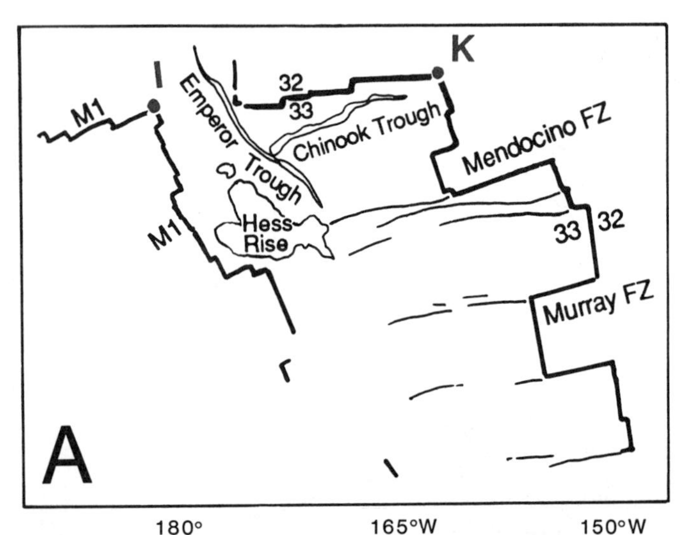

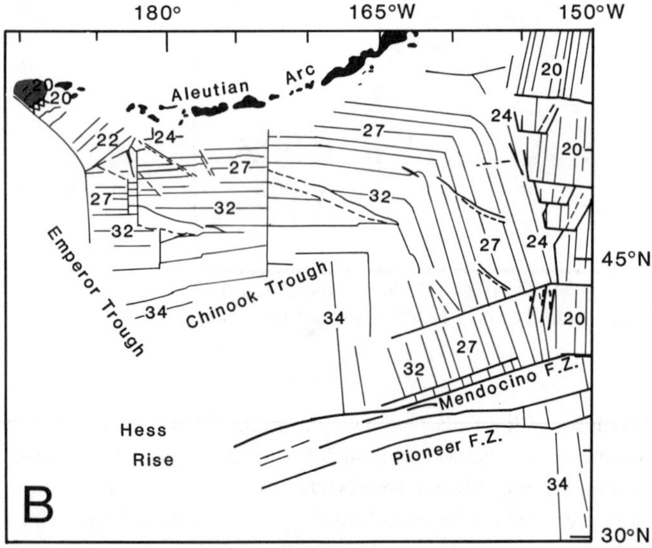

Figure 5. A: Map patterns of isochrons M1 (121 Ma) and 32r (72 Ma) and the intervening Cretaceous quiet zone with anomalous topographic features. Dots are locations of Izanagi-Farallon-Pacific triple junction (I), and the Kula-Farallon-Pacific triple junction (K). There is no straightforward way that (I) can evolve directly into (K). B: Magnetic isochrons in the northeastern Pacific, modified after Atwater and Severinghaus (1989) and Atwater (1989). A small piece of the Kula Plate (red) trapped on the Pacific plate, is preserved south of the trench in the western part of the Aleutian Arc. The Kula Plate most likely had its origins along the Chinook Trough.

CENOZOIC FRAGMENTATION OF THE FARALLON PLATE

The size of the Farallon plate in the Late Cretaceous was impressive. Its spreading center with the Pacific extended north-south more than 10,000 km. The immensity of the Farallon plate was short-lived, however. In the early Cenozoic it began to break up, becoming increasingly fragmented with time. The lineation patterns in the northeast Pacific (Fig. 2) document this slow disintegration.

The first disruption of the Farallon plate occurred about chron 24 (55 Ma), when its northern part broke off from the rest, forming the large "Vancouver" plate. This change is shown in Figure 2 by a rather abrupt change in direction of the northern fracture zones, the sudden appearance of a set of propagating rifts, and the creation of two new transform faults, the Sila and Sedna (Caress and others, 1988). The new boundary between the Farallon and Vancouver plates lay between the Pioneer and Murray fracture zones, where a narrow neck had developed in the Farallon plate as the East Pacific rise approached North America. The misalignment between the Vancouver and Farallon plates was small; the relative motion was only about 2 cm/yr. The trace of the Vancouver-Farallon-Pacific triple junction that is left in the Pacific plate can be seen in Figure 2 as a set of curving, toothlike disjunctures in anomalies 19–13 offshore from San Francisco. Apparently, a pair of propagating rifts alternately shifted the junction north and south in a 10-m.y.-year duel (Atwater and Severinghaus, 1989). At 30 Ma (anomaly 10), the plates in the vicinity of the Pacific-Vancouver-Farallon junction abruptly shattered, and two microplates—the Monterey and Arguello plates—appeared, moving slowly away to the southeast and east-southeast from the Pacific plate. These, in turn, gradually disappeared beneath the rim of North America until the last remaining spreading center stalled and the last small piece of the Monterey plate, now located southwest of San Francisco was captured by the Pacific about 19 Ma (Lonsdale, 1989b).

With the appearance of the two microplates at 30 Ma, the Vancouver and Farallon plates lost contact with one another, and about 25 Ma the Farallon plate broke in two again at the Galapagos spreading center. The remaining plates, renamed from north to south the Juan de Fuca, Guadalupe, and Nacza plates, were relatively small and continued to decrease in size with the encroachment of the Americas plates. Their motions, as recorded by their spreading histories with respect to the Pacific, grew less and less stable. The relative direction of motion of the Juan de Fuca plate shifted first counter-clockwise and then more and more clockwise. In response to these changes, numerous propagating rifts appeared and removed most transform offsets, leaving the ridge crest remarkably long and straight by chron 6 (20 Ma), and then gradually added the transform offsets (Wilson, 1988; Johnson and Holmes, 1989).

South of the Murray fracture zone, spreading of the Guadalupe plate away from the Pacific was also unstable: the spreading direction shifted first clockwise, then counter-clockwise, then clockwise again. Then, about 14 to 12 Ma, spreading is believed to have stalled along the entire length of ridge crest off Baja California so that the remaining narrow sliver of the Guadalupe plate was added to the Pacific plate (Fig. 2; Lonsdale, 1989a and b; Spencer and Normark, 1989). To the south, the Mathematician microplate appeared for a time, then the East Pacific Rise propagated northward past it, finally establishing the present Cocos-Pacific plate boundary about 3.5 Ma (Mammerickx and others, 1988).

MODERN SPREADING CENTERS AND THEIR OFFSETTING FEATURES

Compared to other ocean basins, the modern north Pacific is poor in spreading centers (Fig. 1). However, those that do exist form a diverse set, spanning spreading rates from medium to ultra-fast, occurring in a variety of more and less stable plate-motion situations, and having various relations to hot spots and triple junctions. They have been studied intensively on all scales and have contributed much to our fund of knowledge of both the large and fine-scale characteristics of medium and fast spreading systems.

On a grand scale, most of the world's ocean floor was created by relatively smooth spreading on sets of spreading centers offset by transform faults; however, variations of this configuration are not uncommon. The modern spreading systems contain a number of types of non-transform offsets and disjunctures: ridge jumps and microplate transfers, propagating rifts, overlapping spreading centers, and other small jogs and dips, most of which have been characterized only in the past few years (Batiza, 1989b). Figure 6 shows the distribution of some of these features along the present Galapagos and East Pacific Rise crests.

The Galapagos spreading center is particularly noted for its clear examples of active propagating rifts. Two propagators are currently moving east and west away from the Galapagos hot spot, and others are apparent in the older spreading record. The propagating tip near 95.5°W has been studied in great detail with nearly every technique available to marine geoscientists, so it presently forms our "type example" for a propagating rift tip (Hey and others, 1989). The propagating rift is steadily extending itself at the expense of the adjacent ridge segment, the "doomed rift," creating a V-shaped wedge of new sea floor edged by "pseudofaults." The lithosphere between the two rifts is sequentially sheared and transferred from one plate to the other as the propagator passes (Figs. 7, 8).

The Juan de Fuca Ridge also contains clear examples of past and present rift propagation (Fig. 2). During the Neogene, a set of nested propagators moved southward, followed by another moving northward to its present site. During the past 0.5 m.y., this propagator made two reversals in direction—a "dueling" (Johnson and Holmes, 1989).

The primary cause for rift-propagation events is unclear. Those on the Galapagos spreading center are propagating away from the hot spot, leading workers to postulate that they may be driven by sublithospheric magma flow out from the spot and/or by the resulting topographic gradients. On the other hand, rift propagation seems to be the mechanism by which mid-ocean ridges reorient themselves. Isochron trends formed on the propagating and doomed rifts tend to be distinctly different from one another, and changes in plate direction are marked in well-mapped, older sea-floor records by the appearance of numerous propagating-rift structures (e.g., Wilson, 1988; Atwater and Severinghaus, 1989). Thus, it seems that either the proximity of a hot spot or the occurrence of a plate-direction change may initiate and drive a rift-propagation event.

Another type of disjuncture, commonly observed at small offsets, is the overlapping of spreading centers, in which two adjoining but slightly misaligned rift tips overlap each other with an intervening, deep overlap basin (Macdonald, 1989). These tend to occur at relatively small offsets, and have a characteristic shape that reflects the stress patterns found around overlapping cracks (Fig. 8). The longer term manifestations of the overlapping spreading centers are not yet well known. In propagating rifts, the propagating and failing rift tips overlap, but it appears that these are only one special class of overlappers. Many overlapping spreading centers seem to be ephemeral, but others are episodic features, recurring at a given spot on the ridge crest or drifting slowly along strike.

Detailed mapping along strike on the ridge crests of both the medium-rate Juan de Fuca ridge and the fast- and ultra-fast–spreading East Pacific rise has led to the discovery that ridge crests seem to be naturally segmented, the ends of the segments being marked by transform faults, propagating rifts, overlapping spreading centers, or small misalignments called devals (Johnson and Holmes, 1989; Macdonald, 1989). This segmentation appears to reflect the structure of the upwelling asthenosphere beneath the ridge axes. The disjunctures all tend to occupy deep spots along the ridge-crest profile and to accompany abrupt changes in geochemical signature, suggesting that they delimit individual upwelling cells (Macdonald, 1989; Batiza, 1989a). Magma is postulated to upwell primarily at the centers of the segments, and to flow sideways to the ends. The relatively low magma supply at the joins is indicated by narrower cross-strike ridge-crest profiles, higher iron and titanium content in the lavas, deeper topography, and weaker or absent magma-chamber reflections in multichannel seismic lines.

One of the most exciting aspects of mid-ocean ridge exploration in recent years has been the discoveries of hydrothermal vents and their related deposits, exotic biological communities, and thermal and water chemistry effects (Haymon, 1989; Johnson and Holmes, 1989; Lonsdale, 1989a). These have been found in various locations along the Galapagos and East Pacific rises (Fig. 6) in the Gulf of California, and on the Juan de Fuca ridge. They range from warm vents (effluent temperatures less than 250 °C) with large clams and giant vestimentiferan worms, to "white smokers" (less than 300°C) streaming through "snow balls" and chimneys encrusted by worm tubes, to "black smokers" billowing from Cu-rich sulfide-sulfate chimneys up to 30 m tall (Fig. 9).

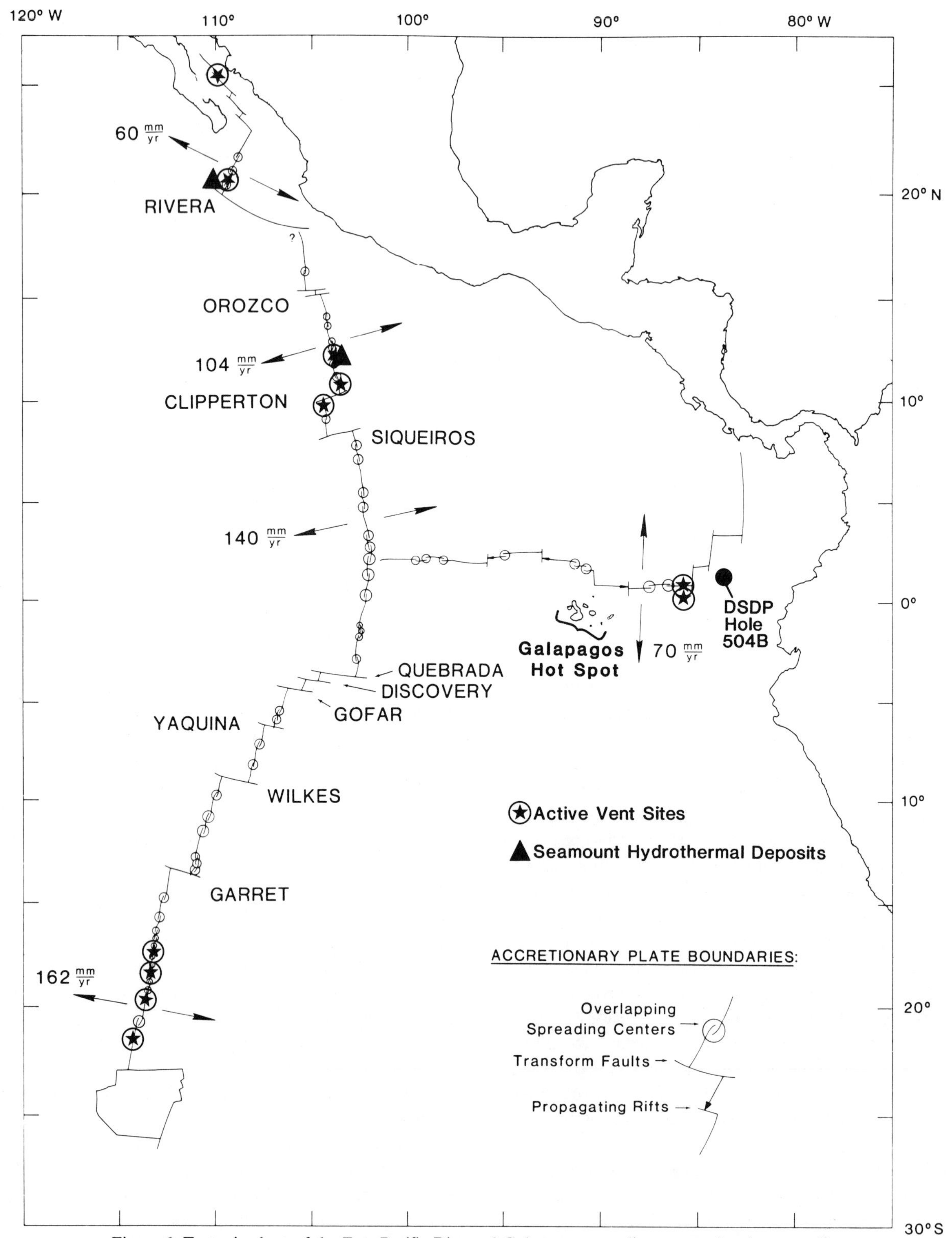

Figure 6. Tectonic chart of the East Pacific Rise and Galapagos spreading center showing spreading centers, transform faults, propagating rifts, and overlapping spreading centers based primarily on Sea-Beam coverage and locations of known sites of hydrothermal venting (from Macdonald, 1989; Haymon, 1989). Solid stars mark sites of active venting; solid triangles mark location of off-axis seamounts associated with hydrothermal mineral deposits. Solid circle shows location of DSDP Hole 504B. Full spreading rates are listed.

The effluent temperatures and flows, deposit types, and animal species are all extremely variable from vent to vent, so each new find holds new surprises: visits to these vents are as exciting as any Jules Verne adventure! The effects of these vents on the lithospheric heat budget, ocean-water chemistry, rock and sediment mineralization, and animal evolution are profound and are little understood at present.

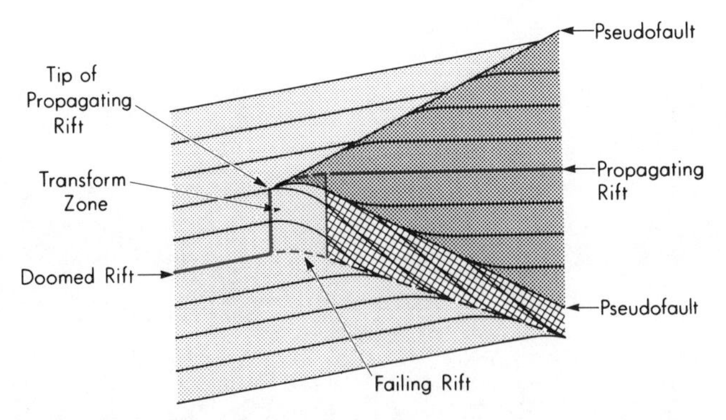

Figure 7. Propagating rift geometry (from Hey and others, 1989). Red lines show active plate boundaries. Propagating rift lithosphere is marked by dark stipple, normal lithosphere created at the doomed rift is indicated by light stipple, transform zone between overlapping rift tips is shown by red stipple, and transferred lithosphere is cross-hatched.

PLATE TECTONIC MODELS FOR RECONSTRUCTING THE INTERACTIONS OF THE OCEANIC PLATES WITH THE SURROUNDING CONTINENTS

The interactions of the oceanic plates of the Pacific with the surrounding continents, important as they are for understanding the geology of the Continental rim, may never be determined as precisely around the rim of the Pacific basin as they can be for the other oceans because most of the intervening plate boundaries are or have been subduction zones.

Quantitative plate reconstructions are usually made using a circuit path along which all plate boundaries crossed are spreading ridges. The primary plate circuit used for Pacific–North American reconstructions is one through Antarctica and crossing the Pacific-Antarctica ridge: Farallon-Pacific-Antarctica-(India)-Africa-North America (Fig. 10). This circuit has been used with considerable success to find rotation parameters, with uncertainties, for the Pacific–North American plate pair at various times in the middle and late Cenozoic (Stock and Molnar, 1988). The global magnetic anomaly and fracture zone data set has greatly improved in recent years, resulting in dramatic decreases in the uncertainties of these reconstructions.

Studies attempting to use the circuit shown in Fig. 10A for Late Cretaceous and early Cenozoic circuits have been more problematic, but an important breakthrough on this problem was recently made by Stock and Molnar (1987) when they documented the relative motions of an additional plate, the Bellingshausen plate in the South Pacific. With the recognition of this plate, consistent circuit solutions can now be constructed back to chron 32 (75 Ma). Unfortunately, for earlier times there is no known plate circuit connecting the Pacific and Pangaean realms.

One problem with circuits across Antarctica is that some extension has occurred between east and west Antarctica, but the amount and age are not well known. Any motion between the two halves of Antarctica will be a source of error in Pangaean-Pacific circuit solutions.

Another approach to Pacific-continent reconstructions is to locate the plates with respect to an "absolute" frame of reference. The most successful, though controversial, of these is the hot-spot frame. It is assumed that the sources for the various volcanic "hot spots" (e.g., Hawaii, Iceland, Yellowstone) form a fixed, stable frame of reference against which the motions of individual plates can be measured. The Pacific plate motion with respect to the hot spots is clearly shown by the Hawaiian seamount chain (0 to 43 Ma) and the Emperor seamount chain (43 to 74 Ma), and plausibly represented by the Line Islands (74 to 100 Ma), (Epp, 1978). Henderson and Gordon (1981) suggested a stage prior to 100 Ma, but this is much more controversial. For the time being, Pacific plate/hot-spot motions before 74 Ma should be used with care and those before 100 Ma should be considered to be no more than interesting speculations. All reconstructions made assuming a fixed global hot-spot frame are only approximations, because the hot spots, in fact, drift slowly with respect to one another. Nonetheless, because they are all that we have to work with for much of the Mesozoic, it is worth following them to see where they lead. The hot-spot circuit for these plate reconstructions is in Figure 10B: Farallon–Pacific–Hot-spots–Africa–North America.

Selected North Pacific reconstructions made using the hot-spot method by Engebretson and others (1985) are shown in Figure 3. The ambiguity concerning the location of the Kula-Farallon boundary, described above, is clear in Figures 3C, 3D, and 3E. Also impressive in the earlier reconstructions is the vast expanse of unknown North Pacific sea floor. We tend to assume that it is populated only by the plates that we know about—Izanagi, Kula, Farallon, Vancouver—but there is plenty of room there for unknown plates as well.

Average relative plate velocities over the intervals between the reconstructions can also be calculated. Figure 11 shows relative velocity histories for a point near San Francisco, found by the hot-spot method (black) and by the circuit method including uncertainties (red). The large uncertainties emphasize that the velocities are only very general indicators of plate motions and should not be used to determine precise rates or small changes. Note that coast-normal velocities of subductions were fast during the Laramide orogeny, although methods disagree about values, and uncertainties are very large. Another useful rendition of the reconstructions can be made by tracing the locations of individual points on individual plates. Examples of such trajectories have been plotted with their uncertainties by Stock and Molnar (1988)

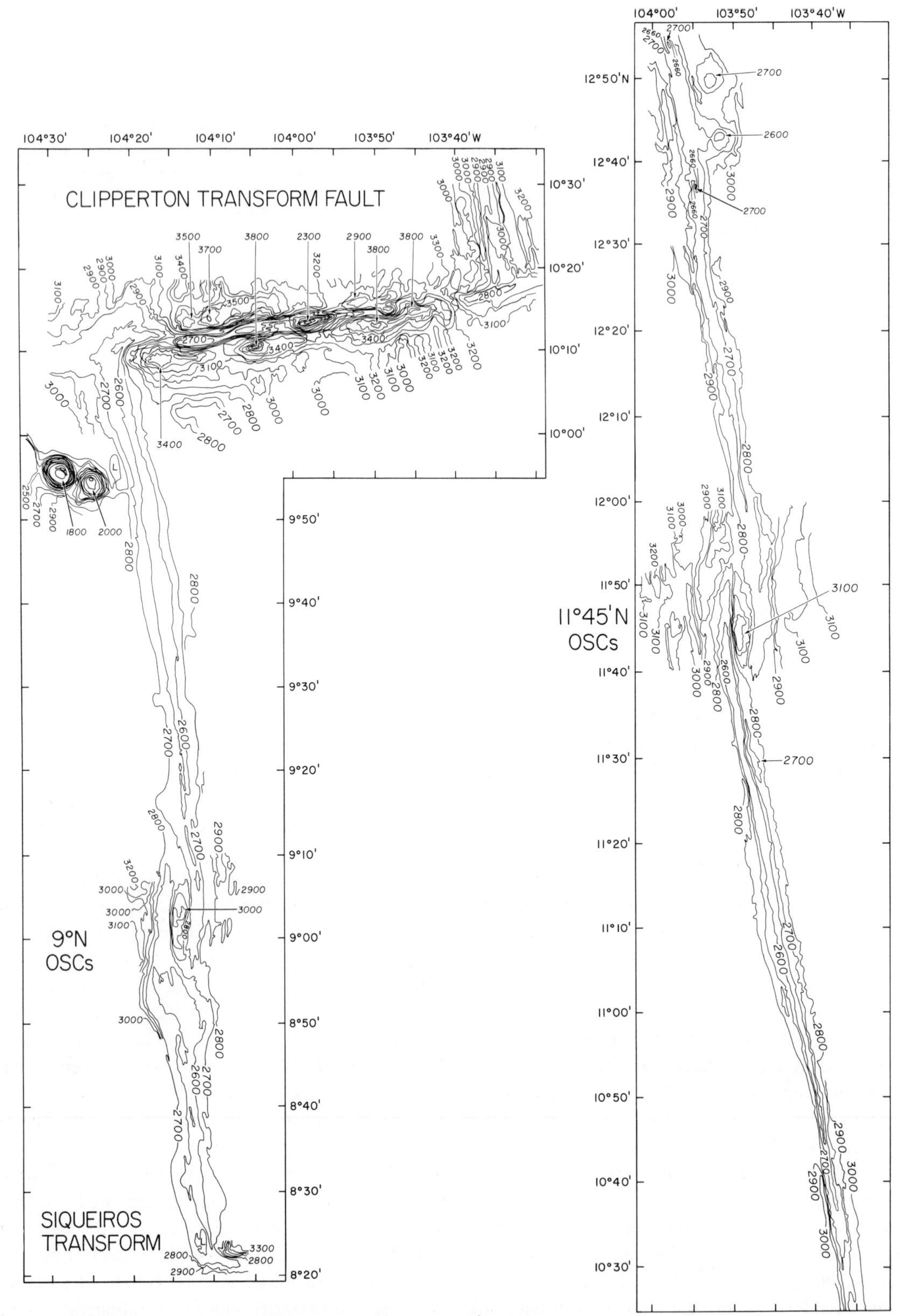

Figure 8. Overlapping spreading center geometry, illustrated in a SeaBeam map of part of the East Pacific Rise crest. Overlapping spreading centers are present near 9°03′N and 11°45′N (from Macdonald, 1989).

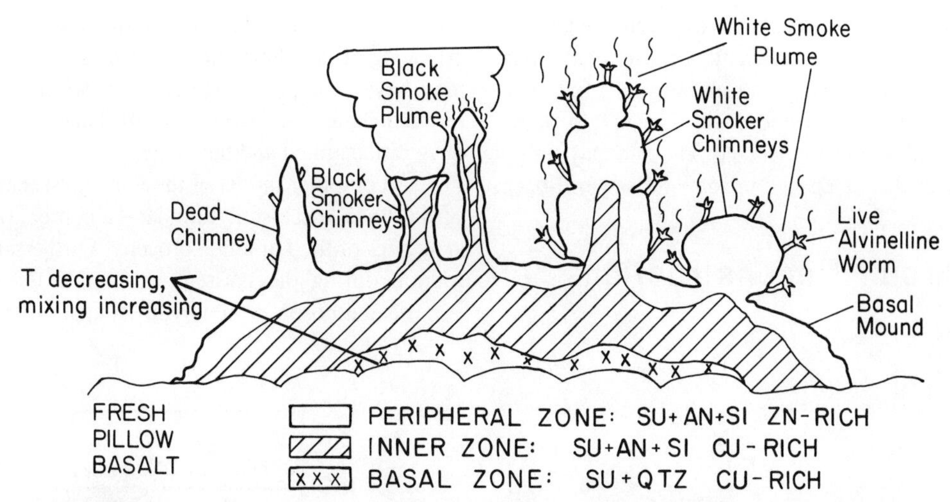

Figure 9. Composite sketch showing features of hydrothermal vent deposits on axis of the East Pacific Rise. Mounds of hydrothermal precipitates, accumulated on top of fresh basalt, are surmounted by chimney edifices. Although little is known about mound interiors, some zoning within mounds is expected by analogy with chimneys and with massive sulfide deposits on land. Simplified sketch of expected zoning is shown here. An outer, peripheral zone of anhydrite (AN) + amorphous silica (ST) + Zn-rich sulfide (SU; dominantly ZnS + FeS_2) is replaced in the interior by an inner zone (cross-hatched) of Cu-rich sulfide ($CuFeS_2$ + FeS_2) + minor anhydrite and amorphous silica. The inner zone may be replaced by a basal zone (cross-pattern) of sulfide ($CuFeS_2$ + FeS_2) + quartz (QTZ). As in chimneys, these zones migrate as thermochemical conditions within the mound evolve. Although not shown here, it is anticipated that zoning around individual fractures cutting through the mound will be superimposed on the simplified zone structure in this sketch (from Haymon, 1989).

from global plate circuits, and by Engebretson and others (1985) from the hot-spot circuit.

The velocities and trajectories are of particular interest for tracing possible paths of "suspect terranes." Alaska and the rim of North America are believed to include numerous displaced terranes, many of which originated far to the south.

One likely transport mechanism for terranes is illustrated in the edges of some modern overriding plates where the subduction direction is oblique. The plate motion tends to be partitioned, compression being taken up at the trench while the strike-slip component appears on faults well inland, so that the rim of the overriding plate is transported sideways. This has been postulated as a mechanism for the truncation of early Mesozoic features, for the common occurrence of Mesozoic right-lateral features in the Sierra Nevada, for the northward transport of Alaskan terranes, and for this dismemberment.

Plate models are only partially supportive of these oblique transport ideas. The tangential velocities calculated for the Farallon plate in Figure 11B are not large, usually near zero. Kula plate tangential velocities were great, but were short-lived. The oblique subduction mechanism may be invoked for transporting North America terranes primarily during the Late Cretaceous, and might account for about 20° to 30° of northward transport. Geologic terranes may also have been transported while embedded within oceanic plates, and then transferred to the edge of the continent when they resisted subduction. Debiche and others (1987) presented an analysis for many such trajectories.

MESOZOIC-CENOZOIC SUBDUCTION IN THE WESTERN UNITED STATES

An inescapable conclusion that can be drawn from any tectonic reconstruction of the Pacific plate is that a great deal of area greater than the present North Pacific basin has been consumed since the Triassic. The continental geologic record of the Pacific rim is full of evidence of this subduction and its variations.

One of the more enigmatic, and plate tectonically accessible, of these subduction variations is recorded by the Laramide orogeny and the subsequent extensional regimes in the Great Basin. Beginning about 80 Ma, magmatism ceased rather abruptly in the western arc, and small patches of magmatic activity appeared to the east as far inland as Colorado. Corresponding in time and space to this shift was the onset of the Laramide compressional regime. These events are believed by many to correspond to a flattening of the subducting slab, similar to the flat slabs presently subducting beneath Peru and central Chile. During the mid-Cenozoic, magmatic activity slowly drifted westward again, narrowing and reestablishing a western belt: a re-steepening of the slab? The profound extension of mid- to late Cenozoic age in the Great Basin has a geographic extent similar to Laramide features, and its onset commonly corresponds approximately to this westward passage of the magmatic arc so that it appears to be related to the removal of the flat slab.

Both the existence of the Laramide flat slab and the cause(s) for its flattening are the subjects of lively debate. This was a time of extra-fast subduction and continental overriding rates, but those factors were probably not sufficient to cause a flattening. The most likely cause was a change in slab buoyancy following the subduction of thickened oceanic crust. The nature of the resteepening of the slab is likewise debated. The slab may simply have lost its buoyancy and steepened in some orderly roll-back. On the other hand, because of slowing of subduction and the younging of the plate being subducted, a great length of the slab may have simultaneously aged and warmed beyond coherence (Severinghaus and Atwater, 1989). Thus, the flat slab may simply have disintegrated and fallen away.

A computer model of the flat-slab scenario, constructed by Bird (1984), successfully simulates a number of the unusual characteristics of the Laramide orogeny. Furthermore, it predicts that friction during the flat-slab era would delaminate the North American lithosphere, removing its upper mantle portion, so that

A. Plate Circuit Reconstructions

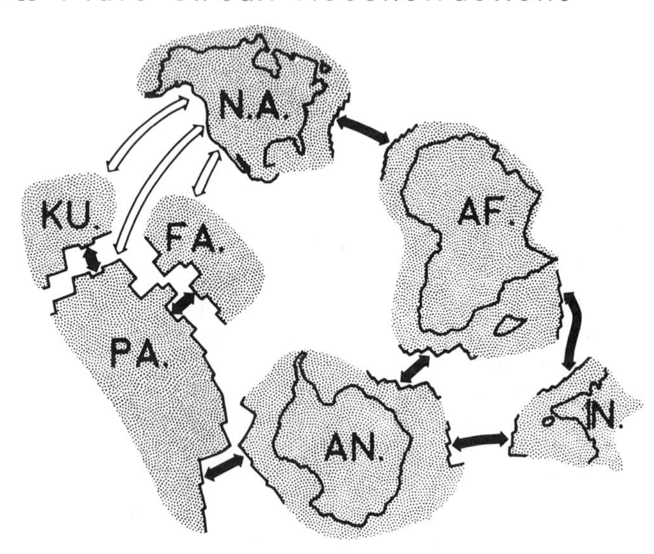

B. Hot Spot Reconstructions

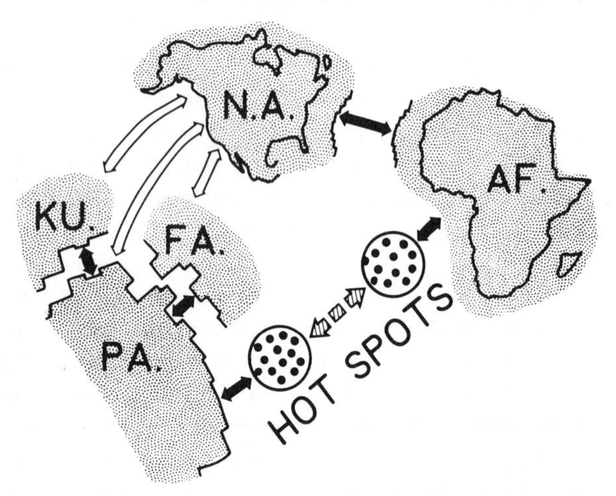

Figure 10. Graphic illustrations of the plate circuits for reconstructions of Pacific–North American relative plate positions. Steps indicated by dark arrows can be reconstructed using sea-floor spreading data. Striped arrow indicates the assumption that the Pacific and Atlantic hot spots form a single frame of reference. Relations indicated by hollow arrows can then be calculated by summing the others (from Atwater, 1989). A: Round-the-world plate circuits of Stock and Molnar (1988) crossing spreading systems to the South Pacific, Indian Ocean, and central Atlantic provide a three- to five-step circuit. B: Hot spot frame circuit of Engebretson and others (1985) using spreading centers in the Pacific and Atlantic oceans and assuming that the hot spots in these two oceans are fixed with respect to each other.

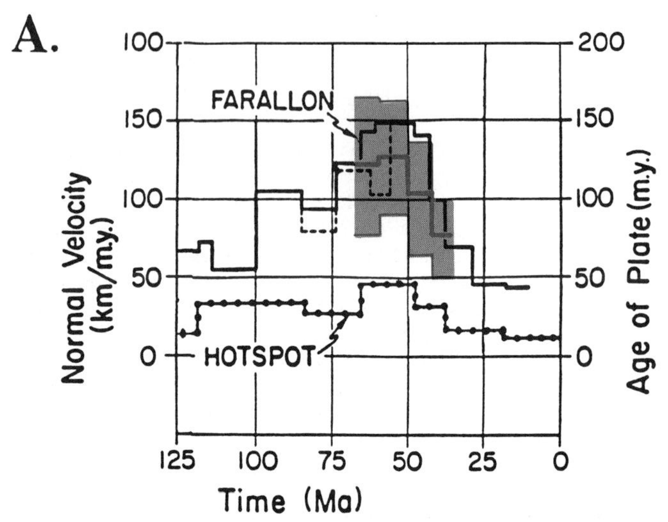

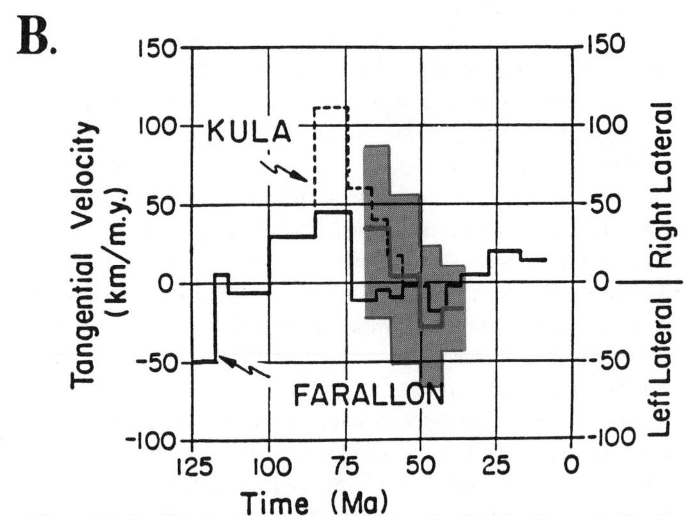

Figure 11. Predicted average relative plate velocities for time steps in the reconstructions, computed for a point near San Francisco, separated into (A) coast-normal and (B) tangential components, perpendicular and parallel, respectively, to N40°W (from Atwater, 1989). Black: Relative velocities of the Farallon and Kula plates and of the hot spot frame with respect to North America (from Engebretson and others, 1985). Red: Relative velocities, with uncertainties of the Farallon plate with respect to North America (from the circuit solutions of Stock and Molnar, 1988).

when the slab was removed, hot asthenosphere would be emplaced directly beneath continental crust. This, in turn, would result in anomalously high heat flow, a thin, weak lithosphere, uplift, and extension(?), all of which are characteristic of the mid- to late Cenozoic Great Basin.

LATE CENOZOIC DEVELOPMENT OF TRANSFORM MARGINS

During the middle and late Cenozoic, the plate regime along the rim of western North America gradually changed from subduction to the present geometry, in which strike-slip extensional regimes predominate. This changeover was a natural consequence of the gradual drift of the spreading system toward the continent. The Farallon plate became steadily narrower until the Pacific-Farallon ridge crest approached the trench.

The geographic unfolding of the ridge-trench collision off California has been approximately reconstructed using the round-the-world plate circuits as shown in Figure 12. The first ridge segments arrived at the trench off southern California and northern Baja California between 28 and 26 Ma, and the first portion of the Pacific-North America plate boundary came into existence, linked to the adjacent subduction regimes by triple junctions. With time, the Mendocino junction migrated northwestward along the coast, changing the tectonic regime in the adjacent continent from subduction to strike-slip as it passed. This motion was consistently north-northwestward, probably with a slower speed in the early to middle Miocene, accelerating to its present speed in late Miocene or Pliocene. The southern (Rivera) triple junction remained approximately stationary off northern Baja California until about 16 Ma. About 14 to 12 Ma, spreading and subduction ceased all along Baja California, and the triple junction shifted far to the south, to the tip of Baja California.

The most obvious consequence of the growth of the Pacific–North America boundary has been the development of the San Andreas system. A primary problem in understanding this development concerns the manner in which the new plate boundary becomes established following the demise of the intervening plate. To study this we may examine the similar but more recent transition that occurred around Baja California following the passage of the Rivera triple junction.

The Pacific–North America boundary was probably established between 14 and 12 Ma, nearly simultaneously all along central and southern Baja. After the triple junction passed, the primary strike-slip plate boundary was established in the continental margin along the Tosco-Abreojos fault zone (Spencer and Normark, 1989). At the same time, extension was occurring inland, forming a proto-gulf and rifting the margin near the Tres Marias Islands. Starting about 5.5 Ma, the primary plate boundary gradually shifted inland, transferring Baja California to the Pacific plate. For about 2 m.y., plate motion was taken up across a broad set of faults until the major throughgoing system was established (Lonsdale, 1989a).

This scenario for the Gulf of California is very similar to that

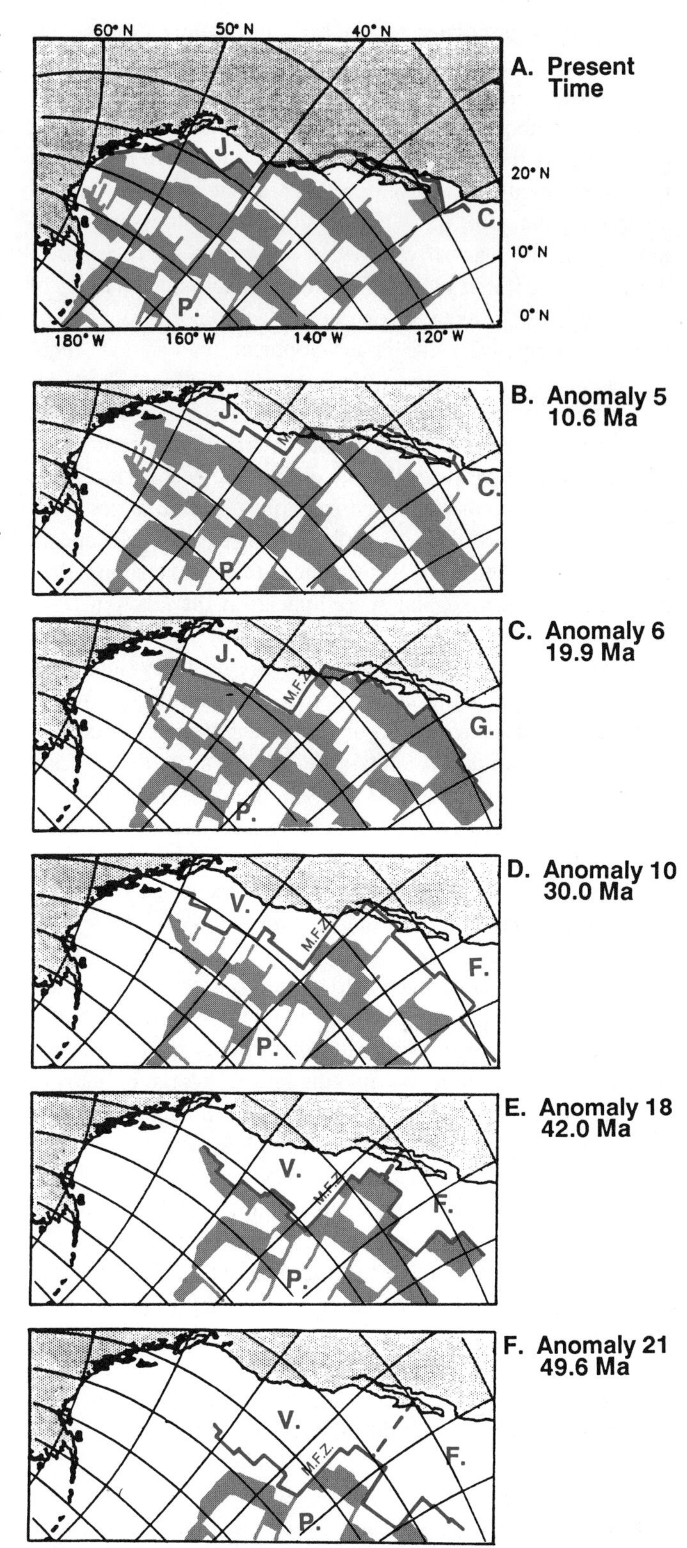

Figure 12. Mid-late Cenozoic reconstructions of the Pacific Plate and the Farallon Plate (and its descendants) with respect to North America for times corresponding to selected prominent magnetic anomalies, constructed using the global plate circuits (from Atwater, 1989—modified from Stock and Molnar, 1988). P.: Pacific plate, F.: Farallon plate, V.: Vancouver plate, G.: Guadalupe plate, J.: Juan de Fuca plate, C.: Cocos plate.

which may be postulated for the early development of the San Andreas system in southern California. The earliest on-land manifestations are the opening of basins and accompanying volcanism, starting about 22 Ma. Presumably the first strike-slip faults lay in the continental margin, because onshore strike-slip fault systems appear to have developed later, about 18 to 16 Ma, and migrated inland over time. Furthermore, the fault systems were more diffuse in their early stages, as implied by the rotations of the Transverse Range blocks. The present situation, with much of the motion being taken up on one or two major throughgoing faults, is a relatively recent development that started about 12 Ma.

After the inception of the Pacific–North America plate boundary, the boundary on North America was continually lengthened northwestward by the drift of the Mendocino triple junction. Because the San Andreas fault direction is not quite parallel to the trend of the coastline and trench, the Mendocino triple junction is intrinsically unstable: as the plates continue their motions, a small triangular space appears at the junction. Two geologic solutions to this geometric instability seem likely. One solution is that the San Andreas boundary regularly shifts sideways, inland, realigning its northern terminus with the trench. Such a shift is currently occurring around Cape Mendocino, where several strike-slip faults have formed more than 70 km inland of the main strand of the San Andreas and are in the process of transferring a continental sliver, the "Humboldt plate," from North America to the Pacific plate (Kelsey and Carver, 1988; Fig. 13). Likewise, the Salinian block was transferred to the Pacific plate when the San Andreas system moved inland in an earlier shift.

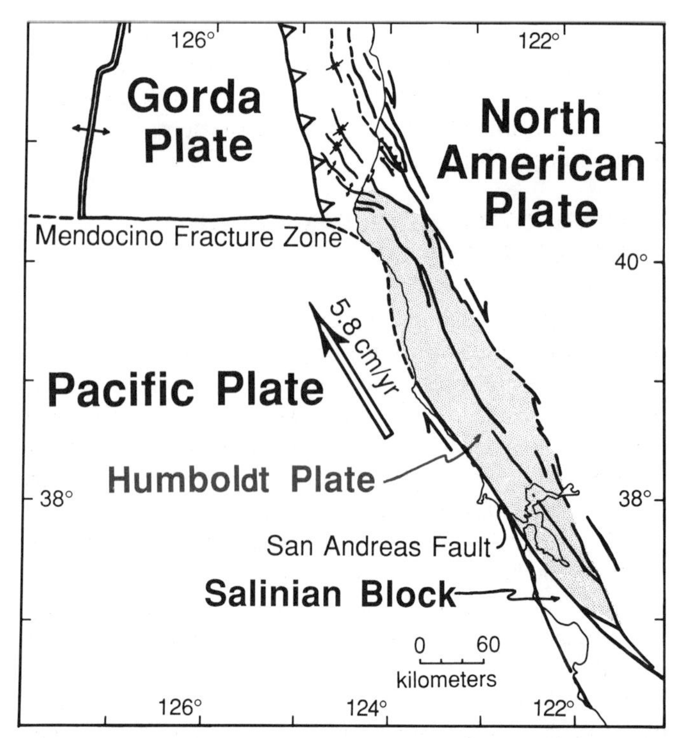

Figure 13. Active faults in the vicinity of the Mendocino triple junction (from Atwater, 1989—modified from Kelsey and Carver, 1988). The main strand of the San Andreas fault lies offshore, but major young faulting also occurs inland of the junction. The "Humboldt plate" (Herd, 1978) may be in the process of being transferred from the North American to the Pacific plate.

A second possible reaction to the geometric instability of the Mendocino triple junction is the formation of extensional basins alongside the triple junction as it passes. It appears that this was also a common solution, because the initiation times of many of the California coastal basins seem to correspond to predicted times for the triple junction passage (Dickinson and Snyder, 1979; Atwater, 1989; McCulloch, 1989).

Southern California and northernmost Baja California are by far the most complicated parts of the San Andreas system. The first contact between the North American and Pacific plates was near this region, and the Riviera triple junction lay offshore from 26 to 16 Ma. During that period, and also the next when the boundary extended southward along the Pacific margin, this region acted as the extensional connection zone between the southern offshore boundary and the onshore displacements of the San Andreas system. About 5.5 Ma, Baja California was transferred to the Pacific plate. This region again acted as a connection zone, but now it was compressional between the inland boundary in the Gulf of California and the more seaward faults of the San Andreas. The complex structures onland, and offshore in the California Borderland as described by Gorsline and Teng (1989), reflect this complicated history.

An exciting recent development has been the recognition of large-scale rotations of intact blocks and the geometric constraints imposed by such rotations. Both the timing and the magnitudes of rotations of geologic blocks are relatively easy to measure using paleomagnetism. Studies of rocks in the Transverse Ranges show that they have been rotated clockwise as large coherent blocks during the Neogene. The time histories of these rotations are interesting, but they also provide powerful constraints on the amount and timing of shear deformation that occurred across the fault systems both north and south of the ranges (Hornafius and others, 1986).

The margin of British Columbia and eastern Alaska is also a transform margin between the Pacific and North American plates. It includes an interplay of strike-slip and compressional regimes (von Huene, 1989a). The plate boundary here lies offshore. The southern segment occupies the continental shelf edge, disrupting the edge in high-angle faults and offsetting fans and channels. A small compressional component appears to be taken up as very slow subduction beneath the Queen Charlotte Islands, although deep strike-slip earthquake focal mechanisms imply that the subducting slab is broken beneath the shelf edge (Riddihough and Hyndman, 1989). Farther north, the boundary lies inland of a sideways-slipping terrane, the Yakutat block. This block is currently colliding with the southern rim of Alaska in an oblique continental collision, so that the Yakutat block is the latest addition to the Alaskan terrane collage (Fig. 14; von Huene, 1989a).

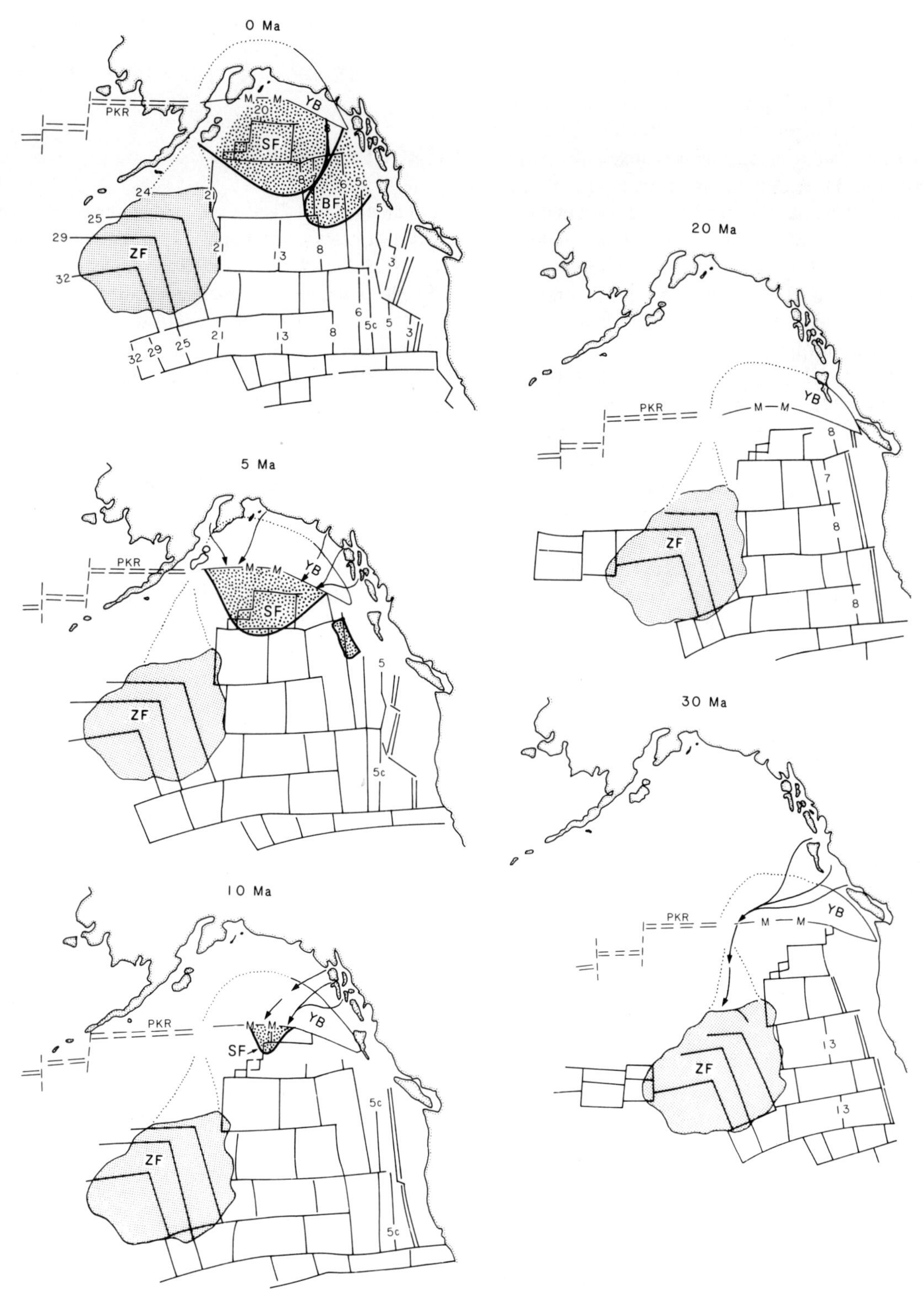

Figure 14. Sequence of diagrams showing relative motion of the North American and Pacific plates during the past 30 m.y. (from von Huene, 1989a). Zodiak Fan (ZF), Surveyor Fan (SF), Baranof Fan (BF), and the Yakutat Block (YB) are back-tracked assuming a fixed position relative to the anomaly pattern and their hypothesized subducted extensions indicated by dotted lines. The southern edge of the Yakutat Block is the slope anomaly (M-M-M), and the failed Pacific-Kula Ridge (PKR), shown by single and triple lines, respectively; major magnetic anomalies and transform fault patterns are also indicated. Plate motion after Engebretson and others (1985).

TECTONICS OF MODERN SUBDUCTION MARGINS

There are three subduction zones active in the Northeast Pacific today. The Cocos plate is subducting beneath Mexico and central America at the Mid-America trench, the Juan de Fuca plate subducts beneath Oregon and Washington in the Cascadia zone, and the Pacific plate is subducting beneath Alaska and the Aleutian Islands (Fig. 1). Recent major advances in our understanding of these margins have resulted from a combination of seismic imaging and deep-sea drilling. Whereas most subduction margins show evidence of accretion of materials at their front edges, we now know that this is not generally a continuous process, that accretion takes various forms, and that strike-slip may play an important disruptive role.

Watkins (1989) describes a detailed transect across the Mid-America trench off southern Mexico. Three separate accretionary modes seem to be active, so that incoming oceanic sediments have several fates. Some are being accreted at the toe of the continental margin (offscraped), as documented by structural details and the age of progression in the accretionary wedge. Some sediments are being underplated onto the base of the margin, as inferred from the fact that the sediments and structures document a slow, steady tilting and uplift. Finally, mass-balance calculations suggest that some of the sediments must be being removed from the system by sediment subduction beneath the continent.

The present accretionary mode has been in operation here for at least 10 m.y., but the occurrence of older crystalline rocks in the margin shows that a major truncation event occurred earlier. Watkins (1989) postulates a strike-slip event as the truncation mechanism and suggests that it may be marked in the sedimentary record by a major subsidence documented to have occurred about 24 to 17 Ma.

A second Mid-America transect off Guatemala shows relatively minor accretion (von Huene, 1989b). Age relations in the wedge here show that there has been little Neogene offscraping, although slow, variable uplift of the shelf edge implies some underplating. A mid-slope discontinuity is most easily explained as a site of strike-slip faulting.

The contrasting histories being documented in the Mid-America subduction systems could be local discrepancies or they could be related to larger plate-motion changes: changes in subduction rate and direction. The Neogene history of Pacific–Guadalupe/Cocos spreading includes many dramatic changes that may be reflected here. Future quantification and refinement of relative plate motions and of subduction histories should give us interesting insight into the detailed subduction interactions and their larger implications.

Work on the Aleutian margin likewise documents some clear changes, the most dramatic being a widespread hiatus, i.e., a major uplift event, at about 40 Ma. This corresponds approximately in time to the change in Pacific plate motion shown by the Hawaiian/Emperor bend and also to the stalling of Kula-Pacific spreading as hypothesized by Lonsdale (1988). Neogene subduction at Alaska and the Aleutians includes major sediment accretion as glacially derived trench fill and the huge sedimentary mass of the Gulf of Alaska enter the subduction zones.

SEDIMENTS OF THE NORTHEAST PACIFIC

E. L. Winterer

INTRODUCTION

The northeast Pacific is blanketed unevenly by a wide variety of sediments ranging in age from mid-Cretaceous to Quaternary. Near the North American continent, terrigenous clastic sediments dominate, and thicknesses are commonly measured in kilometers; tectonic deformation of sediments, especially of pre-Quaternary sediments, is the rule. Farther seaward, in the pelagic realm, biogenous and authigenic components are increasingly important, and thicknesses are measured in tens to hundreds of meters. These sediments are virtually undeformed by tectonism. In the following sections we take up these two realms separately, first describing sediments along the continental margins, from north to south, and then the oceanic sediments. The discussion of margin sediments is limited to relatively undeformed (i.e., easily imaged by seismic reflection methods) sediments deposited in fairly deep water (bathyal and abyssal).

The enormous areas of Pacific oceanic crust that have been subducted beneath, or have been accreted in one way or another to North America over the past 160 m.y. have carried a freight of sediment, some of it of immediate continental derivation, some of distant, oceanic provenance. It is thus important to understand the compositions and facies patterns of these sediments, not only as an end in itself, but also in the context of North American geology. The distribution of sediments on the remaining lithospheric plates of the Pacific provides us with models for the reconstruction of the sedimentary cover of now-vanished or dismembered plates. The detailed record of global climatic changes preserved in the oceanic sediments serves as a backdrop to the more provincial records of the North American continent.

The margin sediments are treated in their regional and tectonic context by von Huene (1989a, 1989b), Riddihough and Hyndman (1989), Duncan and Kulm (1989), McCulloch (1989), Normark and Gutmacher (1989), Gorsline and Teng (1989), Spencer and Normark (1989), Lonsdale (1989), and Watkins (1989). The oceanic sediments are dealt with by Barron (1989), Leinen (1989), Piper and Heath (1989), and Theyer and others (1989). These sources have been utilized extensively in the preparation of this overview.

At any one time, the types of sediment being deposited in the deep northeast Pacific varied geographically according to a number of factors: the biological productivity of the surface waters, which controls the rate of supply of skeletal remains of planktonic organisms; the biogeography of the shelled plankton, which is reflected in the relative proportions and species of diatoms, radiolarians, coccolithophorids, and foraminifers from place to place; the rate and sources of supply of terrigenous materials from the continents, through eolian, surface-current, or bottom-current transport; the rate and sources of supply of volcanic ash; the proportions of various authigenic minerals being formed near the sediment-water interface; the local position of the calcite compensation depth (CCD) and the lysoclines for foraminifers and coccoliths, which control the degree of dissolution of calcareous sediment; the efficacy of bottom currents and downslope transport, which can erode and redistribute sediments; and the processes of post-burial diagenesis, which further modify the sediments by compaction, dissolution, cementation, and recrystallization.

Sediments deposited close to the North American continent

General patterns. Near the continent, terrigenous sediments delivered to the coast by streams and glaciers dominate. Most of this material remains on the margin, either on the inner shelf or trapped in offshore structural basins. Where the margin is narrow, sediment transported by turbidity currents is deposited on the deep ocean floor, over oceanic crust. In some places, trenches along the ocean-continent boundary capture most of the sediment. Elsewhere, in places unprotected by marginal traps or a trench, fans commonly build far seaward from the margin.

A veil of hemipelagic sediment, consisting of fine-grained terrigenous debris carried by surface currents and turbid flows, extends seaward from the coast. The geographic extent and proportions of the continental materials depend on local conditions of sediment supply rate, the patterns of surface currents, and the physiography of the margin. Fine terrigenous sediment and volcanic ash from Central and South American volcanoes carried west by the west-flowing North Equatorial Current are detectable in pelagic sediments as far west as about 120°W, nearly 3,000 km from the source.

From the Aleutian and Alaskan coasts, ice rafts have transported both coarse and fine material from the continent southward to about 45°N, and this is mixed with the normal pelagic clays and diatomaceous muds of the North Pacific.

Biogenic sediment is locally an important component of sediments deposited near the continent. The fertility of North American coastal waters is generally relatively high, owing to upwelling of nutrient-rich waters. In some places, biogenous sediment predominates, either because of exceptionally high biologic productivity, as in the Gulf of California, or because of shielding of the site from dilution by terrigenous sediment, as in the seaward basins of the Southern California Borderland.

The North American margins, from the Aleutians to the equator, are of two basic types: convergent margins, generally with trenches; and transform margins, commonly with the major modern transform fault located a little inland from the ocean-continent boundary. The trench-bordered margins differ significantly from the transform margins in the pattern of accumulation of continent-derived terrigenous sediments on the deep-sea floor, and sedimentation patterns off the transform margins differ considerably among themselves according to the degree of sediment trapping between the master transform and the ocean floor. The trenches are variably filled with turbidite sediments that bypassed the continental slope via submarine canyons, but in some places sediments overflow the trenches to spill onto the adjacent ocean floor. Some of the transform margins, on the other hand, are free of traps, and large turbidite fans extend seaward from these. Other transform margins are in fact passive margins, with the active transform far inland, and with sediment-trapping basins within the margin. In the following sections, the sediments deposited opposite each of the margin segments are discussed in turn, from north to south.

Aleutian margin. Terrigenous sediments in the eastern part of the Aleutian Trench, close to sediment sources on the Alaska mainland, are about 3 km thick where they enter the subduction zone, but trench sediments thin westward along the Alaska Peninsula and the Aleutian chain.

Yakutat and Queen Charlotte Islands margin. From the eastern end of the Aleutian Trench in the Gulf of Alaska to the triple junction near the southern end of the Queen Charlotte Islands, the continental margin is a transform margin, strongly faulted and lineated, with only a narrow continental shelf or rise. Terrigenous sediments, delivered to the margin from the glaciated mountains, have accumulated to thicknesses of at least 5 km at the foot of the margin. Although the age of the oceanic crust along the margin is as old as Oligocene, most of the sediment thickness is believed to be post-Miocene.

Two major submarine fans extend about 1,000 km seaward from the margin: the Surveyor Fan in the Gulf of Alaska, and the Baranof Fan off the Queen Charlotte Islands margin (Fig. 14). The Baranof fan complex consists of glacially derived sediment from multiple sources along British Columbia and southeast Alaska. It has been sliding northward past the continent since late Miocene time, successively tapping different sediment sources, but no part of the fan has been subducted. The Surveyor fan began building in the mid-Tertiary, probably far south of its present position. It has moved along the transform faults into the Gulf of Alaska, where parts of the fan have been subducted at the eastern end of the Aleutian Trench.

The largest submarine fan in the northeast Pacific, the Zodiac Fan, began to form in late Eocene time, but ceased growth at the end of the Oligocene. Although the fan is juxtaposed against the Aleutian Trench and has a channel system radiating south from a point close to the trench, the northwest movement of the Pacific Plate during the past 40 m.y. requires that the fan have originated far to the southeast of its present location.

Juan de Fuca margin. The slowly convergent margin (orthogonal velocity about 1.6 cm/yr) landward of the Juan de Fuca spreading ridge system reveals no physiographic trench because the rate of sediment supply to the abyssal plain and to the several turbidite fans (nearly 1 km/m.y. on the distal Astoria Fan) exceeds the subsidence/subduction rates in the convergence zone. A terrigenous sediment pile estimated to be about 2.5 km thick overlies oceanic crust beneath the Astoria Fan. The Juan de Fuca Ridge system forms a seaward barrier for terrigenous sediments, except in a few spots where there are narrow gaps (Fig. 15).

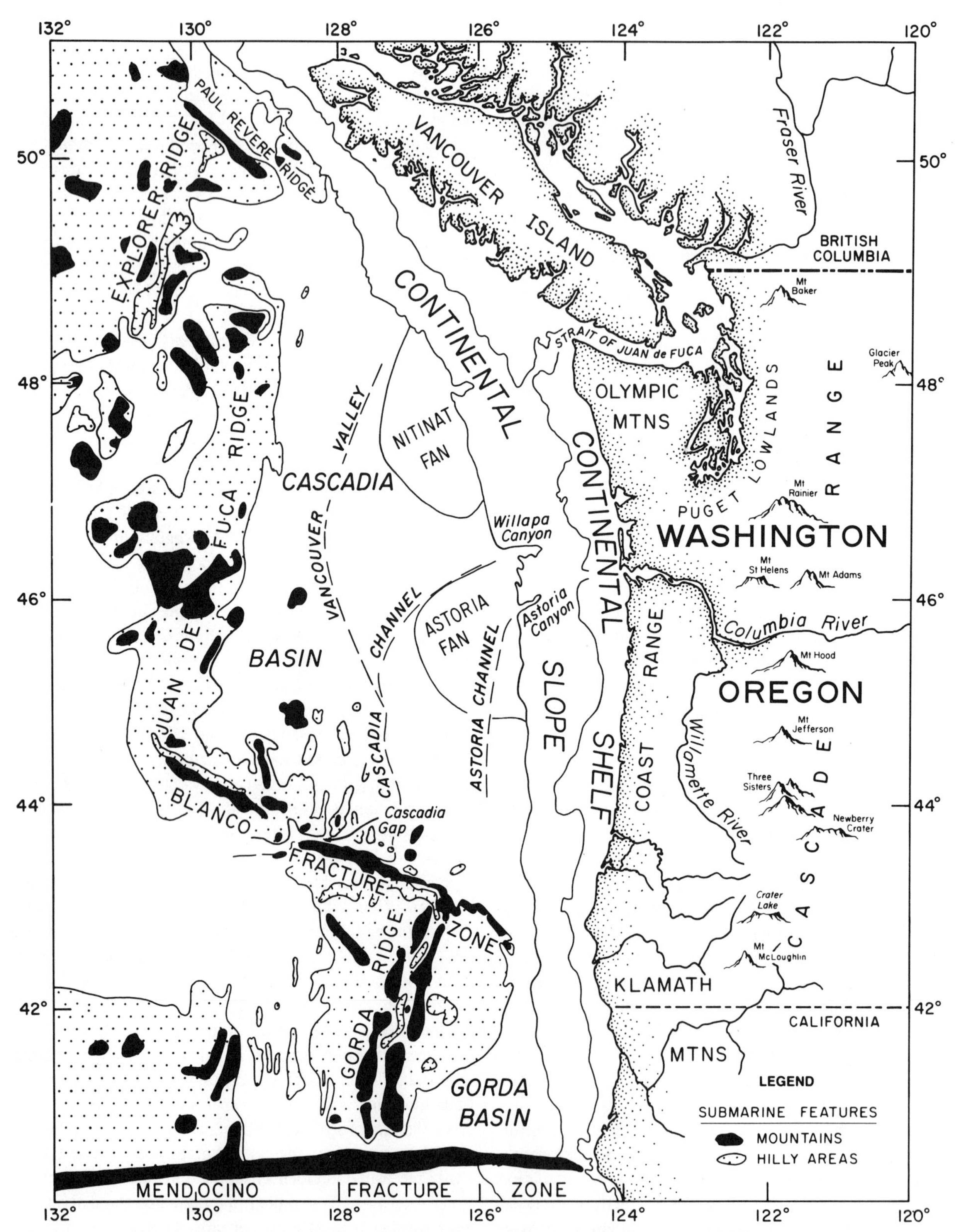

Figure 15. Physiography of the Juan de Fuca Plate, continental margin, and Cascades (from Duncan and Kulm, 1989).

California margin. From the Mendocino triple junction southward to the mouth of the Gulf of California, the North American margin is essentially a transform margin, but the width and complexity of the transform zone makes for very different conditions of sediment trapping from place to place.

From Cape Mendocino to Point Conception, the California margin is 50 to 100 km wide. A series of elongate fault-controlled Neogene basins and highs, arranged subparallel to the coast, results in much sediment from the continent being trapped before it is dispersed onto the deep ocean floor (Fig. 16). Nonetheless, two large terrigenous turbidite fans, the Delgada and Monterey fans, extend about 300 km seaward from central California. The Delgada fan results from the overtopping of an offshore basin, and the Monterey fan is fed by a canyon system that is not intercepted by a Neogene offshore basin. These fans began to develop in mid-Tertiary time, as the adjacent margin was converted from convergent to transform. The Pacific Plate has carried the fans and most of the feeding canyon systems progressively northward with respect to the North American Plate. The fan sediments are as much as 3 km thick in some places, and the Monterey fan locally buries oceanic basement relief of as much as 2 km.

From Point Conception southward to Cape Viscaino, the continent-ocean boundary is relatively straight, but the coastline curves inland, enclosing a borderland about 900 km long and as much as 250 km wide, and comprising about two dozen elongate basins and their intervening structural highs, some surmounted by islands (Fig. 17; Gorsline and Teng, 1989). In the present morphology, which was formed near the end of the Miocene, basin floors occupy about 15 percent of the area. Sediments brought by streams from the mainland are trapped in these basins so that virtually no terrigenous material reaches the deep ocean floor beyond the borderland.

The nearshore basins receive the most sediment, and those farther offshore receive less (Fig. 18). The innermost basins (Ventura and Los Angeles) are filled to overflowing and are topped by fluvial deposits. The immediately offshore basins have about 1 to 2 km of fill, dominated by turbidites. The intermediate basins contain thick blankets of mainly hemipelagic clay, interspersed with turbidites introduced from surrounding banks during glacial lowstands of sea level. The outermost basins are dominated by slowly deposited biogenic pelagic sediments. A few basins have their sill depth within the oxygen minimum, and their basin-floor sediments are seasonally laminated.

Southern Baja California. From the Viscaino Peninsula southward to the tip of Baja California, the continent-ocean boundary is nearly straight and lies along the trace of an extinct subduction zone that died in middle Miocene time, about 14 to 12 Ma. The trench associated with that zone is still visible in the bathymetry as the Cedros Deep. The margin itself is cut by an extinct transform fault system (the San Benito and Tosco-Abrejos faults) parallel to the trace of the trench, which was active between about 12 and 3.5 Ma. In the period prior to and immediately following cessation of subduction, an active submarine fan, the Magdalena Fan, built westward across the trench onto the Guadalupe plate and extended lobes along the trench axis for at least 200 km laterally. The fan was at least 450 m thick in some places, but did not extend far westward because of the barrier of the dying spreading ridge that lay only about 50 km west of the trench. Since middle Miocene time, hemipelagic sediments have continued to fill the old trench, but most terrigenous sediment is probably trapped in the fault-controlled basins on the margin (Fig. 19).

Gulf of California. The Gulf of California has been formed by oblique northwestward drift of Baja California from the Mexican mainland, initiated about 5 to 6 Ma (Lonsdale, 1989a). Beginning about 3.5 Ma, the Gulf became the principal locus of interplate motion between the Pacific and North American plates, and since then a series of small, deep-water pull-apart basins have gradually evolved. Terrigenous sediments come chiefly from the large rivers draining the Mexican mainland and from the Colorado River, which empties into the head of the gulf. These sediments are dispersed by both surface currents and turbidity currents. Muddy turbidites in the Guaymas Basin accumulate at a rate of about 1 mm/yr. Because of intense upwelling in the gulf, plankton production rates, especially of diatoms, are very high, and diatom remains constitute about half the sediment in some of the basins.

Sediments accumulating on basin slopes in the oxygen minimum (about 300 to 800 m) are rich in organic carbon, and are generally very finely laminated, chiefly reflecting summer clastic pulses against a fairly steady rain of diatom remains. Rapid sedimentation buries even the active spreading centers in the basins, and these very young sediments are locally intruded by volcanic sills and altered by diagenesis accelerated by high heat flow.

Middle America margin. For 3,000 km, from the mouth of the Gulf of California to the Panama Fracture Zone, the North American margin is bordered by a subduction zone marked by the Middle America Trench (Fig. 20). Tehuantepec Ridge intersects the trench in the Gulf of Tehuantepec and divides the margin into two halves with contrasting structural styles. To the north, the continental shelf is narrow, and a steep continental slope leads down to the trench; to the south, as far as the Costa Rica–Nicaragua border, the shelf is underlain by a wide fore-arc basin. The result is an important difference in the supply of terrigenous sediment to the ocean floor: the northern margin is incised by many submarine canyons that carry sediment from the coast directly down to the trench, but the southern margin has fewer canyons and the forearc basin probably traps much sediment from the continent. The northern trench segment is well nourished with turbidite sands from the canyons (Fig. 21), and the turbidity currents carry sand laterally along the trench axis between canyon mouths. These trench sediments are scraped off and underplated beneath the continental margin as the oceanic plate is subducted. The southern margin appears not to be accreting significant amounts of sediment, although there is about 150 m of local trench turbidite fill near the mouth of San Jose Canyon, where the most intensive seismic and drilling work has been concentrated.

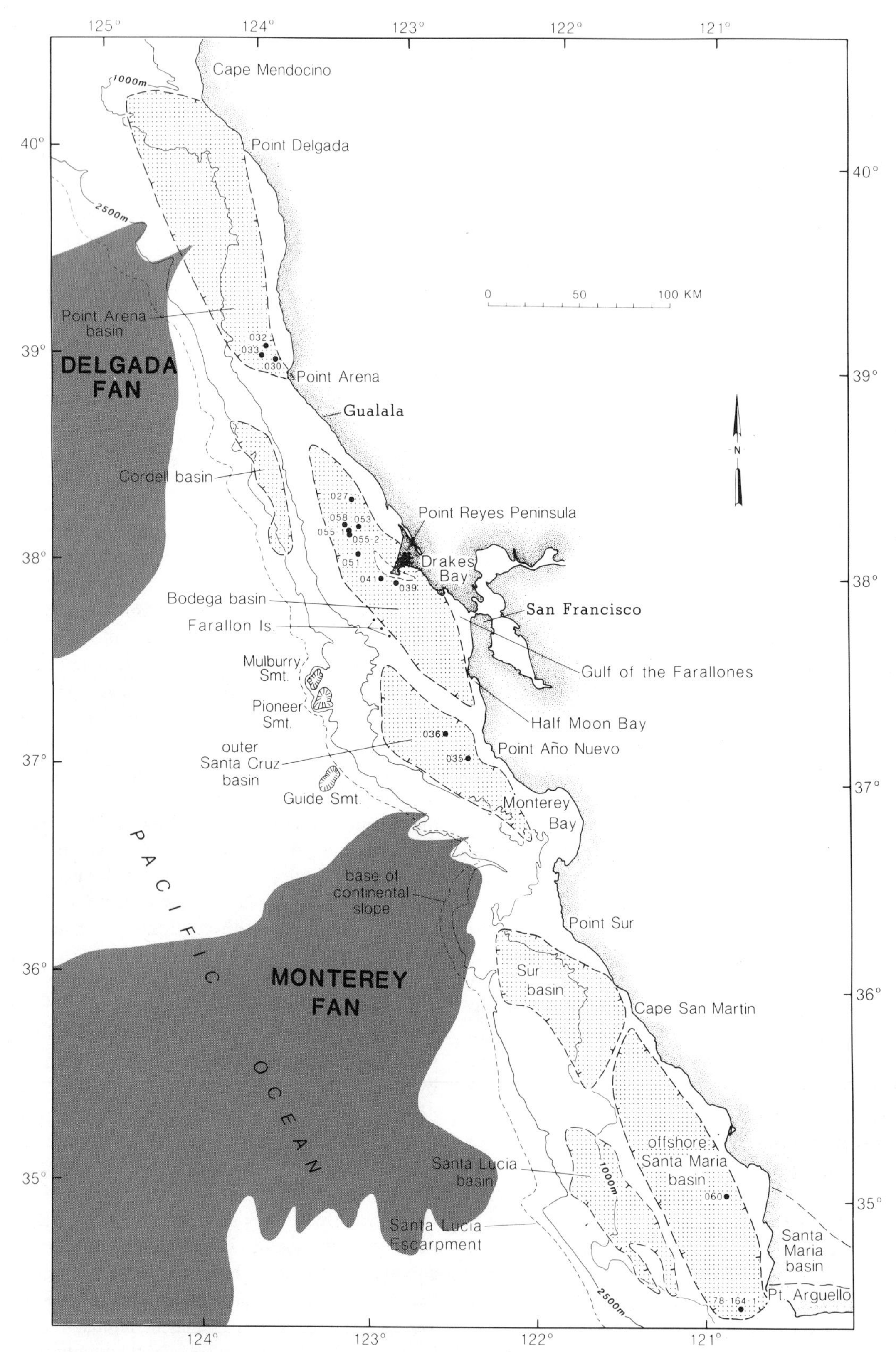

Figure 16. Map showing generalized boundaries of late Tertiary shelf and slope basins on the central California continental margin (from McCulloch, 1989). Delgada and Monterey fans shown in red.

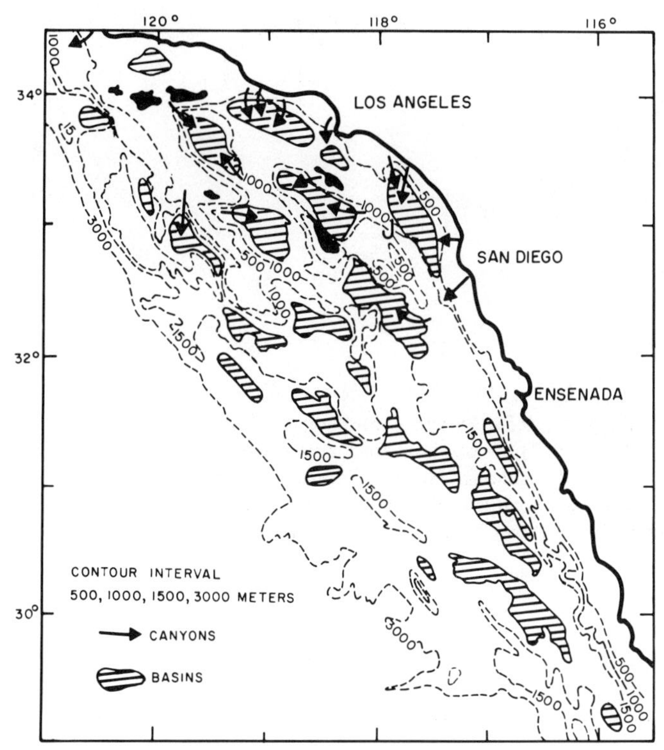

Figure 17. Sedimentary basins of the California Borderland (from Gorsline and Teng, 1989).

Panama-Colombia Margin. Although the Pacific margin of Panama and Colombia to the equator is bordered by discontinuous remnants of trenches that trap as much as 1.5 km of terrigenous sediment, the thickness (400 to 700 m) of sediment in the Panama Basin seaward of the trenches (Van Andel and others, 1971) suggests that appreciable quantities of hemipelagic material have been transported beyond the foot of the margin since formation of the ocean crust about 25 Ma, possibly mainly in the past few million years, since extinction of the active subduction zone and transfer of the Gulf to the Caribbean plate.

Sediment facies distributions on the deep ocean floor

Plate stratigraphy. Plate stratigraphy, which describes the interrelations between the stratigraphy of sediments in ocean basins and the kinematics of the lithospheric plates on which the sediments are deposited (Berger and Winterer, 1973), provides a framework for understanding the distribution of sediments in the northeast Pacific. The plate-kinematic evolution of the Pacific since mid-Cretaceous time is complex, but two essential features of this evolution are of great importance in understanding the distribution of sediments in three dimensions. (1) The Pacific Plate has been moving northwest, resulting in a progressive 30° to 40° northward shift in latitude since the mid-Cretaceous (Epp, 1978; Jarrard and Clague, 1977). Thus, for example, sediments deposited under the equator in Cretaceous time are now located in mid-latitudes, buried beneath sediments formed progressively farther north. (2) Sea floor created at a spreading ridge subsides as it ages, with the result that younger layers in the accumulating sediment pile are deposited in progressively deeper water (provided that sediment build-up rates do not exceed lithospheric

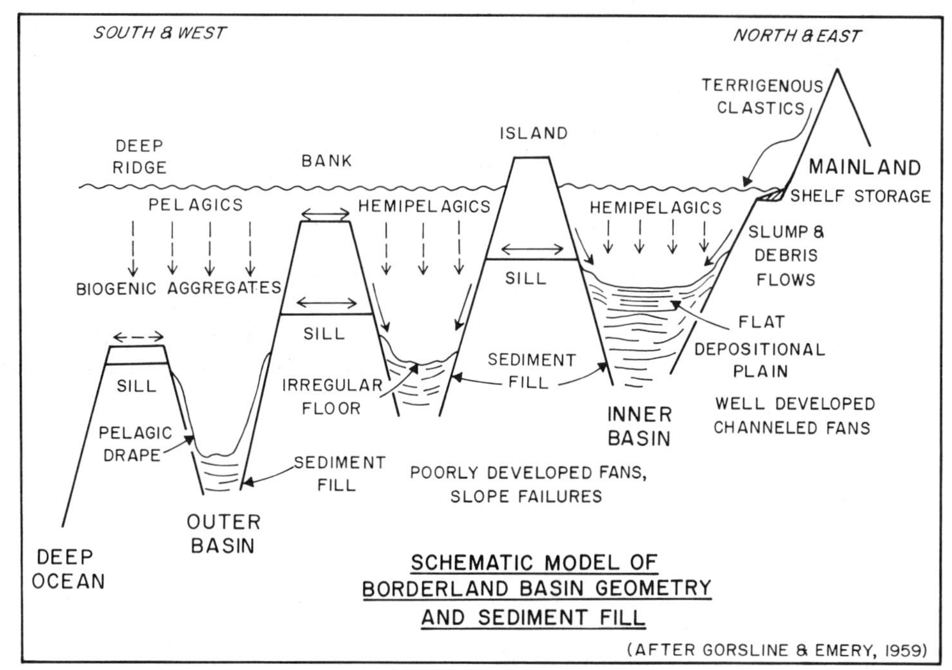

Figure 18. Schematic sedimentation model of the Borderland (from Gorsline and Teng, 1989).

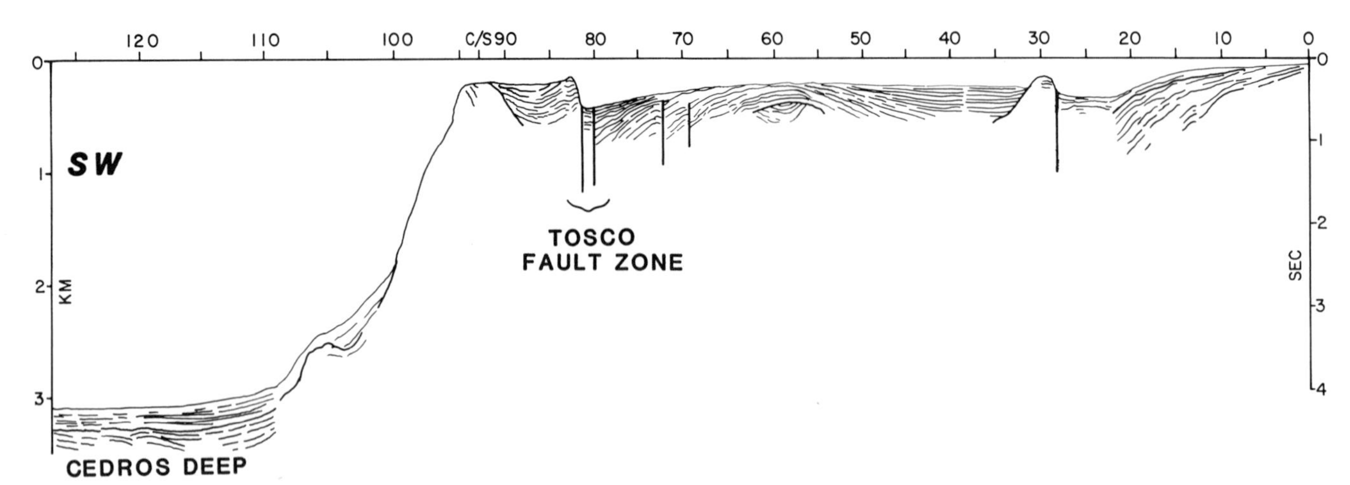

Figure 19. Line drawing of single-channel seismic reflection profile showing typical morphology across the continental margin of Baja California south of Cape Viscaino. The Tosco fault zone, now inactive, marks the trace of a transform fault, active between 12 and 3.5 Ma. Although much sediment is trapped in the fault basins on the margin, the Magdalena Fan has filled the extinct trench (Cedros Deep) and spilled onto the adjacent ocean floor (from Spencer and Normark, 1989). Horizontal scale in kilometers; vertical scale in seconds of two-way travel time.

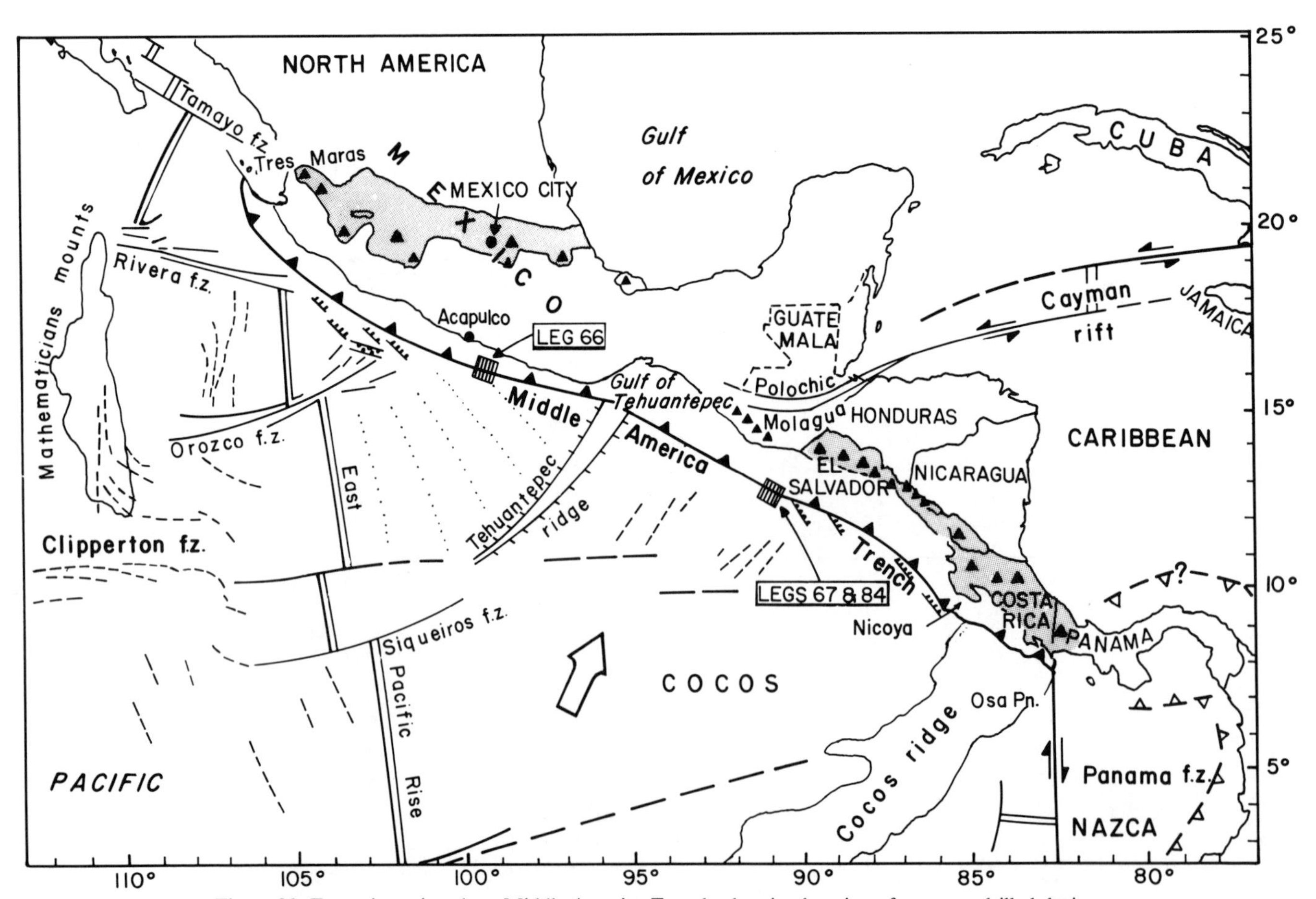

Figure 20. Tectonic setting along Middle America Trench, showing location of transects drilled during DSDP Legs 66, 67, and 84 (from Watkins, 1989).

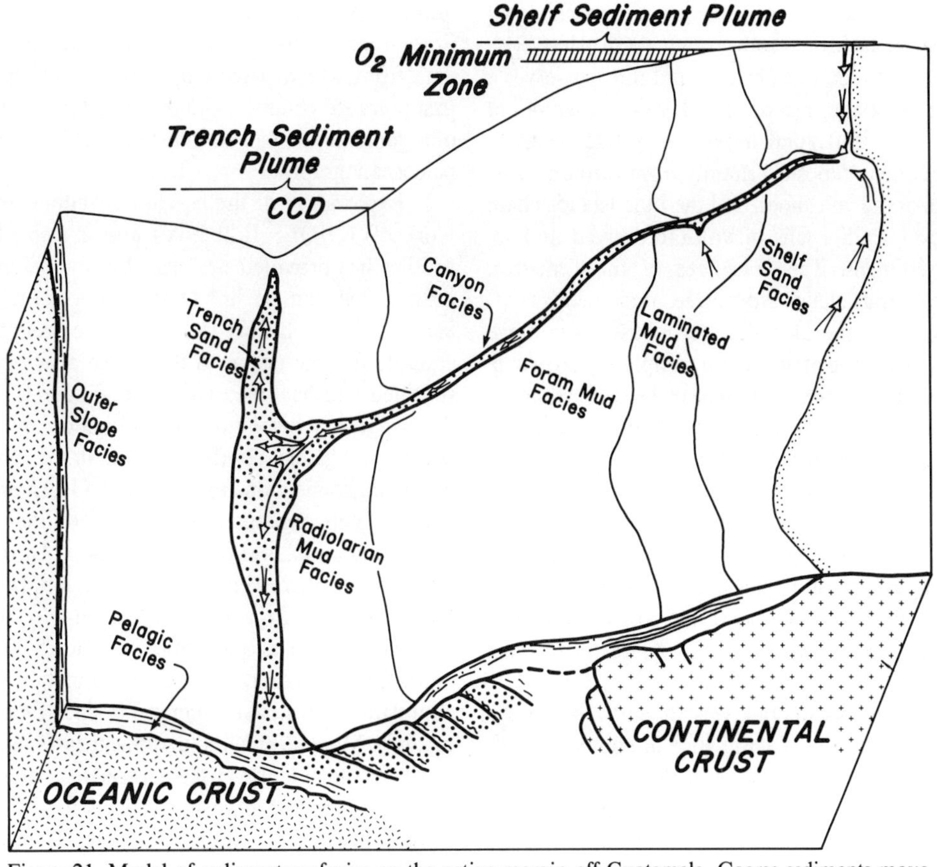

Figure 21. Model of sedimentary facies on the active margin off Guatamala. Coarse sediments move from the coast directly to the trench via submarine canyons, thus bypassing the slope, where muddy sediments accumulate (from Watkins, 1989).

subsidence rates). In a general way, this results in carbonate-rich sediments in the lower part of the sediment column and carbonate-poor sediments in the upper part, although regional differences in dissolution levels produce complications in this general trend (Berger and Winterer, 1973).

Regional facies distributions. On the deep ocean floor, away from direct continental influences, several sedimentary realms with gradational boundaries can be discriminated. Along the equator, in a zone a few degrees wide, the surface-water fertility is exceptionally high because of equatorial upwelling. Biogenous sediments predominate here, and have accumulated during the Cenozoic to a thickness of about 500 m. The rate of accumulation is highest directly at the equator. Above the lysocline for foraminifers and coccoliths, the sediments are calcareous, but become progressively enriched in biogenous silica below the lysocline. Beneath the CCD, equatorial sediments are mainly radiolarian ooze. The northward component of motion of the Pacific Plate during the Cenozoic has progressively displaced older equatorial sediments northward, while cooling and subsidence of lithosphere spreading from the East Pacific Rise carries ocean crust gradually into deeper water. Thus, layers at the base of any column of sediment were deposited at ridge-crest depths, generally above the lysocline, and overlying layers record dissolution conditions at progressively deeper levels in the sea. Because the CCD is deeper beneath the equatorial high-productivity belt than outside the belt, the equatorial calcareous sediments grade northward into radiolarian ooze. The Pacific Plate motions that have carried Pacific sea floor diagonally beneath the equator have produced complex stratigraphic sequences.

There is a very large zone, centered on the North Pacific central gyre and extending between about 10° and 40°N, where surface waters are relatively infertile. The dominant sediments at depths below the CCD (about 3500 m) in this region are very slowly deposited pelagic brown clay, largely of eolian origin. The mineralogy of the sediments indicates derivation from arid lands, both in Asia and North America.

North of about 50°N is a northern zone, where high fertility of surface waters has favored deposition of diatomaceous ooze during much of the Neogene.

Close to the axis of oceanic spreading ridges, sediments commonly have special characteristics of composition, such as enrichment in iron and manganese, resulting from release and dispersal of these elements from hydrothermal vents along the spreading axis. A thickness of a few meters of sediments of this type forms the base of the sedimentary column in most drill holes in the abyssal Pacific.

Elevated areas in the ocean basin, the oceanic plateaus and seamounts, have special facies on and around them. Hess Rise was above the CCD for much of its history and thus preserves a mid-latitude pelagic carbonate record. The Hawaiian seamount chain is flanked by a wide flexural moat, partly filled with as much as 1 km of sediment deposited mainly from turbidity currents from the flanks of the volcanoes, and the Line Islands chain is bordered by thick turbidite fans of volcano-derived and redeposited pelagic sediment. The volcanoes of the Emperor, Hawaiian, and Line Islands chains are fringed or capped by carbonate reefs and banks, some of which persist as atolls above sunken foundations, and some of which are completely drowned. Bottom currents are generally accelerated near the steep slopes of seamounts, and as a consequence, many seamounts are rimmed by a narrow erosional or nondepositional moat.

Cenozoic sediments

Equatorial region. The Cenozoic sediments of the equatorial Pacific record deposition of a thick lens of biogenous sediments on the Pacific Plate as it subsided and moved obliquely northward across an oceanographic zone of relatively high fertility.

During the Cenozoic, ocean crust was added to the Pacific (and Farallon) plates at the East Pacific Rise in equatorial latitudes at rates of 5 to 10 cm/yr. Cooling of the lithosphere has caused progressive subsidence as the lithosphere moves away from the rise. For example, Eocene crust has subsided from rise crest depths of about 2,700 m to about 5,000 m. At the same time, northward motion of the Pacific Plate parallel to the hotspot traces of the Emperor (65 to 43 Ma) and Hawaiian (43 to 0 Ma) seamount chains displaced crust northward at 3 to 5 cm/yr.

Equatorial fertility is caused by divergence and upwelling. At the equator, divergence of the surface 100 m of water is maintained by the change in sign of the Coriolis effect; west-flowing waters are deflected to the right (north) in the Northern Hemisphere and to the left (south) in the Southern Hemisphere. Productivity diminishes gradually westward along the equator, and sharply about 2 to 4° north and south of the equator, to about 10 to 20 percent of its equatorial value. The increased calcareous shell production in surface waters depresses the depth at which carbonate accumulation and dissolution rates are in balance (the CCD).

The gross effect of this combination of northward plate motion, subsidence, and passage through a fertile belt is a lens of mainly calcareous Cenozoic sediment as much as 600 m thick. The effect of northward plate motion is to place the axis of greatest thickness at about 4°N. A conceptual model for stratigraphic columns within the lens is shown in Figure 22. In the equatorial region, the stratigraphic sequence is nearly complete, with only a few relatively small hiatuses, and the abundance of planktonic microfossils of all four major groups—foraminifers, coccoliths, radiolarians, and diatoms—enables correlation, especially in the Neogene, with a precision of about 1 m.y. The state of preservation of foraminifers provides information on the position of the lysocline and the CCD, and the oxygen- and carbon-isotopic stratigraphy of benthic and planktonic foraminifers yields data from which paleotemperatures and temperature gradients, past polar ice volumes, and the global production and burial rates of organic matter can be inferred. The lens is a treasure house for paleoceanography.

Exploration of the equatorial sedimentary lens with a network of JOIDES drill holes and a web of seismic reflection profiles has provided the basis for a coherent regional geologic history that can be linked to global ocean history. The main feature of this history is a stepwise change from the warm, equable Eocene ocean to the Pleistocene ocean that is strongly stratified and has steep latitudinal gradients. The changes reflect the progressive isolation of Antarctica and the installation of continental glacial conditions there in the Oligocene, the closing of Pacific connections to the Indian Ocean and to the Caribbean and the concomitant development of the present-day meridional circulation, and the deterioration of global climate, leading finally to Northern Hemisphere glaciation. In the equatorial zone, the changes led to a marked deepening of the CCD in the late Oligocene, from about 3,500 to about 5,000 m, and thus to a marked increase in carbonate accumulation rates. Carbonate accumulation rates have tapered off since then, with notable fluctuations. Many of the fluctuations in carbonate dissolution levels, recognizable as shifts in the carbonate content of drill cores, can also be recognized in seismic reflection profiles over much of the equatorial Pacific. Dating of these levels in drill holes has established that the shifts correspond to times of global changes in deep-water circulation, resulting in nondeposition or erosion elsewhere in the Pacific.

North-central Pacific. North of the equatorial zone of high productivity, sediments are less and less biogenous. Beneath the subtropical gyre, on the deep ocean floor away from the influence of volcanoes, only brown clay, mainly of eolian origin, is present. The clay is unfossiliferous except for microscopic fish debris and is commonly enriched in zeolites, barite, and iron- and manganese-rich oxides. Mineralogically, the clay typically comprises about 30 to 40 percent illite, 10 to 15 percent each of chlorite, quartz, plagioclase, and kaolinite, and 0 to 5 percent smectite. Chlorite increases northward, reflecting high-latitude weathering; kaolinite and smectite increase eastward, reflecting North American dust contributions. The accumulation rate of the clay decreases from west to east, reflecting the dominantly Asian provenance of the wind-borne sediment. The accumulation rate for sediments older than about 15 Ma was about 20 to 50 mg/cm/k.y., but after that time, rates increased by a factor of about 10 in the Pleistocene, reflecting the onset of Northern Hemisphere glaciation and the load of loess-derived dust carried by the westerlies. Clay older than about 15 Ma generally contains less illite and quartz and more zeolite, smectite, and amorphous material than younger clays and is more enriched in transition elements, such as Fe, Mn, Co, Cu, Ni, and Zn. The differences may reflect the lower flux of dust during the earlier, more humid times.

Far northern and eastern Pacific. North of the subarctic front, at about 40°N, the surface waters are cooler and more fertile than in the subtropical gyre. Sedimentation is more rapid, both because of high production rates of diatom remains and because of contributions of detrital clays and volcanic ash from the land. The diatomaceous component appears first in significant proportions in middle Miocene strata. In more deeply buried sequences the diatom silica has been dissolved and recrystallized as chert. Ice-rafted debris in oceanic sediments on the Pacific Plate appears first in the Pliocene.

The California current dominates the eastern margin of the northeast Pacific from about 40°N where the west wind drift in the North Pacific is deflected southward as it approaches the coast. It transports cool, fertile waters as far south as 23°N, so that oceanic sediments in this region are enriched in biogenous carbonate and silica.

Where the central North Pacific brown clay province grades laterally into the more biogenous sediments near the continental margin and in the equatorial sediment lens, the succession is punctuated by a series of hiatuses, representing times of nondeposition or erosion. Changing oceanographic and climatic conditions are ultimately responsible for creating the hiatuses. In the Neogene, these are attributed to intensification of flow of bottom waters, tied to periods of growth of the Antarctic ice cap. Many

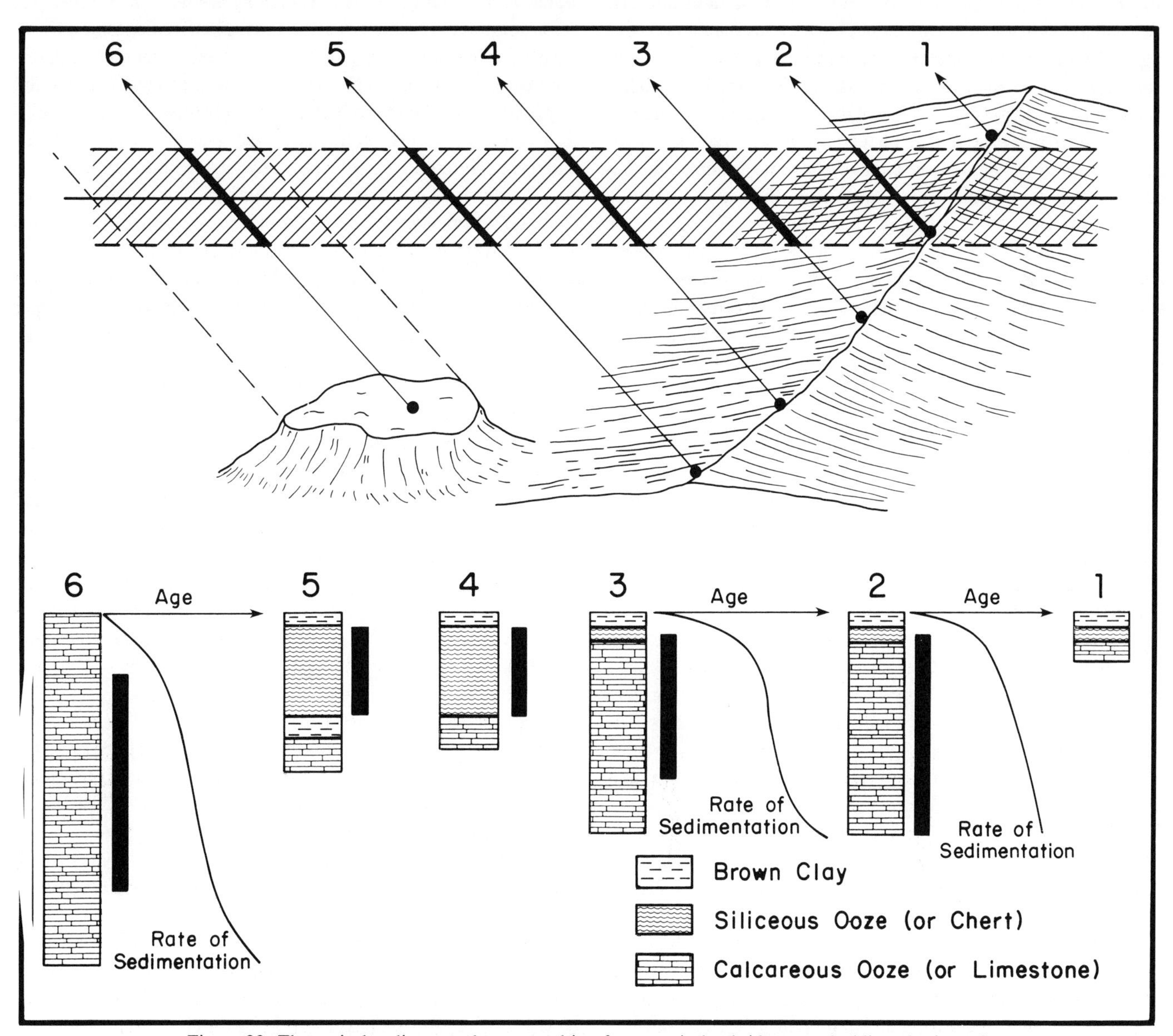

Figure 22. Theoretical sediment columns resulting from vertical subsidence and oblique horizontal motions of sea floor beneath the equatorial high-productivity belt (diagonal ruling in upper panel) (from Theyer and others, 1989). Crossing of the equatorial zone shown by black bars beside columns in lower panel. Rate of accumulation of carbonates and silica increases where the crossing is shallower than the CCD (cases 2, 3, and 6), or of silica without carbonate where the crossing is below the CCD.

of the hiatuses documented in JOIDES cores in the North Pacific Neogene have been correlated to hiatuses in other parts of the world ocean. These can be recognized, and more precisely dated, as dissolution events in the equatorial lens.

Mesozoic sediments

The large region of the northeast Pacific underlain by Cretaceous crust has been barely explored by drilling. Thus, we have only the sketchiest notion of the distribution of Cretaceous sediments there. Because of the northward component of Pacific plate motions, Cretaceous sediments are now located from 20° to 40° north of their original latitudes of deposition. What few data that are available suggest that in middle Cretaceous time, the CCD was at depths of about 3500 m, and perhaps was a little deeper in Late Cretaceous time near the equator (Thierstein, 1979). Sediments deposited above the CCD are mainly limestone, chalk, and marlstone; sediments deposited below are mainly zeolitic brown clay. Chert nodules are common in the limey sediments and occur in the clays much more abundantly than in comparable Cenozoic facies.

A notable feature of the Mesozoic sequences on oceanic plateaus in the Pacific is the occurrence of organic-rich sediments at certain levels. On Hess Rise, limestone with organic-rich laminae occurs in Albian and Cenomanian strata deposited at a paleodepth of about 1,000 m (Vallier and others, 1981), probably in the oxygen minimum zone.

Sediments on and around seamounts

Three long seamount chains rise above the deep-sea floor in the western part of the northeast Pacific, and these have special sediments on and around them. The oldest chain is the Line Islands chain, stretching from about 17°N to about 10°S and comprising many guyots and a few living atolls. The flanks of the central part of the chain, near the equator, are buried beneath thick archipelagic aprons. Cores from JOIDES drill holes (Jackson and others, 1976) through these aprons show the edifices to be of Campanian age, with a cap of shallow-water sediments. The shallow-water conditions were maintained through Maastrichtian time, and there was at least local rejuvenation of reefal conditions in the Eocene, associated with renewed volcanism.

The Hawaiian chain erupted progressively from about 42 Ma until now, and shows the classical development of a flexural moat, partly filled with volcanic and minor amounts of reefal debris transported by turbidity currents, debris flows, and slides down the flanks of the volcanoes. Volcanic islands at the younger end of the chain are fringed by coral reefs, and atolls cap seamounts in the northwestern part of the chain up to about 28°N, near the northern limit of hermatypic coral growth, where the subsidence rate of the seamounts is faster than the upward growth rate of the reefs.

The Emperor chain was generated over the same hot spot that produced the Hawaiian chain, from about 65 to 42 Ma. Drilling and dredging show the seamounts to be capped by shallow-water bryozoan-algal limestone. This assemblage is characteristic of temperate rather than tropical waters and suggests that the Hawaiian hot spot may have migrated south with respect to the Earth's pole of rotation since Eocene time.

Hydrogenous and hydrothermal sediments

Hydrogenous sediments, precipitated inorganically from sea water or from pore waters in the upper few tens of centimeters, are a common occurrence in the northeast Pacific, especially in areas far from the diluting influence of rapid biogenous or terrigenous sedimentation. The major members of the hydrogenous component in pelagic sediments of the northeast Pacific are the oxyhydroxides of iron and manganese, barite, and the silicates phillipsite, clinoptilolite, smectite, palygorskite, and sepiolite.

Modern sediments forming close to the East Pacific rise and the basal sediments resting on oceanic basaltic basement at many JOIDES drill sites have high transition-metal contents. The combined mineralogical, isotopic, and chemical data suggest they formed from hydrothermal solutions resulting from basalt–sea water reactions at the rise crest. The solid phases crystallized at low temperatures under the strong influence of sea water.

Ferromanganese oxides (todorokite, birnessite, δ-MnO_2, and poorly crystallized Fe oxides) occur as fine particles, coatings and encrustations, as dispersed micronodules, and as macronodules that are abundant on the ocean floor in some places. The minor elements Ni, Cu, and Co can total more than 3 weight percent in some nodules. Compositions of nodules vary regionally: in the belt near 12°N, where nodules are very abundant, Ni and Cu contents are high, Mn/Fe ratios are greater than 2, and todorokite is abundant; in the central North Pacific, Ni and Cu are generally less than 1.5 percent and δ-MnO_2 is the only mineral. On seamounts, ferromanganese crusts generally contain Co as the dominant minor element.

Phillipsite is the most abundant zeolite in the near-surface sediments of the North Pacific, exceeding 50 weight percent on a carbonate-free basis in some samples. It mainly forms from alteration of basaltic glass. It is probably metastable, decreasing in abundance to zero at about 300 m burial depth. Smectite also probably forms from alteration of basaltic glass, but it may result from reaction between biogenic silica and FeO(OH) to form nontronite.

Barite is enriched in sediments along the East Pacific Rise and along the equator. It reaches concentrations of 1 to 5 percent of the sediment in some places. The East Pacific Rise barite may be largely of hydrothermal origin, while the equatorial barite may be precipitated inorganically from pore waters.

THE HAWAIIAN-EMPEROR CHAIN

R. W. Decker

INTRODUCTION

Intraplate volcanism within the Pacific Plate is most obvious in Hawaii and the Hawaiian-Emperor volcanic chain. This chain forms a global relief feature of the first order.

The Island of Hawaii lies at the southeastern end of the Hawaiian-Emperor volcanic chain—a dogleg ridge, largely submarine, stretching nearly 6,000 km across the North Pacific Ocean basin (Fig. 2). From Hawaii the chain extends northwestward along the Hawaiian Ridge to a major bend beyond Kure Atoll. North of the bend the chain continues in a northward direction as the submarine ridge of the Emperor Seamounts. Volcanoes are active at the southeast end of the chain and become progressively older to the northwest. Most of this volcanic chain, with an estimated area of 1,200,000 km^2, lies beneath the ocean. Only the Hawaiian Islands and a few atolls of the Hawaiian Ridge, totaling some 6,878 km^2, rise above the sea.

The following discussion is drawn directly from sections in the chapter on the Hawaiian-Emperor Chain in Winterer and others (1989), and chapters in Decker and others (1987).

Tectonics, geochronology, and origin

The Hawaiian-Emperor Chain consists of at least 107 individual volcanoes with a total volume of about 1 million km^3. The bend between the Hawaiian and Emperor Chains reflects a major change in Pacific Plate motion at 43.1 ± 1.4 Ma and probably was caused by collision of the Indian subcontinent into Eurasia and the resulting reorganization of oceanic spreading centers and initiation of subduction zones in the western Pacific. Ages of the volcanoes at the northwesternmost end of the Emperor chain are 75 to 80 Ma. The volcanoes of the chain were erupted onto the floor of the Pacific Ocean without regard for the age or preexisting structure of the ocean crust.

Hawaiian volcanoes erupt lava of distinct chemical compositions during four major stages in their evolution and growth (Table 1). The earliest stage is a submarine alkalic preshield stage, which is followed by the tholeiitic shield stage. The shield stage probably accounts for >95 percent of the volume of each volcano. The shield stage is followed by an alkalic postshield stage, during which a thin cap of alkalic basalt and associated differentiated lava covers the tholeiitic shield. After several million years of erosion, alkalic rejuvenated-stage lava erupts from isolated vents. An individual volcano may become extinct before the sequence is complete. The alkalic preshield stage is known only from recent study of Loihi seamount, at the southeasternmost end of the chain. Lava from later eruptive stages has been identified from numerous submerged volcanoes located west of the principal Hawaiian Islands.

Volcanic propagation rates along the chain (Fig. 23) are 9.2 ± 0.3 cm/yr for the Hawaiian Chain and 7.2 ± 1.1 cm/yr for the Emperor Chain. A best fit through all the age data for both chains gives 8.6 ± 0.2 cm/yr.

Alkalic rejuvenated-stage lava is generated during rapid change from subsidence to uplift as the volcanoes override a flexural arch created by loading the new shield volcano on the ocean lithosphere. Thus, lava erupts on an older shield during formation of a new large shield volcano 1,900 ±30 km to the east. The duration of the quiescent period preceding eruption of rejuvenated-stage lava decreases systematically from 2.5 m.y. on Niihau to <0.4 m.y. at Haleakala, reflecting an increase in the rate of volcanic propagation during the past few million years.

Paleomagnetic data indicate that the Hawaiian hot spot has remained fixed during the past 40 m.y., but prior to that time the hot spot was apparently located at a more northerly latitude. The most reliable data suggest about 7° of southward movement of the hot spot between 65 and 40 Ma.

Numerous hypotheses have been formulated to explain the mechanism of the hot spots. These fall into four types: propagating fracture hypotheses, thermal or chemical convection hypotheses, shear melting hypotheses, and heat injection hypotheses. A successful hypothesis must explain the propagation of volcanism along the chain, the near-fixity of the hot spot, the chemistry and timing of the eruptions from individual volcanoes, and the detailed geometry of volcanism. None of the geophysical hypotheses proposed to date is fully satisfactory. However, the existence of the Hawaiian swell suggests that hot spots are indeed hot. In addition, both geophysical and geochemical hypotheses suggest that primitive undegassed mantle material ascends beneath Hawaii. Petrologic models suggest that this primitive material reacts with the ocean lithosphere to produce the compositional range of Hawaiian lava.

Petrology of Hawaiian lava

Hawaiian petrology continues to be a subject of great scientific interest. Several developments over the past three decades have substantially increased our knowledge of the processes by which basaltic magma is generated in the mantle, transported to storage in the crust, and erupted onto the surface (Fig. 24). Significant areas of study include the following.

1. Active volcanism at Kilauea volcano, including the study of lava lakes ponded in pit craters. Lava lakes have provided natural laboratories in which numerous petrologic processes associated with cooling, crystallization, and differentiation of basaltic magmas have been quantified. The detailed study of Kilauea lava chemistry in time and space has resulted in recognition of other petrologic processes, including storage of chemically distinct mantle-derived magma batches and mixing of these parental magma batches with magma stored and fractionated in the rift zones. Geodetic and seismological studies at Kilauea have been critical in establishing a context in which the petrologic data can be evaluated. One unsolved question is the source of the magma for each active volcano. Seismic evidence suggests a common

TABLE 1. HAWAIIAN ERUPTIVE PRODUCTS

Eruptive Stage	Rock Types	Eruption Rate	Volume (%)
Rejuvenated stage	Alkalic basalt Basanite Nephelinite Nepheline melilitite	Very low	<1
Postshield stage	Alkalic basalt Transitional basalt Ankaramite Hawaiite Mugearite Benmoreite Trachyte	Low	~1
Shield stage	Tholeiitic basalt Picritic tholeiitic basalt	High	95-98
Preshield stage	Basanite Alkalic basalt Transitional basalt	Low	~3

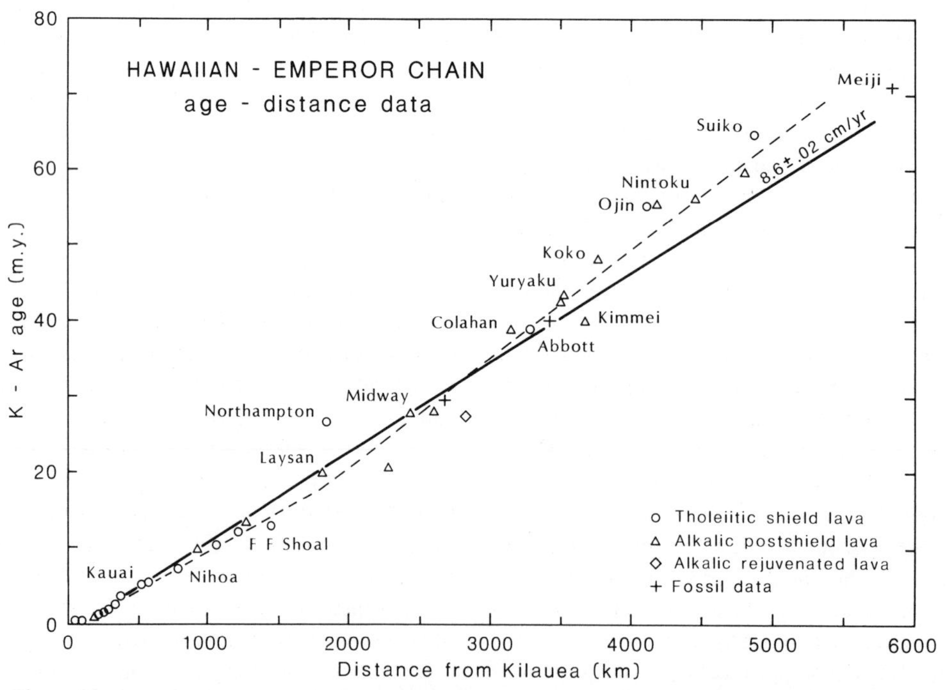

Figure 23. Age of volcanoes in the Hawaiian-Emperor chain as a function of distance from Kilauea (from Clague and Dalrymple, 1989). The solid line is a least-squares cubic fit to the data and represents an average rate of propagation of volcanism of 8.6×0.2 cm/yr. Dashed line is a two-segment fit using data from Kilauea to Gardner, and Laysan to Suiko.

staging area at 40 km depth, whereas petrologic studies show that each active volcano has unique chemical characteristics, indicating isolated storage regions.

2. Detailed study of the recently discovered Loihi Seamount, the newest volcano in the Hawaiian Chain, has revealed a preshield alkalic stage similar, but not identical, to the postshield alkalic stages on the subaerial volcanoes.

3. Detailed stratigraphic studies of individual volcanoes, using major-element chemistry, trace-element chemistry, and radioactive-isotope systems, show diversity of chemical evolution in each volcano in the chain, particularly within the alkalic stage that follows construction of a tholeiitic shield. There is also diversity in the chemical and isotopic relations linking shield lava to postshield lava. The combined isotopic and chemical data have revealed significant complexity in the source mantle for Hawaiian lava, both within the stratigraphic record of single volcanoes and among different volcanoes. The origin of Hawaiian magma, as defined by depth and degree of partial melting, enriched versus depleted sources, and mineralogy of the source mantle, is unresolved at present. The increasing amount of data indicates a need for more definition of the structure and composition of the Earth's mantle from such diverse disciplines as seismic tomography and the experimental physics of melting and melt transport.

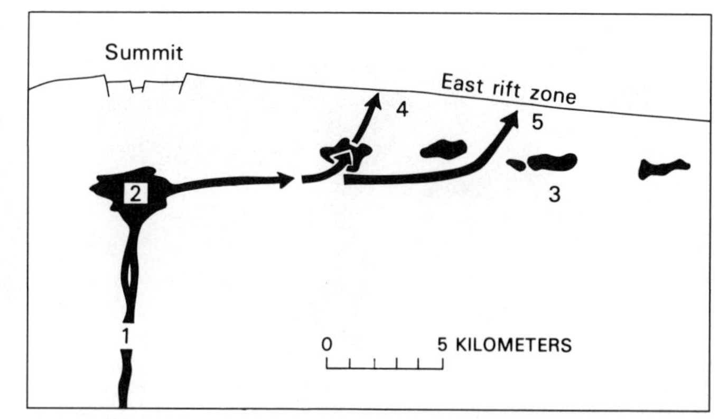

Figure 24. Simplified model of magma storage and eruption at Kilauea (modified from Wright and Fiske, 1971, Fig. 9). 1: Conduit through the volcanic pile defined seismically; 2: shallow storage reservoir, defined from both geodetic measurements and as an aseismic zone; 3: isolated pockets of magma produced by intrusions into the rift zones. Eruptions at the summit are fed directly from the top of the central reservoir. Most eruptions on the rift are fed from lower in the central reservoir and may either become mixed with stored rift magma (4) or have direct access to the surface (5). Infrequently, stored rift magma may be erupted independently.

Seismicity and tectonics of Hawaii

Earthquake-hypocenter data collected by the Hawaiian Volcano Observatory from 1960 to 1983 provide a wealth of information on the active processes of Kilauea's magma system. Two classes of earthquakes can be recognized. The magma conduits produce "volcanic earthquakes" that occur in episodic swarms often accompanied by tilt changes or eruptions. "Tectonic earthquakes" on Kilauea's flanks and in some parts of the upper mantle occur more continually and are punctuated with mainshock-aftershock sequences. Volcanic earthquakes also have smaller magnitudes, a greater proportion of small events, and frequent association with tremor. Three-dimensional earthquake patterns and separation of volcanic and tectonic seismicity can be visualized in a series of hypocenter depth slices and cross sections. Earthquakes reveal a magma system consisting of a vertical conduit from Kilauea caldera to about 60 km depth, two shallow rift zones radial to the caldera, and a shallow magma reservoir joining these three conduits.

The shallow magma chamber reservoir is an aseismic zone beneath the south edge of Kilauea caldera. The reservoir is surrounded on two sides by intensely active rift conduits centered near 3 km depth, above by a seismically active cap in the caldera mostly between 1 and 2 km depth, and below by the vertical magma conduit having earthquakes as shallow as 7 km. The deformation centers are mostly between 2 and 4 km depth, near the top of the seismic zone that is between 3 and 7 km depth. Inflation of the reservoir produces earthquakes above by extension in the summit region, and in the adjacent rift conduits by slow magma intrusion into the rifts.

The vertical magma conduit, as defined by earthquakes, consists of two parts: a narrow, nearly vertical pipe between 7 and 20 km depth mostly having swarms of volcanic earthquakes, and a zone that widens into a diffuse and south-dipping region between 20 and 60 km depth. Earthquakes in the deeper conduit are larger in magnitude and more continuous in time, as if tectonic in origin. Earthquakes below 40 km depth merge with the Hawaiian hot spot below Kilauea, Loihi, and Mauna Loa Volcanoes. Kilauea's deep earthquakes also join a band of seismicity along the island's south coast, which is probably caused by shear stress applied from Kilauea's mobile south flank and by the growing and asymmetrical weight of the Kilauea shield. The number of earthquakes in the vertical conduit dropped dramatically at the time of the magnitude 7.2 Kalapana earthquake in 1975. This decrease indicates that conduit earthquakes are partly driven by regional stresses derived from the seaward push of the south flank.

The vertical distribution of conduit earthquakes shows pronounced gaps near depths of 5, 13, and 20 km. The first gap results from the magma reservoir between 3 and 7 km depth, and the gap at 13 km is probably bounded by the Moho and the prevolcanic oceanic sediments. The depth of 20 km is also a gap for earthquakes in the surrounding lithosphere, marks the change from volcanic-style earthquakes above to tectonic below, and is probably the zone of the neutral stress axis in the lithosphere bending under the island's weight. The vertical magma conduit thus is similar to a passive, weak zone in the lithosphere that triggers earthquakes mainly driven by regional stresses.

The rift zones of Kilauea produce shallow earthquake swarms of varied intensity and complexity arising from periods of

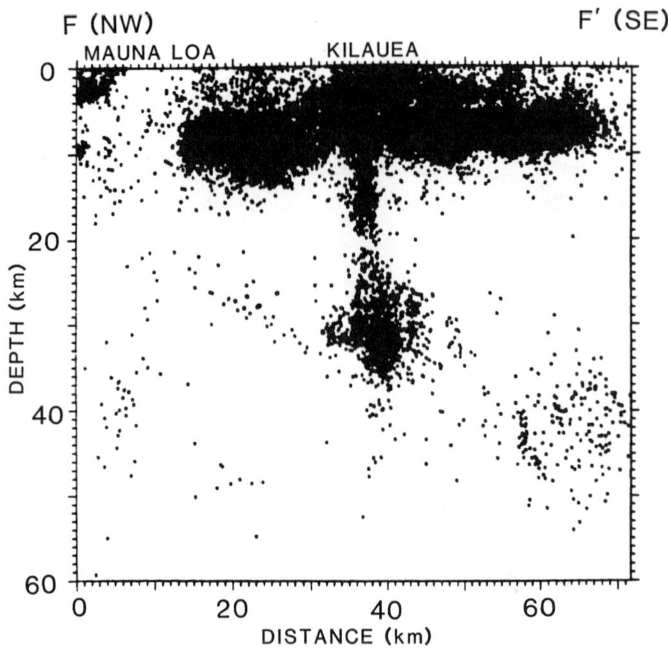

Figure 25. Cross-section through Kilauea and part of Mauna Loa (from Klein and Koyanagi, 1989). Earthquakes from 1970 to 1983 with calculated errors in position of 4 km or less are included. Hypocenters are projected into the section from 10 km on both sides.

summit inflation, slow intrusions, and rapid intrusions that may also result in eruptions. Slow intrusions may feed the rifts adjacent to the caldera during inflation, send slow pulses of magma (and hence earthquakes) down the rifts, or be aseismic, except at the terminus of the intrusion where magma collects. The computer plot in Figure 25 shows the depth and shape of the seismic zone.

Magma and eruption dynamics

Eaton and Murata's (1960) cross section of Kilauea Volcano (Fig. 26) remains the basic model of how Hawaiian volcanoes work. Magma forms by partial melting of mantle rock at depths between 60 and 170 km in a specific area of the mantle known as the Hawaiian hot spot. The melt accumulates by migrating through small fractures, or by shear coalescence, into volumes large enough to ascend. The ascensive pressure is caused by the greater density of the rocks surrounding and overlying the magma. Ascent through the lithosphere occurs in discontinuous conduits that are generated by magmafracting. Apparently there are enough of these ascensive conduits that the magma is supplied to a shallow reservoir system 3 to 7 km beneath the summit caldera at rates that vary by less than an order of magnitude over time scales of months to decades. When the shallow magma reservoir fills to about lithostatic pressure, magmafracting emplaces dikes upward or laterally into the rift zones, and those dikes that reach the surface erupt. Eruptions at high volume rates rapidly reduce the pressure in the shallow magma reservoir and are of brief duration. Long-lived eruptions occur at low volume rates and are sustained by the resupply of magma from depth. Lava fountains are produced by the rapid expansion of magmatic gases (H_2O, CO_2, and SO_2) at near-surface pressures. Major caldera collapses, sometimes associated with explosive eruptions, occur repeatedly at intervals of a few thousand years. One probable cause of these collapses is intrusion or eruption on the submarine rifts which produce draindown of the shallow reservoir system.

Hydrothermal systems in Hawaii

The east rift zone of Kilauea volcano is composed of a northeast-trending complex of dikes and fractures extending more than 100 km from the summit caldera to the ocean floor. Geological, petrological, and geophysical data indicate that substantial volumes of molten magma are intruded into and stored within the east rift dike complex and that parts of the rift have temperatures exceeding the Curie point of basalt. The shallow ground-water hydrology and chemistry of the lower rift are strongly affected by natural thermal discharge from the rift and indicate a continuous heat-loss rate estimated at 291 megawatts. Several deep geothermal wells drilled into the lower rift have confirmed the presence of high temperatures and of an active hydrothermal system associated with the rift. The maximum temperatures encountered in deep wells approach the critical point of water (374°C), but show a sharp decline on the southern boundary of the rift.

Petrologic studies of drill cuttings from the wells have shown that intermittent, intense hydrothermal alteration has occurred to

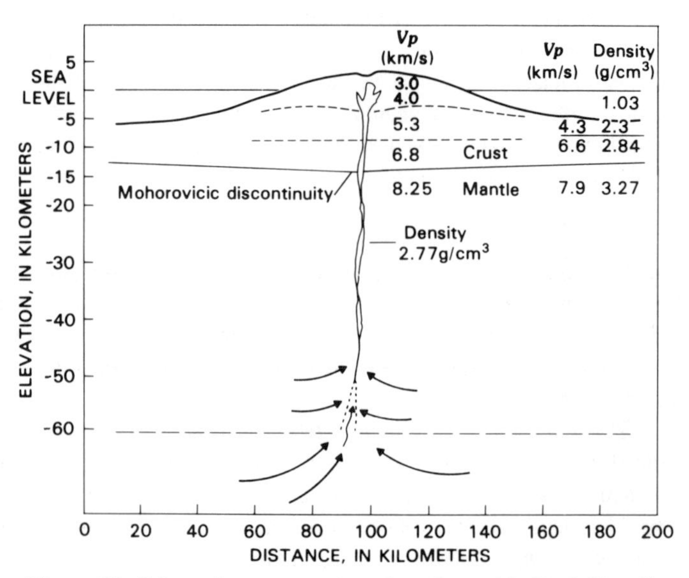

Figure 26. Schematic cross section through an idealized Hawaiian volcano (modified from Eaton and Murata, 1960). Magma from a source about 60 km deep streams up through conduits and collects in a shallow reservoir beneath the caldera. Occasional discharges of lava from the shallow reservoir through dikes that split to the surface constitute eruptions. Note the slight depression of the M-discontinuity beneath the volcano. Vp is the velocity of seismic P waves.

depths of at least 2.5 km. The alteration phases present indicate that metamorphism reaches the greenschist facies; they also have strong similarities to alteration suites in mid-ocean-ridge hydrothermal systems. Chemical data from the deep fluids suggest that the primary source of recharge to the reservoir is meteoric water in the interior of the rift but that saline water is present on the southern boundary. Production data from the wells also indicate that accessible parts of the hydrothermal system are capable of producing both dry steam and hot brine. The data that have been gathered to the present indicate that the hydrothermal system associated with the Kilauea east rift zone is actively evolving and has characteristics ranging from low-temperature benign fluids to high-temperature, highly aggressive fluids that may provide both an economically viable geothermal resource and a natural laboratory for the study of ore-forming and geochemical-cycling processes.

SOME FUTURE DIRECTIONS

E. L. Winterer, T. M. Atwater, and R. W. Decker

In the plate tectonic realm, a number of important questions concern aspects of the Kula plate: its motion history between 55 and 43 Ma, and the timing and nature of its demise. Because many proposed terrane trajectories use the motions of the Kula plate, this is quite important. Also, the geometry of the Kula-Farallon boundary must be deciphered. Barring some unexpected breakthrough in our oceanic predictive capabilities, this will probably be worked out from tectonic patterns on North America.

The steady improvements in the global plate circuit solutions hold great promise. Comparison of them with local and global hot-spot frames, as well as the refining of the latter is also vital, because the hot spots may be our only way to reconstruct mid-Mesozoic plate motions in the Pacific. Quantification of the timing and magnitude of motions between East and West Antarctica is crucial for the improvement of plate circuit solutions.

Our understanding of Cenozoic geology in the western United States is increasing rapidly with refinement of structural and magmatic data and concepts in the Great Basin. With improvements in our understanding of unusual subduction geometries such as the proposed Laramide flat slab and its steepening, and with increasingly good reconstructions of the subduction parameters, we may soon be able to make detailed correlations between the plate kinematics and continental geologic events.

Also, as the uncertainties in late Cenozoic plate circuit reconstructions decrease and our California structural data base improves, we can make increasingly detailed correlations between events in the San Andreas system and in the larger Pacific–North America motions. We may finally be arriving at the level of precision in plate reconstructions that will allow us to go beyond general statements and productively compare hill- and mountain-sized geologic events with specific planet-sized plate events.

The next few years should see an integration of our ideas about the array of ridge-crest offset types and their relations to mantle dynamics. It is not clear if the various types of offsets all form a continuum or if they are distinct features resulting from distinct causes.

The exploration of ridge crest hydrothermal vents has been exciting; however, we still have a great deal to learn about almost every aspect of them. Single vent chimneys, and perhaps whole fields, appear to be quite ephemeral and fast-changing, so that generalizations from any single time-set of observations can be highly misleading. It will be particularly interesting to monitor the development of some of these features through time.

The recent detailed seismic and drilling transects have led to major advances in our understanding of the difficult environment of subduction margins. More transects need to be done, and they need to be combined with detailed plate history calculations. Particularly interesting is the role of strike-slip in the subduction margins and the ways in which strike-slip and compressional deformations are partitioned there.

Another problem in the convergent margins is the question of the dewatering of sediments conveyed into the margin on the oceanic plate. Drill samples from the margins indicate there has been extensive water loss, but the mechanisms remain obscure. Seismic profiles suggest that at least some of the water escapes along well-defined paths that terminate in mud volcanoes, but we have no quantitative data on the importance of this style as opposed to more diffuse pathways. The volumetric importance of dewatering is as yet unknown, but it could rival hydrothermal circulation at the spreading ridge crests, which is viewed as a major determinant in controlling the chemistry of the oceans.

An element in the complex set of processes that disperse sediments across the continental margin, and that needs more attention, is downslope creep and slump, at scales from millimeters to kilometers, Improved reflection seismic images are beginning to reveal the possible quantitative importance of these mass movements, and more detailed structural studies on the land make the distinction between tectonic and gravity mélanges. We need proper assessment of the relative roles of compressional tectonics and gravity processes in modern active margins.

Oceanic sediments, especially those deposited in areas of high productivity, offer the possibility of time resolution on the order of the Milankovitch frequencies, and thus the possibility of global correlation of events with great precision. Rhythmically deposited sequences provide us with means to order closely linked events and to estimate rates of change. The advent of new coring methods in the Ocean Drilling Program that make possible the recovery of continuous, undisturbed sequences of pelagic sediments representing many millions of years of sedimentation, also makes possible the detailed stable-isotope, magnetic-intensity, and lithologic studies required for very-high-resolution stratigraphy.

The important role of global fluctuations in sea level in determining the character of stratigraphic sequences on continental margins is widely appreciated, but the expression of these fluctuations in the deep sea has not been adequately explored. Major hiatuses and changes in carbonate content in Neogene pelagic sediments in the Pacific, corresponding to sea-level fluctuations inferred from seismic records on continental margins, have been documented (Mayer and others, 1986), but such correspondence is not yet established for pre-Neogene times, when the extent, or even the presence of continental glaciers is uncertain or doubtful. The methods used for the Neogene studies need to be applied to older sediments, where possible.

Future investigations of the Hawaiian-Emperor chain that are likely to improve understanding of its origin and development will probably focus on the structure and dynamics of the Hawaiian hot spot, and mapping the submarine geology of the island flanks and seamounts. Ongoing sonar surveys by GLORIA of the submarine Exclusive Economic Zone surrounding the state of Hawaii have already provided a wealth of information that is currently being digested and interpreted. Seismic tomography may be the technique to provide significant new information on the deep structure and dynamics of the hot spot. Time and curiosity will tell.

REFERENCES CITED

Chapters in Volume N of *The Geology of North America* that are cited in this chapter are listed below, along with the full citation for the volume.

Winterer, E. L., Hussong, D. M., and Decker, R. W., editors, 1989, The Eastern Pacific Ocean and Hawaiian Islands: Boulder, Colorado, Geological Society of America, The Geology of North America, v. N (in press).

Atwater, T., 1989, Plate tectonic history of the northeast Pacific, Ch. 5.

Atwater, T., and Severinghaus, J., 1989, Tectonic maps of the northeast Pacific, Ch. 4.

Barron, J., 1989, The late Cenozoic stratigraphic record and hiatuses of the northeast Pacific—Results from the Deep Sea Drilling Project, Ch. 15.

Batiza, R., 1989a, Petrology and geochemistry of the eastern Pacific spreading centers, Ch. 10.

—— , 1989b, Failed rifts, Ch. 12.

Clague, D. A. and Dalrymple, G. B., 1989, Tectonics, geochronology, and origin of the Hawaiian-Emperor volcanic chain, Ch. 13.

Duncan, R. A., and Kulm, L. D., 1989, Plate tectonic evolution of the Cascade arc-subduction complex, Ch. 22.

Gorsline, D. S., and Teng, L. S-Y., 1989, The California continental borderland, Ch. 24.

Haymon, R., 1989, Hydrothermal processes and products on the Galapagos Rift and East Pacific Rise, Ch. 9.

Hey, R. N., Stinton, J. W., and Duennebier, F. K., 1989, Propagating rifts and spreading centers, Ch. 11.

Johnson, H. P., and Holmes, M. L., 1989, Evolution in plate tectonics; the Juan de Fuca Ridge, Ch. 6.

Klein, F. W., and Koyanagi, R. Y., 1989, The seismicity and tectonics of Hawaii, Ch. 13.

Leinen, M., 1989, The pelagic clay province of the North Pacific Ocean, Ch. 16.

Lonsdale, P., 1989a, Geology and tectonic history of the Gulf of California, Ch. 26.

Macdonald, K. C., 1989, Tectonic and magmatic processes on the East Pacific, Ch. 7.

Mammerickx, J., 1989, Large-scale undersea features of the northeast Pacific, Ch. 2.

McCulloch, D. S., 1989, Evolution of the offshore central California region, Ch. 23.

Normark, W. R., and Gutmacher, C. E., 1989, Major submarine fans of the California continental rise, Ch. 19.

Piper, D. Z., and Heath, G. R., 1989, Hydrogenous sediments, Ch. 17.

Riddihough, R., and Hyndman, R. D., 1989, Queen Charlotte Islands margin, Ch. 21.

Spencer, J. E., and Normark, W. R., 1989, Neogene plate-tectonic evolution of the Baja California sur continental borderland and the southern Gulf of California, Ch. 25.

Theyer, F., Vincent, E., and Mayer, L. A., 1989, Sedimentation and paleoceanography of the central equatorial Pacific, Ch. 18.

von Huene, R., 1989a, Continental margins around the Gulf of Alaska, Ch. 20.

—— , 1989b, The Middle America convergent plate boundary, Ch. 28.

Watkins, J., 1989, The Middle America Trench off southern Mexico, Ch. 27.

Berger, W. H., and Winterer, E. L., 1973, Plate stratigraphy and the fluctuating carbonate line, *in* Hsü, K. J., and Jenkyns, H. C., eds., Pelagic Sediments—on the land and under the sea; International Association of Sedimentologists Special Publication: Oxford, Blackwell, p. 11–48.

Berggren, W. A., Kent, D. V., Flynn, J. J., and van Couvering, J. A., 1985, Cenozoic geochronology: Geological Society of America Bulletin, v. 96, p. 1407–1418.

Bird, P., 1984, Laramide crustal thickening event in the Rocky Mountain foreland and Great Plains: Tectonics, v. 3, p. 741–758.

Caress, D. W., Menard, H. W., and Hey, R. N., 1988, Eocene reorganization of the Pacific–Farallon Spreading Center north of the Mendocino fracture zone: Journal of Geophysical Research, v. 93, p. 2813–2838.

Debiche, M. G., Cox, A., and Engebretson, D. C., 1987, The Motion of Allochthonous Terranes across the Pacific Basin: Geological Society of America Special Paper 207, 49 p.

Decker, R. W., Wright, T. L., and Stauffer, P. H., editors, 1987, Volcanism in Hawaii: U.S. Geological Survey Professional Paper 1350, v. 1, 839 p., v. 2, 1677 p.

Dickinson, W. R. and Snyder, W. S., 1979, Geometry of triple junctions related to San Andreas transform: Journal of Geophysical Research, v. 84, p. 561–572.

Eaton, J. P., and Murata, K. J., 1960, How volcanoes grow: Science, v. 132, p. 925–938.

Engebretson, D. C., Cox, A., and Gordon, R. G., 1985, Relative Motions Between Oceanic and Continental Plates in the Pacific Basin: Geological Society of America Special Paper 206, 59 p.

Epp, D., 1978, Age and tectonic relationships among the volcanic chains on the Pacific plate [Ph.D. thesis]: Honolulu, University of Hawaii, 199 p.

Henderson, L. J., and Gordon, R. G., 1981, Oceanic plateaus and the motion of the Pacific plate with respect to hot spots: EOS (American Geophysical Union Transactions), v. 62, p. 1028.

Herd, D. G., 1978, Intracontinental plate boundary east of Cape Mendocino, California: Geology, v. 6, p. 721–725.

Hornafius, J. S., Luyendyk, B. P., Terres, R. P., and Kamerling, M. J., 1986, Timing and extent of Neogene tectonic rotation in the western Transverse Ranges, California: Geological Society of America Bulletin, v. 97, p. 1476–1487.

Jackson, E. D., and Schlanger, S. A., eds., 1976, Initial reports of the Deep Sea

Drilling Project: Washington, D.C., U.S. Government Printing Office, v. 33, 973 p.

Jarrard, R. D., and Clague, D., 1977, Implications of Pacific island and seamount ages for the origin of volcanic chains: Reviews of Geophysics and Space Physics, v. 15, p. 57–76.

Kelsey, H. M., and Carver, G. A., 1988, Late Neogene and Quaternary tectonics associated with northward growth of the San Andreas transform fault, northern California: Journal of Geophysical Research, v. 93, p. 4797–4819.

Kent, D. V., and Gradstein, F. M., 1985, A Cretaceous and Jurassic geochronology: Geological Society of America Bulletin, v. 96, p. 1419–1427.

Lonsdale, P., 1988, Paleogene history of the Kula Plate—Offshore evidence and onshore implications: Geological Society of America Bulletin, v. 100, p. 733–754.

—— , 1989b, Structural patterns of the Pacific floor offshore of Peninsular California, *in* Simoneit, B. and Ness, G., eds., Gulf and Peninsula Provinces of the Californias: American Association of Petroleum Geologists Memoir 47 (in press).

Mammerickx, J., and Sharman, G. F., 1988, Tectonic evolution of the North Pacific during Cretaceous Quiet Period: Journal of Geophysical Research, v. 93, p. 3009–3024.

Mammerickx, J., Naar, D. F., and Tyce, R. L., 1988, The Mathematician Paleoplate: Journal of Geophysical Research, v. 93, p. 3025–3040.

Mayer, L. A., Shipley, T. H., and Winterer, E. L., 1986, Equatorial Pacific reflectors as indicators of global oceanographic events: Science, v. 233, p. 761–764.

Menard, H. W., 1964, Marine Geology of the Pacific: New York, McGraw-Hill, 271 p.

Sager, W. W., Handschumacher, D. W., Hilde, T.W.C., and Bracey, D. R., 1988, Tectonic evolution of the northern Pacific Plate and Pacific-Farallon-Izanagi triple junction in the late Jurassic and early Cretaceous (M21–M10): Tectonophysics, v. 155, p. 345–364.

Severinghaus, J., and Atwater, T. M., 1988, Geometry and condition of the subducted Farallon plate beneath western North America during the late Cenozoic: Geological Society of America Abstracts with Programs, v. 20, p. 230.

—— , 1989, Cenozoic geometry and thermal condition of the subducting slabs beneath western North America, *in* Wernicke, B., ed., Geological Society of America Memoir (in preparation).

Stock, J., and Molnar, P., 1987, A revised history of early Tertiary plate motion in the southwest Pacific: Nature, v. 325, p. 495–499.

—— , 1988, Uncertainties and implications of the Late Cretaceous and Tertiary position of the North America relative to the Farallon, Kula, and Pacific Plates: Tectonics, v. 7, p. 1339–1384.

Tamaki, K., and Larson, R. L., 1988, The Mesozoic tectonic history of the Magellan microplate in the western central Pacific: Journal of Geophysical Research, v. 98, p. 2857–2874.

Thierston, H. R., 1979, Paleoceanographic implications of organic carbon and carbonate distribution in Mesozoic deep sea sediments, *in* Talwani, M., Hay, W., and Ryan, W.B.F., eds., Deep Drilling Results in the Atlantic Ocean—Continental Margins and Paleoenvironment: American Geophysical Union, Maurice Ewing Series, p. 249–274.

Vallier, T. L., Rea, D. K., Dean, W. E., Thiede, J., and Adelseck, C. G., 1981, The geology of the Hess Rise, central North Pacific Ocean, *in* Thiede, J., and Vallier, T. L., eds., Initial reports of the Deep Sea Drilling Project: Washington, D.C., U.S. Government Printing Office, v. 62, p. 1031–1072.

Van Andel, T. H., Heath, G. R., Malfait, B. T., Heinrichs, D. F., and Ewing, J. I., 1971, Tectonics of the Panama basin, eastern equatorial Pacific: Geological Society of America Bulletin, v. 82, p. 1489–1580.

Wilson, D. S., 1988, Tectonic history of the Juan de Fuca Ridge over the last 40 million years: Journal of Geophysical Research, v. 93, p. 11863–11876.

Wright, T. L., and Fiske, R. S., 1971, Origin of the differentiated and hybrid lavas of Kilauea Volcano, Hawaii: Journal of Petrology, v. 12, p. 1–65.

MANUSCRIPT ACCEPTED BY THE SOCIETY JANUARY 27, 1989

Printed in U.S.A.

The Geology of North America
Vol. A, The Geology of North America—An overview
The Geological Society of America, 1989

Chapter 11

Geologic history of the Caribbean and Central America

Thomas W. Donnelly
Department of Geological Sciences, State University of New York, Binghamton, New York 13901

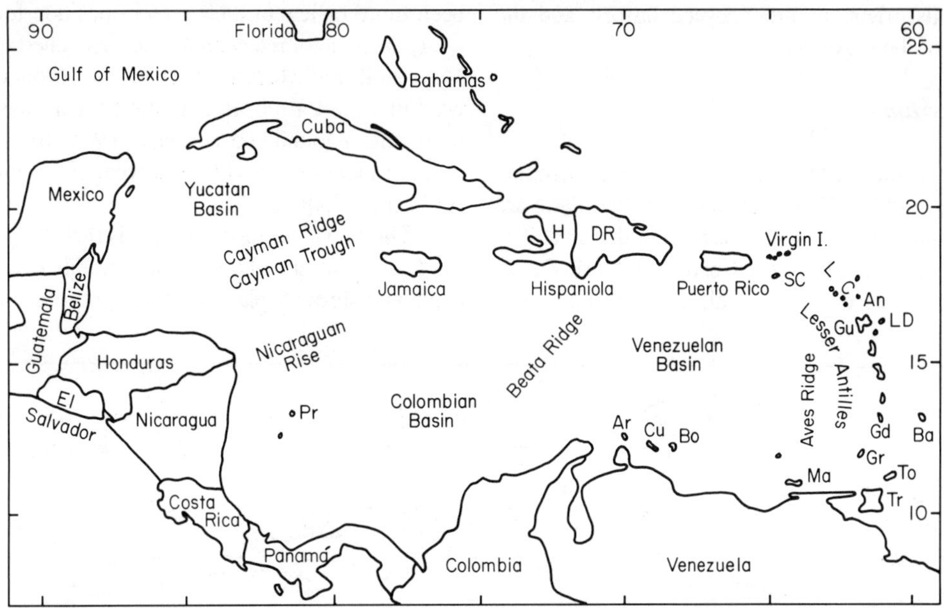

Figure 1. Map of the Caribbean. Pr = Providencia; Ar = Aruba; Cu = Curaçao; Bo = Bonaire; Ma = Margarita; Tr = Trinidad; To = Tobago; Gr = Grenada; Gd = Grenadines; Ba = Barbados; LD = La Désirade; Gu = Guadeloupe; An = Antigua; L C = Limestone Caribbees; SC = St. Croix; H = Haiti; DR = Dominican Republic.

INTRODUCTION

The Caribbean area as defined here includes the Greater Antilles, Lesser Antilles, the northern boundary of South America, and Central America (Fig. 1); it spans approximately 7,800 km in an east-west direction and 3,900 km in a north-south direction. Although the geology of this region should be considered along with that of Mexico and the Gulf of Mexico, these areas form separate chapters in this book. This chapter is in part a condensation of numerous contributions prepared for the synthesis volume on the Caribbean region by Case and Dengo (1989). Further details are available in that book.

Modern geological interest in the Caribbean has centered on its Cretaceous to Recent orogenic belts that resulted from plate interactions between North and South America. The Caribbean is the site of America's most extensive Cretaceous and Cenozoic oceanic-continental tectonic zone and has (along with the Aleutians) its only real island arcs. It has the majority of the active volcanic centers of the New World and a major share of the destructive earthquakes.

The goal of the Caribbean geologist is to reconstruct the history of a minor "plate" whose extensive internal deformation belies the strict application of this term. This "plate" has been broken and twisted within the jaws of three major plates (Farallon, North America, and South America), whose relative motions have changed dramatically from Jurassic to Recent time. However, the average motion among the three plates since the middle Cretaceous has been one of roughly east-west compression, and the aim of this paper is to place the geologic history in the context of these changing major plate motions.

Donnelly, T. W., 1989, Geologic history of the Caribbean and Central America, *in* Bally, A. W., and Palmer, A. R., eds., The Geology of North America—An overview: Boulder, Colorado Geological Society of America, The Geology of North America, v. A.

Geological challenges

The central problems of Caribbean geologic evolution are the origins of the numerous fragments of pre-Cretaceous terranes, their juxtaposition with younger terranes formed during the late Mesozoic separation of the Americas, and the subsequent complicated compressive interactions among these major plates. Although all Caribbean geologists agree that the central theme of Caribbean tectonic evolution has been the Neogene relative eastward movement of the Caribbean Plate (very likely the Caribbean moved very little as the Americas plates moved westward in a hot-spot reference frame), there is considerable disagreement as to the place of its origin, its pre-Neogene history, and the amount and timing of the movement.

Identification of terranes

Perhaps the single most serious obstacle to an understanding of the tectonic history of the Caribbean region is that there are relatively few exposures of pre-Cretaceous rock in this area. The cores of the Maya and Chortis blocks of Central America (Fig. 2) have long been recognized to contain Paleozoic or older rock, and similarly old rocks have been recognized in northern Venezuela. More recently, a unit previously considered to be Cretaceous in the Serranía del Interior of northern Venezuela has been recognized as Permian, and metamorphic rocks of central Cuba are now recognized as Precambrian. Even the extensive occurrences of Jurassice rocks in Pinar del Río, Cuba, have eluded attempts toward regional correlation.

Tectonic history

There have been two views of Caribbean geological history. The original view was that the elements of the Caribbean have been more or less in their present position for a very long (certainly since pre-Cretaceous) time (Schuchert, 1935; Weyl, 1973; Meyerhoff and Meyerhoff, 1972). A corollary of this view has been that the Caribbean may not have always been oceanic, but represents a foundered continent (Woodring, 1954). The latter view was laid to rest with the advent of seismic refraction studies (Officer and others, 1957, 1959).

The prevalent modern view is that the geologic elements of the Caribbean have had a highly mobile history, which must be explained through plate-tectonic synthesis. Pindell (Pindell and

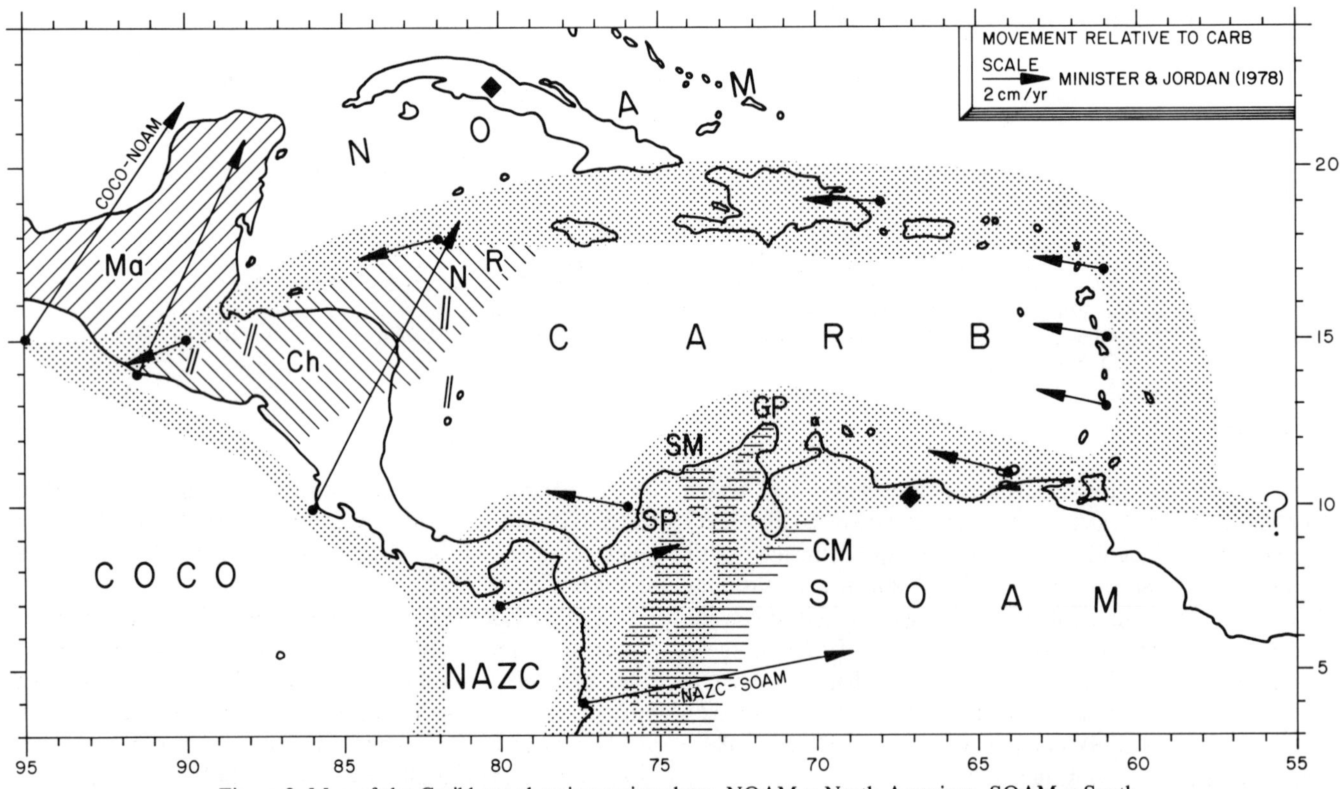

Figure 2. Map of the Caribbean showing major plates: NOAM = North American, SOAM = South American; CARB = Caribbean; COCO = Cocos; NAZC = Nazca. Vectors show present plate motions according to Minster and Jordan (1978). Stippled pattern shows the boundary zone of the Caribbean plate. Diagonal line patterns show Maya (Ma) and Chortis (Ch) blocks, including the extension of the latter to the Nicaraguan Rise (NR). Lined patterns show Precambrian-Paleozoic cores of Andean ranges (SM = Santa Marta, GP = Guajira Peninsula; SP = Sierra de Perijá; CM = Cordillera de Mérida). Solid diamonds indicate occurrence of Precambrian metamorphic rocks in Cuba and ?early Paleozoic metamorphic rocks in north-central Venezuela.

Barrett, 1989) has become the main exponent of this approach, which includes a Pacific origin of the Caribbean "Plate" and its Cretaceous to Cenozoic movement into its present position. While Neogene eastward movements of the Caribbean "Plate" are manifest, contemporary workers have differed in its amount and timing. This chapter presents arguments that the movement was smaller and earlier than many other workers have concluded.

A major obstacle to reconstruction of the Caribbean "Plate" is that the plate is itself poorly defined. The plate is not a rigid body surrounded by sharply defined tectonic zones (Fig. 2). Instead, the border zones show pervasive young deformation over distances into the plate that make up a substantial fraction of the area of the plate itself; there is further evidence from marine geology of a long history of internal deformation of the plate; and there is increasing evidence that small subplates around the periphery of the plate may have separate histories.

A further obstacle to a tectonic synthesis is that the history of the relative motions of the North American, South American, and Farallon (later the Cocos) Plates (Fig. 3) has been poorly understood. This latter problem is especially important, because the Mesozoic–Cenozoic history of plate interactions suggests that the relative compressive interaction of the Farallon Plate (and its two middle Cenozoic derivatives: the Cocos and Nazca Plates) with the American plates is far more important than the relatively minor interaction between the American plates themselves.

Stratigraphic overview

The older (pre-Jurassic) terranes of the Caribbean consist of more or less scattered fragments in four general areas: (1) the Maya Block basement of Guatemala and Belize—metamorphics with late Paleozoic sedimentary cover; (2) the Chortis block of Honduras and southeastern Guatemala—basement with low-grade metasedimentary cover of unknown age; (3) Precambrian metamorphic rocks of central Cuba; and (4) minor occurrences of older metamorphic rocks of northern Venezuela and Colombia. Recently, Permian fossils in bioclastic limestones (Tucutunemo Limestone) from the Serranía del Interior of northern Venezuela were identified by Benjamini and others (1987). Available evidence does not permit a correlation of these terranes either with each other or with terranes of North America or South America. Ross (1979) suggests a communality of the Permian fusuline faunas from Texas, Belize, Guatemala, and northern South America, and from this communality he concludes that southern North America, the Maya block, and northern South America were more or less juxtaposed prior to the Mesozoic breakup of the Americas.

There are relatively few occurrences of Jurassic rocks within the Caribbean area. The most extensive occurrences of marine Jurassic sedimentary rocks are within Cuba (carbonates and clastics) and in northern Venezuela (dominantly clastics). Continental red-bed deposits of southern Mexico, Guatemala, and northern South America have yielded some Jurassic fossils (also Early Cretaceous in Mexico). In Honduras these beds appear to grade eastward into marine facies.

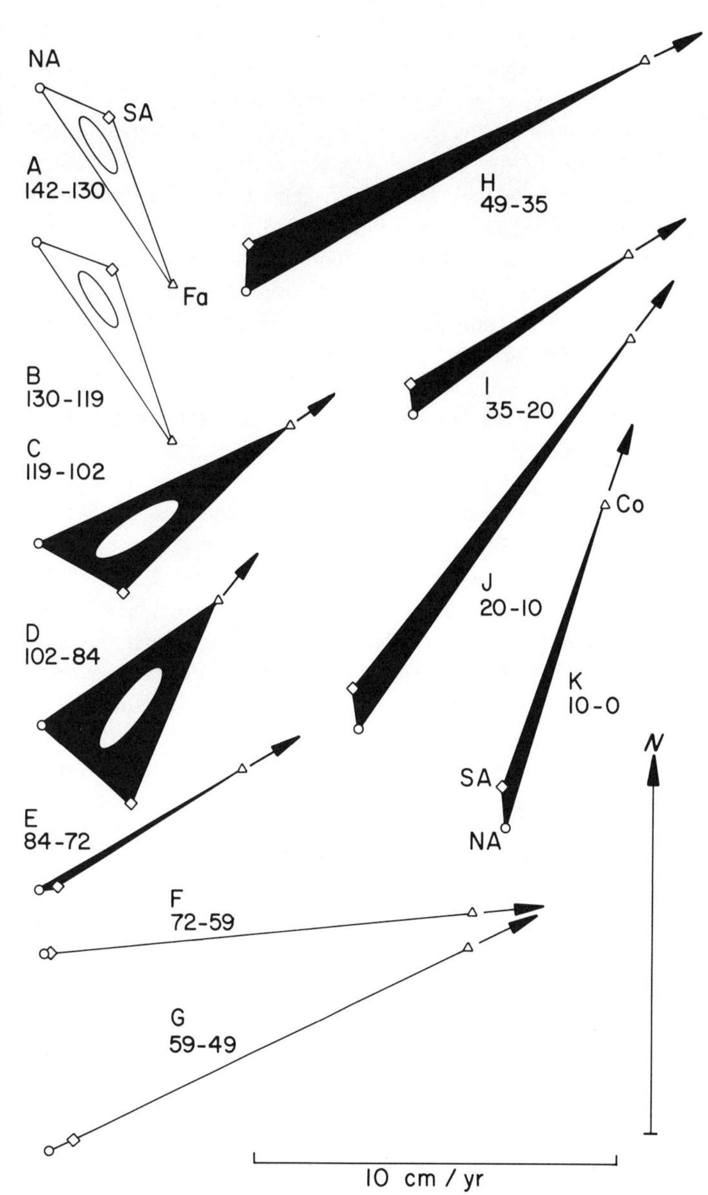

Figure 3. Triangles of vectors showing relative motions among the North American, South American, and Farallon (later Cocos) Plates, derived from rotations given in Pindell and others, 1988. Ages are shown for each triangle, and the scale shows the motion rate. North America is an open circle, South America an open diamond, and the Farallon/Cocos Plate an open triangle. Triangles A and B show divergence among all three plates (ellipse pattern); triangles C and D two show northeast convergence from the Farallon Plate (solid pattern) and southeast divergence between the American plates (ellipse); triangles E, F, and G show compression in the east or northeast direction, and very little relative motion between the American plates; triangles H, I, J, and K show northeast convergence of the Farallon/Cocos Plate and minor north-south convergence between the American plates.

The Early Cretaceous around the Caribbean consists mostly of thin units of diverse lithologies but dominated by carbonate rocks. The lower stratigraphic limit in most areas is at about the Albian level, at which time there are thick limestones, many of which are dolomitic (Guatemala, Cuba). In the Greater Antilles this is the time of inception of island-arc volcanic activity.

The Late Cretaceous is more lithologically varied in the Caribbean. In the Greater Antilles (and probably in Central America, where they are buried) calc-alkaline volcanic rocks form a large fraction of this interval. The entire Late Cretaceous succession in the Caribbean region appears to reflect a regional transition from relatively stable conditions with differential vertical movement (dominantly carbonate-rich units) to a relatively mobile condition, with strong compressive tectonics and accompanying island-arc volcanism.

Units of Paleogene age in the Caribbean are generally local and of highly diverse lithologies. In many areas they are apparently partly or dominantly continental, and they are commonly sparsely fossiliferous. Volcanic lithologies are conspicuous, and there are probably more volcanic units of this age in Central America and the Lesser Antilles than are recognized.

Neogene sedimentary units of the Caribbean area are commonly similar to modern offshore sediments and are dominantly carbonate or mud-rich facies. The distribution of Neogene volcanic facies mirrors the occurrence of modern volcanic centers with only minor exceptions. In some parts of the Greater Antilles and Central America, relatively thick Neogene clastic sections exposed on land indicate impressive young vertical movements.

NORTHERN CENTRAL AMERICA

Northern (or nuclear) Central America is divided into the Maya and Chortis blocks, separated by the Motagua suture zone of central Guatemala (Donnelly and others, 1989a). These blocks are distinct terranes that have been assigned widely different histories and provenances by various authors. I take the view that their original positions were not widely separated (hundreds rather than thousands of kilometers).

Maya block

The basement of central Guatemala (Maya block) is Paleozoic or older and consists of medium- to high-grade gneisses and schists with minor marbles named the Chuacús Series. This series is dominantly metasedimentary and granitic, and is not presently correlatable with terranes of Mexico or North America. Overlying this basement is an extensive late Paleozoic sedimentary series (Santa Rosa) with widespread Early Permian fossils and scattered pre-Permian fossils. The late Paleozoic sedimentary rocks extend into Chiapas, Mexico (López Ramos, 1981). The pre-Permian sedimentary rocks are dominantly shales and sandstones overlain by Permian shales and dolomitic limestones. Some granitoids in Guatemala, Chiapas, and Belize of poorly defined late Paleozoic age are older than this sedimentary series.

The nearest well-known terrane with abundant rocks of Early Permian age is Texas and its extension into northern and northeastern Mexico (López Ramos, 1981), but two features of the Maya block have no analogue in Texas and northern Mexico: the occurrence of the Bladen volcanic series at the Pennsylvanian–Permian boundary, and an Early Permian deformation seen in eastern Guatemala. Intruding this series in Belize, and possibly also in Guatemala, are several small granitic plutons of Early Triassic age.

Overlying the metamorphic basement and the Paleozoic series with an extensive unconformity is a Late Jurassic–Early Cretaceous red-bed series (Todos Santos) passing upward to thick dolomitic limestones (Cobán/Ixcoy), which contains, especially to the north beneath southern Mexico, thick gypsum units. The thickness of the pre-Albian portion of this section is unknown. At about the Albian–Cenomanian boundary, this unit passes upward to platform limestones that are locally highly fossiliferous (Campur). At the end of the Cretaceous and into the early Cenozoic, the limestones are overlain by locally thick clastic flysch (Sepur). Local continental clastic rift-basin units (Subinal) of Eocene age are in turn overlain by mid- to late Cenozoic volcanic cover, especially toward the Pacific Coast.

Chortis block

The Chortis block is the Caribbean's one certain "exotic terrane." Evidence for its original position is limited, but the prevailing view, which is supported by paleomagnetic evidence (Gose and Swartz, 1977), is that it represents a fragment of western Mexico that moved southward to its present position.

The Chortis block basement consists of a gneissic series (Las Ovejas Series in Guatemala; Omoa of northwestern Honduras) and a younger, lighly metamorphosed series of limy and shaly sedimentary rocks. The basement gneisses, where extensively studied in Guatemala, appear to represent a metavolcanic series with intercalated marbles, intruded by granitoid plutons of several possible ages (Horne and others, 1976), which are themselves deformed prior to the Late Cretaceous. Superincumbent shaly and locally limy metasediments (Cacaguapa, San Diego) have not yielded fossils.

The older rocks are overlain by a diverse, locally thick, and largely undated clastic unit (Honduras Group of Horne and others, 1989); portions were previously called Todos Santos, Metapán, and El Plan). The earliest of these units (El Plan) is a thick, badly exposed, marine clastic sequence with scattered Jurassic fossils. The sequence passes upward to largely unfossiliferous siliciclastic sediments, which are found scattered widely over a large portion of the Chortis block.

Overlying carbonate and continental clastic units have been stratigraphically controversial. A dominantly Albian, locally thick reefal limestone sequence (Yojoa) is overlain by a coarse clastic unit (Valle de Angeles). The latter unit has a prominent and widespread Cenomanian limestone unit dividing the clastics into lower and upper parts.

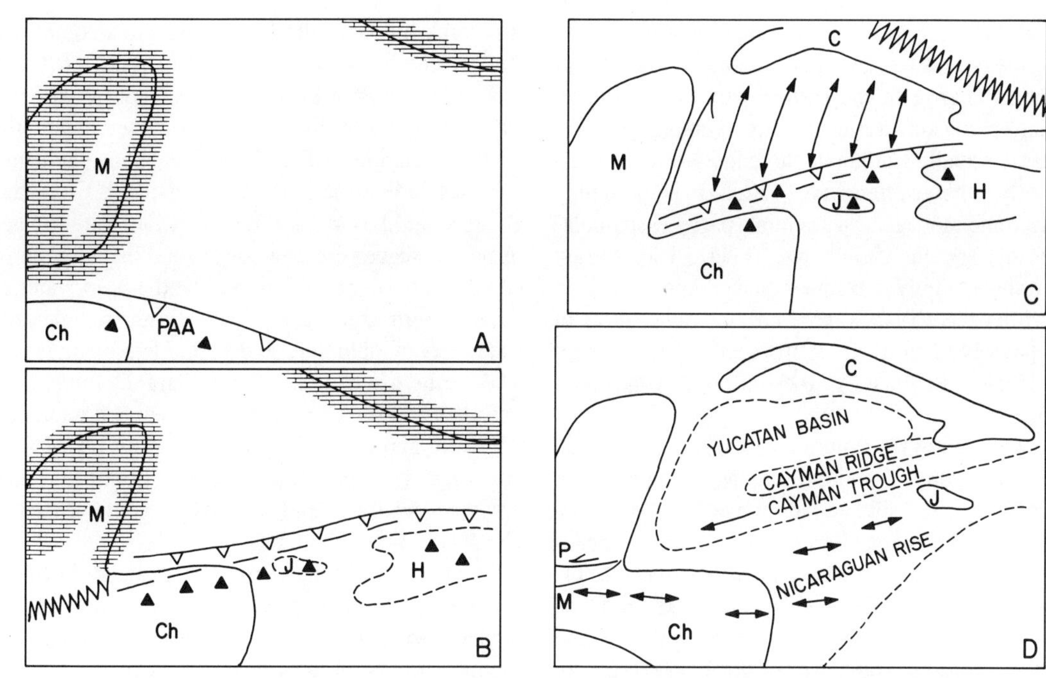

Figure 4. Four sketch maps showing the evolution of the northwestern Caribbean. Brick pattern shows thick passive-margin carbonates of the Maya block (M) Florida-Bahama margin. Solid triangles indicate magmatic activity associated with subduction. A: middle Cretaceous. The proto-Antillean arc (PAA) is shown attached to the northern margin of the Chortis block (Ch). B: early Maastrichtian. Collision of the Chortis (Ch) and Maya blocks (M) is indicated by zigzag line in eastern Guatemala. The dashed line shows the possible locus of later opening of the Yucatan Basin. Early positions of Jamaica (J) and Hispaniola (H) are also shown. C: end Cretaceous or early Paleogene: opening of the Yucatan Basin shown by double-headed arrows. The suturing of Cuba (C) and the Florida-Bahama bank during the Paleogene is shown as a zigzag line. The dashed line shows the locus of later opening of the Cayman Trough. D: Neogene. Spreading (double-headed arrows) within the northern Chortis block (Ch) leaves it eastern end submerged as the Nicaraguan Rise. The Cayman Ridge is a remnant of the subduction zone formed during opening of the Yucatan Basin. P = Polochic fault; M = Motagua fault (suture) zone; C = Cuba; J = Jamaica; H = Hispaniola.

The Cenozoic of the Chortis block consists mainly of local continental clastic units (Subinal), a widespread Miocene ignimbrite unit or units (Matagalpa, Padre Miguel), and locally thick Neogene volcanic deposits around modern volcanic centers along the Pacific margin.

Motagua Suture Zone

The Motagua River of central Guatemala is the site of a suture zone between the Chortis and Maya blocks (Fig. 4). The basement rocks of the two terranes place high-grade metamorphics of contrasting facies in juxtaposition across a narrow fault zone. The Mesozoic sedimentary series on either side also are quite different: abundant dolomites to the north overlain by limestones and, higher, by flysch, contrast with limestones to the south overlain by thick continental clastics and interbedded thin limestone.

The structural style of the zone is dominated on the north side by north-vergent thrusts that were rotated, close to the suture zone, into high-angle faults during Neogene uplift. These thrusts, which occur in a belt along the southern front of the Sierra de Chuacús and Sierra de las Minas, juxtapose older metamorphic and sedimentary units with ophiolitic debris (El Tambor), including thick serpentines.

On the south side, south-vergent thrusts have less tectonic transport than those on the north. In the axis of the suture zone occur ophiolitic rocks (El Tambor), latest Cretaceous platform carbonates, and a rift-facies red-bed unit (Subinal).

The age of the suturing event has been established as latest Cretaceous by two independent means. Several $^{39}Ar/^{40}Ar$ dates of separate metamorphic minerals establish the age as very close to 66 to 70 Ma (J. Sutter, personal communication, 1984). Also, a major allochthonous ophiolite (Oxec ophiolite) slide mass derived from the suture zone is structurally emplaced directly above flysch containing pelagic foraminifera of late Campanian age.

GREATER ANTILLES

The Greater Antilles consist of a core of Cretaceous through Paleogene island-arc volcanic rocks and a lightly deformed Neogene sedimentary sequence. With the possible exception of western Cuba, there is no reason to suspect continental crust beneath these islands, and chemical and isotopic evidence seems to exclude such a basement for the eastern part of this arc. The style of volcanism seems to change in the eastern part from an early island-arc submarine volcanic association to an emergent, more mature island-arc association in about the middle of the Cretaceous. Structurally, the western part (Cuba) is a highly thrust-faulted tectonic collage, the central part (Hispaniola) shows less thrusting, and the eastern part (Puerto Rico–Virgin Islands) seems to show mainly movement on high-angle faults. In several places within these islands there are ophiolites, most of which seem to have been thrust from the south of the present islands and to represent fragments of the Caribbean Cretaceous basalt association.

Neither the western nor the eastern extensions of the Greater Antilles have been identified. Granitoid plutons on the northern margin of the Chortis suggest a western continuation of at least a part of the chain along this margin; but there is no igneous activity of the appropriate age on the Maya block. To the east the Limestone Caribbees contain Paleogene igneous rocks similar to those on the Virgin Islands, and there are scattered drilled and dredged Cretaceous volcanic rocks within the northern Lesser Antilles.

Cuba

The stratigraphy and structure of Cuba have long provided some of the most challenging problems of all Middle American geology. The island itself is most meaningfully divided into three zones (west, mainly Pinar del Río; central, the bulk of the island; and east, mainly Oriente). Each of these zones shows different structural styles and somewhat distinctive stratigraphy. Within these zones, the rock units are distributed in terranes separated for the most part by major thrusts trending approximately parallel to the long axis of the island. These terranes have been given various names; Lewis (1989) summarizes these. Other valuable references for this island include Hatten and others (1989), and Pardo (1975).

The oldest Cuban rocks are metamorphics (Renne and others, 1989) and consist of tectonically isolated fragments of granite and marble (Socorro complex) that have an age close to 900 Ma. Their relation to other terranes is unknown, but the absence of an indication of a Pan-African age in these materials suggests to these authors that a correlation must be sought to the west rather than the east.

Western Cuba consists mainly of north-vergent thrust packages of Jurassic to Cretaceous clastics and limestones, with minor ophiolite occurrences. There are few mid- to Late Cretaceous deposits typical of island-arc associations and no granitoids of that age. A major problem here is the lack of a correlation of the earlier units (such as the San Cayetano clastics) with Jurassic units outside of Cuba.

Central Cuba has been the main focus for tectonostratigraphic syntheses of the island. The structural geology of this part of the island is dominated by major north-vergent thrust faults that stack lithologically diverse units in a complex arrangement. The northernmost zone (which includes the Cayo Cocos and Remedios zones of Lewis, 1989) consists dominantly of layered carbonate and evaporite-carbonate sediments that form the southern margin of the Florida–Bahama platform. The central zone (including the Placetas, Camajuaní, Cifuentes, Jatibonico, Zulueta, and Las Villas zones of various authors) is, as the welter of names suggests, a composite zone including Jurassic through Cretaceous sediments that may be the deep-water equivalents of the northern zone, along with clastic sediments and tectonic fragments of ophiolite, and of the basement mentioned above. The southern zone (Zaza, Santa Clara, Domingo, Cabaiguán) has been considered the eugeosynclinal zone. It is allochthonous from the south and consists of two major but not always distinguishable rock types: ophiolite of oceanic origin, and probable island-arc volcanic rocks and associated sediments intruded by Late Cretaceous granitic plutons.

Eastern Cuba lacks the conspicuous thrust-fault-separated zones of the remainder of the island. Rock units there have a higher volcanic and a lower clastic and carbonate component and resemble the Antillean island arc assemblages of the Cretaceous and early Cenozoic; indeed, the southern massif is geologically similar to Hispaniola. Ophiolitic rocks in the southern zone were locally metamorphosed to blueschist facies in the Paleogene.

Any tectonic history of Cuba must include recognition of terranes of varying lithology and origin consisting dominantly of Jurassic and Cretaceous rock units. The identification of the northern zone of central Cuba with the Florida–Bahama platform is clear, but the provenance of the remaining units is less so. The abundant ophiolitic rocks could be correlated with the Caribbean Cretaceous basalt event; alternatively they might represent older oceanic crust outside of the arc. The island-arc rocks resemble those of the remainder of the Antilles, but their stratigraphy is much less well known. In central Cuba many of the Cretaceous sediments are of pelagic facies. The Jurassic and Cretaceous sediments, especially of western Cuba, are particularly enigmatic, and their correlation beyond Cuba is a problem of primary importance. The Proterozoic metamorphics of central Cuba will probably ultimately be found to resemble those of either the Chortis or Maya blocks.

Analyzed by itself, Cuba can be considered to be a tectonic and stratigraphic collage that was thrust against the Florida–Bahamas block. The thrusting has been dated largely as Eocene, but there are strong indications of Late Cretaceous movements.

Hispaniola

Hispaniola is composite but lacks the extreme stratigraphic diversity of Cuba. There are no correlatives of the Jurassic–Cretaceous sedimentary sequences seen in Pinar del Río nor to the shelf-edge evaporite-carbonate facies of northern Cuba. In other respects, but perhaps not in the proportions of rock types, Hispaniola is similar to central and especially eastern Cuba. The Neogene history is characterized by a dominance of strike-slip faults that have juxtaposed elongate elevated areas across broad valleys. The most valuable reference is Lewis and others (1989a); additional references are Bowin (1975) for the Dominican Republic, and Maurrasse (1982) for Haiti.

In northern Hispaniola, metamorphosed sedimentary rocks and ophiolitic fragments with a locally distinctive blueschist mineralogy represent an accretionary complex deformed in early mid-Cretaceous and again in Paleogene times.

The oldest rocks of Hispaniola occur mainly in the central part of the island and are divisible into two lithologic series: island-arc volcanics (largely siliceous) and basalt of oceanic affinity. For both lithologic types, there exist metamorphic and nonmetamorphic representatives. It is tempting to conclude in each case that the metamorphosed rocks are correlative with the nonmetamorphosed, and there are important similarities in detail. The Early Cretaceous island-arc volcanic association (Los Ranchos) is notable for its abundant siliceous members and for its resemblance to the Water Island Formation of the Virgin Islands. The Amina and Maimón schists, which form a long belt extending from central Dominican Republic into northern Haiti, are lithologically similar to these rocks, but occur separated from them to the south of a major fault zone.

The older mafic units are mafic schists and amphibolites (Duarte) that have the composition of oceanic crust, but with some LIL-enriched examples, and an unmetamorphosed basalt with a large fraction of hyaloclastic material (Siete Cabezas), which has yielded a Santonian age (radiolaria, E. Pessagno, personal communication, 1986). The Duarte is intruded by granitoid plutons of about 90 Ma; it has also yielded radiometric ages of 123 and 127 Ma (hornblende, K-Ar; Bowin, 1975; Kesler and others, 1977), the significance of which is not clear. In southern Hispaniola there are unfoliated basalts (Dumisseau, Bahoruco), which are mainly pre-Campanian and which consist of "normal" MORB (mid-ocean ridge basalt) compositions and LIL (large-ion lithophile element)-enriched varieties. The latter are very similar to both some Duarte metabasalts and to the basalt recovered at DSDP Site 151 on the Beata Ridge (Donnelly and others, 1973; Sen and others, 1988). The correlation of these unusual basalts from the Beata Ridge to southern and central Hispaniola shows that Caribbean crust extends north at least to this latitude.

The central Cordillera of Hispaniola is underlain by a regularly zoned series of rock units trending approximately parallel with the topographic alignment (WNW). The zones, from northeast to southwest, are as follows; (1) discontinuously exposed unfoliated older volcanic rocks of island-arc aspect (Los Ranchos), (2) a major southwest-dipping thrust-fault zone (Hispaniola fault zone, Hatillo thrust), (3) foliated rocks apparently correlated with the Los Ranchos (Amina-Maimón), (4) unfoliated volcanic rocks of island-arc aspect (Peravilla), (5) a major peridotite body, (6) unfoliated basalt and hyaloclastite (Siete Cabezas), (7) mafic metamorphics (Duarte) intruded by foliated tonalite plutons, (8) later Cretaceous island-arc volcanic materials of the Tireo and equivalents. Late Cretaceous and early Cenozoic unfoliated plutons intrude several of these units. The zonal occurrence of these units suggests that they are mainly slices of parallel faults, but there is no simple way to explain the juxtaposition of units of this variety of lithology and degree of metamorphism. The Los Ranchos may be the only autochthonous unit present; the remainder are units juxtaposed during a Late Cretaceous or Paleogene thrusting event.

The Los Ranchos and its metamorphosed equivalents represent the early stage of an island arc, which I tentatively interpret as north facing. The Duarte and the younger Siete Cabezas represent the Caribbean crust originally south of (behind) the arc. The Tireo represents a later stage of the development of the arc, and still later, limestones were deposited widely, especially in the west. The earliest deformation was middle Cretaceous and resulted in obduction and metamorphism of the Duarte and its intrusion by granitoid plutons. The collision of the Greater Antilles with the Florida–Bahamas platform in the Paleogene resulted in major thrusting from the north. Uplift accompanying this collision created thick Paleogene clastic units on the south side of the Cordillera Central and olistostromal units in northern Hispaniola. Certainly the younger subduction is from the north.

The stratigraphic and tectonic history of southern Hispaniola is somewhat different than that of the remainder of the island. The oldest bedrock unit is relatively undeformed Caribbean Cretaceous basaslt that outcrops along the elevated southern peninsula and is overlain in part by mainly pelagic Late Cretaceous limestones. The mode of emplacement of the oceanic basalt in Haiti is not clear. There are no associated major thrusts beneath these units, and the deformation appears to consist mainly of abundant high-angle faults. An unpublished airborne magnetic anomaly profile shows a strong remanent, low-inclination anomaly that suggests the body is largely undeformed. It would appear that a part of the Caribbean sea floor was more or less simply uplifted as a tectonic wedge in a transpressonal regime, probably during Paleogene strike-slip motion.

Puerto Rico and the Virgin Islands

Puerto Rico and the Virgin Islands contain probably the most complete range of rock types associated with a purely oceanic island arc in the entire world. The pre-arc basement is not seen, and nonradiogenic lead isotopes indicate no continental materials were involved in any way with the early arc magmatism (Armstrong and Cooper, 1971). Almost all of the rocks exposed here play some role in the formation of an arc; a small but significant occurrence of ophiolitic rocks in southwestern Puerto Rico (Bermeja Complex) represents an allochthonous fragment of nonarc materials. There are several references for Puerto Rico and the Virgin Islands, including Mattson and others (1989), and, for the Virgin Islands, Donnelly (1966) and Whetten (1966).

The oldest autochthonous island-arc deposits are keratophyres and spilites (Water Island) in the Virgin Islands and their more poorly exposed equivalents in the pre-Robles of Puerto Rico. These belong to the PIA (primitive island arc) magma series and represent the earliest deep submarine volcanic deposits of the nascent island arc; they pass upward to shallow water, and thence to an emerged island arc. The ages of inception of volcanism are unknown, but the latest phase of purely submarine activity is about at the Aptian-Albian boundary. Mid-Cretaceous emergence brought thick concomitant sedimentation, and younger magmas tended to intrude as granitoid plutons instead of erupting as volcanics. Virtually all of the associated sedimentary facies are volcaniclastic, with minor lenticular limestones.

Magmatic activity diminished near the end of the Cretaceous, and the early Cenozoic was a time of large vertical fault movements and more limited magmatic activity. The latest magmatism in Puerto Rico is Eocene; plutonism continued on a small scale in the Virgin Islands into the Oligocene.

Jamaica

Jamaica is relatively small and rugged, and geological study is hampered by poor access and extensive cover of a well-developed karst formed in widespread middle Cenozoic limestones. The most useful references are Draper (1989) and Arden (1975).

The oldest dated rocks of Jamaica are Early Cretaceous and crop out in widespread but rather limited areas. Correlations within the island are difficult, and correlations beyond the island are essentially impossible. The earliest units are limestones of earliest Cretaceous age and have no correlatives in other islands of the Greater Antilles nor in Central America. The remainder of the early stratigraphic section consists of dominantly clastic, carbonate, and volcanic facies typical of other more island-arc associations of the Greater Antilles. The volcanic association is not clear but may be correlable with the PIA suite. At the end of the Cretaceous the section is dominated by thick ignimbritic volcanics and clastic sediments similar to coeval rock units of Hispaniola and Puerto Rico.

A Paleocene–early Eocene rift-valley sedimentary association (Wagwater) forms a conspicuous northwest-southeast belt across the island. Associated bimodal mafic and felsic volcanics are typical of a rifting environment (Jackson and Smith, 1979).

The Cenozoic history of this island is dominated by submergence (perhaps with the exception of the higher part of the Blue Mountains) and deposition of a widespread limestone (mid-Eocene to mid-Miocene). However, later Cenozoic history has been one of uplift, with higher rates on the north side of the island.

LESSER ANTILLES

The Lesser Antilles are dominantly a Neogene volcanic chain with a deformed outer accretionary complex (Barbados) and with remnants of Paleogene and older volcanic centers. Tectonic reconstructions of the Caribbean tend to treat the Lesser Antilles as an entity more or less similar to its present form during most of the Cenozoic. Such a consideration is unrealistic, and the presence of scattered emergent and submarine older volcanic centers may be an indication that the present arc has formed on fragments of older arcs. The most useful reference is Maury and others (1989); additional references are Westercamp (1988), and Bouysse (1984).

Volcanic islands

The Lesser Antilles consist of an older, outer arc ("Limestone Caribbees") and an inner, active volcanic arc. The older arc forms a roughly continuous extension of the eastern Greater Antilles arc. It is not clearly traceable south of Antigua, but the morphology of eastern Guadeloupe suggests that it is underlain by similar materials. East of Guadeloupe the island of La Désirade has a basement containing Jurassic and Early Cretaceous rocks; it resembles nothing else in the Lesser Antilles, but is very similar in part to the oldest rocks of the eastern Greater Antilles. South of Guadeloupe there is no evidence of an older arc.

The present volcanic arc, reviewed most recently by Westercamp (1988), is a typical oceanic island arc, with its oldest elements dating back to basal Miocene, and there is no clear evidence that all, or even any, of the presently active volcanic centers are built on Paloegene or older arc materials. Most of the recent attention focused on the volcanic Lesser Antilles has centered on the problem of the origin and differentiation of the magmas, and of the putative role of sediment or crustal contamination of some of these magmas.

Barbados and the older elements of the southern Lesser Antilles

The island of Barbados has long been an enigma in the geology of the Lesser Antilles. The island consists of three rock units (Speed and Larue, 1982): a basal complex of Paleocene to late Eocene clastic sediments of continental provenance with interbedded pelagites; a series of nappes of middle Eocene to middle Miocene pelagic sediment; and a cover of Pleistocene reefs.

The basal complex has quartz-rich turbidites, which have inspired nearly a century of geological speculation. Their composition demonstrates a continental South American provenance, but sediments of this coarseness more than 300 km from the mainland are provocative. The oceanic nappes overlying the basal complex are thrust onto this complex from the northwest, which places them in a fore-arc basin between the site of Barbados and the volcanic arc of the Lesser Antilles.

The Paleogene of the southern Lesser Antilles arc is dominantly volcanogenic wacke with pelagic sediment interbeds. Speed (1985) has noted that the deformation of the older rocks of Barbados, Grenada, and some of the Grenadines resulted from compression from the north. He convincingly placed both of these in a fore-arc complex of a Paleogene island arc, which faced south toward South America and collided with that continent during the Eocene.

NORTHERN SOUTH AMERICA

Northern South America consists of the northern margins of Colombia and Venezuela, the offshore Venezuelan islands, the Dutch ABC islands (Aruba, Bonaire, Curaçao), Trinidad, and Tobago. Northern Colombia is dominated by fragments of the dismembered branches of the Andes and will not be treated here.

Offshore islands

The belt of islands extending from Aruba on the west to Tobago on the east contains lithic elements of a Cretaceous island arc plus occurrences of Cretaceous oceanic basalt similar to others in the Caribbean. The belt extends eastward through the northern range of Trinidad to Tobago. The older lithic units of this belt are as follows: (1) a metabasite (La Rinconada) of Margarita, stated by Maresch (1974) and Beets and others (1984) to underlie the oldest sedimentary rocks; (2) a Jurassic–Cretaceous shelf-sediment series (Caracas, Juan Griego); (3) island-arc volcanic series of Bonaire (Washikemba) and Tobago related by Donnelly and Rogers (1978) to the PIA series, and its metamorphic equivalent on Tobago (Frost and Snoke, 1989); and (4) a basaltic series on Aruba and Curaçao, with a minor correlative on Trinidad (Sans Souci) and possible minor equivalents on the smaller Venezuelan offshore islands. The interpretation of these units within the offshore belt and their correlation with lithologically similar units of northern Venezuela continue to be controversial topics.

Onshore pre-Mesozoic terranes

The older Venezuelan and Colombian terranes are divisible into two series: (1) scattered terranes cored with Paleozoic or Precambrian metamorphic rocks that are more or less aligned with the central and eastern branches of the Colombian and Venezuelan Andes (including disjunct occurrences of gneiss within the coast ranges of Venezuela, such as the Sebastopol gneiss), and (2) late Paleozoic sedimentary series (Sierra de Perijá, Cordillera de Mérida, and the disjunct occurrence in the dominantly Mesozoic–Cenozoic coast ranges of northern Venezuela of the late Paleozoic Tucutunemo Limestone (Benjamini and others, 1987).

Coastal belt of Venezuela

Venezuela is rimmed on its northern margin by a broad coastal belt with strike parallel to the coast (east-west). The belt was originally interpreted as a series of more or less autochthonous ranges, but following the imaginative suggestion of Hess, first the Villa de Cura belt (Fig. 5) and subsequently nearly all of the major units of this area have been considered to be allochthonous.

The tectonostratigraphic units of this belt are: (1) small bodies of metamorphic rocks of older terranes, whose correlations are not understood (Sebastopol Gneiss); (2) a belt of metamorphosed mafic rocks along the coast (Tacagua); (3) a late Paleozoic limestone (Tucutunemo) amidst undated metamorphic rocks; (4) a Jurassic–Early Cretaceous shelf sedimentary sequence with notable amounts of dark phyllites (Caracas); (5) an allochthonous belt of tectonically mixed metamorphic and igneous rocks of an island-arc complex along with possible oceanic basalt fragments (Villa de Cura nappe); and (6) a post-Caracas Group series of Late Cretaceous and Cenozoic sedimentary rocks forming first a normal shelf sequence, and later a clastic wedge in a marginal basin, including clastic debris shed from the front of the advancing Villa de Cura allochthon.

The relative tectonic relations of these units have been controversial. Following Hess's suggestion that the Villa de Cura complex was an allochthon, several scenarios have been developed. Menédez (1967) presents the first and perhaps the most valuable of these, showing that the Villa de Cura was a nappe derived from the north at the end of the Cretaceous; later modifications are by Beck (1983), Stephan and others (1980), Beets and others (1984), and most recently, by Benjamini and others (1987). The major problems associated with the interpretation of this belt are in the provenance and tectonic history of the lithic units and their correlation with units beyond northern Venezuela.

The correlation of the Villa de Cura belt with the volcanic rocks of the offshore islands has been suggested by many authors, most recently Beets and others (1984). This suggestion seems highly likely, and I would even suggest that some lithic units these authors did not correlate may in fact be highly correlatable (El Carmén Formation with picrites of Curaçao Lava). Perhaps the most interesting and valuable correlation is between the siliceous volcanics of Bonaire and the metavolcanic units of the Villa de Cura. There is a possible age discrepancy: the Villa de Cura rocks were metamorphosed and intruded at about 100 Ma, and the end of the volcanism on Bonaire is about 88 Ma. This discrepancy might not be too severe; the Bonaire rocks span a considerable but unknown amount of time, and their nearest correlatives on Tobago (Sharp and Snoke, 1988; Frost and Snoke, 1989) show Cenomanian and Albian ages. More distant correlatives with this suite (La Désirade, Virgin Islands, Puerto Rico, Hispaniola) consistently show Albian and older ages.

The many occurrences of mafic volcanic rocks that occur both within the Villa de Cura nappe and scattered more or less on or in the Cacagua-Tinaco belt (Benjamini and others, 1987) present a major problem in correlation. The Tiara Lava occurs as part of a fairly complete ophiolite complex, but most other basalts are more isolated. Other units (also including the Tiara) occur in juxtaposition with datable fossil occurrences, which place them in the Early or middle Cretaceous. At least one occurrence (Los Naranjos volcanics) seems to occur within the Paleozoic Tucutunemo Formation, leading Benjamini and others (1987) to query the ages of all of these units. However, there are no known basalts of late Paleozoic age in the western Andes. While the stratigraphic position of these bodies is one of the major challenges of Venezuelan geology, it seems at present that all of them will probably eventually be related to late Mesozoic

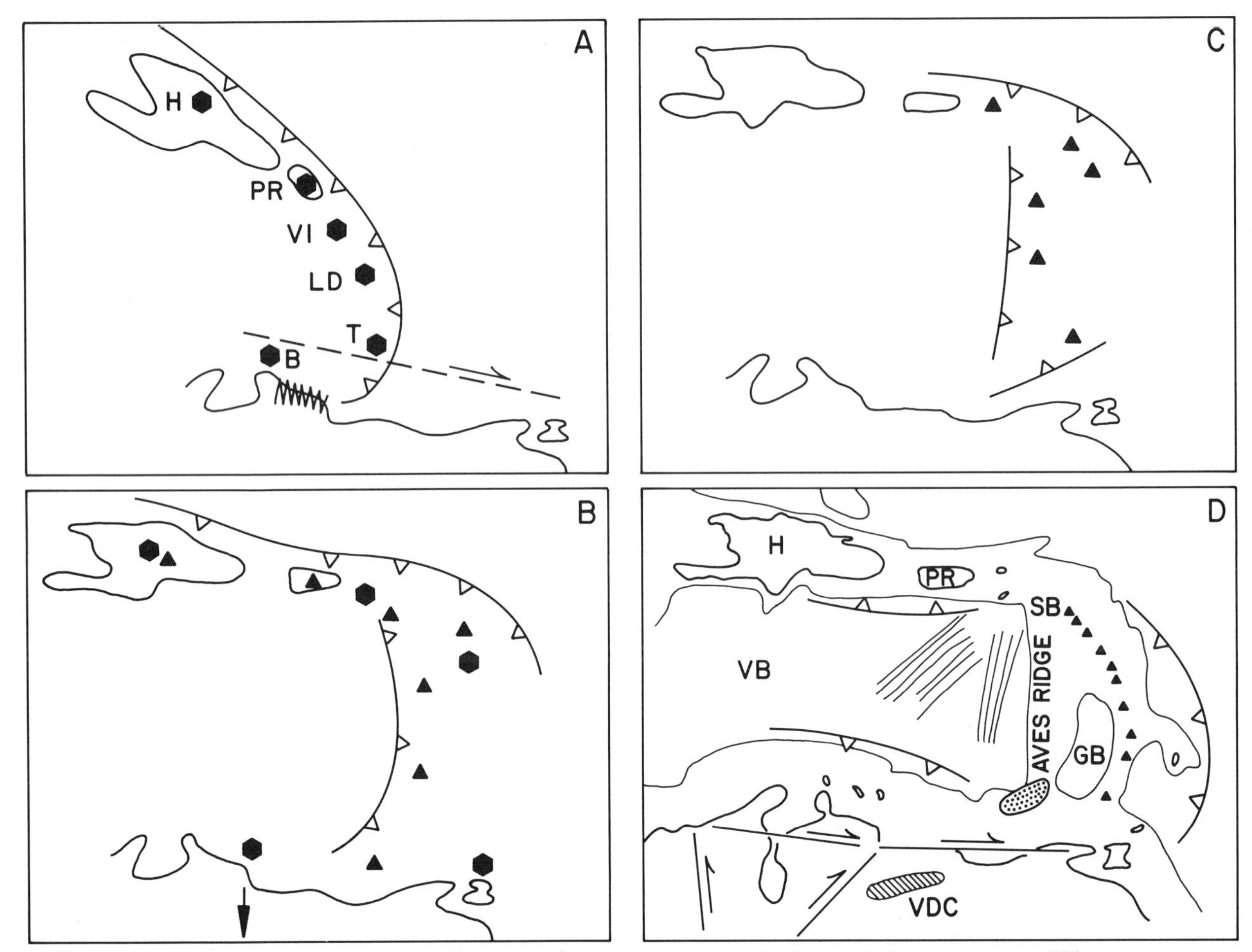

Figure 5. Four sketch maps showing evolution of the eastern Caribbean. Solid hexagons are PIA associations showing the early island arc; solid triangles are later calc-alkaline volcanic centers. A: Late Cretaceous, showing the proto-Antillean arc moving eastward and starting to collide with northern South America. Dashed line shows fault that will later separate Bonaire (B) from Tobago (T). H = Hispaniola, PR = Puerto Rico; VI = Virgin Islands; LD = La Désirade. B: latest Cretaceous: severed proto-Antillean arc is joined by a second, west-facing arc behind the Aves Ridge. Arrow at bottom shows beginnings of southern movement of Villa de Cura allochthon. C: Paleogene. Atlantic-facing subduction continues in northern and southern ends of Antillean arc system, along with continued subduction on Aves Ridge. D: Recent. Thin line shows 2,000-m isobath, solid lines in eastern Venezuelan Basin (VB) show magnetic anomalies (Ghosh and others, 1984). Subduction zones shown on northern and southern boundaries of Venezuelan Basin. Lines with arrows show strike-slip motions on major faults of northern South America. Dotted circle encloses latest Cretaceous granitoids of La Blanquilla and southern Aves Ridge. Lined circles shows the Villa de Cura allochthon (VDC); GB = Grenada Basin; SB = Saba Bank; H = Hispaniola; PR = Puerto Rico.

basalts seen elsewhere, with coastal and offshore complexes of Aruba, Caraçao, and northern Trinidad providing the most proximate examples.

A complete geologic history of this area will probably elude us for several more years. However, the following points seem clear: A coastal belt of Jurassic–Cretaceous age sediments formed at about the same time as on offshore island-arc belt. Subduction was active in this belt during the late Early Cretaceous and led to the formation of high-P metamorphic suites. At some point in the latest Cretaceous, much of this belt was obducted onto the South American mainland. The allochthons continued to slide southward until the middle Cenozoic.

Additional evidence from paleomagnetism has been sought to elucidate the structural history of this deformation. Numerous sites on the offshore islands as well as onshore Venezuela have yielded widely scattered declinations (Skerlec and Hargraves, 1980; Hargraves and Skerlec; 1982; Stearns and others, 1982) with a tendency to show clockwise rotation. A problem for paleomagnetic interpretation will be to determine how much of the rotation of declinations reflects the rotation of large terranes and how much is a local ("ball bearing") effect formed during later Cenozoic eastward movement of the Caribbean Plate.

The beginning of obduction cannot be pinpointed precisely. The oldest autochthonous formation with ophiolitic debris in

Venezuela is the Garrapata Formation (Coniacian), but its dominantly serpentine debris might not be derived from the coastal subduction zone. By the beginning of the Cenozoic, mafic and other metamorphic debris identifiable with the Villa de Cura nappe appears in the Guárico Formation admixed with debris derived from a southerly continental source. It seems most likely that the various elements of this orogen, from the offshore island-arc chain to the sedimentary series of interior Venezuela, are all more or less in their original location. To have moved any of them a long distance (many hundreds of kilometers) would require that a suture south of the Guárico be found, and such a suture seems not to occur. This point must be emphasized, because many reconstructions of the Caribbean require that the coastal belt of Venezuela be derived from a far westerly area, possibly the Pacific margin. In order for the terrane to be allochthonous beginning during the middle Cenozoic (as suggested by Pindell and Dewey, 1982), the debris from the Guárico must not contain materials derived from any of these nappes.

SOUTHERN CENTRAL AMERICA

The part of the Caribbean from Honduras to northern Colombia has been perhaps the most frustrating area for geological research of the Caribbean region. Virtually all of the area is covered by late Cenozoic volcanic deposits and their sedimentary equivalents on the Caribbean coast. The only exceptions are exposures of Jurassic–Cretaceous bodies of oceanic basalt with associated pelagic sediments, and a few limited areas in which Late Cretaceous orogenic sedimentary rocks are found.

The oldest unit of Central America is the Nicoya Complex of northwestern Costa Rica. Correlative exposures are found in eastern Costa Rica (Osa Peninsula) and Panamá (Azuero Peninsula); further correlatives have been suggested from Guatemala to Colombia (Donnelly and others, 1989b) and throughout the Caribbean. The Nicoya Complex actually is two complexes: a pre–Late Jurassic oceanic basalt complex with especially abundant intrusive facies, and above an intervening 50-m-thick pelagic sequence (Punta Conchal), a late Albian through Santonian basaltic complex with sparse sedimentary interbeds (Schmidt-Effing, 1979; Azéma and others, 1979). The older Nicoya (Matapalo) is undoubtedly ocean crust, and the Punta Conchal a pelagic superincumbent sequence. The upper Nicoya (Esperanza), however, poses interpretive problems. Donnelly and others (1989b) have called attention to its chemical and stratigraphic similarity to the Cretaceous basaltic province and correlated it with this event. However, it is now located west of the bounding orogenic zone of Central America, and correlation to materials within the Caribbean must explain its location on the outside of the arc. In this sense it is analogous to the Duarte and Siete Cabezas of Hispaniola, which are now found northeast of much of the contemporaneous arc.

Overlying the Nicoya Complex is a thick sedimentary sequence (Sabana Grande), which provides the earliest (early Campanian) evidence for compressive deformation and associated sedimentation in the Costa Rica area. Lundberg (1982) has described many of the elements of this orogen, including that its sedimentary debris does not contain identifiable fragments from a continental source. However, exposures of these rocks are limited, and the pre–late Cenozoic history of southern Central America remains enigmatic. The importance of the early orogenic deposits is great: if the Caribbean Plate originated in the Pacific and moved passively into its present position, there should be no subduction zone on the western margin. The time of initiation of this zone represents the time at which the relative eastward movement of the Caribbean Plate was impeded; the evidence before us now places this in the Campanian.

The late Cenozoic history is dominated by the growth of Neogene volcanic centers along the Pacific coast and the more local development to the east of a series of alkalic centers that extend to Hispaniola. Along the Pacific coast, locally thick deposits of Neogene clastic sediments testify to the creation of deep fore-arc basins followed by dramatic uplift.

MARINE GEOLOGY

As a result first of extensive seismic refraction and profiling, and later of two campaigns of the Deep Sea Drilling Project (part of Leg 4 and all of Leg 15), the nature of the oceanic part of the Caribbean has become fairly well known. However, this area has turned out to be more complex than originally suspected, and several more legs of drilling will be required to answer some of the important questions posed both by the earlier drilling and by more recent geophysical surveys. Most of the discussion that follows refers to the eastern part of the Caribbean—the Venezuelan Basin; the western basins (Colombian, Yucatán) are relatively poorly known.

The crust of the Caribbean plate

Officer and others (1957) noted that the Caribbean crust was much thicker than normal oceanic crust. They offered several possible explanations, of which the most likely was that the crust was oceanic crust that had been modified by extensive igneous intrusions. Edgar and others (1973) identified this material as the previously mysterious seismic horizon B″ and found that the Venezuelan Basin was underlain by a widespread basalt (dominantly very shallow intrusives) whose latest age was about Coniacian. Because this material is much younger than material found on many of the surrounding islands, and because it predates the divergence of the two Americas by 100 m.y. or more, its identification immediately raised the question as to whether "normal" oceanic crust, of Jurassic age, might be found beneath it.

Linear magnetic anomalies were identified by Donnelly (1973a), but were not stated to have resulted from sea-floor spreading. Ghosh and others (1984) interpreted these anomalies as earliest Cretaceous spreading anomalies, which would have to be beneath the middle Cretaceous basalt event. There are several problems with this interpretation, although the results are broadly consistent with the required early spreading. In the first place, the velocities of spreading according to these authors (less than 1 cm/yr) are less than half the inter-American divergence rate. A higher rate could be explained by positing a convergent margin on either of the American plates; a lower rate would require a second ridge to make up the deficit. This latter case might be permitted if contemporaneous spreading occurred in the Gulf of Mexico, but present knowledge of the Gulf suggests that spreading there was earlier. Second, the anomalies themselves are suspiciously parallel to topographic lineaments and buried scarps of the Venezuelan Basin, and in some instances, buried scarps and magnetic anomalies coincide. Diebold and others (1981) noted a correlation between magnetic anomalies and structural grain but still considered that the magnetic anomaly represented an isochron.

I believe that most past analyses have failed to capture the essence of the role of the Caribbean Plate because they have failed to note the striking evidence for internal deformation of the plate. Edgar and others (1973) presented a synthesis of sediment thicknesses in the central Venezuelan Basin based on numerous seismic reflection profiles. Using as datum planes for their analysis the seismic reflectors A″ (middle Eocene cherts, roughly 40 Ma) and B″ (strongly lithified limestones directly above dolerite sills, roughly 88 Ma), they showed that there was a strong structural grain of the plate as shown by buried scarps in horizon B″, isopachs of materials between B″ and A″, and in isopachs of the post-A″ sediment. To these we add the scarps on the sea floor (mapped by Case and Holcombe, 1980) and interpreted as slip lines by Burke and others (1978), and the faulted scarps at which A″ outcrops (Edgar and others, 1971). The interpretation of seismic reflection profiles does not always make clear the distinction between deeply buried faults and pelagic sediment drapes, but some of the profiles shown by Diebold and others (1981) show a deeply buried A″ that appears to have been faulted. Thus, the post-B″ deformation of the plate is substantial, and post-A″ deformation is less extensive but obvious in numerous places within the plate. Immediate conclusions from these observations are (1) the burden of proof will have to be on the proposer that the magnetic anomaly pattern of the Venezuelan Basin results from sea-floor spreading of any age, (2) the rough B″ of Diebold and others (1981) is exactly that and not crust of an older age, and (3) deformation prior to B″ remains unknown, deformation between B″ and A″ was major, and deformation has continued subsequent to A″.

A recent paper by Bowland and Rosencrantz (1988) shows that much of the Colombian basin is underlain by crust similar to that of the Venezuelan Basin. This contribution is especially important in that it shows that this crust occurs close to the Pacific margin occurrences of the Nicoya Complex, and its equivalents.

Pelagic sediment history

Known Caribbean pelagic sediments are younger than Coniacian and consist dominantly of calcareous and siliceous varieties. The earlier sediments (Late Cretaceous) differ from either Atlantic or Pacific sites (with the exception of site 144 of DSDP Leg 14; Guyana Basin) in having locally abundant carbonaceous facies in the Santonian. The early Cenozoic is highly siliceous in tropical Pacific, Caribbean, and tropical Atlantic sites, which demonstrates the existence of a broad passage open to deep water between the oceans at that time. Donnelly (1989) has used the upward disappearance of a siliceous component in the Atlantic and the Venezuelan Basin to indicate the times of formation of a barrier ridge (about 45 Ma) in the Lesser Antilles or Aves Ridge and the closure of the Central America isthmus (about 15 Ma).

IGNEOUS HISTORY

The igneous history of the Caribbean is remarkably well known as the result of decades of extensive studies, both of the typical calc-alkaline volcanoes of Central America and the Lesser Antilles, as well as of older suites of rocks abundant throughout the region. The igneous rocks of the Caribbean are probably better known than for any other orogenic zone of the world.

For this section I have drawn almost entirely on Donnelly and others (1989b), using also some more recent contributions.

Cretaceous oceanic basalts

One of the most important discoveries of DSDP Leg 15 was that Horizon B″, drilled at five sites, was a vast area of shallow basaltic sills intruding pelagic sediment of about 88 Ma. The discovery provided a linkage among the diverse basaltic suites of similar age around the Caribbean that had each been considered to belong to a different and special tectonic phenomenon. Clearly the basalts were the top of the thick crust found earlier by Officer and others (1957, 1959), and equally clearly they lacked many of the attributes of typical oceanic crust. Horizon B″ is smooth, in contrast to rough oceanic crust. The sediments above the Venezuelan Basin sites show no basal iron enrichment. The basalts were initially referred to as a flood basalt event (Donnelly, 1973b) and correlated with scattered circum-Caribbean Cretaceous basalts. Although Duncan and Hargraves (1984) have treated the Caribbean as an earlier stage of the undeniable Neogene hot spot of the Galapagos, the vast amounts of eruptives, the almost complete absence of eruptions at central localities producing topographic edifices, the widespread, smooth horizon B″, and the predominant MORB–like chemistry of the basalts all argue instead for a plateau origin (oceanic flood basalt). Stratigraphic and petrological data in hand at the present time place occurrences in Panamá, Costa Rica, Guatemala, central Hispaniola, Jamaica, Belize (subsurface), Trinidad, Aruba, Curaçao, and northern and western Colombia, in this suite. Not all authors have agreed with this interpretation. I believe all occurrences are consistent with obduction during compressive deformation, in most cases at the end of the Santonian. Deformation of the bodies varies from minor (Costa Rica, Curaçao, southern Hispaniola) to major, with metamorphism (Puerto Rico, central Hispaniola, northern Venezuela). It is most realistic to think of this province as analogous to some oceanic basaltic plateaus, such as the Ontong Java plateau in the south Pacific. However, whereas the latter lies in approximately its original state and position, the Caribbean Plate has been tectonized around its perimeter, and fragments are found on almost all surrounding land areas.

Fossils within the complex have mainly been dated as Albian through Santonian, but there are Campanian ages for Hispaniola and Nicaraguan Rise sites, and some Pacific coast sites show minor volcanic activity into the Paleogene. Beneath the basalt in Costa Rica is a 50-m-thick radiolarite sequence, which has been interpreted in two different ways. According to a German group (summarized in Gursky and others, 1982), the radiolarite is overlain by basalt in eruptive contact. According to a French group (summarized in Bourgois and others, 1984), the radiolarite is thrust over the younger basalt and places no age constraints on it. The radiolarite contains Late Jurassic through Cenomanian fossils, and the interpretation of its contact with the younger basalt remains an important problem for Caribbean geology.

In the broad sense, the basaltic province includes a great variety of igneous and associated sedimentary facies. The basalt is dominantly pillowed in many places, but unpillowed flows and shallow sills are numerous. Associated sediments include widespread pelagites. Locally (Hispaniola, Aruba) there are conglomerates of basaltic or macrofossil debris, indicating emergence of the complex. Hyaloclastites are especially conspicuous in Venezuela, Trinidad, and central Hispaniola.

According to major and minor elements, the basalt is generally indistinguishable from MORB. Compositional variants are noted in several places: high-Mg basalts (called picrites in Curaçao and komatiites in Isla Gorgona, Colombia) are apparently variants of this basalt, and poorly preserved high-Mg basalts from Costa Rica may belong here also. A LIL-enriched basalt has already been noted from the Beata Ridge (DSDP site 151). Its equivalents are widespread in southern Hispaniola; further possible equivalents occur in the metamorphic terrane of central Hispaniola (Duarte metabasalts). Although much, probably most, of the basalt is like MORB, the high-Mg occurrences suggest a very high degree of melting not seen at modern ridge sites. The LIL-enriched variant can be matched with a few ridge samples but is not typical of this environment. There is no distinctive character of this basalt that states where it was erupted, and unfortunately we do not yet have a good understanding of the total time span involved.

The basaltic province is vast (3,000 km by 1,000 km within the Venezuelan and Colombian Basins; larger if Cuban basalts are included). Not knowing the thickness of the basalt or the age of its inception, we do not know the rate of eruption, but even a lower limit of possibilities would have been impressive. There are vast basalt suites of about the same age (Ontong Java Plateau and other mid-Pacific plateaux; possibly also the Cyprus and Oman ophiolites) scattered around the world. These plateaux signify vigorous mantle melting, but in no place do they produce well-defined hot-spot islands.

In general, the magmatism stops sharply at about 88 Ma. However, there are minor occurrences, especially in the western Caribbean and in Central America, of later Cretaceous and Paleogene basalts, many of which show a slight tendency to LIL enrichment. There are buried seamounts in the Venezuelan Basin that might be further examples (e.g., aborted DSDP site 145). These are interpreted here as minor late manifestations of the event.

Primitive Island Arc suite

The PIA suite characterizes the early stages of the Antillean island arc and is better developed in the Caribbean than at any other place in the world.

The initial description of the PIA suite of island arc volcanic rocks came from the Virgin Islands (Donnelly, 1966; Donnelly and Rogers, 1978, 1980), emphasizing six aspects of this volcanism: its stratigraphically low position (the age is still poorly known but is probably Aptian–Albian or older), the evidence for high intrinsic water content of the magmas, the absence of intercalated clastic sediments or other indications of an association with an emergent island arc, the abundance of highly siliceous lavas, the nonradiogenic Pb isotopes, and the low values of many LIL elements. This suite seems to indicate early stages of calc-alkaline magmatism but with no involvement of subducted sediments and in a topographically subdued, submarine island arc.

The Virgin Islands volcanic history began with deep-water volcanism, shallowed toward the end of Water Island time, and was subaerial during Louisenhoj time (Albian). (An incorrect reference to a Turonian–early Santonian age for these beds in Mattson and others, 1989, is based on a fossil misidentification.) Correlative suites have been identified in many other parts of the Caribbean. The Los Ranchos of Hispaniola (and its probable metamorphosed equivalents, the Amina and Maimón schists), is dominantly siliceous, and has minor sedimentary interbeds. In Puerto Rico, units of this affinity are grouped under the name pre-Robles. The basal complex of La Désirade consists of two dominant lithologies. The westernmost siliceous complex is very similar to the Virgin Islands with a possibly minor difference: there are conspicuous trondhjemites, which are absent in the Virgin Islands, and which yield a latest Jurassic Pb-U zircon age. The volcanic rocks of Tobago form a suite remarkably similar to the Virgin Islands and pre-Robles of Puerto Rico, with basaltic-andesite pyroclastics dominant. The age of magmatism is Albian to Cenomanian (Sharp and Snoke, 1988). A large consanguinous plutonic complex is intruded in the volcanic units, and is the only substantial occurrence of plutonic rocks from this association. The Washikemba Formation of Bonaire is the final in situ example of this association. With dominant highly siliceous rocks, it is compositionally parallel to the Virgin Islands. At the top there are Coniacian fossils; this complex is the only one containing post-Albian fossils in the Caribbean. The Villa de Cura nappe of Venezuela contains abundant metamorphosed equivalents of this formation.

Aside from the evidence that these deposits represent early stages of an island arc, the most important aspect of this volcanism is that the identified centers can be reconstructed into a single arc spanning the diverging Americas during the Early Cretaceous. The length of this arc is unknown, but large gaps between some of these centers imply that it might have been far shorter than at present. The polarity of subduction has not been established for any of the centers; Lewis and others (1989b) suggest that it faced south, but I prefer a north-facing polarity (Donnelly, 1966) for the Virgin Islands and, presently, for the entire arc.

In each occurrence the PIA series precedes the more normal calc-alkaline (CA) series. In Puerto Rico the time of transition is between the Albian and Turonian, but in Bonaire there are PIA volcanics as young as Coniacian. Establishing the age of this transition is important; presently it appears that the more normal CA magmatism follows the termination of the basalt event. Noting that the bulk of ages established within the PIA are Albian or Aptian, I suggest that the PIA series is roughly coeval with the basalt event.

Calc-alkaline suites

Beginning approximately in the Albian to Turonian, and not overlapping the PIA series in any one location, volcanics of the more typical calc-alkaline (CA) suite were erupted widely in the Greater Antilles. These accumulated dominantly as pyroclastics in stratigraphic sections with thick intercalated sediments, they are mainly andesitic, and they are typically enriched in LIL elements. There are widespread plutons of the same material, especially toward the end of the Cretaceous.

In contrast with the PIA series, the CA volcanics are enriched in LIL elements, less siliceous on the average, and contain more radiogenic Pb isotopes. The stratigraphically lowest of the CA volcanics of Puerto Rico are shoshonitic and conspicuously high in potassium. In each of the islands of the Greater Antilles (except for Cuba, which is imperfectly known) the Cretaceous igneous rocks vary considerably in potassium content, evidently reflecting a greater depth of differntiation, rather than a difference in the material present at the locus of fusion.

The transition from PIA to normal CA is accompanied by the appearance of conspicuous intercalated sediments. Thus, the early island arc is submarine and forms in an oceanic environment relatively free from strong compressive deformation, and the later arc represents strong compression, with emerging centers providing thick sediment, much of which is later subducted.

In the Paleogene the CA series was represented in the northern and southern Lesser Antilles and in Central America. In the Neogene the activity continued through the Lesser Antilles and Central America.

Cenozoic suites associated with rifting

During the Paleogene the CA magmatism of the Greater Antilles largely ended, except in the eastern Greater Antilles (extending into what is now the northern Lesser Antilles) where this activity continued until well into the Oligocene. The eastward movement of the Caribbean Plate created local rift environments along both the northern and southern borders of the Caribbean. The best known of these is the Wagwater trough of Jamaica, but the Oligo-Miocene Falcón suite of Venezuela, a cluster of earliest Oligocene alkalic granitoid plutons in northern Central America, and the diabase dike swarm of Puerto Rico and the Virgin Islands are further examples.

The early and middle Miocene ignimbrites of Honduras (Padre Miguel) are a slightly younger suite evidently formed during broad crustal rearrangement of the Chortis block.

In the northwestern Caribbean, widespread alkalic magmatism appeared in the late Neogene. The most abundant examples are in Hispaniola and Costa Rica, but there are numerous other examples in Honduras, Nicaragua, Jamaica, and in offshore locations. This activity is too widespread to be related to any single structural feature, such as a subducted slab from the Pacific or Greater Antilles. Instead, it signals the inception of a new tectonic style at a still-undetermined time, probably in the late Miocene (the oldest example is the Low Layton basalt from Jamaica). I interpret this event as indicating pervasive spreading of the entire northwestern part of the Caribbean Plate and regard it as further evidence that the Caribbean Plate cannot be regarded as a single rigid entity.

TECTONIC HISTORY OF THE CARIBBEAN

Reconstruction of the tectonic history of the Caribbean is hindered by lack of knowledge of the provenance of terranes, by imprecise knowledge of the history of coherence or noncoherence of the Caribbean Plate, and by lack of knowledge of interactions between the plate and its borderlands in a long period of mainly compressive interactions among the Farallon and two American Plates.

In the following analysis I make use of the most current estimates for the relative motions of the Farallon (Cocos in the Neogene), North American, and South American Plates (from Pindell and others, 1988). These relative motions suggest four periods, each with their own characteristic tectonic ambience. I assume, as outlined above, that the Caribbean "Plate" itself deformed internally throughout this history and hence has no simple, knowable plate movement.

The motion description is "Caribocentric"; that is, the Caribbean is here described as moving relative to the Americas. However, in a hot-spot reference frame, the Caribbean is probably nearly static, and the North and South American Plates move westward past it.

Relative plate movements since the end of the Jurassic

Figure 3 shows a series of triangles of vectors representing the relative motions of the three major plates since about the end of the Jurassic (the pre-Cretaceous motion of the Farallon Plate with respect to the American plates has not yet been solved nor even conjectured). The vectors have been calculated using the rotation parameters of Pindell and others (1988) for a point in northern Central America. The pre-Cretaceous history is not shown, because the movement of the Farallon Plate has not been determined. I assume that Jurassic history was dominated by the formation of an oceanic crust between rapidly diverging American plates.

The first stage of relative motion shown here (triangles A and B) covers the period of 142 to 119 Ma, or roughly the Neocomian and Barremian. A state of pure tension existed: the American plates were diverging at 2 to 3 cm/yr, and the Farallon Plate diverged from both of them at a higher rate, 4 to 6 cm/yr.

The second stage (triangles C and D) covers the time period 119 to 84 Ma, which corresponds approximately to Aptian through Santonian. This is also the period of the Cretaceous "quiet zone" and appears to correspond to the Cretaceous basalt event. In this stage the Farallon Plate converged with the two American plates, which were still diverging from each other. This was a period of compression in one direction (at about 5 to 8 cm/yr) and tension in the other (at about 3 cm/yr).

The third stage (triangles E, F, and G) represents the period 84 to 49 Ma, which is approximately Campanian through early middle Eocene. In this stage the convergence of the Farallon Plate increased to about 13 cm/yr, and the azimuth of this compression became more easterly. The North and South American Plates moved very little with respect to each other; thus an immense external stress was created by the Farallon Plate impinging on the nonyielding American plates.

The fourth stage (triangles H, I, J, and K) covers the period 49 to 0 Ma, or middle Eocene through Recent. In this period the Farallon convergence continued and the azimuth gradually swung to a more northerly direction. The rates of convergence decreased to about 9 cm/yr. The North and South American Plates converged during this period at an average rate slightly less than 1 cm/yr. In the region of the Lesser Antilles, this convergence was about one-fourth this amount.

Problem area 1: Yucatan Basin, Cayman Trough, and the Motagua fault

The northwestern Caribbean is the site of one of the most troublesome and enduring geological disputes in the Caribbean region. Holcombe and others (1973) found that the mid–Cayman Trough was the site of very young spreading, making this the only area of current ocean-crust formation in the entire Caribbean. Further analysis of magnetic anomalies (most recently by Rosencrantz and others, 1988) has shown that there exists a recognizable central sequence with a total spreading velocity of about 1.5 cm/yr since the late Oligocene and a likely earlier sequence with a velocity of about 2.5 cm/yr beginning in the middle Eocene. The interpretation has minor internal difficulties: some prominent magnetic anomalies are clearly not part of a spreading sequence, and the interpretation requires ridge jumps and asymmetric spreading. The older part of the sequence is not convincing, and some of the heat-flow measurements toward the extremities are too high for the proposed ages of their crust. Few people doubt that the Cayman Trough has been the site of young spreading, but a question remains whether the entire 1,000-km opening has been accomplished by east-west spreading, or whether there was an earlier stage of north-south opening followed by a later east-west stage. Even with deep-sea drilling it may not be easy to resolve this question.

The consequences of Cayman Trough spreading are very important for the Cenozoic history of the Caribbean. If there has been 1,000 km of east-west spreading since the middle Eocene, and if this spreading has been only slightly asymmetric, then we should be required to find about 1,000 km of post–middle Eocene sinistral offset across one or more faults extending west from this trough through northern Central America. The problem is that we do not do so, and field work to date seems to limit the maximum offset to about 130 km on the Polochic fault, mainly of Neogene age (Burkart, 1978). We are nearly 900 km short of finding the necessary offset.

The Motagua fault zone itself has been considered as the most likely site for the missing offset. The problem with this zone is that the complex of faults, which includes but is not limited to the Cabañas fault that moved violently in 1976, includes no fault across which there is much lithic contrast of Cretaceous and Paleogene rock units. The Eocene Subinal Formation displays almost identical facies on either side of this fault, even though this formation shows a gradual change in a space of tens of kilometers eastward (down the valley). Across other faults, almost identical lithofacies can be found on each side of the fault in at least one place. Perhaps the most striking example of a lithic match is of two large amphibolite bodies found about 50 km east of Guatemala City. These amphibolites are metamorphosed mafic igneous rock identified with the apparent Cretaceous basalt complex occurrences; the age of metamorphism is early Maastrichtian, as discussed in Donnelly and others (1989a). In both occurrences the amphibolites dip north, as shown by their gravity signatures (Donnelly, unpublished), and in both cases the complexes contain minor bodies of eclogite. The known occurrences of rocks of this type in northern Central America are limited to these two areas, and a movement of 900 km of the fault would then have had to bring into juxtaposition amazingly similar rock facies with special characteristics. The occurrence of these bodies at the northern and southern limits of the Motagua fault zone effectively eliminates any of the faults of this zone individually, or all of them collectively (as well as any buried faults within the valley), from consideration as the candidate fault for the missing offset.

If we look for the missing 900-km movement elsewhere in northern Central America, we do not find likely candidate zones. If northern Central America was mainly blanketed by Neogene sediment, then we could propose buried fault zones with relatively impunity, but the vast areas of exposed Paleogene and older rocks have made accounting for 1,000 km of Cenozoic fault movement essentially impossible.

There are two ways in which this discrepancy might be resolved, not including finding a hitherto unrecognized major fault zone. The first calls for the total east-west opening of the Cayman Trough to be limited to 500 km, with the remainder resulting from an early north-south opening. I regard this as less likely but consistent with the geophysical and topographic data. The second calls for the opening to be accompanied by a considerable stretching of the Chortis block, so that the fault zone and spreading center have not been fixed relative to the Chortis block. This suggestion is prompted by the observation that, in contrast with the Maya block to the north, the entire Chortis block has abundant grabens oriented approximately north-south, as well as minor sinistral splays of the northern bounding fault zone. The Nicaraguan Rise has even more striking north-south scarps, and the large north-south trough adjacent to Providencia Island is one of the most prominent topographic features of Central America. Adjacent to many of these grabens are Neogene alkali basalt eruptive centers (Lake Yojoa, Providencia Island, etc.). Cenozoic stretching of the Chortis block alleviates the problem of accounting for the many hundred kilometers of east-west opening and also may account for the submergence of the Nicaraguan Rise.

The Yucatan Basin was found, on the basis of a single reversed seismic refraction profile, to have a crust similar to that of normal ocean, in contrast to the Venezuelan and Colombian Basins (Ewing and others, 1960). Hall and Yeung (1980) proposed that the faint magnetic lineations of the basin, its heat flow, and its depth of crust were consistent with a Late Cretaceous–Paleogene age for the basin. The magnetic analysis is not completely convincing; there is, for one thing, no center of symmetry about an ancestral mid-basin ridge. However, the overall conclusion seems sound and is generally consistent with the geology of Cuba and (considering how little we know of it) the Cayman Ridge. I believe that a sphenochasmic opening of the Yucatan Basin during the latest Cretaceous swept diverse fragments northward (older Chortis basement and superincumbent sediments, Chortis-margin Cretaceous orogen, older oceanic crust, and superincumbent pelagites) to a collision with the Florida–Bahamas passive margin. Figure 4 outlines the stages of this development.

The tectonic development of Cuba and the Yucatan Basin is closely linked with the history of the Chortis block. A Cayman Trough opening of 1,000 km places the early Cenozoic Chortis block against the Maya block with essentially no continental crust protruding east of the present-day coast of Belize. In this conventional view the advancing Caribbean plate with Cuba on its northern margin swept past the entire Chortis block on its way to its present position. My view that the Chortis block protruded far to the east of the Maya block requires that the Yucatan Basin open as a sphenochasmic basin after the Chortis block reached its easterly position. A protruding Cretaceous Chortis block leaves much of Cuba (the western half) tectonically shadowed during Late Cretaceous movement of the Greater Antilles northward. Thus, while the Greater Antilles from eastern Cuba eastward was developing as a vigorous island arc, western Cuba underwent no such development, and its later assembly as a thrust collage included very few elements that could be related to a Late Cretaceous island arc.

Jamaica poses further enigmas. The earlier Cretaceous stratigraphy is not similar to what is seen in other parts of the Greater Antilles, and in fact some of the earliest Cretaceous Antillean strata are found on this island. The volcanic series and associated granitoid plutonics at the end of the Cretaceous are very similar to examples from Hispaniola and Puerto Rico, but the earlier volcanic series are not so clearly correlative. Jamaica may be a tectonically composite island formed in part from older passive-margin stratigraphic and igneous elements and in part from island-arc elements of Late Cretaceous age. Possibly a latest Cretaceous opening of the Yucatan Basin resulted in the northern transport of older oceanic and Chortis margin slices to an ultimate collision with the Florida-Bahamas passive margin (Cuba) and a southern subduction margin with magmatism on the northern Chortis block, Nicaragua Rise, and Jamaica.

Problem area 2: The eastern Caribbean

Instead of a central problem, there are a host of problems associated with the eastern Caribbean. One of these is the relation of the Greater Antilles to the Lesser Antilles and the corollary problem of the extension of the mainly Mesozoic Greater Antilles to the east. A second problem is the nature of the Aves Ridge and its placement among the other elements of the eastern Caribbean. Perhaps the most contentious problem is the proposed major Neogene eastward movement of the Caribbean Plate relative to South America, as would be required by the 1,000 km offset of the Cayman Trough linked to a rigid Caribbean Plate. Another problem is the correlation of older rock units of the southeastern Caribbean with elements on the northern boundary. I have outlined four stages in the history of the eastern Caribbean in Figure 5.

The first problem—the extension of the Greater Antilles into the Lesser Antilles—has only been recognized as a problem in the last few decades. Earlier than this, it was simply assumed that tectonic evolution of the Greater Antilles stopped at the end of the Mesozoic and began then in the Lesser Antilles. However, the discovery of pre-Cenozoic igneous rocks in the Lesser Antilles and the identification of extensive Paleogene CA igneous activity in the eastern Greater Antilles showed that a clear division at a time break did not occur. Occurrences of Mesozoic igneous rocks are still sparse in the Lesser Antilles. Except for the isolated island of La Désirade, all of the occurrences consist of dredged or drilled examples. However, in spite of their limited number, the location of these occurrences shows that Cretaceous igneous activity is widespread, including dredged rocks along the eastern front of the Lesser Antilles arc (Fox and Heezen, 1975), along the Aves Ridge 300 km to the west, and in the bottom of the Saba Bank well (Bouysse and others, 1985). The dredged examples consist of tuffaceous sediment with a datable biogenic component; the Saba Bank occurrence is 65-Ma igneous rock at the bottom of the well. St. Croix could be considered to belong to this province rather than to Puerto Rico; its well-known Late Cretaceous sedimentary rocks and intrusions (Whetten, 1966; Speed and others, 1979) then provide further examples.

Neither in the southern Lesser Antilles nor in the Aves Ridge south of its central part have Cretaceous rocks been identified. The dredged granitoid rocks from the southern end (Fox and Heezen, 1975) have been shown to be essentially identical with granitoids occurring widely on the adjacent South America shelf, of which La Blanquilla Island is the closest example (Donnelly and Rogers, 1978). An earlier report of Cretaceous rocks from the Grenadines has now been shown to be false (Andreieff and others, 1988).

The Aves Ridge is an enigmatic marine feature that figures heavily in the Late Cretaceous–Paleogene tectonic history of the Caribbean. Its western boundary is remarkably linear, and it is emergent only at the insignificant, sand-covered Aves Island. Deep-sea drilling (DSDP sites 30 of Leg 4 and 148 of Leg 15) on the southern end show no volcanic activity during the Neogene but yield little evidence for the arc structure. The arc is commonly interpreted as an inactive island arc, and, noting the dredged volcanic rocks of Late Cretaceous and Paleogene age, I follow this interpretation here. However, most interpretations have its subduction from the east and require it to have preceded the Lesser Antilles by a trench jump prior to the Miocene. I take the somewhat novel view, however, that its polarity was from the west and not from the east. There are some geophysical observations to support this view and none to support the opposite view.

A gravity profile of the arc (Bowin, 1976) shows a thickened welt of lower density material, resembling a normal island arc but lacking an obvious polarity. A few seismic refraction lines in the adjacent Venezuelan Basin to the west show that the mantle appears to deepen, and low-velocity sediment thickens markedly as the arc is approached (Edgar and others, 1971).

Deformation of the eastern Venezuelan Basin is shown by the pattern of magnetic anomalies, which changes abruptly at about 65.5° longitude to north-south, or parallel to the Aves Ridge. I believe these anomalies result from normal faulting associated with subduction. In the eastern Caribbean the moving plate began to subduct beneath the Aves Ridge in the latest Cretaceous; much of the faulting shown in the profiles of Diebold and others (1981) occurred at this time. The rough B″ zone in the southeastern Venezuelan Basin is a highly faulted zone where a depressed B″ was covered by more than 2 km of sediment over a broad area (map of Case and Holcombe, 1980).

Cretaceous rocks in the northern Lesser Antilles province occur over a width of 300 km across the arc. A single Cretaceous arc would have to have been tectonically fragmented in such a way that its fragments were broadly scattered. It is more likely that there were in fact two Cretaceous arcs, one on the outer edge (Limestone Caribbees) and one on the inner edge (Aves Ridge). The existence of two coeval arcs requires subduction with opposite polarities in the Late Cretaceous. The thickened, buoyant Caribbean crust should not be easily subducted beneath the island arc (Burke and others, 1978), but it is clearly being subducted today. By the end of the Cretaceous this crust would be several tens of millions of years old and hence cooler, less buoyant, and more subductable than in its original state.

The Grenada Basin to the east has been and continues to remain mysterious. Bouysse (1988) has interpreted this as a small oceanic basin formed as a sort of mirror image to the Cayman Trough by Neogene spreading parallel to the Lesser Antillean arc. Its 6 km of well-layered pelagic sediment places some restrictions on its age. If the sediment is as old as 60 Ma at the crustal contact, then the Cenozoic sedimentation rate is 100 m/m.y., which is about ten times the average for the Venezuelan Basin pelagic section, and of the same order of magnitude as the late Neogene drilled sections on the southern Aves Ridge (sites 30, 148, DSDP). A younger Grenada Basin that formed in response to Miocene and younger volcanic activity of the Lesser Antilles (a "back-arc" basin) would have a prohibitively high sedimentation rate. Unfortunately, there is no magnetic or structural fabric to further elucidate the history of this basin, and I interpret it simply as a remnant of the Caribbean crust between two younger island arcs on either side.

The lithic units of northern South America are interpreted as remnants of the proto-Antillean arc (Bonaire, Tobago, Villa de Cura allochthon), a Caribbean basalt event (Aruba, Curaçao, Trinidad, Tiara, and similar allochthonous units of Venezuela), and a later Cretaceous continental margin orogen or offshore island arc (Hooiberg pluton of Aruba; granitoid pluton or plutons of Venezuelan offshore islands; southern-derived Knip series volcanogenic sediments of Curaçao). These have been tectonically mingled during the Late Cretaceous collision of the proto-Antillean island arc with the South America borderland.

The lithic and temporal similarities among the diverse fragments of early island-arc occurrences in the Caribbean imply a once-continuous proto-Antillean arc that must have been breached in the Late Cretaceous by a relative eastward moving Caribbean Plate. The severed ends of the Antillean arc were then located across the span of the protruding Caribbean plate, which is the span of the present Lesser Antilles. La Désirade is probably a remnant of this arc. The relative eastward movement of the Caribbean Plate, from the time of original formation of the primitive island-arc series until the end of the Cretaceous, has resulted in episodic stretching of an originally short island arc. Successively later volcanic centers grew upon the stretched and separated early fragments, and in the gaps between them, and were stretched and severed in turn. A hypothetically complete palinspastic restoration of the arc would show that the length has increased with time.

The post-Mesozoic relative eastward movement of the Caribbean Plate, as seen in the southeastern Caribbean, has been minimal according to this analysis. Donnelly and Rogers (1978) correlated the dredged granitoids of the Aves Ridge with those of nearby La Blanquilla Island on the shelf. This correlation forces any post-Cretaceous fault movement to have been north of the dredged granitoids (12°20′N), which is within the plate itself. The onshore movement of the Villa de Cura allochthon at the beginning of the Paleogene, and its shedding of clastic debris into the Guárico Basin, places the entire offshore complex, with its Caribbean crust component, approximately in its present position at this time. Also, the collision of the Paleogene island arc of the southern Lesser Antilles with the South America borderland in the Eocene is entirely consistent with little or no subsequent eastward movement of the Caribbean Plate (Speed, 1985).

SUMMARY

Stage 1. Jurassic to Early Cretaceous rifting

The earliest stage (Fig. 6) of Caribbean history is the least controversial but is recorded in an uncomfortably sparse lithic record. The required rapid (2 to 3 cm/yr) movement of the combined South American–African Plates away from the North American Plate formed a rapidly accreting oceanic crust. The passive margin of the two continents is not identified, except that evaporite-limestone-dolomite terranes of the Gulf of Mexico and Florida-Bahamas are logically marginal facies of this event. On the western margin are found red-bed deposits in southern Mexico, northern Central America, and northwestern South America.

The lithic remains of Jurassic oceanic crust are limited in the Caribbean to occurrences of basaltic rocks in the lower (Matapalo) part of the Nicoya Complex, and the Siquisique ophiolite of Venezuela. An occurrence of Jurassic radiolarian chert within the Bermeja Complex of Puerto Rico is a possible additional example.

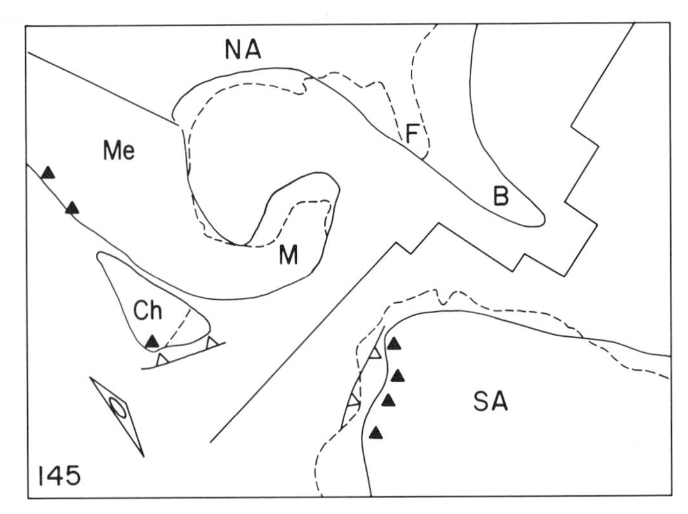

Figure 6. Sketch map showing the Caribbean at the end of the Jurassic, about 145 Ma. The Chortis block (Ch) has separated from Mexico (Me). Possible subduction zones adjacent to the spreading Caribbean crust are suggested because of the occurrence of Late Jurassic igneous rocks (solid triangles) on the adjacent terranes as indicated. The triangle in the lower left is taken from Figure 3 and shows the triangle of motion vectors, with divergence indicated by the ellipse. NA = North America; SA = South America; M = Maya block; F = Florida; B = Bahamas.

Stage 2. Cretaceous basalt event

The middle Cretaceous basalt event (Figs. 7, 8) was one of the major events of the Caribbean, but probably had an eastern Pacific origin. The occurrence in some places of evidence of subaerial environments, and the intriguing occurrences of what appear to be buried seamounts in the Venezuelan Basin suggest that there were volcanic prominences built on this plateau surface.

I do not offer here an explanation for the basalt event. However, I note that it occurred during the interval represented by plate convergence in one direction and divergence in the other. Both the initiation of this peculiar tectonic ambience and the basalt event itself are not precisely dated, the first because of the Cretaceous magnetic quiet zone and the second because of a lack of fossil control for the early stages of the event. However, it is plausible to suggest that they coincide at the beginning as they apparently do at the end. Because the Cretaceous basalt event has apparently coeval counterparts in other parts of the world, and because, regardless of the surficial tectonic-igneous environment, the rate of magma upwelling during that interval was undeniably high, it is further plausible to believe that the internal conditions that led to magnetic quiescence led also to extensive mantle melting.

Probably the significant aspect of this event for Caribbean geologic development was the formation of a thickened crust that could not be readily subducted, especially when young. Thus, the basalt event has defined closely the extent (but perhaps not the shape) of the Caribbean Sea, which has largely survived the subsequent compressive ravages of surrounding plates.

The termination of the event in most parts of the Caribbean was about 88 to 85 Ma (Coniacian–Santonian) and slightly younger in the west (Fig. 8). In many places, obduction of fragments of this thickened crust occurred near the end of the Santonian, and there are several places where the obducted complex is overlain by Campanian limestones (Costa Rica, Puerto Rico, Panamá). The initiation in Central America and the intensification in the Greater Antilles and northern South America of island-arc activity indicates that this is one of the critical turning points in Caribbean geologic history.

Figure 7 shows the Caribbean at an early stage of the basalt event. The Chortis block has separated from Mexico and moved southward at an earlier time when the Farallon Plate was moving southward; the basaltic crust narrowly separating this from the Maya and Mexican blocks was not the same as the Caribbean basalt and could better be likened to a Cretaceous Cayman Trough.

A proto-Antillean arc is shown spanning the Americas and flanking the thickening Caribbean crust, which is an area of extensive basalt eruption. The arc formed at the zone of lithic contrast, with cold, probably altered, oceanic crust to the northeast and a hot crust thickening beneath basalt eruptives to the southwest. Although the arc was a locus of subduction, its formation was not a response to an applied compressive stress. More

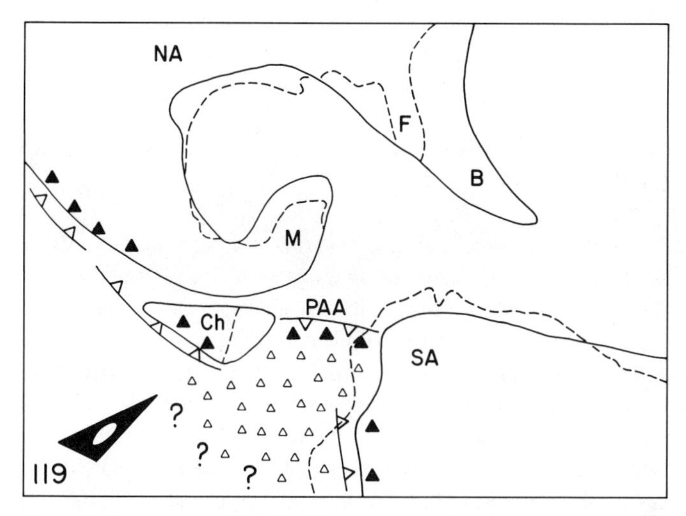

Figure 7. Sketch map of the Caribbean in the Aptian, about 119 Ma. The proto-Antillean arc (PAA) is shown spanning the gap between the Chortis block (Ch) and South America (SA). The pattern of open triangles shows the beginning of the Caribbean Cretaceous basalt plateau behind the island arc. The triangle of motion vectors (from Fig. 3) shows convergence (solid pattern) to the northeast and divergence (ellipse) to the southeast. Solid triangles are calc-alkaline volcanic centers. M = Maya block; NA = North America; F = Florida; B = Bahamas.

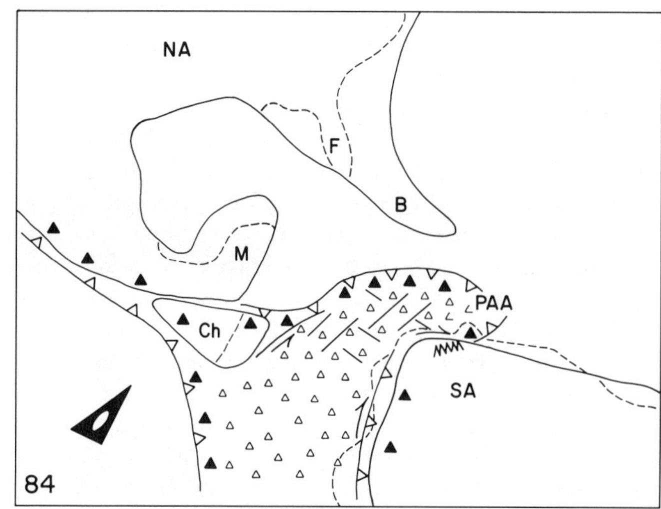

Figure 8. Sketch map of the Caribbean in late Santonian, about 84 Ma. The Chortis block (Ch) is about to collide with the Maya block (M). The Caribbean plate is moving eastward into the gap between the Americas and deforming internally (diagonal lines). The southern end of the proto-Antillean arc (PAA) is colliding with South America (SA). The basalt eruptions of the central Caribbean are generally still active (open triangles), but becoming inactive in the east (incomplete small triangles). The triangle of motion vectors is similar to that for Figure 7. Solid triangles are calc-alkaline volcanic centers. NA = North America; F = Florida; B = Bahamas.

likely the arc occupied the snout of a thickening basalt accumulation; the gradual outward spread of this accumulation created subduction at its boundary with older oceanic crust. Fragments of this proto-Antillean arc extend from Cuba to northern South America. The arc was mainly an oceanic island arc with a very high ratio of accumulated igneous rocks to sedimentary rocks. Apparently, few parts of this arc were emergent until approximately the middle Cretaceous. The southern part of this arc was sufficiently active that subducted volcanic rocks were metamorphosed at high pressures.

I interpret the arc as having formed fringing the plateau basalt event and moving eastward locked with this plateau. Alternatively, the proto-Antillean arc and the plateau basalt might have been quite unrelated. Subduction might have been from the west, and the thickened plateau basalt then advanced until it reached the subduction zone, which could not accommodate this section. The problem with the interpretation is that the time of cessation of the basalt event, the time of initiation of significant compressive deformation, and the time at which the American plates ceased to diverge at high velocity appear to nearly coincide. This would make the cessation of the basalt event and the collision of an advancing oceanic plateau with the subduction zone a coincidence, which seems a less attractive hypothesis.

Figure 8 shows the configuration of the Caribbean at the end of the basaltic event.

Stage 3. Compression: Island arcs and suturing

The onset of regional compression is considered to be the time at which the South American and North American Plates ceased to diverge. Convergence from the west drove the arc and basalt plateau to the east, but because the American plates were no longer diverging, there ceased to be a growing inter-American void for this plate to occupy. The result was that the Caribbean Plate deformed extensively internally and on its margins, which became vigorously compressive orogens. The southern part of the Antillean arc rotated and collided with South America. The originally continuous arc was breached on the east by the advancing plate and divided into two separated segments, each of which continued as a vigorous orogen: the Greater Antilles and its extension into the Limestone Caribbees, and the orogen bordering the South American margin.

The entire margin of the Caribbean (including the Lesser Antilles as part of a proto-Antilles, which had not taken its present form) was a compressive, subductive, magmatic orogen during the Late Cretaceous. A sharp change occurred at about the end of the Cretaceous. The Chortis block collided with the Maya block (from which it had perhaps not been widely separated) in the Maastrichtian. In the southern Caribbean the proto-Antillean island arc collided with the South America mainland, and the Villa de Cura block was obducted onto the continental margin. The Greater Antilles collided with the Florida-Bahama block in the Paleogene. The result of these collisions was that the Caribbean Plate was now hemmed in on the north and south as well as being compressed. The only relief possible from the impinging Farallon Plate was continued subduction along the Pacific margin and a breakout to the east. Thus, the tectonic style of both the northern and southern margins became dominated by strike-slip movement along the northern and southern boundaries of the Caribbean Plate.

Figure 9 shows the configuration of the Caribbean at about the end of the Cretaceous. The basalt event itself almost entirely ended at the end of the Santonian, although a few eruptive centers continued to be active into the early Paleogene, especially on the western side. The Chortis block had been sutured in the early Maastrichtian onto the Maya block in approximately its present position. The proto-Antilean arc moved northward and eastward; its western end became relatively inactive because of the tectonic shadow effect of the Chortis prominence. Suturing of the southern Antillean arc with South America continued. The Villa de Cura nappe moved onto the South American mainland during the earliest Cenozoic and started to shed volcanic and metamorphic debris into the Guárico trough. After the Greater Antilles sutured with the Florida-Bahama block in the Paleogene, there was no further subduction, except at its eastern end, which probably faced more to the east than at present.

Central America remained the site of active convergent island-arc activity to the south and compressive continental margin activity to the north. All that presently remains are restricted exposures of island-arc sedimentary and volcanic sequences in the south and a few granitoid plutons in the north; the rest is either buried beneath extensive later volcanic cover or removed by tectonic erosion during later subduction.

Stage 4. Mid-Cenozoic relative eastward movement of the Caribbean plate

Following the suturing on the northern and southern borders of the Caribbean during the latest Cretaceous and Paleogene, most of the deformation of the plate was taken up by eastward movement. Strike-slip movements along the northern and southern margins created small rift basins, such as the Wagwater trough of Jamaica and the Falcón basin of northern Venezuela. Subduction continued in the eastern Greater Antilles, the Limestone Caribbees of the Lesser Antilles, and also in the southern Lesser Antilles. Figure 10 shows the region at about the end of the Eocene.

Convergence of the Farallon Plate (which split into the Nazca and Cocos Plates in mid-Cenozoic time) resulted in a continuation of the convergent tectonics of the Pacific margin of Central America. I believe that the Caribbean was broadly open to the Pacific Ocean through what is now southern Central America, largely on the basis of high rates of biogenic silica

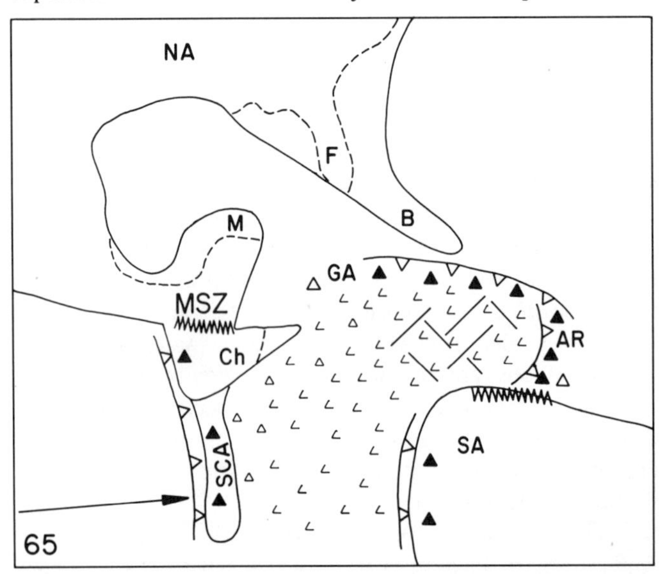

Figure 9. Sketch map of the Caribbean at the end of the Cretaceous, about 65 Ma. The Chortis block (Ch) has sutured with the Maya block (M) and is locked in position (MSZ = Motagua suture zone). The Caribbean plate continues to move eastward and pushes the Greater Antilles (GA) aside to the north. The western end of the GA is tectonically shadowed behind the protruding Chortis block and ceases to undergo subduction (open large triangles indicate inactive island arc). The basalt event has ended (incomplete triangles), except for some loci in the western part of the area. Southern Central America (SCA) is still located at a considerable distance from South America (SA). The second, west-facing subduction zone behind the Aves Ridge (AR) is shown. The triangle of motion vectors is virtually a straight line, indicating little relative motion between the Americas. Solid triangles are calc-alkaline volcanic centers. NA = North America; F = Florida; B = Bahamas.

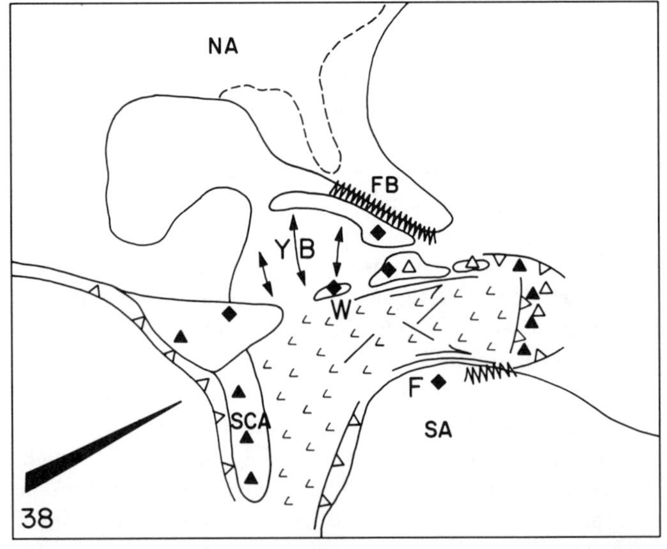

Figure 10. Sketch map of the Caribbean in late Eocene, about 38 Ma. The opening of the Yucatan Basin (YB) sweeps fragments of the Chortis margin, and the older Caribbean ocean floor against the Florida–Bahama platform (FB), forming a complex thrust collage. Minor relative compression between the Americas and continued convergence of the Farallon/Cocos Plate causes strike-slip motion along the northern and southern margins of the Caribbean during a breakout to the east. (The American plates are moving westward and the Caribbean remains static; thus there is a relative eastward motion of the Caribbean.) Southern Central America (SCA) is approaching northern South America (SA); the gap will close in middle Miocene. Solid diamonds indicate rift-basin associated magmatism on these margins (W = Wagwater; F = Falcón). The triangle of motion vectors shows convergence among all three plates, with the principal azimuth east-northeast. Solid triangles are active, and open triangles inactive, calc-alkaline volcanic centers. NA = North America.

sedimentation in the western Atlantic, Caribbean, and eastern tropical Pacific Oceans during the Paleogene (Donnelly, 1989).

Igneous activity of the Caribbean during the Paleogene is largely unknown on the Pacific margin, dominated by probable rift-associated basaltic and alkalic suites (Cuba, Hispaniola, Jamaica, Venezuela, Puerto Rico, Virgin Islands), and contains fairly normal island-arc calc-alkaline suites in the east (Virgin Islands, Limestone Caribbees, southern Lesser Antilles). Some granitic plutons with Paleogene K-Ar ages in northern Venezuela may be older plutons reheated by the movement of the Villa de Cura nappe. The transition from typical island-arc sedimentary and volcanic facies in the Greater Antilles to rift-associated facies in the Paleogene reflects the cessation of subduction in all but the eastward end of this arc.

Stage 5. Neogene to Recent compression and internal spreading

Figure 11 shows the Neogene to Recent deformation of the Caribbean. Presently the Cocos plate impinges on Central America nearly in a northerly direction, and the western Caribbean Plate has responded by spreading at nearly right angles to this applied stress. The most dramatic new developments during this interval were, first, the formation of extensive ignimbrites in Honduras, and subsequently, the formation of numerous grabens in the northwestern Caribbean, next to several of which are located highly alkalic volcanic centers. This graben development probably began during the Paleogene (evidence of clastic sediment-filled troughs found in drilling on the Nicaragua Rise; Holcombe, 1989). Very likely the Cayman Trough spreading center itself is only one manifestation of this spreading, which is here within oceanic crust, making it a wagging tail rather than the entire tectonic dog.

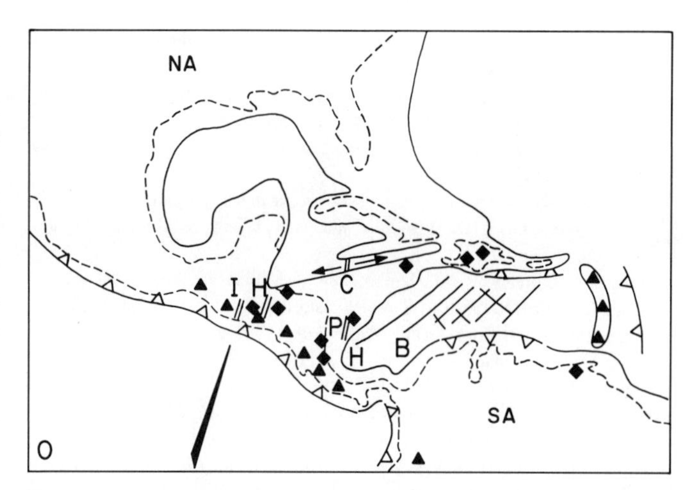

Figure 11. Sketch map of the Caribbean at present, showing continued subduction on the eastern and western borders. Solid lines approximate the Hess (H) and western Beata (B) escarpments; the remainder are stylized representations of many smaller scarps. Solid diamonds indicate alkalic magmatism associated with rifting; solid triangles are calc-alkaline volcanic centers. The paired lines in the Chortis block are young grabens (I = Ipala graben; H = Honduras depression; C = mid-Cayman rift; P = Providencia basin). The triangle of motion vectors shows that the convergence of the Cocos Plate has swung into a nearly northern direction. NA = North America; SA = South America.

Conclusion

The history of the Caribbean is dominantly a history of major plate interactions, and the major turning points in its history are times at which the movements among the three adjacent tectonic plates changed their azimuth or velocity abruptly. As our knowledge of igneous and stratigraphic history improves, the regional correlation of events becomes more evident. Perhaps the biggest single impediment to an understanding of the history of the region, however, has been the previous consideration of the Caribbean Plate as a rigid, coherent body, which has necessarily forced its surrounding regions into improbable configurations. The present approach emphasizes a problem often overlooked in plate reconstructions: the vast scale of plate phenomena forces us to realize that over distances of hundreds of kilometers, horizontal compressive forces cannot be transmitted through plates only a hundred or so kilometers thick. Unimpeded, they can, and apparently do, slide across the globe on a frictionless lower boundary, but upon encountering marginal resistance they must deform pervasively. The history of the Caribbean "Plate" has been a superb illustration of this scale problem.

REFERENCES CITED

Andreieff, P., Westercamp, D., and Bouysse, P., 1988, Révision de l'âge du substratum volcanique et sédimentaire de l'île d'Union (Grenadines, Petites Antilles méridionales); Absence de Crétacé supérieur, présence d'Eocene: Comptes Rendus Academie de Science, Paris (II), v. 306, p. 79–82.

Arden, D. D., Jr., 1975, Geology of Jamaica and Nicaragua Rise, *in* Nairn, A.E.M., and Stehli, F. G., eds., Ocean Basin and Margins, v. 3: Plenum Press, p. 617–661.

Armstrong, J. L., and Cooper, J. A., 1971, Lead isotopes in island arcs: Bulletin Volcanologique, v. 35, p. 27–63.

Azéma, J., Sornay, J., and Tournon, J., 1979, Découverte d'Albien supérieur á Ammonites dans le matérial volcano-sédimentaire du "complexe de Nicoya" (province de Guanacaste, Costa Rica): Comptes Rendus, Société Géologique de France, fasc. 3, p. 129–131.

Beck, C., 1983, Essai sur L'évolution géodynamique des Caraïbes sud-orientales: Bulletin de la Société Géologique de France (7), v. 25, p. 169–183.

Beets, D. J., and 6 others, 1984, Magmatic rock series and high-pressure metamorphism as constraints on the tectonic history of the southern Caribbean, *in* Bonini, W. E., Hargraves, R. B., and Shagam, R., eds., The Caribbean-South American plate boundary and regional tectonics: Geological Society of America Memoir 162, p. 95–130.

Benjamini, C., Shagam, R., and Menéndez, V., A., 1987, (Late?) Paleozoic age for the "Cretaceous" Tucutunemo Formation, northern Venezuela; Stratigraphic and tectonic implications: Geology, v. 15, p. 922–926.

Bourgois, J., Azéma, J., Baumgartner, P. O., Tournon, J., Desmet, A., and Aubouin, J., 1984, The geologic history of the Caribbean–Cocos Plate boundary with special reference to the Nicoya ophiolite complex (Costa Rica) and

D.S.D.P. results (Legs 67 and 84 off Guatemala)—a synthesis: Tectonophysics, v. 108, p. 1–32.

Bouysse, P., 1984, The Lesser Antilles island arc; Structure and geodynamic evolution, *in* Biju-Duval, B., Moore, J. C., and others, eds., Initial Reports of the Deep Sea Drilling Project: Washington, D.C., U.S. Government Printing Office, v. 78a, p. 83–103.

——, 1988, Opening of the Grenada back-arc basin and evolution of the Caribbean Plate during the Mesozoic and early Paleogene: Tecatonophysics, v. 149, p. 121–143.

Bouysse, P., Andreieff, R. M., Baubron, J. C., Mascle, A., Maury, R. C., and Westercamp, D., 1985, Aves swell and northern Lesser Antilles ridge; Rock-dredging results from Arcante 3 cruise, *in* Mascle, A., ed., Géodynamique des Caraïbes; Symposium Paris, 5–8 Février 1985: Editions TECHNIP, p. 65–75.

Bowin, C. O., 1975, The geology of Hispaniola, *in* Nairn, A.E.M., and Stehli, F. G., eds., Ocean Basin and Margins, v. 3: Plenum Press, p. 501–522.

——, 1976, Caribbean gravity field and plate tectonics: Geological Society of America Special paper 169, 79 p.

Bowland, C. L., and Rosencrantz, E., 1988, Upper crustal structure of the western Colombian basin, Caribbean Sea: Geological Society of America Bulletin, v. 100, p. 534–546.

Burkart, B., 1978, Offset across the Polochic fault of Guatemala and Chiapas, Mexico: Geology, v. 6, p. 328–332.

Burke, K., Fox, P. J., and Sengor, A.M.C., 1978, Buoyant ocean floor and the evolution of the Caribbean: Journal of Geophysical Research, v. 88, p. 375–386.

Case, J. E., and Dengo, G., eds., 1989, The Caribbean region: Boulder, Colorado, Geological Society of America, The Geology of North America, v. H (in press).

Case, J. E., and Holcombe, T. L., 1980, Geologic-tectonic map of the Caribbean region: U.S. Geological Survey Miscellaneous Investigations Map I-1100, scale 1:2,500,000.

Diebold, J. B., Stoffa, P. L., Buhl, P., and Truchan, M., 1981, Venezuela basin crustal structure: Journal of Geophysical Research, v. 86, p. 7901–7923.

Donnelly, T. W., 1966, The geology of St. Thomas and St. John, U.S. Virgin Islands, *in* Hess, H. H., ed., Caribbean Geological Investigations: Geological Society of America Memoir 98, p. 85–176.

——, 1973a, Magnetic anomaly observations in the eastern Caribbean Sea, *in* Edgar, N. T., and Saunders, J. B., and others, eds., 1973, Initial Reports of the Deep Sea Drilling Project: Washington, D.C., U.S. Government Printing Office, v. 15, p. 1023–1029.

——, 1973b, Late Cretaceous basalts from the Caribbean, a possible flood basalt province of vast size [abs.]: EOS Transactions of the American Geophysical Union, v. 54, p. 1004.

——, 1989, History of marine barriers and terrestrial connections—Caribbean paleogeographic inference from pelagic sediment analysis, *in* Woods, C., ed., Biogeography of the West Indies: E. J. Brill (in press).

Donnelly, T. W., and Rogers, J.J.W., 1978, The distribution of igneous rock suites around the Caribbean: Geologie en Mijnbouw, v. 57, p. 151–162.

——, 1980, Igneous series in island arcs; The northeastern Caribbean compared with worldwide island-arc assemblages: Bulletin Volcanologique, v. 43, p. 347–382.

Donnelly, T. W., Melson, W., Kay, R., and Rogers, J.J.W., 1973, Basalts and dolerites of Late Cretaceous age from the central Caribbean, *in* Edgar, N. T., Saunders, J. B., and others, eds., 1973, Initial Reports of the Deep Sea Drilling Project: Washington, D.C., U.S. Government Printing Office, v. 15, p. 989–1012.

Donnelly, T. W., Horne, G. S., Finch, R. C., and López Ramos, E., 1989a, Northern Central America—the Maya and Chortis blocks, *in* Case, J. E., and Dengo, G., eds., The Caribbean region: Boulder, Colorado, Geological Society of America, The Geology of North America, v. H (in press).

Donnelly, T. W., and 10 others, 1989b, History and tectonic setting of Caribbean magmatism, *in* Case, J. E., and Dengo, G., eds., The Caribbean Region: Boulder, Colorado, Geological Society of America, The Geology of North America, v. H (in press).

Draper, G., 1989, Jamaica, *in* Case, J. E., and Dengo, G., eds., The Caribbean Region: Boulder, Colorado, Geological Society of America, The Geology of North America, v. H (in press).

Duncan, R. A., and Hargraves, R. B., 1984, Plate tectonic evolution of the Caribbean region, *in* Bonini, W. E., Hargraves, R. B., and Shagam, R., eds., The Caribbean-South American plate boundary and regional tectonics: Geological Society of America Memoir 162, p. 81–93.

Edgar, N. T., Ewing, J. I., and Hennion, J., 1971, Seismic refraction and reflection in Caribbean Sea: American Association of Petroleum Geologists Bulletin, v. 55, p. 833–870.

Edgar, N. T., Saunders, J. B., and others, 1973, Initial Reports of the Deep Sea Drilling Project: Washington, D.C., U.S. Government Printing Office, v. 15, 1137 p.

Ewing, J. I., Antoine, J., and Ewing, M., 1960, Geophysical measurements in the western Caribbean and in the Gulf of Mexico: Journal of Geophysical Research, v. 65, p. 4087–4126.

Fox, P. J., and Heezen, B. C., 1975, Geology of the Caribbean crust, *in* Nairn, A.E.M., and Stehli, F. G., eds., Ocean Basin and Margins, v. 3: Plenum Press, p. 421–466.

Frost, C. D., and Snoke, A. W., 1988, Tobago, West Indies—petrochemical evidence of a fragment of a Mesozoic island arc: Geological Society of America Abstracts with Programs, v. 20, p. A60.

Frost, C. D., and Snoke, A. W., 1989, Tobago, West Indies, a fragment of Mesozoic oceanic island arc—Petrochemical evidence: Journal of the Geological Society of London (in press).

Ghosh, N., Hall, S. A., and Casey, J. F., 1984, Seafloor spreading magnetic anomalies in the Venezuelan basin, *in* Bonini, W. E., Hargraves, R. B., and Shagam, R., eds., The Caribbean-South American plate boundary and regional tectonics: Geological Society of America Memoir 162, p. 65–80.

Gose, W. A., and Swartz, D. K., 1977, Paleomagnetic results from Cretaceous sediments in Honduras—tectonic implications: Geology, v. 5, p. 505–508.

Gursky, H. J., Schmidt-Effing, R., Strebin, M., and Wildberg, H., 1982, The ophiolite sequence in northwestern Costa Rica (Nicoya Complex)—outlines of stratigraphical, geochemical, sedimentological, and tectonic data: Quinto Congreso Latinoamericano de Geologia, Argentina, Actas, v. 3, p. 607–619.

Hall, S. A., and Yeung, T., 1980, A study of magnetic anomalies in the Yucatan basin; Transactions of the 9th Caribbean Geological Conference, Santo Domingo: Memorias, Conferencia Geologica del Caribe, v. 9, p. 519–526.

Hargraves, R. B., and Skerlec, G. M., 1982, Paleomagnetism of some Cretaceous-Tertiary igneous rocks on Venezuelan offshore islands, Netherlands Antilles, Trinidad, and Tobago: Transactions of the 9th Caribbean Geological Conference, Santo Domingo: Memorias, Conferencia Geológica Caribe, v. 9, p. 509–517.

Hatten, C. W., Somin, M., Millan, G., and Renne, P., 1989, Tectonostratigraphic units of central Cuba: Proceedings of the 11th Caribbean Geological Conference, Barbados (in press).

Holcombe, T. L., Vogt, P. R., Matthews, J. E., and Murchinson, R. R., 1973, Evidence for sea-floor spreading in the Cayman Trough: Earth and Planetary Science Letters, v. 20, p. 357–371.

Holcombe, T. L., Ladd, J. W., Westbrook, G., Edgar, N. T. and Bowland, C. L., 1989, Caribbean marine geology—ridges and interior basins of the plate interior, *in* Dengo, G. and Case, J. E., eds., The Caribbean Region: Boulder, Colorado, Geological Society of America, The Geology of North America, v. H (in press).

Horne, G. S., Clark, G. S., and Pushkar, P., 1976, Pre-Cretaceous rocks of northwestern Honduras—basement terrane in Sierra de Omoa: American Association of Petroleum Geologists Bulletin, v. 60, p. 566–583.

Horne, G. S., Donnelly, T. W., and Finch, R., 1989, The geology of the Chortis block, northern Central America, *in* Case, J. E., and Dengo, G., eds., The Caribbean Region: Boulder, Colorado, Geological Society of America, The Geology of North America, v. H (in press).

Kesler, S. E., Sutter, J. F., Jones, L. M., and Walker, R. L., 1977, Early Caribbean basement rocks in Hispaniola: Geology, v. 5, p. 245–247.

Jackson, T. A., and Smith, T. E., 1979, The tectonic significance of basalts and dacites in the Wagwater belt: Geological Magazine, v. 116, p. 365–374.

Lewis, J. F., 1989, Cuba, *in* Case, J. E., and Dengo, G., eds., The Caribbean region: Boulder, Colorado, Geological Society of America, The Geology of North America, v. H (in press).

Lewis, J. F., Draper, G., Bowin, C., Bourdon, L., Maurrasse, F., and Nagle, F., 1989a, Hispaniola, *in* Case, J. E., and Dengo, G., eds., The Caribbean Region: Boulder, Colorado, Geological Society of America, The Geology of North America, v. H (in press).

Lewis, J. F., and 7 others, 1989b, Geology and tectonic evolution of the northern Caribbean margin, *in* Case, J. E., and Dengo, G., eds., The Caribbean Region: Boulder, Colorado, Geological Society of America, The Geology of North America, v. H (in press).

López Ramos, E., 1981, Geología de México, v. 3: Mexico City, privately published, 446 p.

Lundberg, N., 1982, Evolution of the slope landward of the Middle America trench, Nicoya peninsula, Costa Rica, *in* Leggett, J. K., ed., Trench–Forearc Geology—Sedimentation and tectonics on Modern and Ancient Active Plate Margins: Geological Society of London Special Publication 10, p. 131–147.

Maresch, W. V., 1974, Plate tectonic origin of the Caribbean mountain system of northern South America—discussion and proposal: Geological Society of America Bulletin, v. 85, p. 669–682.

Mattson, P., Draper, G., and Lewis, J. F., 1989, Puerto Rico and the Virgin Islands, *in* Case, J. E., and Dengo, G., eds., The Caribbean Region: Boulder, Colorado, Geological Society of America, The Geology of North America, v. H (in press).

Maurrasse, F., 1982, Survey of the geology of Haiti; Guide to the field excursions in Haiti, March 3–8, 1982; Miami Geological Society, 103 p.

Maury, R., Westbrook, G., Baker, P., Bouysse, P., and Westercamp, D., 1989, Lesser Antilles, *in* Case, J. E., and Dengo, G., eds., The Caribbean Region: Boulder, Colorado, Geological Society of America, The Geology of North America, v. H (in press).

Menédez, A., 1967, Tectonics of the central part of the western Caribbean mountains, Venezuela—Proceedings of the International Conference on Tropical Oceanography: University of Miami, p. 103–132.

Meyerhoff, A. A., and Meyerhoff, H. A., 1972, Continental drift. IV: The Caribbean "Plate"; Journal of Geology, v. 80, p. 34–60.

Minster, B., and Jordan, T. H., 1978, Present day plate motions: Journal of Geophysical Research, v. 83, p. 5331–5354.

Officer, C. B., Ewing, J. I., Edwards, R. S., and Johnson, H. R., 1957, Geophysical investigations in the eastern Caribbean; Venezuelan basin, Antilles island arc, and Puerto Rico outer trench: Geological Society of America Bulletin, v. 68, p. 359–378.

Officer, C. B., Ewing, J. I., Hennion, J. L., Harkrider, D. G., and Miller, D. E., 1959, Geophysical investigations in the eastern Caribbean—summary of the 1955 and 1956 cruises, *in* Ahrens, L. H., Press, F., Rankama, K., and Runcorn, S. K., eds., Physics and Chemistry of the Earth, v. 3: Pergamon Press, p. 17–109.

Pardo, G., 1975, Geology of Cuba, *in* Nairn, A.E.M., and Stehli, F. G., eds., Ocean basin and margins, v. 3: Plenum Press, p. 553–615.

Pindell, J. L., and Barrett, S. F., 1989, Geological evolution of the Caribbean region; A plate tectonic perspective, *in* Case, J. E., and Dengo, G., eds., The Caribbean Region: Boulder, Colorado, Geological Society of America, The Geology of North America, v. H (in press).

Pindell, J., and Dewey, J. F., 1982, Permo–Triassic reconstruction of western Pangea and the evolution of the Gulf of Mexico/Caribbean region: Tectonics, v. 1, p. 179–211.

Pindell, J. L., and 6 others, 1988, A plate-kinematic framework for models of Caribbean evolution: Tectonophysics, v. 155, p. 121–138.

Renne, P. R., and 6 others, 1989, $^{40}Ar/^{39}Ar$ and U-Pb evidence for Late Proterozoic (Grenville-age) continental crust in north-central Cuba and regional tectonic implications: Precambrian Research (in press).

Rosencrantz, E., Ross, M. I., and Sclater, J. G., 1988, Age and spreading history of the Cayman Trough as determined from depth, heat flow, and magnetic anomalies: Journal of Geophysical Research, v. 93, p. 2141–2157.

Ross, C. A., 1979, Late Paleozoic collision of North and South America: Geology, v. 7, p. 41–44.

Schmidt-Effing, R., 1979, Alter und Genese des Nicoya Komplexes, einer ozeanischen Paläokruste (Oberjura bis Eozän) im südlichen Zentralamerika: Geologischen Rundschau, v. 68, p. 457–494.

Sen, G., Hickey-Vargas, R., Waggoner, D. G., and Maurrasse, F., 1988, Geochemistry of basalts from the Dumisseau Formation, southern Haiti—implications for the origin of the Caribbean Sea crust: Earth and Planetary Science Letters, v. 87, p. 423–437.

Sharp, W. D., and Snoke, A. W., 1988, Tobago, West Indies; Geochronological study of a fragment of a composite Mesozoic oceanic island arc: Geological Society of America Abstracts with Programs, v. 20, p. A60.

Skerlec, G. M., and Hargraves, R. B., 1980, Tectonic significance of paleomagnetic data from northern Venezuela: Journal of Geophysical Research, v. 85, p. 5303–5315.

Schuchert, C., 1935, Historical geology of the Antillean–Caribbean region: New York, Hafner, 811 p.

Speed, R. C., 1985, Cenozoic collision of the Lesser Antilles arc and continental South America and the origin of the El Pilar fault: Tectonics, v. 4, p. 41–69.

Speed, R. C., and Larue, D. K., 1982, Barbados—architecture and implications for accretion: Journal of Geophysical Research, v. 87, p. 3633–3643.

Speed, R. C., Gerhard, L. C., and McKee, E. H., 1979, Ages of deposition, deformation, and intrusion of Cretaceous rocks, eastern St. Croix, Virgin Islands: Geological Society of America Bulletin, v. 90, p. 629–632.

Stearns, C., Mauk, F. J., and Van der Voo, R., 1982, Late Cretaceous–early Tertiary paleomagnetism of Aruba and Bonaire (Netherlands Antilles): Journal of Geophysical Research, v. 87, p. 1127–1141.

Stephan, J.-F., Beck, C., Bellizzia, A., and Blanchet, R., 1980, La chaîne caraïbe du Pacifique á l'Atlantique: Bureau de Recherches Géologique et Minieres Memoir 115, p. 38–59.

Westercamp, D., 1988, Magma generation in the Lesser Antilles; Geological constraints: Tectonophysics, v. 149, p. 145–163.

Weyl, R., 1973, Die Paläogeographische Entwicklung Mittelamerikas: Zentralblat für Geologie und Paläontologie, v. 1, no. 5/6, p. 432–466.

Whetten, J. T., 1966, Geology of St. Croix, U.S. Virgin Islands, *in* Hess, H. H., ed., Caribbean Geological Investigations: Geological Society of America Memoir 98, p. 122–239.

Woodring, W. P., 1954, Caribbean land and sea through the ages: Geological Society of America Bulletin, v. 65, p. 710–732.

MANUSCRIPT ACCEPTED BY THE SOCIETY NOVEMBER 30, 1988

ACKNOWLEDGMENTS

It is a pleasure to acknowledge the many colleagues who supplied me with papers in press or preparation in order to help me with the task of compiling this paper. Manuscripts prepared for Case and Dengo 1989) were supplied by Rene Maury, Bill MacDonald, Troy Holcombe, Jim Case, Gren Draper, John Lewis, Paul Mann, and Jim Pindell. Other important manuscripts were supplied by Jim Pindell, Bob Speed, Carol Frost, Paul Renne, and Charles Hatten. I am grateful to Bert Bally for comments on the first draft and am deeply indebted to Pete Palmer for detailed editorial assistance. My sincere thanks to all of these colleagues.

Printed in U.S.A.

The Geology of North America
Vol. A, The Geology of North America—An overview
The Geological Society of America, 1989

Chapter 12

The evolution of the Appalachian chain

Nicholas Rast
Department of Geological Sciences, University of Kentucky, Lexington, Kentucky 40506

INTRODUCTION: HISTORICAL BASIS OF IDEAS

The outlines

The Appalachian chain is a Paleozoic megastructure, bordering eastern North America. On land the exposed part of the chain stretches more than 3,000 km from Newfoundland in the northeast to Alabama in the southwest (Fig. 1). To the northwest the chain is adjacent to the Laurentian craton of Precambrian rocks, or to their platformal cover; to the southeast, gently inclined Meso-Cenozoic coastal strata of the Atlantic shelf cover the deformed Appalachian formations. Elucidation of the geology of the Appalachian Mountains has had almost two centuries of history (Faill, 1985). The chain was first defined in the southern and central states of the eastern United States, and then extrapolated northward into New England and Canada (Rodgers, 1970). Thus, even early in the history of their investigation, the Appalachians were divided into northern, central, and southern sectors (Fig. 1). South of New York the early work was conducted by state geological surveys, among which those in Pennsylvania, Virginia, and North Carolina were especially active. From the 1870s onward the U.S. Geological Survey expanded its activities in the region.

The foundations for the present understanding of Appalachian geology were laid by the Geological Survey of New York, personified by James Hall, and the Geological Surveys of Pennsylvania and Virginia, from where the brothers W. B. and H. D. Rogers conducted their investigations. While *Hall* (*1883*) stressed the stratigraphic-paleontologic aspects of the rocks composing the Appalachians, the *Rogers brothers* (*1843*) were more concerned with the physical structures of the strata. Hall's impetus led to the paleostratigraphic approach, and he was the first to advance the notion of a basinal geosyncline; the Rogers brothers developed the structural geology of the geosynclinal strata. Another contemporary, *Dana* (*1873*), took the first strides toward the geotectonic interpretation of the Appalachian chain. He inferred that the deformation of geosynclinal rocks must have been produced by tangential forces. This story has been comprehensively discussed by *Kay* (*1951*). In Canada, the leader of Appalachian investigations was *Sir William Logan* (*1861, 1862*), the first director of the Canadian Geological Survey. He traced the boundary (now Logan's line) between deformed Appalachian strata and the undeformed (actually, less deformed) cratonal cover in eastern Canada, thus initiating the continuous mapping of structural boundaries in the field.

To augment the valiant effort of the U.S. Geological Survey, including such indefatigable geologists as A. Keith and later G. W. and A. Stose and P. B. King in the south and C. D. Walcott in the north, university professors and their students soon joined in the field. Thus many universities both in the United States and Canada became centers of Appalachian studies. Consequently the existing literature is voluminous; in this chapter, mainly broader ideas are discussed and papers with large reference lists quoted. Fuller accounts are given in Hatcher and others (1989).

Much recent borehole and geophysical information has become available for the subsurface extension of the Appalachians beneath the Atlantic Coastal Plain and the continental shelf of North America (e.g., *Higgins and Zietz, 1983*; Thomas, 1985; *Haworth and Jacobi, 1983*; *Lefort and Haworth, 1984*; Thomas and others, 1989; Hutchinson and others, 1988). The combination of well, gravity, magnetic, and seismic data allows the recognition of rock types as well as significant boundaries that separate rocks of different original geographic positions. For instance, in Georgia, Alabama, and Florida a suture that separates Paleozoic rocks of North American affinity from those of African affinity has been detected (review in Tauvers and Muehlberger, 1987). In the southeastern United States, it is possible to demonstrate that the Appalachians continue on strike only a short distance southwest below the Gulf Coastal Plain (Horton and others, 1984) and are then cut off by major transform faults (Fig. 2).

The tectonic trend of the Appalachian chain is affected by a series of major inflections, shown in the tectonic lithofacies map compiled by *Williams* (*1978*). These are called promontories if convex toward the Atlantic Ocean, and reentrants or embayments if convex toward the Laurentian craton. Thomas (1977) ascribed these structures to the configuration of the margin of the Laurentian craton, against which the Paleozoic Appalachian structures have been pressed to produce arcuate structural trends within a deformed variably metamorphosed and polyorogenic mountain belt.

Rast, N., 1989, The evolution of the Appalachian Chain, *in* Bally, A. W., and Palmer, A. R., eds., The Geology of North America—An overview: Boulder, Colorado, Geological Society of America, The Geology of North America, v. A.

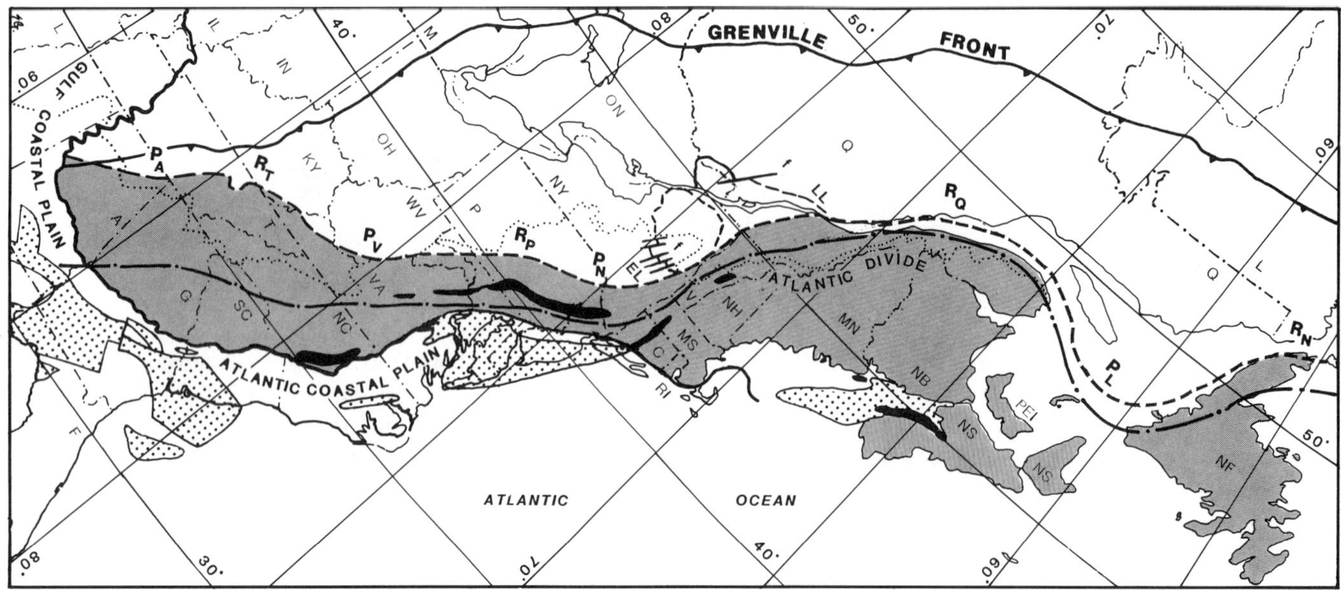

Figure 1. The outlines and margins of the Appalachian orogen. Canadian provinces: NB, New Brunswick; NF, Newfoundland; L, Labrador part of Newfoundland; NS, Nova Scotia; ON, Ontario; PEI, Prince Edward Island; Q, Quebec. U.S.A. states northeast to southwest: MN, Maine; V, Vermont; NH, New Hampshire; M, Michigan; NY, New York; MS, Massachusetts; C, Connecticut; RI, Rhode Island; IN, Indiana; OH, Ohio; P, Pennsylvania; IL, Illinois; KY, Kentucky; WV, West Virginia; VA, Virginia; T, Tennessee; NC, North Carolina; A, Alabama; SC, South Carolina; G, Georgia; F, Florida. Promontories (P) and recesses (R). P_A - Alabama, R_T - Tennessee, P_V - Virginia; R_P - Pennsylvania; P_N - New York; R_Q - Quebec; P_L - Laurentian; R_N - Newfoundland. Some cratonic faults indicated by f. LL, margin of Laurentian shield. Thick dashed line, Appalachian deformation front, known as Logan's line along Quebec recess. Dot-dash line is edge of Grenville basement in the orogenic belt. Black areas, main (Triassic to Jurassic) grabens on land; under the sea or coastal plain these are coarsely stippled. Red overlay pattern covers the extent of the exposed parts of the orogen.

Within the Appalachian orogen lie strips (Fig. 1) of post-orogenic early Mesozoic (Triassic-Jurassic) sedimentary and volcanic rocks, deposited in grabens or half grabens. Associated with these deposits are extrusive basalts, and also, from Newfoundland to Georgia, numerous, mainly mafic Permian(?) to Jurassic dikes and sills (*King, 1971*; McHone and Butler, 1984). Mesozoic plutonic activity occurred mainly in a more restricted area of New England and Quebec, where it ranges in age from the Triassic to Cretaceous (*Foland and Faul, 1977*).

The Triassic-Jurassic sediments form parts of a weakly deformed, broken and disjointed cover over Paleozoic and earlier rocks. The still less deformed Cretaceous to Quaternary strata form the continuous Atlantic Coastal Plain and also occur in isolated exposures within the orogenic belt including those in karstic sinkholes in Pennsylvania (*Pierce, 1965*), as lacustrine and alluvial sediments in Nova Scotia (*Stevenson, 1959*), and lignite coal in Brandon, Vermont (*Traverse and Barghoorn, 1953*).

The present topographic surface of the Appalachians rises to just over 2 km in the south-central part and up to 1.9 km to the north in New Hampshire. A conventional interpretation of the Appalachian topographic relief has been in terms of a probably sub-Cretaceous peneplain (reviews in *Thornbury, 1965*; *Bostock, 1970*). This has an apparent plausibility because both on the mainland of Canada and in the southeastern United States the Appalachian uplands are generally higher to the northwest and lower to the southeast, toward the Atlantic Ocean. *Hack (1980*, 1982), however, makes a case that Appalachian areas of high relief, but similar altitudes, reflect differential erosion of resistant, siliceous rocks. The broader tectonic uplift that has occurred is associated with upwarping, which in the southern Appalachians has resulted in a large, gentle domal structure that has been partially eroded.

Throughout the Mesozoic and Tertiary and even Recent times, faulting has occurred in the Appalachians (*Brown and Oliver, 1976*; *Hack, 1980*). This faulting and local upwarping are presumably related to the above-mentioned domal uplift. *Mathews* (*1975*) has deduced that at least 2,000 m of rocks have been eroded off the uplifted Appalachians in Cenozoic time. Yet, the nature and duration of uplift is not settled. *Hack* (*1980*) and Rodgers (1982), on the basis of Meso-Cenozoic fossils found in sinkholes located on old erosion surfaces well below the present-day peaks, maintain that throughout Meso-Cenozoic times the relief was considerable.

Some of the uplift must be relatively young (Hack, 1982), but some must have been old and in some localities differential. Thus Levine (1986), on the basis of reflectance of organic matter

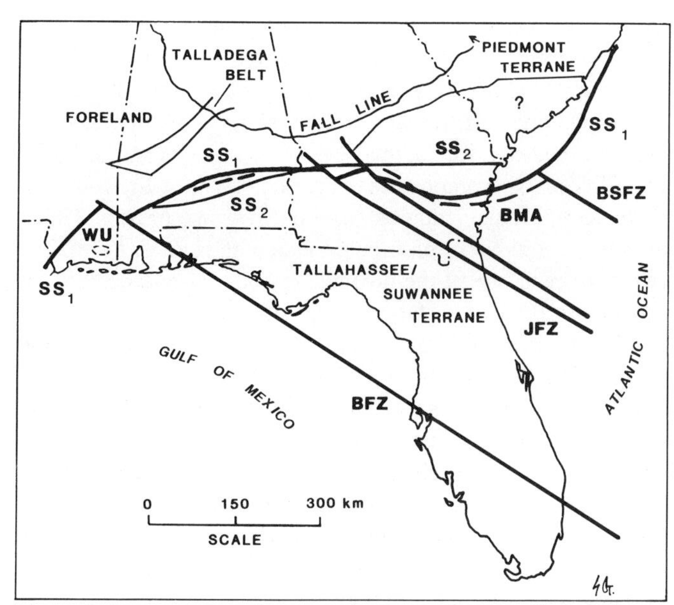

Figure 2. Interpretation of terranes in the southeastern United States. Major geophysical and structural data: Straight lines, faults; BFZ, Bahamas fault zone; BSFZ, Blake Spur fault zone; JFZ, Jacksonville fault zone. Fall line is the northern margin of Coastal Plain deposits, continuation of the Talladega Appalachian belt under these is shown; WU, position of Wiggins uplift of basement metamorphics; BMA, dashed line, Brunswick magnetic anomaly; SS_1 - Suture between the Appalachian belt and the Tallahassee-Suwannee (Suwannee) terrane adopted here from data by Horton and others (1984), Tauvers and Muehlberger (1987), Dallmeyer (1987); SS_2 - suture according to Thomas and others (1989).

and coal rank in eastern Pennsylvania, suggests localized denudation of 6 to 9 km. For this, a prolonged and spasmodic period of erosion is needed. A broader uplift of 5 to 7 km in New York State has been claimed recently by Friedman (1987) from fluid inclusion studies.

A regional structure reflecting uplift is the unconformity under the Atlantic Coastal Plain deposits, which varies in inclination from 0.025 in eastern Delaware to 0.007 in Georgia. Below this unconformity lie truncated Mesozoic basins (Fig. 1) and the intervening deformed and metamorphosed Paleozoic or Precambrian strata. *Judson* (*1975*) suggested that the denudation of the Appalachian chain involved a progressive migration of the continental divide from the southeast to the northwest, and that therefore the former Triassic-Jurassic divide at present lies below the Atlantic Coastal Plain sediments. *Oberlander* (*1985*), however, considers a piecemeal development of denudation through drainage of newly uplifted parts of the orogen. If so, control by resistant rock units was especially important (Mills *in* Mills and others, 1987). North of Cape Cod, the Coastal Plain deposits are restricted to the continental shelf, although occasional exposures of Pleistocene sediments fringe parts of the coast. Modern work in Canada will be summarized in volumes of *The Geology of North America* being prepared by C. E. Keen and Harold Williams. In Canada and Maine the present topography is influenced not only by trend-parallel fluviatile erosion, but also by the effects of the Pleistocene glaciation, which produced a highly dissected surface and many fjord-type estuaries.

Tectonic divisions

The earlier research in the Appalachians was conducted either south of New York where divisions were based largely on topography (c.f., *Willis, 1893*), or in the northern Appalachians (c.f., *Dawson, 1888*) where the age of the rocks was used as the important criterion. This distinction, in modified forms, still survives. Thus, in the southern and central Appalachians (Fig. 3) the broad general units are the Cumberland and other plateaus grouped as the Appalachian Plateau, the Valley and Ridge, Blue Ridge, and Piedmont Provinces, while in the north reference is made to anticlinoria and synclinoria, the former with cores of pre-Silurian rocks and the latter with Siluro-Devonian strata. Rodgers (1970) and *Williams* (*1978*), who have attempted to rationalize the system and to trace the southern divisions northward (Fig. 3), have only partially succeeded. Thus, now the provinces in the south and the anticlinoria and synclinoria in the north in many publications are used mainly as geographic locations to which positions of various geologic features are referred. *Williams* (*1978*) has attempted to trace through the so-called tectonostratigraphic belts (Fig. 3), which he and others proposed in 1972 and 1974 in Newfoundland. He produced a map (*Williams, 1978*) that still forms a template for reference. The map is based on the assumption that linear tectonostratigraphic belts with more or less homogeneous stratigraphy and structure, as first recognized in Newfoundland, can be traced throughout the Appalachians and that these belts represent specific geotectonic fossilized environments reflecting original Ordovician paleogeographic elements, tectonically assembled as an orogenic belt.

The idea of tectonic assembly was propounded by Bird and Dewey (1970), who proposed that the northern Appalachians were formed as a result of head-on approach and ultimate collision of Laurentia (Laurentian craton) and the so-called Avalon platform (*Williams, 1964*) since then referred to as (1) Avalon prong (*Dewey and Kidd, 1974*), (2) Avalon microcontinent (*Schenk, 1978*), (3) Avalon plate (Rast and Skehan, 1983), or (4) Avalon terrane (Williams and Hatcher, 1983). Between Laurentia and the Avalon terrane an oceanic domain was suggested that was margined by continents and included continental shelves, island arcs, back-arc basins, and the associated sedimentary and igneous rocks, which upon collision were thrust (obducted) onto the continental edge. The obducted masses enclose in them sheet-like massifs of layered mafic and ultramafic rocks referred to as ophiolites (*Dewey, 1974*). These were interpreted as remnants of oceanic lithosphere that in general mark a suture between the collided plates. The early Paleozoic carbonates at the Laurentian cratonal edge were explained as a carbonate bank (*Rodgers, 1968*). The edge of the Avalon plate lacked such a bank because it moved in from higher latitudes and a long distance across an ocean. Clastic sediments were commonly interpreted as accumulations in euxinic environments (black graptolitic shales), rapidly subsiding troughs (turbidites), or on continental slopes (contourites). The proposed collision implied that to the east of the main Appalachian belt lay a continental land (Avalon plate). The existence of such land (Appalachia) was suspected by *Dana (1873)* and claimed by Schuchert (1930), but they thought of the rocks intervening between Laurentia and Appalachia as infillings of an ensialic geosyncline, whereas the adherents of plate tectonics (*Dewey, 1969*; *Williams and others, 1972*; *McKerrow and Ziegler, 1972*; *Neuman, 1972*) explained these rocks as diverse, polygenetic infillings of basins in and around an ocean and its islands. The theory of plate tectonics, as used in the seventies, is elegantly expounded by *Smith (1976)*.

The timing of the closure of the proposed ocean (Iapetus or Iapetos) excited much speculation. It was known for some time that the Appalachians yielded evidence for several episodes of orogeny. Schuchert (1930), in the northern Appalachians, recognized: (1) an unnamed Late Cambrian episode; (2) a middle to late Ordovician (Taconian) event; (3) a mid-Devonian Acadian deformation; and (4) the late Carboniferous–Permian Appalachian (now Alleghanian) orogeny. Later, but still prior to the burst of plate tectonics, *Lilley (1966)* identified the late Proterozoic Avalonian orogeny in Newfoundland, while Neuman (1967) presented strong evidence for a Late Cambrian–Ordovician orogenic episode, now known as the Penobscottian, in Maine.

A different approach was developed by relating isotopic dating of intrusive rocks and regional metamorphic peaks to corresponding episodes of orogeny. However, the actual dating of metamorphic climaxes is difficult, and most figures obtained are ages of cooling (Dallmeyer, 1978). *Osberg (1983)* pointed out that the evidence for thermal events is areally restricted (c.f., Fig. 3). Thus, the Penobscottian episode was at first restricted to north-central Maine, although isotopic evidence for it was soon found in central Newfoundland (Williams and others, 1976). The causes of each one of the orogenic episodes also demanded an explanation. One of the far-reaching publications in this regard is that by Williams and Hatcher (1983), in which they employ the notion of suspect terranes, first developed in the western United States (*Coney and others, 1980*). This idea implies that closely juxtaposed belts and blocks may have acquired their position after arrival from distal unknown locations. The juxtaposition (docking) may arise by strike-slip faulting, transpressive collision, or compressive collision. The evidence for the age of docking is provided by the unconformable stratigraphic overstep of younger formations, discordant formations, thrusts, discordant post-docking intrusions, and continuous metamorphic zones passing from block to block (Zen, 1988).

At first, really large blocks (Fig. 4) such as the Avalon belt were considered as terranes (Williams and Hatcher, 1983). Keppie (1985), however, introduced the term *composite terrane,* for the collage of smaller terranes of the Avalon belt, and the possibility of its division into these smaller constituent fragments became very real. Originally the Avalon platform (terrane) was defined as

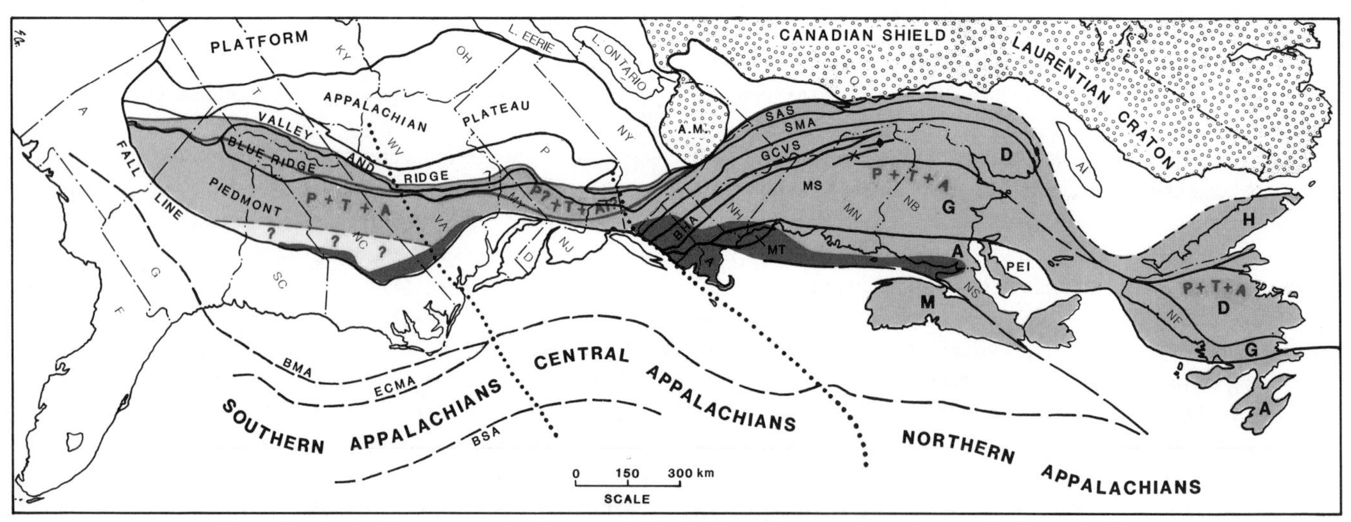

Figure 3. Appalachian structural and metamorphic divisions. States and provinces as in Figure 1 with additions of NJ, New Jersey; D, Delaware; MY, Maryland; AM, Adirondack Mountains. Structural divisions of northern, central, and southern Appalachians delineated by coarse dotted lines. In the northern sector, Canadian subdivisions: A, Avalon zone; G, Gander zone; D, Dunnage zone; H, Humber zone as per *Williams (1978).* American subdivisions: SAS, Saint Albans synclinorium; SMA, Sutton Mountain anticlinorium; GCVS, Gaspe-Connecticut Valley synclinorium; BHA, Bronson Hill anticlinorium; MS, Merrimack synclinorium (Kearsarge central Maine); MT, Merrimack trough; BMA, Brunswick magnetic anomaly; ECMA, East Coast magnetic anomaly; BSA, Blake Spur anomaly. Red, Alleghanian metamorphism. Dark pink, (P[?] + T + A) Penobscottian(?) + Taconian + Acadian metamorphism, and (P[?] +T+Al[?]) Penobscottian (?) + Taconian + Alleghanian (?) metamorphism; the Alleghanian (?) being very low grade or retrogressive. Light pink, metamorphism of the Carolina terrane, possibly Taconian.

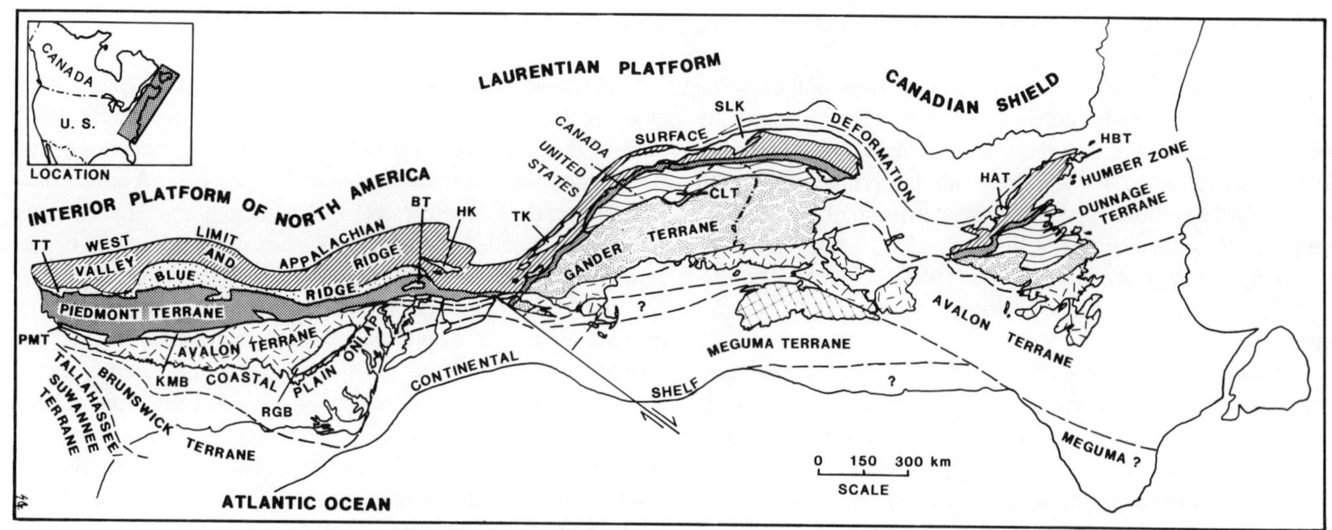

Figure 4. Terrane map of eastern North America mainly after Williams and Hatcher (1983). Possible extensions of the Meguma terrane are shown by (?). Smaller letters identify terranes, from north to south: HBT, Hare Bay terrane; HAT, Humber Arm terrane; CLT, Chain Lakes terrane; SLK, St. Lawrence klippe; TK, Taconic klippe; HK, Hamburg klippe; BT, Brunswick terrane; RGB, Raleigh-Goochland belt; KMB, King's Mountain belt; TT, Talladega terrane; PMT, Pine Mountain belt. Of the labeled terranes, the existence of the Brunswick terrane is doubtful (c.f., Fig. 2).

a partly deformed late Precambrian block of volcanic and volcaniclastic rocks (about 600 Ma) and more or less coeval plutons. The volcanic sequence is interbedded with turbiditic deposits. Throughout the northern Appalachians, the Precambrian rocks of the Avalon belt are conformably to unconformably overlain by Cambro-Ordovician shelf strata containing an Acado-Baltic fauna (Rast and others, 1976; Skehan and others, 1978). Therefore the Cambrian to Lower Ordovician cover of this type is commonly included in the definition of the Avalon terrane. The Avalon terrane, when traced to the southern Appalachians, changes both lithological and paleontological aspect of its cover; the lower Paleozoic volcanic rocks show calc-alkaline volcanicity, there are no carbonates, and the faunas start resembling Armorican assemblages. Thus, Secor and others (1983) suggested that the Carolina Slate Belt, formerly considered as the Avalon terrane, is a Cambrian volcanic arc of unknown exotic, possibly African, provenance to be called the Carolina terrane.

An even more direct correlation with Africa is widely claimed for Paleozoic rocks of the Tallahassee-Suwannee terrane (Fig. 2), which is hidden under the coastal plain deposits, on the basis of faunas and the age of micas (Dallmeyer, 1987) in the Lower Ordovician sandstone that forms the lowest part of the Paleozoic succession. The fauna of this succession has distinct Gondwanan affinities. The underlying calc-alkaline volcanic formations are also similar to those of the Mauritanide and parts of Rokelide chains of west Africa.

Since, according to current views, in Ordovician times Africa (Gondwana) was separated from Laurentia and Baltica by a wide ocean, both the Suwannee and possibly the Carolina terranes are considered separate from the Avalon terrane. However, in late Precambrian time it is likely that all the pieces of the Avalon terrane (Newfoundland, New Brunswick, Nova Scotia, Boston), as well as North and South Carolina (Rast and Skehan, 1983) were near the West African craton terrane and therefore were all, including the basement of the Suwannee, parts of the same plate. Thus, the contrasting stratigraphic nature of the terrane's cover rocks arose through segmentation of this terrane in the latest Precambrian to Early Cambrian interval (circa 570 Ma). Yet there is evidence that even prior to this time the plate consisted of partly or completely disjointed fragments of a late Precambrian island arc, because details of the Precambrian succession, despite the similarities of volcanic and sedimentary lithologies, cannot be correlated from one major block to another. This collage of Precambrian blocks (Rast, 1980) is referred to as the Avalonian *superterrane,* which was fragmented into major blocks during Iapetus rifting (*Rast and others, 1988*). In the northern Appalachians and the Acado-Baltic region these blocks were linked by the overstepping Cambrian sediments populated by the Acado-Baltic fauna, while in the southern Appalachians the overstepping sediments had different faunas more like those of Armorica or Gondwana. Therefore I prefer to exclude the lower Paleozoic sediments from the definition of the superterrane, but to retain them in the definition of the composite terrane.

The Avalon composite terrane shows signs of several stages of deformation and assembly (*O'Hara and Gromet, 1985*). Docking of individual parts within the present composite collage and to North America, therefore, occurred at different times. Vick and others (1987) consider that the Carolina terrane in the south docked to Laurentia in Ordovician time. Alleghanian docking is favored for a part of the Avalon terrane in southeastern New England (Secor and others *in* Rankin and others, 1989), whereas the Tallahassee-Suwannee terrane (Fig. 2), with a lithologically similar basement, probably also docked in late Paleozoic time (Dallmeyer, 1987).

One indirect consequence of the development of the terrane concept is that long-range correlations, either along or across the orogenic trend, became suspect; paleogeographic reconstructions acquired a new flavor of uncertainty, and the terminology had to be modified. For instance, the traditional division of Blue Ridge–Piedmont Provinces lay along the Brevard fault zone (*Hatcher, 1978a, b*), but Williams and Hatcher (1983) included part of the traditional eastern Blue Ridge of North Carolina in the Piedmont terrane.

Another important idea that has arisen in the last few years is that each orogenic episode, and particularly the Alleghanian, is largely thrust conditioned, and that in association with the thrusts, large strike-slip structures affected geologic relations both across and along the orogen. In this regard, folds are commonly considered and discussed in the context, and as a consequence, of thrusting.

Geophysical insights

While speculations on the origins of many of the Appalachian structural patterns have been advanced by geologists, in the last two decades their ideas have been progressively guided by data and hypotheses derived from geophysics. Studies of gravity and magnetics led to the identification of major structures at depth, and their extension from land and sea. By 1980, two regional geophysical maps were published as companions to the tectonic lithofacies map by *Williams (1978)*. These geophysical maps, one of which represents Bouguer gravity anomalies (*Haworth and others, 1980*) and the other magnetic anomalies (*Zietz and others, 1980*), have helped the charting of many transatlantic correlations, as well as the delineation of terranes (Williams and Hatcher, 1983). For example, the recognition of paired (–ve and +ve) anomalies along the Appalachians with an intervening steep gravity-gradient (Fig. 3) suggests positions of ancient sutures (M. D. Thomas, 1983).

Large-scale seismic studies in the Appalachians were initially restricted to refraction studies, especially on the North American continental shelf (e.g., *Drake and others, 1959*). Yet it is with the introduction of reflection studies by the U.S. Geological Survey, Geological Survey of Canada, and COCORP and other University-based groups that the subsurface structure of the Appalachians became interpretable (c.f., Cook and others, 1979; Ando and others, 1983; Phinney and Roy-Chowdhury, 1989). This approach has been especially significant for the understanding of Appalachian thrut tectonics.

The collage-like nature of Appalachian geologic patterns made the application of paleomagnetic studies especially useful (c.f., *Bambach and others, 1980*; *Van der Voo, 1982,* 1988; *Kent and Opdyke, 1980*) in palinspastic reconstructions, although at times changes in interpretation have been drastic (Kent and Opdyke, 1985).

THE BASEMENT—WHERE IT ALL BEGAN

As noted at the beginning of this chapter, the Appalachian chain is a polyorogenic belt that originated at the southeastern edge of the Laurentian craton. The outboard margin craton was originally placed at the northwestern edge of the Avalon composite terrane (*Williams, 1964*), but in the southern Appalachians this idea demanded modifications, since here the whole of the Avalon composite terrane is within the mobile orogenic belt.

The Laurentian craton adjacent to the Appalachian chain consists principally of plutonic and metasedimentary rocks, deformed and, circa 950 to 1,100 Ma (Grenville orogeny), metamorphosed into gneisses, which in the northern Appalachian sector are widely associated with charnockites, anorthosites, and supracrustal paragneisses. Farther south, Grenville gneisses have a generally more orthogneissic aspect (*Rankin and others, 1983,* 1989). In both the northern and south-central Appalachians, tectonic inliers of these rocks occur in large external massifs (Hatcher, 1983; W. A. Thomas, 1983) within the belt. Thomas suggested that in the south, during the Alleghanian orogeny, these massifs formed a major ramp. It is also possible to interpret northern massifs such as the Berkshires and Green Mountains (Fig. 5) and the Long Range massif in Newfoundland in the same way. In the southern Appalachians, external massifs are sliced by Alleghanian and possibly Acadian thrusts. Each of the blocks overlying a single major overthrust has been named by Bartholomew and Lewis (1984) as a massif. Rankin and others (1989) suggest regrouping the smaller blocks into the Shenandoah massif (northern Blue Ridge, Fig. 5), mainly in Virginia, and the French Broad massif (southern Blue Ridge, Fig. 5), mainly in North Carolina. The former, like the Adirondack rocks, contains abundant charnockites, while these are rare in the southern Blue Ridge. Here, as proposed for southern Virginia by Bartholomew (1983), this may be due to Paleozoic retrogression, but Rankin and others (1989) suggest that an initial Proterozoic difference existed, because there are some rare charnockitic rocks in areas of Paleozoic metamorphism (e.g., *Gulley, 1985*). The Paleozoic charnockites may have been produced because of deficiency of fluids associated with Paleozoic metamorphism.

In Georgia, a small massif of Grenvillian rocks (Corbin) is a mylonitized granite gneiss emplaced in a meta-arkose (Fig. 5), but it also includes charnockitic rocks (McConnell and Costello, 1984). The nearby Mulberry Rock Gneiss, may also be Grenvillian (*McConnell and Abrams, 1984*). The separation of such gneisses from the main southern Blue Ridge massifs and of the latter from the northern Blue Ridge massifs is attributed to Alleghanian thrusting.

In the Piedmont Province of the southern and central Appalachians, as well as in southwestern parts of the northern Appalachians, lie internal massifs, exposed in dome-like structures, interpreted as thrust-bound windows (Rankin and others, 1989) or as slices within thrust sheets. Thus, the dashed line bounding Grenville rocks in the United States, shown on Figure 1 of *Muehlberger (1980)*, has to be moved eastward. Farrar (1984)

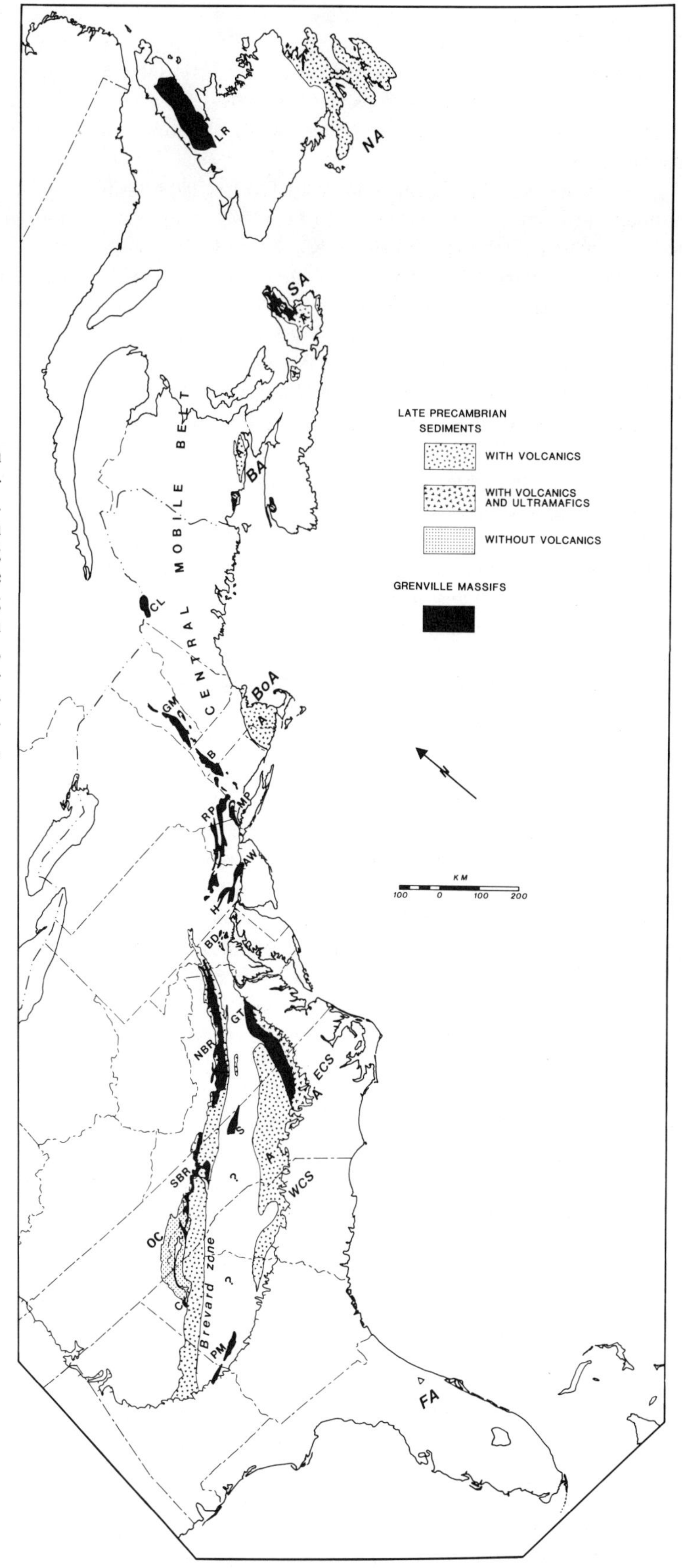

Figure 5. The distribution of Grenville gneissose and Avalonian superterrane massifs from north to south in the Appalachian orogenic belt. States and provincial outlines as in Figures 1 and 3. LR, Long Range; NA, Newfoundland Avalonian; SA, Scotian Avalonian with cores of gneisses, some being probably Grenville; BA, Brunswick Avalonian with a core of probably Grenville age rocks; CL, Chain Lakes; GM, Green Mountains; B, Berkshire; BoA, Boston Avalonian; RP, Reading prong, MP, Manhattan prong; H, Honeybrook upland; AW, Avondale Westchester; BD, Baltimore gneiss domes; NBR, Northern Blue Ridge; GT, Goochland terrane; WCS, Western Carolina Slate; ECS, Eastern Carolina Slate; S, Sauratown Mountains; A–A′, Carolinas "Avalonian"?; SBR, Southern Blue Ridge; OC, Ocoee; C, Corbin; PM, Pine Mountain belt; FA, Florida (Avalonian?) in subsurface.

has persuasively argued that the gneissose Goochland terrane of Grenville (Fig. 5) extends into the Raleigh area. While the external massifs have recognizable Grenvillian structural style, the internal massifs in the southern Appalachians, as Hatcher (1983) pointed out, are affected by late Paleozoic deformation and metamorphism.

In the northern Appalachians there are few internal massifs, although in Nova Scotia, gneisses with Grenville isotopic ages have been found (*Olszewski and others, 1981*; Currie, 1983; *Gaudette and others, 1983*). The ages of these possibly Grenville rocks (Fig. 5) are of the order of 900 to 1,000 Ma, and some of the older massifs have covers of younger sediments. If the above age determinations are confirmed, then Proterozoic massifs exist well to the east of the Waterbury dome (*Dietsch, 1986*) in Connecticut, thus across the Iapetus suture marked by remnants of ophiolites.

In general, the larger external massifs have covers of Precambrian and/or Cambrian sediments or metasediments, which are mainly clastic at the base. In the northern and central Appalachians, such Precambrian sediments are relatively thin, but in the southern Appalachians they reach great thicknesses (over 12 km) and have been interpreted as deposits within multiple grabens (*Schwab, 1977,* Schwab and others, 1988; *Tauvers, 1982*; Rast and Kohles, 1986) that are attributed to late Precambrian rifting.

The Grenville massifs can be placed in four geologic settings:

1. Westernmost massifs include Grenville basement unconformably overlain by first late Proterozoic and then Early Cambrian (circa 740 to 580 Ma) clastic sediments and volcanic rocks associated with Iapetus rifting. In places the late Precambrian deposits are separated from the transgressive Cambrian by disconformities (Rast and Kohles, 1986), but elsewhere an apparent continuity exists. In the northern and central Appalachians these cover strata are accompanied by volcanic rocks that are regionally bimodal and include large volumes of basalts (e.g., the Catoctin Formation) and rhyolites, which are especially noted north of the 36th parallel (Rankin and others, 1989). The disconformity between the late Proterozoic Catoctin Volcanics and the overlying clastic Cambrian Chilhowee Group is post-rifting.

2. Massifs lying just to the west of a line of dislocation, which may be the early Paleozoic Hayesville fault line (Fig. 6) throughout the southern Appalachians, and the Cameron line in the northern Appalachians. These massifs are associated with diverse groups of clastic or volcanogenic metasediments, attributed to either late Precambrian or early Paleozoic ages (Rankin, 1975). The metasediments, so far only partially mapped, enclose and are associated with a large number of ultramafic (Misra and Keller, 1978) and mafic (Misra and McSween, 1984) bodies. Many of these are interpreted as disjointed ophiolites (e.g., *Hatcher and others, 1984*; Abbott and Raymond, 1984).

The widespread enclosing metasediments-metavolcanics, which in the literature are commonly divided into lithostratigraphic units (groups, formations, members), are best understood as either lithotectonic units or as metamorphic suites (Abbott and Raymond, 1984) assembled in places as mélanges; their ages are still indeterminate. It is very likely that this situation also exists in the northern Appalachians, where the most significant of such Proterozoic massifs is the granulitic Chain Lakes massif (Fig. 5), introduced by *Boudette* (*1970*) and dated by *Naylor* (*1975*) as circa 1,500 Ma. *Cheatham* (*1985*) suggests that the massif is a twice metamorphosed (770 and 405 Ma) 3-km-thick pile of metavolcanics and metasediments and that large fragments of this massif are dispersed farther east. *Rankin and others* (*1983*) suggest that at least some of the massif consists of retrogressed orthogneiss. Although the circa 1,500 Ma zircon age implies a non-American affinity, it should be remembered that other old pre-Grenville lithologies are known from the Appalachians (e.g., the Stage Road Layered Gneiss in Virginia; Sinha and Bartholomew, 1984). Within the Canadian Shield the metasedimentary Grenville Supergroup of Ontario and Quebec is dated as 1,200 to 1,310 Ma (Sangster and Bourne, 1982).

3. Grenville massifs in the Inner Piedmont. In the southern and central Appalachians to the southeast of the Brevard zone (Fig. 5), these are relatively rare, while in the corresponding belt in the northern Appalachians (Central Mobile Belt of *Williams, 1964*), they are effectively absent. Since the Inner Piedmont of the southern Appalachians is just as affected by thrusting as other belts, it may be that the absence of Grenville rocks from within it, but the presence of numerous ophiolitic fragments (e.g., *Drake and Morgan, 1981*), indicate that the Inner Piedmont was formed or accumulated on oceanic basement. In the northern Appalachians of Newfoundland the belt equivalent to the Inner Piedmont is referred to as the Dunnage, which has a thick lower Paleozoic succession. Gravity and magnetics of the submarine northeastward extension of the Dunnage belt suggest that it is underlain by oceanic crust (Haworth and Miller, 1982), although Van der Pluijm (1987) projects underlying continental crust.

4. Southern Piedmont easternmost Grenville rocks. These occur in the Pine Mountain and the Sauratown Mountain belts (*Hatcher and others, 1984*; *Hooper and Hatcher, 1988*; Rankin and others, 1989), and *Farrar* (1984, *1985*) suggested their existence in the Raleigh belt, where they are spatially closely associated with the Carolina Slate belt, which may be considered as part of the Avalon composite terrane. Horton and others (1986) suggest that the Carolina Slate is allochthonous over the underlying Raleigh belt, and that the allochthony is associated with an ophiolitic mélange, implying that the slates have been transported westward. Thus the intervening thrust has been explained as a suture separating Laurentian Grenville rocks from those of the outboard Avalon composite terrane of suspect original position.

Avalon superterrane

In the northern Appalachians, older Grenville(?)-age rocks in Nova Scotia appear to be unconformably overlain by sedimentary rocks attributed to the Avalon composite terrane. Since the introduction of plate tectonics into Appalachian geology (Bird and Dewey, 1970) the Avalon composite terrane has been considered to have African affinities and to have been separated from the Laurentian craton by the Iapetus Ocean. Thus the possible presence of a basement of Grenville age rather than the 1,600 to 1,800 Ma age of the West African craton (c.f., *Olszewski, 1978*; Olszewski and Gaudette, 1982) has to be explained.

In the Avalon superterrane of New Brunswick and Nova Scotia, a metasedimentary group (ca. 800 Ma?) underlies the typical Avalonian volcanic sequence (Rast and Skehan, 1983; O'Brien and others, 1983). The group (Green Head in New Brunswick) consists of marbles, quartzites, and meta-argillites and resembles the Grenville Supergroup of Ontario and Quebec, but these strata may also represent the Stromatolite Series of West Africa (*Caby, 1987*).

Odom and Fullagar (1984) suggested that the initial rifting of the Grenville basement to produce the Iapetus Ocean occurred ca. 680 to 700 Ma. In the northern Appalachians, *Strong and others* (*1978*) suggested what they called an aborted rift, now accepted at ca. 760 Ma, which they identified by the thick accumulation of mafic volcanic rocks and by emplacement of gabbro. I now suggest that the period from 680 to 760 Ma was a stage when those blocks of Grenville gneisses, which are now covered by Avalonian rocks, not only rifted but then, also drifted

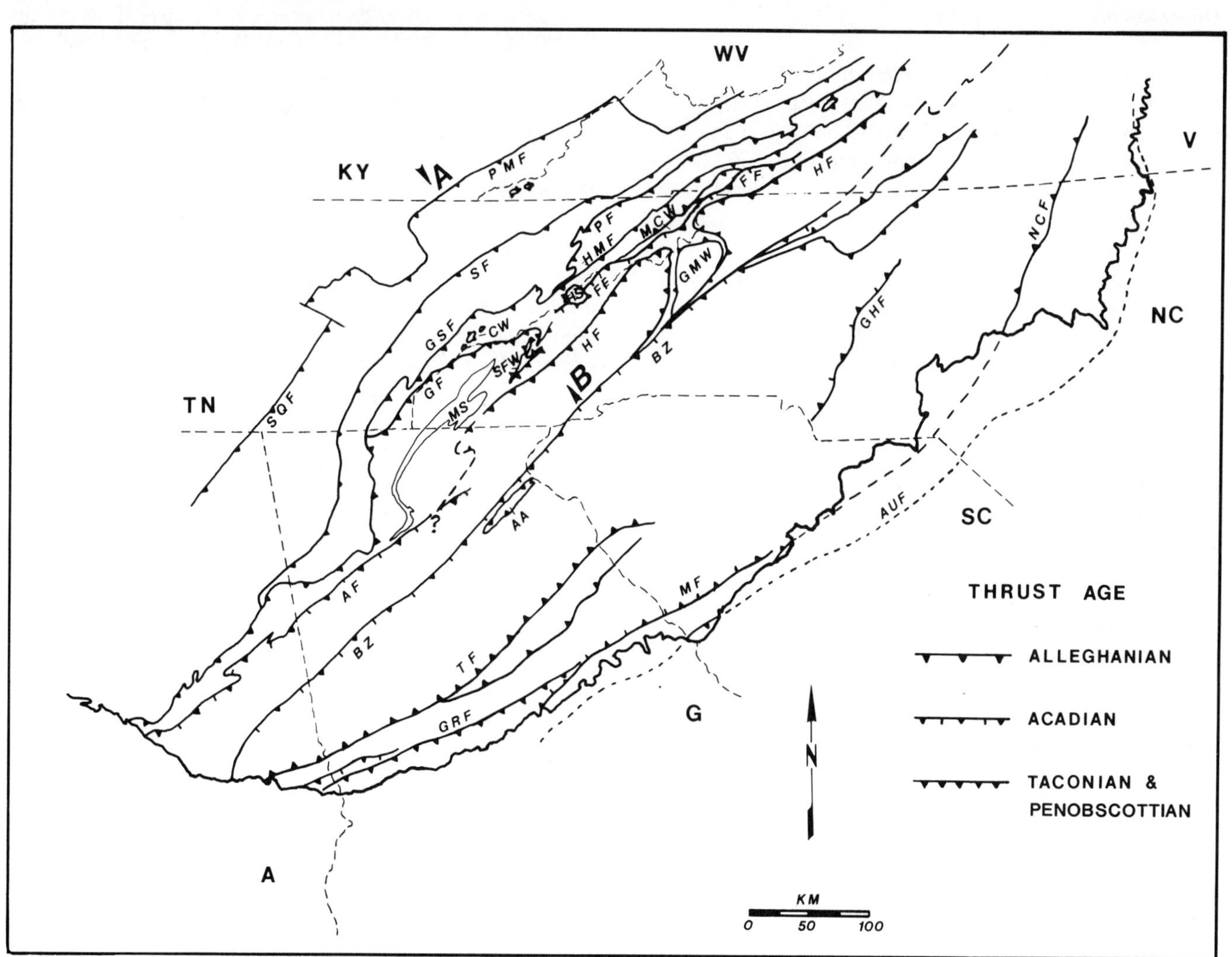

Figure 6. Overthrusts in the southern Appalachians. States in large letters: A, Alabama; G, Georgia; KY, Kentucky; NC, North Carolina; SC, South Carolina; TN, Tennessee; VA, Virginia; WV, West Virginia. State boundaries, thin dashed lines. Overthrusts, faults, and associated low-angle normal faults from northwest to southeast: PMF, Pine Mountain fault; SQF, Sequatchie Valley Fault; SF, Saltville fault; PF, Pulaski fault; GSF, Great Smoky fault; HMF, Halstead Mountain fault; GF, Greenbrier fault; FF, Fries fault; AF, Allatoona fault; HF, Hayesville fault; BZ, Brevard zone; TF, Tauliga fault; GHF, Gold Hill fault; GRF, Goat Rock fault; MF, Modoc fault; NCF, Nutbrush Creek fault; AUF, Augusta fault. Thick dashed lines continuations of faults. Windows from southwest to northwest: CW, cove windows; SFW, Smoky Faults window; HS, Hot Springs window; MCW, Mountain City window; GMW, Grandfather Mountain window. Outliers from northwest to southeast: MS, Murphy syncline; AA, Alto allochthon. ? indicates uncertain junction. Arrows marked A and B show line of section in Figure 9.

away, to form a basement to the Avalon volcanic rocks. Two stages of Proterozoic rifting are now accepted by Krogh and others (1988). In the southern Appalachians the evidence for ca. 700 Ma rifting rests first in the alkalic Crossnore Plutonic Series (Odom and Fullagar, 1984) and associated extrusives of somewhat disputed ages (c.f., Rankin and others, 1989); there is also evidence in dike swarms (see below) and in probably penecontemporaneous grabens and half grabens such as those that accommodate the 12-km-thick supracrustal Proterozoic Ocoee Supergroup (Rast and Kohles, 1986).

Dike swarms

The Precambrian Avalon succession, particularly in Newfoundland (O'Brien and others, 1983), is very thick and probably records a series of episodes of accumulation (Krogh and others, 1988) over a long time interval (minimum 760 to 550 Ma). One method of subdividing this interval is with reference to dike swarms. Such swarms are identified on both Laurentian and Avalon sides of the orogen.

The dikes of the late Precambrian swarms are generally mafic and in the Laurentian craton are much less deformed than the enclosing gneisses. *Strong and Williams (1972)* and, more recently, Williams and others (1985) described these from Long Range (Fig. 5) massif of Newfoundland. Similar dikes are known farther south, and Ratcliffe (*1983,* 1987a, b) attempted to correlate such dikes from the Taconics of New York and Vermont and the Reading Prong with the northern Blue Ridge, where such dikes are considered as feeders of late Precambrian volcanic rocks such as the Catoctin Formation (*Reed and Morgan, 1971*; Rankin and others, 1989), which is composed of mafic lavas of much debated age, although probably ca. 600 Ma. However, at the border of Tennessee and North Carolina, Goldberg and others (1986) have dated somewhat similar dikes as 734 $\pm$ 26 Ma. In the Long Range, isotopic dating leads to somewhat controversial results. Williams and others (1985) report that some dikes cut a granite dated as 602 $\pm$ 10 Ma, but not the local latest Precambrian–Cambrian metasediments. Earlier dating from a different locality by the K/Ar method (*Pringle and others, 1971*) yields an age of ca. 805 Ma. *Stukas and Reynolds (1974)* maintain that the true age is 605 $\pm$ 10 Ma, and the date of 805 Ma is a consequence of preferential absorption of radiogenic argon.

The 600-Ma dates of the eastern part of the northern Appalachians are normally attributed to the rift inception of the Iapetus Ocean. The age discrepancy with the dikes of the southern Appalachians has been attributed by Williams and others (1985) to diachronism. Alternatively, it is possible that two episodes of rifting have occurred; the first, at 700+ Ma, was of the same general age as the emplacement of Crossnore alkali granites, and the second, at 600 Ma, led to the development of the Catoctin lavas.

At the Avalon edge of the orogen the evidence for two stages of rifting is also identified. Rast (1979) described dikes from southern New Brunswick and suggested that they indicate a stage in the opening of the Iapetus Ocean. Rast and Dickson (1982) pointed out that two main stages of dike emplacement can be recognized: earlier, much deformed alkaline xenolithic dikes, and later, less deformed dikes belonging to a swarm of subvertical multiple intrusions of mainly tholeiitic diabases. The former are abundant in the ca. 800-Ma Green Head metasediments, while the latter crosscut ca. 600-Ma intrusive granitoids, but are not found in the overlying Cambrian strata. This two-stage record, I maintain, reflects two separate stages of rifting.

Elsewhere in Gondwana terranes, two stages of late Proterozoic dikes (rifting) have been documented. Caby (*1987*) records ca. 800 Ma and 580 Ma dikes from West Africa; Lindsey and others (1987) describe such dikes (900 Ma and 600 Ma) from Australia. In all these cases it is proposed that the dikes represent rifting apart of a late Proterozoic continent (c.f., Piper, 1987).

Avalonian orogeny

At approximately the same time as the emplacement of dikes (rifting) many of the Avalonian blocks were affected by the so-called Avalonian orogeny associated with the emplacement of calc-alkaline granitoids. The orogeny was first recorded from Newfoundland (*Lilley, 1966*) and subsequently from New Brunswick (Rast and Skehan, 1983). Similar late Proterozoic deformational events are known from the Carolinas (*Glover and Sinha, 1973*; Harris and Glover, 1988) as the Virgilina orogeny, and from Anglesey as the Monian orogeny (Gibbons, 1987; Dallmeyer and Gibbons, 1987). The imprint of these late Proterozoic movements on some dikes in New Brunswick led Nance (1987) to interpret them as originally transtensional within an island arc. Nance suggests that the orogeny was caused by the collision of the arc with the Laurentian Shield and resulted in the closure of the "Avalon Sea." This "sea" was probably a rifted ocean (proto-Iapetus) that developed during the first stage of rifting, ca. 800 to 700 Ma. In Africa, Bertrand-Sarfati and others (1987), and in France, *Ziegler (1982)*, also reported close connections between the latest Proterozoic dikes and orogenic movements.

PALEOZOIC EVENTS—HOW IT ALL DEVELOPED

Succession

On the Laurentian craton and the Avalon superterrane, the diachronous (Palmer, 1971) Cambrian transgression resulted in the formation of epicontinental seas and passive margins. In the southern Appalachians (*Colton, 1970*), transgression against the Laurentian shield started in late Proterozoic time, first generating a fairly thick sequence of Early Cambrian clastic sediments (Chilhowee Formation) that was succeeded by carbonates of Middle and Upper Cambrian and Ordovician times (Table 1), which ultimately formed a bank 2 to 4 km thick that was continuous through the northern Appalachians.

TABLE 1. PALEOZOIC STRATIGRAPHIC SUCCESSION OF LAURENTIAN PLATFORM ADJACENT TO AND IN THE SOUTHERN AND CENTRAL APPALACHIAN BELT

Chronostratigraphy		Lithology and Approximate Maximum Thickness on the Craton	Lithology and Thickness in Northwest (Valley and and Ridge) part of the Orogenic Belt
Permian 286–245 Ma		Clastics (Red beds); 200 m	None
Pennsylvanian 320–286 Ma		Clastics—conglomerates, sandstones, shales, coals; 1,500 m	Clastics—conglomerates, sandstones, shales, and coals; 1,500 m
Mississippian 360–320 Ma		Calcareous shales and sandstones; 700 m, exceptionally much thicker Carbonates; 300 m Clastics—sandstones and shales; 200 m	Clastics—sandstones, shales, coals, carbonates; 600 m
Devonian 408–360 Ma	late	Clastics—conglomerates, shales, sandstones; 2,000 m	Clastics—sandstones and shales; 3,000 m
	Mid.		Conglomerates
	Early	Siluro-Devonian carbonates, evaporites, clastics; 350 m	Siluro-Devonian Carbonates, evaporites, shales; 1,000 m
Silurian 438–408 Ma		Clastics—sandstones, shales, minor carbonates; 100 m	Clastics—sandstones; 200 m
Orodovician 505–438 Ma		Shales and carbonates; 250 m Carbonates; 500 m Unconformity	Unconformity or paraconformity, Red Beds; 500 m Clastics–Shales, sandstones Cambro–Ordovician Carbonate Bank with some shaley horizons passes up and to the east into Martinsburg turbidites up to 4,000 m in thickness – up to 3,500 m
Cambrian 570–505 Ma		Carbonates; 600 m Thin clastics (Lower Cambrian), shales and carbonates	Clastics; 800 m

The fauna throughout the carbonate bank is of American type, and in magnitude there is no other analogue (modern or ancient) of such a bank (Rodgers, 1987). Palmer (1971), however, indicated that it was not a simple bank, even in Cambrian time, and its detailed development depended on the interaction with the siliciclastic sediments deposited to the east and west (present day) of the bank; indeed *Chow and James* (*1987*) interpreted Cambrian carbonates as having been deposited in major cycles.

Cambrian sediments deposited on the Avalonian superterrane basement were mainly clastic marine formations, with occasional indications of volcanogenic components, mainly in those parts now in the southern Appalachians (Carolinas) where they collectively reach 5 km in thickness. In the Central Mobile Belt to the west, well-authenticated Cambrian sediments are rare.

Early Ordovician rocks occur on the Avalon composite terrane in Newfoundland as shale-sandstone facies (which contain in places hematitic iron ores), in Nova Scotia and New Brunswick as carbonaceous shales, and in Boston Avalon blocks(?) as volcanic rocks (Billings, 1982). In the southern Appalachians (Carolinas) there are no Ordovician deposits. In the Tallahassee-Suwannee terrane, Ordovician shales and sandstones have distinct Gondwanan faunal affinities. But this terrane is considered to be outside of the Appalachian orogen.

Well-authenticated Ordovician sediments also occur in the broad belt between the Avalon composite terrane and the Laurentian platform. They tend to vary in thickness and consist of various, at present incompletely correlated, black euxinic pelites, metaturbidites, banded calcareous clastics, and abundant metavolcanics. Clastic wedges of Ordovician age have been discussed by Thomas (1977). In particular the wedge associated with the Taconian orogeny has recently been discussed by Rodgers (1987).

Siluro-Devonian strata are widespread on the Laurentian platform; they are made up in part of carbonate facies, although Late Devonian beds are generally clastic and form a thick clastic wedge in and to the west of the central and southern part of the northern Appalachians (*Boucot, 1968*). In the Central Mobile Belt the Siluro-Devonian is generally unconformable on deformed Ordovician rocks (Hatch, 1982) in the northern Appalachians, but such rocks have not been dated with certainty in the south, except for Alabama (Tull, 1982). Devonian sediments have also been identified in the Suwannee terrane.

Upper Devonian clastic formations in both the northern and southern Appalachians pass up, in many places without a break, into Carboniferous rocks that are mainly terrestrial, coal-bearing, and of variable thickness. In some localities great thicknesses exist (8 km in the Magdalen Islands) and are attributed to deposition in local basins (McCutcheon and Robinson, 1987). Throughout the Carboniferous section in the Canadian sector, shallow-marine incursions are widespread.

In Carboniferous time the distinction between the Central Mobile Belt and the platforms disappeared since Carboniferous sediments lie unconformably on previously deformed and metamorphosed rocks of the Avalon superterrane and the mobile belt, and in the southern Appalachians overstep onto the lower and middle Paleozoic formations of the Laurentian craton.

Orogenies

To understand the Paleozoic section as a whole, a conventional sequence of orogenies and episodes has been introduced in the literature; these are discussed below.

Penobscottian and Taconian. In the northern Appalachians there are three significant localities in the Central Mobile Belt where Cambrian rocks are authenticated. (1) In Newfoundland there are the deformed metasedimentary and granitic rocks of the Dunnage belt (Dewey and others, 1983). (2) In east-central Maine, *Neuman* (1967, *1972*) recognized the Grand Pitch Formation of quartzose turbidites and slates and suggested that it is Cambrian on the basis of a problematic organism, *Oldhamia.* Also, ophiolitic rocks of Cambrian age have been recognized (*Boudette, 1982*; Boone and Boudette, 1989). (3) Lastly, in the Taconic klippen of the United States and western Newfoundland (Fig. 4), Cambrian rocks have long been recognized (c.f., Zen, 1967) and are considered in the United States sector to lie paraconformably on late Precambrian, post-Grenville strata (Stanley and Ratcliffe, 1985, Fig. 3). Although the bulk of the Taconic succession is argillaceous, there are carbonate breccias derived probably from the North American carbonate bank, variably interpreted as olistostromes or mélanges (discussion in Rast and Horton, 1989), containing fossils ranging from Cambrian to Ordovician (discussed in Rodgers, 1970, p. 79). On the basis of the general lithology of the succession in the Taconic klippen of the United States, Stanley and Ratcliffe (1985) suggest an allochthonous derivation of the klippen from the east of the external massifs and thus from the Central Mobile Belt.

The lower Paleozoic succession in the Central Mobile Belt is thin and is frequently referred to as starved. Yet, Ordovician sediments in the Central Mobile Belt are much more widely exposed and much thicker than the Cambrian. The Ordovician sediments generally consist of fine to intermediate clastics dominated by black shales. Along the western margin of the belt (Fig. 3), widespread volcanics are usually interpreted to represent a volcanic arc (Rodgers, 1987) or arcs (Boone and Boudette, 1989) in an oceanic setting, while relicts of the ocean are preserved as ophiolitic complexes. Boone and Boudette (1989) identify two lines of such complexes: (1) Hurricane Mountain in Maine with a possible extension to the Elmtree inlier of New Brunswick (*Rast and Stringer, 1980*), and (2) the Baie Verte–Brompton line in Quebec and Newfoundland (*Williams and St-Julien, 1982*). Each of these lines is interpreted as a collisional suture, where rocks of the opposing terranes suffered an orogenic encounter between an island arc and a continental block. The Hurricane Mountain linear terrane represents a ca. 500-Ma event, while the Baie Verte–Brompton line is a ca. 460-Ma event. Rodgers (1971) integrated both deformational episodes into the Taconic (Taconian) orogeny. It is now customary to refer to the first event as the Penobscottian and the second as the Taconian *sensu stricto*.

The Hurricane Mountain (Penobscottian) terrane (Boone and Boudette, 1989), which is well developed in Maine and New Brunswick, is cut off by a major fault in southwestern Maine and cannot be identified farther south in New Hampshire. In the central and southern Appalachians, however, there is also considerable evidence for a Penobscottian(?) episode of Cambrian age in the Blue Ridge and Piedmont belts. Pavlides (1981, 1989) has identified a Cambrian island arc associated with mélanges indicative of a collisional event (see also *Brown, 1986*) in the Piedmont of Virginia. *Drake and Lyttle* (*1981*) also indicate it in the Virginia Piedmont. Drake and others (1989) make a point that the internides (Central Mobile Belt of this chapter) in the southern Appalachians, like the northern Appalachians, show evidence for Penobscottian deformation and attribute the Hayesville thrust system in the Blue Ridge to it (Fig. 6). In the eastern Piedmont, Secor and others (1986) have recognized what they have called the Delmar event, which is bracketed between 530 and 415 Ma and may be Penobscottian.

Along the western margin of the northern Appalachians the Taconian (*sensu stricto*) is widely recognized. The colliding arc is here positioned at the Bronson Hill anticlinorium (Fig. 3). In general the Taconian event is considered to have occurred in Llandeilo to Caradoc times, although in Newfoundland the corresponding deformation may be older. This is normally explained as resulting from the diachroneity of orogenic events. Recent work also shows that the Avalon superterrane in the southern Appalachians and adjacent areas has been affected by Taconian events (Glover and others, 1983; Dallmeyer and others, 1986).

Both Penobscottian and Taconian events are associated with

mélanges, which predate Taconian metamorphism and are concurrent with extensive overthrusting involving the obduction of ophiolites. In the southern Appalachians the ophiolites are not as continuous or well preserved as in the northern Appalachians. Ophiolite fragments are dispersed throughout extensive, mainly metasedimentary units (e.g., Ashe Formation of North Carolina), that may be mélanges on a large scale (Abbott and Raymond, 1984). Mélanges can also be recognized in the central Appalachians Piedmont (Rast and Horton, 1989). I suggest that the mélange belt marks a suture of Penobscottian or Taconian collisions, and it is partly in the Blue Ridge and partly in the Piedmont because its parts were displaced on the originally transcurrent (Edelman and others, 1987) Brevard Fault (Figs. 5, 6) and its splays. To the southeast, Hatcher (1987) recognizes a tenuous line, which he calls the central Piedmont Suture, that separates the Carolina terrane of Avalonian affinities from the rocks related to the North American continent. This suture possibly marks the docking of the Carolina terrane to North America, and I interpret it as the position of the "Avalon Sea" in the southern Appalachians. In part, this margin coincides with the steep gravity gradient between the axes of regional positive and negative gravity anomalies, discussed by M. D. Thomas (1983), among others.

The Penobscottian and Taconian orogenic events are accompanied by extensive metamorphic effects and granite plutonism. However, in the northern Appalachians these earlier events are commonly largely overprinted by Acadian structures and metamorphism (*Laird and others, 1984*; Stanley and Ratcliffe, 1985), and in the southern Appalachians by Alleghanian events (Hatcher, 1987).

Taconian deformation evidently involved major thrusting that resulted in the development of a marginal foredeep (*Quinlan and Beaumont, 1984*; Beaumont and others, 1987) and also a peripheral bulge (Jacobi, 1981; *Quinlan and Beaumont, 1984*; c.f., Mussman and Read, 1986). The theoretical basis (Fig. 7) for this conclusion was furnished by Bally and others (1966). Hiscott and others (1986) have suggested that the foredeep is somewhat discontinuous and that it is usually filled by Ordovician flysch and mud derived from Taconian overthrusts. If the cause were an arc-continent collision, then the oceanic stretch that was subducted under Laurentia—now represented by the Baie Verte–Brompton line of ophiolites—could have been a back-arc basin (Upadhyay and Neale, 1979; Edelman, 1988) rather than a whole ocean (discussed by Williams, 1979, p. 797). It is quite possible that in the southern Appalachians the repetition of subduction in Penobscottian and Taconian times led to the repetition of Ordovician flysch deposition in the Ordovician section of the Valley and Ridge Province (Rodgers, 1971).

Acadian. The Acadian event is well represented in the northern Appalachians, where it is recognized by polyphase deformation and intrusion of postorogenic granites. The deformation affects rocks as old as Precambrian, but in particular it affects Siluro-Devonian sediments of the Central Mobile Belt that are well represented both in Canada and the United States.

The termination of Taconian movements resulted in the development of a completely new depositional setting spread over the eroded stumps of the Taconian system in an environment that was partly oceanic and partly shallow sea continental. At the edge of the Laurentian craton the synorogenic clastic rocks of the Taconian orogen are covered by an unconformable Siluro-Devonian succession that starts with clastic deposits and is succeeded by a bank of carbonate rocks of mid-Silurian to mid-Devonian age, and then by a clastic wedge attributed to Acadian erosion (Table 1). In the Valley and Ridge Province, Silurian rocks are well known and are disconformably(?) covered by Late Devonian sediments. The Talladega terrane (Fig. 6), sandwiched between the Valley and Ridge and the Central Mobile Belt, shows a Siluro-Devonian sequence (Tull, 1982), the relationships of which to the rest of the belt are being investigated.

The unconformity between Ordovician and Silurian strata in the northern Appalachians of western Newfoundland (*Williams, 1977*), New Brunswick (*Helmsteadt, 1971*; Rast and Stringer, 1980), Quebec (St-Julien and Hubert, 1975), and in New England (Hatch, 1982) marks post-Taconian readvance of Silurian seas. The Silurian sediments vary from entirely clastic to mixed clastic-carbonate shelf sequences, except in the southeastern part of the Mobile Belt (Dunnage Zone), where in New Brunswick and central Maine, turbidites are predominant (Bradley, 1983). The Siluro-Devonian rocks of southern New Brunswick are laterally continuous into the coastal Maine complex and are unconformably overlain by postorogenic reddish Upper Devonian Perry Formation (*Schluger, 1973*). Although *Donohoe and Pajari* (*1974*) date the Acadian deformation responsible for the stratigraphic break in this area as Gedinnian, Osberg and others (1989), on the basis of the work done in the Central Mobile Belt (which they call the Medial New England Terrane), develop a polyphase Acadian chronology. They point out that the turbiditic central belt is bordered on either side by volcanic belts: (1) the Piscataquis in north-central Maine and New Brunswick, and (2) the Coastal Maine Belt extending from southern New Brunswick into coastal Maine. These were formed in a rift environment, which was then superseded by a compressive environment. In the Nashoba terrane in the Boston area, there are intrusive manifestations ranging in age from Ordovician to Early Silurian, and in the adjacent Liberty-Owington antiform of southern Maine there are Carboniferous granites. Thus, Osberg and others (1989) suggest that Acadian plutons have a Middle Ordovician to Carboniferous age range. The volcanic belt of coastal Maine, however, yields ages at the Silurian-Devonian boundary, which are consistent with a Gedinnian or later date for deformation. The plutons associated with the Piscataquis belt (Fig. 3) yield an age of circa 412 Ma and are later deformed by the Acadian movements. The earliest undeformed Acadian plutons have a range of ages, but at least one case suggests that the Acadian deformation was Early Devonian (Lyons, 1979). Silurian ages of some Acadian plutons are reported from central New Brunswick (*Bevier and Whalen, 1988*).

The age of Acadian regional metamorphism is set by the Emsian age of the fossiliferous metamorphosed Littleton Formation in New Hampshire. The age of penetrative deformation is recorded by Robinson and others (1982) from the deeper part of the orogen in Massachusetts as pre–380 Ma, but possibly as old as 401 Ma. *Guidotti and others (1983)* recognize two syntectonic stages, the first pre–394 Ma and the second post–380 Ma. All this suggests a late Early Devonian inception of deformation and metamorphism in the northern Appalachians. Dallmeyer and Van Breeman (1981) report the latest Devonian metamorphism as contemporaneous with plutons of 394 to 381 Ma.

The large, post-tectonic "Acadian" granites have been interpreted by Osberg and others (1989) to be the products of heat locked up under a lid formed by Acadian thrusting.

Van der Voo (1988) and Rast (1988), after Autran and Cogné (1980), suggest that the Acadian orogeny occurred because of the jamming of a large number of small terranes (plates) between the convergent Laurentian and West African cratons. One of the largest of the small plates was the Meguma terrane. This terrane of lower to mid-Paleozoic strata is well represented in southern Nova Scotia. It probably then continues southwestward offshore parallel to the coast of Maine (Fig. 3) and as far as southeast Massachusetts (c.f., Hutchinson and others, 1988). The Meguma succession consists of a thick lower Paleozoic to Devonian sequence of mainly clastic rocks that suffered a series of strike-slip movements along the Chedabucto fault zone (Schenk, 1983). The Meguma had dextral displacement of some 475 km in Early Devonian time, and 280 km in Late Devonian time. During its resultant collision with southern New Brunswick at circa 375 to 410 Ma (Dallmeyer and Keppie, 1987), a steep axial cleavage developed under greenschist–lower amphibolite metamorphic conditions. Later granitic intrusions were emplaced from ca. 375 to 315 Ma. The cleavage dates the collisional Acadian deformation here, but later Carboniferous complex metamorphic

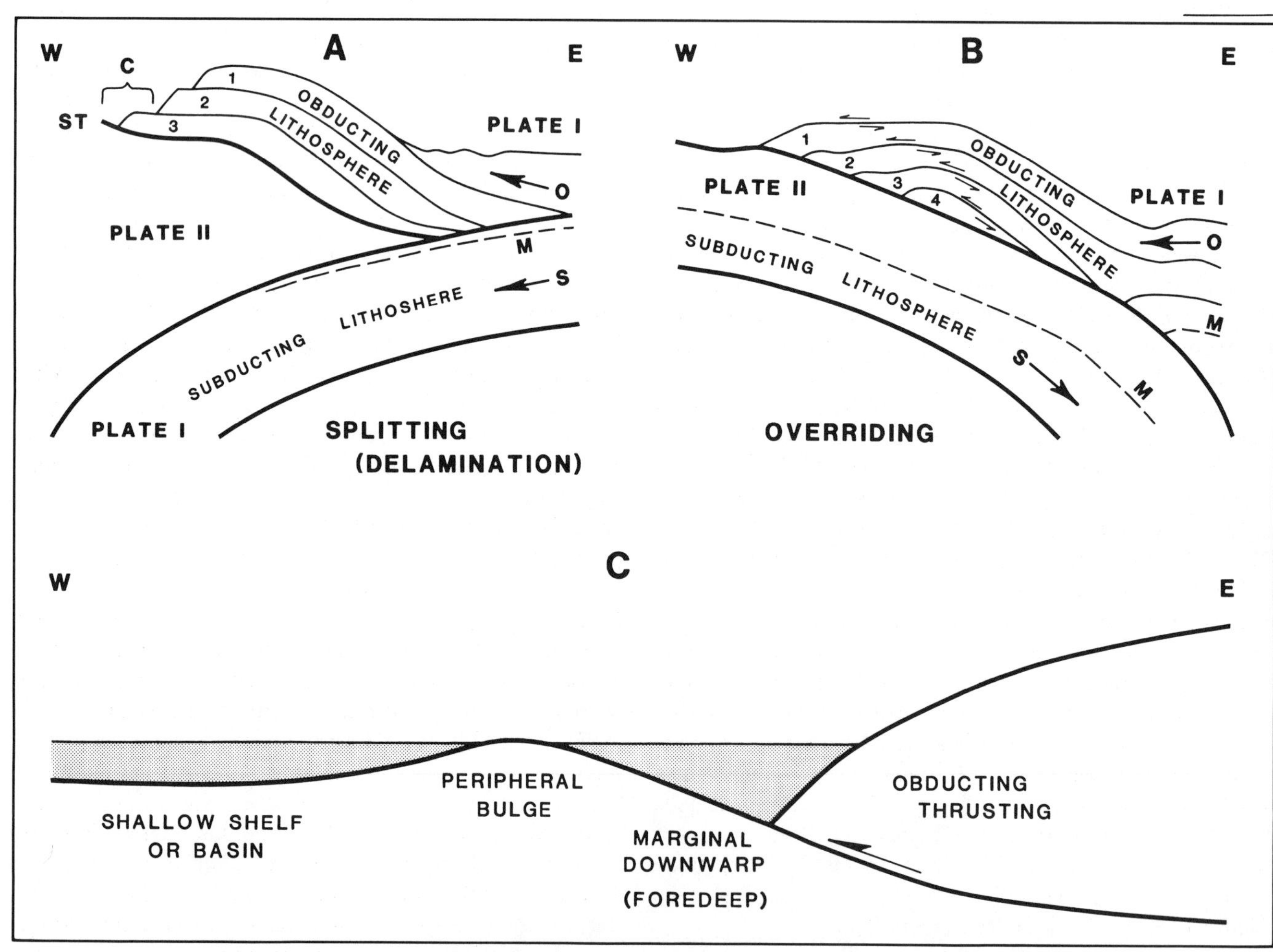

Figure 7. Theoretical possibilities of collisional episodes. A, delamination of lithosphere into obducting part (o) consisting of continental or island arc with ophiolites; and subducting part (G), consisting of the upper mantle. M is position of the Moho discontinuity, but it can also be at the bottom of the obducted plate; ST, sole thrust. This is a model for the southern Appalachians. B, overriding, when two continental plates collide without delamination and one overrides the other, thickening plate 1 at the collisional interface. This model may be applicable to the northern Appalachians during the Taconian or Alleghanian orogeny (c.f., Stockmal and others, 1987, Fig. 2). C, enlarged schematic representation of part of schema A as shown. (After Bally and others, 1966.)

recrystallization and structures affect the same rocks. These findings seem to tie the Acadian orogeny closely to the Alleghanian orogenic cycle. The interpretation of Acadian orogenic deformation, which varies from place to place, requires a recourse to multiple docking of terranes. Both collisional thrusts and transpressive strike-slip Acadian structures are common in the orogen (Ferrill and Thomas, 1988). Van der Voo (1988) evaluated the successive Acadian-Alleghanian episodes using paleomagnetic data and proposed that they represent two collisions, separated by a period of rifting.

In the Dunnage terrane of Newfoundland, according to Karlstrom and others (1982), there is a continuity of Ordovician to Silurian successions and tectonism, which cannot be attributed to separate Taconian and Acadian orogenies. Clearly, if the Dunnage terrane were entirely allochthonous and had not docked to the rest of Newfoundland until the Late Devonian, (c.f., Colman-Sadd and Swinden, 1984; Wonderley and Neuman, 1984), this would be entirely possible. Secor, Murray, and Glover (*in* Rankin and others, 1989) indicate that the absence of Acadian structures from the Boston Avalon block may mean that it also may have docked to the North American continent in post-Acadian times.

Osberg and others (1989), in discussing the Acadian orogeny in the southern Appalachians, indicate that the distribution of its effects is patchy. This may be the result of heavy overprinting (*Dallmeyer, 1986*) by the Alleghanian orogeny, or because strike-slip mechanisms were in places more important than thrusting (Ferrill and Thomas, 1988).

In the central and southern Appalachians, Acadian orogenic overprint normally cannot be disentangled from the Alleghanian, and therefore the Acadian orogeny in these parts of the orogen has been largely ignored.

The ultimate rise and erosion of the Acadian orogen in the northern and central Appalachians produced a large Catskill delta complex mainly in New York State, Pennsylvania, Virginia, and West Virginia. *Ettensohn* (*1985,* 1987) has interpreted the intense cyclicity of Catskill sediments to reflect tectonic oscillations. He has recognized the spatial shift in depocenters of sedimentation in terms of tectophases of Acadian orogeny. The thick sedimentary sequence in the Catskills implies that in southern New England, New York State, and the central Appalachians, Acadian thrusting was vigorous. In the southern Appalachians, however, the thin Early to mid-Devonian sequence in Kentucky and Tennessee implies that the possible Acadian thrust front was so distant as not to influence sedimentation on the craton. Van Tassell (1987), however, explains the Catskill cycles in terms of astronomic periods. The fact that there is no continuous belt of upper Devonian sedimentation parallel to the Acadian orogenic belt, and especially so in the southern Appalachians, suggests that Acadian thrusting was localized.

Alleghanian. The Acadian events were almost immediately succeeded by the Alleghanian period of contemporaneous sediment accumulation and orogenesis (Thomas, 1977; Rast, 1984; Ferrill and Thomas, 1988). After the Acadian orogeny in the northern Appalachians of eastern Canada and the United States, a broad upland area was formed. It was subsequently eroded down to an irregular faulted platform to be invaded by the Carboniferous sea from the east. Initial basal clastic sediments (Late Devonian and early Carboniferous) were deposited in sub-basins. Later, Windsor carbonates and evaporites of a shallow seaboard spread inland as far as central New Brunswick (*McCutcheon, 1981*). The deposition did not take place in a completely stable environment, and penecontemporaneous faults became guides to volcanic activity in central and southern New Brunswick (Fyffe and Barr, 1986; Rast, 1984) in Mississippian time, and as sites of small basins throughout the Canadian Maritime provinces. In Pennsylvanian time, most deposits were clastic, terrigenous, and in part fluviatile (Rust, 1981). Pennsylvanian fluviatile coarse sediments are found north as far as the Gaspé Peninsula of Quebec (Fig. 8) and west as far as the border with Maine. In New Brunswick and Nova Scotia there are coal-bearing deposits. The central New Brunswick syncline, in which the Carboniferous sediments are preserved, plunges north-northeast; thus, in the axial region on Prince Edward Island (Fig. 8), Permian strata are present (*Van de Poll and Forbes, 1984*).

In Nova Scotia, Carboniferous deposits are found both south and north of the Cobequid-Chedabucto fault. These sediments are variable in thickness (Table 2) and commonly overlie volcanogenic breaks, depending on which small sub-basin the deposits occupy.

In Newfoundland, Carboniferous strata are associated with the Cabot fault where they occupy the St. Georges and the Deer Lake–White Bay sub-basins (Fig. 8).

Apart from the Carboniferous deposits of the Canadian Maritime basin, the only other major areas of Carboniferous sedimentation in the northern Appalachians are the Narragansett and Norfolk basins of Rhode Island and Massachusetts (Quinn, 1971; Skehan and others, 1986), which are grabens in the Boston Avalon terrane and where the Carboniferous sequences are entirely of Pennsylvanian age, largely fluviatile and coal-bearing.

The mechanisms of formation of Carboniferous depositional basins in the Maritimes and Rhode Island has had diverse explanations: (1) Belt (1968) suggested that the basins were post-Acadian grabens; (2) Bradley (1983), and following him, Ferrill and Thomas (1988) proposed that they are transtensional, strike-slip–generated structures; (3) McCutcheon and Robinson (1987) claimed that they are produced by subsidence in response to thrusting. The third hypothesis recognizes two stages of basin formation; the mid-Devonian Acadian, and the upper Carboniferous Alleghanian. In parallel, the widespread Late Devonian to upper Carboniferous volcanic rocks of the Maritime basin change from tholeiitic to mildly alkalic and imply a rift environment. At present, it seems that an association of basins with faults is demonstrated; therefore, at least some of the basins are transtensional. Whether or not this hypothesis applies to all basins requires further studies.

In the northern Appalachians, plant-bearing Carboniferous strata show polyphase deformation (Mosher and Rast, 1984), and this is now well known down the Appalachian chain, as shown in

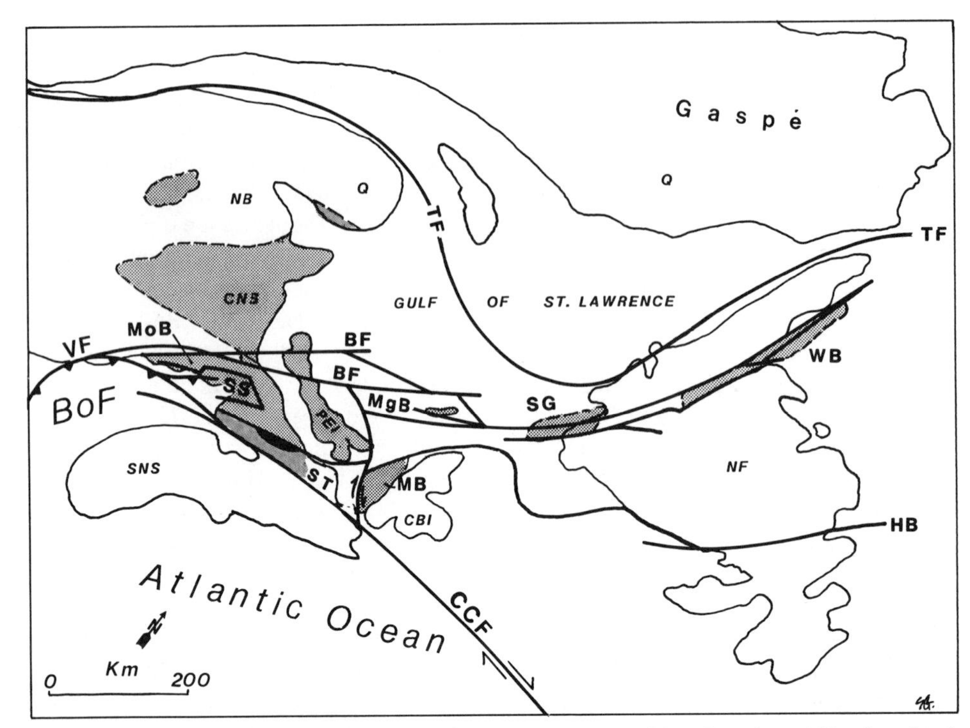

Figure 8. The distribution of principal Carboniferous basins in Maritime Canada and Newfoundland. The basins on land are shown in gray stipple. Regions and provinces in italics: NB, New Brunswick; Q, Quebec; NF, Newfoundland; PEI, Prince Edward Island; SNS, Southern Nova Scotia; CBI, Cape Breton Island; Bof, Bay of Fundy. Basins from east to west: WB, White Bay; SG, Saint George; MB, Mabou; MgB, Magdalen; ST, Stellarton; MoB, Moncton; SS, Sackville sub-basin; CNS, Central New Brunswick syncline and outliers to the northwest of it. Faults: CCF, Cobequid-Chedabucto; HB, Hare Bay (Dover) fault; BF, Belle Isle, note two possible continuations; TF, Taconian front; VF, Variscan front, teeth mark direction of dip of thrust plane.

Pennsylvania (Geiser and Engelder, 1983), Virginia (Bartholomew, 1987), and Alabama (Tull, 1984). As a result, Wintsch and Lefort (1984) have interpreted two episodes of deformation related to the direction of collisional impact between Laurentia and Gondwana. The collisional interpretation of the Alleghanian orogeny is now widely accepted (for review see Rast, 1988) although until recently intracratonic deformation was advocated.

In southeastern New Brunswick along the northwestern coast of the Bay of Fundy (Rast and others, 1984), a late Carboniferous belt of deformation is bounded by a thrust front, which *Rast and Grant* (1973, *1977*) refer to as the Variscan. The front passes laterally into the Cobequid-Chedabucto fault zone (Minas Geofracture), which is a dextral transcurrent fault (Keppie, 1982). Rast (1988) suggests that forward movement of southern Nova Scotia was the indentor for the thrust front. In the Boston Avalon area, Skehan and others (1986) suggest underthrusting of a block of Avalonian beneath the North American continent in Rhode Island. This has also been recognized by Wintsch and Fout (1982) in Connecticut.

While in the northern Appalachians the strongest effects of the Alleghanian orogeny are peripheral to the eastern Canadian provinces and American states, in the southern and central Appalachians the Alleghanian orogeny is widespread and pervasive.

Here the Carboniferous succession is well displayed in the Appalachian Plateau and Valley and Ridge Provinces (Table 1). Earlier Carboniferous (Mississippian) rocks consist of turbidites, black shales, carbonates, and mixed carbonate-clastic sequences, while later Carboniferous (Pennsylvanian) rocks are generally fluviatile coarse clastics with occasional marine bands. The work of COCORP investigators (Cook and others, 1979) and of Harris and Bayer (1979) shows that much or even the whole orogen in the southern Appalachians is allochthonous on a sole thrust (Fig. 9). Similar allochthony has been implied by many for the northern Appalachians, at approximately the site of Logan's line. *Geiser* (*1982*), for instance, has proposed that the age of "Taconian" cleavage in the northern Appalachians may be Alleghanian. Most workers in the northern Appalachians (Rowley and Kidd, 1981; Stanley and Radcliffe, 1985; Drake and others, 1989) do not accept this, since there are no indications of Alleghanian metamorphism or tectonic activity in northwestern Connecticut, New York, Vermont, or Quebec, and also because deformed and cleaved Ordovician strata are overlain unconformably by the little-deformed Devonian Manlius Formation (Bosworth and Vollmer, 1981). In New York State the post-Taconian pre-Alleghanian undeformed Cortland igneous complex cuts both Taconian structures and metamorphic zones (Ratcliffe and others, 1982). In the central Appalachians, the Alleghanian and Taconian orogenic fronts are somewhat proxi-

TABLE 2. STRATIGRAPHY OF CARBONIFEROUS ROCKS OF MARITIME CANADA IN NEW BRUNSWICK AND NOVA SCOTIA

Chronostratigraphic Unit	Age (Ma)	Main Lithostratigraphic Units (Groups)	and Thicknesses	Facies
Early Permian	286–258			Red Beds
Stephanian	296–286	Pictou	3,500 m (Pictou–Cumberland)	Clastics with coals (3,000 m)
Westphalian D				
C				
B		Cumberland		Coal-bearing coarse clastics
A	315–296	Riversdale	3,000 m (Riversdale–Canso)	Quartz pebble conglomerates and sandstones
Namurian	333–315	Canso		Shales and sandstones
Visean	352–333	Windsor	2,000 m	Marine carbonates and evaporites
Tournaisian	360–352	Horton*	3,000 m	Upward-fining clastics with volcanics
Late Devonian	374–360			

*Part of Horton is Middle Devonian; Pictou ranges from Westphalian to Early Permian. All stratigraphic junctions between groups are diachronous; rift-related major unconformities exist between rift-related earlier sediments, orogenic deformation, and uplift-related later sediments. Thicknesses vary partly as a result of the migration of Windsor salt. The greatest cumulative thickness is in Magdalen Islands (8,000 m).

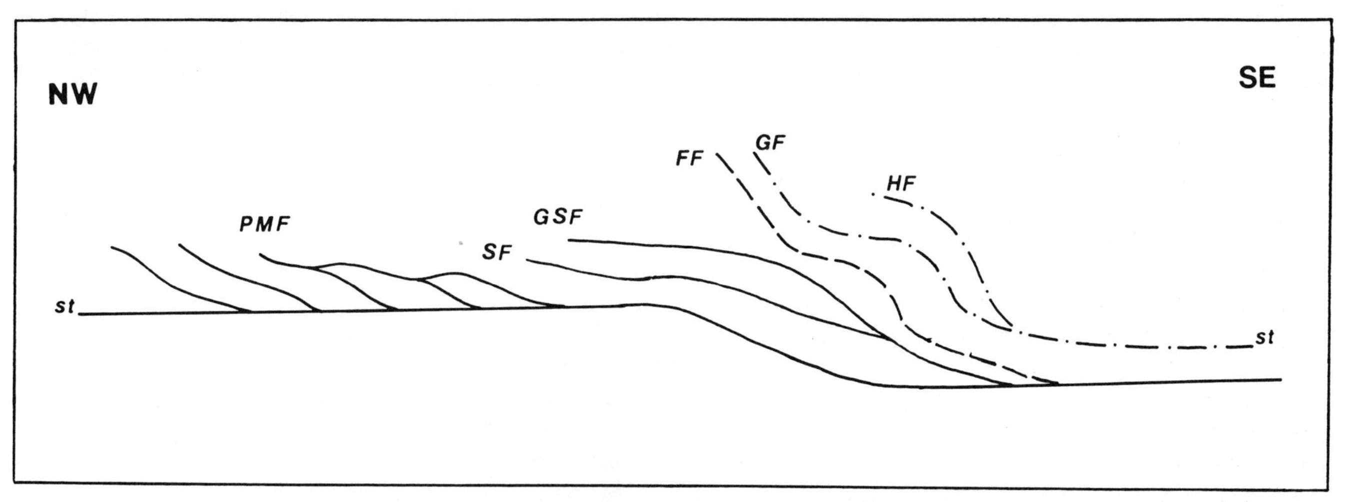

Figure 9. Diagrammatic stacking of overthrusts in the southern Appalachians (Line A–B, Fig. 6). Alleghanian structures, including the sole thrust (st) in solid lines; Acadian faults in dashed lines, Taconian and Penobscottian faults in dot dash lines. From northwest to southeast: PMF, Pine Mountain fault; SF, Saltville fault; GSF, Great Smoky fault; FF, Fries fault; GF, Greenbrier fault; HF, Hayesville fault.

mate (*Drake, 1980*). In the southern Appalachians the Taconian front lies in Tennessee at the border of the Blue Ridge and Valley and Ridge, and farther south in Alabama it is possibly within the Valley and Ridge, while the Alleghanian front lies to the east of it.

The development of Alleghanian thrusts, which was emphasized by Rich as far back as 1934, has been extensively investigated, and there is a voluminous literature for the southern and central Appalachians cited by Neathery and Thomas (1983), Hatcher (1987), Wiltschko *in* Geiser and others (1989), and Bartholomew (1987). Literature for the northern Appalachians is cited by *Mosher (1983)*, *Mosher and Rast (1984),* and Skehan and others (1986) for southeastern New England; by Rast and others (1984) for New Brunswick; and by Smith and Collins (1984) for Nova Scotia.

In the south, the Valley and Ridge represents a fold-and-thrust belt, with the sole thrust (décollement) climbing stepwise (Fig. 9) over early Paleozoic rocks. The décollement continues under the Blue Ridge and the Alabama Piedmont, but above the décollement lie residual blocks of Taconian, Penobscottian, and Acadian thrust packages, which have been carried "piggy back" by the Alleghanian major thrusts (e.g., Rast and Kohles, 1986). The strongest evidence for this is provided by reflection geophysical profiles. One of the latest and the most accurate of these (J. Costain, personal communication, 1988) is illustrated on Plate 8. In the north a much narrower thrust-deformed belt is wedged between Nova Scotia and southern New Brunswick.

The erosion products of the extensive Alleghanian overthrusting were deposited on the craton. These deposits, which range in age from Late Devonian to Early Permian, form clastic wedges laid down in marginal foredeeps on the Laurentian craton.

Alleghanian regional metamorphism (Fig. 3) is well manifested throughout the Piedmont (summary in Hatcher, 1987), and its lower grade greenschist zones encroach on most of the Blue Ridge, producing retrogression, although there is little evidence for it in the Valley and Ridge (*Harris and others, 1981*), except as anchimetamorphism. The high-grade metamorphic effects in the Piedmont coexist with granitoids.

Late Carboniferous granitoids are recorded in the Piedmont of the southern Appalachians. In the northern Appalachians, small bodies have been claimed from New Brunswick (Rast and others, 1984; disputed by *Currie, 1984*) and from Nova Scotia (Dallmeyer and Keppie, 1987). In southern Maine, numerous bodies of mid-Carboniferous granites (ca. 325 Ma) have been recognized recently (Aleinikoff and others, 1985; *Hayward and Gaudette, 1984*). Lux and Guidotti (1985) point out that a high amphibolite–facies terrane surrounds these granites, implying an early phase of Alleghanian thermal activity. The metamorphism may have been generated as a result of emplacement of the granite into the uncooled deep part of the Acadian orogen (*Guidotti and others, 1986*). However, inclusion of these granites within the Acadian thermal event (Osberg and others, 1989) transgresses the usual definition of the Acadian. In this chapter, a post-Acadian age for metamorphism is preferred because neighboring Acadian plutons are isotopically disturbed.

Alleghanian granites of the southern Appalachians yield ages varying from mid-Carboniferous to Permian (Fullagar and Butler, 1979; Dallmeyer, 1988). In the central Appalachians the Alleghanian(?) metamorphism appears to be mid-Carboniferous (Sutter and others, 1985), although since the $^{40}Ar/^{39}Ar$ technique was used, the dates may represent a cooling age of a rising Acadian orogen. Dallmeyer (1988) discusses the isotopic dating problems of the Alleghanian orogeny.

The Alleghanian event, attributed to the collision of Gondwana and the Laurentian craton (Dewey and Burke, 1973; Keppie, 1985; Rast, 1988), was thus prolonged and polyphase. In Permian time the Alleghanian orogenic belt was greatly reduced by erosion, and in Triassic time it became an area affected by the tension that marked the opening of the Atlantic Ocean, but that is another story.

A KINEMATIC SCHEME—HOW DOES IT ALL FIT?

There are at present numerous partial or complete models of evolution of the Appalachian chain. Hatcher and others (1989) in the companion volume on the Appalachian–Ouachita orogen in the United States present several. Part of the problem is that it has become conventional to present models in cross sections. While this may be justifiable for those events that are collisional, it ignores all rotations, strike-slip movements, and large-scale strain of major blocks. Therefore, in the following discussion I shall employ diagrammatic map views of the developing mountain chain and will supplement them by new information from western Europe and Africa. Despite the existing time scales of the Phanerozoic, it is more convenient to discuss events in terms of stratigraphic time rather than to use isotope dates, which are still in a state of flux. Where, however, translation from one to another becomes desirable, I use the time scale of Palmer (1983), although there are a number of splendid recent multi-author reviews (*Harland and others, 1982; Odin, 1982;* and *Snelling, 1985*).

There are two prevalent views, based on paleomagnetism, as to the distribution of cratons in Proterozoic times; the more widely held is that of Irving and McGlynn (1976) who interpreted the evolution of the Grenville orogen in terms of multiple phases of plate mobilism. The second is by Piper (*1985,* 1987), who has proposed a Proterozoic supercontinent analogous to a later Pangaea. Regardless of the early Proterozoic events, the relationships that Piper (1987) outlines for the late Proterozoic of North America include a well-supported proposal of a late Proterozoic combined Laurentian-Baltic craton (supercontinent). The Grenville orogenic belt then stretched from Laurentia to Baltica, although its margin against oceanic crust is indeterminate. The breakup of the supercontinent occurred between the future North America and Baltica, leading to early rifing (Fig. 10a). Piper (1987) envisaged this episode of rifting at ca. 575 Ma. However, based on geologic evidence from both North America and Africa, this event is ca. 750 Ma in North America and 800 Ma in Africa (*Caby, 1987;* Bertrand-Sarfati and others, 1987).

The earliest rift-related volcanics and plutons had a somewhat alkaline composition. Fragments of both continents formed separate smaller terranes (microcontinents) with rocks of diverse ages in the intervening ocean (Fig. 10b). An island arc was formed and was separated from Laurentia by an oceanic stretch or an inland sea that is here called the proto-Iapetus Ocean. The arc originated on the disjointed blocks of Laurentia (Fig. 10b), and possibly of Baltica and even Gondwana, as well as fragments of oceanic crust (Rast, 1980).

In late Precambrian time (ca. 600 Ma) the arc suffered a compressional event (the Avalonian orogeny). During the Avalonian orogeny the arc was caught in a compressive vise between the microcontinents and Laurentian craton, with a resultant accretion and deformation of the intervening sediments and the formerly isolated microterranes into a newly consolidated accretionary superterrane (A, Fig. 10c), which extended parallel to the edge of Baltica at least as far as present-day Poland (Ziegler, 1984). This superterrane was called Armorica by *Van der Voo* (*1982*), and the Avalon superterrane was a part of it. A late Precambrian compressional orogenic episode (580 to 620 Ma) is also widely recorded from regions to the east of the West African craton (Bertrand-Sarfati and others, 1987). To the north of that craton in Morocco the lower Infracambrian (*Michard, 1976, 1978*) crust was formed. *Schenk* (*1978*) and Piqué (1983) pointed out the similarity of the lower Infracambrian volcanogenic and sedimentary rocks of Morocco to Precambrian rock of the Avalon superterrane of Canada. It is thus suggested that the ca. 600-Ma consolidation produced a unified Avalonian-Armorican terrane (c.f., Rast and Skehan, 1983; Fig. 10c). The late Precambrian Avalonian-type volcanicity of Morocco was succeeded by Cambro-Ordovician deposits with Ordovician faunas more closely related to Florida rather than to the rest of the eastern U.S. Avalonian superterrane. Hence the Tallahassee-Suwannee terrane is now accepted as a former part of the West African region (Dallmeyer, 1987) that became isolated on the American side during the Mesozoic split of Pangaea.

Latest Precambrian–earliest Cambrian time saw the splitting of Armorica (570 Ma) with a resultant generation of several oceanic and continental blocks (Fig. 10d). It is quite possible that in the process of late Precambrian fragmentation Armorica was broken into several large blocks, of which that involving the Avalon superterrane of the British Isles, Newfoundland, and New Brunswick–Nova Scotia was only one large block, while the Carolinas formed another; moreover, the block that is now the Tallahassee-Suwannee terrane remained adherent to the West African craton. Within Armorica, and possibly north Africa, there were large grabens generated, such as the Welsh graben (geosyncline of *Jones, 1938*) and possibly one in which sediments of the Meguma terrane accumulated (Schenk, 1983); the latter may have formed in the proto-Tethys during the separation of Armorica from Gondwana (Africa and South America). However, the original provenance of the Meguma is highly disputable (Schenk, 1981).

One of the new oceans that was formed between Laurentia and Avalon superterrane was the Iapetus. Within it, in Cambrian and Early Ordovician time, island arcs developed and collided with the North American continent, resulting in the Penobscottian and Taconian orogenic episodes. Sturt (1984), in Norway, deciphered a Cambro-Ordovician (530 to 490 Ma) collision of an arc with Baltica (Finnmarkian orogeny), which produced nappes accompanied by ophiolites. The symmetrical Finnmarkian-Penobscottian event represents the first phase of the closure of the Iapetus Ocean. There is no indication in Norway of the Taconian orogeny, which generates obduction onto North America (Stockmal and others, 1987).

The split of Armorica resulted not only in the formation of the Iapetus Ocean, but also the separation of Armorica by the Rheic Ocean where the mid-European Caledonides were formed. Ziegler (1984) considers it as a branch of a broader ocean known as the proto-Tethys. The history of the Appalachians during Cambrian to Devonian time is much influenced by the opening and closing of the Iapetus Ocean (*McKerrow, 1982*).

The Iapetus Ocean effectively closed when a volcanic arc terrane collided with the Laurentian craton. This is recognized in the United States and Canada, but not in England, Ireland, or Scandinavia. Taconian events in the central and southern Appalachians (Lash, 1987) suggest that Iapetus may have closed by the subduction of the oceanic part of the North American plate (c.f., Fig. 7A). Williams (1979) also suggested this for Newfoundland, and lately Hutton and Murphy (1987) proposed Ordovician closure in the Southern Uplands of Scotland and the cessation of arc activity on either side of the closing ocean. Elders (1987), however, suggests that very large sinistral strike-slip displacements occurred between Caradocian and Early Devonian times, because of oblique subduction of the Iapetus Ocean under the Laurentian margin. This direction of subduction is contrary to that normally accepted for the northern Appalachians. He claims that granitic boulders from Newfoundland exist in Scottish Paleozoic conglomerates. The presence of Grenville granitic rocks in County Mayo, Ireland (Winchester and Max, 1987), indicates the proximity of northern Ireland to Laurentia at some time since the Precambrian. In Scandinavia, however, Scandian (Late Silurian) orogeny is widely recognized (Sturt and others, 1975; Roberts and Gee, 1985), and because a parallel event is recorded from Greenland (*Escher and Watt, 1976*), it is clear that the Iapetus Ocean there did not close until the end of Silurian time (Caledonian orogeny). Thus the Taconian orogeny produced a partial closing of the Iapetus Ocean, but there were still large areas of ocean remaining (Fig. 10e).

Rast and Stringer (*1980*) suggested that post-Taconian (Silurian) deposition in North America began in depressions as a result of post-Taconian rifting. A similar idea has been advanced by Osberg and others (1989) as one alternative explanation for the Acadian orogeny of the northern Appalachians. The other explanation was that the Acadian orogeny was caused by the

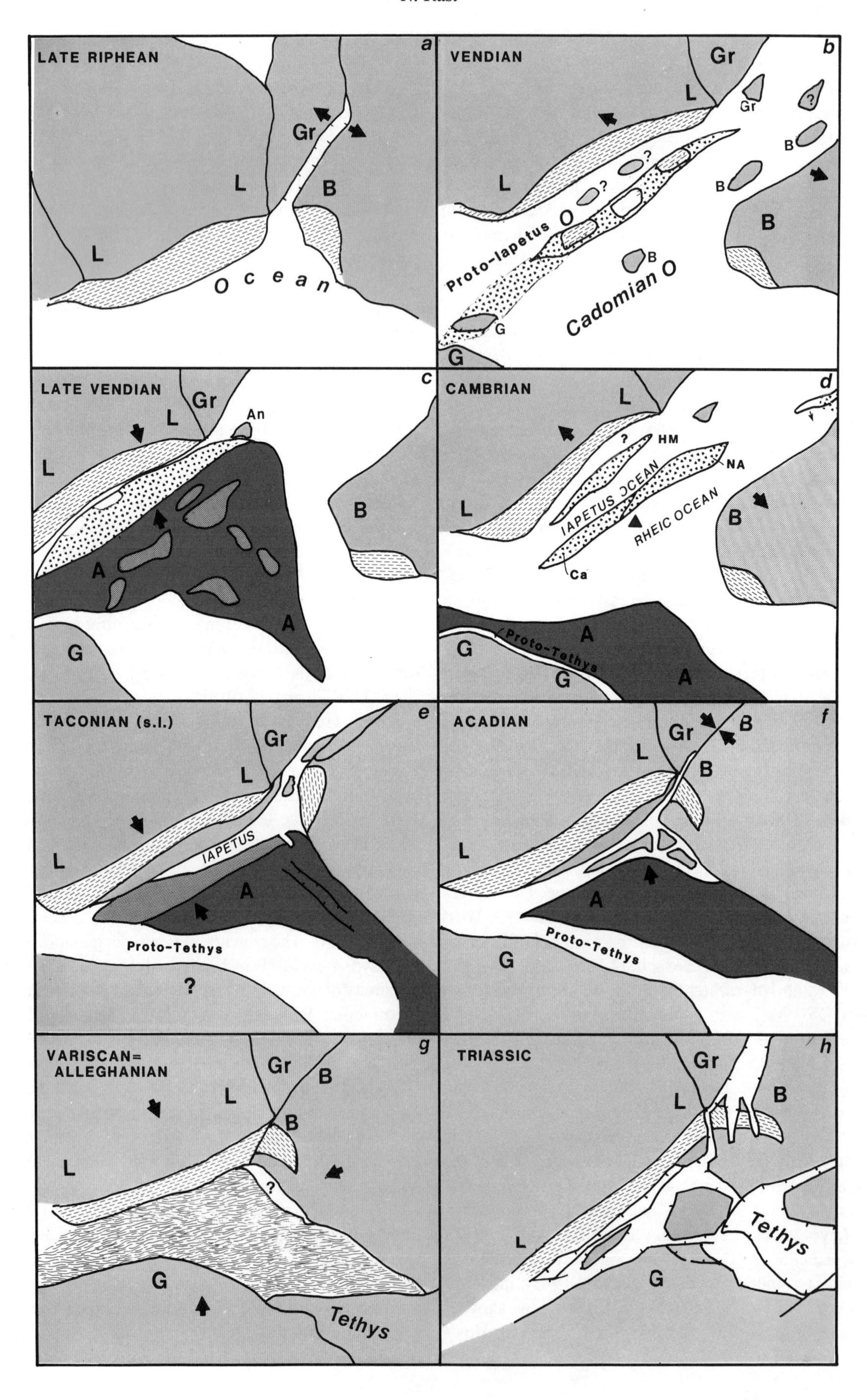

LATE RIPHEAN
a
Gr
L
B
L
Ocean
VENDIAN
b
Gr
L
Gr
?
B
B
L
B
Proto-lapetus O
Cadomian O
B
G
G
LATE VENDIAN
c
Gr
L
An
L
B
A
A
G
CAMBRIAN
d
L
?
HM
NA
L
IAPETUS OCEAN
RHEIC OCEAN
B
Ca
A
G
Proto-Tethys
G
A
TACONIAN (s.l.)
e
Gr
L
IAPETUS
L
A
Proto-Tethys
?
ACADIAN
f
Gr
B
L
B
L
A
Proto-Tethys
G
VARISCAN=
ALLEGHANIAN
g
Gr
B
L
B
L
?
G
Tethys
TRIASSIC
h
Gr
L
B
L
Tethys
G

closure of the Rheic Ocean. Rast (1988) has proposed that the Acadian orogeny resulted from the collision of blocks caught up among Laurentia, Baltica, and Gondwana (Fig. 10f). Autran and Cogné (1980) and *Ziegler (1982)* consider that there may be two separate events, Caledonian (end-Silurian) and Acadian or Ligerian (Early to medial Devonian). In Greenland, Scandinavia, the British Isles, and Ireland, Caledonian orogeny is recognized as end-Silurian, although signs of a possible but local Acadian event are claimed from Anglesey (Bevins and others, 1986). In Scandinavia, late post-Scandian events are recorded by Roberts and Gee (1985). Yet, all of the true Devonian-"Acadian" manifestations in northern Europe are slight. In the United States and Canada, Silurian events, such as the Salinic unconformity in New England (Hatch, 1982), are localized and feeble. In Brittany, it appears that Devonian (Acadian) orogenic events are widespread and are broadly contemporaneous with those of North America. Thus it is possible that the Acadian orogenic belt of North America continues not into England but into France (*Rast and Skehan, 1986;* Fig. 11). This is an old problem raised by *Termier (1914)*, and the last word has not been said on it. In conclusion, it seems that the Iapetus Ocean was closed mainly in end-Silurian time, and the Rheic Ocean by Early to medial Devonian, giving rise to the Old Red Sandstone continent.

The advent of Carboniferous sedimentation over parts of Europe, North Africa, and North America presaged the initiation of the Variscan-Alleghanian orogenic cycle (Rast, 1984, 1988), which culminated in Permian time to generate the supercontinent Pangaea. This cycle caused a complete closure of all the oceanic domains between Europe, North America, and Africa; it also caused the amalgamation of all intervening Avalonian terranes, as well as the Meguma, into the Variscan orogen (Fig. 10g). In North America (Cook and others, 1979; Hatcher, 1987) and Europe (Matte, 1986), thrusting transported remnants of pre-

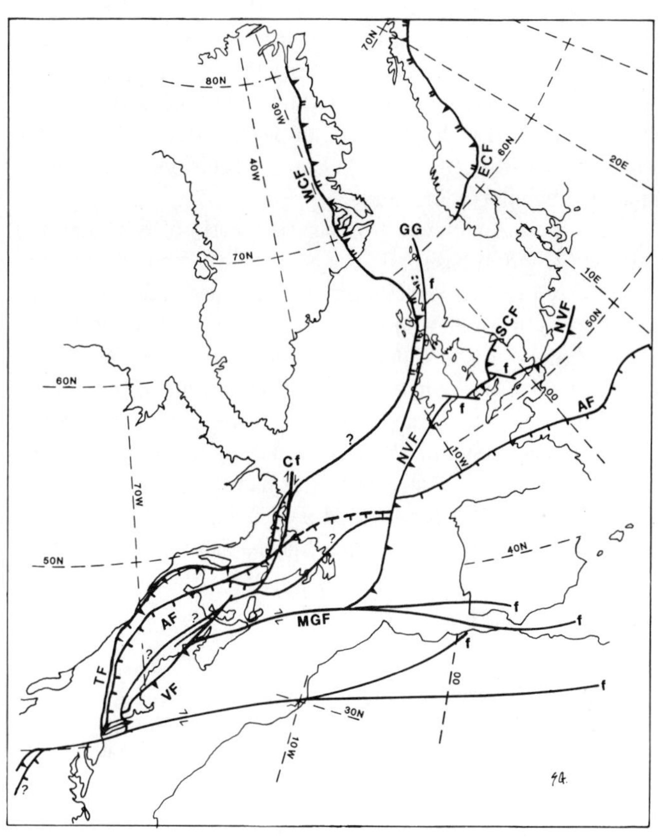

Figure 11. The fit of tectonic relationships across the Atlantic Ocean. Thrust fronts are indicated by teeth against which upper plate has moved. From north to south: ECF, eastern Caledonian front; WCF, western Caledonian front; SCF, southern Caledonian front; NVF, northern Variscan front; VF, Variscan front of North America; AF, Acadian front; TF, Taconian front. Transcurrent-transform faults indicated by f: GG, Great Glen fault; Cf, Cabot fault; MGF, Minas Geofracture (Cobequid-Chedabucto fault zone). After Rast (1988); Autran and Cogné (1980); Lefort and Haworth (*1984*).

Figure 10. Diagrammatic (topological) development of the Appalachian belt with palinspastic inferences. Continental domains in red: A, Armorica; B, Baltica; G, Gondwana; GR, Greenland; L, Laurentia; AN, Anglesey. Oceanic domains, blank. Fragments of these masses are denoted by smaller, identical letters. Dashes, Grenville belt and its fragments; solid triangles, volcanic arcs; flow lines, Variscan-Alleghanian orogenic belt; black lines, faults and sutures. Consolidated cratons unornamented; questionable domains, ?; rifted margins ticked toward the oceans. Note: for reference the Grenville belt is indicated in all diagrams, but completely consolidated terranes considered as continental are shown as such. Directions of movement of continental massifs are shown by black arrows.

a, 800 to 700 Ma late Riphean rifting; b, 700 to 630 Ma Vendian continuation of early rifting formation of continental fragments (terranes) and generation of Avalon island arcs on a diverse, partly oceanic partly continental basement; c, ~600 Ma, late Vendian Avalonian-Cadomian orogeny closing the proto-Iapetus Ocean and much of the Cadomian Ocean. Consolidation of Armorica into a large superterrane from preexisting fragments, possible island arcs, etc.; d, Late Precambrian–Early Cambrian rifting, splitting of Avalon superterrane (NA) and possibly of Hurricane Mountain (HM) and Carolinas (Ca) superterranes from Armorica and formation of the Iapetus, Rheic, and proto-Tethys Oceans joining with one branch of the last in a triple junction (▲). Armorica was separated from Gondwana by a narrow oceanic stretch, the future proto-Tethys. Arrows indicate direction of migration of Penobscottian arcs. e, Taconian partial closing of the Iapetus Ocean in the north, and collision and consolidation of terranes in the south, with formation of rifts in Armorica; f, Caledonian closure of the Iapetus Ocean between Greenland and Laurentia and beginnings of the Acadian (Ligerian) orogeny; g, Variscan-Alleghanian formation of Pangaea and intervening consolidation of the Variscan orogen; h, Triassic splitting.

viously orogenically deformed rocks to the west in North America and to the north in Europe (Fig. 11). The transport was complex, involving polyphase tectonic and metamorphic events. The magnitude of transport was so large that Pindell and Dewey (1982) suggested widespread crustal delamination (c.f., Phinney and Roy-Chowdhury, 1989). In Europe, collisional events were separated by intervening rifting.

In North America the Narragansett basin of New England and the Stellarton basin of Nova Scotia have been attributed to large transcurrent movements that accompanied and followed the thrusting. Some of these faults may have been reactivated Acadian structures. Even though the proposed Late Devonian–Carboniferous, large, sinistral strike-slip faults in North America and Britain have now been rejected (Kent and Opdyke, 1985), evidence is accruing for Taconian strike-slip faults suggested by *Hutton (1987)* from Britain, and Acadian large strike-slip faults claimed by *Ziegler (1982)* and Ferrill and Thomas (1988). Strike-slip faults transverse to the Alleghanian tectonic trend are known and established, and at least one has been studied in detail (Eisbacher, 1970; Keppie, 1982; Mawer and White, 1987) and others suggested (Rast, 1984). These faults partly coincide with the boundaries of salients and recesses, although trend-parallel faults advocated by Webb (1969) in the northern Appalachians are also coming to light in the southern Appalachians (Edelman and others, 1987). These phenomena imply that major orogenies are complex and are associated with compressive transpressive and transcurrent movements.

The post-Permocarboniferous volcanic and sedimentary events in the Appalachians were essentially related to the opening (Fig. 10h) of the Atlantic Ocean (McHone and Butler, 1984; Manspeizer, 1988). The process of reactivation of Alleghanian thrust faults is now widely discussed, and in some cases explicit geophysical evidence offered (Ratcliffe and others, 1986). By Early Triassic time the Appalachian chain clearly reached maturity and started breaking apart in response to Mesozoic rifting.

SELECTED REFERENCES*

Abbott, R. N., Jr., and Raymond, L. A., 1984, The Ashe metamorphic suite, northwest of North Carolina; Metamorphism and observations on geologic history: American Journal of Science, v. 284, p. 350–375.

Aleinikoff, J. J., Moench, R. H., and Lyons, J. B., 1985, Carboniferous U-Pb age of the Sebago batholith, southwestern Maine: Geological Society of America Bulletin, v. 69, p. 990–996.

Ando, C. J., Cook, F. A., Oliver, J. E., Brown, L. D., and Kaufman, S., 1983, Crustal geometry of the Appalachian orogen from seismic reflection studies, *in* Hatcher, R. D., Williams, H., and Zietz, I., eds., Contributions to the tectonics and geophysics of mountain chains: Geological Society of America Memoir 158, p. 83–102.

Autran, A., and Cogné, J., 1980, La zone interne de l'orogene varisque dans l'ouest de la France et sa place dans le developpement de la chaine hercynienne: 26th International Geological Congress in Paris, Colloque C. 6, p. 90–11.

Bally, A. W., Gordy, P. L., and Stewart, G. A., 1966, Structure, seismic data, and orogenic evolution of southern Canadian Rockies: Canadian Petroleum Geology Bulletin, v. 14, p. 337–381.

Bartholomew, M. J., 1983, Palinspastic reconstruction of the Grenville terrane in the Blue Ridge geologic province, southern and central Appalachians, U.S.A.: Geological Journal, v. 18, p. 241–254.

——, 1987, Structural evolution of the Pulaski thrust system, southwestern Virginia: Geological Society of America Bulletin, v. 99, p. 491–510.

Bartholomew, M. J., and Lewis, S. E., 1984, Evolution of Grenville massifs in the Blue Ridge geological province, southern and central Appalachians, *in* Bartholomew, M. J., ed., The Grenville event in the Appalachians and related topics: Geological Society of America Special Paper 194, p. 229–254.

Beaumont, C., Quinlan, G. M., and Hamilton, J., 1987, The Alleghanian orogeny and its relationship to the evolution of the eastern interior, North America, *in* Beaumont, C., and Tankard, A. J., eds., Sedimentary basins and basin-forming mechanisms: Canadian Society of Petroleum Geologists Memoir 12, p. 425–446.

Belt, E. S., 1968, Post-Acadian rifts and related facies, eastern Canada, *in* Zen, E-an, White, W. S., Hadley, J. B., and Thompson, J. B., Jr., eds., Studies of Appalachian Geology; Northern and Maritime: New York, Interscience, p. 95–113.

*A full listing of references, including those shown in italics in the text, is on a microfiche accompanying this volume.

Bertrand-Sarfati, J., Morissine-Pouchkine, A., and Caby, R., 1987, Les correlations du Proterozoique au Cambrien en Afrique de l'Ouest—nouvelle interpretation géodynamique: Geological Society of France Bulletin, ser. 8, v. 3, p. 855–865.

Bevins, R. E., Gibbons, W., Harris, A. L., and Kelling, G., 1986, The Caledonian rocks of Britain, *in* Fettes, D. J., and Harris, A. L., eds., Synthesis of the Caledonian Rocks of Britain: Reidel, Dortrecht, p. 1–27.

Billings, M. P., 1982, Ordovician cauldron subsidence of the Blue Hills Complex, eastern Massachusetts: Geological Society of America Bulletin, v. 93, p. 909–920.

Bird, J. M., and Dewey, J. F., 1970, Lithosphere plate–continental margin tectonics and the evolution of the Appalachian orogen: Geological Society of America Bulletin, v. 81, p. 1031–1061.

Boone, G. M., and Boudette, E. L., 1989, Accretion of the Boundary Mountains Terrane within the northern Appalachian orthotectonic zone, *in* Horton, J. W., and Rast, N., eds., Mélanges and olistostromes in the U.S. Appalachians: Geological Society of America Special Paper 228, p. 17–42.

Bosworth, W., and Vollmer, F. W., 1981, Structures of the Middle Ordovician flysch of eastern New York; Deformation of synorogenic deposits in an overthrust environment: Journal of Geology, v. 89, p. 551–568.

Bradley, D. C., 1983, Tectonics of the Acadian orogeny in New England and adjacent Canada: Journal of Geology, v. 91, p. 391–400.

Colman-Sadd, S. P., and Swinden, H. S., 1984, A tectonic window in central Newfoundland?; Geological evidence that the Appalachian Dunnage zone may be allochthonous: Canadian Journal of Earth Sciences, v. 21, p. 1349–1367.

Cook, F. A., Albaugh, D. S., Brown, L. D., Kaufman, S., Oliver, J. E., and Hatcher, R. D., 1979, Thin skinned tectonics in the crystalline southern Appalachians—COCORP Seismic-reflection profiting of the Blue Ridge and Piedmont: Geology, v. 7, p. 563–567.

Currie, K. L., 1983, Repeated basement reactivation in the northeastern Appalachians: Geological Journal, v. 18, p. 223–239.

Dallmeyer, R. D., 1978, $^{40}Ar/^{39}Ar$ ages hornblende and biotite across the Georgia Inner Piedmont—Their bearing on late Paleozoic–early Mesozoic tectonothermal history: American Journal of Science, v. 278, p. 124–149.

——, 1987, $^{40}Ar/^{39}Ar$ Age of the detrital muscovite within Lower Ordovician sandstone in the coastal plain basement of Florida—Implications for west African terrane linkages: Geology, v. 15, p. 998–1001.

——, 1988, Late Paleozoic tectonothermal evolution of the western Piedmont and eastern Blue Ridge, Georgia; Controls on the chronology of terrane accretion and transport in the southern Appalachian orogen: Geological Society of America Bulletin, v. 100, p. 702–713.

Dallmeyer, R. D., and Gibbons, W., 1987, The age of blueschist metamorphism in Anglesey, North Wales—evidence from $^{40}Ar/^{39}Ar$ mineral dates of the Penmynydd schists: Geological Society of London Journal, v. 144, p. 843–852.

Dallmeyer, R. D., and Keppie, J. D., 1987, Polyphase late Paleozoic tectonothermal evolution of the southwestern Meguma Terrane, Nova Scotia—evidence from $^{40}Ar/^{39}Ar$ mineral ages: Canadian Journal of Earth Science, v. 24, p. 1242.

Dallmeyer, R. D., and Van Breeman, O., 1981, Rb-Sr whole-rock and $^{40}Ar/^{39}Ar$ mineral ages of the Togus and Hallowell quartz monzonite and Three Miles Pond granodiorite plutons, south-central Maine; Their bearing on post-Acadian cooling history: Contributions to Mineralogy and Petrology, v. 78, p. 61–73.

Dallmeyer, R. D., Wright, J. E., Secor, D. T., Jr., and Snoke, A. W., 1986, Character of the Alleghanian orogeny in the southern Appalachians, Part II, Geochronological constraints on the tectonothermal evolution of the eastern Piedmont in South Carolina: Geological Society of America Bulletin, v. 97, p. 1329–1344.

Dewey, J. F., and Burke, V.B.S., 1973, Tibetan, Variscan and Precambrian basement reactiviation, products of continental collision: Journal of Geology, v. 81, p. 683–692.

Dewey, J. F., Kennedy, M. J., and Kidd, W.S.F., 1983, A geotraverse through the Appalachians of northern Newfoundland, *in* Rast, N., and Delany, F. M., eds., Profiles of orogenic belts: American Geophysical Union Geodynamics Series, v. 10, p. 205–242.

Drake, A. A., Jr., Sinha, A. K., Laird, J., and Guy, R. E., 1989, The Taconic orogen, *in* Hatcher, R. D., Jr., Thomas, W. A., and Viele, G. W., eds., The Appalachian–Ouachita orogen in the United States: Boulder, Colorado, Geological Society of America, The Geology of North America, v. F-2 (in press).

Edelman, S. H., 1988, Ophiolite generation and emplacement by rapid subduction hinge retreat on a continent-bearing plate: Geology, v. 16, p. 311–313.

Edelman, S. H., Liu, A., and Hatcher, R. D., Jr., 1987, The Brevard zone in South Carolina and adjacent areas—an Alleghanian orogen-scale dextral shear zone reactivated as a thrust fault: Journal of Geology, v. 95, p. 793–806.

Eisbacher, G. H., 1970, Deformation mechanics of mylonitic rocks and fractured granites in Cobequid Mountains, Nova Scotia, Canada: Geological Society of America Bulletin, v. 81, p. 2009–2020.

Elders, C. F., 1987, The provenance of granite boulders in conglomerates of the northern and central belts of the Southern Uplands of Scotland: Geological Society of London Journal, v. 144, p. 853–863.

Ettensohn, F. R., 1987, Rates of relative plate motion during the Acadian orogeny based on the spatial distribution of black shales: Journal of Geology, v. 95, p. 572–582.

Faill, R. T., 1985, Evolving concepts of the central and southern Appalachians, *in* Drake, E. T., and Jordan, W. M., eds., Geologists and ideas; A history of North American geology: Boulder, Colorado, Geological Society of America, Centennial Special Volume 1, p. 19–46.

Farrar, S. S., 1984, The Goochland granulite terrane; Remobilized Grenville basement in the eastern Virginia Piedmont, *in* Bartholomew, M. J., ed., The Grenville event in the Appalachians and related topics: Geological Society of America Special Paper 194, p. 215–227.

Ferrill, B. A., and Thomas, W. A., 1988, Acadian dextral transpression and synorogenic sedimentary succession in the Appalachians: Geology, v. 16, p. 577–672.

Friedman, G. M., 1987, Vertical movements of the crust—Case histories from the northern Appalachian basin: Geology, v. 15, p. 1130–1133.

Fullagar, P. D., and Butler, J. R., 1979, 325 to 265 m.y. old granitic plutons in the Piedmont of the southeastern Appalachians: American Journal of Science, v. 279, p. 161–185.

Fyffe, L. R., and Barr, S. M., 1986, Petrochemistry and tectonic significance of Carboniferous volcanic rocks in New Brunswick: Canadian Journal of Earth Sciences, v. 23, p. 1243–1256.

Geiser, P., and Engelder, T., 1983, The distribution of layer parallel shortening fabrics in the Appalachian foreland of New York and Pennsylvania—Evidence for two non-coaxial phases of the Alleghanian orogeny, *in* Hatcher, R. D., Williams, H., and Zietz, I., eds., Contributions to the tectonics and geophysics of mountain chains: Geological Society of America Memoir 158, p. 161–176.

Geiser, P. A., Snoke, A. W., Mosher, S., Hatcher, R. D., Jr., Thomas, W. A., and Wiltschko, D. V., 1989, The Alleghanian orogen, *in* Hatcher, R. D., Jr., Thomas, W. A., and Viele, G. W., eds., The Appalachian and Ouachita Regions in the United States: Boulder, Colorado, Geological Society of America, The Geology of North America, v. F-2 (in press).

Gibbons, W., 1987, Menai Strait fault system—An early Caledonian terrane boundary in north Wales: Geology, v. 15, p. 744–747.

Glover, L., III, Speer, J. A., Russell, G. S., and Farrar, S. S., 1983, Ages of regional metamorphism and ductile deformation in the central and southern Appalachians: Lithos, v. 16, p. 223–245.

Goldberg, S. A., Butler, J. R., and Fullagar, P. D., 1986, The Baskerville dike swarm; Geochronology and petrogenesis of Late Proterozoic basaltic magmatism in the Southern Appalachian Blue Ridge: American Journal of Science, v. 286, p. 403–430.

Hack, J. T., 1982, Physiographic divisions and differential uplift in the Piedmont and Blue Ridge: U.S. Geological Survey Professional Paper 1265, 49 p.

Harris, C. W., and Glover, L., III, 1988, The regional extent of the ca. 600 Ma Virgilina deformation—Implications for stratigraphic correlation in the Carolina terrane: Geological Society of America Bulletin, v. 100, p. 282–298.

Harris, L. D., and Bayer, K. C., 1979, Sequential development of the Appalachian orogen above a master décollement—a hypothesis: Geology, v. 7, p. 568–572.

Hatch, N. L., Jr., 1982, Taconian line in western New England and its implications to Paleozoic tectonic history, *in* St-Julien, P., and Beland, J., eds., Major structural zones and faults of the northern Appalachians: Geological Association of Canada Special Paper 24, p. 67–85.

Hatcher, R. D., Jr., 1983, Basement massifs in the Appalachians; Their role in deforation during the Appalachian orogenesis: Geological Journal, v. 18, p. 255–266.

——, 1987, Tectonics of the southern and central Appalachian internides: Annual Review of Earth and Planetary Sciences, v. 15, p. 337–362.

Hatcher, R. D., Jr., Thomas, W. A., and Viele, G. E., 1989, The Appalachian–Ouachita orogen in the United States: Boulder, Colorado, Geological Society of America, The Geology of North America, v. F-2 (in press).

Haworth, R. T., and Miller, H. G., 1982, The structure of Paleozoic oceanic rocks beneath Notre Dame Bay, Newfoundland, *in* St-Julien, D., and Beland, J., eds., Major Structural Zones and Faults of the Northern Appalachians: Geological Association of Canada Special Paper 24, p. 149–173.

Hiscott, R. N., Pickering, K. T., and Beeden, D. R., 1986, Progressive filling of a confined Middle Ordovician foreland basin associated with the Taconic orogeny, Quebec, Canada: International Association of Sedimentologists Special Publication 8, p. 309–325.

Horton, J. W., Jr., Zietz, I., and Neathery, T. L., 1984, Truncation of the Appalachian Piedmont beneath the Coastal Plain of Alabama—Evidence from new magnetic data: Geology, v. 12, p. 51–55.

Horton, J. W., Blake, D. E., Wylie, A. S., and Stoddard, E. F., 1986, Metamorphosed mélange terrane in the eastern Piedmont of North Carolina: Geology, v. 14, p. 551–555.

Hutchinson, D. R., Klitgord, K. D., Lee, M. W., and Trehu, A. M., 1988, U.S.G.S. Deep seismic reflection profile across the Gulf of Maine: Geological Society of America Bulletin, v. 100, p. 172–184.

Hutton, H. W., and Murphy, F. C., 1987, The Silurian of the Southern Uplands and Ireland as a successor basin to the end-Ordovician closure of Iapetus: Geological Society of London Journal, v. 144, p. 765–772.

Irving, E., and McGlynn, J. C., 1976, Proterozoic magnetostratigraphy and the tectonic evolution of Laurentia: Royal Society of London Philosophical

Transactions, v. A280, p. 433–468.

Jacobi, R. D., 1981, Peripheral bulge—a causal mechanism for the Lower/Middle Ordovician unconformity along the western margin of the northern Appalachians: Earth and Planetary Science Letters, v. 56, p. 245–251.

Karlstrom, K. E., Van der Pluijm, B. A., and Williams, P. F., 1982, Structural interpretation of the eastern Notre Dame Bay area, Newfoundland—regional post-Middle Silurian thrusting and a symmetrical folding: Canadian Journal of Earth Sciences, v. 19, p. 2325–2341.

Kent, D. V., and Opdyke, N. D., 1985, Multicomponent magnetization from the Mississippian Mauch Chunk Formation of the central Appalachians and their tectonic implications: Journal of Geophysical Research, v. 90, p. 5371–5383.

Keppie, J. D., 1982, The Minas, geofracture, *in* St-Julien, D., and Beland, J., eds., Major structural zones and faults of the northern Appalachians: Geological Association of Canada Special Paper 24, p. 263–280.

—— , 1985, The Appalachian collage, *in* Gee, D. G., and Sturt, B. A., eds, The Caledonide orogen; Scandinavia and related areas: Chichester, John Wiley and Sons, p. 1217–1226.

Krogh, T. E., Strong, D. F., O'Brien, S. J., and Papezik, V. S., 1988, Precise U-Pb zircon dates from the Avalon terrane in Newfoundland: Canadian Journal of Earth Sciences, v. 25, p. 442–453.

Lash, G. G., 1987, Geodynamic evolution of the Lower Paleozoic central Appalachian foreland basin, *in* Beaumont, C., and Tankard, A. J., eds., Sedimentary basins and basin-forming mechanisms: Canadian Society of Petroleum Geologists Memoir 12, p. 413–423.

Levine, J. R., 1986, Deep burial of coal-bearing strata, Anthracite region, Pennsylvania—Sedimentation or tectonics?: Geology, v. 14, p. 577–580.

Lindsey, J. F., Korsch, R. J., and Wilford, J. R., 1987, Timing the breakup of a Proterozoic supercontinent—evidence from Australian intracratonic basin: Geology, v. 15, p. 1061–1064.

Lux, D. R., and Guidotti, C. V., 1985, Evidence for extensive Hercynian metamorphism in western Maine: Geology, v. 13, p. 696–700.

Lyons, J. B., 1979, Stratigraphy, structure and plutonism east of the Bronson Hill anticlinorium, New Hampshire, *in* Skehan, J. W., and Osberg, P. H., eds., The Caledonides in the U.S.A.: Geological excursions in the northeast Appalachians: Weston, Massachusetts, Weston Observatory, p. 73–92.

Manspeizer, W., 1988, Triassic–Jurassic rifting and opening of the Atlantic—An overview, *in* Manspeizer, W., ed., Triassic–Jurassic rifting—Continental breakup and the origin of the Atlantic passive margins: New York, Elsevier Science Publishers, p. 52–59.

Matte, P., 1986, Tectonics and plate tectonics model for the Variscan Belt of Europe: Tectonophysics, v. 126, p. 329–374.

Mawer, C. K., and White, J. C., 1987, Sense of displacement on the Cobequid–Chedabucto fault system, Nova Scotia, Canada: Canadian Journal of Earth Sciences: v. 24, p. 217–223.

McConnell, K. I., and Costello, J. D., 1984, Basement-cover rock relationships along the western edge of Blue Ridge Thrust sheet in Georgia, *in* Bartholomew, M. J., ed., The Grenville Event in the Appalachians and related topics: Geological Society of America Special Paper 194, p. 263–280.

McCutcheon, S. R., and Robinson, P. T., 1987, Geological constraints on the genesis of the Maritimes basin, Atlantic Canada, *in* Beaumont, C., and Tankard, A. J., eds., Sedimentary basins and basin-forming mechanisms: Canadian Society of Petroleum Geologists Memoir 12, p. 287–298.

McHone, J. G., and Butler, J. R., 1984, Mesozoic igneous provinces of New England and the opening of the North Atlantic Ocean: Geological Society of America Bulletin, v. 95, p. 757–765.

Mills, H. H., Brakenridge, G. R., Jacobson, R. B., Newell, W. L., Pavich, M. J., and Pomeroy, J. S., 1987, Appalachian mountains and plateaus, *in* Gray, W. L., ed., Geomorphic Systems of North America: Boulder, Colorado, Geological Society of America, Centennial Special Volume 2, p. 5–50.

Misra, K. C., and Keller, F. B., 1978, Ultramafic bodies in the southern Appalachians—A review: American Journal of Science, v. 278, p. 389–418.

Misra, K. C., and McSween, H. Y., Jr., 1984, Mafic rocks of the southern Appalachians—A review: American Journal of Science, v. 284, p. 294–318.

Mosher, S., and Rast, N., 1984, The deformation and metamorphism of Carboniferous rocks, in Maritime Canada and New England, *in* Hutton, D.H.W., and Sanderson, D. J., eds., Variscan tectonics of the North Atlantic region: Geological Society of London Special Publication 14, p. 233–244.

Mussman, W. J., and Read, J. F., 1986, Sedimentology and development of a passive to convergent-margin unconformity; Middle Orodovician Knox unconformity, Virginia Appalachians: Geological Society of America Bulletin, v. 97, p. 282–295.

Nance, R. D., 1987, Model for the Precambrian evolution of the Avalon terrane in southern New Brunswick, Canada: Geology, v. 15, p. 753–756.

Neathery, T. L., and Thomas, W. T., 1983, Geodynamics transect of the Appalachian orogen in Alabama, *in* Rast, N., and Dalany, F. M., eds., Profiles of orogenic belts: American Geophysical Union Geodynamics Series, v. 10, p. 301–308.

Neuman, R. B., 1967, Bedrock geology of the Shin Pond and Stacyville quadrangles, Penobscot County, Maine: U.S. Geological Survey Professional Paper 524–I, p. 1–137.

O'Brien, S. J., Wardle, R. J., and King, A. F., 1983, The Avalon Zone—a pan-African terrane in the Appalachian orogen of Canada: Geological Journal, v. 18, p. 195–222.

Odom, A. L., and Fullagar, P. D., 1984, Rb-Sr whole-rock and inherited zircon ages of the plutonic suite of the Crossnore Complex, southern Appalachians, and their implications regarding the time of opening of the Iapetus Ocean, *in* Bartholomew, M. J., ed., The Grenville event in the Appalachians and related topics: Geological Society of America Special Paper 194, p. 255–280.

Olszewski, W. J., Jr., and Gaudette, H. E., 1982, Age of the Brookville Gneiss and associated rocks, southeastern New Brunswick: Canadian Journal of Earth Sciences, v. 19, p. 2158–2166.

Osberg, D. H., Tull, J. F., Robinson, P., Hon, R., and Butler, J. R., 1989, The Acadian orogeny, *in* Hatcher, R. D., Jr., Thomas, W. A., and Viele, G. W., eds., The Appalachian–Ouachita orogen in the United States: Boulder, Colorado, Geological Society of America, The Geology of North America, v. F-2 (in press).

Palmer, A. R., 1971, The Cambrian of the Appalachian and eastern New England regions, eastern United States, *in* Holland, C. H., ed., Cambrian of the New World: New York, Interscience, p. 169–217.

—— , 1983, The Decade of North American Geology 1983 geologic time scale: Geology, v. 11, p. 503–504.

Pavlides, L., 1981, The Central Virginia volcanic-plutonic belt; An island arc of Cambrian(?) age: U.S. Geological Survey Professional Paper 1231–A, 34 p.

—— , 1989, Early Paleozoic composite mélange terrane and its origin, Central Appalachian Piedmont, Virginia and Maryland, *in* Horton, J. W., Jr., and Rast, N., eds., Mélanges and olistostromes of the U.S. Appalachians: Geological Society of America Special Paper 228, p. 137–193.

Phinney, R. A., and Roy-Chowdhury, K., 1989, Reflection seismic studies of crustal structure in the eastern United States, *in* Pakiser, L. C., and Mooney, W. D., eds., Geophysical Framework of the United States: Geological Society of America Memoir 172 (in press).

Pindell, J., and Dewey, J. F., 1982, Permo–Triassic reconstruction of western Pangea and the evolution of the Gulf of Mexico/Caribbean region: Tectonics, v. 1, p. 179–211.

Piper, J.D.A., 1987, Paleomagnetism and the continental crust: New York-Toronto, Open University Press, Halsted Press, John Wiley and Sons, 434 p.

Piqué, A., 1983, Structural domains of the Hercynian belt in Morocco, *in* Schenk, P. E., ed., Regional trends in the geology of the Appalachian–Caledonian–Hercynian–Mauritanide orogen: Dordrecht, D. Reidel Publishing Company, p. 339–346.

Quinn, A. W., 1971, Bedrock geology of Rhode Island: U.S. Geological Survey Bulletin 1295, p. 1–65.

Rankin, D. W., 1975, The Continental margin of eastern North America in the southern Appalachians—The opening and closing of the proto-Atlantic Ocean: American Journal of Science, v. 275–A, p. 298–336.

Rankin, D. W., Drake, A. A., Jr., Glover, L., III, Goldsmith, R., Hall, L. M.,

Murray, D. P., Ratcliffe, N. M., Read, J. F., Secor, D. T., Jr., and Stanley, R. S., 1989, Pre-orogenic terranes, *in* Hatcher, R. D., Jr., Thomas, W. A., and Viele, G. W., eds., The Appalachian-Ouachita orogen in the United States: Boulder, Colorado, Geological Society of America, The Geology of North America, v. F-2 (in press).

Rast, N., 1979, Precambrian meta-diabases of southern New Brunswick—The opening of the Iapetus Ocean?: Tectonophysics, v. 59, p. 127–137.

—— , 1980, The Avalonian plate in the northern Appalachians and Caledonides, *in* Wones, D. R., ed., The Caledonides in the U.S.A.: Blacksburg, Virginia Polytechnic Institute and State University Department of Geological Sciences Memoir 2, p. 63–66.

—— , 1984, The Alleghanian orogeny in eastern North America, *in* Hutton, D.H.W., and Sanderson, D. J., eds., Variscan tectonics of the North Atlantic region: Geological Society of London Special Publication 14, p. 197–218.

—— , 1988, Variscan Alleghanian orogen, *in* Manspeizer, W., ed., Triassic-Jurassic rifting; Continental breakup and the origin of the Atlantic passive margins: Amsterdam-New York, Elsevier Science Publishers, p. 1–27.

Rast, N., and Dickson, W. L., 1982, The Pocologan mylonite zone, *in* St-Julien, P., and Beland, J., eds., Major structural zones and faults of the northern Appalachians: Geological Association of Canada Special Paper 24, p. 249–261.

Rast, N., and Grant, R. H., 1973, Transatlantic correlation of the Variscan-Appalachian orogeny: American Journal of Science, v. 273, p. 572–579.

Rast, N., and Horton, J. W., Jr., 1989, Mélanges and olistostromes in the Appalachians of the United States and mainland Canada; An assessment, *in* Horton, J. W., Jr., and Rast, N., eds., Mélanges and olistostromes of the U.S. Appalachians: Geological Society of America Special Paper 228, p. 1–15.

Rast, N., and Kohles, K. M., 1986, The origin of the Ocoee Supergroup: American Journal of Science, v. 286, p. 593–616.

Rast, N., and Skehan, J. W., 1983, The evolution of the Avalonian Plate: Tectonophysics, v. 100, p. 257–286.

Rast, N., O'Brien, B. H., and Wardle, R. J., 1976, Relationships between Precambrian and Lower Paleozoic rocks of the "Avalon Platform" in New Brunswick, the Northeast Appalachians, and the British Isles: Tectonophysics, v. 30, p. 315–338.

Rast, N., Grant, R. H., Parker, J.S.D., and Teng, H. C., 1984, The Carboniferous succession in southern New Brunswick and its state of deformation, *in* Neuvième Congrés International de Stratigraphie et de Géologie du Carbonifère, Comptes Rendus, Washington, Champaign-Urbana, v. 3, p. 13–22.

Rast, N., Skehan, J. W., and Hussey, A. M., II, 1988, The role of the Avalon superterrane (ST) in Paleozoic orogenic development of the northern Appalachians: Geological Society of America Abstracts with Programs, v. 20, p. 63–64.

Ratcliffe, N. M., 1987a, High TiO_2 metadiabase dikes of the Hudson Highlands, New York and New Jersey—Possible late Proterozoic rift rocks in the New York recess: American Journal of Science, v. 287, p. 817–850.

—— , 1987b, Basaltic rocks in the Rensselaer Plateau and Chatham slices of the Taconic allochthon—Chemistry and tectonic setting: Geological Society of America Bulletin, v. 99, p. 511–528.

Ratcliffe, N. M., Armstrong, R. L., Mose, D. G., Seneschal, R., Williams, N., and Baiamonte, M. J., 1982, Emplacement history and tectonic significance of the Cortland complex, related plutons and dike swarms in the Taconide zone of southeastern New York based on K-Ar and Rb-Sr investigations: American Journal of Science, v. 282, p. 358–390.

Ratcliffe, N. M., Burton, W. C., D'Angelo, R. M., Costain, J. K., 1986, Low-angle extensional faulting, reactivated mylonites, and seismic reflection geometry of the Newark basin margin in eastern Pennsylvania: Geology, v. 14, p. 766–770.

Rich, J. L., 1934, Mechanics of low-angle overthrust faulting as illustrated by Cumberland thrust block, Virginia, Kentucky, and Tennessee: American Association of Petroleum Geologists Bulletin, v. 18, p. 1584–1694.

Roberts, D., and Gee, D. G., 1985, An introduction to the structure of the Scandinavian Caledonides, *in* Gee, D. G., and Sturt, B. A., eds., The Caledonide Orogen—Scandinavia and Related Areas: Chichester, John Wiley and Sons, p. 55–68.

Robinson, P., Tracy, R. J., Hollocher, K. T., and Dietsch, C. W., 1982, High grade Acadian regional metamorphism in south-central Massachusetts, *in* Joesten, R., and Quarrier, S. S., eds., Guidebook for fieldtrips in Connecticut and south-central Massachusetts: 74th Annual Meeting New England Intercollegiate Geological Conference, Storrs, Connecticut, p. 289–339.

Rodgers, J., 1970, The Tectonics of the Appalachians: New York, Wiley Interscience, 271 p.

—— , 1971, The Taconic orogeny: Geological Society of America Bulletin, v. 82, p. 1141–1178.

—— , 1982, The life history of a mountain range—The Appalachians, *in* Hsü, K. J., ed., Mountain building processes: New York, Academic Press, p. 229–241.

—— , 1987, The Appalachian Geosyncline, *in* Schaer, J. P., and Rodgers, J., eds., The Anatomy of Mountain Ranges: Princeton, New Jersey, Princeton University Press, p. 241–258.

Rowley, D. B., and Kidd, W.S.F., 1981, Stratigraphic relationships and detrital composition of the Medial Ordovician flysch of western New England; Implications for the tectonic evolution of the Taconic orogeny: Journal of Geology, v. 89, p. 199–218.

Rust, B. R., 1981, Alluvial deposits and tectonic style—Devonian and Carboniferous successions in eastern Gaspé, *in* Miall, A. D., ed., Sedimentation and Tectonics in Alluvial Basins: Geological Association of Canada Special Paper 23, p. 49–76.

Sangster, A. L., and Bourne, J., 1982, Geology of the Grenville Province and regional metallogenesis of the Grenville Supergroup, *in* Hutchinson, R. W., Spence, C. D., and Franklin, J. M., eds., Precambrian Sulphide Deposits: Geological Association of Canada Special Paper 25, p. 91–125.

Schuchert, C., 1930, Orogenic times of the northern Appalachians: Geological Society of America Bulletin, v. 41, p. 701–724.

Schenk, P. E., 1981, The Meguma Zone of Nova Scotia—A remnant of western Europe, South America, or Africa?, *in* Kerr, J. M., and Ferguson, A. J., eds., Geology of the North Atlantic borderlands: Canadian Society of Petroleum Geologists Memoir 7, p. 119–148.

—— , 1983, The Meguma terrane of Nova Scotia, Canada—an aid in trans-Atlantic correlation, *in* Schenk, P. E., ed., Regional trends in the geology of the Appalachian-Caledonian-Hercynian-Mauritanide orogen: Dordecht, D. Reidel Publishing Company, p. 121–130.

Schwab, F. L., Nystuen, J. P., and Gunderson, L., 1988, Pre-Arenig evolution of the Appalachian-Caledonide orogen—Sedimentation and stratigraphy, *in* Harris, A. L., and Fettes, D. J., eds., The Caledonian-Appalachian orogen: Geological Society of London Special Publication 38, p. 75–92.

Secor, D. T., Jr., Samson, S. L., Snoke, A. W., and Palmer, A. R., 1983, Confirmation of the Carolina Slate belt as an exotic terrane: Science, v. 221, p. 649–650.

Secor, D. T., Jr., Snoke, A. W., Bramlett, K. W., Costello, O. P., and Kimbrell, O. P., 1986, Character of the Alleghanian orogeny in the southern Appalachians; Part I, Alleghanian deformation in the eastern Piedmont of South Carolina: Geological Society of America Bulletin, v. 97, p. 1319–1328.

Sinha, A. K., and Bartholomew, M. J., 1984, Evolution of the Grenville terrane in the central Virginia Appalachians, *in* Bartholomew, M. J., ed., The Grenville event in the Appalachians and related topics: Geological Society of America Special Paper 194, p. 175–186.

Skehan, J. W., Palmer, A. R., Smith, A. T., and Belt, E. S., 1978, Significance of fossiliferous Middlie Cambrian rocks of Rhode Island to the history of the Avalonian microcontinent: Geology, v. 6, p. 694–698.

Skehan, J. W., Rast, N., and Mosher, S., 1986, Paleoenvironmental and tectonic controls of sedimentation in coal-forming basins of southeastern New England, *in* Lyons, P. C., and Rice, C. L., eds., Paleoenvironmental and tectonic controls in coal-forming basins of the United States: Geological Society of America Special Paper 210, p. 9–30.

Smith, L., and Collins, J. A., 1984, Unconformities, sedimentary copper mineralization and thrust faulting in the Horton and Windsor groups, Cape Breton Island and central Nova Scotia: Neuvième Congrés International de stratigraphie et de Géologie Carbonifère, Comptes Rendus, Washington, Champaign-Urbana, v. 3, p. 105–116.

St-Julien, P., and Hubert, C., 1975, Evolution of the Taconian orogen in the Quebec Appalachians: American Journal of Science, v. 275–A, p. 337–362.

Stanley, R. S., and Ratcliffe, N. M., 1985, Tectonic synthesis of the Taconian orogeny in western New England: Geological Society of America Bulletin, v. 96, p. 1227–1250.

Stockmal, G., Colman-Sadd, S. P., Keen, C. E., O'Brien, S. J., and Quinlan, G., 1987, Collision along an irregular margin: A regional plate tectonic interpretation of the Canadian Appalachians: Canadian Journal of Earth Sciences, v. 24, p. 1098–1107.

Sturt, B. A., Pringle, J. R., and Roberts, D., 1975, Caledonian nappe sequence of Finnmark, Northern Norway, and the timing of orogenic deformation and metamorphism: Geological Society of America Bulletin, v. 86, p. 710–718.

Sturt, B. A., 1984, The accretion of ophiolitic terrains in the Scandinavian Caledonides: Geologie en Mijnbouw, v. 63, p. 201–212.

Sutter, J. F., Ratcliffe, N. M., and Mukasa, S. B., 1985, $^{40}Ar/^{39}Ar$ and K-Ar data bearing on the metamorphic and tectonic history of western New England: Geological Society of America Bulletin, v. 96, p. 123–136.

Tauvers, P. R., and Muehlberger, W. R., 1987, Is the Brunswick magnetic anomaly really the Alleghanian suture?: Tectonics, v. 6, p. 331–342.

Thomas, M. D., 1983, Tectonic significance of paired gravity anomalies in the southern and central Appalachians, *in* Hatcher, R. D., Jr., Williams, H., and Zietz, I., eds., The tectonics and geophysics of mountain chains: Geological Society of America Memoir 158, p. 113–124.

Thomas, W. A., 1977, Evolution of Appalachian salients and recesses from reentrants and promontories in the continental margin: American Journal of Science, v. 277, p. 1233–1278.

—— , 1983, Basement-cover relations in the Appalachian fold and thrust belt: Geological Journal, v. 18, p. 267–276.

Thomas, W. A., Chowns, T. M., Daniels, D. L., Neathery, T. L., Glover, L., III, and Gleason, R. J., 1989, The subsurface Appalachians beneath the Atlantic and Gulf Coastal Plains, *in* Hatcher, R. D., Jr., Thomas, W. A., and Viele, G. E., eds., The Appalachian–Ouachita orogen in the United States: Boulder, Colorado, Geological Society of America, The Geology of North America, v. F-2 (in press).

Tull, J. F., 1982, Stratigraphic framework of the Talladega Slate Belt, Alabama Appalachians, *in* Bearce, D. N., Black, W. W., Kish, S., and Tull, J. F., eds., Tectonic studies in the Talladega and Carolina Slate Belts, southern Appalachian orogen: Geological Society of America Special Paper 191, p. 3–18.

—— , 1984, Polyphase Late Paleozoic deformation in the southeastern foreland and northwestern Piedmont of the Alabama Appalachians: Journal of Structural Geology, v. 6, p. 223–234.

Upadhyay, H. D., and Neale, E.R.W., 1979, On the tectonic regimes of ophiolite genesis: Earth and Planetary Science Letters, v. 43, p. 93–102.

Van der Pluijm, B. A., 1987, Timing and spatial distribution of deformation in the Newfoundland Appalachians; a "multi-stage collision" history: Tectonophysics, v. 135, p. 15–24.

Van der Voo, R., 1988, Paleozoic paleogeography of North America, Gondwana and intervening displaced terranes—Comparisons of paleomagnetism with paleoclimatology and biogeographical patterns: Geological Society of America Bulletin, v. 100, p. 311–324.

Van Tassell, J., 1987, Upper Devonian Catskill delta margin cyclic sedimentation; Brallier, Scherr, and Foreknobs formations of Virginia and West Virginia: Geological Society of America Bulletin, v. 99, p. 414–426.

Vick, H. K., Channel, J.E.T., and Opdyke, N. D., 1987, Ordovician docking of the Carolina Slate Belt; Paleomagnetic data: Tectonics, v. 6, p. 573–584.

Webb, G. W., 1969, Paleozoic wrench faults in Canadian Appalachians, *in* Kay, M., ed., North Atlantic geology and continental drift: American Association of Petroleum Geologists Memoir 12, p. 754–786.

Williams, H., 1979, Appalachian orogen in Canada: Canadian Journal of Earth Sciences, v. 16, p. 792–807.

Williams, H., and Hatcher, R. D., Jr., 1983, Appalachian suspect terranes, *in* Hatcher, R. D., Williams, H., and Zietz, I., eds., Contributions to the tectonics and geophysics of mountain chains: Geological Society of America Memoir 158, p. 33–54.

Williams, H., Dallmeyer, R. D., and Wanless, R. K., 1976, Geochronology of the Twillingate granite and Herring Neck Group, Notre Dame, Newfoundland: Canadian Journal of Earth Sciences, v. 13, p. 1591–1601.

Williams, H., Gillespie, R. T., and Van Breeman, O., 1985, A late Precambrian rift-related igneous suite in western Newfoundland: Canadian Journal of Earth Sciences, v. 22, p. 1727–1735.

Winchester, J. A., and Max, M. D., 1987, A displaced and metamorphosed peralkaline granite related to the Late Proterozoic Labrador and Gardar suites—The Doolough granite of County Mayo, northwest Ireland: Canadian Journal of Earth Sciences, v. 24, p. 631–642.

Wintsch, R. P., and Fout, J. S., 1982, Structure and petrology of the Willimantic dome and the Willimantic fault, *in* Joesten, R., and Quarrier, S. S., eds., Guidebook for Field Trips in Connecticut and southcentral Massachusetts: New England Intercollegiate Geological Conference, v. 74, p. 465–482.

Wintsch, R. P., and Lefort, J. P., 1984, A clockwise rotation of Variscan strain orientation in southeastern New England and regional implications, *in* Hutton, D.H.W., and Sanderson, D. J., eds., Variscan tectonics of the North Atlantic region: Geological Society of London Special Publication 14, p. 245–252.

Wonderley, P. F., and Neuman, R. D., 1984, The Indian Bay Formation—Fossiliferous Early Ordovician volcanogenic rocks in the northern Gander Terrane, New Terrane, Newfoundland, and their regional significance: Canadian Journal of Earth Sciences, v. 21, p. 525–532.

Zen, E-an, 1967, Time and space relationships of the Taconic allochthon and autochthon: Geological Society of America Special Paper 97, 107 p.

—— , 1988, Evidence for accreted terranes and the effect of metamorphism: American Journal of Science, v. 288-A, p. 1–15.

Ziegler, P. A., 1984, Caledonian and Hercynian crustal consolidation of western and central Europe—A working hypothesis: Geologie en Mijnbouw, v. 63, p. 93–108.

MANUSCRIPT ACCEPTED BY THE SOCIETY DECEMBER 2, 1988

ACKNOWLEDGMENTS

This chapter is dedicated jointly to E.R.W. Neale and R. D. Hatcher, Jr. Neale started with a four-member faculty at Memorial University in Newfoundland, and with the help of M. J. (Ben) Kennedy, D. F. Strong, and Harold (Hank) Williams, built it into one of the foremost centers of Appalachian studies. Hatcher, through his personal drive and energy, has made major contributions to understanding the southern Appalachian sequence and structure.

I would also like to thank J. W. Skehan, S. J., Kieran O'Hara, Stewart Farrar, Damien Nance, Ken Currie, Kevin Kohles, and many other friends and colleagues for numerous discussions and consultations. If I have not conveyed their points of view adequately, it is my regret and responsibility.

A. R. Palmer and A. W. Bally reviewed the manuscript and made many constructive comments. Jean Kelley and Rebecca Meacham typed the successive versions, and Steven Grebb prepared most of the figures. John Costain kindly contributed the plate of seismic profiles, and their geological interpretation was prepared by R. D. Hatcher, Jr. Two figures are modifications of those produced by Kevin Kohles. Part of the expense for preparation of this chapter was defrayed by the donations of the Chevron Oil Company, California.

Printed in U.S.A.

The Geology of North America
Vol. A, The Geology of North America—An overview
The Geological Society of America, 1989

Chapter 13

The Arctic Islands

H. P. Trettin
Geological Survey of Canada, 3303 33rd Street NW, Calgary, Alberta T2L 2A7, Canada

INTRODUCTION

The Canadian Arctic Archipelago, perched on the northern rim of the continent, is about 1.3 million km^2 in area, including intervening waters (Fig. 1; Plate 9, index). Parry Channel, a seaway connecting Baffin Bay with the western Arctic Ocean, separates the Queen Elizebeth Islands to the north from another group of islands to the south. Rugged mountain ranges with extensive ice caps in the eastern part of the archipelago, and plateaus, lowlands, and a coastal plain in the western part, are all dissected by numerous channels and fiords (Dawes and Christie, Ch. 3).[1]

Outlines of the geography and rudiments of the geology were established during the last century and the first half of this century. This work was done by ship, with sledges, or on foot, under hardship and often tragic circumstances (Christie and Dawes, Ch. 2). A coherent stratigraphic-structural framework has emerged from subsequent systematic surface studies, which have been supported by helicopters since 1955. Paleontology, always at the forefront of Arctic earth science, has provided the basis for both regional correlations and reconstructions of the geologic history. Petroleum exploration has been active in the islands since the early 1960s, and by 1987, 176 wells had been drilled and more than 65,000 km of seismic reflection lines had been shot. The well data have been absorbed into the stratigraphic framework, and a few instructive seismic interpretations have been released (e.g., Harrison and Bally, 1988), but the bulk of the seismic work remains unpublished. Gravity surveys (Sobczak, Ch. 5A) and deep seismic refraction surveys, both carried out from the late 1950s onward, have permitted construction of crustal cross sections in the western parts of the islands (Sweeney and others, 1986; Sobczak and others, Ch. 5B), while aeromagnetic surveys (Coles, Ch. 5D), electrical conductivity studies (Niblett and Kurtz, Ch. 5E), and analyses of seismicity (Forsyth and others, Ch. 5C) have elucidated other aspects of crustal structure and tectonics.

Evolution of the tectonic nomenclature reflects advances in both understanding of the local geology and in general tectonic theory. Schuchert (1923) made the first synthesis of North American geology that included the Arctic, but it was based on scanty data. He saw the Precambrian Shield fringed in the north by a Franklinian geosyncline that received clastic sediments from a Precambrian borderland, Pearya, extending along the northwestern margin of the Arctic Islands. The geological discoveries of the 1950s and early 1960s, interpreted in terms of Marshall Kay's geosynclinal concepts, led to a revised framework, summarized by Thorsteinsson and Tozer (1970). The Franklinian Geosyncline was divided into a miogeosyncline and eugeosyncline, the latter now including Pearya, which was abandoned as a separate entity. It was recognized that the geosyncline was terminated by a mid-Paleozoic event, named the Ellesmerian orogeny. The Carboniferous to Paleogene strata overlying the eugeosyncline were incorporated in the Sverdrup Basin, which was terminated by the mid-Tertiary Eurekan orogeny. The Sverdrup Basin is unconformably overlain in the northwest by Neogene to Recent strata of another new province, the Arctic Coastal Plain. In broader compilations, the name "Innuitian Orogen" was used for the Phanerozoic region affected by the Ellesmerian and Eurekan orogenies, and the name "Arctic Platform" for the undeformed Phanerozoic cover of the Canadian Shield farther south.

From the early 1970s onward, attempts have been made to apply the new plate tectonic concepts. It was realized that the Franklinian region contains exotic elements such as Pearya, now regarded as a composite microcontinent with Caledonian affinities (Trettin, 1987). Therefore, the term "geosyncline" (implying that the rocks are more or less in place) was exchanged for the (noncommittal) term "mobile belt," and the terms "miogeosyncline" and "eugeosyncline" were replaced by "shelf" and "deep water basin," respectively. The deposits of the Arctic Coastal Plain were reinterpreted as the thin edge of an Arctic continental terrace wedge (Balkwill, 1979), which becomes thicker and longer ranging offshore (Balkwill, 1979).

CRYSTALLINE BASEMENT AND PROTEROZOIC SEDIMENTARY AND VOLCANIC SUCCESSIONS OF THE CANADIAN SHIELD

The Precambrian Canadian Shield, consisting of crystalline basement and Proterozoic sedimentary and volcanic supracrustal

[1]This summary has been abstracted from a volume in this series on the Arctic Islands and North Greenland. Contributions to that volume are cited here by chapter and listed alphabetically at the beginning of the references. Adequate reference lists are given in those chapters; references here are kept to a minimum because of space limitations.

Trettin, H. P., 1989, The Arctic Islands, *in* Bally, A. W., and Palmer, A. R., eds., The Geology of North America—An overview: Boulder, Colorado, Geological Society of America, The Geology of North America, v. A.

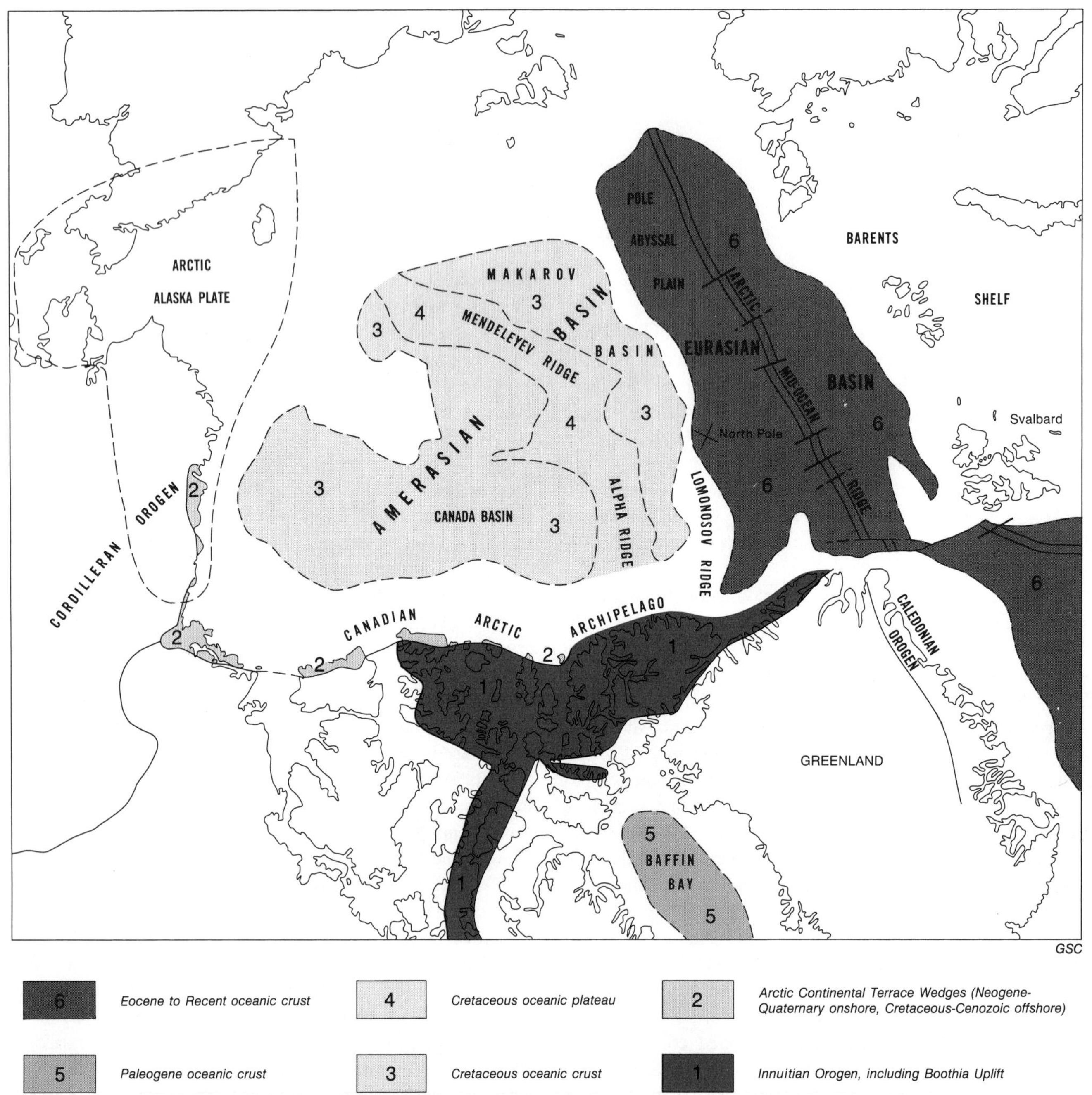

Figure 1. Tectonic setting of Innuitian orogen; oceanic features adapted from Churkin and Johnson (1983) and other sources. For geographic names, see index to Plate 9 (lower right).

sequences, is widely exposed in the southeastern parts of the archipelago and extends into the adjacent Arctic Platform as salients and outliers, such as the core of the Boothia Uplift, Minto Arch, Melville Horst, and the Wellington and Duke of York Highs (exhumed hills on the Proterozoic–Cambrian erosion surface; Fig. 2). The shield extends under the Arctic Platform and Franklinian mobile belt, but its northern limit in the subsurface has not yet been delimited. The crystalline basement probably represents a number of relatively small continental plates of Archean age, welded together in a series of early Proterozoic orogenies (Hoffman, this volume).

Clastic sediments of probable late Early and early Middle Proterozoic ages are exposed only on southern Victoria Island (Fig. 2, unit 2). More widely exposed deposits were laid down in a basin, or a series of basins, created by an extensive rifting event at about 1.2 Ga (Fig. 2, unit 3). The basin fill consists of basal clastic sediments and basalt of late Middle Proterozoic age, overlain by sedimentary deposits that probably range in age far into

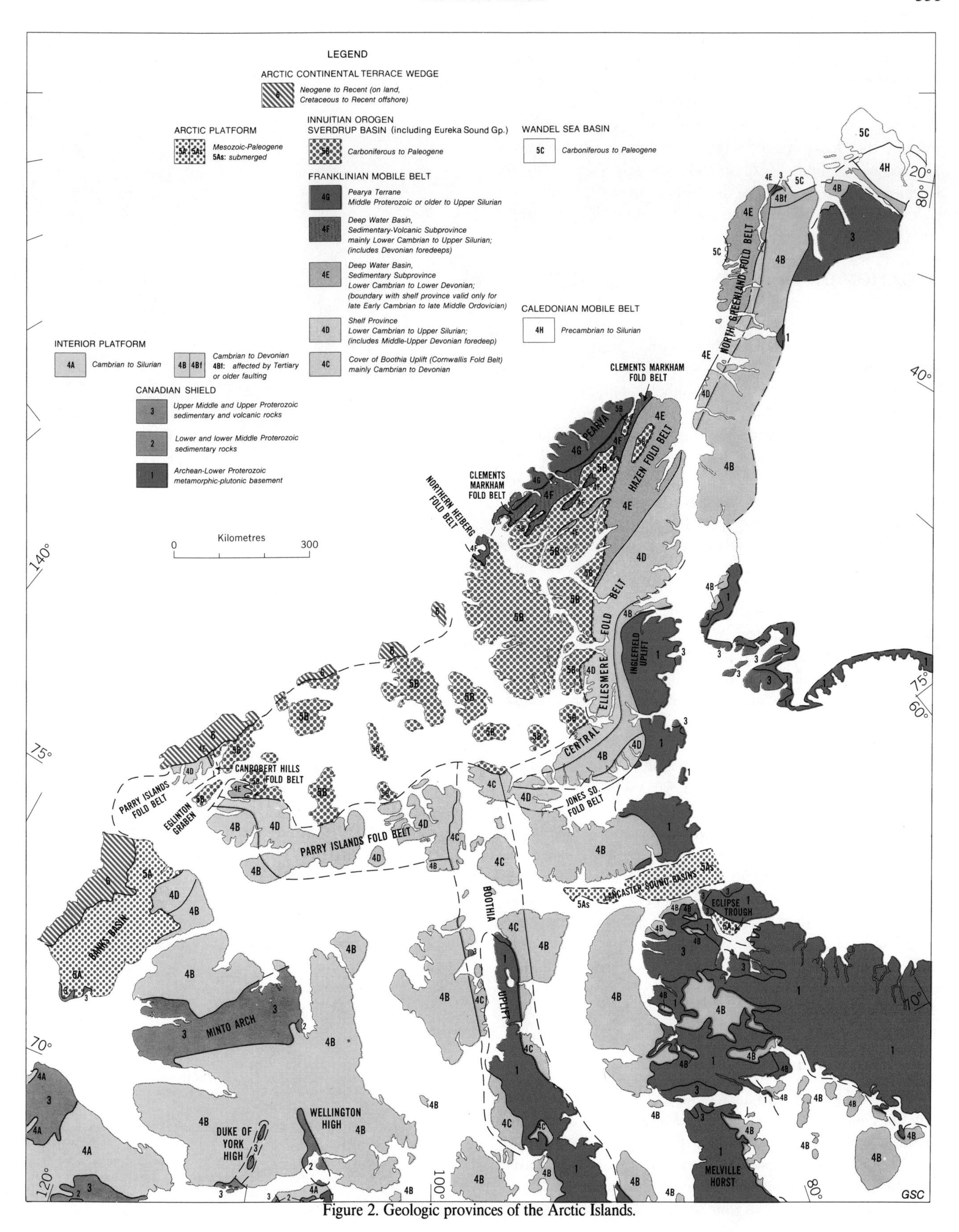

Figure 2. Geologic provinces of the Arctic Islands.

the Late Proterozoic (Vendian). Extending from the southwestern Arctic Islands to northeastern Greenland, the erosional remnants of these deposits form the oldest major succession that shows the Innuitian trend. However, the tectonic significance of this succession—whether it represents a passive margin related to a proto-Arctic Ocean or a series of intra-cratonic basins—is uncertain because of limited exposure (Frisch and Trettin, Ch. 6). Seismic reflection data suggest that a Proterozoic succession 10 to 12 km thick, with several unconformities, underlies Melville Island (Kanasewich and Berkes, 1988).

INITIATION OF FRANKLINIAN MOBILE BELT

The early history of the Franklinian mobile belt is poorly known. Analogy with the Cordilleran and Caledonian mobile belts suggests that it was initiated by a rifting event in the Late Proterozoic, probably represented by the Franklin diabase dike swarm, tentatively dated at 750 Ma, and basic volcanics and intrusions on Victoria Island (Natkusiak Formation) that have given K-Ar ages of 635 to 640 Ma. Poorly dated mafic volcanics and associated sediments of possible Late Proterozoic or earliest Cambrian age occur also in northern Axel Heiberg and northwestern Ellesmere Islands. Apart from these predominantly volcanic units, and glaciogenic sediments in northeastern Greenland, the uppermost Proterozoic to lowermost Cambrian strata of the Franklinian mobile belt are covered (Frisch and Trettin, Ch. 6). In the central and southern parts of the Arctic Islands, late Early Cambrian and younger strata of the Franklinian shelf or Arctic Platform are separated from Proterozoic or older rocks of the shield by an angular unconformity that probably is due to late Proterozoic thermal uplift and rifting, followed by early Paleozoic thermal subsidence.

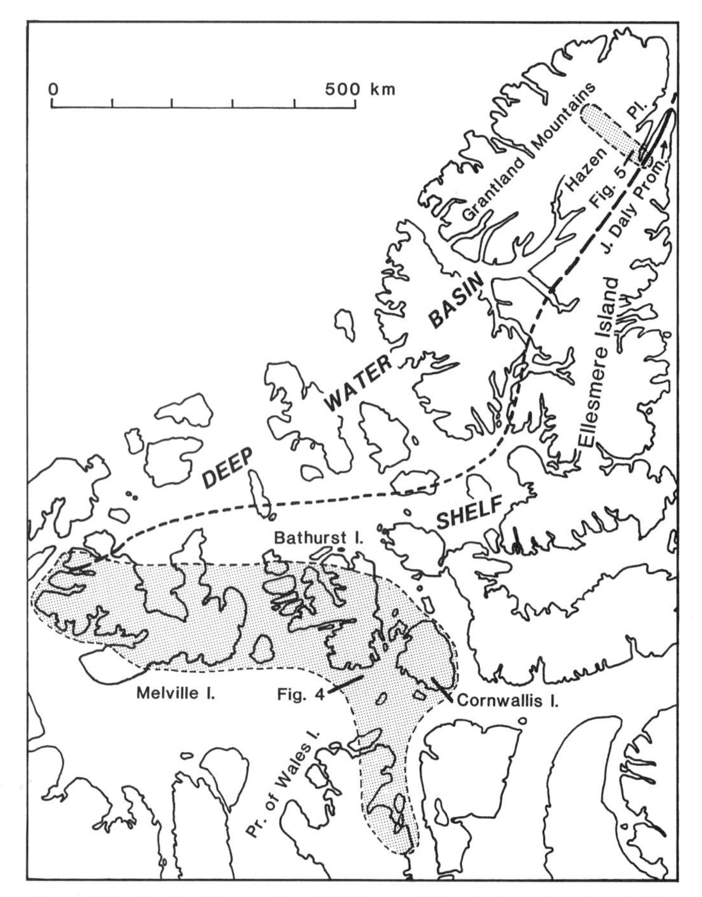

Figure 3. Index for Figures 4 and 5. The shelf-basin boundary is valid for latest Early Cambrian to Late Ordovician time.

EARLY CAMBRIAN TO EARLY DEVONIAN BASIN DEVELOPMENT AND DEPOSITION

The Cambrian to Lower Devonian succession was deposited in two first-order provinces: shelf and deep-water basin. The latter, in turn, is divisible into a southeasterly sedimentary subprovince and a northwesterly sedimentary and volcanic subprovince (Trettin and others, Ch. 8). The shelf and the southeasterly sedimentary subprovince can be traced from northeastern Greenland (Higgins and others, Ch. 7) to the southwestern Arctic Islands, but the northwesterly sedimentary and volcanic subprovince is exposed in northern Ellesmere and Axel Heiberg Islands only.

Franklinian shelf and Arctic Platform

The Franklinian shelf and Arctic Platform are stratigraphically continuous; the boundary between them is structural and coincides with the limit of folding. This region (Plate 9, A-G; Fig. 2) received a succession of predominantly shallow marine sediments, mainly carbonates with lesser proportions of clastics and evaporites, that thickens from some 500 m in Foxe Basin to about 9 km at the shelf margin in Ellesmere Island. The subsidence probably was caused not only by Early Cambrian rifting and subsequent lithospheric cooling, but also by loading of the adjacent basin with rapidly accumulating sediment gravity flows.

The stratigraphic record indicates a series of transgressions and regressions that seem to conform to some degree with continent-wide patterns. The transgressions increased in extent from Cambrian to Ordovician time, attaining an all-time maximum in the late Middle and Late Ordovician. The regressions are marked by disconformities that die out on the outer shelf or slope. Some probably are due to uplift and others to eustatic drops in sea level. A widespread but subtle disconformity near the Ordovician-Silurian boundary is commonly attributed to a fall in sea level caused by glaciation in the Sahara.[2]

[2]At present, information is insufficient to describe the lower Paleozoic stratigraphy of the Arctic Islands in terms of the transgressive-regressive cycles now recognized in the upper Paleozoic and Mesozoic record (see below). Instead, the shelf succession has been divided into major and minor time rock slices (labeled P, for platform, in Figs. 4 and 5; for location see Fig. 3) that are bounded by unconformities or by significant changes in lithology or facies configuration. The problem that remains to be clarified is to what extent the unconformity-bounded sequences established by Sloss for the continental interior are applicable in this tectonically more active region.

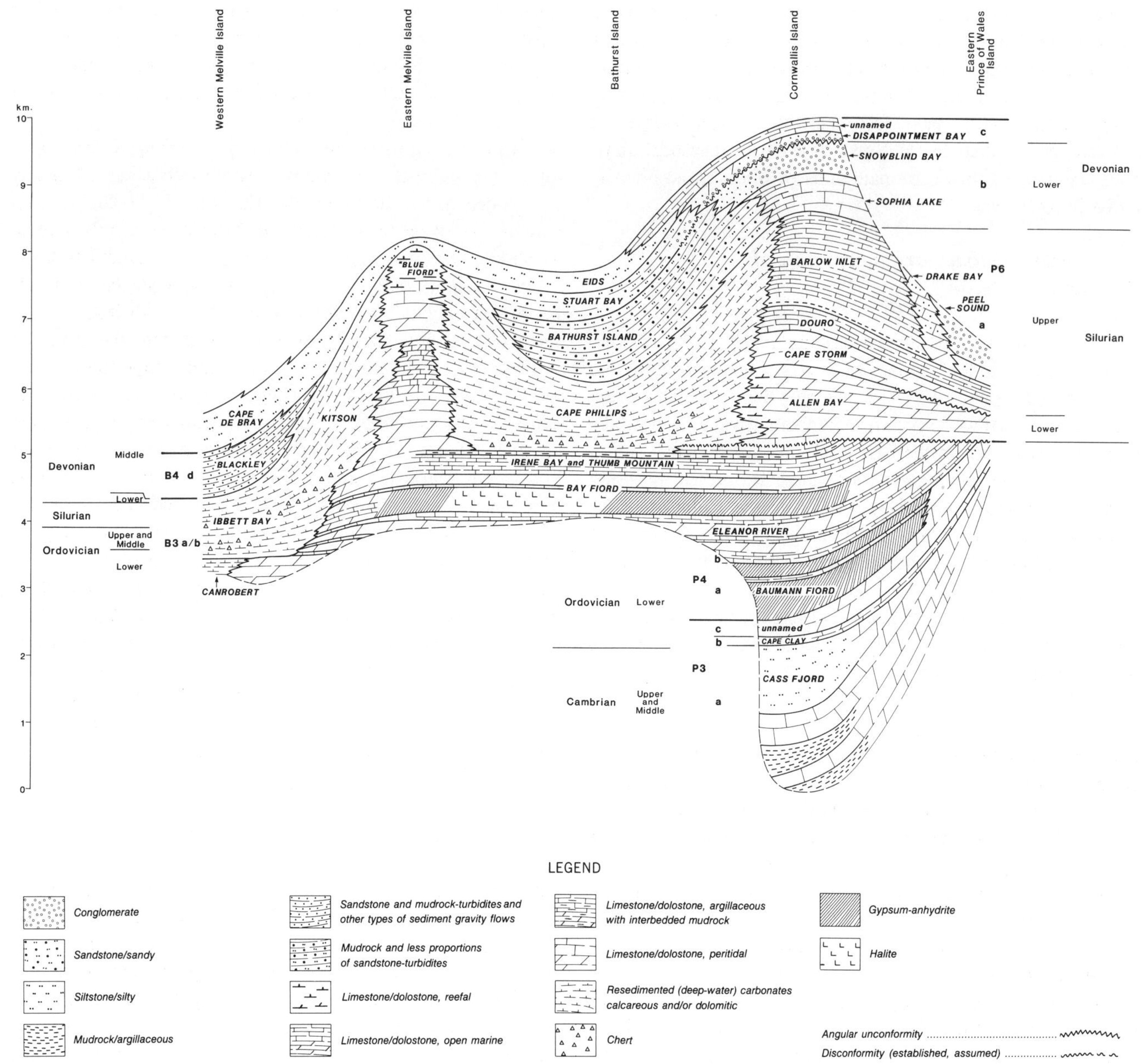

Figure 4. Restored lower Paleozoic stratigraphic cross section, Prince of Wales Island to Melville Island (from U. Mayr in Trettin and others, Ch. 8).

Shelf architecture was characterized by alternation of two basic modes, the distally steepened ramp and the rimmed shelf. The shelf margin retreated cratonward during the Early Cambrian, and again in latest Ordovician to Early Devonian time, when isolated carbonate buildups, surrounded and overlain by deep-water sediments, developed in some areas near the previous shelf edge. The largest of these, extending from Cameron Island to northeastern Melville Island, persisted from Late Ordovician to Middle Devonian (early Eifelian) time; others were terminated earlier by clastic sedimentation or drowning (Plate 9, F-I; Figs. 3 and 4).

The carbonate sediments of the Franklinian shelf and Arctic Platform include a great variety of limestones and dolostones deposited in subtidal to supratidal settings. Clastic sediments, derived from the cratonic interior, consist mainly of quartzose or arkosic sandstone, and mudrock, deposited in outer shelf to shoreline, rarely fluvial environments. The most important clastic unit, of late Early Cambrian age (Plate 9, B), thickens from 0 to 19 m on Devon Island (Rabbit Point Formation) to 1.5 km in east-central Ellesmere Island (Ellesmere Group). Considerable proportions of clastic sediments are associated with carbonates in other formations of Early Cambrian to earliest Ordovician age.

Two important evaporitic formations, the Lower Ordovician Baumann Fiord and the Lower to Middle Ordovician Bay

Fiord, were deposited in a large intrashelf basin (or lagoon) that was separated from the deep-water basin by a narrow rim of carbonate buildups. Primary textures of the evaporites and associated carbonates indicate subtidal settings. In Bay Fiord time, this basin had a central halite facies, surrounded by anhydrite and dolomite facies (Plate 9, D). Small amounts of supratidal anhydrite occur in various carbonate units of Middle Cambrian to Early Devonian age.

Southeasterly sedimentary subprovince of the deep-water basin

The deposits of this subprovince are linked with the Franklinian shelf by interlocking facies changes. Four major units and several subunits (labeled B1, B2, B3a, etc.; B for basin) are recognized in the northwestern part of the subprovince in northern Ellesmere Island where the base of the deep-water succession is concealed, and equivalents of these units are present in North Greenland (Higgins and others, Ch. 7). In the southeastern (or marginal) part, units 1 and 2 are absent and units 3 and/or 4 overlie shelf carbonates with generally conformable but locally disconformable contact.

Unit 1 (Nesmith beds) consists of resedimented impure carbonates (lime mudstone to pebble conglomerate) and associated mudrocks that are probably mid–Early Cambrian in age (Plate 9, A; Fig. 5, unit B1).

Unit 2 (Grant Land Formation) comprises perhaps 2 km of quartzose and feldspathic sandstone and minor pebble conglomerate, interlayered with varicolored mudrock. It is the deep-water equivalent of the upper Lower Cambrian Ellesmere Group, and like the latter, was derived from the North American craton (Plate 9, B; Fig. 5, unit B2). The sandstones were deposited by sediment gravity flows in middle to upper parts of submarine fans.

Unit 3 (Hazen, Canrobert, Ibbett Bay, Cape Phillips Formation, etc.) consists of varying proportions of fine-grained siliciclastic sediments (mainly mudrock, minor very fine grained sandstone) derived mainly from the North American craton, resedimented carbonates, and chert (commonly radiolarian, also secondary). The unit is highly diachronous with an overall age range from latest Early Cambrian to earliest Middle Devonian (Plate 9, C-J; Figs. 4 and 5, unit B3). Downwarping of the outer shelf, mainly in Late Ordovician to Early Silurian time, caused younging of the base of the deposits in southeasterly or southerly directions.

Most carbonate sediments were derived from the shelf margin and slope and transported to the basin by slumps, slides, and sediment gravity flows, but some lime mud probably was deposited from suspensions generated on the shelf by storms. The size-grade and proportion of the carbonates, and the total thickness of unit 3, decrease with distance from the shelf margin, whereas the proportion of chert increases in that direction. Throughout the basin, the proportion of chert also increases upward in the succession, concomitant with increasingly extensive marine transgressions on the craton. Starved basin conditions existed in the northern part of the sedimentary subprovince, where the entire uppermost Lower Cambrian to Lower Silurian (mid-Llandovery) succession is only 250 m thick, about 5 percent of the thickness of correlative shelf units.

Unit 4 comprises a thick (locally >2.8 km) succession of sandstone, mudrock, and minor conglomerate deposited mainly by sediment gravity flows (flysch). The unit is highly diachronous with an overall age range from Late Ordovician or Early Silurian to Middle Devonian (Plate 9, F-J; Figs. 4 and 5, unit B4). Paleocurrent directions and age relationships indicate that the flysch prograded longitudinally from northeast to southwest, and age relationships show that it also encroached onto the craton in southeasterly directions. The sandstones are compositionally immature, as they include carbonate detritus from terrestrial (orogenic) sources in addition to quartz, feldspar, phyllosilicates, chert, etc.; the detrital carbonate and noncarbonate components are mixed thoroughly and in fairly constant proportion. Five different terrestrial sources have been identified: the Caledonian Mountains at the northeastern termination of the basin (Late Ordovician to Early Devonian or later); a source of similar composition north of Ellesmere Island (Early Silurian); Pearya (Late Silurian); and the cratonic Boothia and Inglefield Uplifts (Late Silurian to Early Devonian, see below). In addition, relatively small amounts of carbonate conglomerate and breccia at the margin of the basin were derived from adjacent shelves. This material differs from the orogenic carbonate detritus by its sporadic occurrence, much larger maximum clast size, and high skeletal content, and is mixed less thoroughly with the noncarbonate detritus.

The development of the shelf-basin transition is known from exposures near the head of Archer Fiord, central Ellesmere Island. There, shelf-basin differentiation, presumably due to deep-seated normal faulting, occurred in the latest Early Cambrian. Subsequently, the relief was accentuated by relatively rapid deposition on the shelf, which kept pace with regional subsidence, and slow sedimentation in the basin. Eventually the slope became too steep to retain shelf-derived sediments. From Early Silurian time onward, rapidly deposited turbidites (flysch) filled the basin and produced a submarine unconformity on the slope where these strata abut Middle and Upper Ordovician shelf-margin carbonates. A preliminary geometric analysis of this slope unconformity indicates a relief of more than 1 km in the latest Ordovician and a slope angle of several tens of degrees. Sedimentary loading of the trough depressed the shelf below the photic zone and thus terminated carbonate production. The drowned shelf then was covered by graptolitic mudrock-carbonate units, succeeded by flysch, or locally covered directly by flysch.

Northwesterly sedimentary-volcanic subprovince of the deep-water basin

The sedimentary-volcanic subprovince forms the Northern Heiberg Fold Belt of Axel Heiberg Island and the Clements Markham Fold Belt of northern Ellesmere Island, which differ in strati-

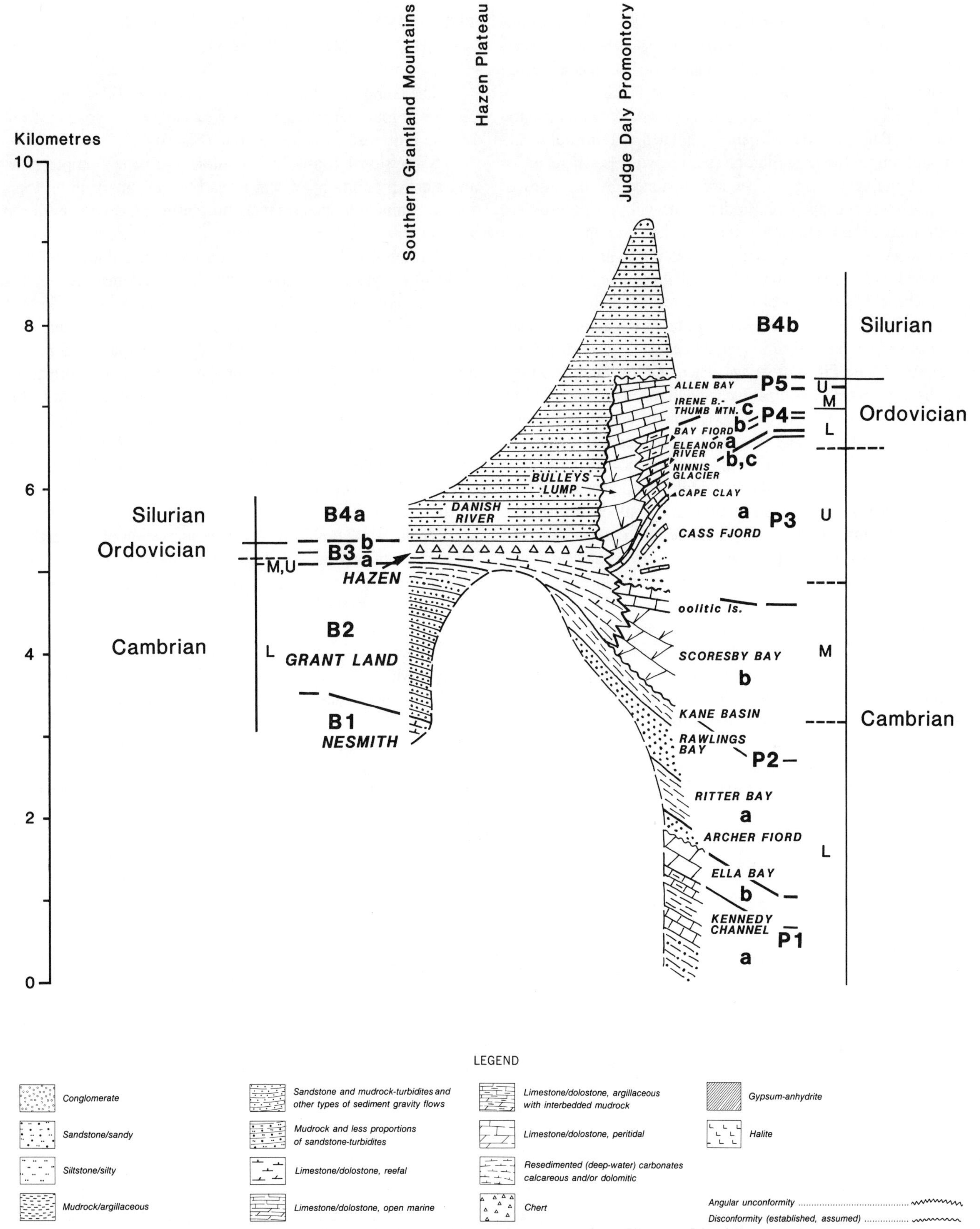

Figure 5. Restored lower Paleozoic stratigraphic cross section, northern Ellesmere Island (for legend see Fig. 4).

graphy and structural trend (see below, Fig. 8). A major transcurrent fault forms the boundary between the sedimentary and sedimentary-volcanic subprovinces in northeasternmost Ellesmere Island (the southern fault of the Feilden Fault Zone [FFZ] in Fig. 14, below). It appears to have had dextral motion during the Paleogene but probably originated as a sinistral strike-slip fault during the Late Silurian (see below). Elsewhere, exposures of the two subprovinces are separated by expanses of younger strata or glaciers. The sedimentary-volcanic subprovince is extremely complex in stratigraphy and structure. In addition to sedimentary units that are broadly comparable to units 2, 3, and 4 of the sedimentary subprovince, it contains four major volcanic units. The oldest consists of highly altered mafic volcanics and associated sediments that are overthrust by Lower Cambrian clastics. The simplest interpretation would be that they are rift-related volcanics of Late Proterozoic age. Their trace-element composition, however, is more compatible with an island arc origin, and if so, they may represent an oceanic terrane of uncertain Proterozoic or early Paleozoic age. Younger volcanic units, intermediate to felsic in composition, with arc characteristics, are of Middle Ordovician, Early Silurian (early–middle Llandovery), and Late Silurian (early Ludlow) ages. A Silurian (Wenlock–lower Ludlow) flysch unit differs markedly in detrital composition and paleocurrent directions from coeval flysch in the adjacent sedimentary subprovince of Ellesmere Island, but is similar to coeval flysch in North Greenland. This relationship, combined with structural considerations (see below), suggests that the Clements Markham Fold Belt was involved in the sinistral strike-slip motion inferred for the Pearya terrane. Moreover, the apparent stratigraphic heterogenity of the Clements Markham Fold Belt suggests that it is not a single tectonic unit, but an assemblage of fault slices.

THE MIDDLE PROTEROZOIC TO LATE SILURIAN RECORD OF PEARYA

The composite Pearya terrane of northern Ellesmere Island consists of four major successions with an overall age range from Middle Proterozoic to Late Silurian (Fig. 6).

Succession I consists of granitoid gneiss; less amphibolite; and small proportions of schist, marble, and quartzite. Isotopic age determinations indicate metamorphism and granitic intrusion at about 1.0 to 1.1 Ga.

Succession II comprises sedimentary and minor volcanic rocks of subgreenschist to amphibolite, predominantly greenschist, metamorphic grade. The stratigraphy is poorly known because of the absence of fossils and very complex structure. The contact with succession I is interpreted as an angular unconformity that became a detachment surface during later deformation. Regional relationships and a zircon age on volcanics from the upper part of the succession suggest a Late Proterozoic to earliest Ordovician age range. The numerous lithologic units fall into three broad categories: basal(?) arkosic sandstones; diamictites, similar to uppermost Proterozoic glaciogenic deposits in the North Atlantic region (especially Svalbard) and in the Cordillera; and a thick, stratigraphically complex succession of shelf carbonate rocks, mudrock, and quartzite that is of passive margin (miogeoclinal) aspect. In addition, there are small amounts of mafic to felsic volcanics and of dark gray chert of deep-water aspect.

Succession III, consisting of metamorphosed sedimentary and volcanic rocks, also is unfossiliferous and complexly deformed. Metamorphism is mainly of subgreenschist grade but locally rises to greenschist and amphibolite grade. The sedimentary rocks, both of shallow- and deep-water aspect, consist of limestone, mudrock, and chert with minor sandstone and dolo-

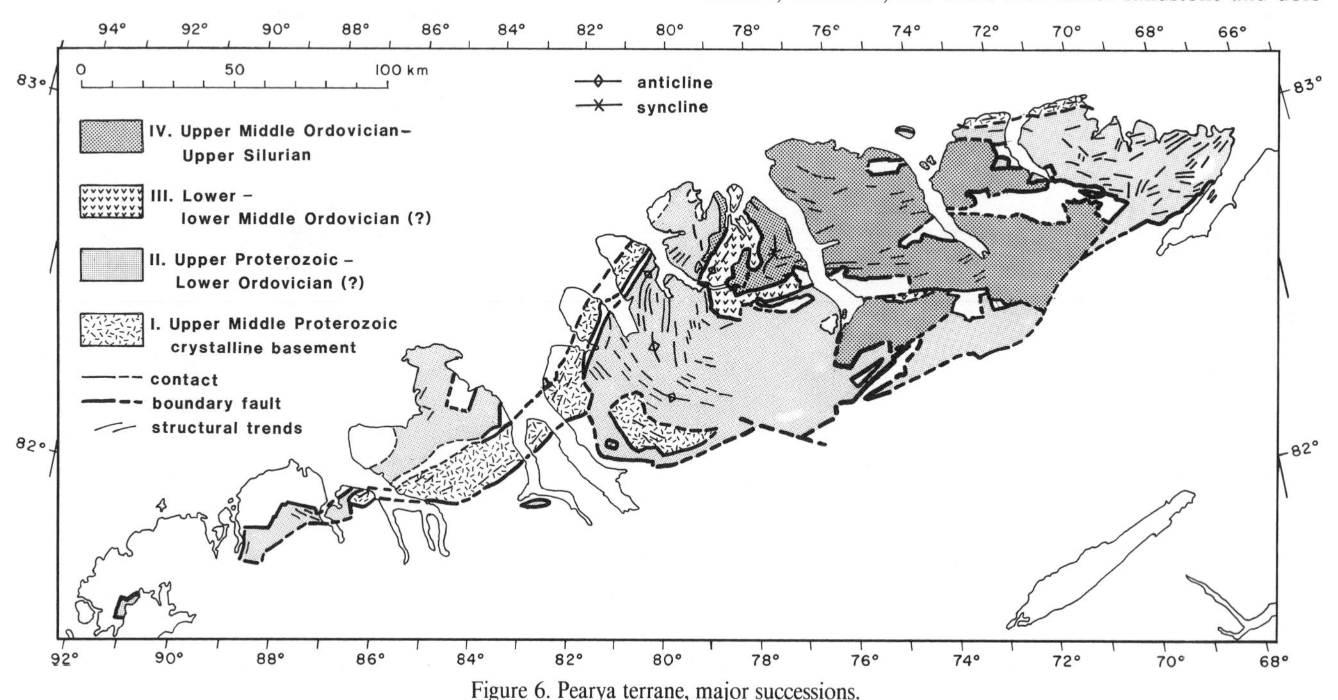

Figure 6. Pearya terrane, major successions.

stone. Abundant volcanic flows and pyroclastics are of andesitic and basaltic composition and seem to have originated mainly in arc-type settings, although ocean-floor basalt may also be present. Unconformably overlain by succession IV, succession III can be no younger than Middle Ordovician (early Caradoc). It is tentatively placed in the Early to early Middle Ordovician on the basis of tectonic considerations.

Arenig ultramafic-mafic complexes. Five fault blocks (or aggregates of fault slices), of ultramafic-mafic plutonic complexes with minor felsic components (Thores Suite) are structurally associated with succession III. Serpentinite, wehrlite, and varieties of clinopyroxenite and hornblendite constitute the ultramafic suite, and varieties of gabbro the mafic suite. The intermediate to felsic suite ranges in composition from hornblende diorite through monzodiorite, quartz monzodiorite and trondjhemite to granodiorite. The lithology and structural setting of the Thores Suite are compatible with the view that it represents dismembered ophiolites, but sheeted dikes and pillow basalt, the most diagnostic members of the ophiolite suite, appear to be absent. Alternatively the Thores Suite may represent subvolcanic complexes, as it has some features in common with Alaskan-type intrusions (apparent absence of orthopyroxene and common occurrence of hornblende). Zircon from a felsic rock in the largest body gave an age of 481 +7/–6 Ma, Arenig according to recent time scales (e.g., Snelling, 1987).

Mid-Ordovician M'Clintock orogeny. An angular unconformity (up to 90°) at the base of succession IV represents the M'Clintock orogeny. The strata above the unconformity are Middle Ordovician (early Caradoc or Blackriveran) in age at some localities and Late Ordovician (Ashgill or Richmondian) at others; the youngest rocks beneath it are probably Middle Ordovician (Llandeilo–Llanvirn; succession III) in age and definitely no older than Arenig (Thores Suite). The structures produced by this event are generally difficult to distinguish from later deformations, but complex folds and faults are apparent beneath the unconformity. The most important structure appears to be a major fault that places succession III against succession II and has associated with it four ultramafic-mafic fault blocks of the Thores Suite. It is tentatively interpreted as a suture that places an arc suite (succession III) and associated ophiolite slices (Thores Suite) against (or upon) a miogeoclinal suite (succession II).

The orogeny was accompanied by Barrovian metamorphism up to amphibolite grade. Muscovite in a schist has given a K-Ar (cooling) age of 452 ± 8 Ma (Caradoc).

At least two granitic plutons with Llandeilo U-Pb ages are related to this orogeny: a fault-bounded body of granodiorite, quartz monzodiorite, and quartz diorite (Markham Fiord Pluton) that probably was produced by subduction (462 ± 11 Ma); and an unaltered intrusive complex (Cape Richards) composed of quartz monzonite, granodiorite, and syenite with alkalic affinity and basement-derived zircon that is of post-tectonic aspect (463 ± 5 Ma).

Succession IV consists of about 7 to 8 km of clastic, carbonate, and volcanic strata that range in age from Middle Ordovician (early Caradoc) to Late Silurian (late Ludlow or Pridoli). The succession is generally conformable but has an internal unconformity of Late Ordovician (Ashgill or early Richmondian) age. A minor volcanic suite near the base of the succession is composed of felsic, partly alkalic rocks that are of rift aspect. A voluminous younger suite of late Caradoc to Ashgill age consists mainly of andesite, i.e., is of arc aspect. The sediments include shallow marine to nonmarine clastics ranging in grade up to boulder conglomerate; shallow marine carbonates; resedimented carbonates and mudrocks of slope and basinal origin (latest Ordovician); and about 1 km of proximal flysch ranging in grade up to cobble conglomerate (Llandovery).

Pearya is related to the Caledonian-Appalachian region by:

(1) The Grenvillian age of its crystalline basement (Fig. 7a).

(2) The Early Ordovician age of its ultramafic–mafic complexes (Fig. 7b). Overlapping ages have been reported from ophiolites in the Appalachians (493.9 +2.5/–1.9 Ma to 477.5 +2.6/–2.0 Ma; Dunning and Krogh, 1985) and Ballantrae, Scotland (481.4 +4.0/–1.9 Ma; Bluck and others, 1980); and slightly older and younger ages from ophiolites in Norway (497 ± 2 to 489 ± 3 Ma and 470 +9/–5 Ma; Dunning and Pedersen, 1988).

(3) The presence of a mid-Ordovician collisional orogen that is comparable in age and style to the Taconian and Grampian orogens (Fig. 7b).

In contrast, the crystalline basement of the Franklinian mobile belt is Archean–Early Proterozoic in age, and the belt was not deformed in the Ordovician. Affinities with the deep-water basin become apparent in latest Ordovician to Early Silurian time, but the Lower Silurian flysch of Pearya differs in composition from coeval flysch in the deep-water basin.

LATE SILURIAN TO EARLY CARBONIFEROUS OROGENIC EVENTS

Pulses of deformation

Five major events, or groups of events, are distinguished (Figs. 8 and 9; Harrison and others, Ch. 12G; Harrison and Brent, Ch. 12H; Okulitch, Ch. 12F; Okulitch and others, Ch. 12C; Trettin, Ch. 12B, 12E).

(1) The accretion of Pearya appears to have been the most important structural event in the history of northern Ellesmere Island, but inferences about its mechanism and age are still somewhat speculative. Available structural information suggests that Pearya was transported by sinistral strike slip as three or more slices and accreted by transpression. Intense deformation, including horizontal ("oroclinal") flexuring occurred when the motion was arrested and the terrane was welded to the Clements Markham Fold Belt, although the latter probably participated in the sinistral motion to some extent. If so, the northwestern part of the Hazen Fold Belt was probably also affected. Limited evidence suggests that this occurred in the Late Silurian, but a Devonian age cannot be excluded.

(2) A Late Silurian–Early Devonian deformation in north-

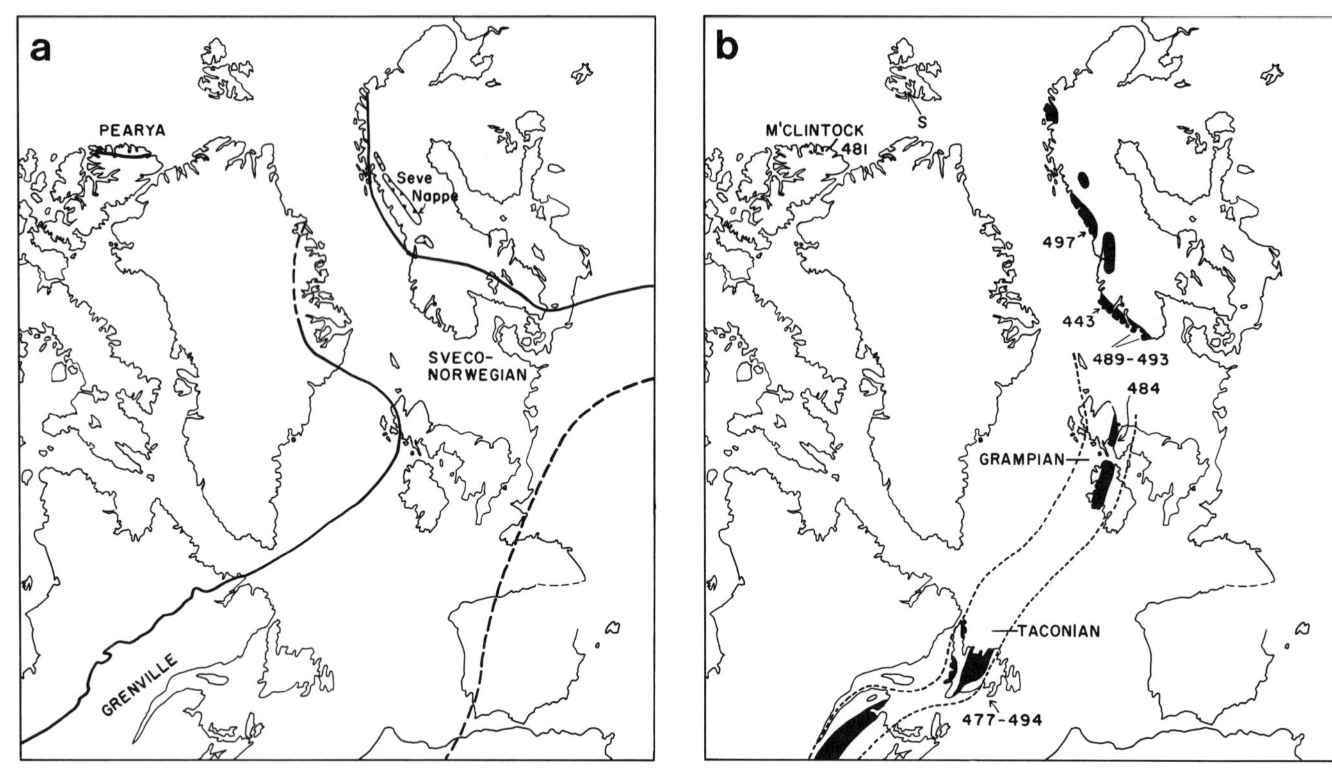

Figure 7. Relations of Pearya terrane with North Atlantic region; base is Cretaceous pre-drift reconstruction of Le Pichon and others (1977). a. (left) Generalized area of Grenville-age basement (adapted from Zwart and Dornsiepen, 1978) (The presence of Grenville-age basement in east-central Greenland is questioned by some authors.) b. (right) Generalized distribution of Taconian and Grampian orogens and ophiolitic rocks (adapted from Williams, 1984), and generalized U-Pb zircon ages (in Ma). S: area of Arenig(?) high-pressure metamorphism in Svalbard (Ohta and others, 1986).

ern Axel Heiberg Island is known from an angular unconformity between upper Lower Silurian deep-water sediments and Lower Devonian (or slightly older) conglomerate and red beds (Plate 9, H). It is speculated to have been caused by southwestward motion of northern Ellesmere Island (Clements Markham Fold Belt and [?] northwestern Hazen Fold Belt), but alternatively may be due to the same stress field that caused the contemporaneous deformation of the Boothia Uplift (see below).

(3) Late Silurian–Early Devonian movements of the Boothia Uplift are known from unconformities and flanking syntectonic sediments (Plate 9, G–I). The Late Silurian movements were restricted to south of Parry Channel, but the Early Devonian movements affected the entire belt. These movements, previously attributed to isostatic basement uplift, are now interpreted as compressional deformation on east-dipping reverse faults. If so, they are due to an east–west compressional regime that affected areas with northerly basement trends. This interpretation has also been applied to Early Devonian movements of the Inglefield Uplift (Plate 9, I), inferred from an unconformity and syntectonic sediments.

(4) A Givetian(?)-Frasnian uplift of the northwestern part of the Hazen Fold Belt (Grant Land Uplift) can be inferred from the composition and paleocurrent directions of syntectonic clastic sediments in the Clements Markham Fold Belt (Plate 9, K). A poorly dated, post-Lochkovian (earliest Devonian), pre-Visean (late Early Carboniferous) deformation in northern Axel Heiberg Island may also have occurred at this time.

(5) A final event of Late Devonian–Early Carboniferous age, the Ellesmerian orogeny, is known from an angular unconformity at the base of upper Lower Carboniferous and younger strata. It affected the entire mobile belt, from North Greenland (Soper and Higgins, Ch. 11A) to Prince Patrick Island, creating a highly sinuous assemblage of fold belts that is more than 375 km wide. Deformation was most intense in previously undeformed areas. Thin-skinned deformation is inferred for the shelf province and adjacent parts of the deep-water basin (North Greenland, Central Ellesmere, and Parry Islands Fold Belts; southeastern and central parts of Hazen Fold Belt); basement was involved on northern Ellesmere Island (Pearya, Clements Markham Fold Belt, northwestern Hazen Fold Belt [?]), southeastern Ellesmere Island (Jones Sound Fold Belt), and the Boothia Uplift. The thin-skinned deformation is best known from reflection seismic surveys of Melville Island, where it occurred mainly above the base of the Lower to Middle Ordovician Bay Fiord evaporite (Harrison and Bally, 1988). There, the shortening was roughly 23 to 27 km (10 to 12 percent). Structural analysis indicates that the deformation progressed both from the interior to the margin of the fold belt and upward in the section.

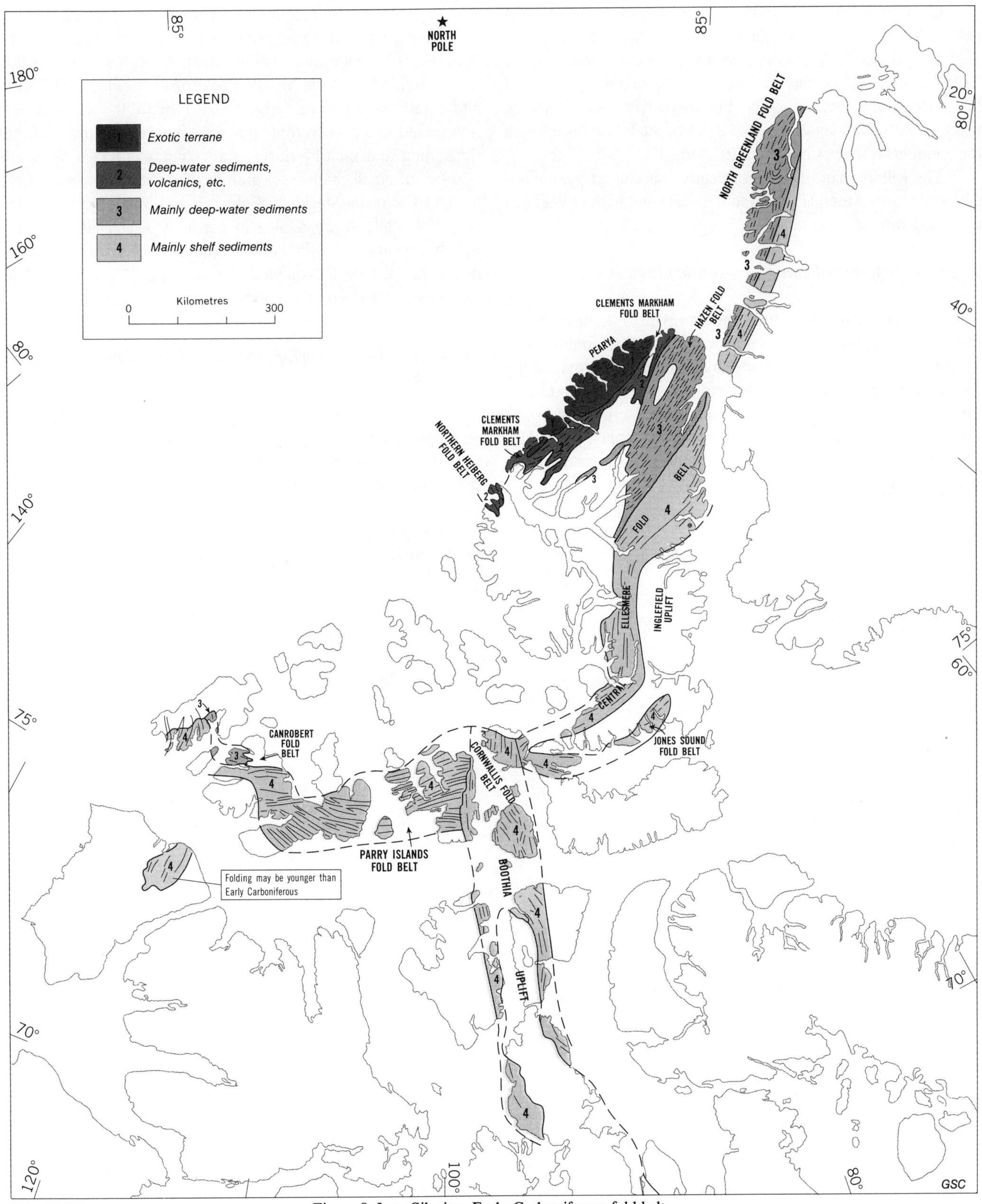

Figure 8. Late Silurian–Early Carboniferous fold belts.

On Prince Patrick Island, the Parry Island and Canrobert Hills Fold Belts cross the margin of the Arctic Archipelago at high angles. Evidence for a coeval deformation also is present in the North Yukon and northern Alaska, but the original position of these areas with respect to the Ellesmerian orogen cannot be restored with confidence until the trend of the fold belts beneath the continental shelves has been determined.

The Ellesmerian orogeny evidently was caused by convergence of North America with another plate that has not yet been identified with any assurance.

Regional metamorphism and granitic plutonism

Silurian and older strata in northwestern Ellesmere Island show metamorphism of upper greenschist and amphibolite grade adjacent to a major fault that appears to have been active during the emplacement of Pearya. Regional metamorphism up to amphibolite grade is also developed in northeastern parts of the deep-water basin in Greenland (Higgins and Soper, Ch. 11B). Elsewhere the Silurian–Devonian metamorphism was of greenschist or subgreenschist grade.

A large pluton of quartz monzonite and granodiorite intrudes the Pearya terrane in northwestern Ellesmere Island (Cape Woods). U-Pb determinations on zircon and sphene indicate that it was derived from the Middle Proterozoic basement of Pearya and emplaced in late Early Devonian time (390 ± 10 Ma). It is interpreted as a post-tectonic intrusion that resulted from crustal thickening and melting during the accretion of Pearya. A fair number of small, high-level granitic plutons are present in the western Clements Markham Fold Belt and in the Northern Heiberg Fold Belt. A small plug in northern Axel Heiberg Island, which appears to be the surface extension of a larger body at depth, has a Late Devonian K-Ar age of 367 ± 25 Ma (Late Devonian), regarded as a minimum age.

Syntectonic basin development and deposition

Clastic sediments derived from Late Silurian to Early Devonian uplifts include (Trettin and others, Ch. 8):

- 3 to 4 km of Lower Devonian (and possibly older) sandstone, mudrock, and conglomerate in northern Axel Heiberg Is-

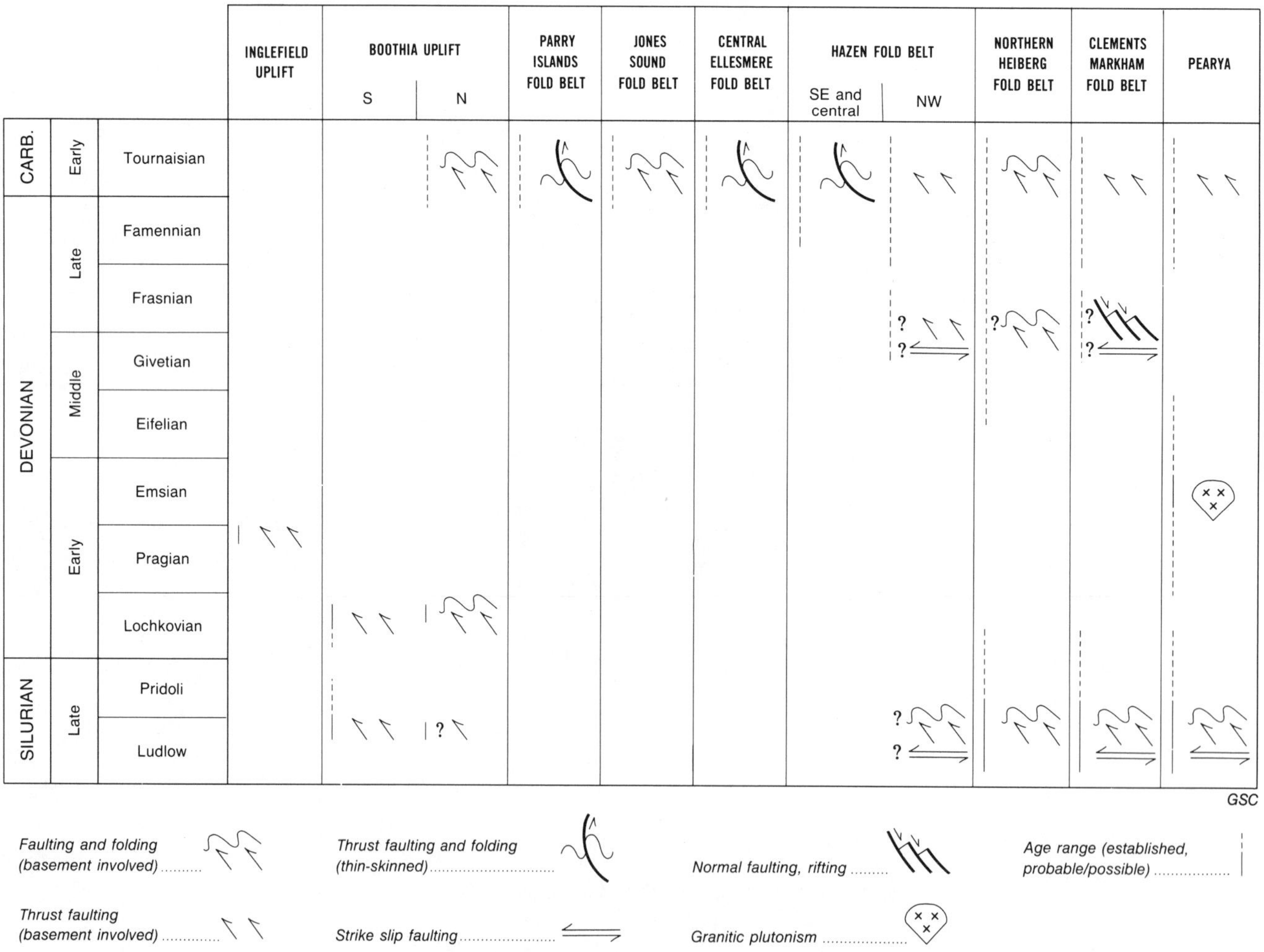

Figure 9. Age and character of deformation in Late Silurian–Early Carboniferous fold belts.

land, deposited in alluvial to shallow marine, deltaic settings (Stallworthy Formation; Plate 9, H). The sediments were derived from Lower Cambrian sandstone and Cambrian–Silurian radiolarian chert.

- 600 to 750 m of Upper Silurian–Lower Devonian sandstone, conglomerate, and mudrock, deposited in alluvial to shallow marine settings on the western and eastern flanks of the southern Boothia Uplift (Peel Sound Formation; Plate 9, G-H) and on the northern Boothia Uplift (Snowblind Bay Formation).
- perhaps more than 2 km of Lower Devonian turbidites (fine-grained sandstone and mudrock), deposited in deep-water settings on the western flank of the northern Boothia Uplift (Bathurst Island and Stuart Bay Formations; Plate 9, H-I).
- a few hundred meters of Lower Devonian sandstone, mudrock, and conglomerate on the western flank of the Inglefield Uplift in central Ellesmere Island (Vendom Fiord Formation; Plate 9, I). The terrigenous sediments were derived from lower Paleozoic and older carbonate and clastic units and deposited in alluvial to shallow marine settings where they became mixed with nondetrital carbonates. An underlying Lower Devonian unit of peritidal sandstone and siltstone, about 1.8 km thick, may also have been derived from that uplift.

By early Middle Devonian time, a foreland basin had been created in the northeastern part of the mobile belt that was fringed by uplands on the northwest, northeast, and southeast. Out of this region, an enormous clastic wedge, composed mainly of sandstone and mudrock with small proportions of conglomerate, prograded to the southwest and west in Middle and Late Devonian time, filling the remnants of the deep-water basin to shelf level, and transforming the shelf into an alluvial plain (Plate 9, J-K; Embry, Ch. 10). Proximal shelf environments (including deltas) were dominated by clastic sediments while distal shelf environments also received carbonates. The preserved maximum thickness of the wedge is about 5 km, but the original thickness, inferred from thermal maturation data, is on the order of 10 km. The eroded part probably was of latest Devonian and Early Carboniferous (Tournaisian) age.

The sandstones consist mainly of quartz with varying proportions of feldspar, mica, chlorite, and chert, the latter derived partly from uplifted strata of the deep-water basin. Provenance studies and paleocurrent directions indicate that the Middle Devonian clastics were derived mainly from northeasterly to southeasterly, largely cratonic sources and that the northern mountains became increasingly important sources during the Late Devonian. Alternations of meandering and braided stream deposits in the alluvial part of the basin probably reflect tectonic events in the hinterland and associated cyclical changes in climatic humidity.

A minor nonmarine basin is represented by perhaps 1 km of Givetian(?) and Frasnian strata in the Clements Markham Fold Belt. These chert-rich sediments probably were derived from the Grant Land Uplift in the northwestern Hazen Fold Belt, an area where the base of the Sverdrup Basin lies on the Lower Cambrian Grant Land Formation (Plate 9, K).

LATE EARLY CARBONIFEROUS TO EARLY CRETACEOUS DEVELOPMENT OF THE SVERDRUP BASIN

The late Early Carboniferous to Late Cretaceous history of the Arctic Islands was dominated by the development of the Sverdrup Basin. The basin is about 1,300 km long, up to 400 km wide (after compressive deformation), and bounded on the northwest by a horst (Sverdrup Rim), which subsided relatively slowly. Up to 3 km of upper Paleozoic strata (Fig. 10; Davies and Nassichuk, Ch. 13; Beauchamp and others, 1989) and up to 9 km of Mesozoic strata (Figs. 11 and 12; Embry, Ch. 14) were deposited in the axial region.

The basin originated during a Carboniferous–Early Permian rifting event, apparent from listric faults with associated coarse clastic sediments. The extensional origin of the basin is also apparent from the fact that the crust is thinner in the axial region than at the margins (37 to 41 km versus 48 km; Sobczak and others, Ch. 5B). The cause of the rifting is uncertain, but on northwestern Melville Island there is evidence for dextral transcurrent motion in Early Permian time (Melvillian disturbance). Permian to Early Cretaceous subsidence, markedly decreasing in rate with time, is attributed to lithospheric cooling that followed this rifting event (Stephenson and others, 1987).

Overall, the basin fill consists mainly of clastic sediments, but with larger proportions of carbonates, evaporites, and chert during the late Paleozoic. The absence of post-Carboniferous evaporites, and the near-absence of post-Permian carbonates (except for minor Middle Triassic occurrences) reflect continental drift from subequatorial to high latitudes, an inference based on paleomagnetism and supported by biostratigraphy and sedimentology. The clastic sediments were derived mainly from areas south and east of the basin, close to the basin margin or remote. Marked fluctuations in sediment supply resulted from episodic uplifts of the craton. Lesser amounts of clastic sediments were derived from sources in the area now occupied by the Amerasian Basin.

Fluctuations of relative sea level, apparent throughout the Carboniferous to Cretaceous interval, have created major stratigraphic sequences (7 in the Carboniferous and Permian, 30 in the Mesozoic succession) that are bounded by disconformities or diastems.

Intermittent rise of Carboniferous evaporite diapirs, from Triassic time onward, produced minor highs within the basin that are marked by relatively thin stratigraphic successions and local unconformities.

During the Late Carboniferous to Middle Jurassic, the Sverdrup Basin extended from northeastern Ellesmere Island to southwestern Prince Patrick Island. A northwest-trending basement arch, the Tanquary High, is apparent in the northeastern part in late Paleozoic to Middle Triassic time. During the Late Jurassic, the Sverdrup Basin proper was connected with a sub-basin on Banks Island via Eglinton graben. The depositional patterns during specific time intervals can be summarized as follows.

Late Early Carboniferous. The oldest unit in the Sverdrup Basin, late Early Carboniferous (Visean) in age and present at a few localities only (Emma Fiord Formation; Fig. 10), consists of up to 300 m of mudrock, lensoid sandstone, fine conglomerate, and coal seams, with lacustrine marlstone rich in organic matter derived from algae ("oil shale") on northwestern Devon Island.

Latest Early Carboniferous to Early Permian. The oldest continuous deposits, resting mainly on the Ellesmerian erosion surface, but locally on the Emma Fiord Formation, are diachronous conglomerates and sandstones with common red beds (Canyon Fiord and Borup Fiord Formations). In northern Axel Heiberg and northwestern Ellesmere Islands, mafic volcanics, in part alkaline (Audhild Formation), occur locally within and above the basal clastics.

Following the initial rifting, and concomitant with later stages of rifting, concentric facies evolved during earliest Late Carboniferous (Namurian) to mid–Early Permian (Artinskian) time (Plate 9, L). Three outer belts are characterized by: (1) nonmarine clastics, confined to southern and eastern margins of the basin and derived from fault scarps in adjacent lower Paleozoic strata (Canyon Fiord Formation); (2) mixed clastic and carbonate sediments deposited in predominantly peritidal to shallow marine settings (Belcher Channel, Antoinette and Tanquary Formations), locally with evaporites (Mount Bayley Formation); and (3) cyclical shelf carbonates (Nansen Formation), locally with basalt (Esayoo Formation) at the top.

In the central parts of the Sverdrup Basin, two or three separate sub-basins developed in which subsidence exceeded deposition so that deep-water conditions prevailed. There, the basal red beds (Borup Fiord Formation) are overlain by a lower unit of halite, anhydrite, limestone, and minor sandstone (Otto Fiord Formation), and an upper unit of cherty limestone, chert, and mudrock (Hare Fiord Formation). Submarine relief of no less than 300 m between shelf and basin is apparent from carbonate tongues (in part debris flows and turbidites) with paleoslopes of more than 35°. The submarine origin of the evaporites is apparent from various criteria, including: position in the axial region of the basin, seaward from marine limestones; presence of marine biota in interbedded limestones; thickness of anhydrite units (typically more than 10 m); and partial preservation of laterally continuous, thin stratification.

Late Early and Late Permian. During the late Early Permian, nonmarine, deltaic, and shallow marine—in part glauconitic—sandstones were deposited at the basin margin (Sabine Bay and Assistance Formations); dark mudrock and spicular chert of deeper water origin in the center (van Hauen Formation; Plate 9, M); and, for a short interval, a local shelf-margin carbonate unit between them ("unnamed" formation of Fig. 10). The youngest dated deposits, of early Late Permian (Wordian) age, are marginal glauconitic sandstones and mudrocks (Trold Fiord Formation), which surround skeletal limestone, cherty limestone, and chert (Degerböls Formation).

Permian–Triassic boundary. Permian marine sedimentation was terminated by a relative fall in sea level that resulted in an extensive disconformity on the shelves. The effects of this regression in the axial deep-water regions are controversial because both lithological evidence for emergence and erosion, and biostratigraphic evidence for continuous sedimentation (i.e., fossils of latest Permian age), are lacking—the uppermost 70 m of the basinal succession are unfossiliferous.

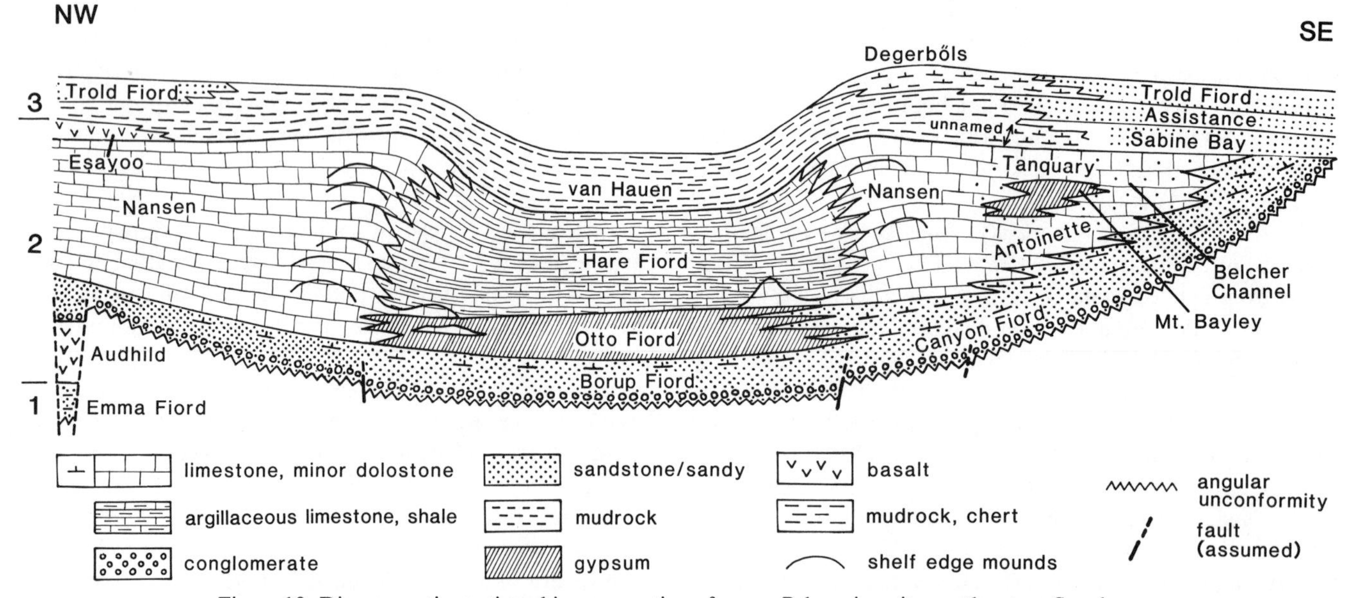

Figure 10. Diagrammatic stratigraphic cross section of upper Paleozoic units, northeastern Sverdrup Basin, western Ellesmere Island (not to scale; from Davies and Nassichuk, Ch. 13). (1) Upper-Lower Carboniferous (Visean); (2) Lower-Upper Carboniferous to mid-Lower Permian (lower Artinskian); (3) Upper-Lower Permian to lower-Upper Permian (Wordian). Beauchamp and others (1989) suggest that the unfossiliferous uppermost part of the Trold Fiord and van Hauen Formations ranges in age to latest Permian.

Early Triassic to Early Cretaceous. Normal sea level was restored in the Early Triassic. Deep-water conditions persisted in the axial region of the basin where a thick succession (locally more than 4 km) of turbidites, in part argillaceous (Blind Fiord and Blaa Mountain Formations), accumulated while coarser sediments were laid down in fluvial-deltaic and shelf settings at the basin margin (Bjorne Formation, Schei Point Group; Plate 9, N). Two depocenters, related to major deltas, are apparent in west-central Ellesmere Island and northern Melville Island.

Deltas prograded across the entire basin during an episode of high sediment supply in latest Triassic to Early Jurassic (Norian to Sinemurian) time (Heiberg Formation; Plate 9, O). Subsequent basinal deposits consist of thinner successions of shallow marine sandstone and mudrock that interfinger in a complex fashion (Plate 9, P-Q; Fig. 12).

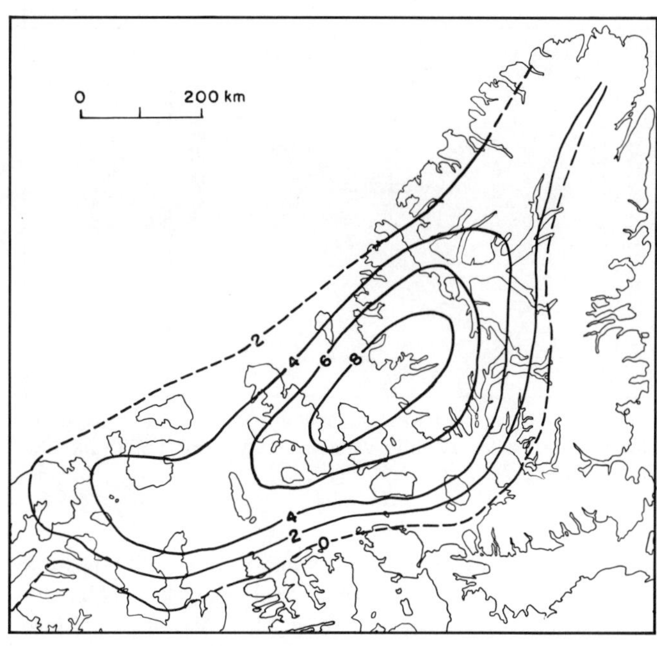

Figure 11. Thickness (in km) of Mesozoic deposits in Sverdrup Basin (adapted from Embry, Ch. 14).

MIDDLE JURASSIC TO LATE CRETACEOUS EVENTS RELATED TO OPENING OF THE AMERASIAN BASIN

A second cycle in the development of the Sverdrup Basin, which was limited to western parts of the islands where it overlapped in age with the first, spans the Middle Jurassic to Late Cretaceous (Embry, Ch. 14). It appears to be related to the

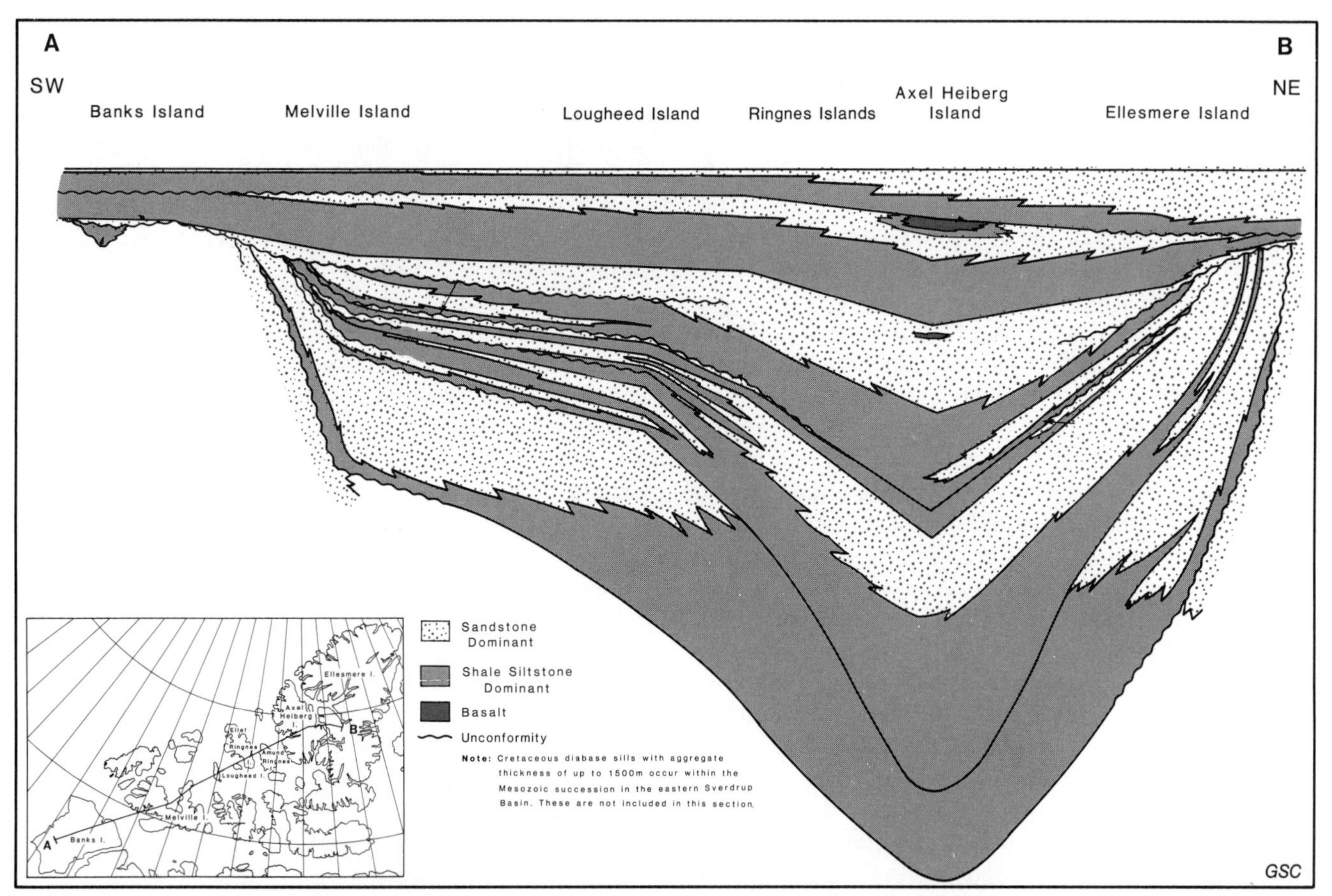

Figure 12. Schematic stratigraphic cross section of Banks and Sverdrup Basins (from Embry, Ch. 14).

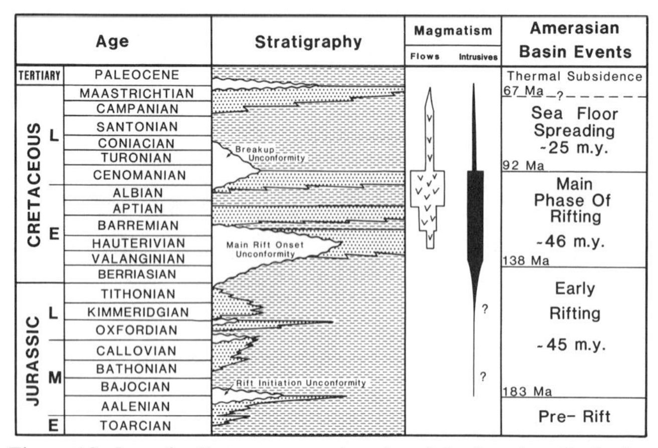

Figure 13. Jurassic–Cretaceous stratigraphy of the Sverdrup Basin: implications for the history of the western Arctic Ocean (Embry and Osadetz, 1988, Fig. 7).

development of the western part of the Arctic Ocean (known as the Amerasian Basin), which comprises the Canada and Makarov Basins together with the intervening Alpha-Mendeleyev Ridge. Seismic evidence has shown that Canada Basin is floored by oceanic crust, and bathymetry and limited bottom samples suggest that the oceanic crust is Cretaceous in age (Sweeney, 1985). However, in contrast to most other oceans of the world, both well-defined magnetic anomalies and drill cores are absent so that inferences about the specific age and mode of formation of this basin can only be based on the geologic history of the surrounding lands.

A series of minor unconformities in Middle and Upper Jurassic strata on the northwestern margin of the Sverdrup Basin are taken by Embry (Ch. 14) to indicate an initial rifting stage of the Amerasian Basin (Fig. 13). The onset of the main stage of rifting probably is marked by a major break within the Lower Cretaceous Series. Uplifts during the main rifting stage produced widespread fluvial deposits (Isachsen Formation [Plate 9, R] and Hassel Formation) during the later part of the Early Cretaceous. The beginning of sea-floor spreading and thermal subsidence probably coincides with an early Late Cretaceous (Cenomanian–Turonian) “breakup” unconformity that is overlain by extensive marine mudrock of Late Cretaceous (Turonian to Campanian) age (Kanguk Formation; Plate 9, S; Embry and Osadetz, 1988).

The main rifting stage was accompanied by extrusion of tholeiitic basalt in Axel Heiberg and northern Ellesmere Islands, most widespread in the late Early Cretaceous (Albian; Fig. 13). The onset of spreading, according to this interpretation, coincides approximately with the emplacement of gabbroic to granitic intrusions in northern Ellesmere Island, the largest of which has yielded an early Late Cretaceous (late Cenomanian) U-Pb zircon age of 92 ± 1 Ma. This was followed by Late Cretaceous (Turonian to Maastrichtian[?]) bimodal and alkaline volcanism.

The fact that these magmatic rocks are concentrated in an area adjacent to the Alpha Ridge of the Arctic Ocean may not be coincidental. The latter, a volcanic(?) edifice about 40 km thick, has been interpreted as a hot-spot track, comparable to the Iceland–Faeroe Plateau (Asudeh and others, 1988).

The tectonic models proposed for the opening of the Amerasian Basin cannot be properly discussed here. Suffice it to state that the oldest mobilistic hypothesis (Carey, 1958), in its present version (e.g., Jackson and others, 1986; Asudeh and others, 1988), envisages counterclockwise rotation of an “Arctic Alaska Plate” comprising northern Alaska and parts of northeastern Siberia (Fig. 1). Although this model is widely accepted now, its enormous implications for the entire pre-Tertiary history of the Arctic Islands, Alaska, and Siberia have not yet been adequately evaluated. A rival hypothesis (e.g., Smith, 1987) proposes that Arctic Alaska attained its present position by sinistral transcurrent motion along the present margin of the Arctic Islands. This reconstruction conflicts with stratigraphic evidence indicating continuity of Arctic Alaska with the northeastern Cordillera (e.g., Richards and others, 1989) rather than with the Arctic Islands.

CRETACEOUS-PALEOGENE EVENTS RELATED TO THE OPENING OF THE LABRADOR BASIN

Early Cretaceous to Oligocene development of the Labrador Basin and related faulting in the southeastern Arctic Islands

The Labrador Basin is a structurally and topographically depressed region that is underlain by oceanic crust and extended continental crust (Balkwill, 1987). The basin is divisible into three physiographic and geologic subprovinces coinciding with the Labrador Sea, Davis Strait, and Baffin Bay (see Fig. 15a, below). Best known is the geologic history of the Labrador Sea, where well-defined magnetic anomalies are present and where extensive geophysical investigations and drilling have been carried out (Srivastava and others, 1981; Balkwill, 1987). Rifting, inferred from fault-bounded wedges of terrigenous clastic sediments and alkali basalt, occurred in Early and early Late Cretaceous time. That the Labrador Sea has oceanic crust is apparent not only from well-developed paired magnetic anomalies, but also from seismic and gravity evidence for an extinct mid-oceanic ridge with a fault-bounded median valley. Sea-floor spreading progressed from south to north; the oldest anomaly in the south (34) is early Late Cretaceous in age, and the oldest in the north (31), latest Cretaceous. The spreading continued to latest Eocene or earliest Oligocene time but ceased before anomaly 13 time (early Oligocene).

Magnetic anomalies are weak in Baffin Bay and absent from Davis Strait, and the tectonic history of these areas is uncertain in detail. However, if sea-floor spreading is accepted for the Labrador Sea, geometric constraints require that this process has also occurred in these two subprovinces.

Post–early Paleozoic normal faults are common in the southeastern and south-central part of the archipelago (Fig. 14). Subvolcanic alkaline intrusions on southeastern Bathurst Island (Fig. 14, FCV), associated with normal faults, have an Eocene

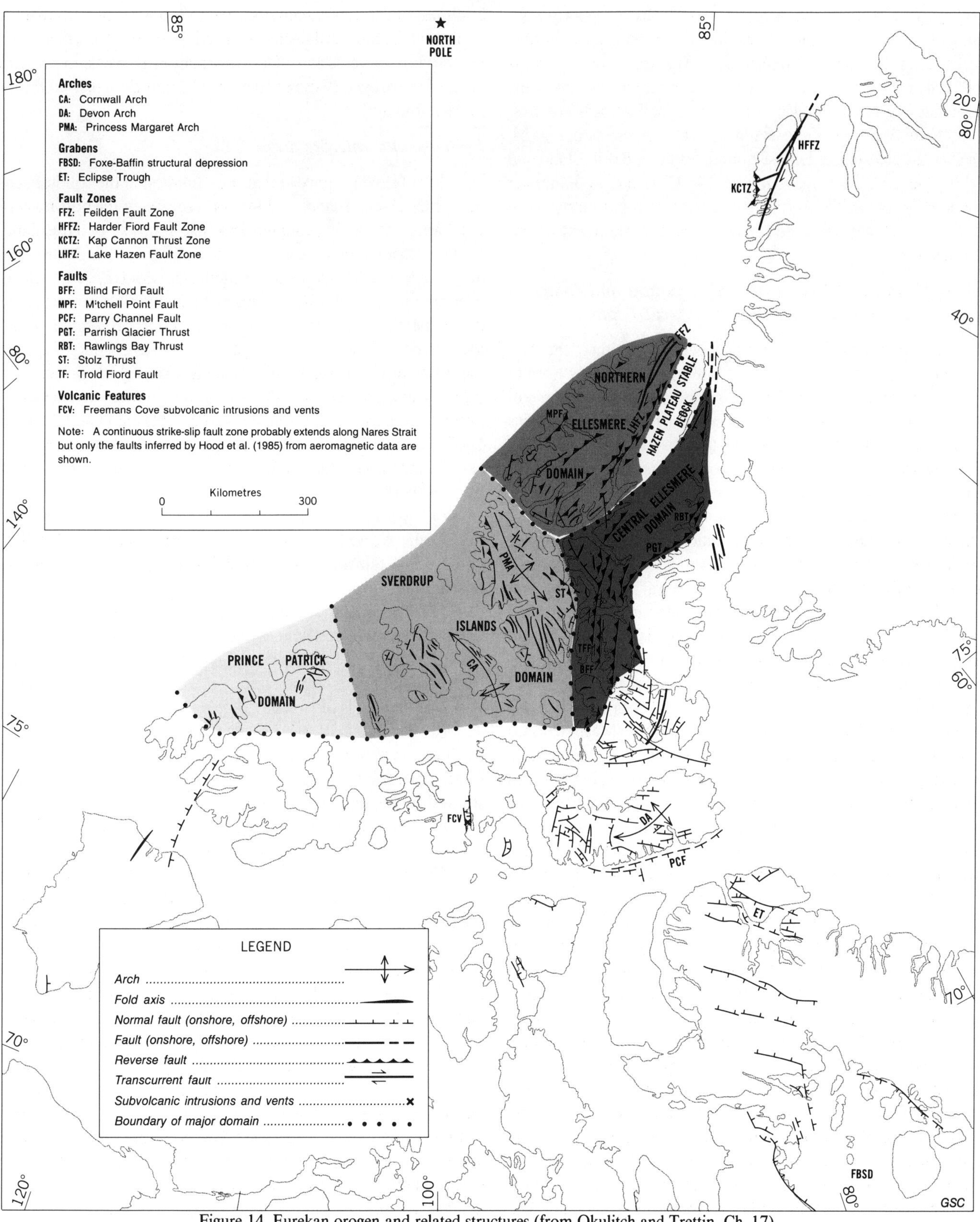

Figure 14. Eurekan orogen and related structures (from Okulitch and Trettin, Ch. 17).

Rb-Sr age. Elsewhere, the ages of these faults are poorly constrained, but it is reasonable to assume that most originated during the development of Baffin Bay. The trend of the faults conforms with the structural grain of the Precambrian crystalline basement in given areas. Major grabens or half grabens are present in Foxe Basin (the Foxe–Baffin structural depression, Fig. 14, FBSD), the environs of Eclipse Sound, northern Baffin Island and Bylot Island (Eclipse trough, Fig. 14, ET), and in Lancaster Sound (Fig. 14, PCF). A system of dextral transcurrent faults in southeastern Ellesmere Island may represent onshore extensions of transform faults.

Latest Cretaceous–Paleogene sedimentation and compressive deformation in the northeastern Arctic Islands

The uppermost Cretaceous-Paleogene succession of the Arctic Islands, assigned to the Eureka Sound Group (locally Formation), is preserved in a number of structural depressions, some of which coincide with original depositional basins or sub-basins (Plate 9, T; Miall, Ch. 15). Locally, it consists of more than 3 km of sandstone and mudrock, with minor amounts of conglomerate, derived from sources within the Sverdrup Basin and around its periphery. Deposition took place in predominantly fluvial and deltaic settings under unstable tectonic conditions. Nonmarine conditions prevailed in the eastern parts of the archipelago, and shallow marine conditions in the north-central and southwestern parts. The regional stratigraphy of these deposits is controversial and difficult to resolve, because of complex facies relations and biostratigraphic problems. Although all can be regarded as syntectonic *sensu lato,* only two facts are established: (1) a major high within the basin (Cornwall Arch, Fig. 14, CA) was truncated by erosion some time between latest Cretaceous (Maastrichtian) and late early Eocene time, and (2) some coarse conglomerates, bordering major thrusts, such as the Stolz thrust (ST, Fig. 14) and the Lake Hazen fault zone (LHFZ, Fig. 14), are middle Eocene and(?) younger in age. Conglomerates adjacent to faults in eastern Ellesmere Island have been tentatively dated as Paleocene, but this remains to be confirmed. The mid-Eocene movements ushered in a phase of climactic deformation that involved the Eureka Sound Group along with older units. The deformed Eocene and older strata are locally unconformably overlain by Miocene(?) and Pliocene strata of the Beaufort Formation.

The term "Eurekan Orogeny" is applied to the deformation of the Eureka Sound Group (and older units), as well as to the preceding arching and thrust faulting in Canada and North Greenland (Okulitch and Trettin, Ch. 17; Soper and Higgins, Ch. 16). The effects of this event were most pronounced in northeastern parts of the Arctic Islands and northernmost Greenland. The orogen is divisible into five major domains, including an internal stable block in northern Ellesmere Island (Okulitch and Trettin, Ch. 17). The domains differ mainly in structural trend, which conforms with Ellesmerian and older trends in given areas. The Sverdrup Islands domain contains two large arches (Cornwall and Princess Margaret, Fig. 14, CA and PMA); elsewhere, the orogen is characterized by thrust faults and associated folds. In addition, sinistral strike-slip occurred in Nares Strait and adjacent to it, and dextral strike-slip occurred in parts of northern and central Ellesmere Island. The deformation is weak in western parts of the orogen (western Sverdrup Islands domain and Prince Patrick domain).

Plate-tectonic interpretation

Kerr (1967) proposed that the extension in the southeastern part of the Arctic Islands and the compression in the northeastern part were caused by counterclockwise rotation of Greenland. Systematic analysis of magnetic anomalies in the Labrador Sea and North Atlantic supports this model (Srivastava, 1985). However, treatment of North America and Greenland as separate rigid plates inevitably suggested that Greenland and Ellesmere Island were initially separated by an ocean that was subducted during the rotation (Fig. 15b). The fact that there is no geologic evidence for such an ocean indicates that spreading, rotation, and deformation all occurred within a single, variably plastic plate (cf., Kerr, 1967; Peirce, 1982). This model explains some known characteristics of the orogen and implies others that have yet to be verified by field work:

(1) Most of the deformation occurred in the weakest part of the plate, i.e., that region where the Precambrian crystalline basement is thin or absent (Franklinian deep-water basin and Sverdrup Basin).

(2) The compressional deformation was not thin-skinned, although some detachment surfaces occur at shallow levels; for example, within a Carboniferous evaporite. Reverse motion on listric normal faults, formed during the initiation of the Sverdrup Basin, probably played a major role.

(3) Deviation of trends from the expected fan pattern must be due to the influence of the inherited fabric. Obliquity of the rotational stress with respect to the latter may explain the dextral strike-slip faulting inferred for parts of Ellesmere Island.

(4) The absolute shortening along arcs related to the pivotal point should increase with distance from the pivot.

The most obvious discrepancy between this plate-tectonic model and field information is timing. Rotation of Greenland seems to have occurred from Early Cretaceous time onward, but significant shortening within the Arctic Islands is not apparent before Eocene or possibly Paleocene time. Another problem concerns the magnitude of sinistral offset along Nares Strait (Dawes and Kerr, 1982). Reconstructions based on magnetic anomalies require no less than 125 km of offset, whereas geologic surface information and aeromagnetic patterns (Hood and others, 1985) permit no more than a few tens of kilometers. However, the discrepancy is much smaller if extensional faulting in the Arctic Islands is taken into consideration. Unknown also are the position and character of the northern limit of the Eurekan orogen. If the orogen is terminated by a transform fault on the Innuitian continental margin, then the counterclockwise rotation of Greenland would have resulted in dextral motion along that fault.

The Eurekan orogeny was coeval with a transpressive deformation in western Spitsbergen and northeasternmost Green-

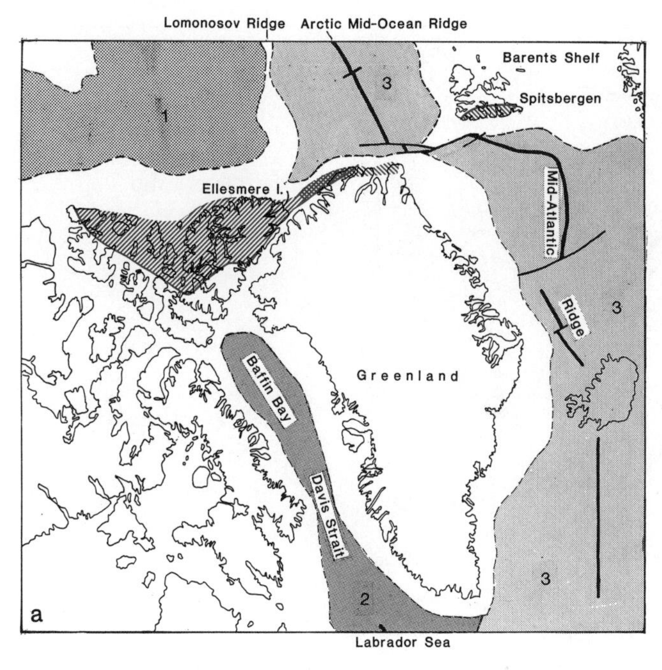

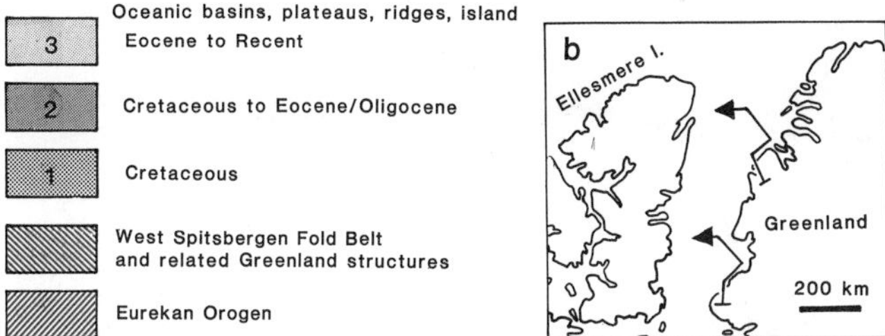

Figure 15. a: Tectonic setting of Eurekan orogen (adapted from Churkin and Johnson, 1983, and other sources). b: Motion of Greenland relative to the Arctic Islands from Late Cretaceous (Campanian) to earliest Oligocene (adapted from Srivastava, 1985, Fig. 9). This reconstruction is based on anomalies 34-13 in the Labrador Sea and North Atlantic, and assumes that Greenland and the Arctic Islands were rigid plates separated by a wide, presumably oceanic, gap in the Cretaceous. However, there is no geological evidence for such a gap and the latter can be eliminated if it is assumed that the rotation of Greenland and the Eurekan orogeny were complementary deformations within a single plate of variable strength. In this case, the gap can be interpreted as the area eliminated by faulting in the Eurekan orogen, and the trajectories (arrows) as indicators of the stress directions during given time intervals.

land, caused by dextral motion of the Barents Shelf relative to the shelf off northeastern Greenland along an east–west transform fault that separates the Arctic and Atlantic mid-ocean ridges (Fig. 15a; Soper and Higgins, Ch. 16). Spreading on the Arctic mid-ocean ridge detached the Lomonosov Ridge, a thin sliver of continental crust, from the Barents Shelf. Differences in spreading rate or direction on the Arctic and Atlantic mid-ocean ridges could have caused motion of the Lomonosov Ridge relative to the Innuitian region, possibly resulting in additional stress on the Eurekan orogen. However, a predrift reconstruction based on isobaths (Le Pichon and others, 1977) did not reveal any offset between the Lomonosov Ridge and Greenland.

MIDDLE TERTIARY TO RECENT TECTONIC AND PHYSIOGRAPHIC DEVELOPMENTS

The middle and late Tertiary sedimentary record of the region is mostly restricted to Miocene(?) and Pliocene deposits on the northwestern margin of the islands that form part of the Arctic continental terrace wedge (Figs. 2 and 16; Miall, Ch. 15). The scarcity of preserved sediments in other areas reflects widespread uplift and erosion, which was most pronounced in parts of the Eurekan orogen and around Baffin Bay (Trettin, Ch. 18).

Differential uplift in the northeastern Queen Elizabeth Islands and North Greenland can be interpreted as isostatic response to Eurekan crustal thickening combined with post-Eurekan erosion. The fact that mountains and negative Bouguer anomalies persist indicates that the crustal roots of the orogen have not yet been eliminated by the interplay of uplift and erosion. Analogy with other mountain belts suggests that the isostatic uplift was intermittent and rapid, but little information is available on related relict erosion surfaces. These cycles of uplift and erosion presumably were of large amplitude (in the order of kilometers) and long duration (millions or tens of millions of years). By comparison, superimposed Quaternary oscillations of the land surface, caused by elastic response to glacial loading and unloading, were of low amplitude (hundreds of meters) and short duration (<1 m.y.).

The mid-Tertiary rise of Precambrian crystalline terranes around Baffin Bay is tentatively interpreted as a delayed shoulder uplift, caused by thermal perturbations in the mantle after the rifting. These positive movements must have been accompanied by renewed normal faulting in Jones and Lancaster Sounds, which remained submerged.

The present fiords and seaways probably originated as a Tertiary drainage system (Fortier and Morley, 1956) that followed faults, fractures, and weakly resistant rock types exposed in folds and grabens. Submarine geomorphic features indicate that this system was deepened and straightened by glaciers, and there is evidence that early Pleistocene glaciers extended across certain channels (Hodgson, Ch. 19). In contrast, later glaciations were restricted to present land areas.

Apart from these major developments, it is worth noting that a meteorite impact formed the 16-km-wide Haughton Crater (Fig. 16) in central Devon Island in Early Miocene time (Thorsteinsson and Mayr, 1987).

RESOURCES

The Arctic Islands contain significant proportions of Canada's resources of metals, petroleum, and coal, but only two base-metal deposits are presently exploited.

Metals (Gibbins, Ch. 20D). A large, high-grade iron deposit occurs in lower Proterozoic metamorphic rocks at Mary River, Baffin Island (Plate 9, index in lower right). Zinc, found in karst cavities in an upper middle Proterozoic (or younger) dolostone of northern Baffin Island, has been mined at Nanisivik (Plate 9,

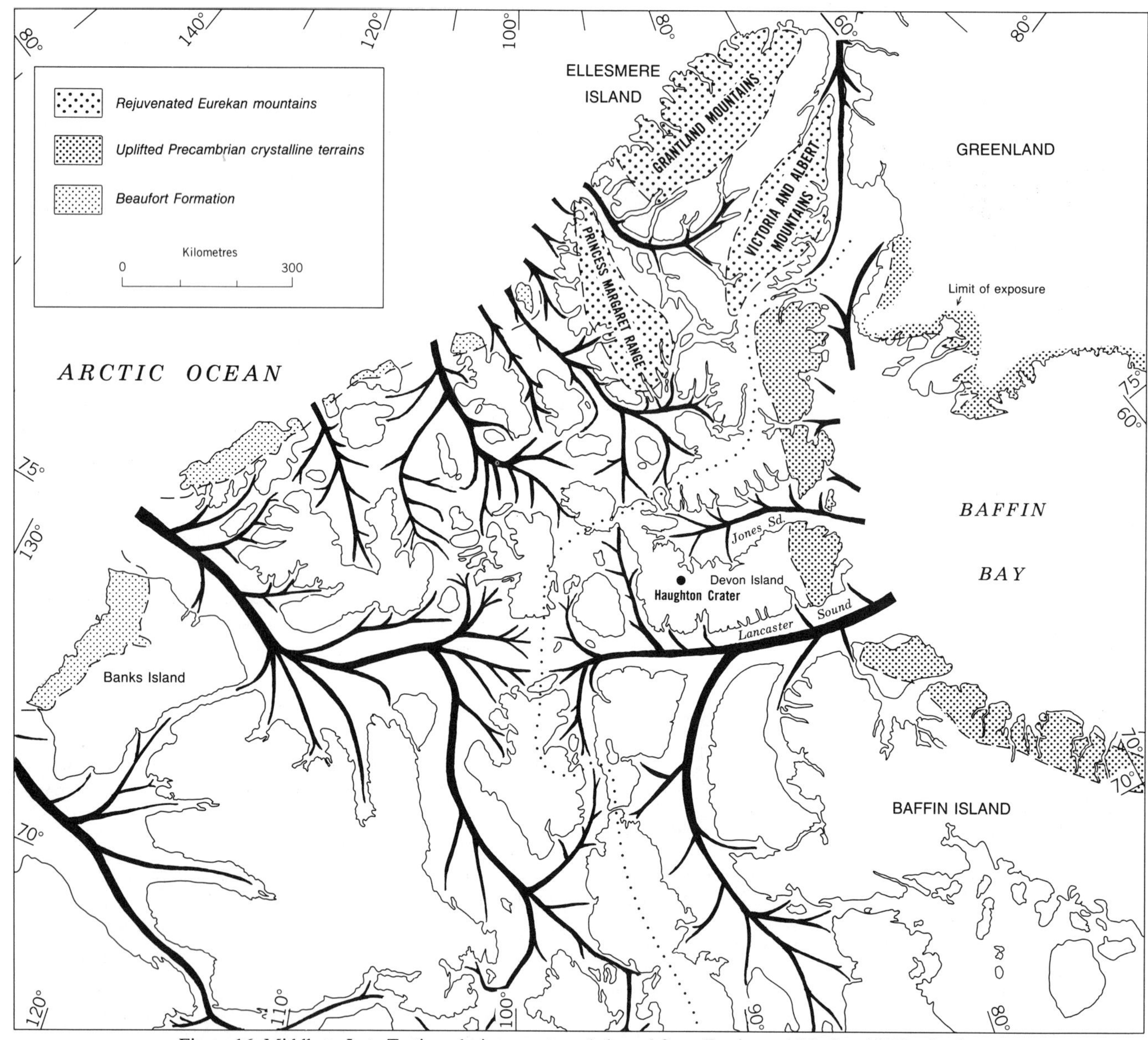

Figure 16. Middle to Late Tertiary drainage pattern (adapted from Fortier and Morley, 1956), physiography, and sedimentary units.

index) since 1976. Past production and current reserves add up to 10 million tonnes of ore containing more than 10 percent zinc, 1 percent lead, and 40 g/t silver. Lead and zinc have been mined at Polaris, Little Cornwallis Island, since 1982 (Plate 9, index). Polaris, like other deposits of the Cornwallis lead–zinc district, is of Mississippi Valley–type and hosted by an Ordovician shelf carbonate unit that was subjected to karsting during Early Devonian movements of the Boothia Uplift. The pre-production ore reserves amounted to 23 million tonnes of 4.3 percent lead (galena) and 14.1 percent zinc (sphalerite). Two significant, but smaller, lead–zinc deposits occur in the vicinity of Polaris, and minor showings are present in other parts of the Boothia Uplift and in the Central Ellesmere Fold Belt.

Petroleum (Embry and others, Ch. 20A). To date, 18 hydrocarbon fields have been discovered. One small oil field is contained in Devonian (Emsian–Eifelian) strata of Cameron Island, at the top of a long-lived and extensive carbonate buildup (Plate 9, I; Fig. 4), where vadose processes and fracturing created vuggy porosity. The remaining 17 fields occur in the western part of the Sverdrup Basin, in sandstones of Late Triassic to Early Cretaceous, predominantly Jurassic age. All are in anticlines, most of which are salt-cored. The petroleum was generated from Middle and Upper Triassic shales in Late Cretaceous–early Tertiary time.

Apart from these discoveries, there are various prospects in the Cambrian to Devonian succession of Arctic Platform and Franklinian shelf, and in the Carboniferous to Cretaceous succession of the Sverdrup Basin. Tertiary prospects are limited to Lancaster Sound and the Arctic Islands Shelf. In 1984, the total of discovered, untapped, recoverable resources in the Arctic Islands was estimated at 686 10^6m^3 (4.3 B bbls) of oil and 2,257 10^9m^3 (79.7 TCF) of gas.

Coal (Bustin and Miall, Ch. 20C). The most important coal resources are in the Maastrichtian-Paleogene Eureka Sound Group of eastern Axel Heiberg and west-central Ellesmere Islands, with lesser occurrences in Cretaceous and Tertiary strata on Banks and Baffin Islands. Surface reconnaissance indicates about 25 × 10^9 tonnes of lignite, 20 × 10^9 tonnes of subbituminous coal, and 5 × 10^9 tonnes of high-volatile bituminous coal.

REFERENCES CITED

Because many references in this chapter are from a more extended synthesis on the geology of the region currently in press, the full citation for that book is given below, and authors, with their chapter titles, are listed alphabetically before the remainder of the reference list.

Trettin, H. P., ed., 1989, Innuitian Orogen and Arctic Platform; Canada and Greenland: Geological Survey of Canada, Geology of Canada, v. 3 (also Geological Society of America, The Geology of North America, v. E) (in press).

Bustin, R. M., and Miall, A. D., Coal resources, Arctic Islands, chapter 20C.

Christie, R. L., and Dawes, P. R., Geographic and geologic exploration, chapter 2.

Coles, R. L., Aeromagnetic field, chapter 5D.

Davies, G. R., and Nassichuk, W. W., Carboniferous and Permian history of the Sverdrup Basin, chapter 13.

Dawes, P. R., and Christie, R. L., Geomorphic regions, chapter 3.

Embry, A. F., Middle–Upper Devonian clastic wedge of the Arctic Islands, chapter 10.

—— , Mesozoic history of the Arctic Islands, chapter 14.

Embry, A. F., Powell, T. G., and Mayr, U., Petroleum resources, Arctic Islands, chapter 20A.

Forsyth, D. A., Hasegawa, H. S., and Wetmiller, R. J., Seismicity, chapter 5C.

Frisch, T., and Trettin, H. P., Precambrian successions in the northernmost part of the Canadian Shield, chapter 6.

Gibbins, W. A., Economic mineral resources, Arctic Islands, chapter 20D.

Harrison, J. C., and Brent, T., Late Devonian–Early Carboniferous deformation, Prince Patrick and Banks Islands, chapter 12H.

Harrison, J. C., Fox, F. G., and Okulitch, A. V., Late Devonian–Early Carboniferous deformation of the Parry Islands and Canrobert fold belts, chapter 12G.

Higgins, A. K., and Soper, N. J., [Devonian–Early Carboniferous] Metamorphism [North Greenland], chapter 11B.

Higgins, A. K., Ineson, J. R., Peel, J. S., Surlyk, F., and Sonderholm, M., Cambrian to Silurian basin development and sedimentation, North Greenland, chapter 7.

Hodgson, D. A., The Quaternary record, chapter 19.

Miall, A. D., Late Cretaceous–Tertiary basin development and sedimentation, Arctic Islands, chapter 15.

Niblett, E. R., and Kurtz, R. D., Conductivity anomalies, chapter 5E.

Okulitch, A. V., Late Devonian–Early Carboniferous deformation of the Central Ellesmere and Jones Sound fold belts, chapter 12F.

Okulitch, A. V., and Trettin, H. P., Cretaceous–Early Tertiary deformation, Arctic Islands, chapter 17.

Okulitch, A. V., Packard, J. J., and Zolnai, A. I., Late Silurian–Early Devonian movements of the Boothia Uplift, chapter 12C.

Sobczak, L. W., Gravity field, chapter 5A.

Sobczak, L. W., Forsyth, D. A., and Overton, A., Crustal structure from seismic and gravity studies, chapter 5B.

Soper, N. J., and Higgins, A. K., [Devonian–Early Carboniferous] Deformation [North Greenland], chapter 11A.

Soper, N. J., and Higgins, A. K., Late Cretaceous–Early Tertiary deformation, North Greenland, chapter 16.

Trettin, H. P., Late Silurian–Early Devonian deformation, metamorphism, and granitic plutonism, northern Ellesmere and Axel Heiberg Islands, chapter 12B.

—— , Middle Devonian to Early Carboniferous deformations, northern Ellesmere and Axel Heiberg Islands, chapter 12E.

—— , Middle and Late Tertiary tectonic and physiographic developments, chapter 18.

Trettin, H. P., Mayr, U., Long, G.D.F., and Packard, J. J., Cambrian to Early Devonian basin development, sedimentation, and volcanism, Arctic Islands, chapter 8.

Asudeh, I., Green, A. G., and Forsyth, D. A., 1988, Canadian expedition to study the Alpha Ridge complex; Results of the seismic refraction survey: Geophysical Journal, v. 92, p. 283–301.

Balkwill, H. R., 1979, A synopsis of Carboniferous to Cenozoic tectonics, *in* Trettin, H. P., and Balkwill, H. R., Contributions to the tectonic history of the Innuitian Province, Arctic Canada: Canadian Journal of Earth Sciences, v. 16, p. 762–769.

—— , 1987, Labrador Basin; Structural and stratigraphic style, *in* Beaumont, C., and Tankard, A. J., eds., Sedimentary basins and basin-forming mechanisms: Canadian Society of Petroleum Geologists Memoir 12, p. 17–43.

Beauchamp, B., Harrison, J. C., and Henderson, C., 1989, Upper Paleozoic stratigraphy and basin analysis of the Sverdrup Basin, Canadian Arctic, *in* Current Research, part G: Geological Survey of Canada Paper 89-1G (in press).

Bluck, B. J., Halliday, A. N., Aftalion, M., and Macintyre, R. M., 1980, Age and origin of Ballantrae ophiolite and its significance to the Caledonian Orogeny and Ordovician time scale: Geology, v. 8, p. 492–495.

Carey, S. W., 1958, The tectonic approach to continental drift, *in* Carey, S. W., convener, Continental drift; A symposium: Hobart, Australia, University of Tasmania, Geology Department, p. 177–358.

Churkin, M., and Johnson, L., coordinators, 1983, Sheet 19, *in* Choubert, G., and Faure-Muret, A., coordinators, Geological world atlas: Paris, UNESCO, scale 1:16 000 000.

Dawes, P. R., and Kerr, J. W., eds., 1982, Nares Strait and the drift of Greenland; A conflict in plate tectonics: Meddelelser om Grønland, Geoscience 8, 392 p.

Dunning, G. R., and Krogh, T. E., 1985, Geochronology of ophiolites of the Newfoundland Appalachians: Canadian Journal of Earth Sciences, v. 22, p. 1659–1670.

Dunning, G. R., and Pedersen, R. B., 1988, U/Pb ages of ophiolites and arc-related plutons of the Norwegian Caledonides; Implications for the development of Iapetus: Contributions to Mineralogy and Petrology, v. 98, p. 13–23.

Embry, A. F., and Osadetz, K. G., 1988, Stratigraphic and tectonic significance of Cretaceous volcanism in Queen Elizabeth Islands, Canadian Arctic Archipelago: Canadian Journal of Earth Sciences, v. 25, p. 1209–1219.

Fortier, Y. O., and Morley, L. W., 1956, Geological unity of the Arctic Islands: Transactions of the Royal Society of Canada, v. 50, p. 3–12.

Harrison, J. C., and Bally, A. W., 1988, Cross-sections of the Parry Islands Fold Belt on Melville Island: Bulletin of Canadian Petroleum Geology, v. 36, p. 311–332.

Hood, P. J., Bower, M. E., Hardwich, C. D., and Teskey, D. J., 1985, Direct geophysical evidence for displacement along Nares Strait (Canada–Greenland) from low-level aeromagnetic data; A progress report, *in* Current Research, part A: Geological Survey of Canada Paper 85-1A, p. 517–522.

Jackson, H. R., Forsyth, D. A., and Leonard, G. L., 1986, Oceanic affinities of the Alpha Ridge, Arctic Ocean: Marine Geology, v. 73, p. 237–261.

Kanasewich, E. R., and Berkes, Z., 1988, Reprocessed and interpreted seismic reflection data from the Arctic Platform, Parry Island Fold Belt, and the Sverdrup Basin on eastern Melville Island, Canadian Arctic Islands: Geological Survey of Canada Open-File Report 1818, 230 p.

Kerr, J. W., 1967, Nares submarine rift valley and the relative rotation of north Greenland: Bulletin of Canadian Petroleum Geology, v. 15, p. 483–520.

Le Pichon, X., Sibuet, J. C., and Francheteau, J., 1977, The fit of the continents around the North Atlantic Ocean: Tectonophysics, v. 38, p. 169–209.

Ohta, Y., Hirajima, T., and Hiroi, Y., 1986, Caledonian high-pressure metamorphism in central western Spitsbergen, *in* Evans, B. W., and Brown, E. H., Blueschists and eclogites: Geological Society of America Memoir 164, p. 205–216.

Peirce, J. W., 1982, The evolution of the Nares Strait lineament and its relation to the Eurekan orogeny, *in* Dawes, P. R., and Kerr, J. W., Nares Strait and the drift of Greenland; A conflict in plate tectonics: Meddelelser om Grønland, Geoscience 8, p. 237–251.

Richards, B. C., Bamber, E. W., Higgins, A. C., and Utting, J., 1989, Carboniferous, *in* Stott, D. F., and Aitken, J. D., eds., Sedimentary cover of the craton; Canada: Geological Survey of Canada, Geology of Canada, no. 6, chapter 4E (also Geological Society of America, The Geology of North America, v. D-1) (in press).

Schuchert, C., 1923, Sites and nature of the North American geosynclines: Geological Society of America Bulletin, v. 34, p. 151–229.

Smith, D. G., 1987, Late Paleozoic to Cenozoic reconstructions of the Arctic, *in* Tailleur, I., and Weimer, P., eds., Alaskan North Slope geology: Pacific Section, Society of Economic Paleontologists and Mineralogists, and The Alaska Geological Society, v. 2, p. 785–795.

Snelling, N. J., Measurement of geological time and the geological time scale: Modern Geology, v. 11, p. 365–374.

Srivastava, S. P., 1985, Evolution of the Eurasian Basin and its implications to the motion of Greenland along Nares Strait: Tectonophysics, v. 114, p. 29–53.

Srivastava, S. P., Falconer, R.K.H., and MacLean, B., 1981, Labrador Sea, Davis Strait, Baffin Bay; Geology and geophysics; A review, *in* Kerr, J. W., and Ferguson, A. J., eds., Geology of the North Atlantic borderlands: Canadian Society of Petroleum Geologists Memoir 7, p. 333–398.

Stephenson, R. A., Embry, A. F., Nakiboglu, S. M., and Hastaoglu, M. A., 1987, Rift-initiated Permian to Early Cretaceous subsidence of the Sverdrup Basin, *in* Beaumont, C., and Tankard, A. J., eds., Sedimentary basins and basin-forming mechanisms: Canadian Society of Petroleum Geologists Memoir 12, p. 213–231.

Sweeney, J. F., 1985, Comments about the age of the Canada Basin, *in* Husebye, E. S., Johnson, G. L., and Kristoffersen, Y., eds., Geophysics of the polar regions: Tectonophysics, v. 114, p. 1–10.

Sweeney, J. F., and 8 others, 1986, Canadian Arctic; Somerset Island to Canada Basin: Geological Society of America, Continent-Ocean Transect G, scale 1:500,000.

Thorsteinsson, R., 1974, Carboniferous and Permian stratigraphy of Axel Heiberg Island and western Ellesmere Island, Canadian Arctic Archipelago: Geological Survey of Canada Bulletin 224, 115 p.

Thorsteinsson, R., and Mayr, U., 1987, The sedimentary rocks of Devon Island, Canadian Arctic Archipelago: Geological Survey of Canada Memoir 411, 182 p.

Thorsteinsson, R., and Tozer, E. T., 1970, Geology of the Arctic Archipelago, *in* Douglas, R.J.W., Geology and economic minerals of Canada: Geological Survey of Canada Economic Geology Report 1, p. 547–590.

Trettin, H. P., 1987, Pearya; A composite terrane with Caledonian affinities in northern Ellesmere Island: Canadian Journal of Earth Sciences, v. 24, p. 224–245.

Williams, H., 1984, Miogeoclines and suspect terranes of the Caledonian–Appalachian Orogen; Tectonic patterns in the North Atlantic region: Canadian Journal of Earth Sciences, v. 21, p. 887–901.

Zwart, H. J., and Dornsiepen, U. F., 1978, The tectonic framework of central and western Europe: Geologie en Mijnbouw, v. 57, p. 627–654.

MANUSCRIPT ACCEPTED BY THE SOCIETY DECEMBER 28, 1988

Published by permission of the Director, Institute of Sedimentary and Petroleum Geology, Calgary. Geological Survey of Canada Contribution 38888.

ACKNOWLEDGMENTS

This summary has been abstracted from contributions to Volume E of this series, on the Canadian Arctic Islands and North Greenland. I am indebted to all participants in this project for sharing with me their knowledge and insights. Because this account is concerned mainly with the Cambrian to Tertiary geology of the Arctic Islands, special thanks go to R. M. Bustin, G. R. Davies, A. F. Embry, W. A. Gibbins, J. C. Harrison, G.D.F. Long, U. Mayr, A. D. Miall, W. W. Nassichuk, A. V. Okulitch, and J. J. Packard, the principal authors or co-authors of chapters on this subject. The manuscript has benefited from critical reading by A. F. Embry, and editing by A. W. Bally and A. R. Palmer.

Printed in U.S.A.

The Geology of North America
Vol. A, The Geology of North America—An overview
The Geological Society of America, 1989

Chapter 14

The Ouachita system

J. Kaspar Arbenz
3964 Wonderland Hill Avenue, Boulder, Colorado 80304

INTRODUCTION

During the Paleozoic, the southern margin of the North American craton underwent one major ocean margin cycle ("Wilson cycle") lasting from the Late Proterozoic into the Permian. Breakup of a preexisting continent may have begun in the Late Proterozoic and lasted to the Middle Cambrian along a series of divergent rifts and transforms, which gave the margin between southern Alabama and northern Mexico an angular appearance. The breakup was accompanied by a system of rift arms and fault systems that reached far into the cratonic interior. The cycle ended with the formation of a collisional orogenic belt known as the Ouachita system.

The Ouachita Mountains of Oklahoma and Arkansas, the Marathon uplift of west Texas, and the Solitario (a small outcrop of Paleozoic rocks west of the Marathon region) are the only outcrop areas of the Ouachita system in the United States (Fig. 1). In northern Mexico, a number of small outcrops of Ouachita-facies rocks appear as inliers of the eastern Cordilleran orogen. The remainder of the frontal elements of the Ouachita system and the entire hinterland are covered by postorogenic Permian, Mesozoic, and Tertiary rocks of the Gulf Coastal Plain. Thus, some 90 percent of this orogenic belt cannot be inspected at the surface and must be mapped from subsurface borehole and geophysical data. Regional tectonic interpretations remain therefore rather tentative, especially in the deep hinterland, where boreholes are sparse.

The foreland of the Ouachita system, on the other hand, abounds in subsurface information, although postorogenic rocks also cover large areas. Because many of the foreland basins are prolific producers of oil and gas, however, thousands of boreholes and kilometers of seismic reflection surveys have yielded an almost unmatched three-dimensional information network.

From Late Cambrian to Early Mississippian time, the continental margin was trailing and passive, receiving stable to moderately subsiding platform sedimentation, while deep-water sediments were laid down off the shelf edge on the slope, rise, and bottom of the adjacent sea. Although this continental margin was the western continuation of the Appalachian margin, the sedimentary sequences, timing, and frequency of orogenic events were in part quite different.

Beginning in middle Mississippian time, deep-water flysch sedimentation with very high sedimentation rates replaced the preceeding slow off-shelf sedimentation. In the Ouachita Mountains, flysch sedimentation ceased in the mid-Pennsylvanian (late Atokan), but in west Texas, some deep-water sedimentation persisted into the Permian. During the Ouachita orogeny, northvergent thrusting transported much of the deep-water facies as an allochthonous thrust belt onto the outer continental shelf.

The tectonostratigraphic history of the Ouachita system has been the subject of many monographs, symposia, and regional summary articles since the early part of the century (e.g., Taff, 1902; Powers, 1928; Miser, 1929, 1934, 1959; van Waterschoot van der Gracht, 1931a, b; King, 1937, 1950, 1975a, b; 1977; Hendricks and others, 1947; Cline and others, 1959; Cline, 1960; Flawn and others, 1961; Keller and Cebull, 1973; Thomas, 1976, 1977a, b; Wickham, 1978; and summary articles in Hatcher and others, 1989). The present chapter serves, therefore, primarily as an update to the earlier publications and as an attempt to point out remaining unresolved problems.

PRE-OROGENIC EARLY AND MID-PALEOZOIC HISTORY OF DEPOSITION AND DEFORMATION

The rifting event that led to the formation of the passive margin of southern North America probably occurred during or sometime before the Middle Cambrian. The onset of rifting cannot be documented in the Ouachita system, but is known to have occurred in late Precambrian time in the southern Appalachians (Rankin, 1975). The overall shape of the margin is generally outlined by the present shape of the compressional thrust belt (Fig. 2) as well as by the distinct gravity signature that identifies the present southern border of the full thickness of continental crust, although the latter may have been somewhat modified by late Paleozoic tectonism and Mesozoic attenuation (Kruger and Keller, 1986). This margin (Fig. 3) can be divided into four, nearly straight segments: (a) a segment trending northwest to southeast between southern Alabama and southeastern Oklahoma; this segment abuts with an almost right angle against the Appalachian margin in southern Alabama; (b) a segment trending north-northeast to south-southwest in central Texas; (c) a south Texas segment trending northwest to southeast; and (d) a

Arbenz, J. K., 1989, The Ouachita system, *in* Bally, A. W., and Palmer, A. R., eds., The Geology of North America—An overview: Boulder, Colorado, Geological Society of America, The Geology of North America, v. A.

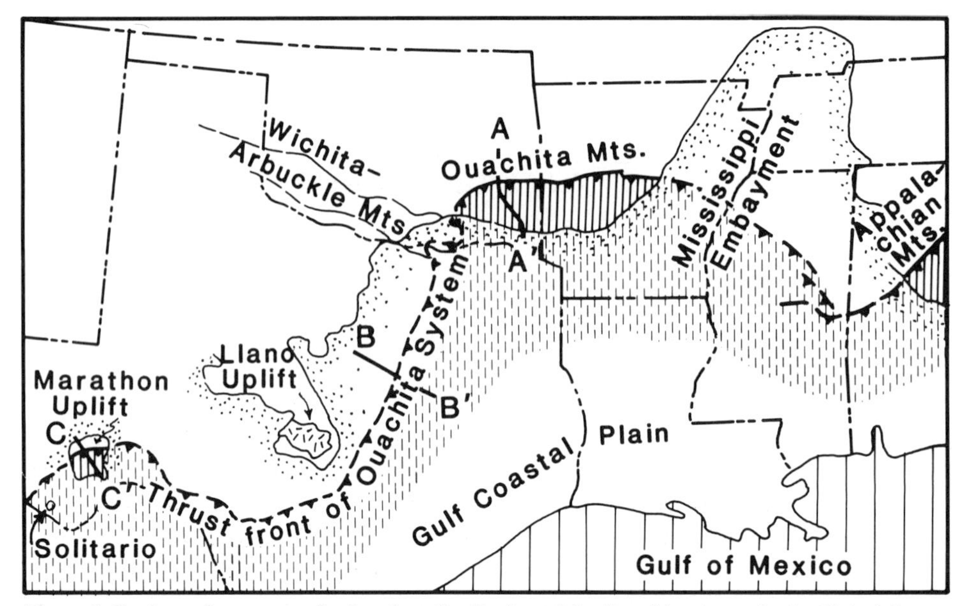

Figure 1. Regions of outcrop and subsurface distribution of the Ouachita system in the United States. For cross sections A–A′, B–B′, and C–C′, see Figure 11. Stipples, northern margin of Cretaceous-Tertiary cover; vertical ruled pattern, outcrop regions of Ouachita system; vertical dashes, subcrop region of Ouachita system.

Marathon segment trending northeast to southwest. Thomas (1976), following Keller and Cebull (1973) and Cebull and others (1976), suggested that this jagged margin was the result of alternating divergent rift and transform sections, and later (Thomas, 1977a) named the two southward-jutting prongs the Alabama and Texas promontories, respectively, and the two northerly reentrants the Ouachita and Marathon Embayments, respectively. During the late Paleozoic orogeny these promontories and embayments became recesses and salients in the thrust front of the Ouachita system.

From the continental margin, several rift and rift-transform basins extended into the interior of the continent (Fig. 3) from the newly opening ocean (Hoffman and others, 1974; Walper, 1977). From east to west these are (a) the extensive Reelfoot–Rough Creek–Rome trough rift and its more easterly subsidiary, the Birmingham basement fault; (b) the southern Oklahoma aulacogen or "leaky transform" (Thomas, 1985); and (c) the poorly documented Delaware aulacogen (Walper, 1977). The Reelfoot–Rome trough rift was the site of a thick, primarily clastic suite of exclusively sedimentary rocks of Early to Middle Cambrian age (Houseknecht and Weaverling, 1983; Ammerman and Keller, 1979). The Southern Oklahoma aulacogen, in contrast, had extensive Cambrian igneous activity (Ham and others, 1964) consisting of an earlier basaltic-gabbroic suite intruded and deposited upon older metasedimentary rocks, and followed by widespread rhyolitic extrusions and granitic epizonal intrusions. These rocks were uplifted and eroded during late Paleozoic orogeny and are well exposed in the Wichita and Arbuckle Mountains of southern Oklahoma. The Delaware rift or aulacogen has not been documented by borehole data and is inferred largely from gravity anomalies (Keller and others, 1989). With the exception of minor rejuvenations of some faults, the rifting stage had ended by Middle Cambrian time, and the southern margin of North America became a passive, trailing margin.

Foreland facies

Relative tectonic stability and proximity to equatorial latitude in the Cambrian (Van der Voo, 1988) were responsible for establishing a huge carbonate platform extending from Canada to west Texas. In the foreland of the Ouachita system this platform displayed major, broad undulations of pericratonic basins and arches. Basinal sags became established above and across the above-mentioned rift arms (Thomas, 1976), while the inter-rift areas remained tectonically positive (Fig. 3). From east to west these are the Nashville dome, the Reelfoot–Mississippi Valley basin, the Ozark uplift, the Oklahoma basin, the Concho arch, the Tobosa basin, and the ancestral Pedernal-Diablo platform (Galley, 1958; Nicholas and Rozendal, 1975; Thomas, 1976, 1977a, b, 1989). These basins and arches retained their tectonic character from the Late Cambrian until the end of the Devonian, the basins receiving more continuous and thicker suites of sediments, the arches being covered by thin, intermittent sections replete with multiple disconformities (Sloss, 1963).

The lithology of the platform sections (Figs. 4, 5) in the foreland of the Ouachita system can be crudely divided into three parts, (1) a basal transgressive part including arkosic, quartzose, and generally glauconitic sandstones and shales (e.g., Lamotte, Timbered Hills, Riley, Bliss); (2) a Late Cambrian to Middle Ordovician shallow-marine to coastal-carbonate section (e.g.,

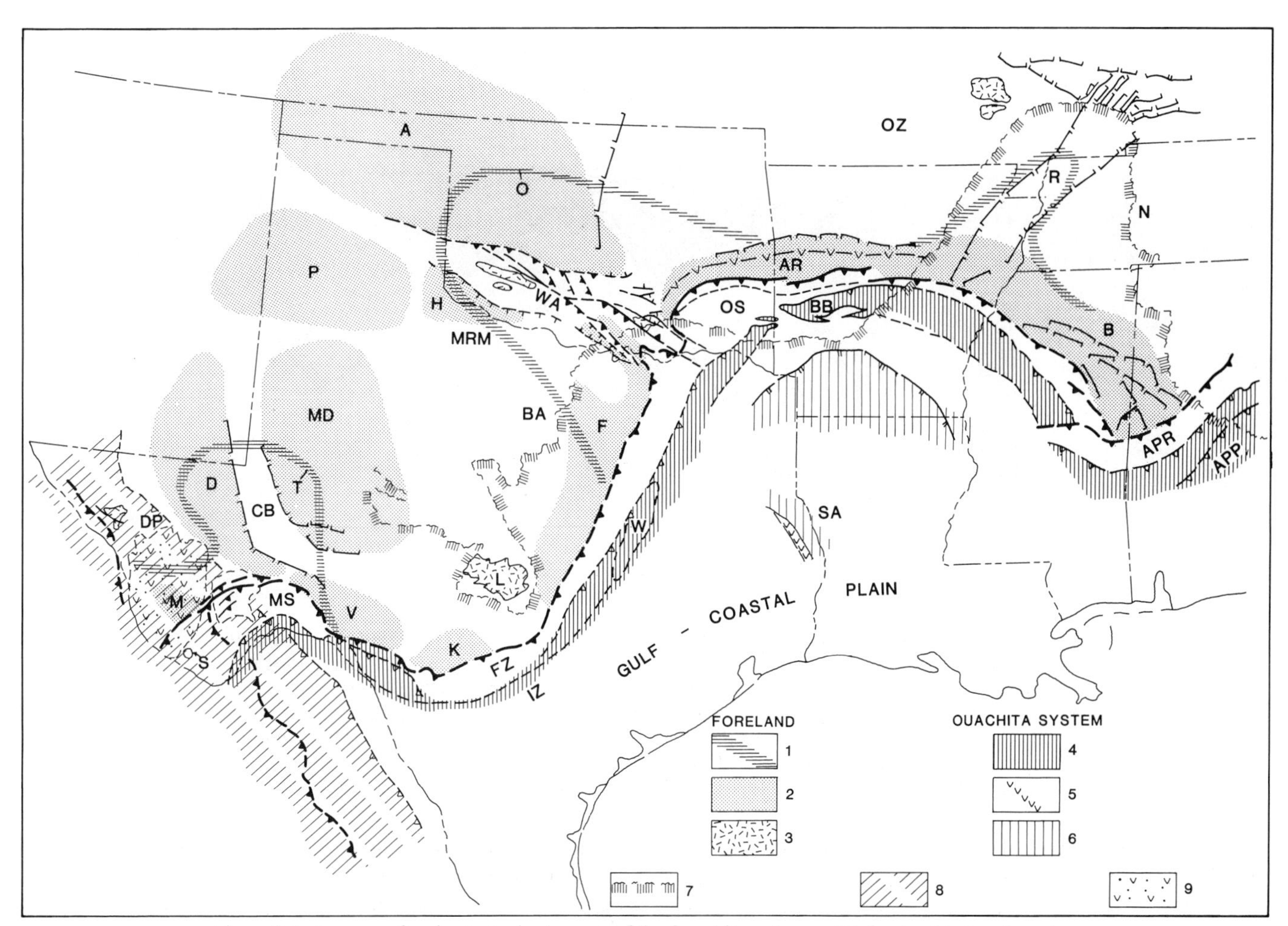

Figure 2. Index map of major tectonic elements of the Ouachita system and its foreland (subsurface after Thomas, 1989, Nicholas and Waddell, 1989). Legend patterns: 1, early Paleozoic basins; 2, late Paleozoic basins; 3, basement outcrops (Precambrian cratonic and Cambrian igneous complex of Wichita Mountains); 4, central uplifts and Interior zone (metamorphosed); 5, late Paleozoic volcanics (Sabine uplift); 6, Desmoinesian and younger successor basin; 7, northern margin of Gulf Coastal Plain; 8, mild overprint by Cordilleran orogen; 9, Davis Mountains volcanics (mid-Tertiary). **Basins on cratonic platform** (from W to E): **Early Paleozoic:** T = Tobosa, O = Oklahoma, R = Reelfoot–Mississippi Valley. **Late Paleozoic synorogenic:** M = Marfa, D = Delaware, V = Val Verde, K = Kerr, MD = Midland, F = Fort Worth (Strawn), P = Palo Duro, H = Hardeman, A = Anadarko, AR = Arkoma, B = Black Warrior. **Uplifts on cratonic platform** (from W to E): DP = Diablo platform, CB = Central Basin platform, L = Llano, BA = Bend arch, MRM = Matador–Red River–Muenster arch, WA = Wichita-Arbuckle, OZ = Ozark, N = Nashville. **Ouachita system** (W to E): S = Solitario, MS = Marathon salient, R = Red River, FZ = Frontal zone, IZ = Interior zone, W = Waco uplift, OS = Oklahoma salient, BB = Broken Bow–Benton uplift, SA = Sabine uplift (postorogenic). **Appalachian system:** APR = Appalachian fold and thrust belt (Ridge and Valley province), APP = Talladega slate belt and Piedmont.

Arbuckle, Wiberns-Ellenburger, El Paso); and (3) a more varied Late Ordovician to Late Devonian suite. During the latter period, craton-derived quartzose sandstones (e.g., St. Peter, Simpson) and transgression-related marine shales (Sylvan, Cason) found their way onto and across the platform of carbonate (Viola, Montoya, Hunton) and cherty (Penters) sediments. The widespread Chattanooga-Woodford transgression brought the preorogenic sequence to a close in much of the Ouachita foreland, although platform conditions continued to exist in some areas that were not affected by the orogeny (e.g., Ozark uplift, Diablo platform).

Ouachita facies

Ever since the early decades of this century it has been recognized that the early to middle Paleozoic rocks exposed in the Ouachita Mountains of Oklahoma and Arkansas, the Marathon uplift, and the adjacent Solitario intrusive uplift of west Texas are drastically different from their foreland sequences (Figs. 4, 5); they were probably emplaced as allochthonous thrust masses and represented some sort of basinal, "geosynclinal" facies (e.g., Miser, 1929) commonly referred to as "Ouachita facies." Particu-

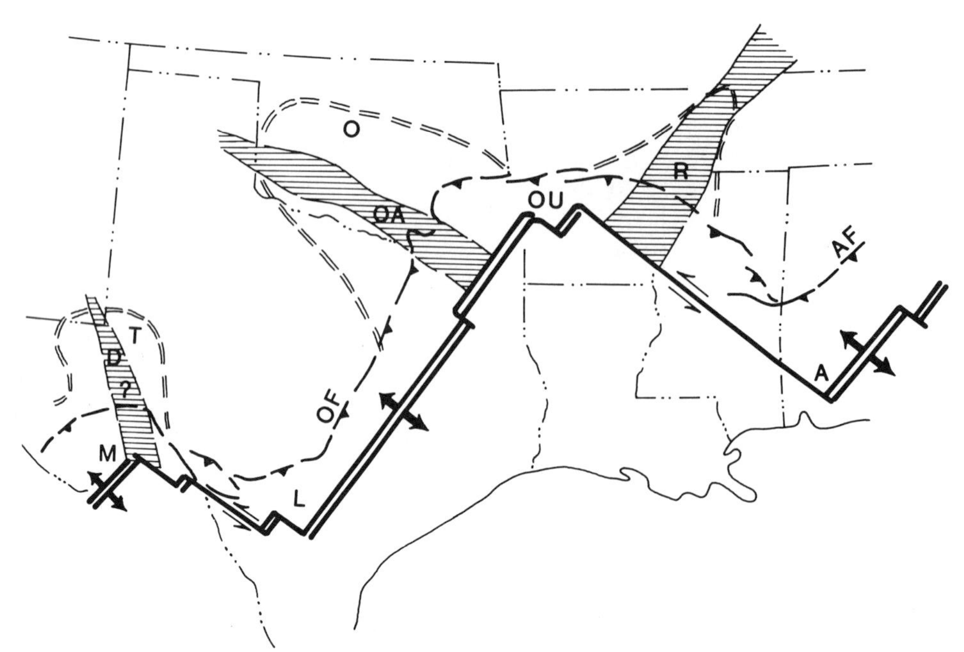

Figure 3. Late Precambrian to Middle Cambrian rift-transform breakup and failed rift arms of the southern continental margin of Paleozoic North America (for possible outboard configuration, see Fig. 14). A = Alabama promontory, AF = late Paleozoic Appalachian thrust front, D = Delaware aulacogen(?), L = Llano (or Texas) promontory, M = Marathon Embayment, O = Oklahoma basin (early Paleozoic), OA = Oklahoma aulacogen, OF = late Paleozoic Ouachita thrust front, OU = Ouachita Embayment, R = Reelfoot rift (with early Paleozoic Mississippi Valley basin), T = Tobosa basin (early Paleozoic). After Cebull and others, (1976), and Thomas (1977a).

larly since the 1950s it has become evident that a good part—if not all—of this sequence must have been deposited in deep water.

Furthermore, it was noted early that the older Paleozoic rocks of the Benton and Broken Bow uplifts of the Ouachita Mountains had undergone mild metamorphism (greenschist facies), are cut by numerous quartz veins, and are mildly to severely tectonized (Honess, 1923; Purdue and Miser, 1923; Miser, 1929; Miser and Purdue, 1929), while the older Paleozoic outcrops of the Potato Hills and the Black Knob Ridge (Oklahoma Ouachitas) and the Marathons (King, 1937) were not metamorphosed. In outcrop, fossil evidence has identified ages from Late Cambrian to Early Mississippian for the preorogenic rocks in these sequences. Although fossils are sparse and the record incomplete, the sections of both the Ouachitas and the Marathons appear to be conformable. In addition, many of the taxa have distinct North American affinities (Ethington and others, 1989).

In modern terms these sequences of dark gray to black shales, silty shales, siliciclastic and carbonate sandstones, detrital limestones, cherts and cherty limestones, conglomerates, and boulder beds are thought to be off-shelf, deep-water (slope to abyssal) deposits laid down by pelagic fallout, turbidity currents, and other mass-flow mechanisms. The following brief remarks are summarized from Lowe (1989) and McBride (1989).

Dark gray and black shales, with minor amounts of greenish gray shales and thin-bedded siltstones, make up nearly 60 percent of the lower and middle Paleozoic of the Ouachita Mountains (Collier, Mazarn, Womble, Polk Creek, and Missouri Mountain Shales). Because they are intensely deformed and cleaved, accurate thickness measurements are difficult to obtain (Bush and others, 1977; Stone and others, 1981). In the nonmetamorphic outcrops of the western Ouachitas of Oklahoma, the black shales of the Womble and Polk Creek display a high organic content typical of rich hydrocarbon source beds (Curiale and Harrison, 1981; Curiale, 1983). In the section of the Marathon uplift, shales are more subordinate (Woods Hollow, Alsate), but shale interbeds in cherts, limestones, and sandstones account for as much as 30 percent of the stratigraphic section (McBride, 1989).

Siliciclastic sandstones are present as major formations in thicknesses of several hundred meters (Ouachitas: Crystal Mountain, Blakely, Blaylock; Marathons: Dagger Flat) and as thin unnamed members in the shales. The petrography of these sandstones can vary considerably, from highly quartzose (Crystal Mountain, Blakely) to lithic (Blaylock, sandstones in Womble) and arkosic (Dagger Flat). They display a variety of bedding and internal sedimentary structures typical of turbidite-fan complexes. In the Broken Bow uplift, Lowe (1989) recognizes two classes of facies and provenance. (a) The first is a quartzitic to slightly arkosic facies associated with clay shale and limestone fragments and with rare paleocurrent indications toward the south and southwest (Crystal Mountain Sandstone and Blakely Sandstone). This facies is inferred to be derived from the craton and to be petrologically related (but not age equivalent) to well-known quartzose sandstones on the shelf (St. Peter–Simpson). The Dagger Flat Sandstone of the Marathons also appears to belong to this facies. (b) The second class is a lithic, overall finer facies (as much as 50/50 quartz to lithic components) characterizing the sandstones and siltstones in the Mazarn and Womble Shales and the Silurian Blaylock Sandstone. Based on paleocurrent directions, this facies seems to be derived from an easterly source. Likewise, a phosphatic sandstone and conglomerate facies in the upper Womble Shale near Little Rock seems to have an easterly source. The Blaylock Sandstone is present only in the Broken Bow uplift and in the southern part of the Benton uplift. The origin of this facies is less distinctly cratonic than facies (a) and—because it is nearly devoid of volcanic debris—suggests as a source the uplift of a passive margin sequence to the northeast, east, or southeast (Lowe, 1989).

Evenly bedded limestones, as micrites, calcisiltites, calcarenites, and conglomerates, generally rhythmically interbedded with shale partings, form a major part (~45 percent) of the Ordovician section in the Marathon uplift (Marathon Limestone, Fort Pena Formation, Maravillas Formation). Most of the limestones are fragmental, and many fragments are clearly derived from shallow-marine environments, such as ooids, stromatolitic structures, whole fossils, and fossil fragments, whereas many shale interbeds contain graptolites. These observations suggest emplacement of the limestone beds into deep water by turbidity currents. In the section of the Ouachita Mountains, limestone plays a subordinate role. Some mainly lens-shaped limestone units up to 15 m thick appear commonly near the top of the Collier Shale (others occur in the middle Mazarn Shale and in the upper Womble Shale). The limestones in the Collier are platy and contain fine- to medium-grained allochems composed of ooids and pellets. Because of the intense deformation it is often difficult to decide whether these lenses are mechanically disrupted, formerly continuous units, or olistoliths. Late Cambrian trilobites with North American affinities have been recovered from such limestone lenses in the Benton uplift near Hot Springs, Arkansas (Hart and others, 1987), indicating that the age span of pre-Mississippian rocks exposed in the Ouachitas and Marathons is the same.

Cherts and novaculites become important and dominant fa-

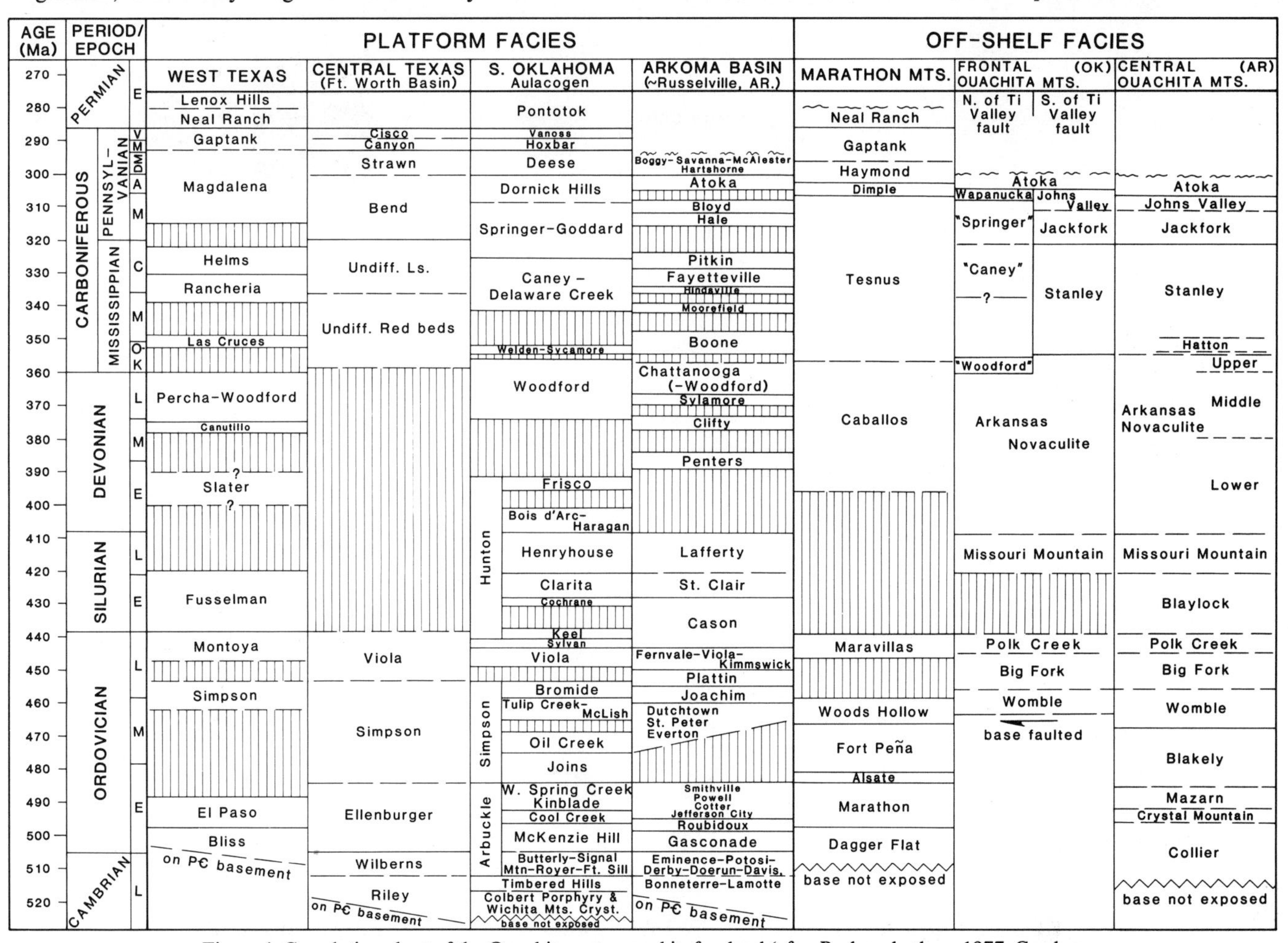

Figure 4. Correlation chart of the Ouachita system and its foreland (after Bush and others, 1977; Gordon and Stone, 1977; Cook and others, 1975; Ethington and others, 1989; Mankin, 1987; Ross, 1986; Sutherland and Manger, 1979). Abbreviations of Carboniferous series (in ascending order): K = Kinderhookian, O = Osagian, M = Meramecian, C = Chesterian; M = Morrowan, A = Atokan, DM = Desmoinesian, M = Missourian, V = Virgilian.

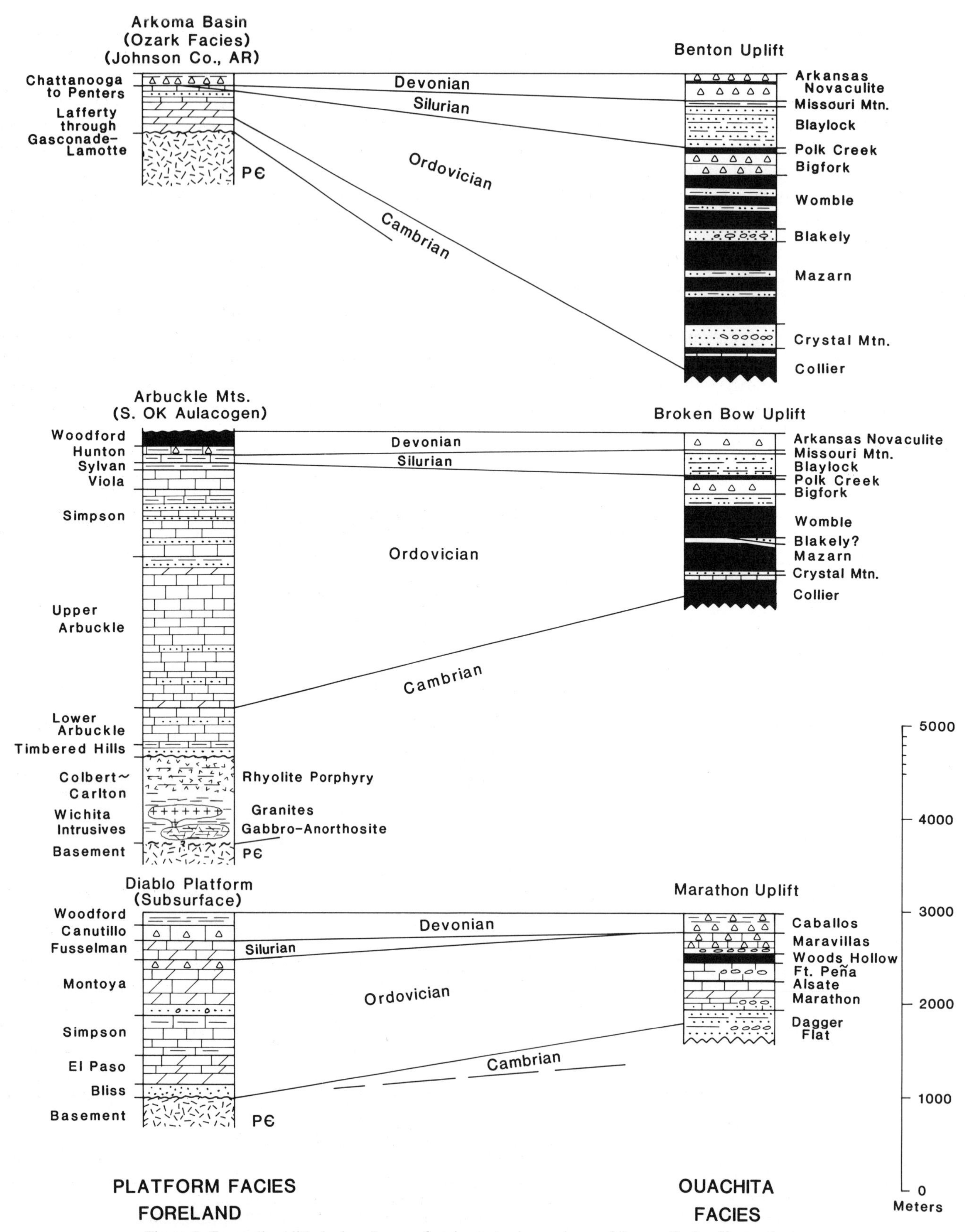

Figure 5. Generalized lithologic columns of major tectonic provinces of the pre-Carboniferous (preorogenic) platform and basin facies (after Bush and others, 1977; Cook and others, 1975; Ham and others, 1964; Lowe, 1989; McBride, 1989; Ross, 1986).

cies near the end of the preorogenic sequence in both the Ouachitas and the Marathons from Late Ordovician to the Early Mississippian. The Ordovician Bigfork (as much as 250 m) and Maravillas (as much as 150 m) Formations (Ouachitas and Marathons respectively) contain abundant beds, 1 to 60 cm thick, of uniformly bedded, organic-rich, black to gray microcrystalline chert, separated by black shale and interbedded with dark, mostly fetid, fragmental limestones and occasional conglomerates. Many pure cherts display ghosts of radiolarians and sponge spicules, but other cherts have textures of chertified calcarenites and calcisiltites. Deposition seems to have occurred in an often anoxic marine basin under hemipelagic and turbiditic conditions.

The Devonian and Early Mississippian Arkansas Novaculite of the Ouachita Mountains and its equivalent in the Marathon uplift, the Caballos Formation, are significant chert-bearing formations comprising one or two massive, milky white novaculite members up to 140 m thick, which pass downward and upward into thin-bedded units of multicolored cherts with some admixtures of quartz sand and silt, limestone, and chert conglomerate, and with shale partings of varied thickness and color. The cherts frequently contain radiolarians, sponge spicules, and spores. Lithologic units in the Marathons are quite persistent; in the Ouachitas they are regionally lenticular, indicating regional disconformities, areas of nondeposition or removal, and lateral gradation into shales. Most of the massive white chert members in the Benton and Broken Bow uplifts of the Ouachita Mountains have undergone a late Paleozoic thermal recrystallization from a cryptocrystalline chert to a polygonal microquartzite (grains up to 100 μm in diameter), which is known and mined as one of the best quality whetstones (Keller and others, 1985). Because of their resistance to erosion, the two chert formations are regional ridge formers that have contributed greatly to the mappability and structural understanding of the Ouachita and Marathon thrust belts.

The origin of some of the chert units remains controversial. Regional pinchout of members of the Arkansas Novaculite and the Caballos Formation, local in-situ brecciation and current-transported conglomerates with quartz detritus, birds-eye–like structures, apparent soil horizons with iron and manganese cements and crusts are some features that characterize these units. Several authors (e.g., Folk, *in* Folk and McBride, 1978; Lowe, 1977, 1989) have concluded from this evidence that during some periods of Devonian sedimentation, shallow-marine and even subaerial conditions may have existed. However, other workers (e.g., McBride and Thomson, 1964; Sholes, 1977; McBride, 1989; Viele and Thomas, 1989) defend a deep-water origin for both chert-bearing formations.

Many of the formations of preorogenic Ouachita facies (Fig. 5) contain conglomerates and boulder beds (Stone and Haley, 1977; Lowe, 1989; McBride, 1989) including in-situ brecciated units, current-transported conglomerates with angular to rounded fragments, and polymodal boulder sands and shales of debris flow and/or gravity slump origin. The fragments consist of a variety of lithologies, some clearly intraclastic (both soft and indurated), some identifiable as debris from shallow-marine environments of the same or older age, and some of truly exotic lithology (igneous, metamorphic, and sedimentary), the provenance of which is not known.

Uncertainties about water depths and about provenance of many units of the preorogenic Ouachita facies, together with an almost total ignorance regarding rock units and terranes in the deep hinterland, lead to even greater uncertainties about the tectonostratigraphic and paleobathymetric framework within which these sequences were deposited. Some possible alternatives will be touched upon at the end of this chapter.

CARBONIFEROUS HISTORY OF DEPOSITION AND DEFORMATION

Flysch facies

The long period of low sedimentation rates of the Silurian and Devonian came to an abrupt end in the Mississippian (Meramecian or earliest Chesterian) with the onset of the late Paleozoic orogeny (Figs. 6, 7) that accompanied the closing of the Paleozoic proto-Atlantic and ended in the collision of Gondwana with North America, and with the assembly of Pangaea. During this phase, enormous amounts of terrigenous clastic sediment poured into the Ouachita trough and came to rest as turbidite fan complexes in an expanse of turbiditic and hemipelagic muds and silts.

In the Ouachita basin proper (i.e., overlying deep-water, preorogenic Ouachita facies) about 6,000 m of such flysch assemblages were deposited in the Mississippian and Morrowan alone (Figs. 6, 7; Morris, 1974, 1989). Paleocurrent indications in the fan complexes are mainly axial from east to west with a dominant sediment supply from northeast and southeast, although there is good evidence of sediment input from a source to the south—possibly an approaching subduction-generated orogenic thrust front (Owen, 1984). A southern source is also indicated for a group of 7- to 40-m-thick rhyodacitic tuffs, which have been mapped near the base of the Mississippian Stanley Group along the southern margin of the outcrop belt of the Ouachita Mountains and pinch out to the north (Niem, 1977). Thicknesses of the Mississippian and Morrowan flysch remain fairly uniform regionally, with the exception of some noticeable thinning of the Morrowan to the northwest near Atoka, Oklahoma, at the western end of the Ouachita Mountains (Hendricks and others, 1947).

During the Atokan, deep-water flysch sedimentation migrated northward onto the continental margin along the southern portions of the present Arkoma basin, where a series of mainly down-to-the-south, Atoka-age, extensional growth faults created a deep-water basin above shallow-marine pre-Mississippian rocks (Buchanan and Johnson, 1968; Berry and Trumbly, 1968; Houseknecht, 1986). These growth faults possibly developed as a response to thrust loading by the approaching orogenic thrust front in the distant south. In the southern Arkoma basin of Ar-

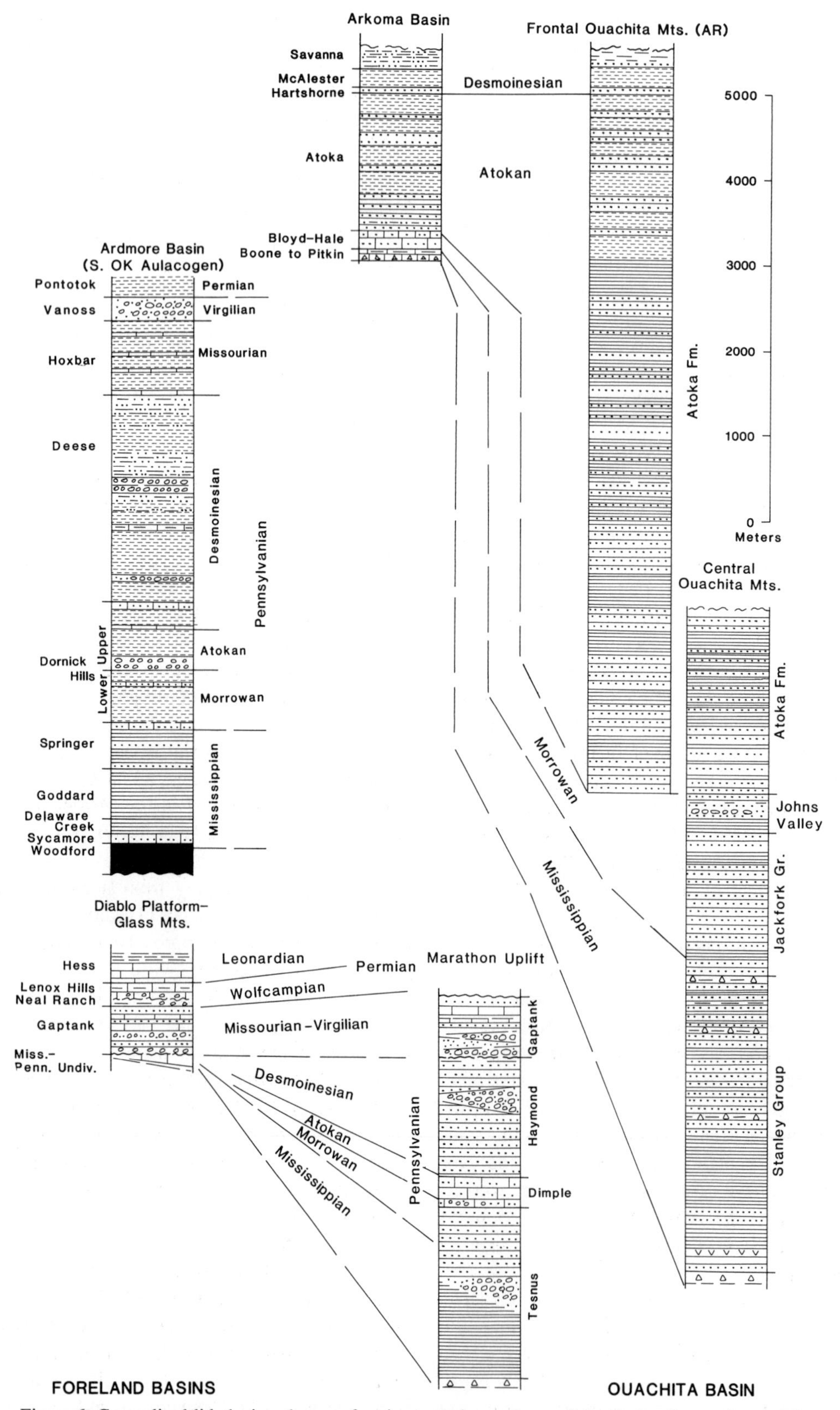

Figure 6. Generalized lithologic columns of major tectonic provinces of the Carboniferous (orogenic) platform and basin facies (after Bush and others, 1977; Cline, 1960; McBride, 1989; Morris, 1989; Sutherland and Manger, 1979; Tomlinson and McBee, 1959).

kansas, some 9,000 m of Atokan flysch have been recognized. Westward axial transport is dominant in the Atokan, but some eastward dispersal existed near the northern basin margin in Oklahoma (Ferguson and Suneson, 1988), and several local, northern source, turbidite fans have been recognized (Morris, 1974, 1989; Houseknecht, 1986). In the central and southern Ouachita Mountains, as much as 2,000 m of Atokan flysch are preserved as erosional, conformable outliers in synclines (Fig. 8). By late Atokan time the flysch basin had filled up, and sedimentation became shallow marine and ultimately fluvial in the Desmoinesian of the Arkoma basin.

As in most flysch assemblages, fossil control is extremely sparse, and many major lithosomes appear to be mildly diachronous. However, throughout the flysch basin of Oklahoma and western Arkansas, thin units of widespread siliceous shale and chert serve as time markers and have been selected as group, formation, and member boundaries (Harlton, 1938; Hendricks and others, 1947; Cline, 1960).

In the Marathon region, the entire flysch sequence is thinner (McBride, 1989) and wedge-shaped, thinning from a maximum of about 4,200 m in the southeast to some 1,500 m in the northwest. Substantial thinning also occurs along strike from northeast to southwest (Muehlberger and others, 1984). Paleocurrent directions are less uniform, indicating a northwesterly dispersal in the Mississippian (Tesnus Formation); a southeasterly, off-shelf direction in the Atokan (Dimple Limestone, a predominantly calcareous turbidite-fan package); and axial, northeast to southwest, in the Desmoinesian (Haymond Formation). Deep-water sedimentation lasted longer than in the Ouachitas in this northwestward migrating and narrowing basin, and ceased only in the earliest Permian (Ross, 1986).

On the basis of bedding sequences and sedimentary structures, a wide range of turbidite-fan subenvironments can be interpreted in the flysch deposits of the Ouachita Mountains and Marathon uplift. These are usually classified according to the criteria developed by Mutti and Ricci Lucchi (1975).

Besides the dominating sand-silt-shale assemblages of the flysch sequences in the Ouachita system, there are also numerous units of pebble-to-boulder conglomerates, olistostromes with scattered boulders, blocks, and slabs as wide as several hundred meters of penecontemporaneously deformed and disrupted slump horizons, and mélange-like chaotic intervals. The boulder beds contain intraclasts (i.e., clasts of lithified and unlithified intraformational material), as well as a vast variety of angular to rounded boulders of older rocks of both known provenance and of unknown origin (Shideler, 1970). Today most workers agree that these conglomeratic units occupy stratigraphic horizons of local to regional dimensions and are the products of a variety of deep-water transport regimes ranging from grain flow to gravity slump, and originating both on the continental margin of North America and the southern orogenic flanks of the basin.

Because many conglomerates are encased in shales or em-

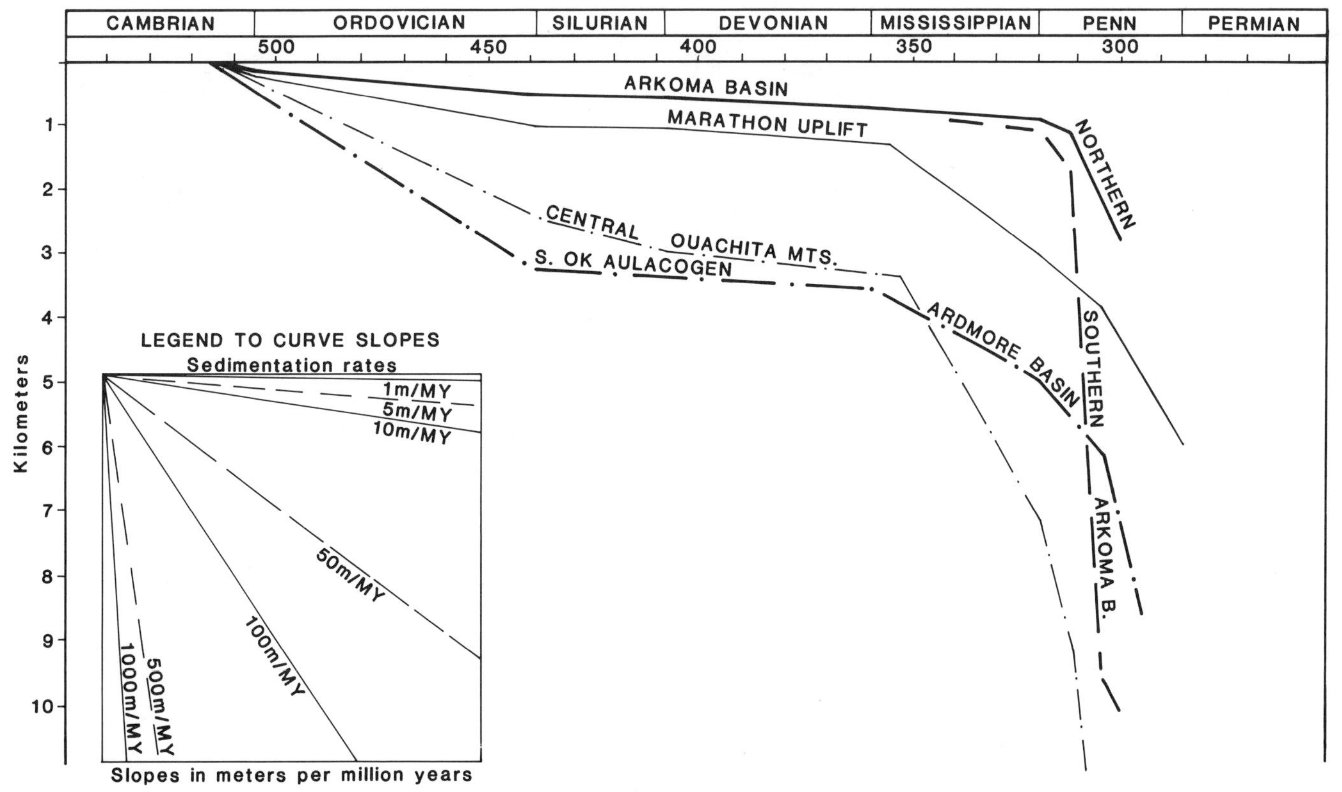

Figure 7. Sedimentation rates in meters per million years for several regions of the Ouachita system and its cratonic foreland.

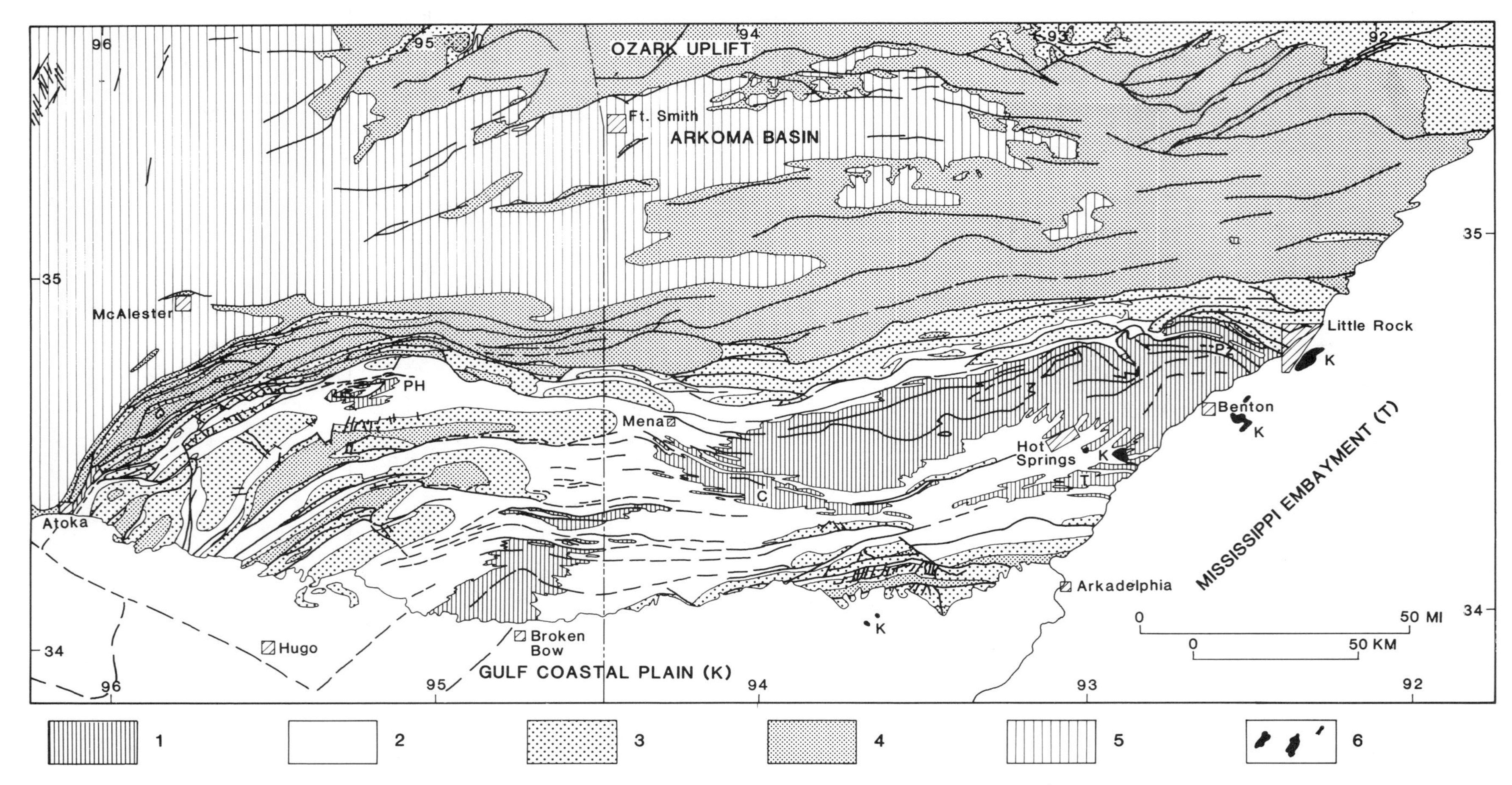

Figure 8. Geologic map of the Ouachita Mountains and the Arkoma basin (simplified after Plate 8, Hatcher and others, 1989). 1. Early and middle Paleozoic (Cambrian through Early Mississippian). 2. Middle and Late Mississippian (Stanley Group of Ouachita facies). 3. Morrowan (Jackfork Group and Johns Valley Formations of Ouachita facies). 4. Atokan. 5. Desmoinesian. 6. Intrusives and/or olistoliths of Paleozoic (Pz) and intrusives of Cretaceous (K) age. PH = Potato Hills, C = Cossatot Mountains, T = Trap Mountains.

bedded in a shaly matrix, they were more readily and more intensely tectonized, especially when these shales became the site of bedding plane faults. Furthermore, it is quite probable that deformation occurred before the flysch was completely dewatered, because the thrust front proceeded in a marine environment. Thus, the deformational fabrics and textures take on many characteristics of mélange-wedges of accretional subduction prisms. This similarity to certain accretionary phenomena of modern deep-sea trench walls has led Viele and Thomas (1989) to propose a model that makes tectonic units out of many of these disrupted, conglomeratic elements. Only very detailed stratigraphic and paleontologic subdivision and mapping will verify or contradict these concepts, which would require that the active, accretionary thrust front had advanced northward into the vicinity of the frontal Ouachitas already in early Morrowan time.

In the flysch series of the Marathon uplift, boulder beds have been known for many decades (Sellards, 1931) and yield some important paleotectonic information. They contain a richly varied assortment of shallow-marine boulders from the North American shelf, but also a multitude of exotic igneous and metamorphic boulders. Of the latter, Denison and others (1969) have determined Middle Devonian to Late Silurian ages, indicating that these boulders could not have come from the North American side of the basin but must have originated from some orogenically uplifted foreign terrane to the south. Recently, unmetamorphosed limestone cobbles of Middle Cambrian age were discovered in a conglomerate band within the Haymond Formation (Palmer and others, 1984); this is an age that is older than any sedimentary rocks known today from the adjacent platform region (e.g., Llano uplift and surrounding subsurface) or from the underlying basinal facies. These boulders indicate (a) that a carbonate platform had been established in the Middle Cambrian on the passive margin, and (b) that they were evidently fed into the basin from a more seaward position of provenance, which must have become buried by the allochthonous thrust sheets.

STYLES OF DEFORMATION

Surface maps from the two major outcrop regions (Figs. 8, 9, 10), amplified by subsurface reflection seismic and borehole information, are the principal sources from which to draw conclusions on the structural styles and tectonic units of the Ouachita system. The system is bordered along its front by a north- and northwest-vergent thrust and fold belt containing multiple and, at some places, folded thrust sheets (Fig. 11; Flawn and others, 1961; King, 1937; Hendricks and others, 1947; Blythe and others, 1988; Bush and others, 1977). North of the Ouachita Mountains, a mildly compressed thin-skinned fold belt, occupying the southern Arkoma basin, lies in front of the highly telescoped frontal imbricated thrust belt. North vergence prevails throughout most of the Ouachita Mountains, with the exception of the central uplifts or core areas (Broken Bow and Benton uplift) where a complex strain history has resulted in south-vergent folds. South of the Benton uplift, north vergence is again present and appears to continue beneath the Mesozoic cover as far as north Texas and Louisiana, where seismic control becomes inconclusive. Northwest vergence also persists throughout the Marathon thrust belt and disappears under the Mesozoic of the Gulf Coastal Plain. Thus, the true width of the thrust belt is unknown.

The vertical distribution of competent, load-bearing units and ductile, shaly, and silty intervals in the outcrop regions is characterized by an abundance of ductile formations in the older deeper parts of the section, and a dominance of very thick, massive, and mostly competent rocks in the Morrowan and younger flysch sequence (Figs. 5, 6, 11). It is evident that this general ductility/competence distribution leads to a structural style that differs considerably from the well-known and much-described style of miogeoclinal thrust belts, which have their main load-bearing members deep in the section and their more ductile units in the younger rocks.

Inspection of surface geologic maps (Figs. 8, 10) and cross sections (Fig. 11) shows that the youngest structural level (upper Mississippian and younger) forms broad synclines and sharp, usually faulted anticlines involving the 4,000+ m of Late Mississippian and younger turbidite fan complexes. In the Ouachitas this competent section comprises the upper Stanley Group, the Jackfork Group, the Johns Valley Formation, and the Atoka Formation. In the Marathons a similar style is produced by the combined competent rocks of the upper Tesnus, Dimple, and Haymond Formations. In plunge view this fold train has the shape of cuspate-lobate folds (Ramsay and Huber, 1987) with the lobes facing the more ductile, less viscous underlying units.

In the older, shale-dominated section, the more competent units are quite thin and tend to seek out their own preferred dominant wave lengths, which are much smaller. Because of the well-bedded nature of the competent rocks (e.g., cherts, well-bedded limestones, and sandstones), chevron folds are common. On plunging map configurations and in mesoscale exposures, several competing wavelengths can often be observed to form complex polyharmonic fold trains (Currie and others, 1962; Ramsay and Huber, 1987). In the Ouachita Mountains, the leading competent units in this overall ductile package are the Crystal Mountain Sandstone, the Blakely Sandstone, and the combined Bigfork-Blaylock-Arkansas Novaculite section. In the Marathons, the Caballos stands out as the dominant competent unit that controls the size and shape of folds.

The intervening ductile shale and limestone sections, which separate differently folded units, must accommodate major and minor disharmonic detachments. Because of the poor exposure of these units, the mechanical details of the decoupling are usually not resolvable. Some authors show these detachment zones as bed-parallel faults or "domain boundaries" (e.g., Fig. 10; Haley and others, 1976; Muehlberger and Tauvers, 1989), while others might interpret them as submarine unconformities, especially where the older rock units seem to be more tightly folded (Welland and others, 1985).

Numerous major thrust faults are recognized (Figs. 9, 11) where contacts of competent marker beds are displaced. Poor

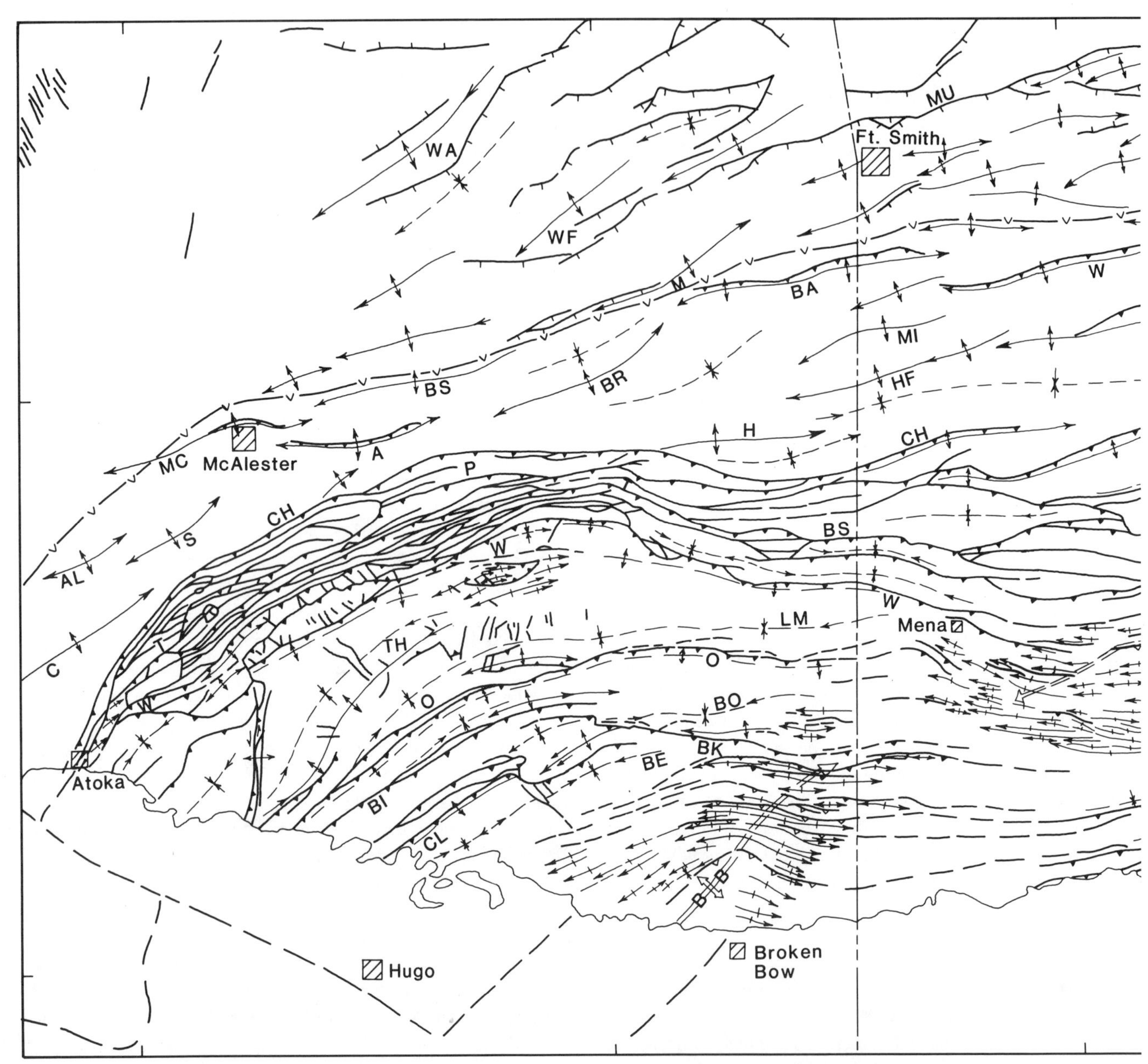

Figure 9. Folds and faults of the Ouachita Mountains and the Arkoma basin. **Folds and faults of the Ouachita Mountains:** AF = Alum Fork thrust, B = Briery fault, BB = Broken Bow uplift, BE = Bethel syncline, BI = Big One fault, BK = Boktukola fault, BO = Boktukola syncline, BT = Benton uplift, CH = Choctaw fault, CL = Cloudy fault, CO = Cowhide fault, G = Graysonia fault, LC = Little Creek fault, LM = Lynn Mountain syncline, O = Octavia fault, P = Pine Mountain fault, PC = Panther Creek fault, S = Skelton fault, T = Ti Valley fault, TH = Tuskahoma syncline, W = Windingstair fault, Y = Y City fault. **Folds and faults of the Arkoma basin and the southern Ozark uplift:** A = Adamson anticline with Carbon fault, AL = Ashland anticline, BS = Burning Springs anticline, BA = Backbone anticline, BM = Bayou Meto anticline, BR = Brazil anticline, C = Coalgate anticline, CA = Cadron anticline, H = Heavener anticline, HF = Hartford anticline, M = Milton anticline, MC = McAlester anticline and Penitentiary fault, MI = Midland anticline, MO = Morrilton anticline, MU = Mulberry fault, PR = Pine Ridge anticline, R = Ross Creek fault, RA = Ranger anticline, S = Savanna anticline, W = Washburn anticline, WA = Warner horst, WF = Whitefield uplift.

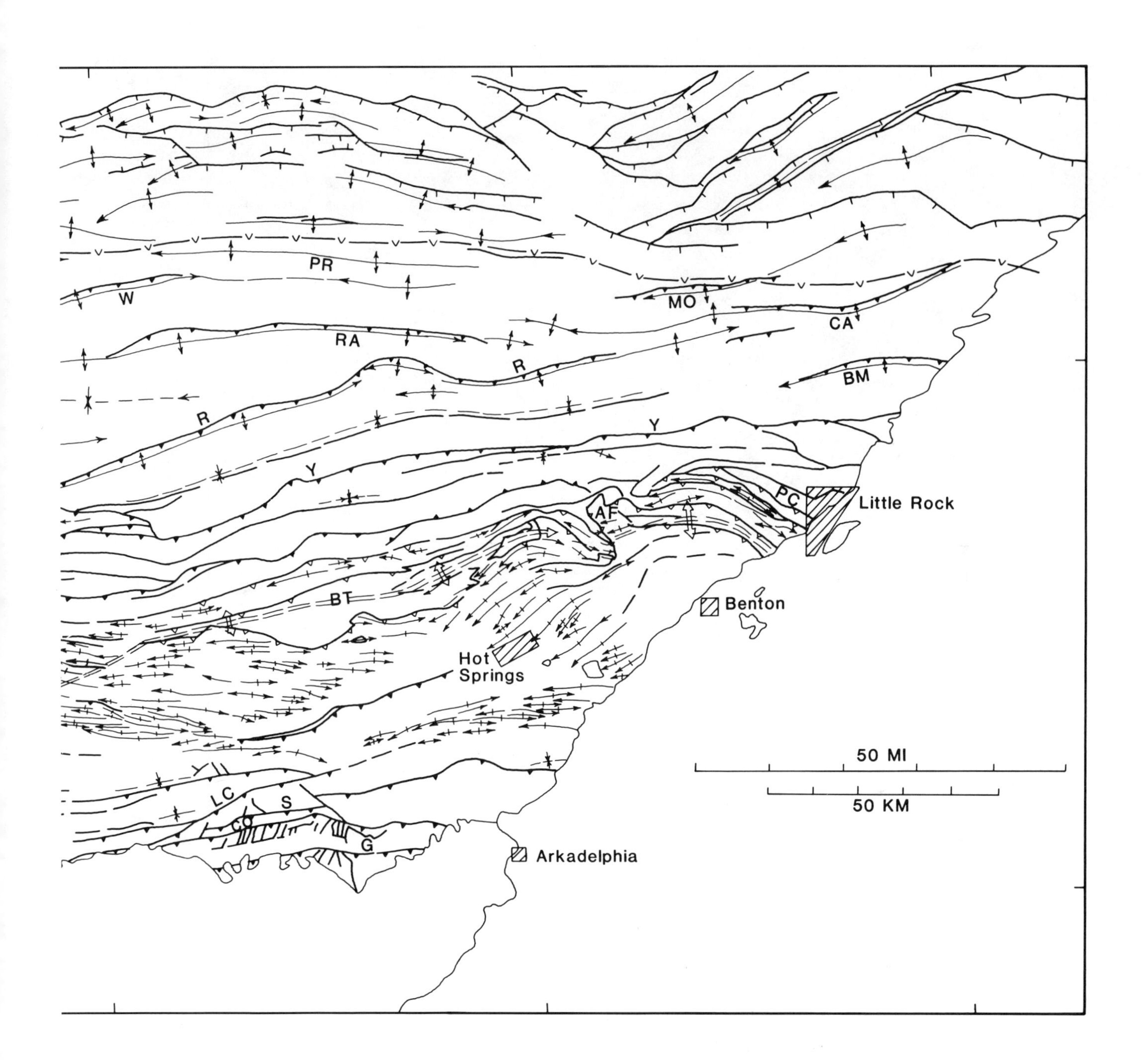
PR
W
MO
CA
RA
R
BM
R
Y
Y
PC
Little Rock
AF
BT
Benton
Hot Springs
50 MI
50 KM
LC
S
CO
G
Arkadelphia

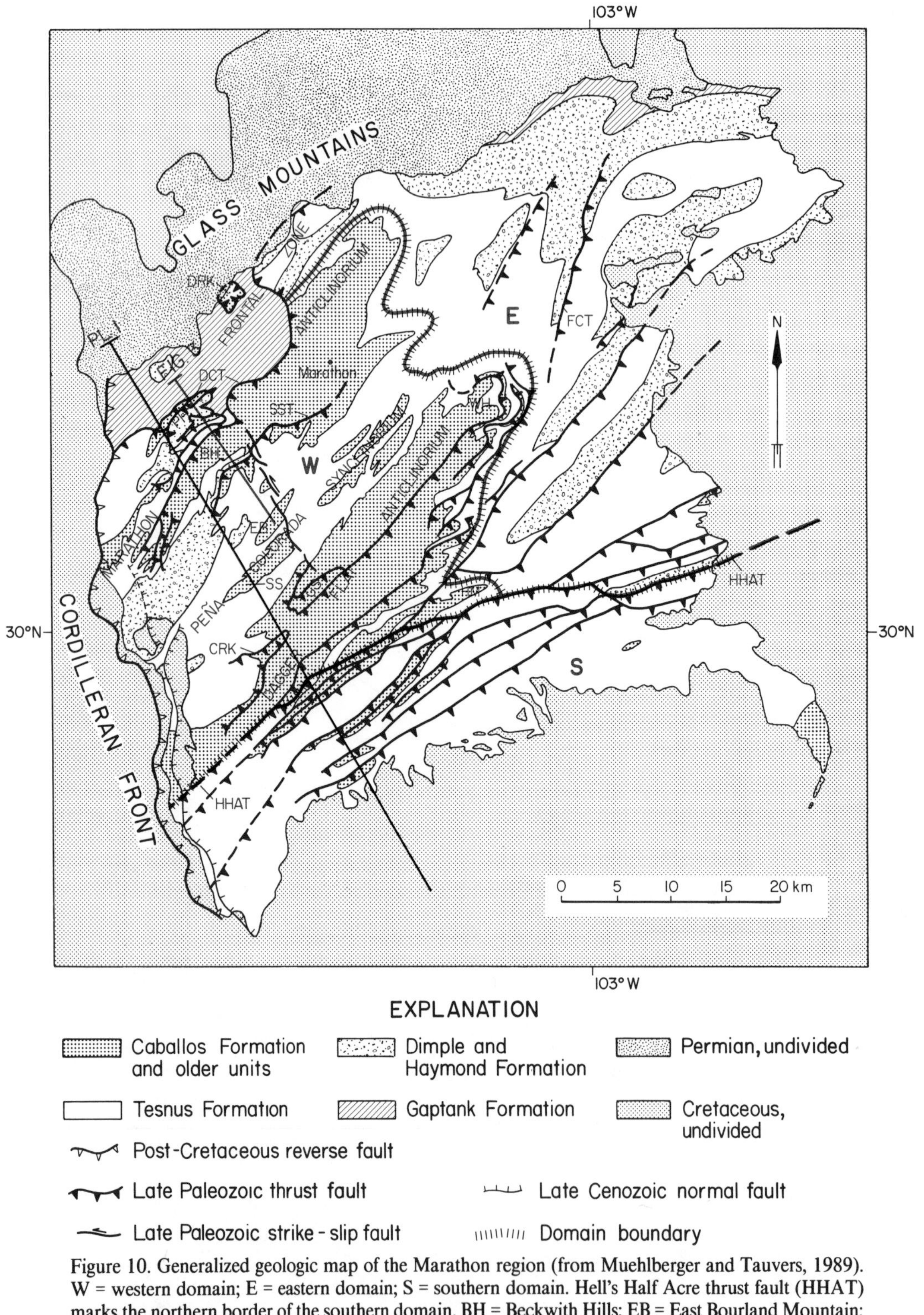

Figure 10. Generalized geologic map of the Marathon region (from Muehlberger and Tauvers, 1989). W = western domain; E = eastern domain; S = southern domain. Hell's Half Acre thrust fault (HHAT) marks the northern border of the southern domain. BH = Beckwith Hills; EB = East Bourland Mountain; GS = Garden Springs area; HM = Horse Mountain; PH = Payne Hills; SS = Simpson Springs Mountain; WH = Warwick Hills; CRK = Combs Ranch klippe; DRK = Decie Ranch klippe; DCT = Dugout Creek overthrust; FCT = Frog Creek thrust.

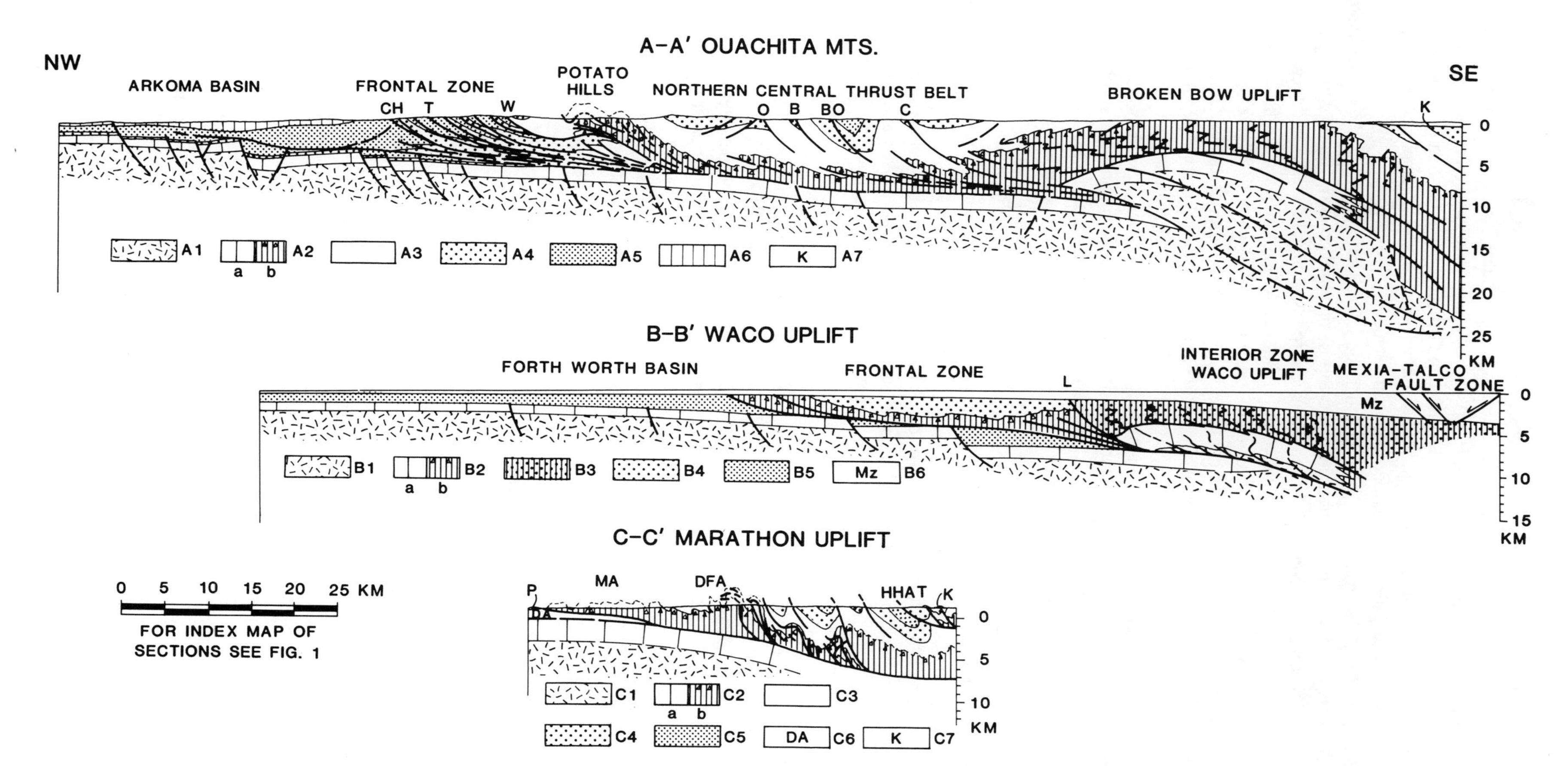

Figure 11. Generalized cross sections across the frontal Ouachita system in Oklahoma and Texas (simplified from Plate 11, Hatcher and others, 1989). Explanation: **Section A–A′:** A1, Precambrian basement; A2a, Cambrian through Mississippian platform rocks; A2b, Cambrian through Early Mississippian deep water rocks (pre-orogenic), triangles represent Ordovician to Devonian cherts; A3, Mississippian flysch; A4, Morrowan flysch and platform rocks; A5, Atoka Formation; A6, Desmoinesian; A7, Cretaceous. Abbreviations: CH = Choctaw fault, T = Ti Valley fault, W = Windingstair fault, O = Octavia fault, B = Boktukola fault, BO = Big One fault, C = Cloudy fault. **Section B–B′:** B1, Precambrian basement; B2a, Cambrian and Ordovician platform rocks; B2b, Cambrian through Early Mississippian deep-water rocks (preorogenic); B3, Cambrian through Carboniferous deep-water rocks; undifferentiated; B4, Morrowan and Atokan flysch; B5, Atoka Formation; B6, Mesozoic undifferentiated. Abbreviations: L = Luling front. **Section C–C′:** C1, Precambrian basement; C2a, Cambrian through Mississippian platform rocks; C2b, Cambrian through Early Mississippian deep-water rocks (preorogenic); C3, Mississippian flysch; C4, Morrowan and Atokan flysch; C5, Haymond Formation; C6, Dugout allochthon, Late Pennsylvanian (DA); C7, Cretaceous. Abbreviations: P = Permian, MA = Marathon anticlinorium, DFA = Dagger Flat anticlinorium, HHAT = Hell's Half Acre thrust.

mappability in the shales usually prevents us from determining whether these major faults actually cut through the entire sequences, including the thick ductile units, or whether they disappear in a multitude of minor faults in the ductile, cataclastically flowing shales. The major thrust faults, where mappable by seismic or borehole control, appear to be listric with little evidence of angular ramps and flats. At the front of the Oklahoma salient of the Ouachita Mountains a great amount of shortening is accomplished by numerous, tightly imbricated thrust slices (Hendricks and others, 1947; Arbenz, 1989).

Late-stage footwall thrusting (duplexing) has resulted in folding of thrust faults. This is particularly well displayed in the Marathon region, where King (1937) demonstrated by down-plunge projection the folding of multiple thrust sheets. In the Ouachita Mountains, similar map configurations indicated folded faults have been recognized, for instance in the Potato Hills (Miser, 1929; Arbenz, 1968).

A very large duplex structure of some 45 km width has been interpreted to underlie the central Benton and Broken Bow uplifts (Fig. 11), where COCORP (Consortium for Continental Reflection Profiling) and proprietary reflection seismic surveys have detected a large antiformal feature beneath the surface anticlinoria (Nelson and others, 1982; Lillie and others, 1983; Arbenz, 1984; Blythe and others, 1988). The special characteristics of the surface geology of these central uplifts had been noticed and described early in this century (Honess, 1923; Purdue and Miser, 1923; Miser and Purdue, 1929) and are summarized by Nielsen and others (1989). The most noteworthy features of these uplifts are summarized below:

a. They represent the major regional outcrop areas of pre-Mississippian rocks in the Ouachita Mountains. The axis of the uplifts trends obliquely across the regional grain of the fold-and-thrust patterns (Fig. 9).

b. Folds are mostly south overturned to recumbent, but show transition to north overturning along the northern and southern margins of the uplifts (Zimmerman, 1984, 1986).

c. Most major faults show down-to-the-north displacements. Honess (1923) shows the faults on his cross sections to have "normal" fault geometry. At two significant places on the Benton uplift, down-plunge views demonstrate major north-vergent thrusting of several kilometers with an overprint of south-vergent folding and minor faulting, for example, the Alum Fork fault (Haley and others, 1976; Nielsen and others, 1989) and the major unnamed fault east of Mount Ida (Soustek, 1979), which itself became refolded. This relationship implies an initial north-vergent thrusting, followed by a complex event of south overturning of both thrust plates and fault surfaces. Nielsen (in Nielsen and others, 1989) believes that the inverse sequence may apply in the Broken Bow uplift. Wherever south overturning is present, it is accompanied by a pervasive north-northwest-dipping cleavage.

d. A large area of both central uplifts shows a low-grade metamorphism (Fig. 12), accompanied by elevated vitrinite reflectance (Desborough and others, 1985; Guthrie and others, 1986; Houseknecht and Matthews, 1985; C. G. Stone, personal communication, 1988), quartz novaculitization (Keller and others, 1985), and by a pervasive invasion by quartz veins (Miser, 1959). Denison and others (1977) reported late Paleozoic radiometric ages for this metamorphism, in places overprinting an earlier Devonian event.

e. Leander and Legg (1988) described the results of a borehole near the top of the Broken Bow uplift, which penetrated 3,570 m of metamorphosed Ouachita facies and then entered and bottomed in foreland facies carbonates at a total depth of 5,784 m. This facies relationship involving the above-mentioned antiform confirms very similar conditions encountered near Waco, Texas, in a borehole described by Vernon (1971) and Nicholas and Rozendal (1975) drilled on an antiformal subsurface structure named the Waco uplift (Figs. 2, 11), where marbleized foreland(?) carbonates and underlying basement rocks were also encountered beneath Ouachita facies rocks. These authors proposed a model of a duplex structure of foreland basement and its cover below a refolded and faulted Ouachita allochthon, a model that was later modified by Nelson and others (1982) in their interpretation of the COCORP seismic survey in the western Benton uplift.

The central uplifts of the Ouachita Mountains and the Waco uplift are parts of a regional positive gravity anomaly or a major gravity gradient (Nicholas and Rozendal, 1975). This gravity feature has received much attention since and is now generally recognized as the southern outboard limit of the North American Paleozoic continental crust (Lillie and others, 1983; Kruger and Keller, 1986; Keller and others, 1989). The crust south and southeast of this gravity anomaly has been modeled to be attenuated transitional or possibly even oceanic crust on which Ouachita facies rocks were deposited. This implies further that the thrust sheets that carry the northernmost occurrence of this facies had to originate south of the central uplifts (i.e., the thrust sheets overlying the Ti Valley, Briery, and Y-City faults of the Ouachitas).

SUBSURFACE CONNECTIONS

The vast area of the Ouachita system that lies beneath late Paleozoic, Mesozoic, and Cenozoic rocks of the Gulf Coastal Plain is still poorly known, and a concise picture of the hinterland and the Pangean suture zone cannot yet be made. The frontal elements, especially in the segment west and south of the Ouachita Mountains, have been penetrated by hundreds of wells as the search for hydrocarbons in the adjacent foreland proceeds beneath the thrust front (Flawn and others, 1961). Also, because small amounts of hydrocarbons have been discovered in Ouachita-facies rocks (Chenoweth, 1989) since the mid-1970s, geophysical exploration and drilling have intensified, but few results have been published (Petroleum Information, 1985). Another problem in interpreting subsurface data is the virtual impossibility of differentiating from drill cuttings the many formations of the flysch series, or of separating them from middle and older Paleozoic siltstones and shales; this leaves only the cherts as somewhat diagnostic lithologies. Around 70 km south and east of the thrust front, usually just southeast of the above-mentioned gravity anomaly, the base of the postorogenic rocks descends to great depths, and borehole information remains very sparse. Nicholas and Waddell (1989) and Thomas (1989) have summarized all existing information and concepts, updating the fundamental framework laid three decades ago by Flawn and others (1961).

Western segment (south and west of the Ouachita Mountains)

On the basis of the visionary groundwork by Powers (1928) and van Waterschoot van der Gracht (1931a, 1931b), and a careful inspection of all existing well data, Flawn and others (1961) established the existence of a nonmetamorphic thrust zone (their "frontal zone") passing southward and eastward into a low-grade metamorphic zone (their "interior zone"). The outcrops of the Marathon belt belong to the frontal zone, and so would that part of the Ouachita Mountains lying north and west of the central Broken Bow and Benton uplifts. Nicholas and Rozendal (1975) and Nicholas and Waddell (1989) pointed out that the northwestern border of the above-mentioned gravity anomaly also correlates with the northwestern limit of the "interior zone," and that the "interior zone" may therefore be a reflection of the band of basement duplex structures recognized from the Waco uplift to the north. In the outcrop south of the Benton uplift and in many bore holes in southern Arkansas and adjacent northern Louisiana and Texas, it is evident that the metamorphism of the Benton uplift drops off to the south (Fig. 12). In south-central and western Texas the well control south of the gravity anomaly is insufficient to document a similar cooling on the seaward side of the interior zone, but the overall gravity interpretation indicates a much-attenuated crustal configuration (Kruger and Keller, 1986; Keller and others, 1989).

A somewhat special feature along the postulated margin of the North American craton in the subsurface of west Texas is the Devils River uplift (Fig. 2), a thrust-faulted basement uplift with a mildly metamorphosed foreland-facies cover (Nicholas, 1983), but without a Ouachita facies allochthon overlying the uplift. It occupies the same regional gravity anomaly, and its metamorphism places the Devils River uplift into the Ouachita interior zone (Keller and others, 1989). The lack of a Ouachita-facies allochthon can be ascribed to pre-Mesozoic uplift and erosion probably during the final stages of the continental collision.

Another tectonostratigraphically significant feature of the Ouachita hinterland is the existence of a large, downbent, post-orogenic successor basin (or "episutural" basin, Bally, 1975), in the region of southern Arkansas and northeast Texas (Fig. 2), the base of which rests with angular unconformity on nonmetamorphic flysch. The northern margin of this basin is fairly well delin-

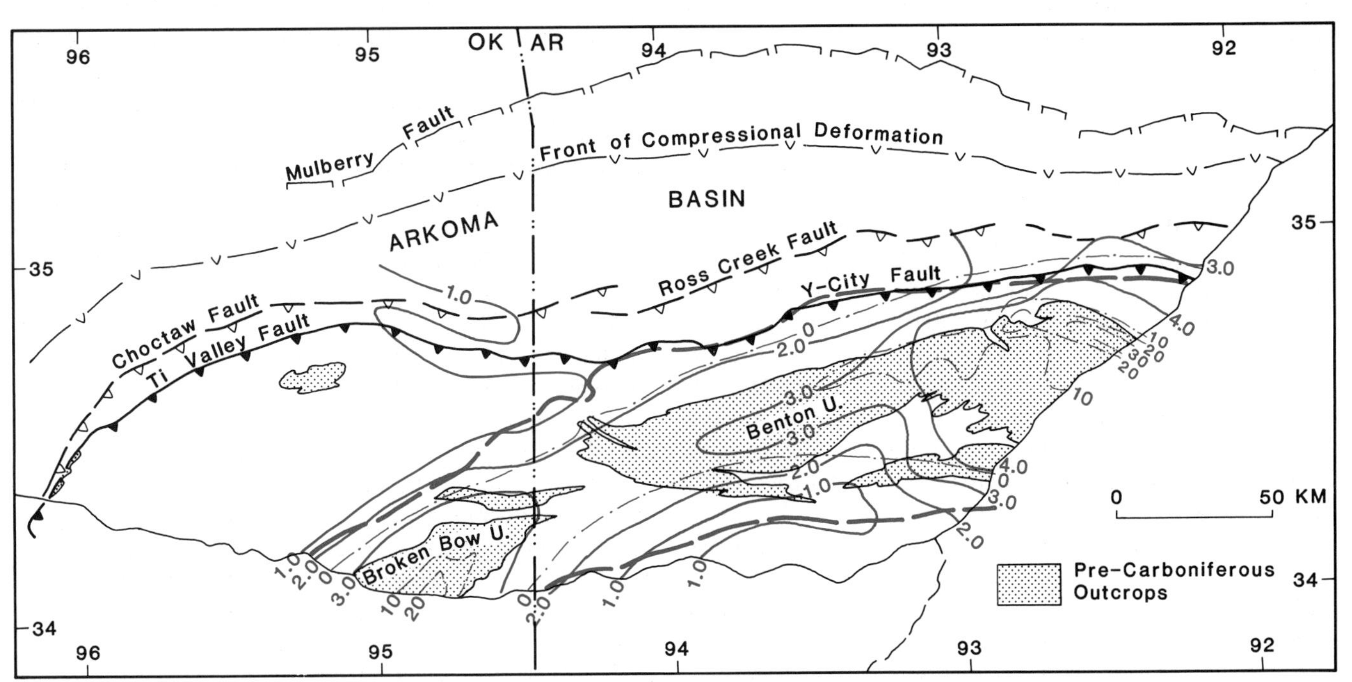

Figure 12. Thermal anomaly of the central uplifts of the Ouachita Mountains manifested by quartz recrystallization, vitrinite reflectance, and quartz veins (from Desborough and others, 1985; Guthrie and others, 1986; Houseknecht and Matthews, 1985; Keller and others, 1985; Miser, 1959).

eated by boreholes and by exploration seismic surveys, and swings in an arc from northeastern Texas to northeastern Louisiana. The eastern, southern, and western limits of this basin are not defined as yet. The youngest synorogenic flysch rocks, truncated by the successor basin sequence, are quite probably Atokan (judging from the outcrops to the north); the oldest rocks of the successor basin consist of a shallow-marine, fossiliferous Desmoinesian carbonate sequence, which grades upward into Late Pennsylvanian and Permian marine carbonates and clastic rocks. This basin was described by Paine and Meyerhoff (1970), Vernon (1971), and Woods and Addington (1973), and was given the somewhat inappropriate name "Texarkana platform." The most significant aspect of this basin is the fact that it dates the latest orogeny in this part of the hinterland with great accuracy as late Atokan. Rocks of the same age and facies have been penetrated by several wells on the Sabine uplift, a long-known domal structure straddling the state line between Texas and Louisiana. There the Desmoinesian carbonates rest on late Paleozoic rhyolite porphyry and tuff, which in turn lie unconformably on Carboniferous flysch (Fig. 2; Nicholas and Waddell, 1989).

In the states of Chihuahua, Coahuila, Nuevo Leon, and Tamaulipas of northern Mexico, rocks from all zones of the Ouachita system and its foreland are known from a number of small outcrop inliers and some exploratory wells in the frontal portions of the Sierra Madre Oriental (Flawn and others, 1961; Handschy and others, 1987). Because of their small size and wide scatter, these occurrences can give only some general constraints to the still-speculative southwestern continuation of the Ouachita system.

Eastern segment

Subsurface control in the Ouachita system between the eastern Ouachita Mountains and the juncture with the Appalachian system remains limited (Thomas, 1976, 1977a, b, 1985, 1989). Subsurface information on the adjacent foreland has delineated the structure and stratigraphy of the Black Warrior Basin as a homoclinal, extensionally step-faulted south flank of the southeastern midcontinent. Much less has been published (Thomas, 1989) about the Reelfoot–Mississippi Valley basin, mainly because commercial accumulations of hydrocarbons have yet to be discovered, and the number of deep well penetrations has consequently stayed low.

The front of the thrust belt east of the Ouachita Mountains is fairly well defined to eastern Mississippi, although identification of formational units is still tentative. Farther east the thrust front is less distinct and continues as a series of right-stepping, en echelon folds of thick Carboniferous rocks, indicating a probable right-lateral strike-slip component along this segment of the Ouachita thrust front. A more interior slate belt, probably a continuation of the central uplift of the Ouachitas, can be traced into central Mississippi (Thomas, 1989).

Because of its much more distinct lithofacies and excellent resolution on proprietary seismic sections, the southwestern and western continuation of the subsurface Appalachians can be traced successfully into central Mississippi, where the information is finally lost beneath the Mesozoic Mississippi salt basin. From these data it is evident that the subsurface thrust system of the Appalachians cuts off and overrides the southeastern extension of the Black Warrior Basin as well as the Ouachita fold and thrust belt farther to the west (Thomas, 1989).

TIMING OF OROGENIC DEFORMATION

The earliest indirect evidence of a constriction of the Ouachita depositional basin and an orogenic uplift of one or more regions of provenance comes in the Meramecian or earliest Chesterian (Mississippian), with the rather sudden influx of large amounts of terrigenous clastic sediments (Fig. 7). The majority of these sediments are being funnelled down the axis of a deep-water trough that parallels the continental margin. The basal contact of the flysch is gradational and regionally conformable. The nearly simultaneous appearance of volcanic tuffs in the southern outcrop of the Ouachita Mountains can be used as confirming evidence for subductional events to the south, while the occurrence of sedimentary, bedded barite deposits at the very base of the flysch sequence in a band along the southern border of the Benton uplift (Hanor and Baria, 1977) may still be related to extensional preflysch phenomena rather than to orogenic ones.

Neither in the Ouachita Mountains nor in the Marathon region can one detect any unequivocal angular unconformity between the base of the flysch section and the late Atokan in tectonically undisturbed areas. Some regional wedging and pinchout of mappable units may be attributed to the depositional shape of turbidite fans. This observation of regional conformity is based on extensive mapping and stratigraphic measurements by numerous authors (e.g., Cline, 1960; Haley and others, 1976; Harlton, 1938; Hendricks and others, 1947; Honess, 1923; King, 1937; Miser, 1929; Miser and Purdue, 1929; Morris, 1974; Walthall, 1967), and implies that structural deformation had not proceeded into the region of the present outcrops. It is evident that this conclusion conflicts with Viele's (in Viele and Thomas, 1989) proposed origin of the Maumelle chaotic zone as an active accretionary prism, which would have affected the entire Ouachita flysch basin since Early Pennsylvanian.

It was pointed out earlier that some of the tectonic disharmonic detachment zones (e.g., the one in the upper Mississippian flysch) could be interpreted as unconformities. However, unpublished mapping by the author shows that the Mississippian structural disharmony never displays any significant stratigraphic cutouts, and that the disharmony does not stay at the same level of the stratigraphic section, indicating that this is indeed a tectonic feature and not an angular unconformity representing an orogenic pulse.

It was also mentioned before that the continental platform under the southern Arkoma basin subsided strongly along several basement growth faults (Fig. 11) during the Atokan (and probably before). This faulting was probably related to thrust loading

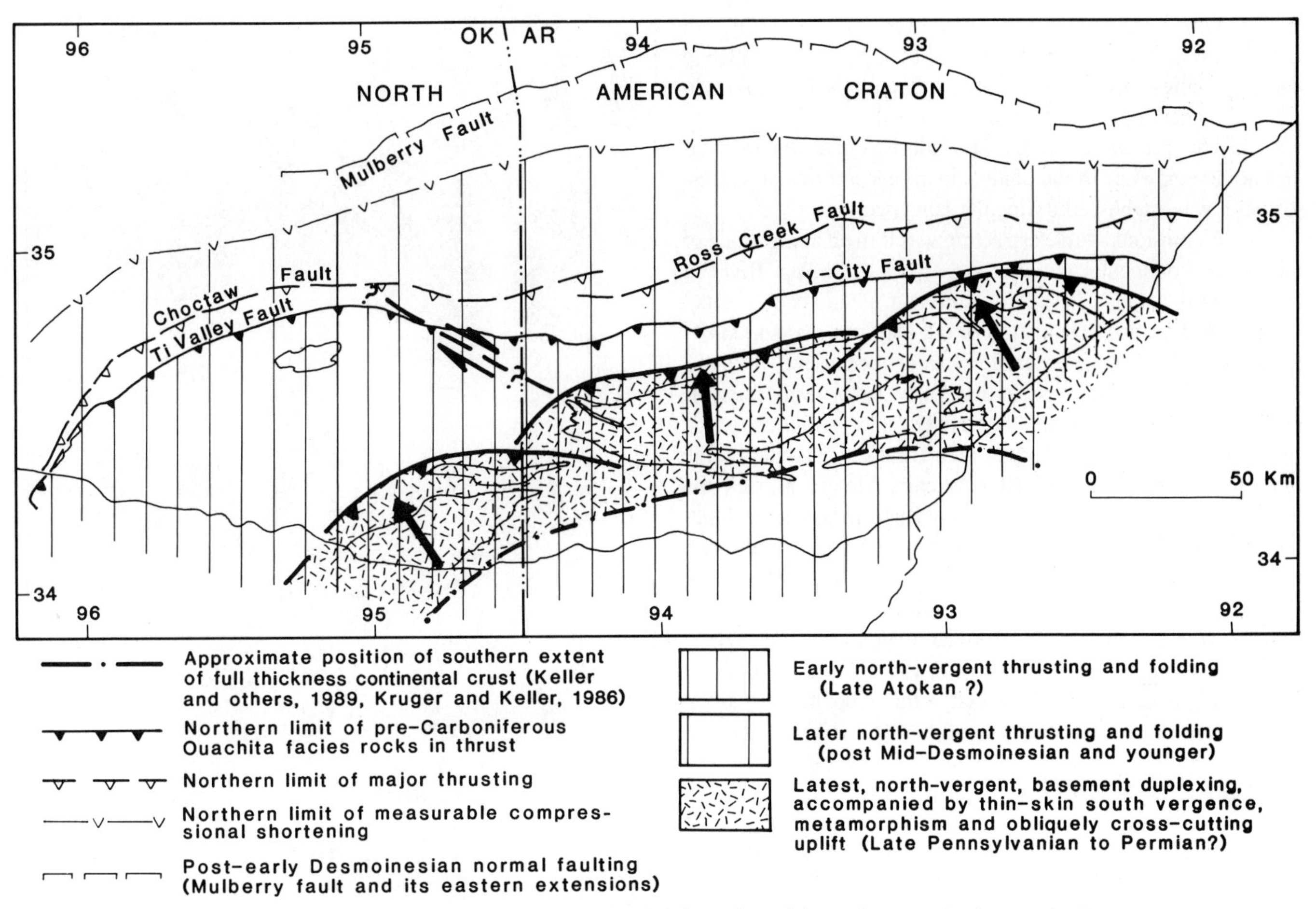

Figure 13. Tentative timing of emplacement and deformation of the major tectonic elements in the Ouachita Mountains.

during the Morrowan, which must have occurred in the hinterland, south of the present surface and subsurface control. The existence of the Desmoinesian and younger, postorogenic successor basin sequence in the subsurface of southern Arkansas and Texas gives clear evidence that Atokan-age thrusting, folding, and subsequent peneplanation had to be terminated by early Desmoinesian. The main compressional event in that part of the orogen had to happen in late Atokan, because all previous flysch units appear to be conformable.

Yet in the Arkoma basin, north of the thrust front of the Ouachita Mountains, beds as young as middle Desmoinesian are still conformably infolded in the synclines of the fold belt. An unconformity separating the Desmoinesian Hartshorne Sandstone from the underlying Atoka Formation, described by Hendricks and Parks (1950) and Haley (1966, 1968), appears still to be more closely related to the extensional growth faulting than to the compressional folding. Thus, it is evident that along the northern margin of the orogen, deformation did not start until middle or late Desmoinesian. Indirect evidence of a major tectonic event at that time comes also from the Ardmore basin, a foreland basin west of the Ouachita thrust front, where the earliest preflysch Ouachita-facies detritus appears in the eastward-coarsening Desmoinesian Devils Kitchen Conglomerate (Tomlinson and McBee, 1959; Denison, 1989).

In the Marathon region, direct evidence for the termination of the orogeny is documented by an angular unconformity between rocks of Wolfcampian and Leonardian (Early Permian) age (Ross, 1986). A Permian age for the close of the orogeny is further suggested by numerous Permian isotopic ages from west Texas to southeastern Oklahoma (Denison and others, 1977; Denison, 1989). On the basis of well-known north-south–trending zones of en echelon, right-stepping faults in north-central Oklahoma (suggesting left-lateral, minor strike slip), Melton (1930) proposed the presence of an effect of Ouachita tectonism in the foreland outside the Ouachitas in Early Permian.

Based on present information, the events of the Ouachita orogeny can be tentatively summarized as follows.

a. Earliest orogenic basin constriction and source activation for flysch sedimentation occurred in the deep hinterland in Mississippian (Meramecian to early Chesterian).

b. Orogenic sediment influx continued through Late Mississippian and Early Pennsylvanian (Morrowan and Atokan), but deformation front did not reach the presently exposed flysch basin until late Atokan.

c. Thrusting and folding deformed the central and southern Ouachita Mountains region in late Atokan, probably obducting and emplacing a Ouachita-facies allochthon on the North American continental margin at that time (Fig. 13).

d. The present deformation front was reached in mid-Desmoinesian, while in the hinterland an unconformable successor basin was established during the same period.

e. A collisional duplex structure was formed along much of the former continental margin west of the Mississippi River in Late Pennsylvanian to Permian, resulting in a band of antiformal ramp structures, an accentuation of the platform margin gravity anomaly, and a thermal event of mild metamorphism.

A more complete record of late Paleozoic orogenic pulses is preserved in the outcrops and the heavily drilled subsurface of the southern Oklahoma aulacogen, the Arbuckle Mountains, the Ardmore basin, the Criner Hills–Wichita Mountains, and the southern margin of the Anadarko basin. Repeated orogenic uplift, followed by truncation and dispersal of coarse clastic sediment, has been documented in Late Mississippian, late Morrowan, Desmoinesian, and late Missourian, with mild rejuvenation of positive structures in the Early Permian (Tomlinson and McBee, 1959; Reedy and Sykes, 1959; Latham, 1970; Brewer and others, 1983; Denison, 1982, 1989). How exactly this record of deformation relates to the Ouachita orogeny is still unresolved.

TECTONIC SUMMARY

The frontal length of the Ouachita system is some 2,100 km, of which only about 430 km are exposed in the Ouachita Mountains and in the Marathon uplift. The entire orogenic hinterland is deeply buried beneath the Gulf Coastal Plain and is known to have undergone varying amounts of extension during the opening of the Gulf of Mexico. Constraining data, especially from the hinterland, are therefore fragmentary, and the regional tectonic history remains the subject of much debate. Many authors have proposed models of the tectonic evolution for parts or all of the Ouachita system, particularly since the emergence of plate tectonics in the 1960s, but space is too limited in this summary to discuss adequately the merits of these proposals. The interested reader is referred to the following list of publications, all of which concern some geotectonic aspects of the Ouachita system: Cebull and others, 1976; Cebull and Shurbet, 1980; Graham and others, 1975; Flawn and others, 1961; Ham and Wilson, 1967; Handschy and others, 1987; Keller and Cebull, 1973; Keller and others, 1989; King, 1959, 1975a, b, 1977; Kruger and Keller, 1986; Lillie, 1984; Lillie and others, 1983; Link and Roberts, 1986; Lowe, 1985, 1989; Meyerhoff, 1973; Nelson and others, 1982; Nicholas and Rozendal, 1975; Paine and Meyerhoff, 1970; Pindell and Dewey, 1982; Rippee,1985; Ross, 1986; Thomas, 1972, 1976, 1977a, b, 1985, 1989; Viele, 1973, 1979; Viele and Thomas, 1989; Walper, 1977; Wickham and others, 1976; Zimmerman and others, 1982.

Most geologists and geophysicists tend to agree today that the southern margin of an intact and nearly autochthonous North American continental crust lay close to the present southern limb of the Benton–Broken Bow uplift in the Ouachita Mountains, and regionally just south and east of the above-mentioned gravity anomaly that extends from west Texas to the Mississippi Embayment. The deep-water oceanic basin, in which the typical preorogenic and early orogenic Ouachita facies rocks were deposited, was probably fault-bounded along its northern rim, judging from the presence of olistostromes and the abrupt appearance of the deep-water facies in the allochthonous thrust belt. That the early Paleozoic continental margin was the result of an angular breakup geometry of alternating rift and transform segments

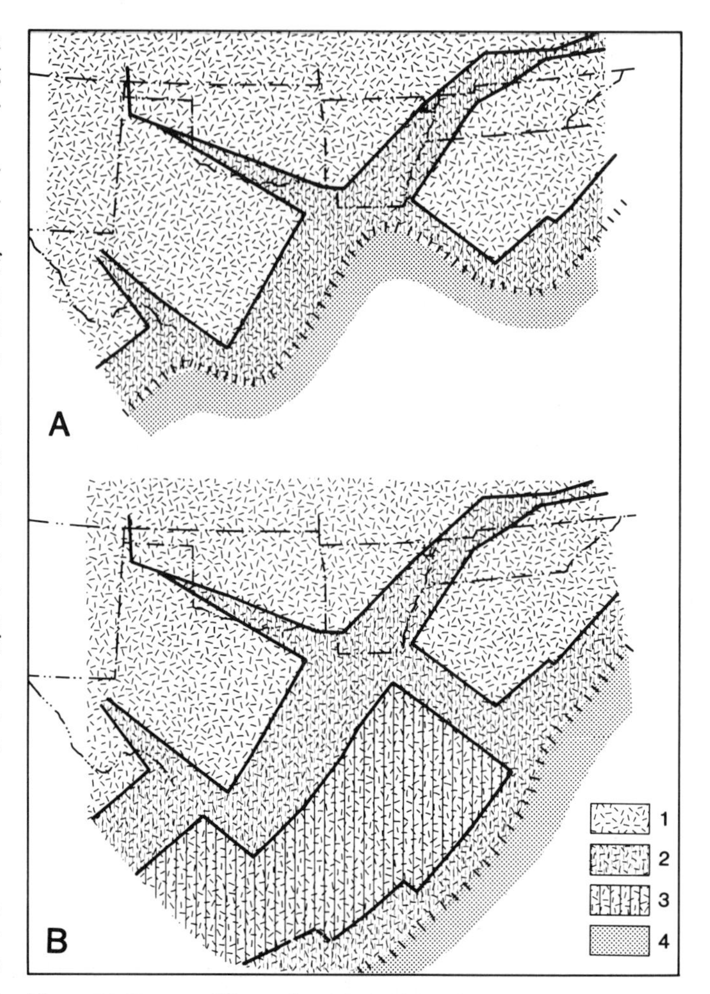

Figure 14. Two possible configurations of the southern continental margin of North America and the tectonic setting of the deep-water Ouachita basin during the early Paleozoic: A. Trailing rift-transform margin facing the open proto-Atlantic Ocean (Iapetus) with three rift basins extending into the craton (after Cebull and others, 1976; Thomas, 1977a; Viele and Thomas, 1989). B. Ouachita trough as a rift basin separated from the open proto-Atlantic by a rifted microcontinent or oceanic plateau that served as an intermittent sediment source and topographic restricting agent (after Lowe, 1985, 1989). Definition of symbols: 1, Continental crust with platform facies cover; 2, Attenuated continental, transitional, and possibly oceanic crust; 3, Attenuated continental crust (less attenuated than 2); 4, Oceanic crust.

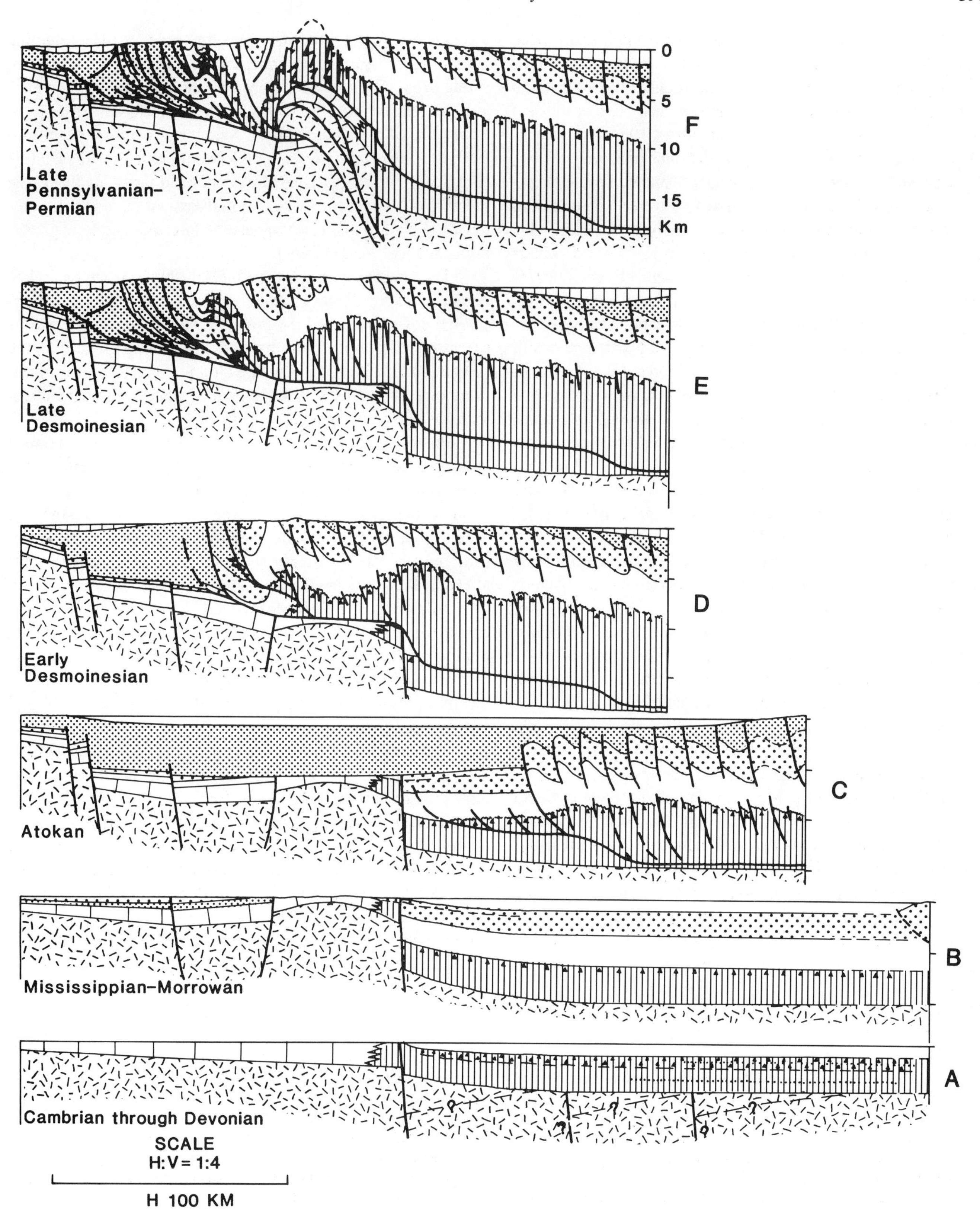

Figure 15. Diagrammatic evolution of depositional and deformational stages of the Ouachita system continental margin (along Section A–A′, Ouachita Mountains, Fig. 11). For discussion see text.

(Fig. 4) is now accepted by many authors (Cebull and others, 1976; Thomas, 1976, 1977b, 1989; Viele and Thomas, 1989). The beginning of rifting is poorly constrained, but by Middle Cambrian a continental carbonate platform had been established on the Llano promontory (Palmer and others, 1984), while igneous activity continued in the south Oklahoma aulacogen.

Less unanimity exists about the depth and size of the ocean basin, in which the Ouachita facies rocks were deposited, and therefore about the nature of the crust underlying the basin. One model (Fig. 14A), originally presented by Cebull and others (1976) and since favored by several authors (Thomas, 1976, 1977b, 1989; Kruger and Keller, 1986; Viele and Thomas, 1989), proposes that the rift-transform margin, mentioned above, became truly the southern continental margin of North America in Cambrian time, facing an open ocean floored by a Paleozoic oceanic crust. Thus, the Ouachita facies rocks of early and middle Paleozoic age represent slope, rise, and/or abyssal sediments, which became obducted and emplaced as an allochthonous mass during the closing phases of that ocean.

The other model (Fig. 14B), suggested by Lowe (1985) and favored by this author, is a plate-tectonic application to ideas dating back to Schuchert (1923), claiming that the Ouachita basin remained a wide rift basin flanked on the outboard side by one or more attenuated microcontinents or ocean plateaus, which could act intermittently as a source of clastic sediments and olistoliths. These outboard barriers could also be the cause for repeated restriction and anoxic conditions, and for basin-center turbidite fans in the rift. The water depth of such a rift could be bathyal but not necessarily abyssal, and the underlying crust could be an attenuated continental (i.e., "transitional") crust, which could exist within a few kilometers of the continental margin. Geographic alignment would associate this rift with the Reelfoot–Rough Creek–Rome trough rift system of the eastern North American craton.

Most authors agree that by the end of the Early Mississippian the Ouachita basin became a narrowing trough receiving vast amounts of clastics and some southern-source volcanics (Fig. 15B). Depending on one's preferred geotectonic model, the south flank of this basin probably was a subductional accretionary thrust front of (a) approaching Gondwana, (b) a mid-oceanic volcanic arc, (c) an unknown foreign terrane, or (d) a returning piece of North America separated from the craton by a Cambrian rifting event. Olistostromes were derived from the cratonic margin (Ouachitas and Marathons) and from the southern tectonic front (Marathons). Much of the continental platform edge from Alabama to west Texas underwent extensional faulting (Fig. 15C)—possibly triggered by continued thrust loading in the hinterland—from Morrowan into mid-Pennsylvanian time, creating deep-water conditions in several foreland basins (e.g., Arkoma and Val Verde basins).

The orogeny reached the Ouachita outcrop region in late Atokan, creating a topographic divide, which separated the depositional environments of the postorogenic Desmoinesian marine successor basin in the south from the continuing foredeep in the Arkoma basin (Fig. 15D). By late Desmoinesian the Atokan and Desmoinesian deposits of the remaining foredeep became themselves mildly compressed (Fig. 15E).

In the Marathon basin, deep-water sedimentation continued in an ever-narrowing channel (Ross, 1986) into the earliest Permian, while an encroaching allochthon transformed the basin into a thrust belt from the close of the Desmoinesian to the late Wolfcampian. Into this Late Pennsylvanian to Early Permian time bracket fall apparently all of the latest observable events affecting the continental margin west of the Mississippi River. The duplexlike basement thrusts (Fig. 15F)—which produced the central uplifts of the Ouachita Mountains (the Broken Bow–Benton uplift), the Waco uplift, the Devils River uplift, and the Sierra del Carmen (Big Bend region), with their attendant metamorphism (Denison and others, 1977; Denison, 1989) and gravity signatures (Keller and others, 1989)—all have isotopic ages indicating latest thermal imprints in the Permian. On the Benton–Broken Bow uplift this duplexing seems to be also the most plausible and opportune time for the formation of the south-vergent overturning and the formation of the pervasive north-dipping cleavage.

On a continental scale these Permian events signal the final closing of the proto-Atlantic Ocean and the assembly of Pangaea. After a period of relative stability in the Late Permian, renewed rifting in the Ouachita-Appalachian hinterland initiated the opening of the Gulf of Mexico and the North Atlantic.

REFERENCES CITED

Ammerman, M. L., and Keller, G. R., 1979, Delineation of Rome trough in eastern Kentucky by gravity and deep drilling: American Association of Petroleum Geologists Bulletin, v. 63, p. 341–353.

Arbenz, J. K., 1968, Structural geology of the Potato Hills, Ouachita Mountains, Oklahoma, *in* Cline, L. M., ed., A guidebook to the geology of the western Arkoma Basin and Ouachita Mountains, Oklahoma: Oklahoma City Geological Society, p. 109–121.

——, 1984, A structural section through the Ouachita Mountains of western Arkansas, *in* Stone, C. G., and Haley, B. R., eds., A guidebook to the geology of the central and southern Ouachita Mountains, Arkansas: Arkansas Geological Commission, p. 76–82.

——, 1989, Ouachita thrust belt and Arkoma Basin, *in* Hatcher, R. D., Jr., Thomas, W. A., and Viele, G. W., eds., The Appalachian–Ouachita orogen in the United States: Boulder, Colorado, Geological Society of America, The Geology of North America, v. F-2 (in press).

Bally, A. W., 1975, A geodynamic scenario for hydrocarbon occurrences: Proceedings, 9th World Petroleum Congress, Tokyo 1975, v. 2, p. 33–44.

Berry, R. M., and Trumbly, W. D., 1968, Wilburton gas field, Arkoma Basin, Oklahoma, *in* Cline, L. M., ed., A guidebook to the geology of the western Arkoma Basin and the Ouachita Mountains, Oklahoma: Oklahoma City Geological Society, p. 86–108.

Blythe, A. E., Sugar, A., and Phipps, S. P., 1988, Structural profiles of the Ouachita Mountains, western Arkansas: American Association of Petroleum Geologists Bulletin, v. 72, p. 810–819.

Brewer, J. A., Good, R., Oliver, J. E., Brown, L. D., and Kaufman, S., 1983, COCORP profiling across the southern Oklahoma aulacogen; Overthrusting of the Wichita Mountains and compression within the Anadarko Basin: Geology, v. 11, p. 109–114.

Buchanan, R. S., and Johnson, F. K., 1968, Bonanza field; A model for Arkoma Basin growth faulting, *in* Cline, L. M., ed., A guidebook to the geology of the western Arkoma Basin and Ouachita Mountains, Oklahoma: Oklahoma City Geological Society, p. 75–85.

Bush, W. V., Haley, B. R., Stone, C. G., Holbrook, D. F., and McFarland, J. D. III, 1977, A guide book to the geology of the Arkansas Paleozoic area: Arkansas Geological Commission, 79 p.

Cebull, S. E., and Shurbet, D. H., 1980, The Ouachita belt in the evolution of the Gulf of Mexico, *in* Pilger, R. H., Jr., ed., The origin of the Gulf of Mexico and the early opening of the central North American ocean; Proceedings of a symposium: Baton Rouge, Louisiana State University Department of Geology–Louisiana Geological Survey, p. 17–26.

Cebull, S. E., Shurbet, D. H., Keller, G. R., and Russell, L. R., 1976, Possible role of transform faults in the development of apparent offsets in the Ouachita–southern Appalachian tectonic belt: Journal of Geology, v. 84, p. 107–114.

Chenoweth, P. A., 1989, Hydrocarbons of the Ouachita trend, *in* Hatcher, R. D. Jr., Thomas, W. A., and Viele, G. W., eds., The Appalachian-Ouachita orogen in the United States: Boulder, Colorado, Geological Society of America, The Geology of North America, v. F-2 (in press).

Cline, L. M., 1960, Stratigraphy of the late Paleozoic rocks of the Ouachita Mountains, Oklahoma: Oklahoma Geological Survey Bulletin 85, 158 p.

Cline, L. M, Hilseweck, W. J., and Feray, D. E., eds., 1959, The geology of the Ouachita Mountains, a symposium: Dallas and Ardmore Geological Societies, 208 p.

Cook, T. D., Bally, A. W., Milner, S., Buffler, R. T., Farmer, R. E. and Clark, D. K., 1975, Stratigraphic atlas of North and Central America: Princeton, New Jersey, Princeton University Press, 272 p.

Curiale, J. A., 1983, Petroleum occurrences and sourcerock potential of the Ouachita Mountains, southeastern Oklahoma: Oklahoma Geological Survey Bulletin 135, 65 p.

Curiale, J. A., and Harrison, W. E., 1981, Correlation of oil and asphaltite in Ouachita Mountain region of Oklahoma: American Association of Petroleum Geologists Bulletin, v. 65, p. 2426–2432.

Currie, J. B., Patnode, H. W., and Trump, R. P., 1962, Development of folds in sedimentary strata: Geological Society of America Bulletin, v. 73, p. 655–674.

Denison, R. E., 1982, Geologic cross section from the Arbuckle Mountains to the Muenster Arch, southern Oklahoma and Texas: Geological Society of America Map and Chart Series, MC-28R, scale 1:250,000.

——, 1989, Foreland structure adjacent to the Ouachita foldbelt, *in* Hatcher, R. D., Jr., Thomas, W. A., and Viele, G. W., eds., The Appalachian–Ouachita orogen in the United States: Boulder, Colorado, Geological Society of America, The Geology of North America, v. F–2 (in press).

Denison, R. E., Kenny, G. S., Burke, W. H., Jr., and Hetherington, E. A., Jr., 1969, Isotopic ages of igneous and metamorphic boulders from the Haymond Formation (Pennsylvanian), Marathon basin, Texas, and their significance: Geological Society of America Bulletin, v. 80, p. 245–256.

Denison, R. E., Burke, W. H., Otto, J. B., and Hetherington, E. A., 1977, Age of igneous and metamorphic activity affecting the Ouachita foldbelt, *in* Stone, C. G., ed., Symposium on the geology of the Ouachita Mountains: Arkansas Geological Commission, v. 1, p. 25–40.

Desborough, G. A., Zimmerman, R. A., Elrick, M., and Stone, C. G., 1985, Early Permian thermal alteration of Carboniferous strata in the Ouachita region and Arkansas River Valley, Arkansas: Geological Society of America Abstracts with Programs, v. 17, p. 155.

Ethington, R. L., Finney, S. C., and Repetski, J. E., 1989, Biostratigraphy of the Paleozoic rocks of the Ouachita orogen, Arkansas, Oklahoma, west Texas, *in* Hatcher, R. D., Jr., Thomas, W. A., and Viele, G. W., eds., The Appalachian–Ouachita orogen in the United States: Boulder, Colorado, Geological Society of America, The Geology of North America, v. F–2 (in press).

Ferguson, C. A., and Suneson, N. H., 1988, Arbuckle source of Atoka Formation, Ouachita Mountains frontal belt, Oklahoma; New evidence from paleocurrents [abs.]: American Association of Petroleum Geologists Bulletin, v. 72, p. 184–185.

Flawn, P. T., Goldstein, A., Jr., King, P. B., and Weaver, C. E., 1961, The Ouachita system: Austin, University of Texas Publication 6120, 401 p.

Folk, R. L., and McBride, E. F., 1978, Origin of the Caballos Novaculite: Society of Economic Paleontologists and Mineralogists, Permian Basin Section, Publication 78–17, p. 101–130.

Galley, J. E., 1958, Oil and geology in the Permian Basin of Texas and New Mexico, *in* Weeks, L. G., ed., Habitat of oil: American Association of Petroleum Geologists, p. 395–446.

Gordon, M. G., Jr., and Stone, C. G., 1977, Correlation of Carboniferous rocks of the Ouachita trough with those of the adjacent foreland, *in* Stone, C. G., ed., Symposium on the geology of the Ouachita Mountains: Arkansas Geological Commission, v. 1, p. 70–91.

Graham, S. A., Dickinson, W. R., and Ingersoll, R. V., 1975, Himalayan–Bengal model for flysch dispersal in Appalachian–Ouachita system: Geological Society of America Bulletin, v. 86, p. 273–286.

Guthrie, J. M., Houseknecht, D. W., and John, W. D., 1986, Relationship among vitrinite reflectance, illite crystallinity, and organic geochemistry in Carboniferous strata, Ouachita Mountains, Oklahoma and Arkansas: American Association of Petroleum Geologists Bulletin, v. 70, p. 26–33.

Haley, B. R., 1966, Geology of the Barber Quadrangle, Sebastian County and vicinity, Arkansas: Arkansas Geological Commission Information Circular 20–C, 76 p.

——, 1968, Geology of the Scranton and New Blaine Quadrangles, Logan and Johnson Counties, Arkansas: U.S. Geological Survey Professional Paper 536–B, 10 p.

Haley, B. R., Glick, E. E., Bush, W. V., Clardy, R. F., Stone, C. G., Woodward, M. B., and Zachry, D. L, 1976, Geologic map of Arkansas: U.S. Geological Survey and Arkansas Geological Commission, scale 1:500,000.

Ham, W. E., and Wilson, J. L., 1967, Paleozoic epeirogeny and orogeny in the central United States: American Journal of Science, v. 265, p. 332–407.

Ham, W. E., Denison, R. E., and Merritt, C. A., 1964, Basement rocks and structural evolution of southern Oklahoma: Oklahoma Geological Survey Bulletin 95, 302 p.

Handschy, J. W., Keller, G. R., and Smith, K. J., 1987, The Ouachita system in northern Mexico: Tectonics, v. 6, p. 323–330.

Hanor, J. S., and Baria, L. R., 1977, Controls on the distribution of barite deposits in Arkansas, *in* Stone, C. G., ed., Symposium on the geology of the Ouachita Mountains, v. 2: Arkansas Geological Commission, p. 42–49.

Harlton, B. H., 1938, Stratigraphy of the Bendian of the Oklahoma salient of the Ouachita Mountains: American Association of Petroleum Geologists Bulletin, v. 22, p. 852–914.

Hart, W. D., Stitt, J. H., Hohensee, S. R., and Ethington, R. L., 1987, Geological implications of Late Cambrian trilobites from the Collier shale, Jessieville area, Arkansas: Geology, v. 15, p. 445–450.

Hatcher, R. D., Jr., Thomas, W. A., and Viele, G. W., eds., 1989, The Appalachian and Ouachita orogen in the United States: Boulder, Colorado, Geological Society of America, The Geology of North America, v. F–2 (in press).

Hendricks, T. A., and Parks, B., 1950, Geology of the Fort Smith district, Arkansas: U.S. Geological Survey Professional Paper 221–E, p. 67–94.

Hendricks, T. A., Gardner, L. S., Knechtel, M. M., and Averitt, P., 1947, Geology of the western part of the Ouachita Mountains, Oklahoma: U.S. Geological Survey Oil and Gas Investigation Map OM–66, scale 1:42,240.

Honess, C. W., 1923, Geology of the southern Ouachita Mountains of Oklahoma: Oklahoma Geological Survey Bulletin 32, Part I, 278 p., Part II, 76 p.

Hoffman, P., Dewey, J. F., and Burke, K., 1974, Aulacogens and their genetic relation to geosynclines, with a Proterozoic example from Great Slave Lake, Canada, *in* Dott, R. H., Jr., and Shaver, R. H., eds., Modern and ancient geosynclinal sedimentation: Society of Economic Paleontologists and Mineralogists Special Publication 19, p. 38–55.

Houseknecht, D. W., 1986, Evolution from passive margin to foreland basin; The Atoka Formation of the Arkoma Basin, south-central U.S.A.: International

Association of Sedimentologists Special Publication 8, p. 327–345.

Houseknecht, D. W., and Matthews, S. M., 1985, Thermal maturity of Carboniferous strata, Ouachita Mountains: American Association of Petroleum Geologists Bulletin, v. 69, p. 335–345.

Houseknecht, D. W., and Weaverling, P. H., 1983, Early Paleozoic sedimentation in Reelfoot Rift [abs.]: American Association of Petroleum Geologists Bulletin, v. 67, p. 1456.

Joustek, P. G., 1979, Structural style of the Ouachita core in a portion of the McGraw Mountain quadrangle, Arkansas [M.S. thesis]: Carbondale, Southern Illinois University, 132 p.

Keller, G. R., and Cebull, S. E., 1973, Plate tectonics and the Ouachita system in Texas, Oklahoma, and Arkansas: Geological Society of America Bulletin, v. 83, p. 1659–1666.

Keller, G.R., Kruger, J. M., Smith, K. J., and Voight, W. M., 1989, The Ouachita system; A geophysical overview, *in* Hatcher, R. D., Jr., Thomas, W. A., and Viele, G. W., eds., The Appalachian and Ouachita orogen in the United States: Boulder, Colorado, Geological Society of America, The Geology of North America, v. F–2 (in press).

Keller, W. D., Stone, C. G., and Hoersch, A. L., 1985, Textures of Paleozoic chert and novaculite in the Ouachita Mountains of Arkansas and Oklahoma and their geological significance: Geological Society of America Bulletin, v. 96, p. 1353–1363.

King, P. B., 1937, Geology of the Marathon region, Texas: U.S. Geological Survey Professional Paper 187, 148 p.

—— , 1950, Tectonic framework of the southeastern United States: American Association of Petroleum Geologists Bulletin, v. 34, p. 309–380.

—— , 1959, The evolution of North America: Princeton, New Jersey, Princeton University Press, 189 p.

—— , 1975a, Ancient southern margin of North America: Geology, v. 3, p. 732–734.

—— , 1975b, The Ouachita and Appalachian orogenic belts, *in* Nairn, A.E.M., and Stehli, F. G., eds., The ocean basins and margins; v. 3, The Gulf of Mexico and the Caribbean: New York, Plenum Press, p. 201–241.

—— , 1977, Marathon revisited, *in* Stone, C. G., ed., Symposium on the geology of the Ouachita Mountains: Arkansas Geological Commission, v. 1, p. 41–69.

Kruger, J. M., and Keller, G. R., 1986, Interpretation of crustal structure from regional gravity anomalies, Ouachita Mountains area and adjacent Gulf Coastal Plains: American Association of Petroleum Geologists Bulletin v. 70, p. 667–689.

Latham, J. W., 1970, Petroleum geology of the Healton field, Carter County, Oklahoma, *in* Halbouty, M. T., ed., Geology of giant petroleum fields: American Association of Petroleum Geologists Memoir 14, p. 255–276.

Leander, M. H., and Legg, T. E., 1988, Potential for subthrust gas fields; Results of recent drilling in the Ouachitas [abs.]: American Association of Petroleum Geologists Bulletin, v. 77, p. 211.

Lillie, R. J., 1984, Tectonic implications of subthrust structures revealed by seismic profiling of Appalachian–Ouachita orogenic belt: Tectonics, v. 3, p. 619–646.

—— , 1985, Tectonically buried continent/ocean boundary, Ouachita Mountains, Arkansas: Geology, v. 13, p. 18–21.

Lillie, R. J., Nelson, K. D., de Voogd, B., Brewer, J. A., Oliver, J. E., Brown, L. D., Kaufman, S., and Viele, G. W., 1983, Crustal structure of Ouachita Mountains, Arkansas; A model based on integration of COCORP reflection profiles and regional geophysical data: American Association of Petroleum Geologists Bulletin, v. 67, p. 907–931.

Link, M. A., and Roberts, M. T., 1986, Pennsylvanian paleogeography from the Ozarks, Arkoma, and Ouachita Basins in east-central Arkansas, *in* Stone, C. G., and Haley, B. R., eds., Sedimentary and igneous rocks of the Ouachita Mountains, part 2: Arkansas Geological Commission, p. 37–60.

Lowe, D. R., 1977, The Arkansas novaculite; Some aspects of its physical sedimentation, *in* Stone, C. G., ed., Symposium on the geology of the Ouachita Mountains: Arkansas Geological Commission, v. 1, p. 132–138.

—— , 1985, Ouachita trough; Part of a Cambrian failed rift system: Geology, v. 13, p. 790–793.

—— , 1989, Stratigraphy, sedimentology, and depositional setting of preorogenic rocks of the Ouachita Mountains, Arkansas and Oklahoma, *in* Hatcher, R. D., Jr., Thomas, W. A., and Viele, G. W., eds., The Appalachian and Ouachita orogen in the United States: Boulder, Colorado, Geological Society of America, The Geology of North America, v. F–2 (in press).

Mankin, C. J., coordinator, 1987, Texas–Oklahoma tectonic region (TOT): COSUNA Project, American Association of Petroleum Geologists.

McBride, E. F., 1989, Stratigraphy and sedimentary history of Pre-Permian Paleozoic rocks of the Marathon uplift, *in* Hatcher, R. D., Jr., Thomas, W. A., and Viele, G. W., eds., The Appalachian and Ouachita orogen in the United States: Boulder, Colorado, Geological Society of America, The Geology of North America, v. F–2 (in press).

McBride, E. F., and Thomson, A., 1964, Sedimentology of the Tesnus Formation, Marathon region, Texas, *in* The Filling of the Marathon Geosyncline, Symposium and Guidebook, 1964 Field Trip: Society of Economic Paleontologists and Mineralogists, Permian Basin Section Publication 64–9, p. 17–21.

Melton, F. A., 1930, Age of the Ouachita orogeny and its tectonic effects: American Association of Petroleum Geologists Bulletin, v. 14, p. 57–72.

Meyerhoff, A. A., 1973, Late Paleozoic of western Gulf Coastal Plain, *in* A study of Paleozoic rocks in Arbuckle and western Ouachita Mountains of southern Oklahoma: Shreveport Geological Society Guidebook, p. 31–37.

Miser, H. D., 1929, Structure of the Ouachita Mountains of Oklahoma and Arkansas: Oklahoma Geological Survey Bulletin 50, 30 p.

—— , 1934, Carboniferous rocks of Ouachita Mountains: American Association of Petroleum Geologists Bulletin, v. 18, p. 971–1009.

—— , 1959, Structure and vein quartz of the Ouachita Mountains of Oklahoma and Arkansas, *in* Cline, L. M., Hilseweck, W. J., and Feray, D.E., eds., The Geology of the Ouachita Mountains; A Symposium: Dallas and Ardmore Geological Society Guidebook, p. 30–43.

Miser, H. D., and Purdue, A. H., 1929, Geology of the De Queen and Caddo Gap Quadrangles, Arkansas: U.S. Geological Survey Bulletin 808, 195 p.

Morris, R. C., 1974, Sedimentary and tectonic history of the Ouachita Mountains, *in* Dickinson, W. R., ed., Tectonics and sedimentation: Society of Economic Paleontologists and Mineralogists Special Publication 22, p. 120–142.

—— , 1989, Stratigraphy and sedimentary history of post-Novaculite Carboniferous rocks of the Ouachita Mountains, *in* Hatcher, R. D., Jr., Thomas, W. A., and Viele, G. W., eds., The Appalachian and Ouachita orogen in the United States: Boulder, Colorado, Geological Society of America, The Geology of North America, v. F–2, (in press).

Muehlberger, W. R., and Tauvers, R. R., 1989, Marathon fold-thrust belt, west Texas, *in* Hatcher, R. D., Jr., Thomas, W. A., and Viele, G. W., eds., The Appalachian and Ouachita orogen in the United States: Boulder, Colorado, Geological Society of America, The Geology of North America, v. F–2 (in press).

Muehlberger, W. R., DeMis, W. D., and Leason, J. O., 1984, Geologic cross-sections, Marathon region, Trans-Pecos Texas: Geological Society of America Map and Chart Series MC–28T, scale 1:250,000.

Mutti, E., and Ricci Lucchi, F., 1975, Turbidite facies and facies associations, *in* Mutti, E., and others, eds., Examples of turbidite facies and facies associations from selected formations of the northern Appenines: 9th International Congress on Carboniferous Stratigraphy and Geology, Field Trip A 11, p. 21–36.

Nelson, K. D., Lillie, R. J., de Voogd, B., Brewer, J. A., Oliver, J. E., Kaufman, S., Brown, C., and Viele, G. W., 1982, COCORP seismic reflection profiling in the Ouachita Mountains of western Arkansas; Geometry and geologic interpretations: Tectonophysics, v. 1, p. 413–430.

Nicholas, R. L., 1983, Structure and stratigraphy of the Val Verde Basin–Devils River uplift, Texas: West Texas Geological Society Publication 83–77, p. 125–137.

Nicholas, R. L., and Rozendal, R. A., 1975, Subsurface positive elements within Ouachita foldbelt in Texas and their relation to Paleozoic cratonic margin: American Association of Petroleum Geologists Bulletin, v. 59, p. 193–216.

Nicholas, R. L., and Waddell, D. E., 1989, The Ouachita system in the subsurface of Texas, Arkansas, and Louisiana, *in* Hatcher, R. D., Jr., Thomas, W. A., and Viele, G. W., The Appalachian and Ouachita orogen in the United States: Boulder, Colorado, Geological Society of America, The Geology of North America, v. F-2 (in press).

Nielsen, K. C., Viele, G. W., and Zimmerman, J., 1989, Structural setting of the Benton-Broken Bow uplifts, *in* Hatcher, R. D., Jr., Thomas, W. A., and Viele, G. W., eds., The Appalachian and Ouachita orogen in the United States: Boulder, Colorado, Geological Society of America, The Geology of North America, v. F-2 (in press).

Niem, A. R., 1977, Mississippian pyroclastic flow and ash fall deposits in the deep-marine Ouachita flysch basin, Oklahoma and Arkansas: Geological Society of America Bulletin, v. 88, p. 49-61.

Owen, M. R., 1984, Southern source for upper Jackfork Sandstone, Ouachita Mountains, Arkansas, *in* Stone, C. G., and Haley, B. R., eds., A guidebook to the geology of the central and southern Ouachita Mountains, Arkansas: Arkansas Geological Commission, p. 116-122.

Paine, W. L., and Meyerhoff, A. A., 1970, Gulf of Mexico basin; Interactions among tectonics, sedimentation, and hydrocarbon accumulation: Gulf Coast Association of Geological Societies Transactions, v. 20, p. 5-44.

Palmer, A. R., DeMis, W. D., Muehlberger, W. R., and Robison, R. A., 1984, Geological implications of Middle Cambrian boulders from the Haymond Formation (Pennsylvanian) in the Marathon basin, west Texas: Geology, v. 12, p. 91-94.

Petroleum Information Corporation, 1985, The Ouachita system; Oil and gas development along the overthrust belt: Petroleum Frontiers, A Quarterly Investigation into the Nation's Most Promising Petroleum Horizons and Provinces, v. 2, no. 3, 98 p.

Pindell, J., and Dewey, J. F., 1982, Permo-Triassic reconstruction of western Pangea and the evolution of the Gulf of Mexico/Caribbean region: Tectonophysics, v. 1, p. 179-211.

Powers, S., 1928, Age of the folding of the Oklahoma mountains; The Ouachita, Arbuckle, and Wichita Mountains of Oklahoma and the Llano-Burnet and Marathon uplifts of Texas: Geological Society of America Bulletin, v. 39, p. 1031-1072.

Purdue, A. M., and Miser, H. D., 1923, Hot Springs, Arkansas, folio: U.S. Geological Survey Folio 215, scale 1:52,500.

Ramsay, J. G., and Huber, M., 1987, The techniques of modern structural geology; v. 2, Folds and fractures: London, Academic Press, p. 309-700.

Rankin, D. W., 1975, The continental margin of eastern North America in the southern Appalachians; The opening and closing of the proto-Atlantic Ocean: American Journal of Science, v. 275-A, p. 298-336.

Reedy, H. J., and Sykes, H. A., 1959, Carter-Knox field, Grady and Stephens Counties, Oklahoma, *in* Mayes, J. W., Westheimer, J., Tomlinson, C. W. and Putman, D. M., eds., Petroleum geology of southern Oklahoma—a symposium: American Association of Petroleum Geologists, v. 2, p. 198-219.

Reinemund, J. A., and Danilchik, W., 1957, Preliminary geologic map of the Waldron Quadrangle and adjacent areas, Scott County, Arkansas: U.S. Geological Survey Oil and Gas Investigations Map OM-192, scale 1:48,000.

Rippee, D. S., 1985, Geology along a cross section through the frontal Ouachita Mountains in Pittsburg, Atoka, and Pushmataha Counties, Oklahoma: Shale Shaker, v. 36, p. 140-154.

Ross, C. A., 1986, Paleozoic evolution of southerm margin of Permian basin: Geological Society of America Bulletin, v. 97, p. 536-554.

Schuchert, C., 1923, Sites and nature of the North American geosynclines: Geological Society of America Bulletin, v. 34, p. 151-230.

Sellards, E. H., 1931, Erratics in the Pennsylvanian of Texas: Austin, University of Texas Bulletin 3101, p. 9-17.

Shideler, G. L., 1970, Provenance of Johns Valley boulders in late Paleozoic Ouachita facies, southeastern Oklahoma and southwestern Arkansas: American Association of Petroleum Geologists Bulletin, v. 54, p. 789-806.

Sholes, M. A., 1977, Arkansas Novaculite stratigraphy, *in* Stone, C. G., ed., Symposium on the geology of the Ouachita Mountains: Arkansas Geological Commission, v. 1, p. 139-145.

Sloss, L. L., 1963, Sequences in the cratonic interior of North America: Geological Society of America Bulletin, v. 74, p. 93-114.

Stone, C. G., and Haley, B. R., 1977, The occurrence and origin of granite—meta-arkose erratics in the Ordovician Blakely sandstone, Arkansas, *in* Stone, C. G., ed., Symposium on the geology of the Ouachita Mountains: Arkansas Geological Commission, v. 1, p. 107-111.

Stone, C. G., McFarland, J. D., III, and Haley, B. R., 1981, Field guide to the Paleozoic rocks of the Ouachita Mountain and Arkansas Valley provinces, Arkansas: Arkansas Geological Commission, 140 p.

Sutherland, P. K., and Manger, W. L., eds., 1979, Mississippian-Pennsylvanian shelf-to-basin transition, Ozark and Ouachita regions, Oklahoma and Arkansas: Oklahoma Geological Survey Guidebook 19, 81 p.

Taff, J. A., 1902, Atoka, Indian Territory, folio: U.S. Geological Survey Folio 79, scale 1:125,000.

Thomas, W. A., 1972, Regional Paleozoic stratigraphy in Mississippi between Ouachita and Appalachian Mountains: American Association of Petroleum Geologists Bulletin, v. 56, p. 81-106.

——, 1976, Evolution of Ouachita-Appalachian continental margin: Journal of Geology, v. 84, p. 323-342.

——, 1977a, Evolution of Apalachian-Ouachitas salients and recesses from reentrants and promontories in the continental margin: American Journal of Science, v. 277, p. 1233-1276.

——, 1977b, Structural and stratigraphic continuity of the Ouachita and Appalachian Mountains, *in* Stone, C. G., ed., Symposium on the geology of the Ouachita Mountains: Arkansas Geological Commission, v. 1, p. 9-24.

——, 1985, The Appalachian-Ouachita connection; Paleozoic orogenic belt at the southern margin of North America: Annual Review of Earth and Planetary Sciences, v. 13, p. 175-199.

——, 1989, The Appalachian-Ouachita orogen beneath the Gulf Coastal Plain between the outcrops in the Appalachian and Ouachita Mountains, *in* Hatcher, R. D., Jr., Thomas, W. A., and Viele, G. W., eds., The Appalachian and Ouachita orogen in the United States: Boulder, Colorado, Geological Society of America, The Geology of North America, v. F-2 (in press).

Tomlinson, C. W., and McBee, W., 1959, Pennsylvanian sediments and orogenies of Ardmore district, Oklahoma, *in* Mayes, J. W., Westheimer, J., Tomlinson, C. W., and Putman, D. M., eds., Petroleum geology of southern Oklahoma—a symposium: American Association of Petroleum Geologists, v. 2, p. 3-52.

Van der Voo, R., 1988, Paleozoic paleogeography of North America, Gondwana, and intervening displaced terranes; Comparisons of paleomagnetism with paleoclimatic and biogeographical patterns: Geological Society of America Bulletin, v. 100, p. 311-324.

van Waterschoot van der Gracht, W.A.J.M., 1931a, The Permo-Carboniferous orogeny in the south-central United States: Verhandelingen der Koninklijke Akademie van Wetenschappen te Amsterdam, Afdeeling Natuurkunde, Tweede sectie, deel 27, no. 3, 162 p.

——, 1931b, Permo-Carboniferous orogeny in the south-central United States: American Association of Petroleum Geologists Bulletin, v. 15, p. 991-1057.

Vernon, R. L., 1971, Possible future petroleum potential of Pre-Jurassic western Gulf basin, *in* Future petroleum provinces of the United States: American Association of Petroleum Geologists Memoir 15, p. 954-979.

Viele, G. W., 1973, Structure and tectonic history of the Ouachita Mountains, Arkansas, *in* De Jong, K. A., and Scholten, R., eds., Gravity and tectonics: New York, John Wiley and Sons, p. 361-377.

——, 1979, Geologic map and cross section, eastern Ouachita Mountains, Arkansas: Geological Society of America Map and Chart Series MC-28F, scale 1:250,000.

Viele, G. W., and Thomas, W. A., 1989, Tectonic synthesis of the Ouachita orogenic belt, *in* Hatcher, R. D., Jr., Thomas, W. A., and Viele, G. W., eds., The Appalachian and Ouachita orogen of the United States: Boulder, Colorado, Geological Society of America, The Geology of North America, v. F-2 (in press).

Walper, J. L., 1977, Paleozoic tectonics of the southern margin of North America: Gulf Coast Association of Geological Societies Transactions, v. 27,

p. 230–241.
Walthall, B. H., 1967, Stratigraphy and structure, part of Athens Plateau, southern Ouachitas, Arkansas: American Association of Petroleum Geologists Bulletin, v. 51, p. 504–528.
Welland, M. J., Cambray, I. W., and Voigt, D. S., 1985, Structural and stratigraphic fabric of the Ouachita thrust belt, Oklahoma and Arkansas: A Paleozoic accretionary complex: Geological Society of America Abstracts with Programs, v. 17, p. 746.
Wickham, J., 1978, The Ouachita foldbelt; A Paleozoic continental margin, *in* Field guide to structure and stratigraphy of the Ouachita Mountains and the Arkoma Basin: American Association of Petroleum Geologists Guidebook for Oklahoma City Meeting, p. 36–52.
Wickham, J., Roeder, D., and Briggs, G., 1976, Plate tectonics models for the Ouachita foldbelt: Geology, v. 4, p. 173–176.
Woods, R. D., and Addington, S. W., 1973, Pre-Jurassic geologic framework, northern Gulf basin: Gulf Coast Association of Geological Societies Transactions, v. 23, p. 92–108.
Zimmerman, J., 1984, Geometry and origin of folds and faults in the Arkansas Novaculite at Caddo Gap, *in* Stone, C. G., and Haley, B. R., eds., A guidebook to the geology of the central and southern Ouachita Mountains, Arkansas: Arkansas Geological Commission, p. 111–115.
——, 1986, The problem of antivergent structures in the Ouachita thrust belt, *in* Stone, C. G., and Haley, B. R., eds., Sedimentary and igneous rocks of the Ouachita Mountains of Arkansas, part 2: Arkansas Geological Commission, p. 79–86.
Zimmerman, J., Roeder, D., Morris, R. C., and Evansin, D. P., 1982, Geologic section across the Ouachita Mountains, western Arkansas: Geological Society of America Map and Chart Series, MC–28Q, scale 1:250,000.

Manuscript Accepted by the Society October 19, 1988

ACKNOWLEDGMENTS

I wish to thank the Geological Society of America for defraying the cost of preparing the figures, and Karen Canfield, who did the drafting. I am especially thankful to Charlie Stone and Boyd Haley for sharing their knowledge with me, and for reviewing the manuscript. Thanks also go to Bill Thomas and Pete Palmer, who reviewed the manuscript and suggested many improvements.

Printed in U.S.A.

The Geology of North America
Vol. A, The Geology of North America—An overview
The Geological Society of America, 1989

Chapter 15

Phanerozoic basins of North America

Albert W. Bally
Department of Geology and Geophysics, Rice University, P.O. Box 1892, Houston, Texas 77251-1892

INTRODUCTION

Much of North America, particularly most of its major population centers, is underlain by sedimentary basins. Within them, ground water and fossil fuel resources are concentrated. It is therefore not surprising that there is a great deal of interest in the history and evolution of the Phanerozoic basins of North America.

In the following I can only highlight but a few significant facets that concern the sedimentary basins of our continent. The main focus will be on the cratonic basin development of North America because many of the other basins are already treated separately in the different chapters of this volume. My aim will be to compare and contrast the many sedimentary basins and to focus somewhat on coeval subsidence patterns in North America.

A very brief summary does not permit one to deal with stratigraphic details. For an introduction to these, the reader is referred to the pertinent volumes of *The Geology of North America* (Sloss, 1988a; Stott and Aitken, 1989) and the following particularly useful references: Douglas, 1970; Mallory, 1972b; Cook and Bally, 1975; Stewart and others, 1977; Howell and McDougall, 1978; Armentrout and others, 1979; Cole and Armentrout, 1979; Reynolds and Dolly, 1983; Lopez-Ramos, 1983a, b, 1985; Flores and Kaplan, 1985; Peterson, 1986; Stanley, 1985; Dott and Batten, 1988. The last two are textbooks that provide much needed introductory paleontological background.

For stratigraphic correlation charts, the reader should consult Douglas (1970) and the series of charts of the COSUNA (Correlation of Stratigraphic Units of North America) series published by the American Association of Petroleum Geologists (see list of charts in Appendix B of this volume).

The topic of this chapter is overwhelming, and comprehensive coverage is not possible. Therefore, I elected to first make a few comments on sedimentary basins in general. Then, three basin types are discussed because their evolution sheds some light on the evolution of the craton of North America. In this context, I will compare and contrast four cratonic basins, four foredeeps, and three basins that evolved from late upper Paleozoic–Triassic episutural basins. The direct comparison of look-alike basins emphasizes differences often obscured by simply lumping them into one class. The second half of the chapter deals with modern sequence stratigraphy as an introduction to a review of various time slices. The sequential review of such time slices emphasizes accumulation rates that illustrate simultaneous subsidence in basins with widely differing origins.

ABOUT GEOSYNCLINES AND BASIN CLASSIFICATIONS

James Hall in 1857 linked the subsidence and accumulation of sediments with the formation of major mountain systems, an idea that was to dominate North American stratigraphic and tectonic thinking. According to Mayo (1985), initial doubts about Hall's basic concepts were due to the perceived difficulty of reconciling his idea with the theory commonly accepted at that time of a contractional origin for mountain ranges. It was James Dwight Dana who particularly objected to Hall's theory ("It is a theory for the origin of mountains with the mountains left out."), but who also in 1873 introduced the term "geosyncline" for Hall's subsiding troughs. Eventually, Dana ended up conceding a relationship between subsidence and mountain building.

Mayo (1985) also tells us that the term "isostasy" was introduced by Dutton in 1889 in a paper that summed up his thinking on "compensatory" movements and crustal equilibria. Dutton apparently presented isostasy as another attempt to de-emphasize the contractional doctrine, which was at that time, all important. Thus, the debates of the past century were the prologue to our current understanding of sedimentary basins. Some hundred years later, the contractional hypothesis is outdated, and the usefulness of the geosynclinal concept is still being debated (Schwab, 1982; Bond and Kominz, 1988), but isostasy has survived.

Today, it may be sensible to appreciate the geosynclinal theory mostly for its historical interest. No doubt, reading Kay's (1951) classic *North American Geosynclines* still is most rewarding if only to understand the reasoning behind the many detailed stratigraphic papers published during this century. Dott (1974) offers a fascinating review of the modern pros and cons of the geosynclinal theory. A milestone in the transition from geosynclines to modern basin studies was Drake and others (1959) who first tried to reconcile modern geophysical-oceanographic obser-

Bally, A. W., 1989, Phanerozoic basins of North America, *in* Bally, A. W., and Palmer, A. R., eds., The Geology of North America—An overview: Boulder, Colorado, Geological Society of America, The Geology of North America, v. A.

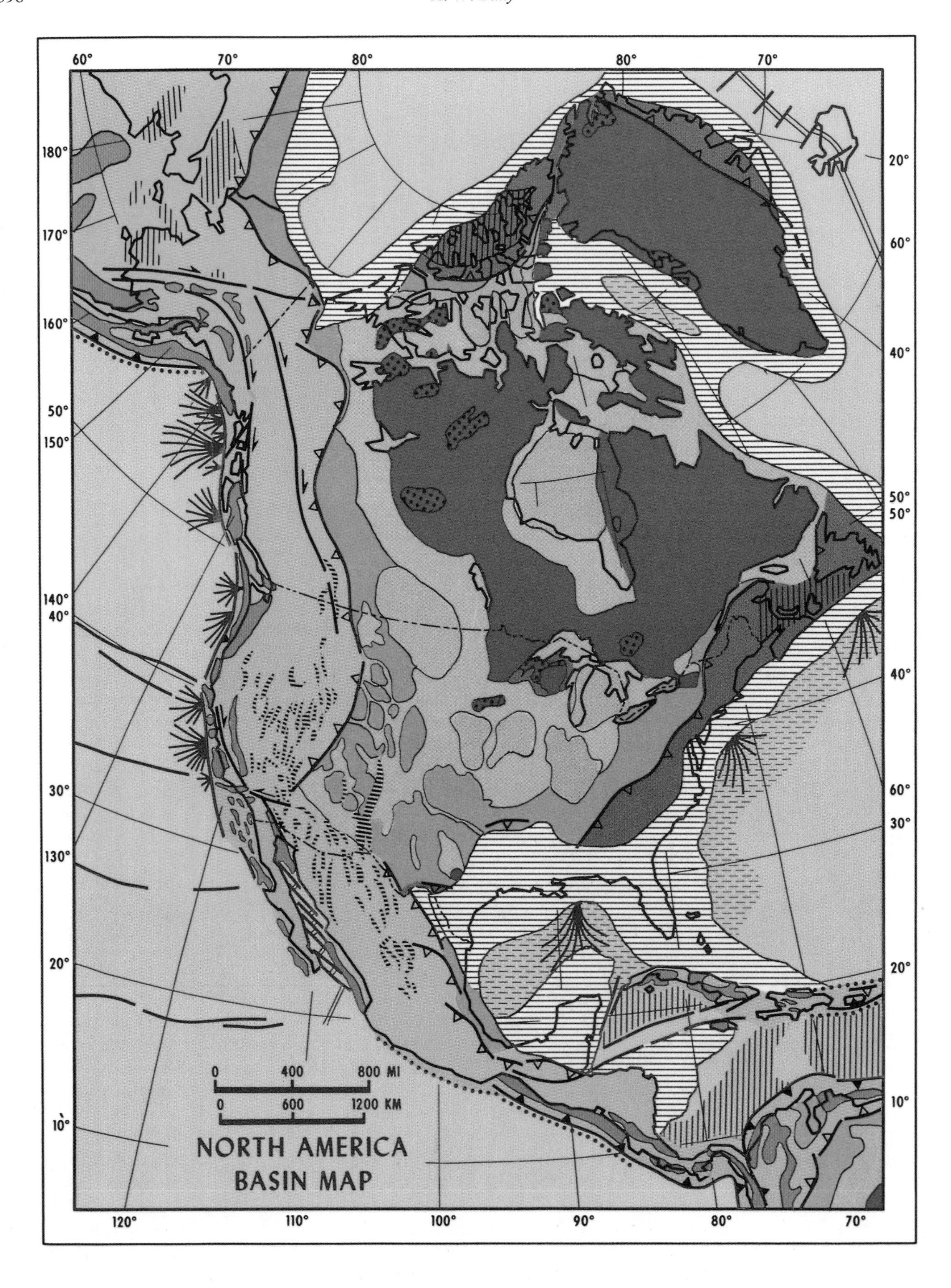
60°
70°
80°
80°
70°
180°
20°
170°
60°
160°
40°
50°
150°
50°
50°
140°
40°
40°
30°
60°
30°
130°
20°
20°
10°
10°
0
400
800 MI
0
600
1200 KM
NORTH AMERICA
BASIN MAP
120°
110°
100°
90°
80°
70°

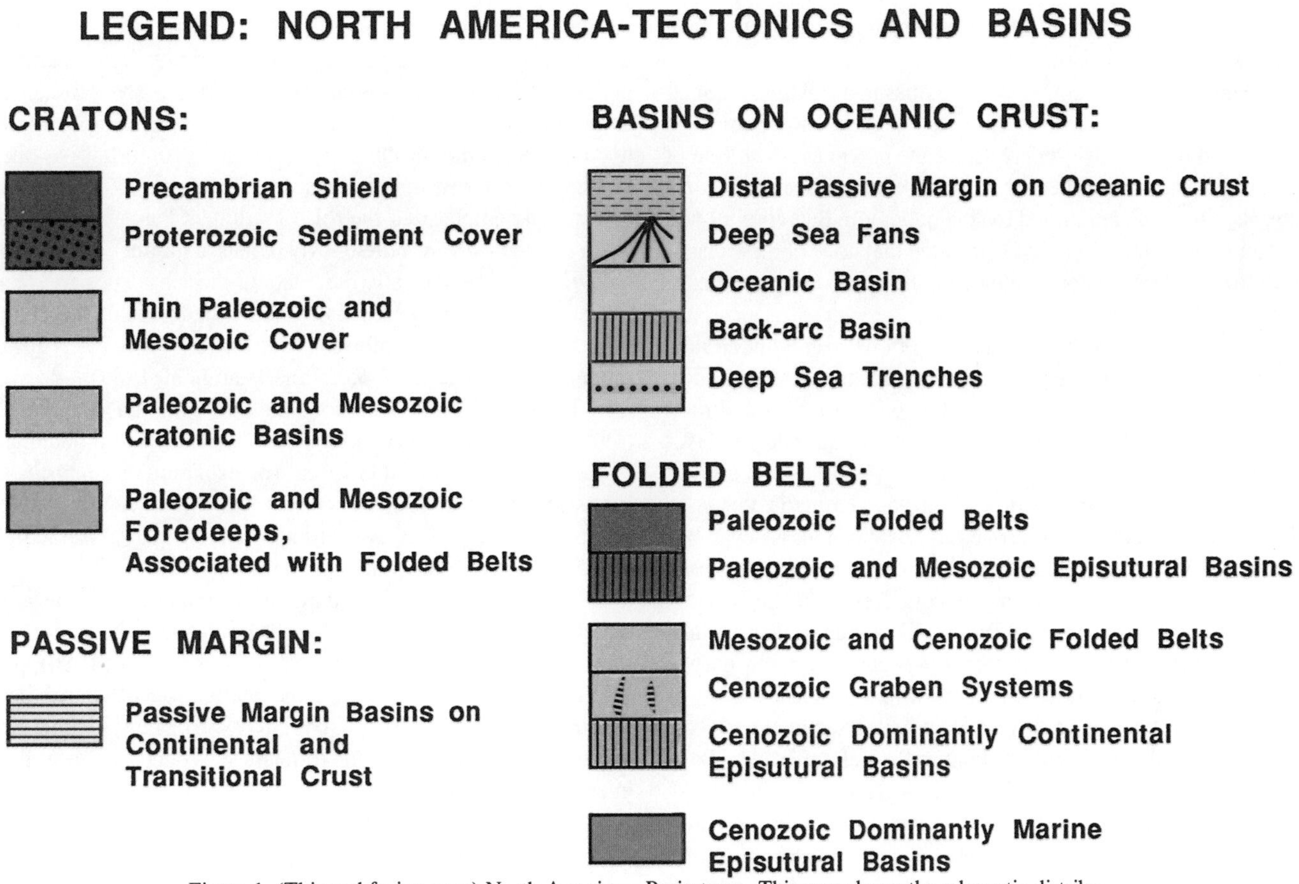

LEGEND: NORTH AMERICA-TECTONICS AND BASINS

CRATONS:

Precambrian Shield

Proterozoic Sediment Cover

Thin Paleozoic and Mesozoic Cover

Paleozoic and Mesozoic Cratonic Basins

Paleozoic and Mesozoic Foredeeps, Associated with Folded Belts

PASSIVE MARGIN:

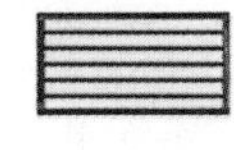

Passive Margin Basins on Continental and Transitional Crust

BASINS ON OCEANIC CRUST:

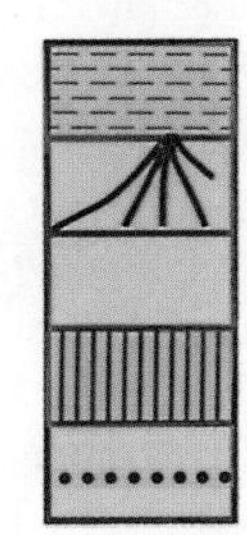

Distal Passive Margin on Oceanic Crust

Deep Sea Fans

Oceanic Basin

Back-arc Basin

Deep Sea Trenches

FOLDED BELTS:

Paleozoic Folded Belts

Paleozoic and Mesozoic Episutural Basins

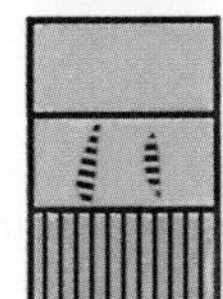

Mesozoic and Cenozoic Folded Belts

Cenozoic Graben Systems

Cenozoic Dominantly Continental Episutural Basins

Cenozoic Dominantly Marine Episutural Basins

Figure 1. (This and facing page) North America—Basin types. This map shows the schematic distribution of various basin types for North America, as based on the classification proposed by Bally and Snelson (1980). Note that the foredeeps of the Laramide U.S. Rocky Mountains and the Paleozoic Ouachita-Marathon folded belts of the southern United States are disrupted by basement-involved uplifts of the cratonic platform. For locations and names of basins and uplifts see Figure 2.

vations with the geosynclinal concept. The subject was again taken up by Dietz (1963) and Dietz and Holden (1974) who proposed that an Atlantic-type passive margin may be viewed as a "miogeocline" that contrasts with a "eugeoclinal" continental rise. In Dietz's view, miogeoclines are no longer necessarily tied to orogenesis. However, sooner or later they are bound to be involved in mountain building (Dott, 1974).

Most modern attempts to salvage the geosynclinal concept with its classifications don't seem to be particularly successful. It may suffice to note that, in hindsight at least, geosynclines were conceptual schemes mostly derived from field geological observations in folded belts. Today we realize that field geological observations alone are insufficient for an adequate understanding of sedimentary basins. We also better appreciate the difficulties inherent in adequate palinspastic reconstructions of folded belts from surface observations alone. Furthermore, before the widespread use of reflection seismic profiles, most authors did not see x-ray–like cross sections of relatively undeformed sedimentary basins.

Instead of further historical musings, let us simply sum up that geosynclinal theory was most relevant in a pre–late tectonic past, but modern plate tectonics have so fundamentally changed our conceptual frame of reference that the old geosynclinal nomenclature is now obsolete. In some areas, like the Appalachians or the Cordillera, force of habit has led to continued usage of the term "miogeosyncline" or "miogeocline" in a sense that is very detached from its original context. In this paper I will occasionally refer to "miogeosyncline" but avoid "miogeocline" because the present-day passive margins present themselves as large basement synclines centering on the transition between oceans and continents (see Diebold and others, 1988).

Today, with the aid of regional seismic profiles and deep wells, we have a much better, but still far from complete, picture of sedimentary basins. It is therefore no surprise to see petroleum geologists attempting to classify basins independently from any traditional classification. But, alas, even here, there is little consensus on which classification to use. In other words, our modern attempts are already less successful than the old geosynclinal scheme. The basin classifications of petroleum geologists share a vague but nevertheless common-sense definition of a sedimentary basin, which requires that the basin is today still more or less intact as a basin. Thus, sediments now folded in orogenic zones are not sedimentary basins! Basin classifications are no more than groupings of perceived analogues.

Among recent attempts to classify basins are Bally and Snelson (1980), and Klemme (1980). Each of these classifications is deficient in that it only crudely details the polyphase evolution of basins. Kingston and others (1983a, b), with a much more complex classification, attempted to do a better job. But, after all was said and done, Helwig (1985) concluded that none of these classifications are satisfactory, although he proposed no better alternative.

Most recent basin-classification efforts were undertaken with the intent to improve potential hydrocarbon reserve forecasts (i.e., if basin A is like basin B, it ought to have a similar potential). Ironically, but unfortunately, in this all modern classifications fail because for each hydrocarbon-rich basin in a given class there will be some hydrocarbon-poor basins in the same class. Thus, the heuristic value of basin classifications is debatable, unless one adopts a method that becomes so complex that each basin appears to be unique. That, of course, is the reality!

Still, modern basin classifications, like many similar intellectual constructs, help to order complex phenomena even though they risk becoming petards on which we hoist ourselves! Let us therefore look at Figure 1 with dignified detachment. As the author of a basin classification, I naturally prefer my own (Bally and Snelson, 1980) as a basis for the legend of the figure. All basins of the Interior Craton of North America are on a Precambrian basement. In contrast, most passive margins of North America have Paleozoic basement; exceptions are the Labrador Sea, Baffin Bay, and East Greenland passive margins, which, like the cratonic basins, are located on a Precambrian basement. Sedimentary basins within the western Cordillera are mostly superposed on a Mesozoic "basement" (i.e., the Cordilleran folded belt).

To further facilitate orientation, Figure 2 lists and locates most of the sedimentary basins of North America.

BASIN MODELS

Preamble

To explain the origin of geosynclines and sedimentary basins, Hsü (1958, 1965) proposed that a continental crust thinned by surficial erosion, following uplift, would lead to isostatically controlled subsidence of sedimentary basins. Gilluly (1955, 1964) added the option of subcrustal erosion as a cause for crustal thinning. These and other authors inspired the beginning of modern subsidence studies. In the early days of plate tectonics, Menard (1969), Sclater and Francheteau (1970), and later, Parsons and Sclater (1977) demonstrated that through time oceanic crust subsided, due to thermal contraction, at exponentially decreasing rates as the newly formed crust moved away from the mid-oceanic ridge.

Subsequently, Sleep (1971) and Kinsman (1975) applied these ideas to the origin of passive margins. Their efforts were greatly encouraged by Falvey's (1974) observation on passive margin reflection seismic profiles, that a rifting phase was commonly separated by a "breakup" unconformity from a drifting phase. The latter phase was characterized by massive subsidence. Even though today the definition of a single breakup unconformity, and the relation of the breakup of the unconformity, is often ambiguous, the concept remains valid. Walcott (1972) quite independently emphasized the role of sediment loading to enhance basin subsidence. Since these early papers, a number of symposia have reviewed periodically the "state of the subsidence art" (e.g., Fisher and Judson, 1975; Bally and others, 1980; Sleep and others, 1980; Kent and others, 1982; Burrus, 1986, 1989; Beaumont and Tankard, 1987; Keen and Beaumont, 1989).

Today, following Beaumont and others (1982a) and Helwig (1985), the simplest way to look at subsidence is to differentiate two basic mechanisms: (1) rifting (or extension) leading to the formation of symmetrical, concave upward, normal-faulted basins; and (2) flexural loading, leading to asymmetrical wedge-shaped and thrust-faulted basins.

Subsidence studies are particularly important if one is to understand (1) the relation of hydrocarbon source beds to major transgressive-regressive facies-cycle wedges (White, 1980), and (2) the thermal evolution and the maturation of source beds within sedimentary basins. Royden (1986) offers a simplified methodology that permits one to relate subsidence and heat flow in extensional basins.

Extensional basins

Extensional basins occur in a variety of tectonic settings such as passive margins, cratonic basins, back-arc basins, and transtensional pull-apart basins. All these basins presumably are associated with an extensional-thermal event that leads to the formation of an attenuated crust. A number of attenuation mechanisms have been invoked: surficial erosion following a thermal uplift (Sleep, 1971; Kinsman, 1975), ductile necking of the whole crust (Artemjev and Artyushkov, 1971), gravity-driven flow toward the ocean following breakup (Bott, 1971; Bott and Dean, 1972), and greenschist-to-amphibolite (Falvey and Middleton, 1981) or gabbro-to-eclogite (e.g., Haxby and others, 1976) phase transitions.

McKenzie (1978) proposed a popular lithospheric stretching model that offered some testing possibilities using crustal data, reflection profiles, and well data. In its simplest and original form, Mackenzie's model permitted the relation of the crustal stretching factor, beta, to crustal thinning obtained from refraction surveys, to tectonic subsidence, and to the thermal evolution of the basin. Initially, crustal thinning was thought of as a combination of thinning within the brittle upper crust by listric normal faulting and ductile stretching in the lower crust (the "pure shear" model of some authors).

Soon a number of authors pointed out that the actual amount of stretching of a given crust was often greatly in excess of what could be observed on seismic reflection profiles. Thus, they proposed modifications of the original stretching model, but

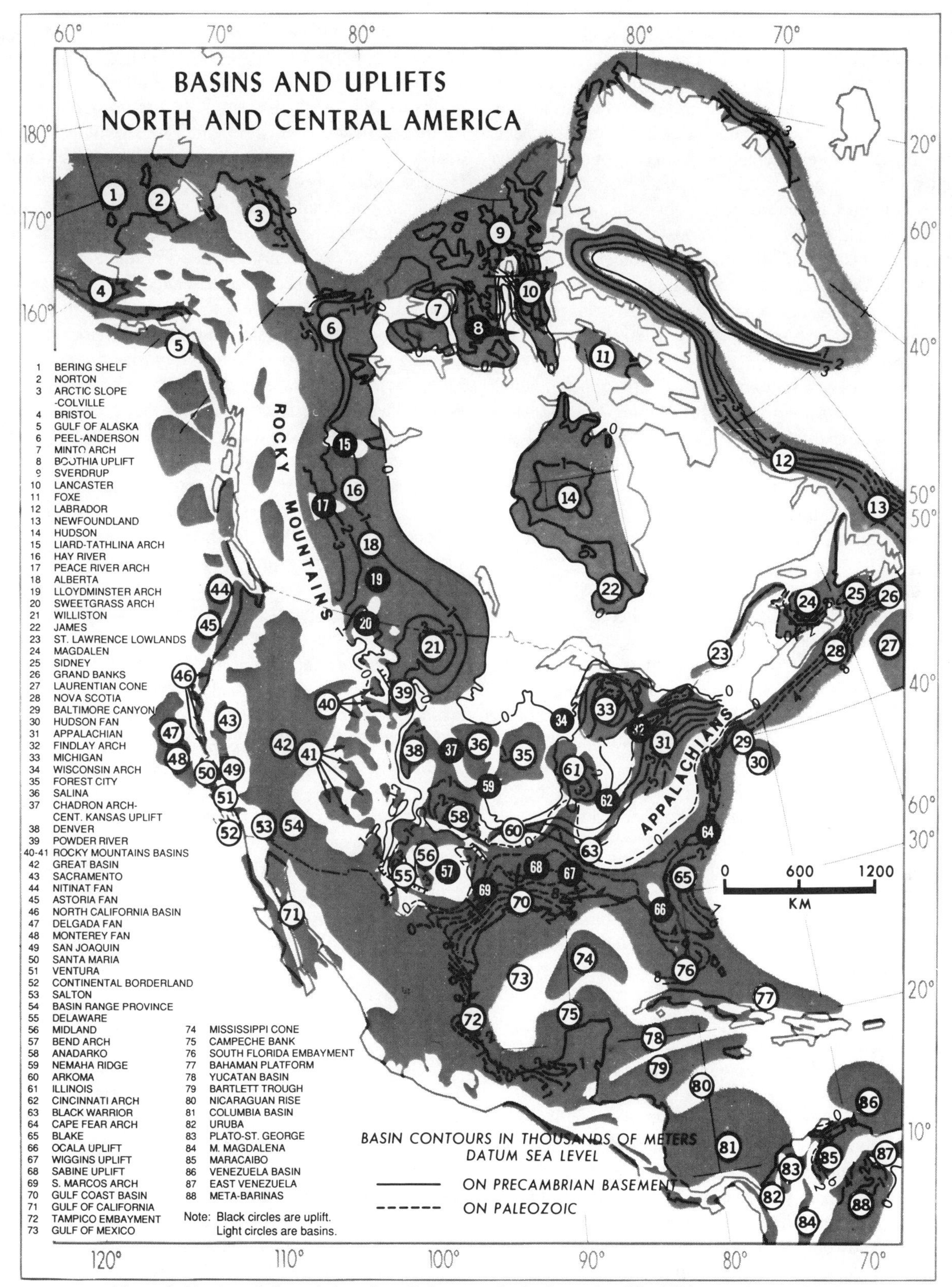

Figure 2. North and Central America—Index map for basins and uplifts. White numbers on black background are uplifts. Black numbers on white background are basins. Black line indicates depth to Precambrian basement in meters, and dashed contours indicate depth to Paleozoic basement in meters.

unfortunately, until now none of the proposed modifications could be tested by additional observations. Many of these modifications of the stretching model remain in the broad class of "spooky" models (i.e., concepts that are intellectually inspiring and certainly physically sound, but not testable by measurements that permit us to differentiate among competing models). Such modified stretching models invoke a number of factors such as alternative fault block geometries (e.g., domino-like extension; Le Pichon and Sibuet, 1981; Angelier and Colletta, 1983); large low-angle normal faults and lithospheric detachments (the simple shear model of Wernicke, 1985); polyphase stretching (e.g., Proffett, 1977); and differential depth-dependent stretching (Sclater and Christie, 1980; Royden and Keen, 1980; Beaumont and others, 1982b).

Today's researchers subtract the effect of sediment loading from a geohistory plot (van Hinte, 1978) using methodologies developed by Perrier and Quiblier (1974), Watts and Ryan (1976), Steckler and Watts (1978), Watts and Steckler (1979), and others. The balance of the subsidence after stripping of the effects of sediment loading (allowing for proper de-compaction) is now commonly referred to as "tectonic" subsidence (Keen, 1979).

Depth-dependent stretching often assumes thermal uplifts that are wider than the rift sensu stricto and therefore they may also accommodate the observed existence of uplifted and subsequently eroded rift shoulders. Such shoulders also have been explained by viscous shear associated with small-scale mantle convection (Steckler, 1985; Moretti and Chenet, 1987) or else by subcrustal erosion due to convective flow (Spohn and Schubert, 1982).

All these models require a better understanding of the rift-related fault geometries. On some North American deep crustal seismic profiles, relevant observations have been made. The following paragraphs briefly mention the more pertinent observations.

Keen and others' (1987) interpretations of crustal reflection profiles suggest that the half-grabens of the Grand Banks of offshore Newfoundland are bounded by major listric fault systems that sole out in the middle or lower crust. The complexity of the Grand Banks normal fault system has also been described in some detail by Welsink and Tankard (1988). In the Basin and Range Province, typically each basin amounts to a half-graben system. Modern reflection-seismic profiles quite clearly illustrate their asymmetrical half-graben character (e.g., Effimoff and Pinezich, 1987). Even so, it is still unclear whether the shallow denudation faults that have been observed, particularly in relation to metamorphic core complexes, may be directly traced into the basinal master faults or whether they are offset by younger and steeper faults. Here, a study of a detailed grid of seismic profiles and its integration with the adjacent surface geology would be needed.

COCORP crustal reflection seismic profiles across the Basin and Range (Allmendinger and others, 1987) also show a tendency for basin-related faults to sole out in the middle or lower crust and to overlie a reasonably continuous Moho.

In other words, in the Basin and Range, and on the Grand Banks, there is no clear support for the lithospheric shear zones as postulated by Wernicke (1985). The Rio Grande Rift could, in principle, offer a good example of the deep geometry of the rift-limiting listric faults. So far, crustal seismic profiles are of a quality that do not permit acceptable constraints for any of the rift models. Industry seismic profiles provide adequate shallow information, but unfortunately, such profiles remain unpublished.

In all cases, the formation and age of the Moho as it relates to the geometry of extensional faults becomes of critical importance. Lower mantle velocities underlying active extensional zones suggest that in active extensional zones, the Moho corresponds to an isotherm that may literally mask any structures intersecting the crust-mantle boundary zone. In other words, the Moho is emplaced toward the end of the extensional activity and may obliterate preexisting structures that could have offset an earlier crust-mantle boundary.

In conclusion, the data on North American rift systems, so far, certainly support the widespread occurrence of transfer-zone–bounded half-graben structures as suggested by Bally (1981) and Gibbs (1984), but the precise nature and geometry of such transfer zones remain to be elucidated. Also, the definition of extensional or transtensional décollement levels within the crust, or perhaps the mantle, is at this time less than satisfactory.

Even allowing for the scarcity of relevant data for the location of extensional decoupling levels within the crust, I accept the overall plausibility of thermally induced subsidence following crustal stretching (e.g., Beaumont and others, 1982a, b; Steckler and Watts, 1978, 1982; Watts and others, 1982; Watts and Thorne, 1984; Issler and Beaumont, 1987).

Compressional, flexural basins

Flexural basin models are all based on the observation that many foreland folded belts are underlain by a regional basement monocline loaded by thrust sheets (see Oldow and others, this volume). Price (1973) suggested that foreland basins (or the synonymous "foredeeps") are due to lithospheric flexure in response to such overthrust loading. The first geodynamic models of foreland basins were proposed by Beaumont (1981), Jordan (1981), and Karner and Watts (1983).

Basin modelers have yet to agree on the rheology of the lithosphere that is being loaded by thrust sheets. Some authors (e.g., Jordan, 1981; Karner and Watts, 1983; Royden and Karner, 1984) visualize an elastic lithosphere, while others (e.g., Beaumont, 1981; Quinlan and Beaumont, 1984; Stockmal and others, 1986; Stockmal and Beaumont, 1987; and Beaumont and others, 1987) assume a viscoelastic lithosphere. Both assumptions lead to acceptable models for foreland subsidence, but they differ in their ability to model unconformities (i.e., sequence boundaries). Elastic models permit rapid relaxation of the lithosphere. On the other hand, viscoelastic models provide for slower relaxation.

Thus, elastic and viscoelastic models both predict an

outward-migrating peripheral bulge, which is often responsible for a characteristic basal foredeep unconformity. However, the viscoelastic model predicts also a reversed mountainward migration of the bulge during phases of decreased loading by thrust sheets.

Quinlan and Beaumont (1984) and Beaumont and others (1987) have been particularly successful in modeling the main stratigraphic sequence boundaries, subsidence, and erosion patterns of the Appalachian Basin, its neighboring arches, and cratonic basins.

More recent work by Royden and Karner (1984) in Italy, but also by Nunn and others (1987) on the Alaskan North Slope, shows that the topographic loads observed are often insufficient to explain foredeep subsidence. According to these authors, additional loads are required that extend into subcrustal levels (i.e., they reflect the load of the subducting slab).

In conclusion, foredeeps are related to foreland folded belts (i.e., the A-subduction process; Bally and Snelson, 1980; Oldow and others, this volume). Thus, the amount of shortening in foreland folded belts suggests limited subduction of the underlying continental margin lithosphere. Loading by thrust sheets and/or the load of the subducted lithosphere creates the moats represented by foredeeps. For a summary of the presumed plate-tectonic controls of foreland-basin subsidence, see Dickinson (1979) and Cross (1986).

As described in the Cordilleran chapter (Oldow and others, this volume), during the Paleocene and the Eocene the Cordilleran foredeep is being dismembered by compressional basement uplifts of the Southern Rocky Mountains. Similar basement uplifts are also observed in the foreland of the Ouachitas (see Arbenz, this volume). In both cases, smaller flexural basins are forming. In a first approximation, Hagen and others (1985) have shown that the small Paleogene basins of the Wyoming foreland, on a smaller scale yet much like the large Cretaceous foredeeps, are characterized by basement homoclines that dip toward and underneath the basement overthrust of Wyoming. Thus, the adjacent Paleogene basins can be modeled as flexural basins that are a result of the load of the adjacent basement uplifts.

FOUR CRATONIC BASINS

North America's sedimentary saucers, its cratonic basins, are deceptively simple, and yet, as will be seen, there is a dearth of adequate explanations for the origin of these basins. I will now compare and contrast the four most important cratonic basins of North America: the Hudson Bay, the Michigan, the Illinois, and the Williston Basins (Fig. 3). First, some key references for these basins are given. The Hudson Bay Basin was poorly known until recently, when regional reflection seismic profiles and exploration wells were published (Dimian, 1983; Quinlan, 1987; Sanford, 1987; Roksandic, 1987). The Michigan Basin has been reviewed recently by Fisher and others (1988) and also has been the subject of a number of modeling studies (Haxby and others, 1976; Sleep and Sloss, 1980; Nunn and others, 1984; Nunn, 1986). Collinson and others (1988) review the Illinois Basin. All four cratonic basins formed during the Paleozoic. The Williston Basin, however, has both a Paleozoic and Mesozoic history. Peterson and others (1985) published some key seismic profiles. Recent overviews are given by Peterson and MacCary (1987) and Gerhard and Anderson (1988). For model studies, the reader is referred to Ahern and Mrkvicka (1984) and Ahern and Ditmars (1985).

The Mesozoic and Cenozoic history is poorly constrained. Jurassic in the center of the Michigan Basin and unusually thick Pleistocene deposits (Sloss, oral communication, 1988) suggest continued development of that basin. On the other hand, glacial erosion and rebound centered on the Hudson Bay has probably eliminated much of the Mesozoic and Tertiary record in that area.

For a comparison of the four main cratonic basins of North America, the paper by Quinlan (1987) is most useful; many of the following points are gleaned from it. Quinlan rightly emphasizes that the four basins have substantial differences among themselves and that lumping them with other cratonic basins of the world, as was done by Bally and Snelson (1980), obscures some very obvious and important differences. In particular, none of the four basins shows a substantial rifting event that may be unambiguously related to it, even though a modest amount of faulting is associated with the initiation of these basins. To be sure, all four cratonic basins originated during the early Paleozoic. Klein and Hsui (1987) attempted to link the initiation of the cratonic basins to the breakup of the Proterozoic supercontinent (see below). Even ignoring the near absence of conspicuous rifting events, strictly coeval initiation cannot be established among the four cratonic basins. Thus, the search for a well-defined initial rifting event is elusive for all four basins.

Cambrian isopachs (Cook and Bally, 1975) suggest that both the Michigan and the Illinois Basins were connected to the south where the Illinois Basin extends into what we now call the Reelfoot rift area. There Ervin and McGinnis (1975), Braile and others (1986), and Hinze and Braile (1988) have postulated a late Proterozoic to Early Cambrian rift that was a precursor of the Mississippi Embayment. The southern Illinois Basin perhaps represents the extension of the Reelfoot graben system (Sexton and others, 1986). That system was reactivated during the Pennsylvanian, and also may be responsible for the recent earthquake activity of the New Madrid area (Zoback and others, 1980). However, the Illinois Basin is far from being centered on the rift system.

The Michigan Basin also is located off-center of an elongate Keewenawan rift system that extends from the Lake Superior region to the southeast (Brewer and others, 1983; Van der Voo and Watts, 1978; Fisher and others, 1988). That rift system is at least 550 m.y. older than the overlying Cambrian sediments. Considerable Paleozoic faulting is reported from the Michigan Basin, but no obvious Paleozoic half-graben systems have been defined to date.

Only the Hudson Bay Basin shows a conspicuous northerly striking structure, which is best described as a half-horst system located in the center of the basin (Dimian, 1983; Roksandic,

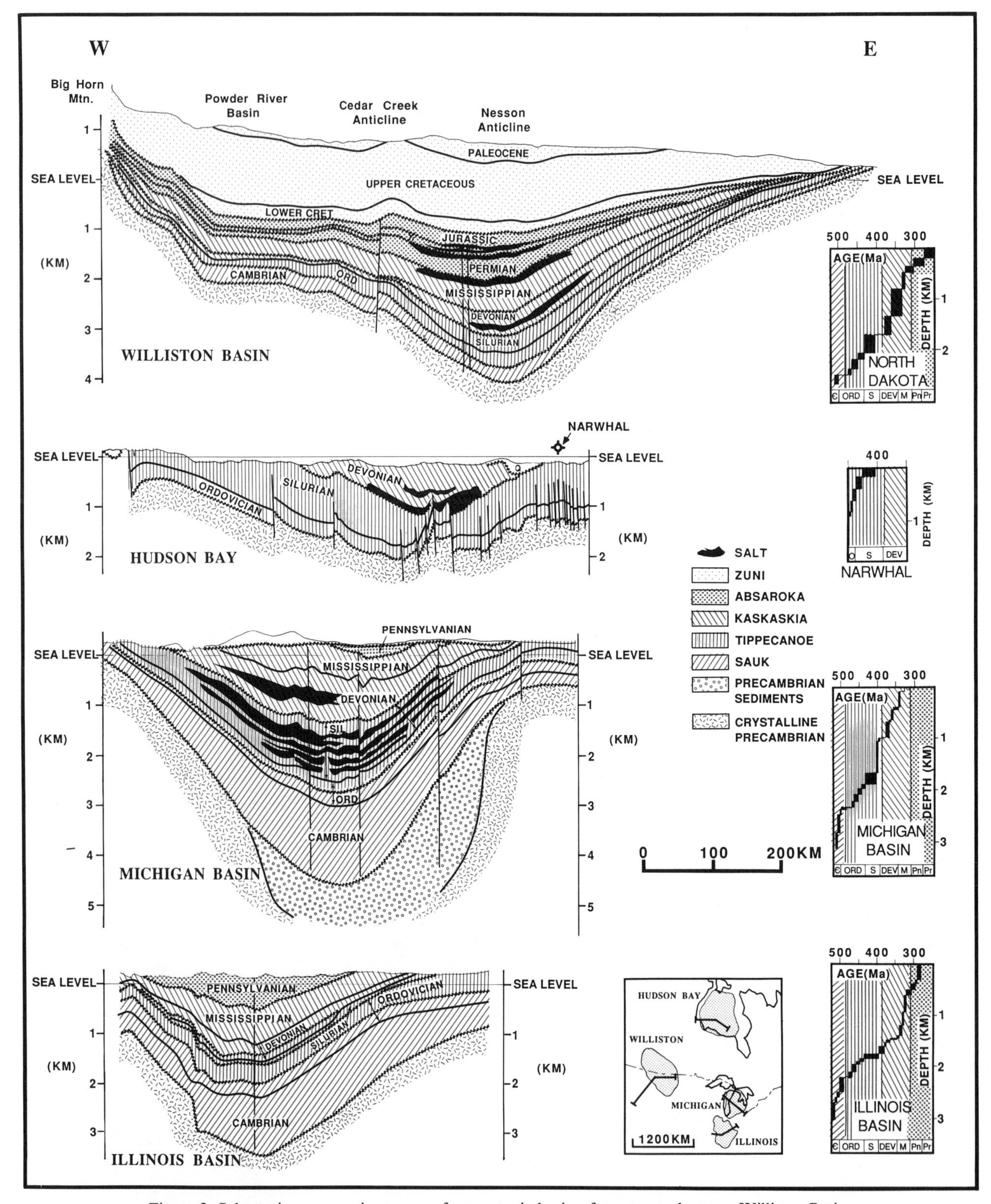

Figure 3. Schematic cross sections across four cratonic basins, from top to bottom: Williston Basin, Hudson Bay Basin, Michigan Basin, Illinois Basin. The cross sections were derived from sections contained in the papers listed in the text. On the right are schematic plots of sediment thickness as a function of age (modified after Quinlan, 1987). Note that the inception times and subsidence rates differ among the four basins, but that the Paleozoic sequence boundaries are common to all basins. Compare also with the Transcontinental cross section shown on Figure 13.

1987; see also Fig. 3). The structure was formed at the beginning of the Late Silurian with Upper Silurian and Lower Devonian pinnacle reefs onlapping on a westward-tilted homocline. Accelerated subsidence leading to the individualization of the Hudson Bay Basin occurred during the Middle and Late Devonian.

Evidence for Paleozoic faulting that would be responsible for the genesis of the Williston Basin is rather subtle. A careful study of the Cedar Creek anticline in the Williston Basin done by Clement (1986) documents (1) a tilting phase during Early Devonian time, (2) reactivation of the main Cedar Creek fault system during Late Devonian, (3) inversion of the fault movement from down to the west during the Devonian to down to the east during the Late Mississippian–Early Pennsylvanian, (4) reactivation in the same sense during the Permo-Triassic, and finally (5) formation of a Laramide inversion anticline during the Paleogene. Again here, as in some of the other cratonic basins, there is no obvious relationship between the formation of the Cedar Creek anticline and the individualization of the Williston Basin.

Also, following Quinlan (1987), with what little evidence we have, there is no strong indication for an elevated Moho centering below the four cratonic basins. Typical Moho depths are on the order of 40 km for three basins. For the Michigan Basin, we have no data. The lower crust seismic P-wave velocity below the Williston and the Illinois Basins is an anomalously high 7.0 to 7.6 km/sec.

Turning to the subsidence history of the four cratonic basins, Quinlan (1987) plotted Paleozoic subsidence rates for all of them (redrafted in part on Fig. 3) and concluded that rapid sediment accumulation occurred in the Michigan Basin during the Late Cambrian to Middle Ordovician as well as during the Silurian; in the Hudson Bay Basin during Late Ordovician and Middle Devonian as well as during the Late Devonian; in the Illinois Basin during the Late Cambrian and the Mississippian; in the Williston Basin during the Middle Ordovician and the Devonian. It can be fairly concluded from a cross section of Figure 3 that the four cratonic basins did not subside to a common rhythm; instead they developed their own individual subsidence rates and history.

In the Williston Basin, Cambrian strata were originally connected with the Cordilleran miogeosyncline. However, only in the mid-Ordovician do we get the first signs of an individualization of the basin.

The Hudson Bay Basin formed part of a widespread Ordovician carbonate platform that perhaps covered most of the Canadian Shield; the basin acquired its circular identity only during the Middle and Upper Devonian.

All four cratonic basins are mostly filled with Paleozoic shallow-water carbonates and evaporites. In the Michigan and Hudson Bay Basins, salt beds are of upper Silurian, and Lower and Middle Devonian age. In the Williston Basin, Middle Devonian salt beds are extensive and extend all the way into the adjacent northern Alberta Basin; more limited salt beds occur in the Mississippian, Permian, Triassic, and Jurassic (Bassett and Stout, 1968; Cook and Bally, 1975; Peterson and MacCary, 1987).

Thus, all four cratonic basins appear to have developed during the Paleozoic, but with accelerated subsidence occurring at different times. No obvious extensional event can be directly related to the subsidence patterns of the four basins, but the Illinois Basin may be in some way associated with the Reelfoot rift system.

Thermal models have been promulgated by a number of authors for all four basins. The Williston Basin and the Michigan Basin suggest an increase in the effective elastic thickness of the lithosphere due to cooling of a thermal anomaly (Haxby and others, 1976; Ahern and Ditmars, 1985). Thus, a thermal event at the inception of the basin subsidence can be modeled to satisfy the stratigraphic information, but again the physical evidence for any thermal event such as rifting is lacking. As is to be expected in situations like this, modelers also like to take refuge in phase transitions, and yes indeed, the preferred gabbro-eclogite phase transition helps to model subsidence in the Michigan Basin (Haxby and others, 1976) and in the Williston Basin (Fowler and Nisbet, 1985). Seismic velocities of the mantle and lower crust provide a mild measure of support for these models. However, the main disadvantage of these concepts is, as pointed out by Quinlan (1987), that the model cannot be used in a predictive sense. In other words, phase transitions are used in an ad-hoc mode when all other explanations fail!

And so, the deceptively simple cratonic saucers of our continent remain unexplained. In addition, the origin of many of the apparently equally simple intracratonic arches is even more obscure. Obviously we need additional information, including more and better geophysical data concerning both the lower crust and the mantle underlying the cratonic basins and arches.

PALEOZOIC AND MESOZOIC FOREDEEPS OF NORTH AMERICA

Preamble

Figure 1 shows the distribution of foredeep basins in North America. The earlier comments on basin models indicated that foredeeps—or the foreland basins of some authors—are due to loading by thrust sheets and/or other lithospheric loads. In this section we will compare and contrast the geology of some of North America's foredeeps.

Bally and Snelson (1980) suggest that foredeeps are directly associated with foreland folded belts. During compression, all deformation in the folded belt merges into one or more regional décollement zones. Toward the interior of the folded belt, these involve and remobilize the pre-orogenic basement; in the exterior zone, they typically involve mostly "miogeosynclinal" sediments. In some cases, such as the Southern Rockies, the basement of the foreland eventually gets caught up in a crustal décollement process (see Oldow and others, this volume). The shared link between the folded belt and the foredeep is a foreland basement homocline that can be followed with reasonable continuity from the craton well into and underneath the interior of the folded belt.

The subduction of continental and transitional lithosphere, the A-subduction process, was originally inferred from the overall shortening observed in décollement systems and from palinspastic reconstructions, both of which entailed the disappearance of the underlying lithosphere. As stated by Struik (1988), in the Canadian Cordillera there may be no need to subduct much of the crust itself, and the same may be said for several other folded belts. However, particularly in collisional ranges like the Appalachians, and the Alpine-Himalayan Ranges, there is no escaping the fact that substantial amounts of passive margin lithosphere were being subducted. This was the shortening problem originally confronting Ampferer when he conceived subduction (Bally and Snelson, 1980). Of course, subducted passive margins are originally underlain by a stretched-attenuated crust, and therefore, if any crust gets subducted, it is bound to be the lower part of a much-attenuated crust. As it is, we certainly do not have an adequate fix on whether substantial amounts of the pre-orogenic lower crust may be subducted or otherwise involved in forming the lithospheric roots of mountain ranges.

To further modify my original description of A-subduction, it should be added that in a Cordilleran setting, wedge-type tectonics (Price, 1986) on a large scale would permit positioning off-scraped terranes on overthrusts that are conjugate to ocean-verging B-subduction–related accretionary wedges. Such a model would view the shortening in foreland folded belts as an accretionary complex involving former passive margin or platform sediments and possibly not require any subduction of passive margin lithosphere at all.

For an overview of the development of foredeeps, an idealized foredeep is shown on Figure 4. From bottom to top, one differentiates (1) the basement; (2) a rifting sequence that was the prelude to (3) a passive margin and/or platform sequence, which corresponds to the former miogeosyncline and its cratonic extension; a complex basal foredeep unconformity and/or wedge of multiple unconformities separates (3) from (4) and (5). This unconformity is significant because it may be interpreted as the record of a migrating peripheral bulge. Sediments overlying the unconformity relate to the thrusting process of the adjacent mountains. Sediments below that unconformity are the record of the precollision shelf margin. (4) A deep-water phase, representing the inception of the foredeep, a situation analogous to the deep-water sill that separates Timor and the outer Banda Arc from the Sahul Shelf of Australia (Montecchi, 1976; Audley-Charles, 1986). This early foredeep phase often is characterized

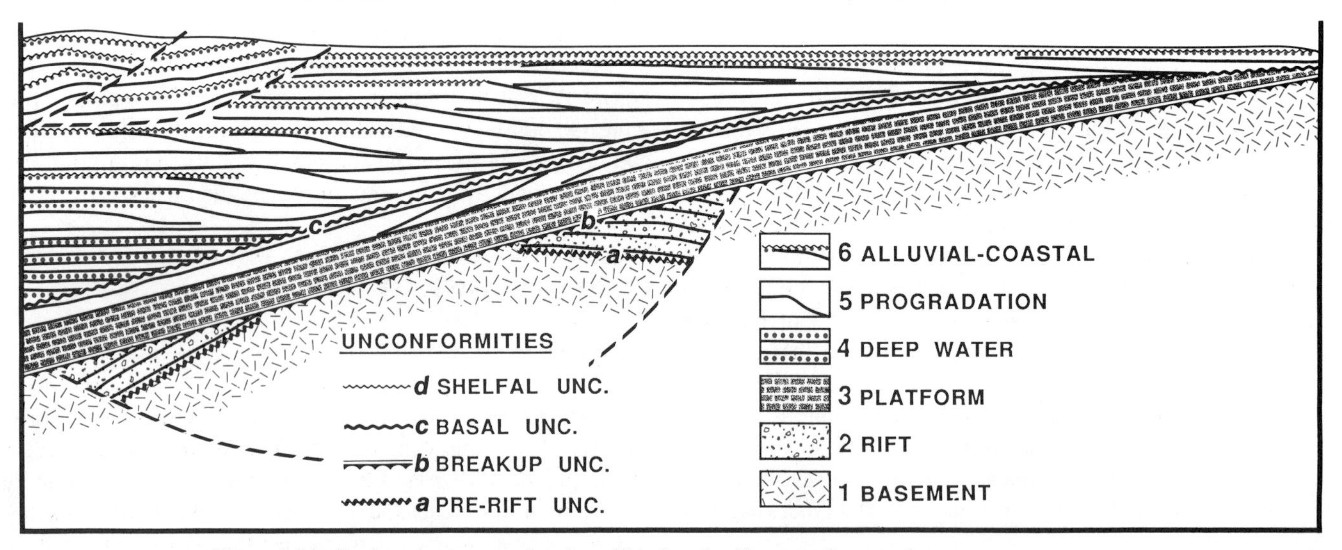

Figure 4. Idealized section across a foredeep. This drawing illustrates features that are common to many foredeeps. Keep in mind that each foredeep has its own individual development, which accentuated one and/or another feature of this idealized diagram. In particular, note four basically different unconformity types: (a) Pre-rift unconformity(ies), which mark the inception of a rifting regime that may or may not be related to the formation of a passive margin. (b) Breakup unconformity(ies). These mark the cessation of significant rifting activity and herald the initial flooding of a passive margin. The updip portions of such passive margins merge into the much thinner cratonic platform covers (see also Fig. 13). Unconformities (a) and (b) are inherited and not directly related to the formation of the foredeep. Of course the platform sequence contains numerous other sequence boundaries that may be due to sea-level changes. (c) Basal foredeep unconformity. This is best described as a complex unconformity, with deep-water deposits that onlap on the subducted distal passive margin, and with updip truncation due to erosion of an outward-migrating peripheral shallow-water bulge. Immediately overlying the basal unconformity a complex downlap surface is observed, which marks the distal end of prograding sediment wedges. (d) Shelfal unconformities that are due to the lowering of the sea level. These unconformities may also erode growing anticlines of the adjacent fold belts. Growing folds would thus enhance unconformities that are due to eustatic sea-level changes.

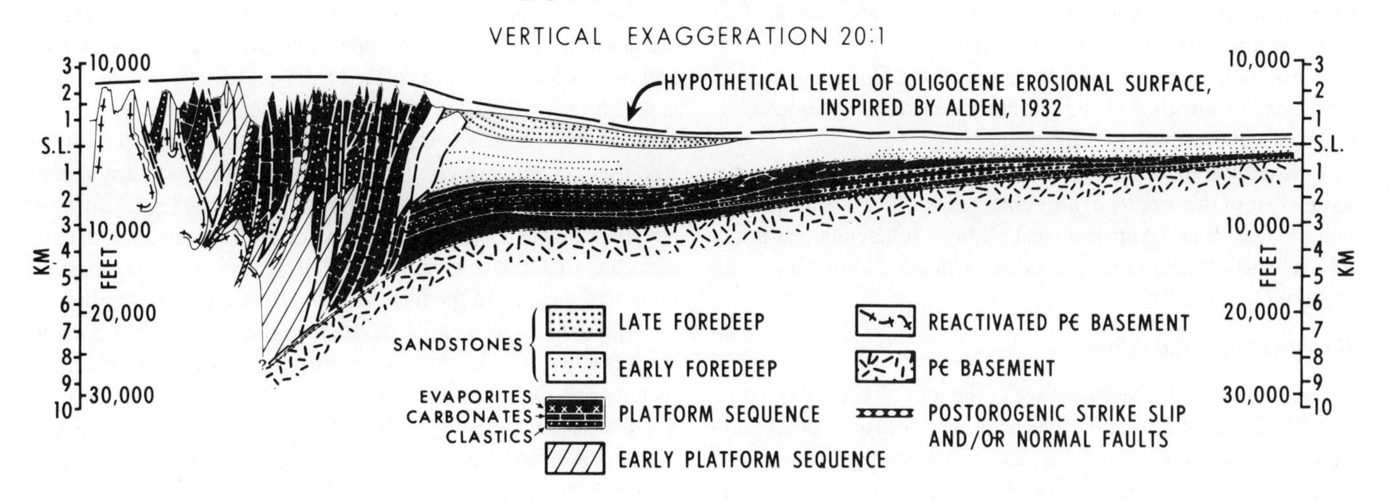

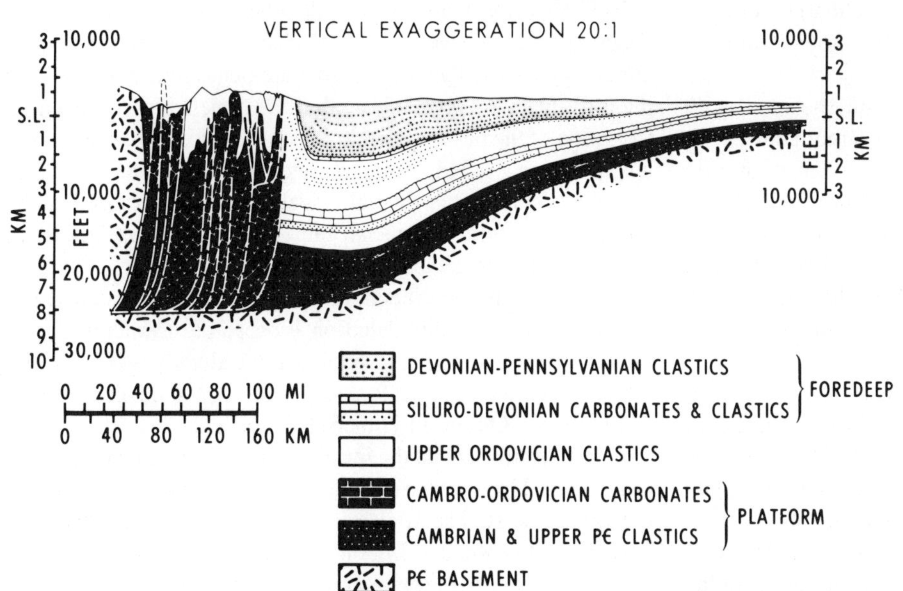

Figure 5. Western Canada and Central Appalachian foredeeps (from Bally and Snelson, 1980). The basement dips underneath the adjacent foldbelts. Underneath the Appalachians, modern reflection seismic profiles suggest a steeper basement dip than the dip shown on this figure. Note that in contrast with the Western Canada foredeep, the Appalachian Basin clastic sequence is interrupted by the deposition of Siluro-Devonian carbonates.

by longitudinal infill with turbidites. (5) A prograding phase where deltaic complexes are seen to prograde from the rising mountain ranges or from the cratonic flank to fill the adjacent moat. (6) A dominantly alluvial-deltaic phase. Note that much of the overthrusting eventually involves the foredeep clastic wedge itself and that the leading edge of the foreland folded belt throughout much of its history remains either below sea level or near sea level.

The evolution of a foredeep records a delicate balance between late- to post-thrusting uplift within the folded belt and subsidence in the adjacent foredeep basins. In the following, I briefly compare and contrast four foredeeps of North America (in brackets are selected key references): (1) The Colville foredeep of the Alaska North Slope Basin (Bird, 1985; Hubbard and others, 1987; Molenaar and others, 1987); (2) The Western Canada Sedimentary Basin (Porter and others, 1982); (3) The Appalachian Basin (Colton, 1970; Milici and de Witt, 1988); and (4) The Arkoma Basin (Sutherland, 1988; Houseknecht, 1986; Arbenz, this volume).

Figure 5 shows greatly simplified versions of the Western Canada Basin and the Appalachian Basin (east-west reversed) with the same vertical exaggeration. The Appalachian foredeep reflects two orogenic loading cycles that correspond to an Ordovician-Silurian Taconic event and to a Devonian to Permian Acado-Variscan event, respectively.

Figure 6 is a sequential evolution of the Colville foredeep, reproduced from Bird (1985). It fairly depicts the characteristic stages of the evolution of a foredeep.

Structural sections that illustrate the inboard margin (i.e., the folded belt of the foredeep) are contained in other chapters in this volume (see Rast [Appalachians], Arbenz [Ouachita-Marathon folded belt], and Oldow and others [Alaska North Slope and western Cordillera]).

Basement age and rifting

Comparing the basement age of the four foredeeps, only the Colville foredeep has a mid-Paleozoic basement, all other foredeeps have a pre-Cambrian crystalline basement. The age and nature of the basement may be inferred from the Precambrian basement map of North America (Hoffmann, this volume).

There is evidence for rifting prior to the deposition of the passive margin-platform sediments (miogeosynclinal) in the deep portion of all four foredeeps, even though the time of rifting is poorly constrained.

Seismic profiles across the Colville Basin show an early extensional basin of Early Mississippian to possibly Late Devonian age (Endicott, of Fig. 6). In excess of 5 km of mostly unknown sediments fill these basins (Fig. 6). Mauch (1985), as well as Hubbard and others (1987), view this deep, extensional system as analogous to the system beneath the Pannonian Basin of Hungary (Royden and Horvath, 1988). Note that the early rift system of the North Slope was inverted during a mid-Mississippian compressional event.

In the Western Canada Basin, there is a vaguely defined Precambrian rift system that has been revealed by geophysics in southern Alberta (Kanasevich and others, 1969). Of course, still farther south the Proterozoic Helena Embayment and the Uinta rifts are candidates for a rifting event that underlies the U.S. Rocky Mountain foredeep. However, these rift systems were formed too early to be associated with the early subsidence of the Cordillera (for reference, see Oldow and others, this volume).

In the Appalachian Basin, the Rome Trough may be a passive-margin–related Lower Cambrian rift system that influenced sedimentation well into the Silurian. Whether that trough can be followed in the Reelfoot rift system still remains to be established (see Plate 10-A).

Finally with regard to the pre-Arkoma platform section, there is no obvious suggestion for rifting under that basin, although the Oklahoma and Reelfoot rift systems of Late Proterozoic to Early Cambrian age strongly suggest that rifting preceded the breakup of the southern U.S. margin.

The foredeep platform

The platform sequence beneath the foredeep includes the cratonic cover and its continuation into the "miogeosyncline" or former passive margin. The Colville foredeep is underlain by a platform sequence that is particularly well displayed on seismic profiles. Mississippian carbonates are overlain by Permo-Triassic clastics and carbonates, and Jurassic clastics. All early Mesozoic and older siliciclastics are derived from a northerly source. There is a consensus that this platform sequence accumulated to the north of the Canadian Arctic Islands and that during the Mesozoic it either rafted and/or rotated toward an island-arc system that was to become the Brooks Range. Thus, the Upper Jurassic and two Lower Cretaceous sequences are separated by unconformities that relate to rifting events within a trailing passive margin of the Alaska Arctic Shelf, which is located to the north of the Colville foredeep and separated from it by the Point Barrow Arch (see Fig. 6). A major unconformity separates the platform sequence of the Colville Basin from the overlying clastic wedge. The platform underlying the Colville foredeep differs from typical North American foredeeps because it represents a rafted fragment of the northern extension of the Innuitian foldbelt of northern Canada (see also Cordillera chapter, Oldow and others, this volume).

The platforms underlying all other North American foredeeps began as passive-margin extensions of the North American craton. Typically, Paleozoic carbonate deposition dominates on these former passive margins (the traditional miogeosynclines). Cessation of the passive-margin regime occurred when an island-arc system or a rafted terrane accreted with the North American continent. Thus, in the Central Appalachians the platform regime terminates by mid-Ordovician time, and in the Ouachita Basin the platform regime ends during the Mississippian.

Whether the Cordilleran miogeosyncline was a passive margin throughout the entire Paleozoic is debatable. Certainly, during the Late Devonian to Mississippian, there already was an Antler foldbelt and an associated foredeep rimming the miogeosyncline. For more, see Oldow and others, this volume.

In western Canada the termination of the platform regime is characterized by a wedge of multiple unconformities that thickens toward the west. The wedge includes Pennsylvanian, Permian, Triassic, and Lower and Middle Jurassic formations with siliclastics, which all derive from a cratonic source (see pre-Cretaceous subcrop map, Plate 10-L).

The basal foredeep unconformity

Although basal foredeep unconformities are quite common in many foredeeps of the world, they have not yet been systemati-

Figure 6. North–south cross section and reconstructions across the Alaska North Slope (from Bird, 1985). The basal foredeep unconformity (c on Fig. 4) overlies the Kingak Formation. Note the sub-horizontal onlap of presumed deep-water shales on the down-dip extension of that unconformity, and the updip truncation of the unconformity, which is related to the cessation of rifting on the passive margin of northern Alaska (for more complex details see Hubbard and others, 1987). Note also the southerly progradation of the Kingak Formation, which contrasts with the northeast progradation of the overlying Cretaceous foredeep clastics.

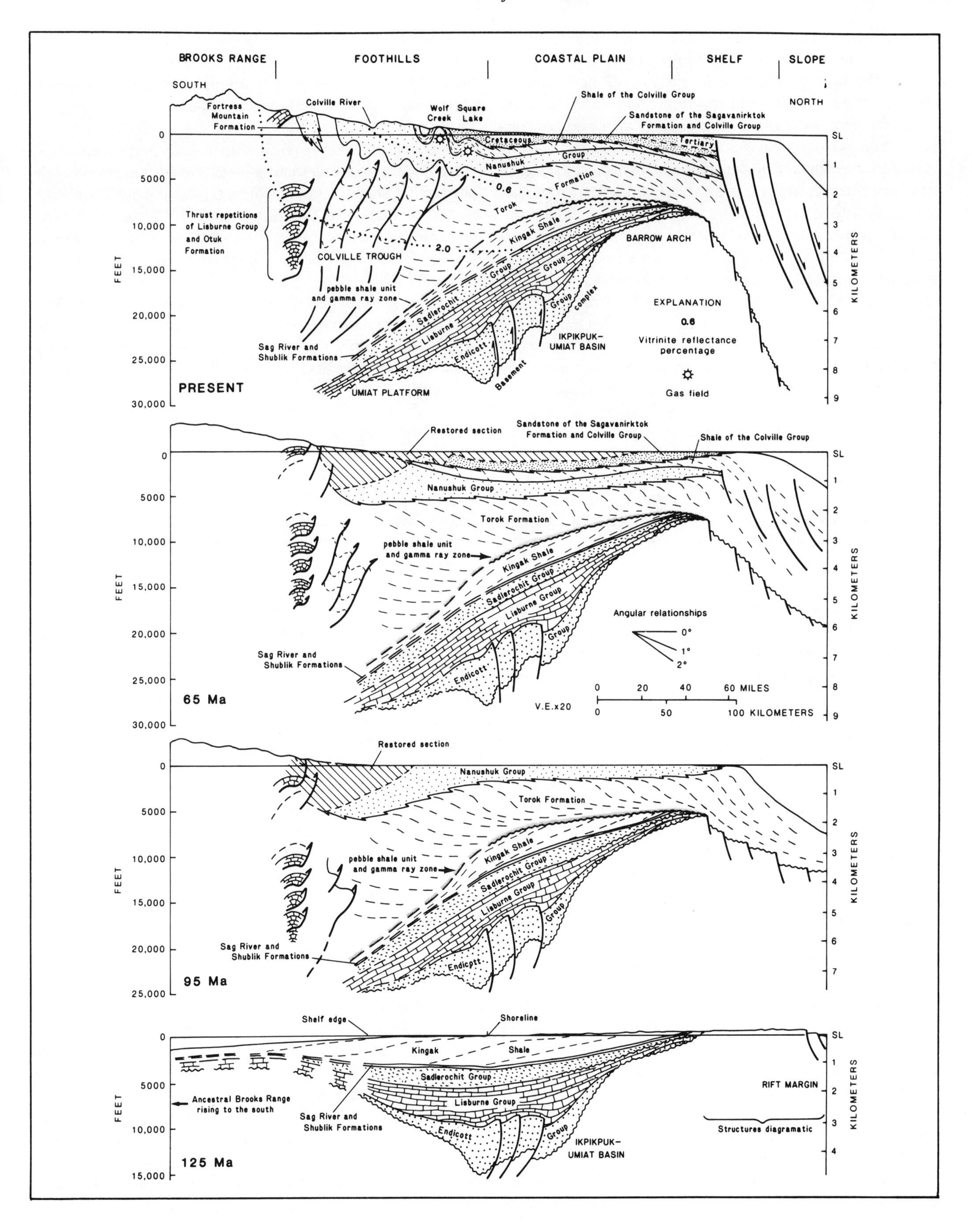
BROOKS RANGE
FOOTHILLS
COASTAL PLAIN
SHELF
SLOPE
SOUTH
NORTH
Fortress Mountain Formation
Colville River
Wolf Creek
Square Lake
Shale of the Colville Group
Sandstone of the Sagavanirktok Formation and Colville Group
Cretaceous
Tertiary
Nanushuk Group
Torok Formation
Thrust repetitions of Lisburne Group and Otuk Formation
COLVILLE TROUGH
Kingak Shale
BARROW ARCH
pebble shale unit and gamma ray zone
Sadlerochit Group
Lisburne Group
Group complex
Endicott
Basement
Sag River and Shublik Formations
IKPIKPUK–UMIAT BASIN
UMIAT PLATFORM
EXPLANATION
0.6
Vitrinite reflectance percentage
Gas field
PRESENT
FEET
KILOMETERS
SL
Restored section
Angular relationships
0°
1°
2°
0 20 40 60 MILES
0 50 100 KILOMETERS
V.E.x20
65 Ma
95 Ma
Shelf edge
Shoreline
Kingak Shale
Ancestral Brooks Range rising to the south
RIFT MARGIN
Structures diagramatic
125 Ma

cally described. Many different manifestations of these unconformities occur in foredeeps in the United States.

On the North Slope of Alaska, there is little doubt that the foredeep sequence begins with uppermost Jurassic to lowermost Cretaceous deep-water clastics, which onlap on the downdip extension of a significant unconformity underlying the Lower Cretaceous (Barremian-Aptian) "Pebble shale" horizon and truncates underlying formations on the updip end. For details see Molenaar and others (1987).

The downdip end of the Western Canada Basin basal foredeep unconformity bifurcates into the already mentioned shallow-water wedge of multiple unconformities. Its eastern-derived sequence of clastics is overlain by shallow-water sediments of uppermost Jurassic age, which for the first time show a western clastic source. Thus, the basal foredeep unconformity on the downdip end is a pre–Upper Jurassic unconformity, and updip the same unconformity merges into the pre-Aptian unconformity. This situation contrasts with the Colville foredeep where the distal basal foredeep unconformity is overlain by deep-water sediments.

In the Paleozoic Arkoma and Appalachian foredeeps, the inception of the foredeep regime is not clearly associated with a distinct basal foredeep unconformity. Nevertheless, marine flysch deposits transgress onto earlier platform deposits.

For the Appalachian foredeep, Quinlan and Beaumont (1984) suggest that the pre-Tippecanoe (pre–Middle Ordovician Chazyan) sequence boundary may be a record of the migrating peripheral bulge of their model. There is no clastic wedge immediately overlying this unconformity; instead, shallow-water carbonate deposition continues. It would be more plausible to search for an unconformity near the base of the Upper Ordovician Martinsburg turbidite sequence, but the reported gradational contact at the base of this formation does not suggest the presence of a significant unconformity. However, Lash (1987) recognized a basal unconformity hiatus at the Middle to Upper Ordovician level at the base of the Martinsburg Formation in eastern Pennsylvania, and Hiscott and others (1986) suggest the presence of foredeep clastics of Middle Ordovician age in Tennessee and southwest Newfoundland. Stratigraphically, the base of the Central Appalachian foredeep sequence is a contact where shallow-water carbonates are overlain by deep-water (Martinsburg) flysch deposits. One would expect, by analogy with the Timor model (Audley-Charles, 1986), that the base of the deep-water flysch sequence onlaps on the passive-margin sequences, but this still requires detailed paleontological proof.

To conclude, the nature of the boundary underlying the foredeep clastic wedge and overlying the preceding platform sequences relates to the initial water depth of the clastic wedge. In a deep-water setting, deep-water foredeep clastics would be superposed on basinal deep-water sediments, and in a shallow-water setting, the foredeep clastic wedge would be superposed on preceding shallow-water deposits.

Thus, in deep water, the dominant feature of the basal foredeep unconformity would be onlap of foredeep sediments on its substratum with no truncation below. In the shallow-water portion of the foredeep unconformity, truncation due to erosion of a migrating peripheral bulge is observed, followed by transgressive sands and/or downlap of a shallow deltaic system on the basal foredeep unconformity.

Whether a foredeep remains dominantly deep water or proceeds to develop into a shallow-water foredeep is obviously dependent on initial crustal thicknesses, passive-margin configurations, and the extent to which a folded belt and its foredeep "overruns" the craton. Some of these factors are described in the foredeep archetypes that have been proposed by Stockmal and others (1986).

Among the four examples discussed here, the Arkoma Basin represents a dominantly deep-water end member, and the Western Canada Basin a shallow-water end member. The next segment will discuss the development of the clastic wedges in each of the four foredeeps.

On the filling of a moat

The clastic wedge, a term used by King (1977), is the infill of the foredeep moat. The character of the infilling sediments changes within one and the same foredeep and also from one foredeep to another. The overall subsidence of the clastic wedge records the continuity of the orogenic process in the neighboring folded belt.

To start with the Colville foredeep of the Alaska North Slope, seismic profiles (Kirschner and others, 1983; Molenaar and others, 1987) show a clear progression of a foredeep infilling process, which is schematized on Figure 6 (95 Ma and 65 Ma). Downdip, in the southern part of the Colville Basin, there are subhorizontal reflectors, presumably representing deep-water Upper Jurassic to lowermost Cretaceous units that onlap onto the north flank of the platform over the distal end of its Middle Jurassic clastics. A spectacular progradation of deltaic systems begins with the Albian (Torok Formation), in a sequence that exhibits topsets, clinoforms, and bottomsets of a prograding deltaic system. Sea-level changes impose southward-impinging transgressive pulses and condensed sections. These transgressive pulses subdivide the overall prograding and shallowing foredeep sequence. Key highstands are within the upper Albian, near the base of the Cenomanian, at the base of the Turonian, and within the Santonian. Foredeep clastics prograde from the southwest to the northeast (i.e., oblique to the basin axis) and terminate in the mid-Pliocene (Molenaar and others, 1987).

The Western Canada foredeep suggests shallow-water sedimentation at its inception. Only later does the foredeep become more marine, and by mid-Albian to mid-Campanian time, the basin is dominated by marine shale sequences. These are punctuated by unconformities and siliclastic lowstand-related influxes during late Albian, upper Turonian, and basal Campanian times.

When discussing sea-level highstands and lowstands within the Cretaceous of the Colville and Western Canada Basins, it must be emphasized that these are vaguely compatible with the

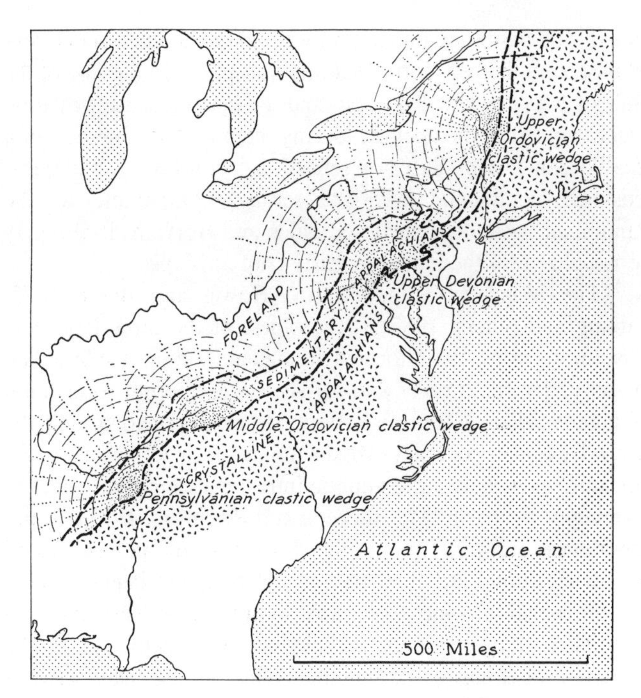

Figure 7. King's (1977) illustration showing the principal clastic wedge deposits of the Appalachian foreland.

chart of Haq and others (1987). Because that chart (for an example see Fig. 11) shows sea-level changes in excruciating detail, a lowstand or highstand that will approximately fit the chart can always be found. Much better documented correlations have yet to be made to justify tracing worldwide lowstands and highstands into these foredeeps. This, of course, is the crux of the debate that centers around orogenic versus eustatic control of the Rocky Mountain foredeep stratigraphy.

Weimer (1983, 1986) provides a particularly clear perspective. According to him, the overall subsidence of the Southern Rocky Mountains foredeep is interrupted by nine major regional unconformities (indicated by asterisks on Fig. 11), which are related to lowered sea levels. Thus, sea-level changes are superposed on the overall foredeep subsidence and they profoundly influence sedimentation and the specific positions of unconformities within the foredeep.

The development of clastic wedges in the Appalachian foredeep was concisely summed up by King (1977) in a classic diagram reproduced in Figure 7. Combining this diagram with the schematic section of Figure 5, the shifting depocenters of the Appalachian foredeep reflect shifting orogenic loads (Quinlan and Beaumont, 1984; Beaumont and others, 1987).

Middle Ordovician flysch-type deposits first occur in the foreland of the Southern Appalachians and the Canadian Appalachians, and then Upper Ordovician deep-water flysch can be followed all along the Appalachians. McIver (1970) has summarized the main features of these turbidite systems.

Shallow-water depocenters are first installed with the Late Ordovician Queenstown Delta. A major nonorogenic relapse occurs during the Siluro-Devonian. During this time, platform carbonates in the Appalachian Basin suggest a break in the progression of deformation of the Appalachians. Early Devonian brings the resumption of alluvial-deltaic systems and their condensed basinal equivalents (e.g., the Catskill Delta of New York). As will be seen later, these basinal equivalents form part of a North America–wide black shale system (Fig. 15). Deltaic depocenters continue to dominate e Appalachian foredeep through the Mississippian and the Pennsylvanian. For an overview of general facies distribution, see Meckel (1970) and McIver (1970).

Summaries of the fill of the Arkoma Basin by Houseknecht (1986) and Sutherland (1988) are most informative. Following the deep-water inception of the Arkoma foredeep during the Late Mississippian and Early Pennsylvanian (Arbenz, this volume), there is the somewhat unusual occurrence of northward-migrating down-to-the-south growth-fault systems at the base of the foredeep. Such normal faulting is perhaps related to bending stresses in the underthrust foreland slab in response to the Ouachita thrust load. Elsewhere in North America, similar normal faults are seen in the Ordovician foredeep of the St. Lawrence Lowland (e.g., Hiscott and others, 1986). During the mid-Pennsylvanian Atoka interval, the Arkoma foredeep is filled with a great thickness of deep-water and fan deposits. A narrow coastal sand strip marks the north flank of the Arkoma Basin. The last stage of the Arkoma foredeep evolution outlines the final infilling of the basin by a "molasse-type" sequence of Desmoinesian (Late Pennsylvanian) alluvial and deltaic sediments. Initially, the source of the coarse clastics is from the north and east, but higher up in the sequence a southerly source from the adjacent Ouachita orogen can be detected. Compressional deformation of the foredeep deposits brings the foredeep cycle to an end.

Recapitulation

All foredeeps of North America are related to the subduction of platforms that began as passive continental margins (i.e., to A-subduction). Only the Colville foredeep involves the fragment of a continent that rafted in during the opening of the Arctic Ocean, while all other foredeeps are superposed on the North American craton. To a first approximation, loading by thrust sheets and/or lithospheric loads adequately explains the subsidence of these foredeeps.

Having stated some of the common denominators, it is important to emphasize the substantial differences in the evolution and basin fill of these foredeeps.

The idealized sketch of Figure 4 shows a basal foredeep unconformity that separates underlying platform/passive margin (i.e., "miogeosynclinal") sequences from overlying clastic sequences that reflect the filling of the foredeep moat. The Paleozoic foredeeps of North America, as well as the Mesozoic Colville foredeep, all begin with a deep-water "flysch" phase. Sediment transport during that phase is mostly basin-parallel. In the Arkoma-Ouachita as in the Appalachian foredeep, the basin fill is superposed on an earlier carbonate platform, indicating dramatic deepening of the platform due to orogenic loading. In the Colville foredeep, the original moat is superposed on the attenuated deep-water edge of the North Slope platform.

In western Canada and the Southern Rocky Mountains, the foredeep record is mostly within shallow-water sediments, and the initial foredeep moat is filled with shallow-water clastics that are superposed on a shallow-water wedge of multiple unconformities.

Note that the down-dip distal portion of a foredeep, as observed on a reflection profile, is not necessarily the record of the inception of that foredeep. Instead, in most cases—particularly in the case of the Rocky Mountains—the early foredeep clastics were overthrust, uplifted, and subsequently eroded. Thus, deep-water foredeeps more closely represent the "birth" of a foreland folded belt (i.e., the moment when an orogenic system started to override a passive margin). In shallow-water foredeeps, the early record is typically involved in overthrusts and eroded. However, the fact that shallow-water sediments are widespread throughout the observable record would suggest that folded belts "overran" much wider areas of the preorogenic continental margins.

The amount of continental "underthrusting," as well as the amount of crustal imbrication within a folded belt, will largely be responsible for the elevation of a mountain range. For the Appalachians and Ouachitas, following Stockmal and others (1986) and Beaumont and others (1987), that elevation would be quite considerable, and cumulative upper Paleozoic erosion would be in excess of 15 to 20 km.

As folded belts emerge from old oceans and continental margins, we see the end of a classical Huttonian cycle. Today's missing link in that cycle is our inadequate knowledge of uplift and erosion rates. These are bound to be elucidated in the near future with the more widespread and increasingly more sophisticated application of fission-track and other uplift-measuring techniques.

THE FORMATION OF MISSISSIPPIAN TO TRIASSIC EPISUTURAL BASINS

Accumulation-rate maps for the Mississippian to Triassic (Plate 10—G, H, I) show conspicuous subsidence centers that were located right on top of the Paleozoic folded belts. We are dealing here with the Magdalen (Gulf of St. Lawrence) and Sidney Basins of the Canadian Maritimes (Howie and Barss, 1975; Rast, this volume), the Sverdrup Basin (Stephenson and others, 1987; Trettin, this volume), and the ancestral Gulf Coast Basin (Worrall and Snelson, this volume). The overall setting of these basins has been previously described by Bally and Snelson (1980); Figure 8, taken and modified from that paper, provides a comparison of them.

The common denominator of the three basins is that they are each superposed on a Paleozoic collisional megasuture and that they formed at a time when the collision was almost completed. The basins are underlain by a highly attenuated continental basement that was formed at their inception. In the case of the Gulf of Mexico, late Paleozoic and Triassic crustal attenuation eventually led to the opening, during the mid–Late Jurassic, of a small oceanic basin. Based on reflection profiles, an overall transtensional continental back-arc setting, comparable to the Pannonian Basin of Hungary (Royden and Horvath, 1988), may be visualized for the Paleozoic early Gulf of Mexico.

The Magdalen/Sidney Basin (Howie and Barss, 1975; Gibling and others, 1987) is the oldest of the three Paleozoic episutural basins, as it formed immediately after the Acadian orogeny. Seismic profiles and surface studies permit recognition of post-Acadian extensional structures that formed during the latest Devonian to Early Mississippian. Both felsic and mafic volcanics as well as some granitic intrusions are coeval with the opening of the basin (McCutcheon and Robinson, 1987). Rapid subsidence occurred during the Mississippian and decreased somewhat during the Pennsylvanian. Subsequent Pennsylvanian compressional tectonics, the Variscan episode of Rast (this volume), led to inversion of the old graben system and to the formation of elongate salt anticlines. Thus, an interplay between early transtensional and later transpressional inversion tectonics is inferred. This situation is similar to the Pannonian Basin, but is also reminiscent of the evolution of some Tertiary basins in California. The detailed evolution of the Magdalen and the adjacent Sidney Basin still needs further study (see also Rast, this volume).

A summary of the evolution of the Sverdrup Basin is given by Trettin (this volume). The initiation of the basin may be somewhat later than the basins of the Gulf of St. Lawrence, as rifting there began during the latest early Carboniferous. Stephenson and others (1987) confirm with their subsidence model that in the Sverdrup Basin an initial Permo-Carboniferous (330 to 265 Ma) rifting phase was followed by thermal subsidence from the Triassic to the earliest Cretaceous (265 Ma to 138 Ma). A second rifting–thermal event occurred during the Barremian-Cenomanian (i.e., 138 to 91 Ma) and is related to the opening of the Arctic Ocean and associated widespread volcanics (i.e., tholeiitic basalts), dikes, and sills. This event was followed by thermal subsidence, which was interrupted by the Late Cretaceous to Tertiary Eurekan orogeny.

Comparing the origin of the Gulf Coast Basin (see Worrall and Snelson, this volume) with the Gulf of St. Lawrence and Sverdrup Basins, there is a substantial difference in the dates of basin inception and above all during the later subsidence story. Increasing evidence supports the formation of a Late Pennsylvanian (i.e., post-Atokan) to Permian, postorogenic basin nested in the concave part of the Ouachita folded belt (Milliken, 1988). Even though seismic data do not yet provide convincing evidence for Late Pennsylvanian normal faulting, the impressive sediment thickness suggests a thermal origin for that upper Paleozoic basin (see Plate 10—I, H). I am tempted to connect this basin with a similar basin suggested by Lopez-Ramos (1969, 1983b) in Mexico. However, specific correlation of Pennsylvanian and Permian sequences of the U.S. Gulf Coast subsurface with the section

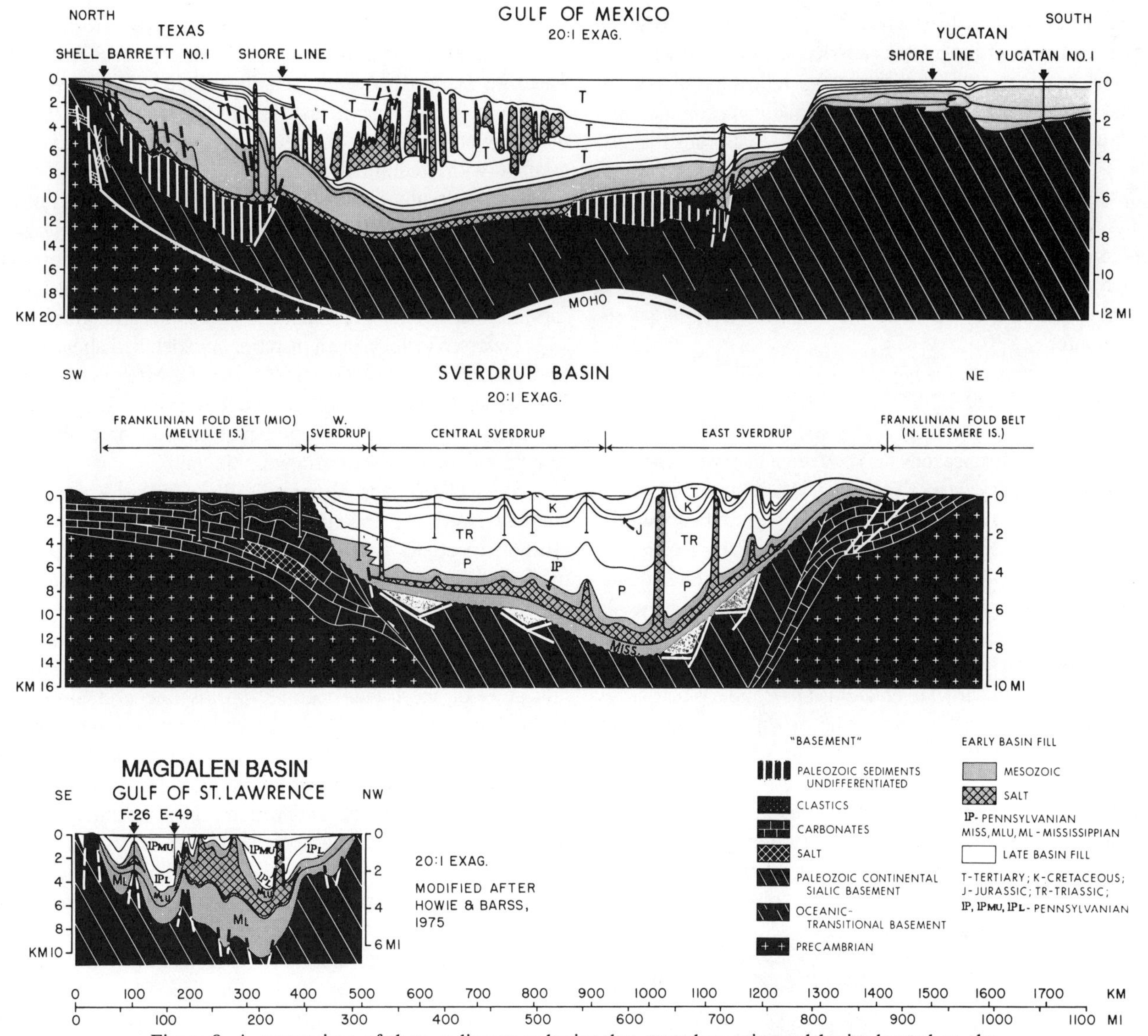

Figure 8. A comparison of three sedimentary basins that started as episutural basins located on the Paleozoic folded belts of North America (modified from Bally and Snelson, 1980). The Paleozoic Magdalen (Gulf of St. Lawrence) Basin serves as a model for the early history of the Gulf of Mexico and the Sverdrup Basins. Paleozoic normal faulting suggested for the Gulf of Mexico and the Sverdrup Basins is hypothetical and needs to be confirmed by deep seismic profiles. Of course, pre-salt Late Triassic-Jurassic normal faulting has been known for some time from the Gulf of Mexico.

reported from Mexico is not clear. In both areas, rift-filling Triassic red beds often overlie the older Paleozoic basin sequences. In the Gulf Coast subsurface, the red beds and some volcanics are associated with half-graben systems. Lopez-Ramos (1969) reports Permo-Triassic granitic intrusions from the subsurface basement of the foreland of the Sierra Madre Oriental. Even allowing for some early Mesozoic strike-slip displacements in Mexico, it appears that the early Gulf of Mexico may be viewed as a Pannonian-type back-arc basin system that formed during the Permo-Pennsylvanian and was replaced by a more conventional back-arc system during the Triassic. The Triassic island arc would be located in Mexico. Thus, considerable crustal attenuation preceded the emplacement of the oceanic crust of the Gulf of Mexico during mid–Late Jurassic time (see Worrall and Snelson, this volume). Subsequent Jurassic to Cretaceous subsidence may well be explained as a consequence of cooling of a Triassic–Early Jurassic rifting event (Buffler and Sawyer, 1985; Dunbar and Sawyer, 1987). Note however, mid-Jurassic Louann evaporites clearly and discordantly overlie the Triassic–Early Jurassic rift systems.

On the Gulf Coast, an additional thermal event is indicated by Upper Cretaceous volcanics. Ultimately, however, much of the Gulf Coast subsidence is related to major Tertiary clastic depocenters and their lowstand fan deposits, infilling a deep-water basin (see Worrall and Snelson, this volume).

To conclude, three episutural basins formed on the Paleozoic folded belts of North America. They were initiated by late Paleozoic to Triassic rifting, which also led to a much-attentuated continental basement. Thermal subsidence followed but was interrupted by (1) late Paleozoic compressional inversion tectonics in the Gulf of St. Lawrence Basin; and (2) Cretaceous thermal events in the Sverdrup and Gulf Coast Basins. Further thermal subsidence in the Sverdrup Basin was terminated by the Eurekan orogeny. The Gulf Coast Basin, however, was invaded by an enormous influx of Tertiary clastics that filled a deep-water basin. Although the Paleozoic episutural basins here described had a comparable origin, they ended up with a widely different subsequent evolution.

SEQUENCE STRATIGRAPHY

In 1948, a conference in New York brought experts together to discuss sedimentary facies. The result was Memoir 39 of the Geological Society of America (Longwell, 1949). In that volume, John Rodgers (p. 130) stated his impression of the meeting as follows: "I have the uncomfortable feeling that everyone attending this meeting is for facies in the same way that everyone while attending church is against sin, and I wonder just how far this allegiance would carry if we found ourselves faced with the stratigraphic equivalent of carnal temptation. The trouble is that facies relations are magnificently convincing when one sees them flashed on the screen, but devilishly difficult to recognize in the field."

In hindsight, it would appear that the authors of the memoir sensed that they were at the limit of time-stratigraphic resolution and that they did as well as they could with what they had. Most important, however, the memoir contained one Gordian knot–cutting paper by Sloss and others (1949), who proposed that the Paleozoic of North America could be split into four sequences (i.e., Sauk, Tippecanoe, Kaskaskia, and Absaroka) that were separated by major breaks. The new names were introduced to avoid conflict with traditional stratigraphic nomenclature. The new concept eventually evolved into the modern definition of a sequence as a "relatively conformable succession of genetically related strata bounded by unconformities and their correlative conformities" (Mitchum and others, 1977, p. 53). Thus, unconformities became the great dividers of regional stratigraphy.

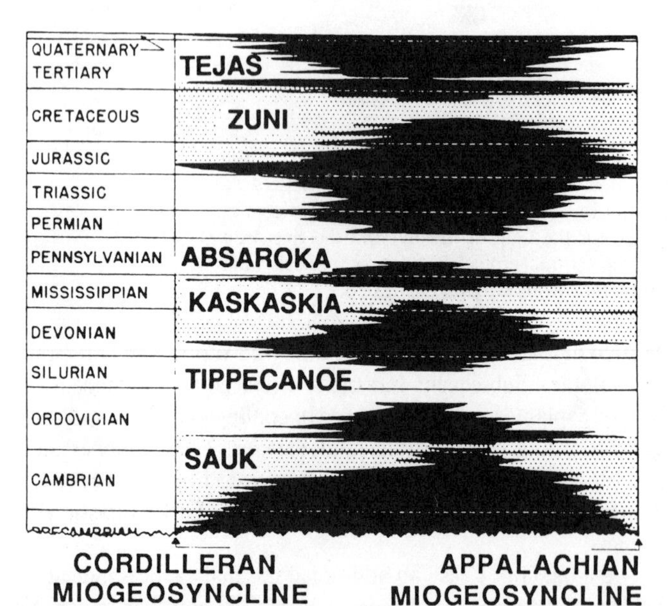

Figure 9. Classic diagram of Sloss (1963) showing time-stratigraphic relationships of the sequences in the North American craton. Black areas represent nondepositional hiatuses; white and stippled areas represent deposition (stippling introduced only to differentiate successive depositional episodes).

Levorsen (1960), in an inspiring booklet, had already shown that interregional unconformities were of great concern to petroleum geologists because they helped to unravel paleogeology and paleogeomorphology. More pragmatically, unconformities were responsible for significant stratigraphic traps.

Sloss (1963) and Wheeler (1963) further expanded and codified North American sequence stratigraphy. Both authors attributed tectonic significance to the sequence boundaries. Figure 9 shows the Sloss (1963) sequence concept, and Tables 1A and 1B show the most recent version. Wheeler even visualized tectonic hiatuses such as the Acadian or Taconic hiatus. In this he followed Stille (1924) who viewed worldwide unconformities as indicators of short-lived tectonic phases (see also Sloss, 1972, 1976). Sloss and Speed (1974) much later parlayed another tectonic perspective into a model that viewed uplift and basin subsidence phases as being controlled by "pulsating asthenospheric" flow between continents and oceans. Thus began a school of thought that viewed stratigraphic sequences as somehow related to tectonic events (see also Johnson, 1971). Sloss (1988d) offers a lively review of the past 40 years of sequence stratigraphy. Because his assessment of "the state of sequence stratigraphy" differs somewhat from mine, the reader is encouraged to read Sloss (1988d).

A major change in perspective to sequence stratigraphy came with the publication of Memoir 26 of the American Association of Petroleum Geologists (Payton, 1977), in which Vail and others (1977) unveiled modern seismic stratigraphy. For the first time it was shown that seismic reflection profiles provided adequate continuity to identify major unconformity-bound stratigraphic sequences and the distribution of prograding and backstepping sediments within these sequences. Together with a detailed explanation of the methodology, Vail and his co-workers from EXXON published coastal onlap curves (Fig. 10), which were at that time viewed to be directly indicative of global sea-level changes. Subsequent publications incorporated much additional research and substantially modified the curves (Haq and others, 1987; Vail, 1987; Van Wagoner and others, 1987).

One of the initial assumptions of modern seismic stratigraphy is that a seismic reflector is a good approximation to a stratigraphic time line. Purists are quick to point out that seismic reflectors only indicate seismic impedance contrasts and that such contrasts do not necessarily correspond to time lines. Empirically, however, it may be said with confidence that such exceptions are

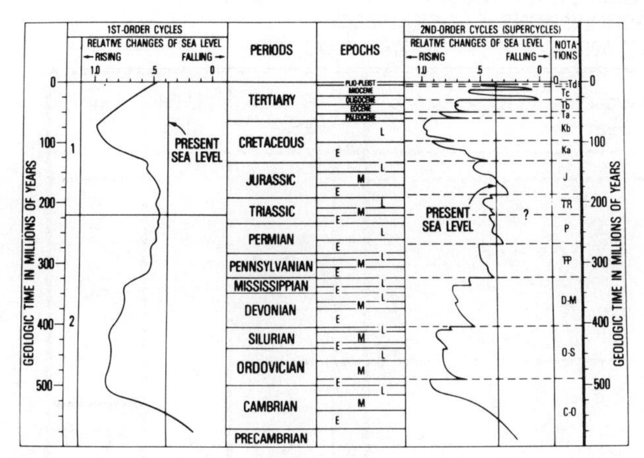

Figure 10. Another classic diagram: Vail and others (1977) show first- and second-order global cycles of relative change of sea level during Phanerozoic time. Compare this diagram with Figure 9 and Figure 11.

in most cases quite obvious, and the overall experience confirms that most reflectors are indeed very good approximations of time lines. The accuracy of a "reflector time line" is obviously a function of seismic resolution. A feeling for seismic time-stratigraphic resolution can be obtained by simply comparing the number of good reflectors with the number of paleontologically well-established time lines in a given area. In most cases, for Mesozoic-Cenozoic reflection profiles, the number of reflectors is greatly in excess of the number of correlatable paleozones, whereas in the Paleozoic cratonic cover of North America, the number of seismic reflectors often may be less than the number of paleozones. In all cases where seismic data quality is good, the continuity of seismic profiles is better than the continuity of outcrop sections.

Variable hiatus values occur along one and the same unconformity, but obviously, strata overlying the unconformity are always younger than strata below the unconformity. Aside from these and other technicalities, the seismic stratigraphic method is well established, and objections are now focused on interpretation of the sea-level curves. Today's curves are quite refined (e.g., Haq and others, 1987; and Vail, 1987). Figure 11 is a simplified segment of the chart published by these authors for the Cretaceous. The new curves show (1) coastal-onlap curves with flat shoulders that correspond to lowstands with their associated lowstand fan complexes, (2) a plot of condensed sections that correspond to maximum flooding and relate to major tectonically controlled cycles, and (3) a plot of the magnitude and types of sequence boundaries and (4) eustatic curves.

After subtracting the effect of tectonic subsidence, Vail and co-workers (Vail, 1987) now present a eustatic curve with many sea-level oscillations representing third-order cycles on the order of 1 to 5 m.y. These cycles change in frequency throughout the Phanerozoic and are packaged into supercycles on the order of about 10 m.y. These in turn are lumped into supercycle sets that last on the order of 30 to 40 m.y., and finally into megacycles, which correspond roughly to the sequences as proposed by Sloss (1988c). Figure 12 (from Vail, 1987) illustrates an idealized sequence with its various systems tracts, which can be recognized on seismic profiles.

Sloss (1988c) emphasizes that Vail's sequences (i.e., Vail's third-order cycles) are much smaller units than the original sequences as perceived by Sloss (compare Fig. 9, 10, and 11). By using sea-level changes as the main rationale for stratigraphic changes, Vail and his colleagues in effect divorced the sequence concept from its original structural connotation; hence the opposition from people who, like Sloss and Stille before, believe, for various reasons, that sequences are representative of structural regimes (e.g., Bally, 1980; Watts and others, 1982; Watts and Thorne, 1984; Cloetingh and others, 1985; Cloetingh, 1989; Summerhayes, 1986). The debate is still going on, and probably will not be resolved in the near future because additional studies and detailed documentation are required. Important points lately emphasized by Vail (1987) are that sequence boundaries may be tectonically enhanced when sea-level changes are superposed on tectonic subsidence regimes and/or on growing structures. In other words, the tectonics may not cause the unconformities; instead, unconformities are superposed on ongoing tectonic processes.

The inception and cessation of tectonic regimes, taken at face value from the literature, often are not correlatable with any of the sequence boundaries that have been proposed. However, in this context the timing of tectonic regimes is much less precise than anything that can be done with seismic stratigraphy.

Folded into the tectonic versus eustatic arguments are often semantic questions that at first glance appear to be casuistic. However, we really do need to resolve what constitutes a tectonic phase on local, regional, and global levels, respectively! In this context, the tectonics of structural geologists differ substantially from the "tectonic" subsidence notions of basin modelers. Furthermore, as I believe, most extensional and compressional tectonics are linked together by common decoupling levels. But unfortunately, the detailed kinematics of whole decoupling systems, including their as yet ill-defined transfer systems, are so far poorly known. Dating one part of any decoupling system does not date the whole system (Bally, 1984).

Sequence stratigraphy began as a very simple concept wherein Sloss (1963) proposed to subdivide the Phanerozoic into six grand sequences, which according to many authors, may have had tectonic significance. Today, sequence stratigraphy has become much more complex. Sloss (1988c) now visualizes some 16 subsequences for the Phanerozoic, and Vail (1987) differentiates 27 supercycles for the Mesozoic only, as opposed to four Mesozoic subsequences proposed by Sloss (1988c). To make matters more difficult, authors insist on using their own preferred time scales. Thus, Sloss (1988c) uses a time scale that already differs in detail from the scale of Palmer (1983); Haq and others (1987), and Vail (1987) differ substantially from all other published scales. Sloss (1963) emphatically declared that his scheme was not an attempt to set up a separate North American chronostratigraphy, but his irreverent student, Vail, and his associates have

TABLE 1A. CORRELATION CHART OF PALEOZOIC SEQUENCES AND SUBSEQUENCES WITH STANDARD STRATIGRAPHIC SUBDIVISIONS (SLOSS, 1988C). INDEX TO STRATIGRAPHIC MAPS (PLATE 10) AND FIGURES FOR THIS CHAPTER

System	Series	Stage	End (Ma)	Subsequence (Ma)	Subsequence	AR Map ◄SC	LITH Map	Fig.
Permian	Lower	Scythian	243	245				
	Ochoa							
		Tatarian	248					
	Guadalupe				Absaroka	I		20
		Kazanian	253		II			
	Leonard	Kungurian	258					
		Artinskian	263					
				268				
	Wolfcamp	Sakmarian	268					
Pennsylvanian	Virgil							16-17
		Stephanian	286					
	Missouri							
		D						
	Des Moines	C			Absaroka	H		
		Westphalian	296		I			
		B						
	Atoka							
		A						
		C						
	Morrow	Namurian B						
Mississippian	Chester	A		330				
		Visean	333					
	Valmayer				Kaskaskia			
	Kinderhook	Tournaisian	352		II	G		
				362			F	15
Devonian		Famennian	360					
	Upper	Frasnian	367			E		
		Givetian	374					
	Middle	Eifelian	380		Kaskaskia			
		Emsian	387		I			
	Lower	Siegenian	394	401		◄D		
		Gedinnian	401					
Silurian		Pridolian	408					
	Upper	Ludlovian	414		Tippecanoe			
	Middle	Wenlockian	421		II			
		Llandoverian	428					
	Lower			438		B		
Ordovician	Upper	Ashgillian	438				C	
		Caradocian	448					
	Middle	Llandeilan	458		Tippecanoe			
		Llanvinian	468		I			
		Arenigian	478	488				
	Lower	Tremadocian	488					
Cambrian					Sauk III			
		Trempealeauan	505					14
	Upper	Franconian				A		
		Dresbachian		515				
					Sauk II			
	Middle		523					
				548				
	Lower		548		Sauk I			
Precambrian	Upper Proterozoic	Ediacaran	590	600				

Letters refer to Plate 10; Numbers refer to text figures.
AR Map–Accumulation rate maps; SC –Subcrop map; LITH Map –Lithofacies maps; Fig – Text figures.

TABLE 1B. CORRELATION CHART OF MESOZOIC AND TERTIARY SEQUENCES AND SUBSEQUENCES (SLOSS, 1988C). INDEX TO STRATIGRAPHIC MAPS (PLATE 10) AND FIGURES FOR THIS CHAPTER

System	Series	Stage	End (Ma)	Subsequence (Ma)	Subsequence	AR Map ←SC	LITH Map	Fig.
Quaternary		Pleistocene	0					
Tertiary	Neogene	Pliocene	2		Tejas III			21
		Miocene	5.1					
		Oligocene	24.6	29				
					Tejas II			
	Paleogene	Eocene	38	39				
					Tejas I			
		Paleocene	54.9	60				
Cretaceous	Upper	Maastrichtian	65		Zuni III	N		
		Campanian	73					
		Santonian	83					
		Coniacian	87.5					
		Turonian	88.5				P	
		Cenomanian	91	96			O	
	Lower	Albian	97.5		Zuni II			
		Aptian	113					
		Barremian	119			M		
		Hauterivian	125					
		Valanginian	131					
				134		← L		
		Berriasian	138					
Jurassic	Upper	Portlandian	144		Zuni I			
		Kimmeridgian	150					
		Oxfordian	156			K		
	Middle	Callovian	163					
		Bathonian	169					
		Bajocian	175					
		Aalenian	181					
				186				
	Lower	Toarcian	188		Absaroka III	J		
		Pleinsbachian	194					
		Sinemurian	200					
		Hettangian	206					
Triassic	Upper	Rhaetian	213					
		Norian	219					
		Carnian	225					
	Middle	Ladinian	213					
		Anisian	238					
	Lower	Scythian	243	245				

Letters refer to Plate 10; Numbers refer to text figures.
AR Map – Accumulation rate maps; SC – Subcrop map; LITH Map – Lithofacies maps; Fig. – Text figures.

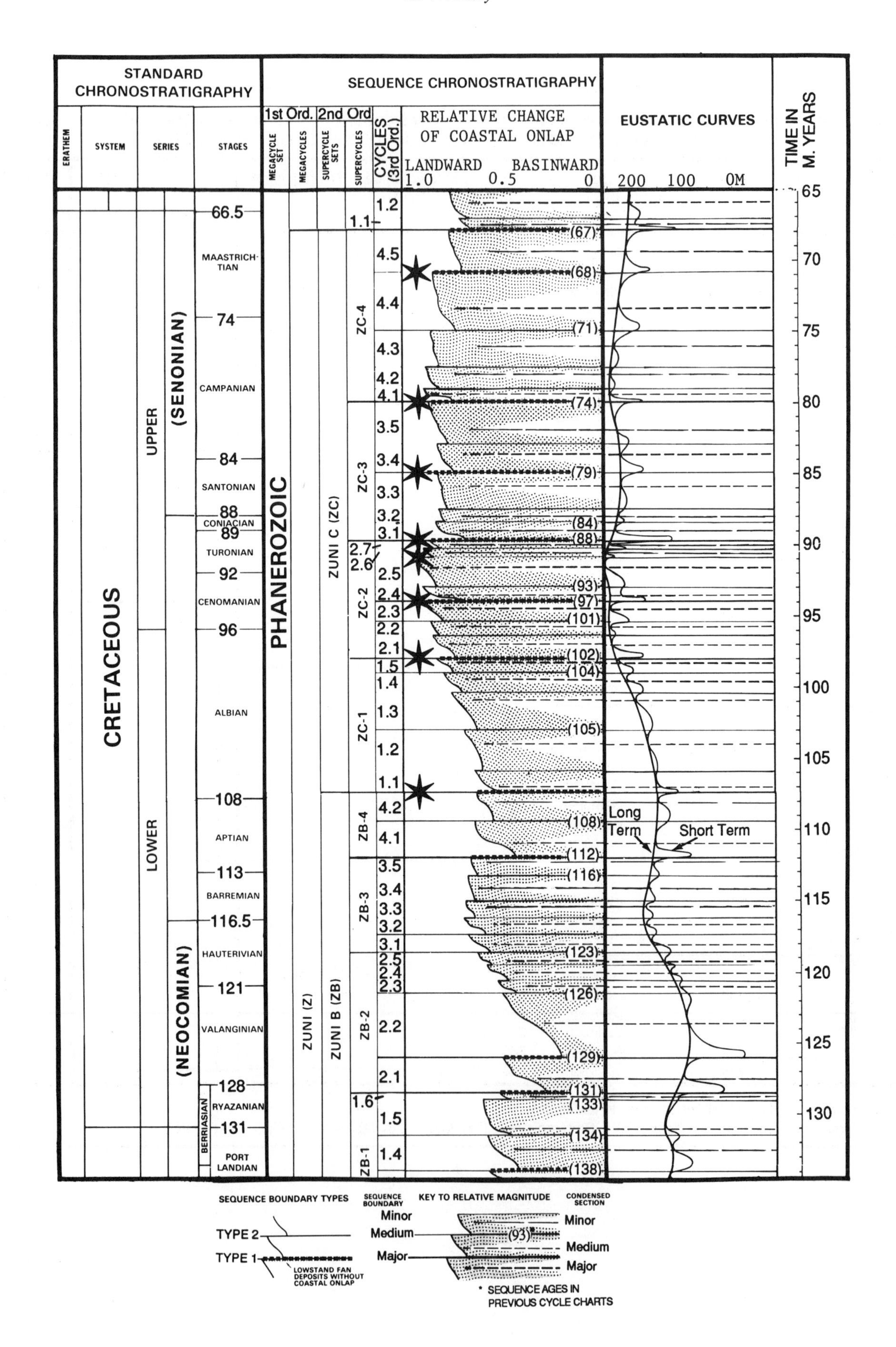
STANDARD CHRONOSTRATIGRAPHY
SEQUENCE CHRONOSTRATIGRAPHY
EUSTATIC CURVES
TIME IN M. YEARS
ERATHEM
SYSTEM
SERIES
STAGES
1st Ord.
2nd Ord
MEGACYCLE SET
MEGACYCLES
SUPERCYCLE SETS
SUPERCYCLES
CYCLES (3rd Ord.)
RELATIVE CHANGE OF COASTAL ONLAP
LANDWARD
BASINWARD
1.0
0.5
0
200
100
0M
CRETACEOUS
UPPER
(SENONIAN)
LOWER
(NEOCOMIAN)
MAASTRICHTIAN
CAMPANIAN
SANTONIAN
CONIACIAN
TURONIAN
CENOMANIAN
ALBIAN
APTIAN
BARREMIAN
HAUTERIVIAN
VALANGINIAN
BERRIASIAN
RYAZANIAN
PORT LANDIAN
PHANEROZOIC
ZUNI (Z)
ZUNI C (ZC)
ZUNI B (ZB)
ZC-4
ZC-3
ZC-2
ZC-1
ZB-4
ZB-3
ZB-2
ZB-1
Long Term
Short Term
SEQUENCE BOUNDARY TYPES
TYPE 2
TYPE 1
LOWSTAND FAN DEPOSITS WITHOUT COASTAL ONLAP
SEQUENCE BOUNDARY
Minor
Medium
Major
KEY TO RELATIVE MAGNITUDE
CONDENSED SECTION
* SEQUENCE AGES IN PREVIOUS CYCLE CHARTS

ended up repackaging the time chronostratigraphy of the whole world in terms of sequences!

Vail's Mesozoic sequence boundaries do not coincide with any of the Sloss sequence boundaries. So, instead of added clarity and simplification, we have new complexities. Some of these complexities are important because they lead to an increased understanding of stratigraphic principles. Above all, the modern development of seismic stratigraphy and sequence stratigraphy has revitalized an important part of our science. Perhaps now the time is ripe to form some kind of working consensus on sequence boundaries and their chronostratigraphic position. Such a consensus, of course, will emanate from committees that unfortunately may eventually degenerate into a new stratigraphic priesthood!

A LATE PROTEROZOIC SUPERCONTINENT AND ITS BREAKUP

The chapter on the Precambrian (Hoffman, this volume) ends with a general perspective on the craton of North America during the Late Proterozoic, when passive margins rimmed the western, northern, eastern, and perhaps the southern margin of North America. The craton was much like Antarctica or Africa today. Implicit in that view is the notion that North America ought to be a fragment of a broken up, Late Proterozoic supercontinent. Morel and Irving (1978) offer a reconstruction of that supercontinent at 600 Ma. That reconstruction, however, like subsequent reconstructions done by Piper (1983, 1987), doesn't show much of North America surrounded by continents prior to a breakup during the Late Proterozoic. Sears and Price (1978) hypothesized a separation of Siberia from western North America about 1,500 Ma, early enough to explain the origin of the thick Middle Proterozoic of the western Cordillera, but too early to relate to the formation of the lower Paleozoic Cordilleran geosyncline (see also Cordillera chapter, Oldow and others, this volume).

Given that reconstructions of the mythical Proterozoic supercontinent remain debatable, one is initially tempted to discard the supercontinent concept for being too speculative. But here it becomes particularly important to follow the subsidence studies undertaken by Armin and Mayer (1983), Bond and Kominz (1984), and Bond and others (1984). These authors depart from the idea that careful reconstruction of the Paleozoic stratigraphy of the Cordillera should permit one to separate a rifting phase from a passive-margin drifting phase, as is often assumed for lithospheric-stretching models. Tectonic subsidence curves are constructed by these authors after removal of the effects of compaction and cementation, and removal of subsidence due to sediment loading. For North America's miogeosynclines, the subsidence curves so obtained are characteristic for thermal subsidence. Their extrapolation backward in time permits postulating a breakup age for North America between 625 Ma and 555 Ma, a time span that is reasonably close to the breakup age postulated by Piper (1983) based on paleomoagnetic data. The proposed breakup age is reasonably compatible with initial rifting ages proposed for the southern Oklahoma aulacogen (Lambert and others, 1988) between 520 and 580 Ma. However, the proposed breakup age is considerably younger than an age ranging from 850 Ma to 820 Ma that was proposed earlier by Stewart (1972, 1976) for the western Cordillera, and by Rankin (1975) for the Appalachians; or else from 750 to 770 Ma for rift-related magmatic events in the Ogilvie-Mackenzie Mountains of northwestern Canada. Trettin (this volume) suggests the initiation of a rifting event in the Franklinian mobile belt of the Canadian Arctic between 750 Ma and 630 Ma, more in harmony with Bond and others (1984).

Klein and Hsui (1987) were satisfied with a thermal origin of the four major cratonic basins of North America and they propose to link the origins of these basins also to the postulated breakup of the mythical Proterozoic supercontinent. However, as already mentioned, the actual evidence for conspicuous rifting related to the formation of these basins is lacking.

The proposed subsidence models and the determination of the breakup time are certainly plausible, and thus, it might seem to be relatively easy to observe Late Proterozoic to early Paleozoic rifting either in outcrop or in the subsurface. In view of the popular consensus concerning the Oklahoma Rift (Hoffman and others, 1974), and also concerning the Reelfoot Rift, these rifts and their marginal faults perhaps should have been actually observed on seismic reflection profiles, or on tightly controlled subsurface sections, but alas, they have only the most rudimentary documentation.

Well-documented Late Proterozoic extension is also rather scarce for the western Cordillera, where rifts are inferred from stratigraphic observations (e.g., Aitken and McMechan, 1989), but specific Late Proterozoic rift reconstructions are not available. For the Appalachian continental margin, Thomas (1977) has made a convincing case for a passive margin with reentrants reflecting increased extension, but here again we lack direct observations (see Arbenz, this volume).

Subsidence studies provide a compelling argument for one or more Late Proterozoic breakup phases of North America. On the other hand, the rift systems associated with that breakup are as yet poorly documented. Reconstructions of the Proterozoic supercontinent also remain nebulous.

Figure 11. Excerpt of the Cretaceous portion of the cycle chart published by Haq and others (1987) and Vail (1987). Note the refined third-order cycles, which are the basis of the chart. Note also the position of sequence boundaries, downlap surfaces, and condensed sections. Haq and others (1987) package third-order cycles into supercycles, supercycle sets, and megacycles. Supercycle sets roughly correspond to the subsequences of Sloss (1988c; see Tables 1A and 1B of this chapter); megacycles correspond to the sequences of the Sloss (1963). Haq and others (1987) use a different time scale than Sloss (1988c). The sea-level curves of Figure 10 (Vail and others, 1977) are now coastal onlap curves. The new eustatic curves were obtained after calculating the effect of tectonic subsidence in many areas (see also Fig. 12). The stars on the diagram mark the position of major unconformities reported by Weimer (1983) from the U.S. Rocky Mountain foredeep. The position of the stars was plotted allowing for the different time scale used by Weimer.

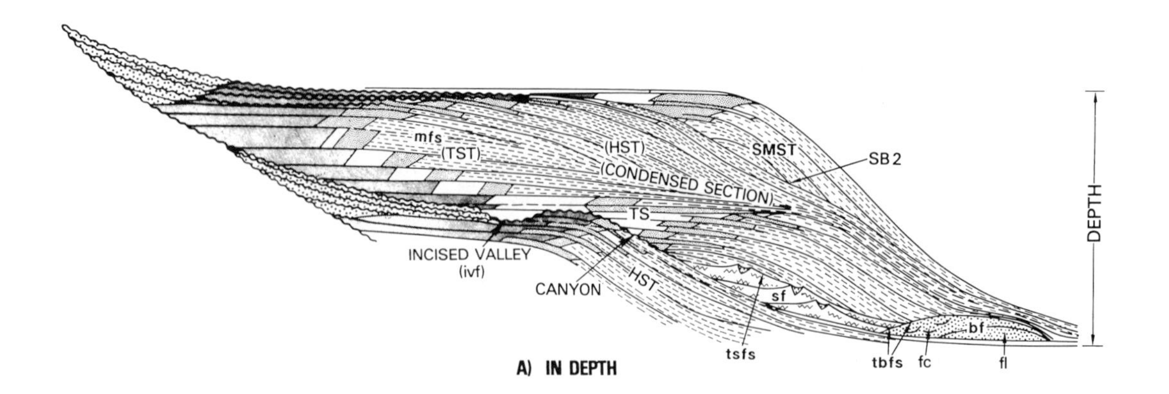
mfs
(TST)
(HST)
SMST
SB 2
(CONDENSED SECTION)
TS
INCISED VALLEY
(ivf)
CANYON
HST
sf
tsfs
bf
tbfs
fc
fl
DEPTH
A) IN DEPTH

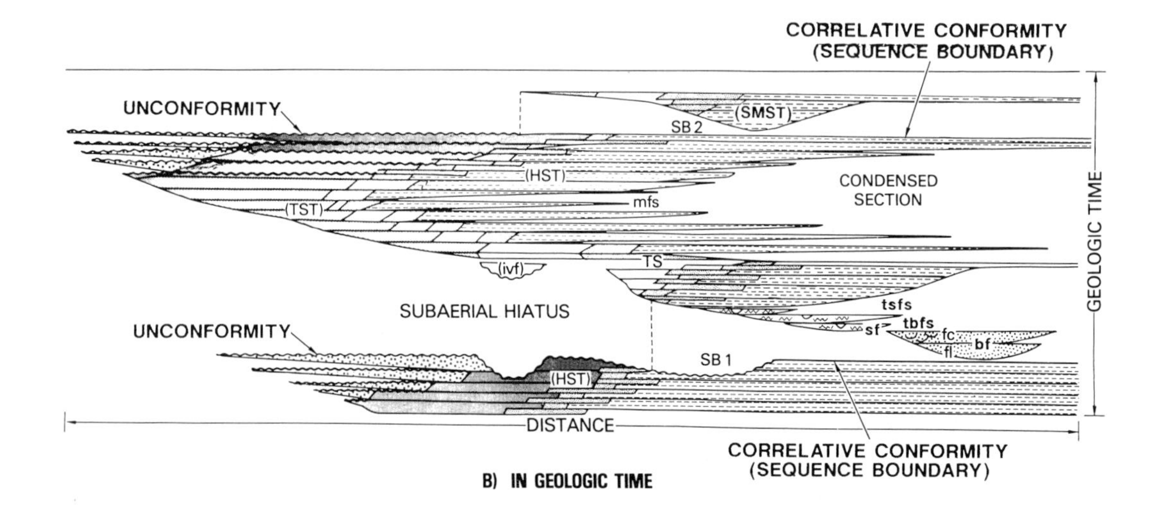
CORRELATIVE CONFORMITY
(SEQUENCE BOUNDARY)
UNCONFORMITY
(SMST)
SB 2
(HST)
CONDENSED
SECTION
mfs
(TST)
(ivf)
TS
SUBAERIAL HIATUS
tsfs
tbfs
sf
fc
fl
bf
UNCONFORMITY
SB 1
(HST)
DISTANCE
GEOLOGIC TIME
CORRELATIVE CONFORMITY
(SEQUENCE BOUNDARY)
B) IN GEOLOGIC TIME

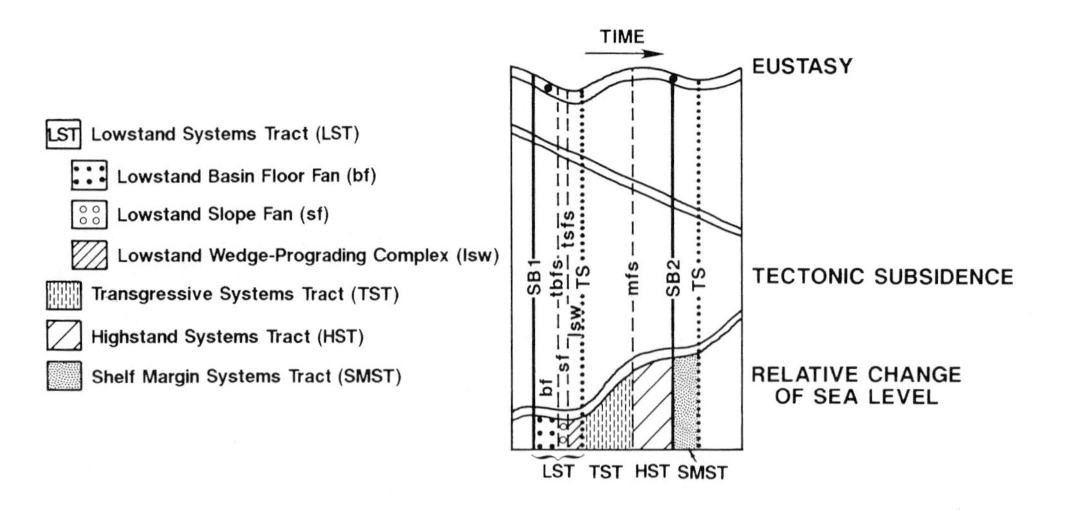
TIME
EUSTASY
LST Lowstand Systems Tract (LST)
Lowstand Basin Floor Fan (bf)
Lowstand Slope Fan (sf)
Lowstand Wedge-Prograding Complex (lsw)
Transgressive Systems Tract (TST)
Highstand Systems Tract (HST)
Shelf Margin Systems Tract (SMST)
SB1
tbfs
tsfs
lsw
TS
mfs
SB2
TS
bf
sf
TECTONIC SUBSIDENCE
RELATIVE CHANGE
OF SEA LEVEL
LST TST HST SMST

LEGEND
ALLUVIAL
COASTAL PLAIN
ESTUARINE/FLUVIAL
SHOREFACE/DELTAIC SANDS
MARINE SILT, MUDSTONE
MARINE SHALE
DEEP-WATER SANDS

THE PALEOZOIC AND MESOZOIC EVOLUTION OF THE CRATON

Preamble

In the following section, the cratonic evolution of North America will be sketched. Plate 10 shows most of the key illustrations. Generalized rate-of-accumulation maps are of some use for an overview of North American realms of subsidence through time. Sloss (1988c) has produced such maps for the United States, and this paper attempts to provide comparable maps for the whole North American continent. Lacking a consensus on sequence boundaries, I had to be practical and decided the following: for the Paleozoic to Lower Jurassic, the Sloss (1988d) sequence boundaries and their ages are accepted (see also Table 1-A and 1-B). For the remainder of the Mesozoic the "subsidence" maps approximate some of Vail's (1987) sequences, but not their time scale. This permits discussion of subsidence regimes and roughly coeval tectonic regimes without necessarily accepting that sequence boundaries ought to be precisely coeval with boundaries separating structural regimes. It must be noted, however, that the only integrated set of published North America–wide Phanerozoic isopachs are contained in Cook and Bally (1975) and that therefore most continent-wide "subsidence" maps have to be derived from the more classical subdivisions of that publication. Three somewhat arbitrary intervals were chosen that would reasonably depict "subsidence" trends from the Middle Jurassic to the end of the Cretaceous. Selected lithofacies and subcrop maps are also shown on Plate 10.

Tertiary subsidence patterns were not included in this chapter because the most important Tertiary basins are treated elsewhere (i.e., in the Gulf of Mexico and the Cordillera chapters; Snelson and Worrall, and Oldow and others, this volume). A small section will attempt to provide a ridiculously brief summary of the Tertiary basins of North America.

A comment about the accumulation-rate maps may be in order. Sloss (1988c) offers similar maps of the conterminous United States. The limitations of North America–wide data and the graphic restrictions imposed by the map scale induced me to produce schematic maps with less differentiation; compare my cutoff rate of more than 40 m/m.y. with the five classes of accumulation rates beyond 40 m/m.y. in Sloss. Of course, a maximum accumulation rate of more than 40 m/m.y. is not sufficiently precise to chart rate changes that may reflect various tectonic subsidence regimes. At the other end of the spectrum, accumulation rates of less than 5 m/m.y. are often due to subsequent erosion. These low rates, and the distribution of large outcrops, are shown simply to provide a more complete idea about sequence distributions. At best, accumulation-rate maps simply are "normalized" isopachs that give a very crude feeling for subsidence rates on a continental scale.

Accumulation rates do not immediately depict subsidence patterns because they make no allowances for decompaction of sediments, paleobathymetry, and sediment-loading effects. The calculation of tectonic subsidence is fraught with uncertainties relating (1) to the quality of the paleobathymetric and stratigraphic input, (2) to the time scale adopted, and (3) to various correction procedures. Systematic regional and continent-wide tectonic subsidence maps are not yet feasible, even though the studies of Quinlan and Beaumont (1984) and Beaumont and others (1987) are most encouraging. Accumulation-rate maps offer a first approximation that permits visualization of synchronous subsidence in the various basins of North America. As such, the maps are useful to describe roughly simultaneous subsidence among basins that have quite different origins.

Figure 13 serves to introduce the relationship between the cratonic and "miogeosynclinal" sequences of the United States. Using the base of the Pennsylvanian as a datum, the section displays the sudden expansion of the cratonic cover into the "miogeosynclines" to the west and east. Note that the sequences can be followed from the craton into the former passive margins of the Appalachians and the Cordillera.

The Sauk sequence. Uppermost Proterozoic through Tremadocian (600 to 478 Ma)

The Sauk accumulation-rate map (Plate 10-A) uses the Table 1 definition of the Sauk sequence (Sloss, 1988c). The sequence rests with profound unconformity on the Precambrian craton of North America. For a view of North America at the end of the Precambrian, see Hoffman (this volume). Moving toward the margin of the craton, significant thicknesses of Proterozoic sediments insert themselves between the crystalline Precambrian shield and the overlying Cambrian; thus, the hiatus between the Precambrian and the Cambrian decreases away from the craton and toward the marginal miogeosynclines of North America. Even in the western Cordillera where the Cambrian-Precambrian hiatus may be relatively brief, there is a consensus that the Cambrian remains separated from the underlying Windermere by an unconformity (Aitken, 1969).

The Sauk sequence divisions of Palmer (1981) have been used by Sloss (1988c) and Aitken and McMechan (1989). These are separated by unconformities or evidence of regression near the end of the Lower Cambrian, and of the Franconian. Stratigraphic maps reveal that the distribution of the Lower Cambrian

◄———

Figure 12. A diagrammatic section illustrating sequence stratigraphy from Vail (1987). This diagram shows typical siliciclastic distributions within sequences and system tracts in depth and in geologic time. The diagram below conceptualizes the relationship between eustasy, a linear plot of tectonic subsidence, sequence boundaries (SB), and transgressive surfaces (TS). Note that the thickness of sediments is primarily controlled by tectonic subsidence, but stratal patterns and lithofacies are dominantly controlled by the rate of relative sea-level change. Downlap surfaces: maximum flooding surface (mfs); top basin-floor fan surface (tbfs); top slope fan surface (tsfs). Lowstand systems tract: incised valley fill (ivf), lowstand wedge prograding complex (lsw); lowstand slope fan (sf); lowstand basin floor fan (bf); fan channels (fc); fan lobes (fl).

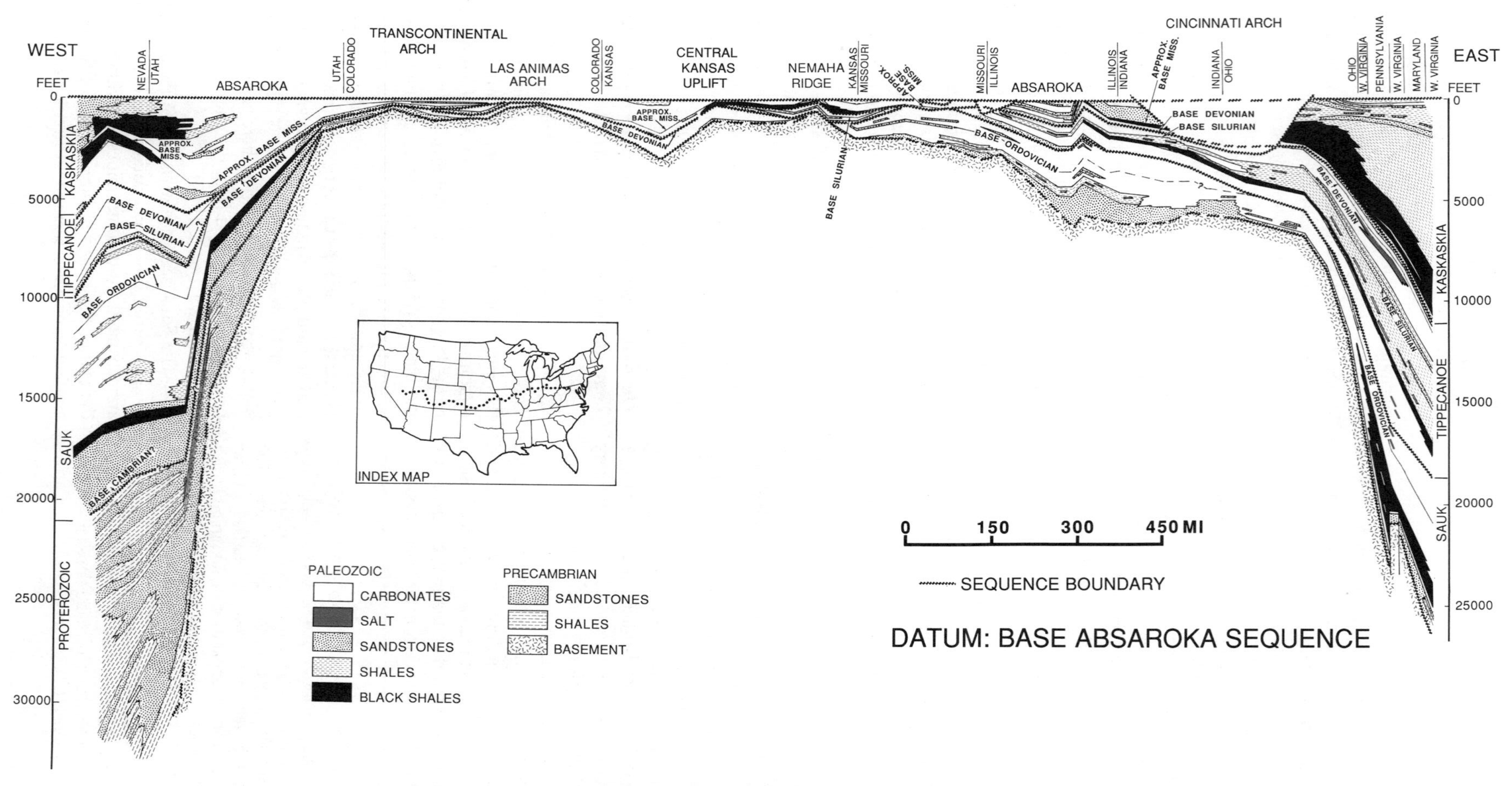

Figure 13. A schematic pre-Pennsylvanian cross section across the United States, based on Adkinson (1966), Colton (1970), and Mallory (1972a), simplified from a section originally compiled by R. E. Farmer (formerly of Shell Oil Company). Note the attenuated section in Colorado coinciding with the Transcontinental Arch. Erosion in Indiana and Ohio indicates the Cincinnati Arch that separates the Illinois Basin from the Appalachian Basins. Rapid expansion of the section toward the Rocky Mountains and the Appalachians illustrates transition into the pericratonic lower Paleozoic passive margin (miogeosynclinal) domain. The break in continuity in western Utah is due to telescoping of stratigraphic thickness across the Utah-Wyoming thrust belt.

Sauk I subcycle, with its basal quartzose clastics, is limited to the Cordilleran and Appalachian folded belts. With the higher Sauk II and III cycles overstepping to the margin of the Canadian Shield, Sauk II ends with a craton-wide offlap and regression, and Sauk III is terminated with a lowering of sea level. Perhaps some of the most spectacular outcrops of the Sauk sequence occur in the Canadian Cordillera, where Aitken (1978) has emphasized the cyclicity of Sauk carbonate deposits.

Figure 14 shows the lithofacies distribution for the Upper Cambrian. A complex lower Paleozoic carbonate shelf margin can be traced discontinuously all along the inner portions of the Cordilleran overthrust belt (for an overview, see Cook and Bally, 1975; Fritz and others, 1989; Stewart and Suczek, 1977), and Oldow and others (this volume) show this carbonate margin generically by lumping Cambrian, Ordovician, and Silurian carbonates without attempting to differentiate individual lower Paleozoic shelf margins, and their various reentrants. Analogous carbonate shelf margins also occur in the northern Appalachians (Rodgers, 1968).

Note that there is no Cambrian reported from the Hudson Bay Basin. Upper Cambrian siliciclastics rim the Canadian Shield, suggesting that the center of the Canadian Shield was exposed during Sauk times. In the midcontinent, the Cambrian deposition was influenced by the Transcontinental Arch, which was greatly accentuated prior to the Middle Devonian.

The Tippecanoe sequence. Arenigian through Gedinnian (478 to 401 Ma)

This interval, following the sequence definition of Table 1A, extends from the Middle Ordovician to the earliest Devonian (Sloss, 1988c) and is shown on Plate 10-B. Sloss proposes a two-fold subdivision into Middle and Upper Ordovician Tippecanoe I, which is separated by a glacial-eustatic unconformity from the Silurian to Early Devonian, Tippecanoe II.

The basal Tippecanoe unconformity oversteps Sauk strata toward the Canadian Shield, and is typically characterized by quartz sands. Most impressive is the fact that sediments of the sequence probably covered the whole of North America. Sediments in the Hudson Bay Basin and remnants on the Canadian Shield suggest primary continuity of the Tippecanoe sequence. The subsequent pre-Kaskaskia erosional surface cuts deeply into all underlying sediments to break up what originally was the record of a great epicontinental sea.

As shown on Plate 10-B, subsidence of the Tippecanoe sequence is accentuated in the Anadarko and Illinois Basins, presumably due to further cooling related to the hypothetical underlying Cambrian rift systems. Similarly, the Williston and Michigan Basins and the Tobosa Basin of west Texas acquired their individuality during the Middle Ordovician to Early Devonian interval.

Plate 10-C shows Upper Ordovician lithofacies. Much of the North American craton is covered by shallow-water carbonates that extend across the whole continent into the Hudson Bay Basin. A carbonate-shelf margin still can be followed along the Cordilleran foreland fold belt; however, along the Ouachita-Appalachian miogeosyncline, a carbonate-shelf margin is not directly observed and therefore has to be inferred.

The craton responds in different ways to overthrusting in mid-Paleozoic times. The Taconic episode of the Appalachians is associated with a foredeep that is initiated early in the Tippecanoe cycle. Lash (1987) notes a basal foredeep unconformity that cuts into the underlying Lower to Middle Ordovician Beekmantown platform carbonates. In the Central Appalachians, the first foredeep deposits that overlie the eroded platform are Upper Ordovician turbidites and shales of the Martinsburg Formation. In the Newfoundland and Southern Appalachians the inception of the foredeep occurred earlier (i.e., during the Middle Ordovician). In turn, folded Upper Ordovician turbidites are cut by a pre-Silurian unconformity, after which foredeep clastic sedimentation derived from the Appalachians resumes for part of the Early and the Middle Silurian. A cessation of orogenic activity during the Late Silurian to Late Devonian (Pridolian to Gedinnian) leads to a break in the foredeep sedimentation and a resumption of carbonate platform sedimentation, with the development of characteristic pinnacle reefs in the Appalachian and Michigan Basins and with the formation of a salt basin in Michigan. The evaporites are low-stand deposits filling in the depression between the reefs.

The effect of the Taconic episode on subsidence is illustrated on Plate 10-C, as indicated by high accumulation rates in the Appalachian Basin. In contrast with the Appalachians, mid-Paleozoic (Pearya) deformation in the Canadian Arctic does not leave much of an imprint on foreland deposits. Similarly, the Paleozoic deformation in the Klamath Mountains of northern California has little if any impact on the foreland of North America. From this it may be deduced that both the Pearya fold belt and the Klamath island-arc system were far offshore and did not influence foreland-platform sedimentation. In other words, in the Arctic and Cordilleran foreland, A-subduction of North American lithosphere had not yet occurred during the mid-Ordovician to Lower Devonian interval. Alternatively for the Pearya folded belt, it has been postulated that this element was rafted in during Late Silurian to Early Devonian strike-slip faulting, and consequently one still would not expect an adjacent foredeep (J. Wheeler, written communication, 1988).

The pre-Kaskaskia unconformity (Combined pre-Devonian and pre-Mississippian subcrop)

The definition and evolution of sedimentary basins in North America is profoundly influenced by an event, as yet poorly defined, that took place before the Middle Devonian. Looking at a subcrop map of the basal Tippecanoe or the base of the Silurian, typically only minor amounts of erosion are observed. Thus, the Silurian of North America is usually underlain by Upper Ordovician. A dramatic contrast is seen on the pre-Kaskaskia subcrop map (see Plate 10-D). However, the map is inaccurate because it does not show the distribution of the Lower Devonian Gedinnian below the sequence boundary; I had no map available that shows the distribution of the Gedinnian in North America.

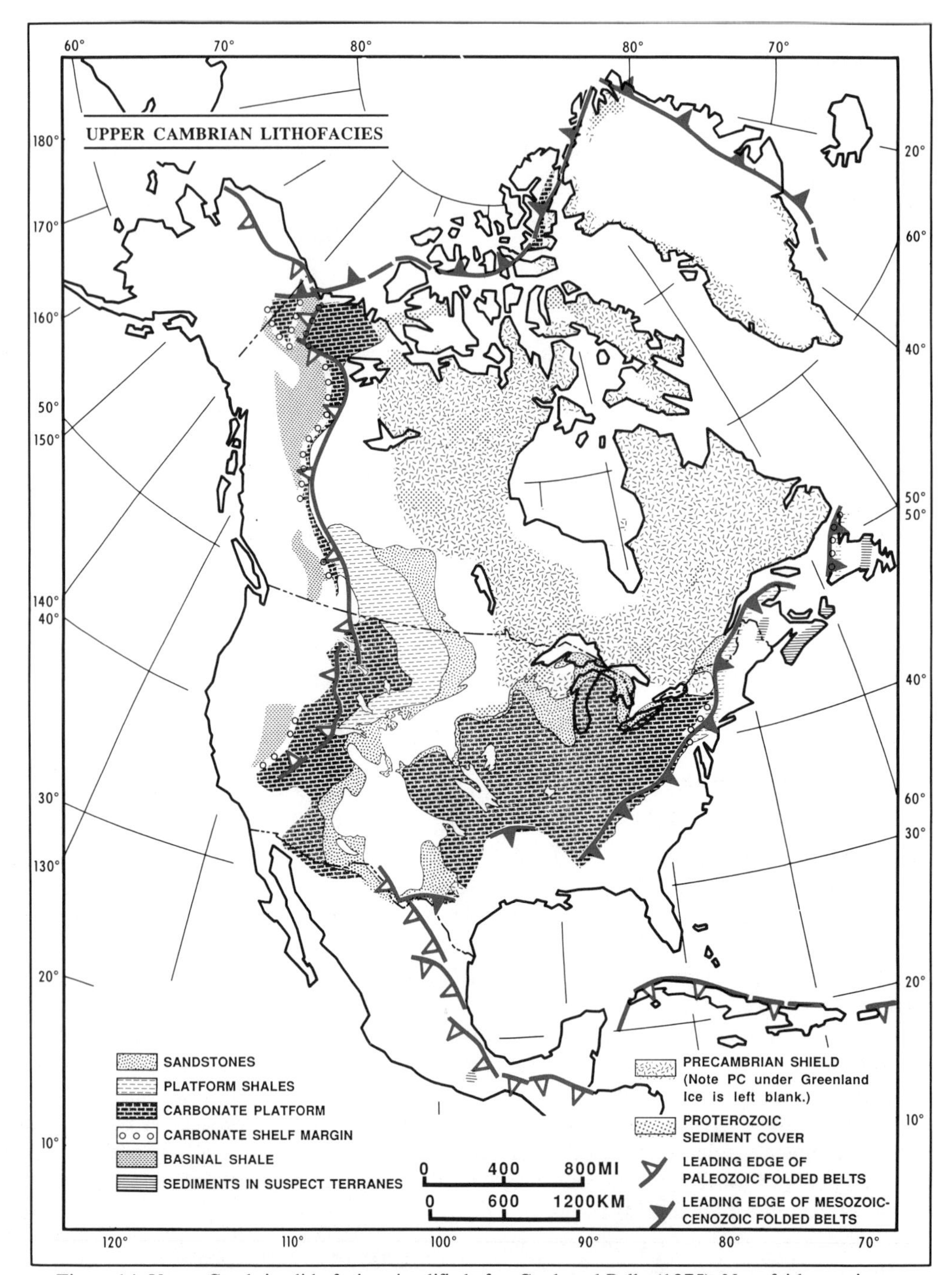

Figure 14. Upper Cambrian lithofacies, simplified after Cook and Bally (1975). Note fairly continuous carbonate shelf margin in the western Cordillera and the northern Appalachians. A carbonate shelf margin may be buried underneath the southern Appalachian and Ouachita allochthons.

In judging the pre-Kaskaskia subcrop map, it is important to keep in mind that the map traces a combined pre-Devonian to pre-Mississippian subcrop. There are numerous uncertainties with a map of this type, which should indeed be more detailed and allow for all the insights obtained by modern sequence stratigraphy. With this precaution in mind, it is nevertheless quite clear that the pre-Kaskaskia sequence boundary mirrors some very unusual cratonic events. Most outstanding among these are the formation of (1) the Boothia uplift–Bell Arch (B.B.A. on Plate 10-D) in the Canadian Arctic (Trettin, Arctic Islands chapter, this volume); (2) the broad pre–Middle Devonian Peace River Arch and its presumed extension, the Keewatin Arch (Sanford, 1987; Cant, 1988; PCA-KA on Plate 10-D); and (3) the strong development of the Transcontinental Arch (T.C.A. on Plate 10-D). The first suggestions for a Transcontinental Arch are already indicated by an onlap of the basal Sauk sediments, and further activity across the arch seems to be indicated during the deposition of the Tippecanoe sequence, but the very significant truncation of Silurian beds seems to be occurring during Late Silurian to Early Devonian time.

Relatively smaller scale features that also involve considerable truncation are the ancestral Sweetgrass Arch and its cousin the Lemhi Arch of the Rocky Mountains, the Cincinnati Arch, and the Nashville and Ozark uplifts.

Note that the axis of the Transcontinental Arch appears to be offset in a left-lateral sense in the Southern Rocky Mountains. I sense that this offset is directly related to later (i.e., Pennsylvanian) transpressional tectonics of the Ancestral Rocky Mountains (see Oldow and others, Cordillera chapter, this volume).

To explain pre-Kaskaskia tectonics, it may be useful to put these into a broader context. During the Devonian and Mississippian the North American continent is surrounded in horseshoe-like fashion by folded belts. This is generically indicated by the distribution of radiometric dates as sketched on the map, and reinforced by a glance at the Kaskaskia I and II accumulation maps. These maps show clearly that the Paleozoic fold belts of North America, with the exception of the Ouachita-Marathon belt, had attached themselves to our continent and that A-subduction took over to control a number of Paleozoic foredeeps characterized by accelerated subsidence rates.

The change from an overall cratonic-miogeosynclinal regime, represented by much of the Sauk and Tippecanoe sequences, to a dominant foredeep regime perhaps put the North American lithosphere under horizontal stress that caused buckling on a lithospheric scale (Cobbold and Davy, 1988), with the reactivation of the Boothia, Peace River, and Transcontinental Arches as main expressions of that deformation.

According to Sanford (1987), these arches may be extended across the Canadian Shield where the Transcontinental Arch is responsible for the separation of the Hudson Bay Basin from the James Bay Basin and where the Keewatin Arch could merge with the Peace River Arch. The Boothia–Bell Arch would separate the Foxe Basin from the Hudson Bay Basin.

Lithospheric warping as an origin for transcontinental arches is rather hypothetical, but needs to be further explored. To do this (1) we need more precise pre-Kaskaskia subcrop maps for North America; (2) there is an urgent need to model and relate mid-Paleozoic arches to the development of adjacent basins; (3) with fission-track studies it should now be possible to better understand the uplift phase on cratonic arches; (4) model studies of continentwide arch systems should give us a better understanding of the rheological properties of the Paleozoic lithosphere of North America; and (5) the pre-Kaskaskia unconformity is an unusual sequence boundary that needs to be explained.

Kaskaskia sequence. Mid-Early Devonian to latest Mississippian (401 to 330 Ma)

Sloss (1988c) proposes to subdivide the Kaskaskia sequence into two subsequences by an unconformity that separates Upper Devonian from the overlying Mississippian (see Table 1). That unconformity is much less profound than the preceeding pre-Kaskaskia unconformity. Consequently, across most of North America, only a minor hiatus occurs between the Devonian and the Mississippian.

The Kaskaskia I subsequence. Mid-Early Devonian to latest Devonian (401 to 362 Ma). The accumulation-rate map (Plate 10-E) shows increased rates of subsidence associated with the northern U.S. Appalachians, in the Parry Island fold belt of the Canadian Arctic, and in the Cordillera of northern Yukon and Nevada. Accelerated subsidence reflects loading of the foreland homocline by adjacent Devonian (Acadian) fold belts. Thus, it is established that these folded belts overthrust the North American craton, causing the subsidence in some very obvious foredeeps, as envisaged by Beaumont (1981) and Quinlan and Beaumont (1984).

On the craton itself, a continuous Alberta–Williston Basin embayment appears, and the Hudson Bay, Michigan, and Illinois Basins further subside, but at different rates. More specifically, late Early to early Middle Devonian sediments are confined to the cratonic basins and the exterior portions of the Appalachian and Cordilleran miogeosyncline.

As with many sequences, basal siliciclastics introduce the Kaskaskia I subsequence of the interior craton. A very large Middle Devonian (Givetian) evaporitic basin—the Prairie Evaporite—extends from the Williston Basin into the northern Alberta Basin. However, much of the cratonal Devonian is dominated by platform carbonates, and by clastic foredeep deposits that extend from the Paleozoic folded belts in the north and west toward the craton (Ettenson, 1985a and b).

Johnson and others (1985) carefully trace eustatic sea-level changes within the Devonian of the Kaskaskia sequence and also across the pre-Kaskaskia boundary into the underlying lower, mostly Devonian sediments in sections where that unconformity merges into its conformable continuation.

Plate 10-F is an Upper Devonian lithofacies map that shows separate Upper Devonian foredeep clastic wedges and carbonate platforms. While recognizing obvious transgressive and regressive cycles, the distribution of the Devonian carbonate shelf margins in northern Canada appears to be overall transgressive (Link, 1950; Bassett and Stout, 1968; Moore, 1989): if we were to strip all basinal sequences from the platform margins and omit minor regressions, we would end up with the schematic "rice-paddy" distribution shown on Figure 3 of Oldow and others (this volume). Of course, that diagram is only a simplified sketch, and the reader is referred to Moore (1989) for a detailed discussion of Devonian correlations.

Plate 10-D illustrates that North America was surrounded by folded belts during Kaskaskia I and Kaskaskia II times. Rast (this volume) and Trettin (this volume) discuss the Devonian collisional history of the Appalachian and Innuitian folded belts. Oldow and others (this volume) discuss and illustrate on their Figure 6 the effect of the Antler transpression. The Antler event is not yet well defined, and particularly in the forelands of the

Alberta Basin and the U.S. Cordillera, the Antler orogeny at this time still has little impact on stratigraphy and subsidence (Gordey and others, 1987). Perhaps this is telling us that Antler transpressional overthrusting may be limited.

Middle and Upper Devonian clastic wedges have been studied in considerable detail in the Catskill delta of the state of New York (Faill, 1985). There, if we accept Sloss (1988c), the base of the Siegenian forms the base of the Kaskaskia I sequence.

A basinal complex of organic-rich black shales corresponds to the distal part of the deltaic system, and within the deltaic system, black shales indicate times of maximum transgression. The basinal black shale facies occurs over much of eastern North America. Referring again to the pre-Kaskaskia subcrop (Plate 10-D), the basinal black shales often are closely overlying the subcropping pre-Kaskaskia strata. The distal ends of the clastic wedges with their black shales are thus visualized as deposits of a restricted epicontinental sea that was floored by the pre-Kaskaskia subcrop (Ettenson, 1985a, b).

Figure 15 shows the distribution of the better known Devonian black shales of North America. The distribution has economic importance because these black shales are the source beds responsible for much of the Paleozoic oil and gas in North America. In the Innuitian, Appalachian, and Ouachita foredeeps, the black shales mature to expel hydrocarbons because they are loaded by additional foredeep clastics during the Late Devonian, Mississippian, Pennsylvanian, and Permian. On the other hand, in the Cordilleran foredeep, maturation of Paleozoic black shales was often insufficient during the Paleozoic, and for instance in Alberta, it was mostly loading by Mesozoic foredeep sediments that permitted the maturation of the underlying Paleozoic source beds.

Thus, on the one hand, the Kaskaskia I sequence may be viewed as a tectonically induced sequence because it is underlain by a tectonically strongly enhanced sequence boundary and because it includes some of the classic foredeep clastic wedges of North America. On the other hand, transgressive and regressive cycles due to eustatic fluctuations explain rather well some of the details of the stratigraphy. Overall, Johnson and others (1985) postulate a strong and sustained sea-level rise during the Givetian and end with the more aggrading cycles of the Famennian.

The Kaskaskia II subsequence. Latest Devonian to Late Mississippian (362 Ma to 330 Ma). As defined by Sloss (1988c) and Table 1, Kaskaskia II coincides reasonably well with the Mississippian, even though Sloss includes some of the latest Devonian and excludes some of the latest Mississippian from this sequence. A monograph by Craig and Connor (1979) describes the Mississippian in the United States. For Canada, much additional information can be found in Richards and others (1989).

The accumulation-rate map (Plate, 1-G) shows substantial subsidence of Mississippian clastic foredeep wedges in the eastern United States. A comparison with the Kaskaskia I accumulation map shows that in response to Alleghanian thrusting, the Mississippian clastic wedge is shifted southward, replicated in model studies by Beaumont and others (1987).

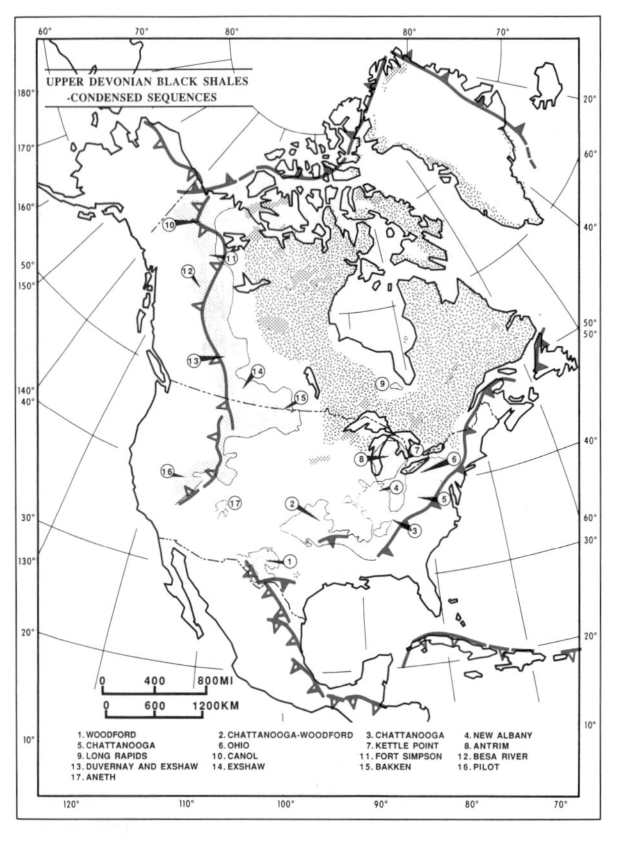

Figure 15. Upper Devonian, black shales–condensed sequences. Compare this map with Plate 10-D, which shows the pre-Kaskaskia subcrop. Note that the black shales are typically deposited close to the pre-Devonian subcrop. Radiometric dates shown on Plate 10-D and additional regional information suggest that during the Upper Devonian the North American continent was surrounded in horseshoe-like fashion by folded belts, effectively insulating the craton from the surrounding Devonian oceans. Access to the ocean was limited to the southwestern United States.

Increased subsidence in the foreland of the Ouachita-Wichita Mountains (i.e., Anadarko, Arkoma, and Black Warrior Basins) also suggests the beginning of orogenic activity to the south. In contrast to the preceding maps, Kaskaskia II subsidence was rather limited in the Arctic Islands. Following the Ellesmerian compressional episode, thin Mississippian sequences were deposited discordantly on the folds of the Parry Island Fold belt. There is some evidence of Mississippian rifting and dextral transtension initiating the development of the Sverdrup Basin (see Trettin, this volume, and the preceding comments on Paleozoic episutural basins).

Over most of the craton, Kaskaskia I sediments onlapped only parts of the pre-Kaskaskia subcrop, but Kaskaskia II (i.e., most of the Mississippian) sediments further overstep the pre-Kaskaskia surface. The Williston Basin is now separated from the Alberta Basin, but connected with the Cordilleran realm of subsidence. The former Peace River Arch appears as a sag, suggesting a negative inversion (Cant, 1988).

Along much of the Cordillera, from Nevada to northern British Columbia and its cratonic foreland, black shales commonly overlie the basal unconformity of Kaskaskia II. In turn, the black shales are often followed by another marine hiatus preceding the deposition of prograding crinoidal limestone ramp-shale packages. Westward-prograding crinoidal limestones follow and merge into the basinal shale facies. These sediments fill the eastern half of the Antler-Prophet foredeep (Poole and Sandberg, 1977; Skipp and others, 1979; Skipp and Hall, 1980; Richards and others, 1989). The often hypothetical western half of the Antler foredeep is best exposed in Nevada, where thick, proximal to distal turbidites of the Diamond Peak Formation fill the clastic foredeep of the Antler folded belt.

In northern Yukon and Alaska, Kaskaskia II is characterized by a well-defined but poorly dated lower boundary and a transitional upper boundary into the Pennsylvanian (i.e., Bashkirian and Moscovian; e.g., Richards and others, 1989). Dramatic appearance of large accumulation rates betrays a poorly understood subsidence history. Extensional basins of Early Mississippian or older age are seen on seismic profiles of the Alaskan North Slope (Mauch, 1985), and the subsequent platform initially thickens and then thins to the south; the sense of progradation appears to be northward. The Alaska North Slope Mississippian differs considerably from that of cratonic North America, and its setting is better evaluated within the context of the much debated circum-Arctic paleogeography. The North Slope of Alaska prior to the Cretaceous opening of the Arctic Ocean was probably located much closer to the Innuitian fold belt and to what today is the Barents Sea.

The Absaroka sequence. Latest Mississippian to Early Jurassic (330 to 186 Ma)

Preamble. A pre-Absaroka subcrop map for North America is difficult to construct. In northern Canada and Alaska, the relevant stratigraphic subsurface information is not detailed enough for a good pre-Pennsylvanian subcrop map, and in the U.S. Midcontinent, the distribution of the Pennsylvanian is greatly influenced by uplifts and basins that developed in the Ouachita foreland (see Arbenz, this volume) and in the Ancestral Rocky Mountains (see Oldow and others, this volume).

In the U.S. Midcontinent, the Absaroka is mostly deposited on Mississippian strata. Within the Paleozoic basins, any hiatus between Late Mississippian (Chester) and the overlying Pennsylvanian is minor, but on basin flanks and the elevated portion of the U.S. craton, Pennsylvanian strata often onlap on pre-Chester Mississippian formations. By the end of Pennsylvanian, the highest portions of the Transcontinental Arch, which remained above sea level during the Mississippian, are completely covered by the onlapping Pennsylvanian strata.

Sloss (1988c) subdivided the Absaroka into three subsequences: (1) the Pennsylvanian to Lower Permian Absaroka I (330 to 268 Ma); (2) the Middle–Upper Permian to Lower Triassic Absaroka II (268 to 245 Ma); and (3) the Middle–Upper Triassic to Lower Jurassic, Absaroka III (268 to 186 Ma). To a first approximation, these subsequences represent different tectonic regimes. They characterize the final assembly of Gondwana following late Paleozoic continental collisions: Absaroka I represents the Ouachita episode, Absaroka I and II correspond to the Alleghanian episode, and Absaroka III represents the rifting phase that led to the opening of the central Atlantic Ocean.

People interested in eustatic interpretations of the stratigraphic record like to emphasize the cyclicity of upper Paleozoic stratigraphy of the U.S. Midcontinent, where sandstone-shale-limestone cycles already show up in the Upper Mississippian. Such cyclical stratigraphy dominates the Pennsylvanian cyclothems of the Midcontinent (Wanless and Shepard, 1936), which have been reviewed by Heckel (1980). Figure 16, taken from that paper, shows the lateral variability of these cyclothems as one proceeds from west to east. Cyclothems represent transgressive-regressive cycles that are likely to be due to glacial eustatic sea-level changes. Heckel notes an approximate frequency of about 400,000 yr for these cycles; a shorter interval than typical 1 to 5 m.y. third-order cycles shown on the chart published by Haq and others (1987). Figure 17, also from Heckel's paper, shows an Upper Pennsylvanian paleogeographic map during a maximum transgression. Note the very narrow seaway between the Ouachita front and the Ancestral Rocky Mountains, which provides access of the sea to the Midcontinent.

Cyclothems and their lateral facies variability make it difficult to make detailed facies maps over thicker intervals, as was done for Figure 18. Nevertheless, much more generalized facies maps do give an impression of the paleogeographic setting of the U.S. Midcontinent during the Pennsylvanian.

Absaroka I subsequence. Latest Mississippian to Early Permian (330 to 268 Ma). The distribution and accumulation-rate map (Pennsylvanian to Permian Wolfcamp) of this subsequence reveals a number of basins and uplifts in the U.S. Midcontinent and shows widespread outcrops in the Appalachian, Michigan, and Illinois Basins (Plate 10-H; see also McKee and others, 1975, 1967a and b).

Subsidence of the eastern United States basins, as modeled by Beaumont and others (1987), shows that the Appalachian, Black Warrior, and Arkoma Basins are best explained by a downdip load of thrust sheets on a basement homocline. For the Appalachian Basin the largest load was emplaced during the Late Pennsylvanian. Much greater loads depressed the Ouachita foredeep (Arkoma Basin) and its equivalent to the east of the Mississippian Embayment (i.e., the Black Warrior Basin).

Northwest of the Ouachitas and the Marathon folded belt (see Arbenz, this volume), we observe a foreland that is highly differentiated into large uplifts and basins. This province extends into the Laramide Wyoming-Colorado Rocky Mountains, where during the last stage of compression, similar basement-involved structures were formed.

The overall structural evolution of the Wichita–Ancestral Rocky Mountains trend is poorly understood. A first-cut interpretation of the pre-Kaskaskia subcrop (Plate 10-D), as mentioned earlier, suggests that during the Pennsylvanian the Transcontinental Arch may have been offset in a left-lateral sense, a proposition that still must be examined by more detailed studies. Note also that Pennsylvanian isopachs generally strike at right angles to the Transcontinental Arch, indicating a profound reorganization of the craton during the Late Carboniferous (Mallory, 1972a; Kluth, 1986).

Pennsylvanian basins and uplifts bridge an area (the Ancestral Rocky Mountains) between the no longer active Antler fold belt to the northwest, and the Ouachita-Marathon system to the southwest. The most prominent uplifts are (1) the Nemaha uplift; (2) the Amarillo-Wichita-Arbuckle uplifts, bounded to the northeast by thrust faults; (3) the Central Basin platform of west Texas, bounded by a reverse fault to the west; and in the Ancestral Rocky Mountains, (4) the Apishapa-Sierra Grande–Front Range; and (5) the Uncompahgre uplift. These uplifts combine with the Ouachita-Marathon folded belt to define a number of Pennsylvanian basins, which may be broadly split into (a) foredeeps immediately adjacent to the folded belt, and (b) intracratonic basins bounded by basement uplifts.

The foredeeps include (1) the Black Warrior, (2) the Arkoma, (3) the Fort Worth and Valverde-Marfa Basins. The inception of these foredeep moats occurred in latest Mississippian to Early Pennsylvanian time, and initially was characterized by down-to-the-south normal faults that are seen on reflection seismic profiles. These faults may perhaps be related to bending stresses within the subducting continental slab.

In the early foredeep phase, turbidites with basin-parallel transport directions were deposited. With time, and in an updip direction, these flysch-type deposits are often substituted laterally and up section by deltaic systems, which, in the Arkoma Basin for instance, prograded from the craton and only later in the Desmoinesian originated from the adjacent Ouachitas (see, Johnson, 1988). By the end of the Pennsylvanian, the Arkoma and Black Warrior Basins were filled with over 3 km of Pennsylvanian sediments, the more westerly Fort Worth Basin contained over 2 km, and the Val Verde and Marfa Basins lesser thicknesses of sediments.

Pennsylvanian intracratonic foreland basins include the Anadarko, Midland, and Delaware Basins, and in the Rocky Mountains, the Eagle, Paradox, and Oquirrh Basins.

The Anadarko Basin (Rascoe and Johnson, 1988) has all the characteristics of a basin that exists due to flexural loading. Implicit in that view, the Wichita-Arbuckle uplift is a northward-verging basement overthrust. There is limited seismic evidence for such overthrusting on the northeast flank of this structure (Brewer and others, 1983). However, Pennsylvanian sediment fill in excess of 3 km suggests that additional factors may be responsible for the subsidence of that basin. Only detailed backstripping and modeling of the tectonic subsidence of the Anadarko Basin will show whether simple flexural loading models will suffice. Additional factors may involve the ancestry of the Anadarko Basin, which straddles the Early Cambrian Oklahoma rift system, possibly Pennsylvanian strike slip faulting, and more hypothetical subsidence mechanisms.

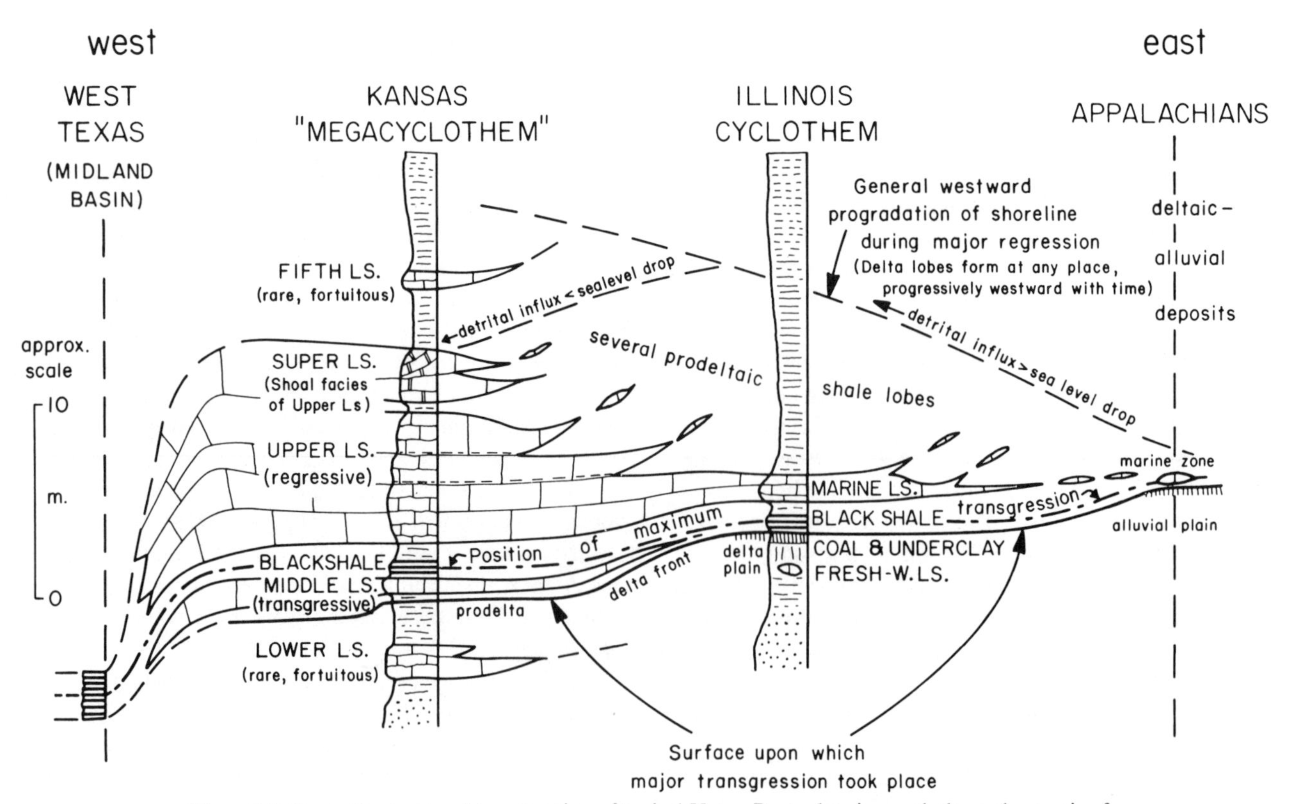

Figure 16. Generalized restored cross section of typical Upper Pennsylvanian cyclothem along axis of Midcontinent sea (from Heckel, 1980).

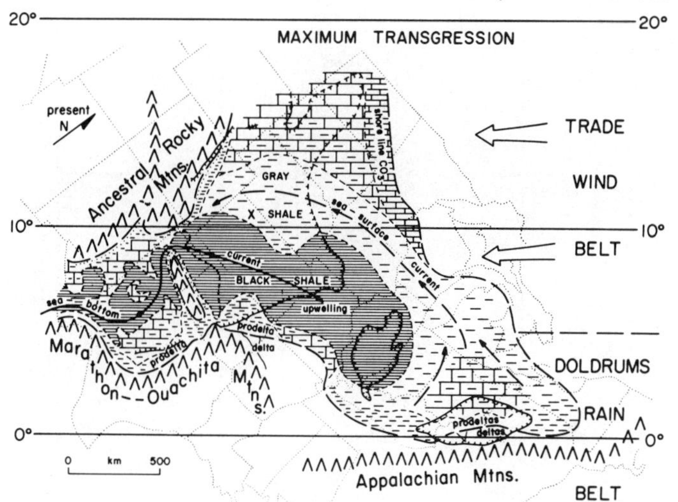

Figure 17. Paleogeographic map showing probable facies relations of Upper Pennsylvanian Midcontinent sea during deposition of offshore shale at phase of maximum transgression (from Heckel, 1980). Hachured lines show outcrop (solid) and subcrop (broken) with hachures showing dip. Short dashes show facies boundaries and north limit of Anadarko Basin; long dashes show extent of sea.

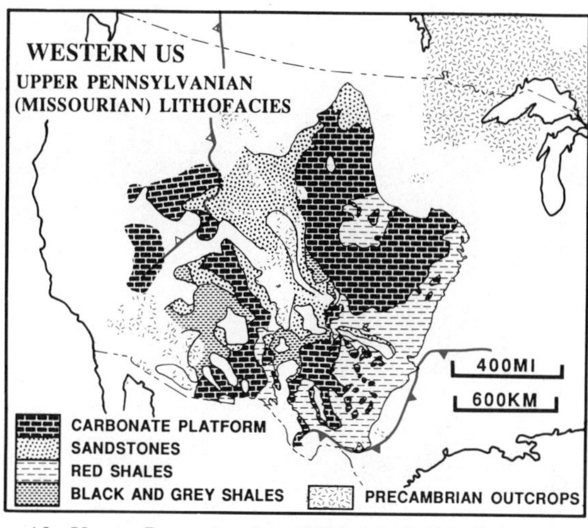

Figure 18. Upper Pennsylvanian (Missourian) lithofacies, simplified from Cook and Bally (1975).

A schematic section across the Anadarko Basin is shown on Figure 19 from Johnson and others (1988). Note that the individualization of the basin occurs at the beginning of the Pennsylvanian, which is separated from the underlying Paleozoic by a basal unconformity. On the south side, a Lower Permian–Pennsylvanian granite-wash clastic wedge extends into the basin. On the updip side, an overall regressive Pennsylvanian carbonate shelf margin is succeeded by a regressive Lower Permian carbonate shelf margin. Only moderate subsidence is reflected by the overlying Permian evaporite sequences.

The Pennsylvanian ancestry of the Permian Basin in west Texas, as described by Frenzel and others (1988), involves the differentiation of two structural highs: the Diablo carbonate platform to the west and the Central Basin platform to the east. These form the margins of the more westerly Delaware Basin and the Midland Basin to the east.

The structural nature of these platforms remains enigmatic. A seismic profile (Fig. 13 of Frenzel and others, 1988) suggests a "half-horst" rather similar to the one reported by Dimian (1983) from the Hudson Bay Basin. On the other hand, there have been reports of reverse faults from the margins of the Central Basin platform, and some authors (i.e., Frenzel and others, 1988) suggest a dextral strike-slip system on the west side of the platform. Be this as it may, at the end of the Pennsylvanian, both the Delaware and Midland Basins developed as individual sags filled with about 500 m of Pennsylvanian sediments. Both basins only reached their full development during the subsequent Absaroka II (Middle–Upper Permian) cycle.

In the Ancestral Rocky Mountains, two important basins, the Eagle and the Paradox, received roughly 3 km of Pennsylvanian sediments, like the Anadarko Basin, the main infilling of the basins was during the mid-Pennsylvanian Desmoinesian interval, but in great contrast to the Anadarko, the centers of the basins were filled with thick evaporitic sequences (see Stevenson and Baars, 1986).

Pennsylvanian isopachs and Absaroka I accumulation rates show that the margins of the Pennsylvanian basins of the Midcontinent extend almost to the Canadian border, suggesting that the influence of Pennsylvanian tectonics on the craton was extensive. However, north of the Canadian border, accumulation-rate maps show an amazingly different picture, with slow accumulation rates limited to the external Canadian Cordillera and its immediate foreland. In northern Yukon and on the Alaska North Slope, Absaroka I stratigraphy is transitional with the underlying Mississippian, but a pronounced hiatus separates this sequence from the overlying Permian and Triassic strata.

To sum up, the Absaroka I cycle in its essence corresponds to the Pennsylvanian. Cratonic subsidence patterns in the east are related to overthrusting in the Appalachians. In the south, however, massive subsidence occurs in foredeeps that are related to the Ouachita-Marathon deformation and to foreland deformation in the Wichita–Ancestral Rocky Mountain trend. For a discussion of the Carboniferous basins superposed on the Appalachian foldbelt, see the earlier comments on Mississippian to Triassic episutural basins.

The Absaroka II subsequence. Middle Permian to lower Triassic (268 to 245 Ma). By the Early Permian, much of Pangaea was welded together. Absaroka II is therefore a sequence that is deposited on the North American portion of that supercontinent. Absaroka II subsidence patterns are superposed on late to syncollisional basins. According to Sloss (1988c) Ab-

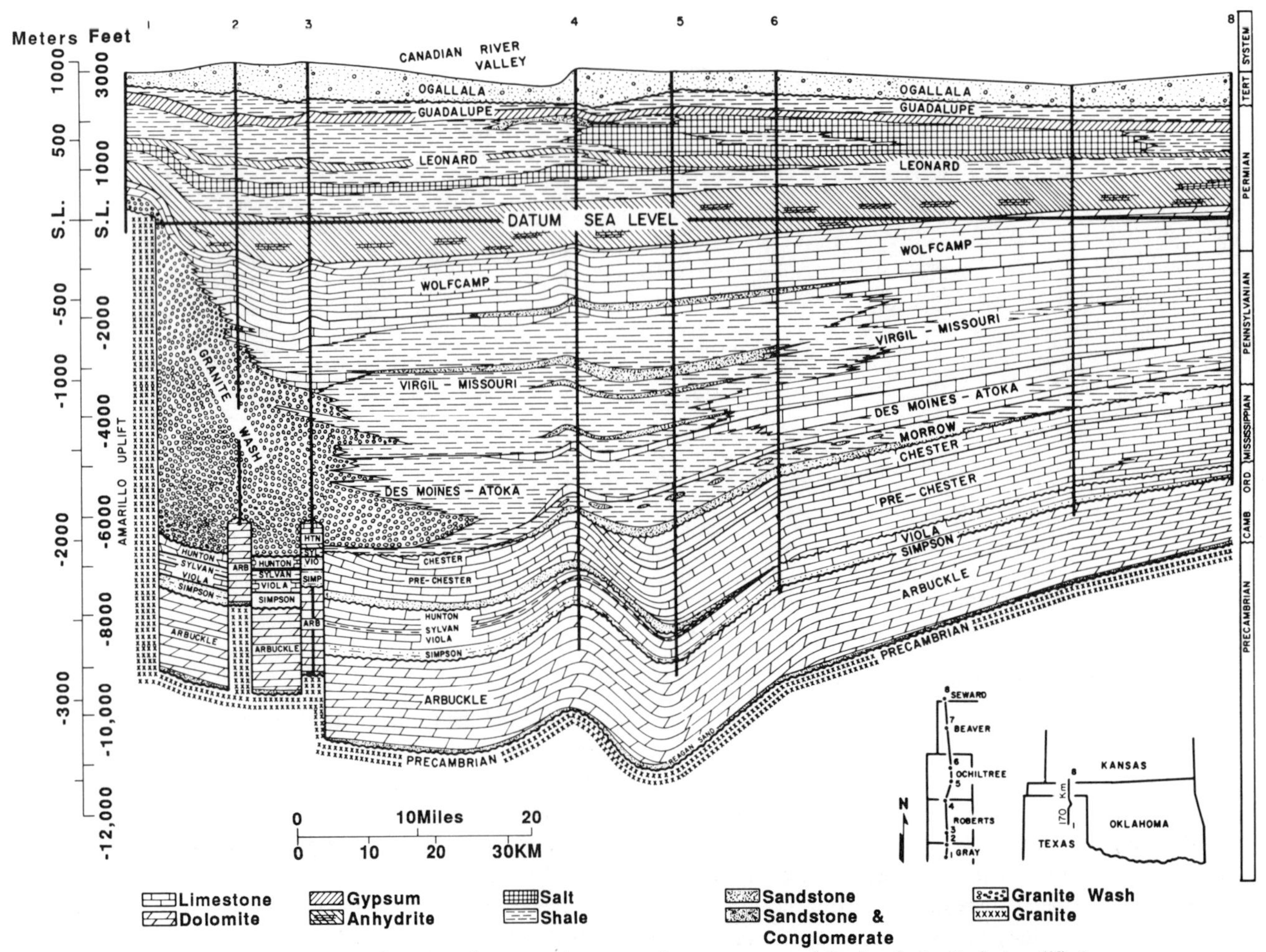

Figure 19. North–south structural cross section across the western part of the Anadarko Basin (modified from Adler and others, 1971). Dip of fault bounding the Amarillo Uplift is not adequately defined, but could be interpreted as a transpressional thrust fault.

saroka II essentially represents the middle to Upper Permian for most of the continent, but in parts of Nevada and the Arctic Islands of Canada, Absaroka II also includes thick Lower Triassic deposits. For details on the Permian of the conterminous United States, the reader is referred to McKee and others (1967a and b). Distribution and accumulation rates for this interval are shown on Plate 10-H.

Accumulation rates in the Appalachian and Ouachita Basins are minimum values because much of the interval has been eroded. From their models and from coal moisture-content studies, Beaumont and others (1987) assume that thicknesses in excess of 6 km were originally deposited in the Appalachian and Arkoma Basins. The explanation may be that during the Permian, the thick basement thrust sheets of the Appalachians and the Ouachitas created a substantial new load on the foreland homocline. The overall agreement of the model with coal moisture-content studies and other measurements of organic metamorphism is quite convincing. Beaumont and others' (1987) model studies also permit estimation of the total thrust loads for the Alleghanian orogeny. They are on the order of 10 to 18 km for the Central Appalachians and on the order of 17 to 20 km for the Ouachitas. Additional uplift studies based on fission-track thermochronometry are needed for the allochthonous basement thrust sheets of these folded belts.

Beaumont and others (1987) visualize a maximum of about 4 km erosion for the undeformed foreland basins, on the order of 7 to 13 km cumulative erosion for the Central Appalachians, and well in excess of 13 km of cumulative erosion for the Ouachitas. These amounts of erosion are stunning, and raise the question of the fate of the eroded material and how much of the unloading was due to as yet unrecognized tectonic unroofing. Of course, the erosion of the folded belts themselves is in part synchronous with the deposition of Absaroka II and Absaroka III sediments.

The Absaroka II accumulation map accentuates the Permian Basin of west Texas and subsidence in the western Cordillera. Although the inception of the Permian Basin of west Texas occurred during the Pennsylvanian, during the Wolfcamp to Ochoa (Artinskian-Tatarian), its subsidence is most dramatic. Best known from the Permian Basin are spectacular prograding Permian carbonate sequences. These were first studied by King

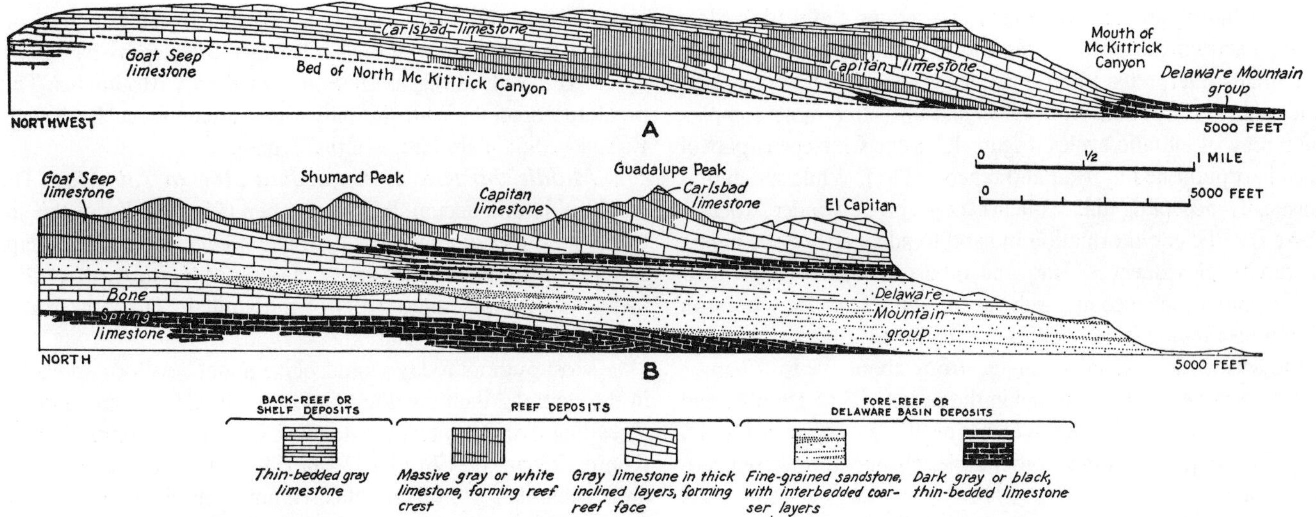

Figure 20. Permian reefs of the Guadelupe Mountains, west Texas. Section A, upper part of sections, Section B, lower part of succession (from King, 1948).

(1948) (Fig. 20; for a summary see also King, 1967). The Permian prograding carbonates are anchored on a platform substratum that was formed during mid-Wolfcampian. Thus, the Permian carbonates prograded outward from the Central Basin platform into the Delaware Basin to the west. Major prograding carbonate complexes also rim the western and northern flanks of the Delaware Basin, as well as the northern and eastern flanks of the Midland Basin (Frenzel and others, 1988). Seismic studies now permit the application of modern sequence stratigraphy to the Permian reef complex (Sarg, 1989).

In the Southern Rocky Mountains, subsidence persists in the Paradox Basin, but there compressional tectonism also led to the formation of northwest-trending elongated salt anticlines that formed during the Permian. Increased accumulation rates for the Absaroka II interval also occur in the western Cordillera, where, following the formation of the Antler foredeep, subsidence persisted during much of the Pennsylvanian (e.g., the Oquirrh Basin and its extensions), the Permian, and the Early Triassic.

The Absaroka III subsequence. Triassic to Early Jurassic (245 to 186 Ma). With the exception of the U.S. Cordillera (McKee and others, 1959) and the Sverdrup Basin (see Trettin, this volume), the accumulation-rate map (Plate 10-J) for this interval is remarkably dull. The map depicts a moment in time when Pangea is still intact, but about to break up. Thus, on the Atlantic Coast the occurrence of numerous half-grabens corresponds to a rifting phase that preceded the mid-Jurassic opening of the Atlantic Ocean. Manspeizer and Cousminer (1988) provide a description of these half-graben systems.

Sloss (1988c) quite rightly found it remarkable that, during the Early Triassic through Early Cretaceous interval, a period of about 150 m.y., there was no significant differentiation of cratonic basins and uplifts in the North American cratonic center.

Triassic to Lower Jurassic sediments accumulated in the Cordilleran miogeosyncline of Nevada, and one is tempted to link suggested accelerated subsidence rates to a hypothetical Sonoman foredeep, but the absence of a clastic wedge in the west discourages this idea. On the other hand, Absaroka III sediments in the western Cordillera are dominantly continental, including widespread eolian sandstones in the Early Jurassic.

To sum up, the Absaroka III sequence reflects the beginning of very stable conditions across North America. Only in the Sverdrup Basin of the Canadian Arctic do we have indications supporting substantial subsidence.

The Zuni sequence. Middle Jurassic to early Paleocene (186 to 60 Ma)

Preamble. Sloss (1988c) has defined this sequence as extending from the Aalenian to the Danian. In general, pre-Zuni (i.e., pre–Middle Jurassic) subcrop maps relate more to syn-Absaroka tectonics than to genuine pre–Middle Jurassic deformation. Thus, the Zuni sequence simply and gradually oversteps Absaroka subcrop patterns. As will be seen later, a pre-Cretaceous subcrop map (Plate 10-L) may be more informative than a pre–Middle Jurassic subcrop map.

The Zuni sequence records the opening and drifting phases of the central Atlantic and the opening and drifting phase of Gulf of Mexico passive margins, as well as the development of the Rocky Mountain and Alaska North Slope foredeeps.

Sloss (1988c) elected to subdivide the Zuni into: (1) Zuni I (latest Early Jurassic, Aalenian to Early Cretaceous, i.e., Berriasian); (2) Zuni II (Early Cretaceous, i.e., Valanginian to early Cenomanian) and; (3) Zuni III (Late Cretaceous, i.e., late Cenomanian to early Paleocene).

Haq and others (1987) and Vail (1987) proposed different and more detailed subdivisions. As an added complication, they used substantially different time scales. A lack of consensus on sequence boundaries and time scales is both frustrating and confusing to the uninitiated, but reflects some very real issues. Foremost among them is the tectonic versus eustatic debate surrounding sequence stratigraphy. To remind the reader, Sloss (1963) started out with an ingeniously simple scheme that he eventually interpreted to represent tectonic cycles; however, Haq and others (1987) and Vail (1987) end up with a more complex hierarchy of eustatic cycles. Figure 12 is the Cretaceous part of the chart published by Haq and others (1987). While still enthusiastically accepting the sequence concept, I wonder whether there is sufficient information in hand to adequately document a hierarchy of sequences. Haq and others (1987) package their cycles into a sequence hierarchy as follows: (1) megacycles with durations ranging from over 70 m.y. to over 100 m.y.; (2) supercycle sets with durations ranging from about 25 to 45 m.y.; (3) supercycles with durations in the order of 5 to 10 m.y.; and (4) cycles of the third order, which typically last between 1 and 5 m.y. The frequency of third-order cycles changes throughout geologic time.

I am convinced that good seismic reflection profiles as well as good outcrop sections permit recognition of third-order cycles, but I also sense that a highly structured hierarchy of these cycles at this time may be premature. Different authors may be tempted to design a hierarchy that fits their respective "cycle philosophies," which in view of the dating uncertainties may be easy to do.

To depict intra-Zuni accumulation rates and thus to provide first approximations of subsidence rates, there is only one integrated set of published North America–wide isopachs available (Cook and Bally, 1975). The interval shown by these maps cannot be easily packaged into any of the proposed Zuni subdivisions. Thus, for the purpose of this overview and as a practical matter, the Jurassic and Cretaceous interval (i.e., much of the Zuni sequence) is subdivided into units that may have some tectonic significance but that unfortunately do not coincide with either the Sloss (1988c) or the Vail and others (1987) subdivisions.

Three units are differentiated as follows; (1) Middle Jurassic to Oxfordian (186 to 156 Ma), which includes much of the pre-collisional Jurassic of the Cordillera and the Alaskan North Slope, some of the pre-collisional Jurassic of the Rocky Mountain foredeep, and sediments associated with the early opening of the Atlantic and Gulf of Mexico; (2) Kimmeridgian to mid-Aptian (156 to 116 Ma), which includes the early foredeep sequences of the Rocky Mountains and the Alaska North Slope as well as sequences on the Atlantic and Gulf of Mexico passive margins; and (3) mid-Aptian to Maastrichtian (116 to 66 Ma), a large stratigraphic package that exhibits massive subsidence in the Gulf of Mexico and the Central Atlantic passive margin as well as in the foredeeps of the Rocky Mountains and the Alaska North Slope.

Sloss (1988c, d) protests that Vail and others (1987) placed the top of the Zuni within the late Maastrichtian, whereas he would prefer to place that boundary within the Paleocene at 60 Ma. I propose, for the time being, to ignore their argument, but it must be pointed out that within the context of the North American craton, there is indeed a substantial change in tectonic regimes occurring around the Cretaceous-Paleogene boundary, as shown by the breakup of the Cretaceous foredeep by basement-involved overthrusting in the Southern Rocky Mountains. This breakup coincides with the individualization of the Paleocene-Eocene sedimentary basins of that region.

Middle Jurassic to Oxfordian (186 to 150 Ma). The distribution and accumulation-rate map (Plate 10-K) of this interval is rather crude because there are no detailed isopach maps available for much of the passive margins of North America. For facies and paleotectonic maps of the United States, the reader should refer to McKee and others (1956).

Most authors today would place initial sea-floor spreading in the central Atlantic within the lower Middle Jurassic, and fast spreading over an interval extending from the Bathonian to the Kimmeridgian, or 176 to 152 Ma (Sheridan, this volume; Vogt and Tucholke, 1986, and this volume; Sheridan and Grow, 1988). The opening of the Gulf of Mexico also occurs during the same interval (see Worrall and Snelson, this volume). Thus, in keeping with thermal subsidence models, accumulation-rate maps for this interval reveal massive subsidence around much of the Gulf of Mexico and the central Atlantic. Note that the evaporites of the Gulf of Mexico and the central Atlantic margin are commonly assumed to be of Middle Jurassic age (i.e., Callovian).

Many authors suggest that the evaporites were deposited before the opening of the Gulf of Mexico, but it must be emphasized that, at least onshore, Middle Jurassic evaporites overlie the principal unconformity that separates the rifting phase from the overlying "drifting" package (e.g., Milliken, 1988). A case may be made for the evaporites being deposited in a desiccated deep depression analogous to the well-known desiccation model for the Messinian of the Mediterranean.

The situation on the Nova Scotia passive margin differs from the Gulf of Mexico because there the salt is presumed to be Early Jurassic, and some authors see the salt as part of a synrift sequence (e.g., Argo Rift; Wade and MacClean, 1989). Others, however, indicate a distribution that follows the rifting phase (Friedenreich, 1987).

On the Grand Banks of Newfoundland, Late Triassic to Early Jurassic extensional systems are followed by late Callovian to Aptian rifts. Subsidence patterns north of Newfoundland, in the northern Atlantic and the Arctic Ocean, are ill defined because Jurassic sediments are confined to half-graben systems that were in part active throughout the Early Cretaceous (e.g., for Newfoundland: Enachescu, 1987; Welsink and Tankard, 1988; for eastern Greenland: Birkelund and Perch-Nielsen, 1976; for the northern Atlantic: Ziegler, 1988; for the Canadian Arctic passive margin: Meneley, 1986; Trettin, this volume).

The Sverdrup Basin appears as a separate subsidence domain that is superposed on a basin already initiated and individualized during the late Paleozoic. On the Arctic passive margin there is evidence for a rifting event that began perhaps during the Early Jurassic and continued during the Early Cretaceous (i.e., through the Aptian; Hubbard and others, 1987).

Turning to the western Cordillera, the moderate subsidence

rates shown on Plate 1-K for the Middle Jurassic to Oxfordian interval on the Alaska North Slope and in the Rocky Mountain foredeep suggest that both foredeeps were only vaguely individualized. This is further supported by the steady southwest progradation of Middle to Upper Jurassic clastics seen on seismic profiles of the North Slope (see Fig. 6).

In the U.S. Cordillera, the paleogeography of this interval, as described by Kocurek and Dott (1983), suggests the deposition of eolian sands and shallow-water marine deposits culminating in the establishment of a marine seaway by the end of Oxfordian time.

To sum up, the Middle Jurassic to Oxfordian interval shows a dramatic increase in subsidence with the opening of the Gulf of Mexico and the early central Atlantic Ocean. Rifting occurs along the passive margins of the Northern Atlantic and the Arctic Ocean. However, the Mesozoic foredeep development of the Rocky Mountains is not yet fully established, suggesting a time lag between the opening of the central Atlantic and the inception of the Rocky Mountain foredeep.

Comments on a pre-Cretaceous subcrop map. Some authors recognize a significant sequence boundary near the base of the Cretaceous. Sloss (1988c) places the base of his Zuni II sequence at 134 Ma (i.e., within the Valanginian), and Haq and others (1988) place the base of this Zuni B2 Supercycle close to the Valanginian-Berriasian Boundary (i.e., 138 Ma of the Palmer [1983] scale, or 128.5 Ma on Haq and other's [1987] time scale). A basal Cretaceous subcrop map (Plate 10-L) is useful as a preamble for the discussion of subsidence patterns during the Cretaceous. Typically across the whole of North America, the Lower Cretaceous oversteps and onlaps the formations shown on the subcrop map.

All along the Gulf Coast and the central Atlantic, the Lower Cretaceous oversteps the zero isopach of the Jurassic and onlaps on the underlying deformed Paleozoic. Thus, the subcrop suggests the presence of a eustatically imposed sequence boundary that provides a break within a subsidence pattern that is still due to cooling following Early Jurassic rifting.

Along the northern Atlantic, Greenland, and Arctic passive margins, Early Cretaceous subsidence follows the formation of Jurassic graben systems or else relates to the formation of Early Cretaceous grabens. The information currently at hand does not yet permit production of a meaningful pre-Cretaceous subcrop map for that area. Such a map no doubt would reveal the spatial relationship between Jurassic and Lower Cretaceous synrift packages.

Subcrop patterns in the foreland of the western Cordillera reveal three distinctly different segments:

1. In the northernmost Northwest Territories of Canada, the strike of subcropping lower and middle Paleozoic formations trends to the east-northeast, a direction that parallels the extension of the front of the Parry fold belt. Here we are either looking at an inherited Paleozoic subcrop pattern, or a subcrop that, in a poorly understood manner, may be related to the opening of the Arctic Ocean.

2. The pre-Cretaceous subcrop segment extending from the latitude of Great Bear Lake to southern Alberta and Saskatchewan parallels the trend of the Canadian (i.e., Alberta, British Columbia) Rocky Mountains. It is the expression of a wedge of multiple unconformities (Bally and others, 1966) that had its inception during the Permo-Pennsylvanian. This subcrop segment may be explained in terms of a migrating peripheral bulge of an ill-defined foredeep related to the Sonoman orogeny or to docking of allochthonous terranes in the west (see Oldow and others, this volume).

3. The southernmost segment of the pre-Cretaceous subcrop extends from southern Alberta and Saskatchewan into the Southern Rocky Mountains of the United States. Most important perhaps is the east-west–trending zero isopach of the Jurassic, which basically separates the U.S. Cordilleran foreland and the Williston Basin from the more northerly foreland of much of the Canadian Cordillera. The distribution and accumulation maps reveal subparallel upper Paleozoic Absaroka I and II zero isopachs (Plate 10-H) to the south of the Jurassic zero limit. Thus, it is as if the southern Cordilleran foreland, with its characteristic Laramide basement-involved deformation style, had an ill-defined lithospheric ancestry. Pre-Cretaceous subcrop patterns show no particular correlation with any deeper Precambrian basement trends, but I feel that somehow during the upper Paleozoic the crustal or lithospheric properties of the Southern Rocky Mountain foreland became differentiated from their northern continuations in Canada. The nature of that differentiation is not understood, but the observations are there!

To conclude, along the passive margins of the continent the pre-Cretaceous subcrop may reveal eustatic sea-level changes superposed on typical plate tectonic subsidence patterns; that is, lithospheric cooling following stretching across the passive margins of the Gulf of Mexico and the central Atlantic. The subcrop of the Cordilleran foreland, however, permits the differentiation of a southern Cordilleran foreland with subcrop patterns that are distinctly different from much of the Canadian Cordilleran foreland. Finally, note that the Alberta–British Columbia foreland subcrop patterns are subparallel to the trend of the adjacent Cordillera; in great contrast to this, the Tertiary Mackenzie Mountains, with their own characteristic structural styles, cut right across these subcrop patterns. Thus, in the Southern Rocky Mountains, Laramide basement-involved structures coincide with earlier pre-Cretaceous subcrop distributions, while in the Mackenzie Mountains such older subcrops do not coincide and are cut by the younger structures.

Kimmeridgian to mid-Aptian (156 to 116 Ma). This interval corresponds to much of the Zuni B sequence (i.e., minus the Zuni B 1 supercycle) as defined by Haq and others (1987).

The accumulation rate map, Plate 10-M, reveals continuing vigorous subsidence along the Gulf Coast and Atlantic passive margins in response to lithospheric cooling that is enhanced by sediment loading. In Mexico and along the U.S. Gulf Coast, a differentiation between highs and lows that is already apparent on the Middle Jurassic–Oxfordian map becomes more accentuated and will persist throughout much of the Cretaceous. Lower Cretaceous carbonate shelf margins are installed on the Gulf Coast. They can, at least in part, be followed along the Central Atlantic margin (see Worrall and Snelson, as well as Sheridan, this volume; Sheridan and Grow, 1988).

In the northern Atlantic and along the Arctic passive margin, accumulation-rate maps are difficult to make because we lack detailed information. But again on the Newfoundland Shelf, distribution of this interval is limited to rift systems (Enachescu, 1987). Little is known about the Kimmeridgian to mid-Aptian interval along the passive margins of the Canadian Arctic, but subsidence in the Sverdrup Basin is still vigorous. In the Mackenzie Delta area and on the Alaska North Slope passive margins, Lower Cretaceous is confined to the infilling of rift systems (Meneley, 1986; Grantz and others, 1979; Grantz and May, 1983; Hubbard and others, 1987).

Turning to the Cordillera, Plate 10-M shows clearly that foredeeps are well established on the Alaska North Slope and in the foreland of the Canadian and U.S. Rocky Mountains. Beginning with the Alaska North Slope, the foredeep begins after the deposition of the southward prograding Middle and Upper Jurassic (Kingak) clastics of Figure 6. Seismic profiles reveal the onlap of presumed deep-water deposits on the sequence boundary near the top of the Upper Jurassic. They indicate massive subsidence associated with the initiation of the North Slope foredeep (the Colville Basin). Crane (1987) described olistostromes of Tithonian to Valanginian, Valanginian, and Hauterivian ages, respectively. These no doubt were associated with an uppermost Jurassic to Lower Cretaceous accretionary wedge that marked the inception of the formation of the Brooks Range and the embryonic Colville foredeep.

Moving farther south to the Canadian Rocky Mountains, we recognize an Upper Jurassic to Lower Cretaceous clastic wedge marking a reversal of transport direction of the sediments, which are now for the first time derived from the west (i.e., from the rising Rocky Mountains). In contrast to northern Alaska, the shallow-water, synorogenic clastic wedge of Alberta and British Columbia is dominated by nonmarine, sometimes coal-bearing formations.

In the U.S. Cordillera, the inception of a foredeep associated with the U.S. Cordillera to the west is first made evident by Upper Jurassic clastics that are derived from the west (Kocurek and Dott, 1983). In particular, the Upper Jurassic Morrisson Formation appears as a northeastward-prograding alluvial system (Peterson, 1972). Further discussion of the dating of deformation and its relation to foredeep sedimentation is in Oldow and others (this volume). For the first time, the Colorado Plateau is covered by clastics that were derived from the southwest. The source of these clastics is still unknown, but could be from as far south as Mexico (Sloss, 1988c).

In summary, the Kimmeridgian to mid-Aptian map (Plate 10-M) suggests further subsidence on the Gulf of Mexico and Central Atlantic passive margins. There is evidence for infilling of extensional rift systems along the Newfoundland–East Greenland passive margins, and along the passive margin of the Arctic. Major foredeeps become differentiated on the North Slope of Alaska and in the foreland of the Cordillera.

Mid-Aptian to Maastrichtian (116 to 66 Ma). Accumulation rates for the mid-Aptian through Maastrichtian interval are shown on Plate 10-N. Along the passive margins of North America, previously established subsidence patterns continue, and so does the foredeep development in northern Alaska and in the Rocky Mountains.

Within the selected interval there are, however, significant facies changes across a "mid-Cretaceous unconformity," a hiatus that is close to the traditional break between the Lower and Upper Cretaceous. These facies changes are illustrated by two simplified lithofacies maps; one for the mid-Aptian through mid-Cenomanian interval (Plate 10-O) and another one for the mid-Cenomanian through Turonian interval (Plate 10-P).

Subsidence patterns in the Gulf Coast follow preceding patterns that were established in mid-Jurassic times. Persistent major high areas are the Yucatan Platform, the Tamaulipas Arch, the San Marcos Arch (an extension of the former Llano Uplift), and the Sabine, Wiggins, and Sarasota highs.

Following palinspastic restoration of the Sierra Madre Oriental, we can visualize, by the end of the Early Cretaceous, a Mexican Cordilleran shelf that was occupied by reefal carbonate complexes and to the west probably faced a back-arc basin associated with an offshore island arc system. The Bisbee Basin may be a remnant of that back-arc system. Note that toward the Caribbean, there was only a very small deep-water outlet corresponding to the Yucatan Straits. Otherwise, the Gulf Coast was virtually surrounded by carbonate-platform margins. However, following the mid-Cretaceous unconformity (i.e., during the Late Cretaceous), the carbonate regime is replaced by a clastic regime that is only interrupted by the deposition of the Coniacian to Santonian Austin Chalk (see also Worrall and Snelson, this volume).

Moving on to the Central Atlantic passive margin, there is a wide carbonate shelf, the Florida-Cuba-Bahama carbonate platform (see Sheridan and Grow, 1988; Sheridan, this volume). To the north a much narrower Jurassic–Lower Cretaceous carbonate platform can be followed into the Baltimore Canyon area. The slope of that platform has subsequently been eroded by marine currents. North of Cape Hatteras, the passive margin is characterized by siliciclastic shallow-water deposits.

In Newfoundland, rifting decreased during this interval, and as in the Gulf Coast, a major regional unconformity separates the lower rifted Cretaceous from overlying Upper Cretaceous limestones. Here there is a mid-Cretaceous unconformity that coincides approximately with the cessation of the rift regime. To the north in the Labrador Basin, rifting that began in the Lower Cretaceous continued well into the Upper Cretaceous (Balkwill, 1987), even though, again, a significant unconformity appears to separate the Lower from the Upper Cretaceous, but here the unconformity appears to be within the rift sequence.

Thus, the mid-Cretaceous unconformity in the Gulf of Mexico does not appear to be related to any major structural event. In Newfoundland the unconformity was found closely following the cessation of a rifting event, and on the Labrador margin the unconformity is found within the synrift sequence. Obviously, better constraints are needed to come up with an adequate understanding, but to a first approximation it would appear that the well-known mid-Cretaceous unconformity is a eustatic event that is superposed on different structural regimes.

The rifting and subsidence history of the passive margins surrounding Greenland is not well known, and the evolution of the passive margin of the Canadian Arctic is equally problematic. With Baffin Bay and the northern Atlantic opening only during the Tertiary, some pre-Tertiary rifting is to be expected in that area. For reconstructions of the northern Atlantic, the reader is referred to Ziegler (1988).

In contrast to Greenland's passive margin, the Arctic margin of North America is associated with the opening of the Amerasian Basin (see Trettin, this volume). Some insight into the evolution and subsidence history of that margin may be gained from the passive margin of northern Alaska (Grantz and May, 1983; Hubbard and others, 1987). There the rifting that precedes the opening of the Amerasian Basin is believed to have occurred during the Early Jurassic through Aptian interval; the breakup is believed to coincide with an unconformity, indicating that subsequent subsidence of the Northern Alaska–Beaufort margin was presumably due to thermal contraction of an attenuated lithosphere.

The Colville foredeep was perhaps initiated before the opening of the Arctic Ocean but it attained its full development during much of the Albian and the Late Cretaceous. In other words, the subsidence in the Colville foredeep and the cogenetic compression of the adjacent Brooks Range coincides with much of the opening of the Amerasian Basin of the Arctic Ocean. The parallel juxtaposition of a passive-margin subsidence domain with that of a foredeep subsidence domain (see Fig. 6) is responsible for the formation of the Point Barrow Arch that separated these two domains (Hubbard and others, 1987).

Finally, some words about the Cordilleran foredeep during the Late Cretaceous. As mentioned in the section on dating of the Cordillera foreland folded belt (in Oldow and others, this volume), much of the shortening that is so dramatically displayed in the décollement thrust belts of the Cordillera occurs during the Late Cretaceous and Paleocene. The subsidence of the foredeep is clearly reflected by the accumulation-rate map (Plate 10-N).

Comparison of the lithofacies map for the mid-Aptian to the mid-Cenomanian (Plate 10-0) with the one of the mid-Cenomanian–Turonian (Plate 10-P) shows some interesting differences. During mid-Aptian to Cenomanian, depocenters are clearly differentiated, with lithic clastics derived from the Cordillera and much cleaner clastics derived from the craton and the shield. During the next interval a continuous marine seaway connecting the Gulf of Mexico with the Arctic Ocean is established.

During the remainder of the Cretaceous, this seaway is gradually closed, as evidenced by the overall regressive nature of the Upper Cretaceous of the Rocky Mountain foredeep. Numerous studies and reconstructions have been made of the Cretaceous foredeep of the western Cordillera. These show shifting strand lines, and the distribution of deltaic and intradeltaic clastic systems, as well as the related coal deposits (McGookey and others, 1972; Stott and others, 1989; Molenaar and Rice, 1988).

Of particular interest is the sequence stratigraphy in the Rocky Mountain foredeep of the United States where Weimer (1983, 1986) has carefully traced unconformities. When plotted on the chart of Haq and others (1987), Weimer's unconformities fit remarkably well with eustatic lowstands (see Fig. 11). This observation strengthens Vail's argument in favor of structural enhancement of sequence boundaries.

Subsidence of the Rocky Mountain foredeep has been explained as due to the load of thrusts by Jordan (1981) and by Beaumont (1981). Both authors produced satisfactory models. Sloss (1988c), however, presents more detailed accumulation-rate maps of the United States part of the foredeep, and wonders about evidence that would explain the high accumulation rates centering around southern Wyoming, northwestern Colorado, and Utah. The distribution of the thrust sheets to the west, that is, the distribution of the load supposedly responsible for the foreland subsidence, is not adequately known. Sloss (1988c) and I agree that there is a pre-Cretaceous ancestry supporting the notion of a Southern Rocky Mountains foredeep reentrant that may be preordained by the earlier evolution of the Cordillera.

Looking at the foredeep as it extends from northeast British Columbia to the southernmost Rocky Mountains, there is an overwhelming impression that throughout much of the Phanerozoic the southern Cordillera persistently showed the highest accumulation rates, and implicitly, probably the highest tectonic subsidence rates. It follows that, assuming comparable rates of shortening, thicker thrust sheets involving thicker sediment and basement slices would be expected, and these would be superposed on a relatively more attenuated crust. This in turn would lead to increased foreland subsidence.

All in all, the arcuate pattern of the foredeep is not too dissimilar from the patterns of the Appalachian foredeep that have been successfully modeled by Quinlan and Beaumont (1984) and Beaumont and others (1987). In the Rocky Mountains, we now need some new studies that attempt to carry balanced structural cross sections within the Basin and Range and, together with additional sections extending from the Mackenzie Mountains to the Southern Rocky Mountains, would lead to acceptable palinspastic maps. These would form the base for reconstructed isopach and facies maps, which in turn would permit detailed three-dimensional subsidence models.

TERTIARY BASINS OF NORTH AMERICA

A comprehensive description of the North American craton and its sedimentary basins would be incomplete without a discussion of the Tertiary evolution of the continent. However, in this volume, Tertiary basin development is discussed within the context of each of the relevant chapters. Figure 21 provides a very simple overview, and the following comments refer specifically to chapters in this volume.

Tertiary sedimentary sequences can be found on all passive margins of North America (Sheridan, this volume). With the exception of the Gulf of Mexico, subsidence rates of North America's passive margins are reasonably well explained by a combination of sediment loading and, particularly for the margins of Greenland, by thermal subsidence. Prograding clastic sediments are widespread on all passive margins. Sea-level lowstands were responsible for the formation of hiatuses on the shelves and the development of deep-sea fans in the deep oceans (see Greenlee, 1988). Continental slopes were the sites of submarine erosion by ocean currents (Popenoe, 1985).

The Gulf of Mexico (Snelson and Worrall, this volume) is, in all respects, an extraordinary basin. Stated in simple terms, following the completion of the Laramide event, the eastern Rocky Mountains and the Colorado Plateau have been severely uplifted since mid-Oligocene time (Curtis, 1975; Flores and Kaplan, 1985). As a consequence, the clastic detritus of the eastern Rocky Mountains was no longer trapped in foredeep basins and their Laramide successors. A major new drainage pattern developed that transported huge quantities of sediments to the Gulf of Mexico where they were deposited in thick Oligocene to Neogene deltaic systems (Winker, 1982). The structural deformation within this basin, due to gravitational salt and shale tectonics, is admirably summarized by Worrall and Snelson (this volume).

Figure 21 shows that all other Tertiary basins of this continent are related to the development of the western Cordillera. Their formation is discussed by Oldow and others (this volume). Three clans of basins may be differentiated:

1. East of the Cordillera, in the Southern Rocky Mountains, compressional basement tectonics led to the formation of large uplifts that broke up the preceding Cretaceous foredeep. Thus, a number of fault-bounded Paleogene basins were formed that are characterized by their fluviatile and/or lacustrine basin sediments (Dickinson and others, 1988).

2. The Basin and Range Province and the Rio Grande Rift are Tertiary extensional systems filled mostly with fluviatile and some lacustrine sediments. These basins are distinctly postorogenic and superposed on the Cordilleran fold belt. It is thought by some that the listric normal and transfer fault systems that reactivated older thrust-fault systems are responsible for the basin geometries of the Basin and Range Province.

3. Finally, along the west coast of North America from Alaska to Mexico we find a number of basins that are all related to late Paleogene and Neogene transtensional and transpressional tectonics. An overview of these is given in Oldow and others (this volume).

What is perhaps most impressive about the evolution of the Tertiary basins is the fact that so many of them are the products of the Cordilleran uplift. That orogeny is directly responsible for all Tertiary basins of western North America, but indirectly also contributed to the Tertiary evolution of the Gulf of Mexico.

CONCLUSIONS

This review of the evolution of the North American craton, its basins and its uplifts, has provided insights as well as new problems. A debate as to what precisely constitutes a craton is tedious, and for the purposes of these conclusions it may suffice to state that Phanerozoic North America had a cratonic center underlain by a Precambrian basement, and that Paleozoic and Mesozoic-Cenozoic folded belts may be viewed as subsequent extensions (additions) to the craton.

Referring back to Figure 1, a large variety of basins can be discriminated, but even within the proposed classes there is such a great variability that the individuality of each basin and each uplift is impressive. Consequently, attempts at classification all appear somewhat artificial. Even so we must simplify to gain any form of overview!

The passive margin basins of North America are perhaps the easiest understood in terms of their relationship to plate tectonics and the sea-floor spreading process. Most of them exhibit one or more rifting events that preceed the deposition of a thick sedimentary wedge. Geophysical models have demonstrated that subsidence on passive margins is caused by a combination of thermal cooling and of sediment loading. Because some passive margins display only single rifting events (e.g., U.S. Atlantic), others multiple rifting events (e.g., Newfoundland and East Greenland), and yet others a less well-defined Paleozoic ancestry (e.g., Gulf of Mexico), an in-depth understanding of these passive margins will come with greater geophysical resolution of their intrastructure.

Our understanding of cratonic basins is unsatisfactory. It is fair to say that most cratonic basins of North America acquired their individuality at different times during the early Paleozoic. A number of models have been proposed for these basins. Both phase changes and/or thermal mechanisms are popular.

The Michigan, Illinois, and Williston Basins have only very meager evidence for extensive precursory rifting at the right time and in the right place. Of special interest is the Hudson Bay Basin, which has a "half-horst" in its center. Perhaps the position of the Central Basin platform between the Delaware and Midland Basins may be comparable to the "half-horst" of the Hudson Bay Basin. Obviously the next question is, "What precisely is a half-horst?" On seismic profiles a half-horst presents itself as a high that appears like one shoulder of a graben system; on its downthrown side, it does not show expansion of the section that is so characteristic for typical half-graben configurations. Until now, this type of structure is barely described, and prior to additional theorizing, a more precise description is desirable.

Common to most if not all cratonic basins of North America, and for that matter many other cratonic basins of the world, are shared major sequence boundaries (Sloss, 1972; Soares and others, 1978). The question is: "Do these sequence boundaries betray an underlying common tectonic cause, or are they simply a eustatic signal that is more or less enhanced in different tectonic regimes?" In an earlier publication, I suggested that the correlatability of Phanerozoic sequences suggested the existence of ubiqui-

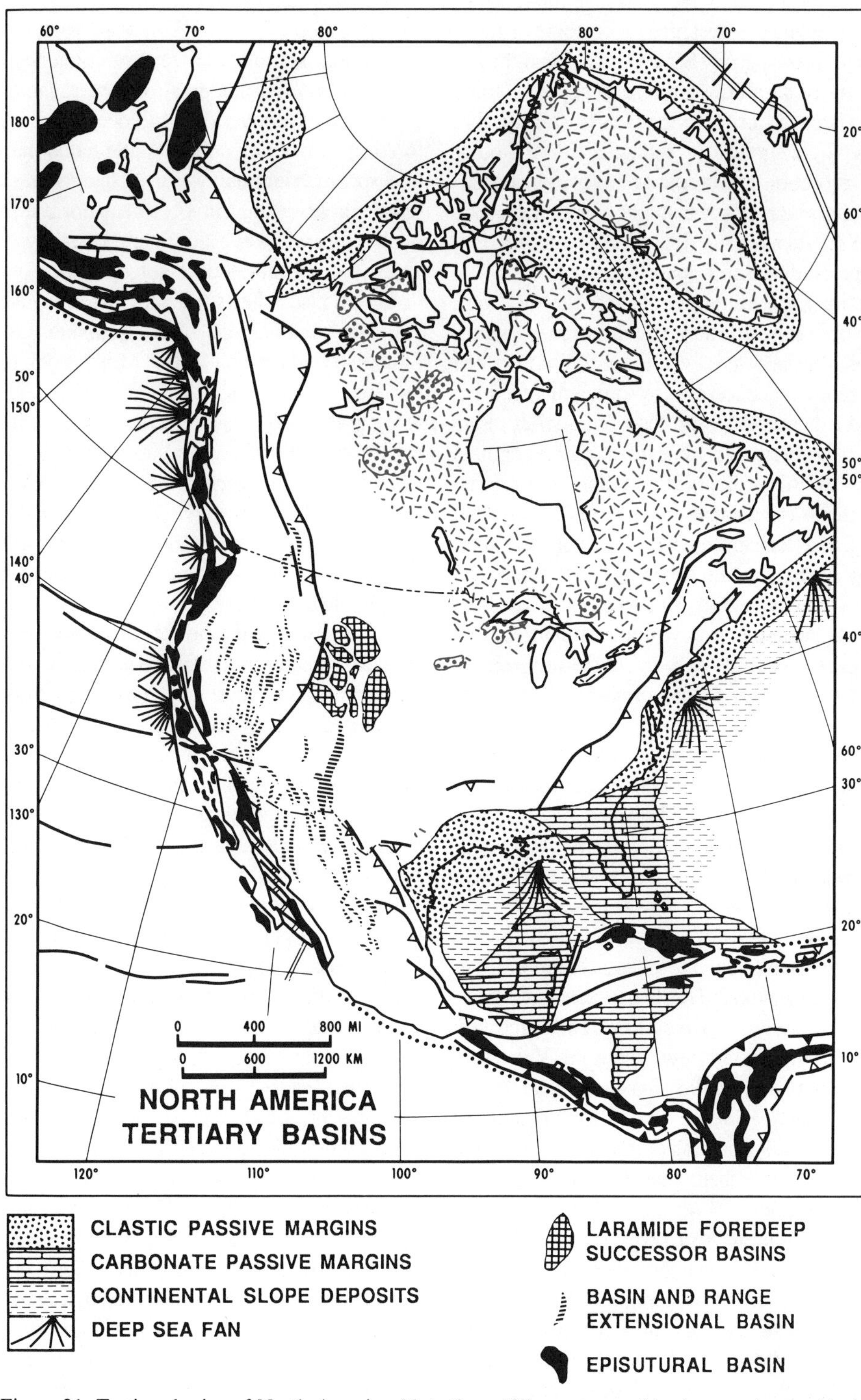

Figure 21. Tertiary basins of North America. Note three different types of basins associated with the formation of the western Cordillera. (a) Episutural basins include mostly marine fore-arc and back-arc basins of the Cordillera, as well as transtensional and transpressional basins associated with strike-slip systems (e.g., San Andreas fault). (b) Extensional basins associated with the formation of the Basin and Range Province. (c) Laramide basins: these are due to the dismemberment of the preceeding Cretaceous foredeep, by compressional and transpressional basement uplifts. For additional details on all three basin types, see Oldow and others (this volume).

tous tectonic regimes (Bally, 1980). Now, under the influence of Vail, I am wavering. A detailed correlation of tectonic regimes with the sequence hierarchies of either Sloss (1988a, b, and c) or Haq and others (1988) is hazardous at best because tectonic regimes last longer and because their varying rates of deformation are not particularly well constrained in geologic time. In other words, the kinematic resolution of tectonic events is not as accurate as the purported definition of often much higher frequency stratigraphic cycles. Yet, there is no doubt that tectonics is a leading cause for both subsidence and uplift.

However, as shown for the cratonic basins, the inception and rate of subsidence between the different cratonic basins varies substantially, a contrast that becomes even more dramatic when foredeeps are considered. The concept of tectonic enhancement of sequences (Vail and others, 1985) and their boundaries offers an excellent working hypothesis. The concept simply recognizes the tectonic nature of subsidence, uplifts, folding, extensional faulting, and other features, and assumes, largely on the notion of steady plate tectonics, that tectonic regimes are typically more long-lived, that is, they fluctuate much less than eustatic sea-level changes. In such a view, unconformities due to eustatic lowering of world sea level are superposed on developing structures both on a regional and a local scale. Thus, unconformities are particularly sensitive time markers that record the progress of structural deformation.

As a working hypothesis, tectonic enhancement is eminently testable. All that is needed is simply to demonstrate for a given eustatic unconformity whether or not a subsidence and/or structural regime continues right across the unconformity. As always, precisely documented paleontological calibration will be decisive in supporting any correlation!

Before leaving cratonic basins, a few words about arches and other cratonic uplifts are offered. These features are particularly poorly defined and understood. The Transcontinental Arch and its Canadian cousin, the Peace River–Keewatin Arch, are outstanding examples. A superficial view of the pre-Kaskaskia map (Plate 10-D) suggests that even allowing for a lower Paleozoic ancestry, there is much evidence for either bending or buckling on a lithospheric level occurring at the same time as the establishment of Devonian folded belts that surround the continent in a horseshoe-like fashion.

Other uplifts may be inversions of preexisting extensional systems, or they may represent a lithospheric thermal event. We need more data and different kinds of observations. Among traditional approaches a detailed reexamination of subcrop patterns and their genesis is required. Additional crustal geophysical data are urgently needed to characterize arches and uplifts, and finally, radiometric and/or fission track dating, combined with measurements of anchimetamorphism, are important to better constrain uplift events in time and space.

Foredeeps dominate much of the Paleozoic and Mesozoic of North America. Models have made a convincing case that the subsidence of foredeeps is due to lithospheric loads and/or the load of piled-up thrust sheets. But so far we have failed to adequately document and explain the great differences between the various types of North American foredeeps. As with cratonic basins, lumping all foredeep (or foreland) basins into one class may be obscuring the most important factors responsible for the development of individual foredeeps. It is intuitively obvious that foredeeps involving a highly attenuated margin will tend toward widespread initial deposition of deep-water ("flysch") sequences, while foredeeps that involve near-normal passive-margin crustal thicknesses will have dominantly shallow-water clastic wedges. Thus, the evolution of a foredeep not only reflects a loading history, it also reflects the nature of the preorogenic passive margin. The basic aspects of the problem have been discussed by Stockmal and others (1986). More geophysical observations are required. These include, particularly, crustal thickness and velocity-layering measurements as well as crustal reflection profiling where justified. Because the basement underlying a foredeep extends well underneath the adjacent folded belt, thus forming the base of what may be loosely called an A-subduction accretionary wedge, it is important to map the downdip projection of that basement underneath the folded belts with reasonable confidence.

If we accept the notion that folded belts represent the mechanical separation of sediments and crustal slices from underlying lithospheric roots, we have less difficulty expressing the subsidence of any foredeep moat in terms of various loading models, but much greater difficulty explaining the uplift of the mountains right next to, and downdip from, the foredeep. Therefore, we still need better information concerning orogenic uplift mechanisms. Here again, quantitative measurements of uplift rates are required.

With regard to sequence boundaries and unconformities, foredeeps emphasize a new set of unconformities. Aside from former passive margin–cratonic unconformities in the platforms that underlie foredeeps, we now can conceptualize two kinds of basal foredeep unconformities (see Fig. 4). A first basal unconformity would relate to erosion of a shallow-water migrating peripheral bulge. A second type of unconformity would be more downdip and separate passive-margin stratigraphy from the overlying embryonic foredeep fill (the Timor model of Montecchi, 1976). Then there are unconformities that emanate from the foreland toward the folded belt (as per Quinlan and Beaumont's 1984 model; Tankard, 1986). Finally, additional unconformities underlie and separate sediments that are deposited and converge toward the axis of growing folded belt structures. The time is ripe for combined seismic stratigraphic and subsidence studies to test in detail the geologic consequences of models that have been presented by our geophysical colleagues.

There are many different kinds of basins directly related to the Tertiary development of the Cordillera. The compressional origin of the basins of the Southern Rocky Mountains foreland is generally understood. This contrasts with our lack of understanding of similar Paleozoic basins in the Ancestral Rocky Mountains and the foreland of the Ouachitas. Progress there will come from better quality and additional specific crustal data. In the Basin and Range Province, judging from the overwhelming volume of recent publications, models often seem to get confused with reality. Yes, there is abundant evidence for extension in the Basin and Range (see Oldow and others, this volume), but so far there is no study that would successfully relate outcrop geology to a grid of seismic data; that is, a study that would relate specifically what we see in the ranges with what we see in the basins, and that would attempt to unravel the specific role, if any, of transfer faulting. Crustal seismic data would need to be reconciled with such studies.

In Oldow and others (this volume), there is a brief review of the multitude of differing episutural basins that occur all along the West Coast from Mexico to Alaska. Superficially, these basins are neatly pigeon-holed in a plate-tectonic frame of reference. There is even overall agreement that transtensional and transpressional mechanisms may be important, but when it comes to any type of firm subsurface documentation, there are few good examples.

To sum up basin studies: it appears that geophysical models are very much ahead of observations. Therefore, models are particularly useful in defining problems and identifying what kinds of data are needed, but they do not necessarily approximate geologic reality. Outstanding among many are two important study targets: (1) three-dimensional seismic stratigraphic studies calibrated by traditional subsurface and paleontological data, and (2) crustal studies aimed at resolving: (a) the downdip projection of faulting within the basement and possibly into the mantle; (b) extensional, transtensional, compressional, and transpressional faulting at the inception of the basin; and (c) the characteristics of the lower crust. With regard to the latter, current reflection seismic methods give unsatisfactory resolution for the lower crust and often make it nearly impossible to differentiate spurious data from what is geologically meaningful.

Finally, some words about stratigraphic sequences, unconformities, and the debate concerning the structural and stratigraphic meaning of them.

First of all, there is an obvious impasse because there is no agreement on sequence boundaries and their specific definition, and there is also no agreement on time scales. Thus, the innocent bystander is forced to dig into the premises of each author or consortium of authors. There are, however, the COSUNA charts (see Appendix) that represent some kind of consensus among traditional stratigraphers, but these charts were produced without much seismic and/or sequence-stratigraphic input.

For the simple sake of coordinated communication, it would be desirable to have a flexible consensus as a working guide. Thus, a condensed COSUNA-like chart that would display such factors as agreed-upon sequence boundaries and maximum transgression, as well as common time standards, needs to be prepared. Such a document could always be updated and modified. However, as mentioned earlier the main danger here is not the chart but the creation of codifying priesthoods.

Much more important than stratigraphic bookkeeping and codifying are perhaps two important conceptual obstacles dealing with sequence stratigraphy. The first deals with the hierarchy of sequences and subsequences, and the second has to do with the origin of unconformities.

For the Mesozoic, Sloss (1988c), Haq and others (1987), and Vail (1987) propose quite different hierarchies. The arguments for the selection of any given sequence hierarchy are not extensively spelled out by any of these authors, but clearly Sloss thinks in terms of structurally controlled sequences while Vail and others emphasize eustatic aspects. For the Paleozoic, there is no contest, because Sloss (1988c) has the corner on the complete Paleozoic market. Yes, there are encouraging attempts to resolve Paleozoic sequence stratigraphy in detail at a solution comparable to that achieved by Vail (1987). Johnson and others (1985) have tried this for the Devonian, and Ross and Ross (1987) have tried this for the Carboniferous and the Permian. But somehow these have to be reconciled with the Sloss sequences.

At this time it may be preferable not to insist any longer on a sequence hierarchy until at least semiquantitative hierarchical principles and criteria have been elaborated. These would have to "measure" the ubiquity of a sequence boundary and, accepting a sea-level concept, correlate it with the order of magnitude of sea-level change.

Turning to the second significant obstacle, as a general geology practitioner and enthusiastic supporter of modern sequence stratigraphy, I remain puzzled by the origin of unconformities. These same unconformities form an important foundation of modern sequence stratigraphy. Perhaps we need a new stratigraphic science: "unconformology" or better perhaps "hiatusology"—the science of what was left out in the geologic record. Without attempting to be systematic and overly learned, here are some unconformity types that need to be further characterized and differnetiated:

- Unconformities characterized by erosional truncation of tilted beds.
- Clear eustatic unconformities within shallow-water sediments with their associated truncation, toplaps, and channel systems.
- Unconformities on passive margin slopes due to slope erosion by ocean currents.
- Unconformities related to shelf-margin canyon systems.
- Deep-water unconformities caused by geostrophic currents.
- Unconformities associated with sediment starvation.
- Unconformities that mark the inception of rifting in shallow and in deep water, respectively.
- The "breakup" unconformity on passive margins.
- The "basal foredeep" unconformity.
- Relaxation unconformities associated with foredeeps.
- Unconformities associated with growing compressional anticlines.
- Unconformities associated with growth-fault systems.
- Unconformities associated with salt-tectonic structures.

Surely numerous other types of unconformities may be added to the list. The point is that while the nature of such unconformities is clear in a number of "textbook" cases, most of the time the origin is not so clear. The genesis of an unconformity is best appreciated in a regional context. As to the structural versus stratigraphic significance of a sequence, we have to determine: (1) whether sea-level changes merely punctuate tectonic events and the associated unconformities become more accentuated because of structural enhancement, (2) whether an unconformity is limited to local structures or areas or is more ubiquitous, or (3) whether structural-kinematic resolution from the plate-tectonic scale to a local scale has sufficient time constraints to be related to specific sequences.

Methods to resolve these questions are in hand, the problem is defined, but we need the stamina necessary to parlay fascinating concepts into carefully documented evidence. Today, this requires intimate cooperation between stratigraphers, paleontologists, and geophysicists.

REFERENCES CITED

Adkinson, W. L., 1966, Stratigraphic cross section of Paleozoic rocks, Colorado to New York: American Association of Petroleum Geologists Publication 4, 58 p.

Adler, F. J., and 11 others, 1971, Future petroleum provinces of the midcontinent, Region 7, *in* Cram, I. H., ed., Future petroleum provinces of the United States—Their geology and potential: American Association of Petroleum Geologists Memoir 15, v. 2, p. 985–1120.

Ahern, J. L., and Ditmars, R. C., 1985, Rejuvenation of continental lithosphere beneath an intracratonic basin: Tectonophysics, v. 120, p. 21–35.

Ahern, J. L., and Mrkvicka, S. R., 1984, A mechanical and thermal model for the evolution of the Williston Basin: Tectonics, v. 3, p. 79–102.

Aitken, J. D., 1969, Documentation of the sub-Cambrian unconformity, Rocky Mountain main ranges, Alberta: Canadian Journal of Earth Sciences, v. 6, p. 192–200.

—— , 1978, Revised models for depositional Grand Cycles, Cambrian of the southern Rocky Mountains, Canada: Bulletin of Canadian Petroleum Geology, v. 26, p. 515–542.

Aitken, J. D., and McMechan, M. E., 1989, Middle Proterozoic assemblages, *in* Gabrielse, H., and Yorath, C. J., eds., The Cordilleran orogen; Canada: Geological Survey of Canada, Geology of Canada, v. 4, chapter 5 (also Geological Society of America, The Geology of North America, v. G-2), (in press).

Alden, W. C., 1932, Physiography and glacial geology of eastern Montana and adjacent areas: U.S. Geological Survey Professional Paper 174, 133 p.

Allmendinger, R. W., Hauge, T. A., Hauser, E. C., Potter, C. J., and Oliver, J., 1987, Tectonic heredity and layered lower crust in the Basin and Range, western United States, *in* Coward, M. L., Dewey, J. F., and Moncock, J. R., eds., Continental extension tectonics: Geological Society of London Special Publication 28, p. 223–246.

Angelier, J., and Colletta, B., 1983, Tensional fractures and extensional tectonics: Nature, v. 301, p. 49.

Armentrout, J. M., Cole, M. R., and TerBest, H., 1979, Cenozoic paleogeography of the western United States, Symposium 3: Pacific Section of the Society of Economic Paleontologists and Mineralogists, 335 p.

Armin, R. A., and Mayer, L., 1983, Subsidence analysis of the Cordilleran miogeocline—implications for timing of late Proterozoic rifting and amount of extension: Geology, v. 11, p. 702–706.

Artemjev, M. E., and Artyushkov, E. V., 1971, Structure and isostasy of the Baikal Rift and the mechanism of rifting: Journal of Geophysical Research, v. 76, p. 1197–1211.

Audley-Charles, M. G., 1986, Timor–Tanimbar Trough—the foreland basin of the evolving Banda orogen, *in* Allen, P. A., and Homewood, P., eds., Foreland basins: International Association of Sedimentologists Special Publication 8, Oxford, Blackwell Scientific Publications, p. 91–104.

Balkwill, H. R., 1987, Labrador basin—structural and stratigraphic style, *in* Beaumont, C., and Tankard, A. J., eds., Sedimentary basins and basin-forming mechanisms: Canadian Society of Petroleum Geologists Memoir 12, p. 17–44.

Bally, A. W., 1980, Basins and subsidence—summary, *in* Bally, A. W., ed., Dynamics of plate interiors: American Geophysical Union Geodynamics Series, v. 1, p. 1–20.

—— , 1981, Atlantic-type margins, *in* Geology of passive continental margins: American Association of Petroleum Geologists Education Course Note Series 19, p. 1–28.

—— , 1984, Tectogenese et sismique reflexion: Bulletin de la Societe Geologique de France, v. 26, p. 279–285.

Bally, A. W., and Snelson, S., 1980, Realms of subsidence, *in* Miall, A. D., ed., Facts and principles of world petroleum occurrence: Canadian Society of Petroleum Geologists Memoir 6, p. 1–94.

Bally, A. W., Gordy, P. L., and Stewart, G. A., 1966, Structure, seismic data and orogenic evolution of southern Canadian Rocky Mountains: Bulletin of Canadian Petroleum Geologists, v. 14, p. 337–381.

Bally, A. W., Bender, P. L., McGetchin, T. R., and Walcott, R. I., eds., 1980, Dynamics of plate interior: American Geophysical Union Geodynamics Series, v. 1, 161 p.

Bassett, H. G., and Stout, J. G., 1968, Devonian of Western Canada, *in* Oswald, D. H., ed., International symposium on the Devonian System: Canadian Society of Petroleum Geologists, v. 1, p. 717–752.

Beaumont, C., 1981, Foreland basins: Geophysical Journal of the Royal Astronomical Society, v. 65, p. 291–329.

Beaumont, C., and Tankard, A., eds., 1987, Sedimentary basins and basin-forming mechanisms: Canadian Society of Petroleum Geologists, 527 p.

Beaumont, C., Quinlan, G. M., and Hamilton, J., 1987, The Alleghanian orogeny and its relationship to the evolution of the eastern interior, North America, *in* Beaumont, C., and Tankard, A. J., eds., Sedimentary basins and basin-forming mechanisms: Canadian Society of Petroleum Geologists Memoir 12, p. 425–446.

Beaumont, C., Keen, C. E., and Boutilier, R., 1982a, A comparison of foreland and rift margin sedimentary basins, *in* Kent, P., and others, eds., The evolution of sedimentary basins: Philosophical Transactions of the Royal Society of London, v. A-305, p. 295–317.

—— , 1982b, On the evolution of rifted continental margins—comparisons of models and observations for the Nova Scotia Margin: Geophysical Journal of the Royal Astronomical Society, v. 70, p. 667–715.

Bird, K. J., 1985, The framework geology of the North Slope of Alaska as related to oil-source rock correlations, *in* Magoon, L. B., and Claypool, C. E., eds., Alaska North Slope oil-rock correlation study: American Association of Petroleum Geologists Studies in Geology 20, p. 3–30.

Birkelund, T., and Perch-Nielsen, K., 1976, Late Paleozoic–Mesozoic evolution of central East Greenland, *in* Escher, A., and Watt, W. S., eds., Geology of Greenland: Geological Survey of Greenland, p. 304–339.

Bond, G. C., and Kominz, M. A., 1984, Construction of tectonic subsidence curves for the early Paleozoic miogeocline, southern Canadian Rocky Mountains—implications for subsidence mechanisms, age of breakup, and crustal thinning: Geological Society of America Bulletin, v. 95, p. 155–173.

—— , 1988, Evolution of thought on passive continental margins from the origin of geosynclinal theory (~1860) to the present: Geological Society of America Bulletin, v. 100, p. 1909–1933.

Bond, G. C., Nickerson, P. A., and Kominz, M. A., 1984, Breakup of a supercontinent between 625 Ma and 555 Ma—new evidence and implications for continental histories: Earth and Planetary Science Letters, v. 70, no. 2, p. 325–345.

Bott, M.H.P., 1971, Evolution of young continental margins and formation of shelf basins: Tectonophysics, v. 11, p. 319–327.

Bott, M.H.P., and Dean, D. S., 1972, Stress systems at young continental margins: Nature, v. 235, p. 23–25.

Braile, L. W., Hinze, W. J., Keller, G.R.F., Lidiak, E. G., and Sexton, J. L., 1986, Tectonic development of the New Madrid Rift complex, Mississippi Embayment, North America: Tectonophysics, v. 131, p. 1–21.

Brewer, J. A., Good, R., Oliver, J. E., Brown, L. D., and Kaufman, S., 1983, COCORP profiling across the southern Oklahoma aulacogen—overthrusting of the Wichita Mountains and compression within the Anadarko Basin: Geology, v. 11, p. 109–114.

Buffler, R. T., and Sawyer, D. S., 1985, Distribution of crust and early history, Gulf of Mexico Basin: Gulf Coast Association of Geological Societies Transactions, v. 35, p. 333–444.

Burrus, J., ed., 1986, Thermal modeling in sedimentary basins: Institut Francais du Petrole Exploration Research Conferences, Paris, Technip, 603 p.

——, 1989, Review of geodynamic models for extensional basin and the example of the Gulf of Lions (northwest Mediterranean)—the paradox of stretching: Bulletin de la Societe Geologique de France (in press).

Cant, D. J., 1988, Regional structure and development of the Peace River Arch, Alberta—a Paleozoic failed rift system?: Bulletin of Canadian Petroleum Geology, v. 36, p. 284–295.

Clement, J., 1986, Cedar Creek—a significant paleotectonic feature of the Williston Basin, *in* Peterson, J. A., ed., Paleotectonics and sedimentation in the Rocky Mountain region, United States: American Association of Petroleum Geologists Memoir 41, p. 213–240.

Cloethingh, S., 1989, Intraplate stresses—a new element in basin analysis, *in* Kleinspohn, K., and Paola, C., eds., New perspective in basin analysis: New York, Springer Verlag (in press).

Cloetingh, S., McQueen, H., and Lambeck, K., 1985, On a tectonic mechanism for regional sea-level variations: Earth and Planetary Science Letters, v. 75, p. 157–166.

Cobbold, P. R., and Davy, P. H., 1988, Continental compressional tectonics; 2 kinds of basins, *in* Abstracts in petroleum tectonics in mobile belts: Bordeaux, Institute Francais du Petrole, p. 10.

Cole, M. R., and Armentrout, J. M., 1979, Neogene paleogeography of the western United States, *in* Armentrout, J. M., Cole, M. R., and TerBest, H., Jr., eds., Cenozoic paleogeography of the western United States: Pacific Section, Society of Economic Paleontologists and Mineralogists, Symposium 3, p. 297–323.

Collinson, C., Sargent, M. L., and Jennings, J. R., 1988, Illinois Basin region, *in* Sloss, L. L., ed., Sedimentary cover–North American craton, U.S.: Boulder, Colorado, Geological Society of America, Geology of North America, v. D-2, p. 383–426.

Colton, G. W., 1970, The Appalachian Basin—its depositional sequences and their geologic relationships, *in* Fisher, F. W., Pettijohn, F. J., and Reed, J. C., Jr., eds., Studies of Appalachian geology: New York, Wiley-Interscience, p. 5–47.

Cook, T. D., and Bally, A. W., 1975, Stratigraphic atlas of North and Central America: Princeton, New Jersey, Princeton University Press, 272 p.

Craig, L. C., and Connor, C. W., eds., 1979, Paleotectonic investigations of the Mississippian System in the United States: U.S. Geological Survey Professional Paper 1010, 559 p.

Crane, R. C., 1987, Cretaceous Olistostrome model, Brooks Range Alaska, *in* Tailleur, I. L., and Weimer, P., eds., Alaskan North Slope Geology: Pacific Section, Society of Economic Paleontologists and Mineralogists, and the Alaskan Geological Society, v. 1, p. 433–440.

Cross, T. A., 1986, Tectonic controls of foreland basin subsidence and Laramide style deformation, western United States, *in* Allen, P. A., and Homewood, P., eds., Foreland basins: International Association of Sedimentologists Special Publication 8, Oxford, Blackwell Scientific Publications, p. 15–40.

Curtis, B. F., ed., 1975, Cenozoic history of the southern Rocky Mountains: Geological Society of America Memoir 144, 279 p.

Dickinson, W. R., 1979, Cenozoic plate-tectonic setting of the Cordilleran region in the United States, *in* Armentrout, J. W., Cole, M. R., and TerBest, H., eds., Cenozoic paleogeography of western United States: Pacific Section, Society of Economic Paleontologists and Mineralogists, Symposium 3, p. 1–13.

Dickinson, W. R., and 6 others, 1988, Paleogeographic and paleotectonic setting of Laramide sedimentary basins in central Rocky Mountain region: Geological Society of America Bulletin, v. 100, p. 1120–1130.

Diebold, J. B., Stoffa, P. L., and the LASE Study Group, 1988, A large Aperture seismic experiment in the Baltimore Canon Trough, *in* Sheridan, R. E., and Grow, J. S., eds., The Atlantic Continental Margin, U.S.: Boulder, Colorado, Geological Society of America, Geology of North America, v. I-2, p. 387–398.

Dietz, R. S., 1963, Collapsing continental rises; An actualistic concept of geosyncline mountain building: Journal of Geology, v. 71, p. 314–333.

Dietz, R. S., and Holden, J. C., 1974, Collapsing continental rises; Actualistic concept of geosynclines—a review, *in* Dott, R. H., Jr., and Shaver, R. H., eds., Modern and ancient geosynclinal sedimentation: Society of Economic Paleontologists and Mineralogists Special Publication 19, p. 14–27.

Dimian, M. V., Gray, R., Stout, J., and Wood, B., 1983, Hudson Bay basin, *in* Bally, A. W., ed., Seismic expression of structural styles, v. 2: American Association of Petroleum Geologists Studies in Geology 13, p. 2.2.4-1 to 2.2.4-4.

Dott, R. H., Jr., 1974, The geosynclinal concept, *in* Dott, R. H., Jr., and Shaver, R. H., eds., Modern and ancient geosynclinal sedimentation: Society of Economic Paleontologists and Mineralogists Special Publication 19, p. 1–13.

Dott, R. H., and Batten, R. L., 1988, Evolution of the Earth: New York, McGraw-Hill, 643 p.

Douglas, R.J.W., ed., 1970, Geology and economic minerals of Canada: Geological Survey of Canada Economic Geology Report 1, 5th edition, 838 p.

Drake, C. L., Ewing, M., and Sutton, G. H., 1959, Continental margins and geosynclines—the east coast of North America north of Cape Hatteras, *in* Physics and Chemistry of Earth: London, Pergamon Press, v. 3, p. 110–198.

Dunbar, J. A., and Sawyer, D. S., 1987, Implications of continental extension for plate reconstructions—an example from the Gulf of Mexico: Tectonics, v. 6, p. 739–755.

Effimoff, I., and Pinezich, A. R., 1987, Tertiary structural development of selected basins—Basin and Range Province, northeastern Nevada, *in* Mayer, L., ed., Extensional tectonics of the southwestern United States; A perspective on processes and kinematics: Geological Society of America Special Paper 208, p. 31–42.

Enachescu, M. E., 1987, Tectonic and structural framework of the northeast Newfoundland continental margin, *in* Beaumont, C., and Tankard, A. J., eds., Sedimentary basins and basin-forming mechanisms: Canadian Society of Petroleum Geologists Memoir 12, p. 117–146.

Ervin, C. P., and McGinnis, L. D., 1975, Reelfoot Rift—reactivated precursor to the Mississippi Embayment: Geological Society of America Bulletin, v. 86, p. 1287–1295.

Ettenson, F. R., 1985a, The Catskill Delta complex and the Acadian orogeny—a model, *in* Woodrow, D. L., and Sevon, W. D., eds., The Catskill Delta: Geological Society of America Special Paper 201, p. 39–49.

——, 1985b, Controls on development of Catskill delta complex basin facies, *in* Woodrow, D. L., and Sevon, W. D., eds., The Catskill delta: Geological Society of America Special Paper 201, p. 65–75.

Faill, R. T., 1985, The Acadian orogeny and the Catskill delta, *in* Woodrow, D. L., and Sevon, W. D., eds., The Catskill delta: Geological Society of America Special Paper 201, p. 15–38.

Falvey, D. A., 1974, The development of continental margins in plate tectonic theory: Australian Journal of Petroleum Explorations, v. 14, p. 95–106.

Falvey, D. A., and Middleton, M. F., 1981, Passive continental margins—evidence for a pre-breakup deep crustal metamorphic subsidence mechanism; *in* Geology of continental margins symposium: Oceanologica Acta, v. 4, p. 103–114.

Fischer, A. G., and Judson, S., 1975, eds., Petroleum and global tectonics: Princeton, New Jersey, Princeton University Press, 322 p.

Fisher, J. H., Barratt, M. W., Droste, J. B., and Shaver, R. N., 1988, Michigan Basin, *in* Sloss, L. L., ed., Sedimentary cover–North American craton, U.S.: Boulder, Colorado, Geological Society of America, Geology of North America, v. D-2, p. 361–382.

Flores, R. M., and Kaplan, S. S., eds., 1985, Cenozoic paleogeography of the west-central United States; Rocky Mountain Paleogeography Symposium 3: Rocky Mountain Section, Society of Economic Paleontologists and Mineralogists, 460 p.

Fowler, C.M.R., and Nisbet, E. G., 1985, The subsidence of the Williston Basin: Canadian Journal of Earth Sciences, v. 22, p. 408–415.

Frenzel, H. N., and 13 others, 1988, The Permian Basin region, *in* Sloss, L. L., ed., Sedimentary cover–North American craton, U.S.: Boulder, Colorado, Geological Society of America, Geology of North America, v. D-2, p. 261–306.

Friedenreich, O. R., 1987, A regional seismic reflection profile in the Scotian basin, offshore Nova Scotia, *in* Beaumont, C., and Tankard, A. J., eds., Sedimentary basins and basin-forming mechanisms: Canadian Society of Petroleum Geologists Memoir 12, p. 71–74.

Fritz, W. H., Cecile, M. P., Norford, B. S., Morrow, D., and Geldsetzer, H.H.J., 1989, Cambrian to Middle Devonian assemblages, *in* Gabrielse, H., and Yorath, C. J., eds., The Cordilleran orogen—Canada: Geological Survey of Canada, Geology of Canada, v. 4 (also Geological Society of America, v. G-2, The Geology of North America) (in press).

Gerhard, L. C., and Anderson, S. B., 1988, Geology of the Williston Basin (United States portion), *in* Sloss, L. L., ed., Sedimentary cover–North American craton, U.S.: Boulder, Colorado, Geological Society of America, Geology of North America, v. D-2, p. 221–242.

Gibbs, A. D., 1984, Structural evolution of extensional basin margins: Journal of the Geological Society of London, v. 141, p. 609–620.

Gibling, M. R., Boehner, R. C., and Rust, B. R., 1987, The Sydney Basin of Atlantic Canada—an upper Paleozoic strike-slip basin in a collisional setting, *in* Beaumont, C., and Tankard, A. J., eds., Sedimentary basins and basin-forming mechanisms: Canadian Society of Petroleum Geologists Memoir 12, p. 269–286.

Gilluly, J., 1955, Geologic contrasts between continents and ocean basins, *in* Poldervaart, A., ed., Crust of the Earth: Geological Society of America Special Paper 62, p. 7–18.

——, 1964, Atlantic-sediments, erosion notes and the evolution of the continental shelf—some speculations: Geological Society of America Bulletin, v. 75, p. 483–492.

Gordey, S. P., Abbott, J. G., Tempelman-Kluit, D. J., and Gabrielse, H., 1987, "Antler" clastics in the Canadian Cordillera: Geology, v. 15, p. 103–107.

Grantz, A., and May, S. D., 1983, Rifting history and structural development of the continental margin north of Alaska, *in* Watkins, J. W., and Drake, C. L., eds., Studies in continental margin geology: American Association of Petroleum Geologists Memoir 34, p. 77–100.

Grantz, A., Eittreim, S., and Dinter, D. A., 1979, Geology and tectonic development of the continental margin north of Alaska: Tectonophysics, v. 59, p. 263–291.

Greenlee, S. M., 1988, Tertiary depositional sequences offshore New Jersey and Alabama, *in* Bally, A. W., ed., Atlas of seismic Stratigraphy, v. 2: American Association of Petroleum Geologists Studies in Geology 27, p. 67–80.

Hagen, E. S., Schuster, M. W., and Furlong, K. P., 1985, Tectonic loading and subsidence of intermontane basins, Wyoming foreland province: Geology, v. 13, p. 585–592.

Haq, B. U., Hardenbol, J., and Vail, P. R., 1987, Chronology of fluctuating sea levels since the Triassic: Science, v. 235, p. 1156–1167.

Haxby, W. F., Turcotte, D. L., and Bird, J. M., 1976, Thermal and mechanical evolution of the Michigan basin: Tectonophysics, v. 36, p. 57–75.

Heckel, P. H., 1980, Paleogeography of eustatic model for deposition of midcontinent Upper Pennsylvanian cyclothems, *in* Fouch, T. D., and Magathan, E. R., eds., Paleogeography of the west-central United States: Rocky Mountain Section, Society of Economic Paleontologists and Mineralogists, Paleogeography Symposium 1, p. 197–215.

Helwig, J. A., 1985, Origin and classification of sedimentary basins: Proceedings of the 17th Annual Offshore Technology Conference Paper 4843, v. 1, p. 21–32.

Hinze, W. J., and Braile, L. W., 1988, Geophysical aspects of the craton, U.S., *in* Sloss, L. L., ed., Sedimentary cover–North American craton: Boulder, Colorado, Geological Society of America, Geology of North America, v. D-2, p. 5–24.

Hiscott, R. N., Pickering, K. T., and Beeden, D. R., 1986, Progressive filling of a confined Middle Ordovician foreland basin associated with the Taconic orogeny, Quebec, Canada, *in* Allen, P. A., and Homewood, P., eds., Foreland basins: International Association of Sedimentologists Special Publication 8, Oxford, Blackwell Scientific Publications, p. 309–326.

Hoffman, P., Dewey, J. F., and Burke, K., 1974, Aulacogens and their genetic relation to geosynclines, with a Proterozoic example from Great Slave Lake, Canada, *in* Modern and ancient geosynclinal sedimentation: Society of Economic Paleontologists and Mineralogists Special Publication 19, p. 38–55.

Houseknecht, D. W., 1986, Evolution from passive margin to foreland basin; The Atoka Formation of the Arkoma Basin, south-central U.S.A., *in* Allen, P. A., and Homewood, P., eds., Foreland basins: International Association of Sedimentologists Special Publication 8, Oxford, Blackwell Scientific Publications, p. 327–345.

Howell, D. G., and McDougall, K. A., eds., 1978, Mesozoic Paleogeography of the Western United States: Pacific Section of the Society of Economic Paleontologists and Mineralogists, 574 p.

Howie, R. D., and Barss, M. A., 1975, Upper Paleozoic rocks of the Atlantic provinces, Gulf of St. Lawrence and adjacent continental shelf: Geological Survey of Canada Paper 74–30, p 35–50.

Hsü, K., 1958, Isostasy and a theory for the origin of geosynclines: America Journal of Science, v. 256, p. 305–327.

——, 1965, Isostasy, crustal thinning, mantle changes, and the disappearance of ancient land masses: American Journal of Science, v. 263, p. 97–109.

Hubbard, R. J., Edrich, S. P., and Rattey, P. R., 1987, Geologic evolution and hydrocarbon habitat of the Arctic Alaska microplate: Marine and Petroleum Geology, v. 4, no. 1, p. 2–34.

Issler, D. R., and Beaumont, C., 1987, Thermal and subsidence history of the Labrador and west Greenland continental margins, *in* Beaumont, C., and Tankard, A. J., eds., Sedimentary basins and basin-forming mechanisms: Canadian Society of Petroleum Geologists Memoir 12, p. 45–70.

Johnson, J. G., 1971, Timing and coordination of orogenic, epeirogenic, and eustatic events: Geological Society of America Bulletin, v. 82, p. 3263–3298.

Johnson, J. G., Klapper, G., and Sandberg, C. A., 1985, Devonian eustatic fluctuations in Euramerica: Geological Society of America Bulletin, v. 96, p. 567–587.

Johnson, K. S., and 7 others, 1988, Southern midcontinent region, *in* Sloss, L. L., ed., Sedimentary cover–North American craton, U.S.: Boulder, Colorado, Geological Society of America, Geology of North America, v. D-2, p. 307–360.

Jordan, T. E., 1981, Thrust loads and foreland basin evolution, Cretaceous, United States: American Association of Petroleum Geologists Bulletin, v. 65, p. 2506–2520.

Kanasewich, E. R., Clowes, R. M., and McCloughan, C. H., 1969, A buried Precambrian rift in Western Canada: Tectonophysics, v. 8, p. 513–527.

Karner, G. D., and Watts, A. B., 1983, Gravity anomalies and flexure of the lithosphere at mountain ranges: Journal of Geophysical Research, v. 88, p. 10449–10477.

Kay, M., 1951, North American geosynclines: Geological Society of America Memoir 48, 143 p.

Keen, C. E., 1979, Thermal history and subsidence of rifted continental margins—evidence from wells on the Nova Scotia and Labrador shelves. Canadian Journal of Earth Sciences, v. 16, p. 502–522.

Keen, C. E., and Beaumont, C., 1989, Geodynamics of rifted continental margins, *in* Keen, M. J., and Williams, G. L., eds., Geology of the continental margin of eastern Canada: Geological Survey of Canada, Geology of Canada, v. 2 (also Geological Society of America, Geology of North America, v. I-1) (in press).

Keen, C. E., Boutilier, R., De Voogd, B., Mudford, B., and Enachescu, M. E., 1987, Crustal geometry and extensional models for the Grand Banks, eastern Canada—constraints from deep seismic reflection data, *in* Beaumont, C., and Tankard, A. J., eds., Sedimentary basins and basin-forming mechanisms: Canadian Society of Petroleum Geologists Memoir 12, p. 101–116.

Kent, P., Bott, M.H.P., McKenzie, D. P., and Williams, C. A., 1982, The evolution of sedimentary basins: London, Proceedings of the Royal Society, 338 p.

King, P. B., 1948, Geology of the southern Guadalupe Mountains, West Texas: U.S. Geological Survey Professional Paper 215, 138 p.

——, 1977, Geological evolution of North America: Princeton, New Jersey, Princeton University Press, 190 p.

Kingston, D. R., Dishroon, C. P., and Williams, P. A., 1983a, Global basin classification system: American Association of Petroleum Geologists Bulletin, v. 67, p. 2175–2193.

——, 1983b, Hydrocarbon plays and global basin classification: American Association of Petroleum Geologists Bulletin, v. 67, p. 2194–2198.

Kinsman, D.J.J., 1975, Rift valley basins and sedimentary history of trailing continental margins, *in* Fischer, A. G., and Judson, S., eds., Petroleum and global tectonics: Princeton, New Jersey, Princeton University Press, p. 83–125.

Kirschner, C. E., Gryc, G., Molenaar, C. M., 1983, Regional seismic lines in the national petroleum reserve in Alaska, *in* Bally, A. W., ed., Seismic expression of structural styles—a picture and work atlas: American Association of Petroleum Geologists Studies in Geology 15, p. 1.2.5-1 to 1.2.5-14.

Klein, G. de V., and Hsui, A. T., 1987, Origin of cratonic basins: Geology, v. 15, p. 1094–1098.

Klemme, H. D., 1980, The geology of future petroleum resources: Revue de l'Institut Francais du Petrole, v. 35, no. 2, p. 337–349.

Kluth, C. F., 1986, Plate tectonics of the ancestral Rocky Mountains, *in* Peterson, J. A., ed., Paleotectonics and sedimentation in the Rocky Mountain region, United States: American Association of Petroleum Geologists Memoir 41, p. 353–370.

Kocurek, G., and Dott, R. H., Jr., 1983, Jurassic paleogeography and paleoclimate of the central and southern Rocky Mountain region, *in* Reynolds, M. W., and Dolly, E. D., eds., Mesozoic paleogeography of the west-central United States, Symposium 2: Rocky Mountain Section, Society of Economic Paleontologists and Mineralogists, p. 101–118.

Lambert, D. D., Unruh, D. M., and Gilbert, M. C., 1988, Rb-Sr and Sm-Nd isotopic study of the Glen Mountains layered complex—initiation of rifting within the southern Oklahoma aulacogen: Geology, v. 16, p. 13–17.

Lash, G. G., 1987, Geodynamic evolution of the lower Paleozoic central Appalachian foreland basin, *in* Beaumont, C., and Tankard, A. J., eds., Sedimentary basins and basin-forming mechanisms: Canadian Society of Petroleum Geologists Memoir 12, p. 413–424.

Le Pichon, X., and Sibuet, J. C., 1981, Passive margins—a model of formation: Journal of Geophysical Research, v. 86, p. 3708–3720.

Levorsen, A. I., 1960, Paleogeologic maps: San Francisco, California, W.H. Freeman and Co., 174 p.

Link, T. A., 1950, Theory of transgressive and regressive (biotherm) development and origin of oil: American Association of Petroleum Geologists Bulletin, v. 34, p. 263–299.

Longwell, C. R., 1949, Sedimentary facies in geologic history: Geological Society of America Memoir 39, 171 p.

Lopez-Ramos, E., 1969, Marine Paleozoic rocks of Mexico: American Association of Petroleum Geologists Bulletin, v. 53, p. 2399–2417.

——, 1983a, Geologia General, v. 1: Universidad Nacional Autonoma de Mexico, 357 p.

——, 1983b, Geologia De Mexico, v. 3: Universidad Nacional Autonoma de Mexico, 453 p.

——, 1985, Geologia De Mexico, v. 2: Universidad Nacional Autonoma de Mexico, 454 p.

Mallory, W. W., 1972a, Regional synthesis of the Pennsylvanian system, *in* Geological atlas of the Rocky Mountain region: Denver, Colorado, Rocky Mountain Association of Geologists, p. 111–127.

——, ed., 1972b, Geological atlas of the Rocky Mountain Region: Denver, Colorado, Rocky Mountain Association of Geologists, 331 p.

Manspeizer, W., and Cousminer, H. L., 1988, Late Triassic to Early Jurassic synrift basins of the United States Atlantic margin, *in* Sheridan, R. E., and Grow, J. A., eds., The Atlantic continental margin, U.S.: Boulder, Colorado, Geological Society of America, Geology of North America, v. I-2, p. 197–216.

Mauch, E. A., 1985, A seismic stratigraphic and structural interpretation of the Middle Paleozoic Ikpikpuk-Umiat Basin, National Petroleum Reserve, Alaska [M.A. thesis]: Houston, Texas, Rice University, 220 p.

Mayo, D. E., 1985, Mountain building theory—the nineteenth century origins of isostasy and the geosyncline, *in* Drake, E. T., and Jordan, W. M., eds., Geologists and Ideas—a history of North American geology: Boulder, Colorado, Geological Society of America Centennial Special Volume 1, p. 1–18.

McCutcheon, S. R., and Robinson, P. T., 1987, Geological constraints on the genesis of the Maritimes Basin, Atlantic Canada, *in* Beaumont, C., and Tankard, A. J., eds., Sedimentary basins and basin-forming mechanisms: Canadian Society of Petroleum Geologists Memoir 12, p. 287–298.

McIver, N. L., 1970, Appalachian turbidites, *in* Fisher, G. W., Pettijohn, F. J., Reed, J. C., Jr., and Weaver, K. N., eds., Studies of Appalachian geology; Central and southern: New York, John Wiley and Sons, p. 69–82.

McGookey, D. P., and 6 others, 1972, The Cretaceous System, *in* Mallory, W. W., ed., Geologic atlas of the Rocky Mountain region: Denver, Colorado, Rocky Mountain Association of Geologists, p. 190–228.

McKee, E. D., and 9 others, 1956, Paleotectonic maps, Jurassic System: U.S. Geological Survey Miscellaneous Geological Investigations Map I–175, 6 p., 9 plates.

McKee, E. D., and 6 others, 1959, Paleotectonic maps of the Triassic System: U.S. Geological Survey Miscellaneous Geologic Investigations Map I–300, 33 p.

McKee, E. D., and 15 others, 1967a, Paleotectonic maps of the Permian System: U.S. Geological Survey Miscellaneous Geological Investigations Map I–450.

McKee, E. D., and 15 others, 1967b, Paleotectonic investigations of the Permian System in the United States: U.S. Geological Survey Professional Paper 515, 271 p.

McKee, E. D., Crosby, E. J., and 16 others, 1975, Paleotectonic investigations of the Pennsylvanian System in the United States: U.S. Geological Survey Professional Paper 853, pt. I, 349 p.; pt. II, 192 p.

McKenzie, D., 1978, Some remarks on the development of sedimentary basins: Earth and Planetary Science Letters, v. 40, p. 25–32.

Meckel, L. D., 1970, Paleozoic alluvial deposition in the central Appalachians—a summary, *in* Fisher, G. W., Pettijohn, F. J., Reed, J. C., Jr., and Weaver, K. N., eds., Studies of Appalachian geology—central and southern: New York, John Wiley and Sons, p. 49–68.

Menard, H. W., 1969, The deep oceanic floor, *in* The Ocean: Scientific American, p. 51–63.

Meneley, R. A., 1986, Oil and gas fields in the East Coast and Arctic basins of Canada, *in* Halbouty, M., ed., Future petroleum provinces of the world: American Association of Petroleum Geologists Memoir 40, p. 143–176.

Milici, R. C., and de Witt, W., Jr., 1988, The Appalachian Basin, *in* Sloss, L. L., ed., Sedimentary cover–North American craton, U.S.: Boulder, Colorado, Geological Society of America, Geology of North America, v. D-2, p. 427–469.

Milliken, J. V., 1988, Late Paleozoic and early Mesozoic geologic evolution of the Arklatex area [M.A. thesis]: Houston, Texas, Rice University, 259 p.

Mitchum, R. M., Vail, P. R., and Thompson, S., III, 1977, Seismic stratigraphy and global changes of sea level, Part 2—The depositional sequence as a basic unit for stratigraphic analysis, *in* Payton, C. E., ed., Seismic stratigraphy—application to hydrocarbon exploration: American Association of Petroleum Geologists Memoir 26, p. 53–56.

Molenaar, C. M., and Rice, D. D., 1988, Cretaceous rocks of the western Interior basin, *in* Sloss, L. L., ed., Sedimentary cover–North American craton, U.S.: Boulder, Colorado, Geological Society of America, Geology of North America, v. D-2, p. 77–82.

Molenaar, C. M., Bird, K. J., and Kirk, A. A., 1987, Cretaceous and Tertiary stratigraphy of northeastern Alaska, *in* Tailleur, I., and Weimer, P., eds., Alaska North Slope Geology: Pacific Section, Society of Economic Paleontologists and Mineralogists and the Alaska Geological Society, v. 1, p. 513–528.

Moore, P. F., 1989, Devonian, *in* Stott, D. F., and Aitken, J. D., eds., Sedimentary cover of the craton; Canada: Geological Survey of Canada, Geology of Canada, v. 5 (also, Geological Society of America, Geology of North America, Volume D-1) (in press).

Montecchi, P. A., 1976, Some shallow tectonic consequences of subduction and their meaning to the hydrocarbon explorationist, *in* Halbouty, M., T., Maher, J. C., and Lian, H. M., eds., Circum-Pacific energy and mineral resources: American Association of Petroleum Geologists Memoir 25, p. 189–202.

Morel, P., and Irving, E. C., 1978, Tentative paleocontinental maps for the early Phanerozoic and Proterozoic: Journal of Geology, v. 86, no. 5, p. 535–561.

Moretti, I., and Chenet, P. Y., 1987, The evolution of the Suez rift—a combination of stretching and secondary convection: Tectonophysics, v. 133, p. 229–234.

Nunn, J. A., 1986, Subsidence and thermal history of the Michigan Basin, *in* Burrus, J., ed., Thermal modeling in sedimentary basins: Paris, Technip, p. 417–440.

Nunn, J. A., Sleep, N. H., and Moore, W. E., 1984, Thermal subsidence and generation of hydrocarbons in Michigan Basin: American Association of Petroleum Geologists Bulletin, v. 68, p. 296–315.

Nunn J. A., Czernlak, M., and Pilger, R. H., Jr., 1987, Constraints on the structure of Brooks Range and Colville Basin, northern Alaska, from flexure and gravity analysis: Tectonics v. 6, p. 603–617.

Palmer, A. R., 1981, Subdivision of the Sauk sequence, *in* Taylor, M. E., ed., Short papers for the Second International Symposium on the Cambrian System: U.S. Geological Survey Open-File Report 81–743, p. 160–163.

——, compiler, 1983, The Decade of North American Geology geologic time scale: Geology, v. 11, p. 503–504.

Parsons, B., and Sclater, J. G., 1977, An analysis of the variation of ocean floor bathymetry and heat flow with age: Journal of Geophysical Research, v. 82, p. 303–327.

Payton, C. E., ed., 1977, Seismic stratigraphy—applications to hydrocarbon exploration: American Association of Petroleum Geologists Memoir 26, 516 p.

Perrier, R., and Quiblier, J., 1974, Thickness changes in sedimentary layers during compaction history—methods for quantitative evaluation: American Association of Petroleum Geologists Bulletin 58, p. 507–520.

Peterson, J. A., 1972, Jurassic system, *in* Geologic Atlas of the Rocky Mountain region: Denver, Colorado, Rocky Mountain Association of Geologists, p. 177–189.

——, 1986, Paleotectonics and sedimentation in the Rocky Mountain Region, United States: American Association of Petroleum Geologists Memoir 41, 693 p.

Peterson, J. A., and MacCary, L. M., 1987, Regional stratigraphy and general petroleum geology of the United States portion of the Williston Basin and adjacent areas, *in* Longman, M. W., ed., Williston Basin—anatomy of a cratonic oil province: Denver, Colorado, Rocky Mountain Association of Geologists, p. 9–43.

Peterson, J. A., Dyer, R. C., and Clement, J. H., 1985, The Williston Basin and structural seismic exploration, *in* Gries, R. R., and Dyer, R. C., eds., Seismic exploration of the Rocky Mountain region: Denver, Colorado, Rocky Mountain Association of Geologists, p. 289–294.

Piper, J.D.A., 1983, Proterozoic paleomagnetism and single continent plate tectonics: Geophysical Journal of the Royal Astronomical Society, v. 74, no. 1, p. 163–197.

——, 1987, Paleomagnetism and the continental crust: J. Wiley and Sons, 434 p.

Poole, F. G., and Sandberg, C. A., 1977, Mississippian paleogeography and tectonics of the western United States, *in* Stewart, J. H., Stevens, C. H., and Fritsche, A. E., eds., Paleozoic paleogeography of the western United States: Pacific Section, Society of Economic Paleontologists and Mineralogists Symposium 1, p. 67–85.

Popenoe, P., 1985, Cenozoic depositional and structural history of the North Carolina margins from seismic stratigraphic analysis, *in* Poag, G. W., ed., Geologic evolution of the United States Atlantic margin: Van Nostrand Reinhold, p. 125–187.

Porter, J. W., Price R. A., and McCrossan, R. G., 1982, The western Canada sedimentary basin, *in* Kent, P., and others, eds., The evolution of sedimentary basins: Proceedings of the Royal Society of London, v. A305, p. 169–192.

Price, R. A., 1973, Large-scale gravitational flow of supracrustal rocks, southern Canadian Rockies, *in* de Jong, K. A., and Scholten, R., eds., Gravity and tectonics: New York, Wiley and Sons, p. 491–502.

——, 1986, The southeastern Canadian Cordillera—thrust faulting, tectonic wedging, and delamination of the lithosphere: Journal of Structural Geology, v. 8, p. 239–254.

Proffett, J. M., Jr., 1977, Cenozoic geology of the Yerington District, Nevada, and implications for the nature and origin of Basin and Range faulting: Geological Society of America Bulletin, v. 88, p. 247–266.

Quinlan, G. M., 1987, Models of subsidence mechanisms in intracrationic basins, and their applicability to North American examples, *in* Beaumont, C., and Tankard, A. J., eds., Sedimentary basins and basin-forming mechanisms: Canadian Society of Petroleum Geologists Memoir 12, p. 463–481.

Quinlan, G. M., and Beaumont, C., 1984, Appalachian thrusting, lithospheric flexure, and the Paleozoic stratigraphy of the Eastern Interior of North America: Canadian Journal of Earth Sciences, v. 21, p. 973–996.

Rankin, D. W., 1975, The continental margin of eastern North American in the southern Appalachians—the opening and closing of the proto-Atlantic ocean: American Journal of Science, v. 275a, p. 298–336.

Rascoe, B., Jr., and Johnson, K. S., 1988, Anadarko basin and Hugoton embayment, *in* Sloss, L. L., ed., Sedimentary cover–North American craton, U.S.: Boulder, Colorado, Geological Society of America, Geology of North America, v. D-2, p. 318–326.

Reynolds, M. W., and Dolly, E. D., eds., 1983, Mesozoic paleogeography of the west-central U.S., Symposium 2: Rocky Mountain Section, Society of Economic Paleontologists and Mineralogists, 391 p.

Richards, B. C., Bamber, E. W., Higgings, A. C., and Utting, J., 1989, Carboniferous, *in* Stott, D., and Aitken, D. L., eds., Sedimentary cover of the craton; Canada: Geological Survey of Canada, Geology of Canada, v. 1 (also, Geological Society of America, v. D-1) (in press).

Rodgers, J., 1968, The eastern edge of the North American continent during the Cambrian and Early Ordovician, *in* Zen, E., and others, eds., Studies of Appalachian geology—northern and maritime: New York, Wiley-Interscience, p. 141–149.

Roksandic, M., 1987, Hudson Bay—its tectonics and evolution, *in* Beaumont, C., and Tankard, A. J., eds., Sedimentary basins and basin-forming mechanisms: Canadian Society of Petroleum Geologists Memoir 12, p. 483–506.

Ross, C. A., and Ross, J.R.P., 1987, Late Paleozoic sea levels and depositional sequences: Cushman Foundation for Foraminiferal Research Special Publication 24, p. 137–149.

Royden, L., 1986, A simple method for analysing subsidence and heat flow in extensional basins, *in* Burrus, J., ed., Thermal modeling in sedimentary basins: Paris, Technip, Collection 44, p. 49–74.

Royden, L., and Karner, G. D., 1984, Flexure of lithosphere beneath Appennine and Carpathian foredeep basins—evidence for an insufficient topographic load: American Association of Petroleum Geologists Bulletin, v. 68, p. 704–712.

Royden, L., and Keen, C. E., 1980, Rifting process and thermal evolution of the continental margin of eastern Canada determined from subsidence curves: Earth and Planetary Science Letters, v. 51, p. 342–361.

Royden, L. H., and Horvath, F. A., eds., 1988, The Pannonian basin—a study in basin evolution: American Association of Petroleum Geologists, Memoir 45, 394 p.

Sanford, B. V., 1987, Paleozoic geology of the Hudson Platform, *in* Beaumont, C., and Tankard, A. J., eds., Sedimentary basins and basin-forming mechanisms: Canadian Society of Petroleum Geologists Memoir 12, p. 483–506.

Sarg, J. F., 1989, Middle-Late Permian depositional sequences, Permian Basin, West Texas–New Mexico, *in* Bally, A. W., ed., Atlas of seismic stratigraphy,

v. 3: American Association of Petroleum Geologists (in press).

Schwab, F. L., ed., 1982, Geosynclines, concept and place within plate tectonics: Benchmark Papers in Geology, v. 74, Hutchinson Ross, 408 p.

Sclater, J. G., and Christie, P.A.F., 1980, Continental stretching—an explanation of the post mid-Cretaceous subsidence of the central North Sea basin: Journal of Geophysical Research, v. 85, p. 3711–3739.

Sclater, J. G., and Francheteau, J., 1970, The implication of terrestrial heat flow observations on current tectonic and geochemical models of the crust and upper mantle of the earth: Geophysical Journal of Royal Astronomical Society, v. 20, p. 509–542.

Sears, J. W., and Price, P. A., 1978, The Siberian connection—a case for Precambrian separation of the North American and Siberian cratons: Geology, v. 6, p. 267–270.

Sexton, J. L., Braile, L. W., Hinze, W. J., and Campbell, M. J., 1986, Seismic reflection profiling studies of a buried Precambrian rift beneath the Wabash Valley Fault Zone: Geophysics, v. 51, p. 640–660.

Sheridan, R. E., and Grow, J. A., 1988, The Atlantic continental margin, United States: Boulder, Colorado, Geological Society of America Geology of North America, v. I-2, 611 p.

Skipp, B., and Hall, W. E., 1980, Upper Paleozoic paleotectonics and paleogeography of Idaho, *in* Fouch, T. D., and Magathan, E. R., eds., Paleozoic paleogeography of the west-central United States: Rocky Mountain Section, Society of Economic Paleontologists and Mineralogists, p. 387–422.

Skipp, B. W., Sando, W. J., and Hall, W. E., 1979, The Mississippian and Pennsylvanian (Carboniferous) Systems in the United States—Idaho: U.S. Geological Survey Professional Paper 1110-AA, p. AA1–AA2.

Sleep, N. H., 1971, Thermal effects of the formation of Atlantic continental margins by continental break-up: Royal Astronomical Society Geophysical Journal, v. 24, p. 325–350.

Sleep, N. H., and Sloss, L. L., 1980, The Michigan Basin, *in* Bally, A. W., Bender, P. L., McGetchin, T. R., and Walcott, P. I., eds., Dynamics of plate interiors: American Geophysical Union, Geodynamics Series, v. 1, p. 93–98.

Sleep, N. H., Nunn, J. A., and Chou, L., 1980, Platform basins: Annual Review of Earth and Planetary Sciences, v. 8, p. 17–34.

Sloss, L. L., 1963, Sequences in the cratonic interior of North America: Geological Society America Bulletin, v. 74, p. 93–114.

——, 1972, Synchrony of Phanerozoic sedimentary tectonic events of the North American craton and the Russian platform: 24th Session, International Geological Congress, Section 4, p. 24–32.

——, 1976, Areas and volumes of cratonic sediments, western North America and eastern Europe: Geology, v. 4, p. 272–276.

——, 1987, Williston in the family of cratonic basins, *in* Longman, M. W., ed., Williston Basin—Anatomy of a cratonic oil province: Rocky Mountain Association of Petroleum Geologists, p. 1–8.

——, 1988a, ed., Sedimentary cover–North American craton, U.S.: Boulder, Colorado, Geological Society of America, Geology of North America, v. D-2, 506 p.

——, 1988b, Conclusions, *in* Sloss, L. L., ed., Sedimentary cover–North American craton, U.S.: Boulder, Colorado, Geological Society of America, Geology of North America, v. D-2, p. 493–496.

——, 1988c, Tectonic evolution of the craton in Phanerozoic time, *in* Sloss, L. L., ed., Sedimentary cover–North American craton, U.S.: Boulder, Colorado, Geological Society of America, Geology of North America, v. D-2, p. 25–52.

——, 1988d, Forty years of sequence stratigraphy: Geological Society of America Bulletin, v. 100, p. 1661–1665.

Sloss, L. L., and Speed, R. C., 1974, Relationships of cratonic and continental margin tectonic episodes, *in* Dickinson, W. R., ed., Tectonics and sedimentation: Society of Economic Paleontologists and Mineralogists Special Publication 22, p. 98–119.

Sloss, L. L., Krumbein, W. C., and Dapples, E. C., 1949, Integrated facies analysis, *in* Longwell, C. R., ed., Sedimentary facies in geologic history: Geological Society of America Memoir 39, p. 91–124.

Soares, P. C., Landim, P.M.B.L., and Fulfaro, V. J., 1978, Tectonic cycles and sedimentary sequences in the Brazilian intracratonic basins: Geological Society of America Bulletin, v. 89, p. 181–191.

Spohn, T., and Schubert, G., 1982, Convective thinning of the lithosphere; A mechanism for the initiation of continental rifting: Journal of Geophysical Research, v. 87, p. 4669–4681.

Stanley, S. M., 1985, Earth and life through time: San Francisco, California, W. H. Freeman, 690 p.

Steckler, M. S., 1985, Uplift and extension at the Gulf of Suez; Indications of induced mantle convection: Nature, v. 317, p. 135–139.

Steckler, M. S., and Watts, A. B., 1978, The Gulf of Lion—subsidence of a young continental margin: Nature, v. 287, p. 425–430.

——, 1982, Subsidence history and tectonic evolution of Atlantic-type continental margins, *in* Scrutton, R. A., ed., Dynamics of passive continental margins: American Geophysical Union, Geodynamics Series, v. 6, p. 184–196.

Stephenson, R. A., Embry, A. F., Nakiboglu, S. M., and Hastaoglu, M. A., 1987, Rift-initiated Permian to early Cretaceous subsidence of the Sverdrup Basin, *in* Beaumont, C., and Tankard, A. J., eds., Sedimentary basins and basin-forming mechanisms: Canadian Society of Petroleum Geologists Memoir 12, p. 213–232.

Stevenson, G. M., and Baars, D. L., 1986, The Paradox—a pull-apart basin of Pennsylvanian age, *in* Peterson, J. A., ed., Paleotectonics and sedimentation in the Rocky Mountain region: American Association of Petroleum Geologists Memoir 41, p. 513–540.

Stewart, J. H., 1972, Initial deposits in the Cordilleran geosyncline—evidence of a Late Precambrian continental separation: Geological Society of America Bulletin, v. 83, p. 1345–1360.

——, 1976, Late Precambrian evolution of North America; Plate tectonic implication: Geology, v. 4, p. 11–15.

Stewart, J. H., and Suczek, C. A., 1977, Cambrian and latest Precambrian paleogeography and tectonics in the western United States, *in* Stewart, J. H., Stevens, C. H., and Fritsche, A. E., eds., Pacific Coast Paleogeography Symposium 1: Pacific Section, Society of Economic Paleontologists and Mineralogists, p. 1–17.

Stewart, J. H., Stevens, C. H., and Fritsche, A. E., eds., 1977, Paleozoic paleogeography of the western United States: Pacific Section, Society of Economic Paleontologists and Mineralogists, 502 p.

Stille, H., 1924, Grundfragen der vergleichenden Tektonik: Berlin, Borntraeger, 413 p.

Stockmal, G. S., and Beaumont, C., 1987, Geodynamic models of the convergent margin tectonics—the southern Canadian Cordillera and the Swiss Alps, *in* Beaumont, C., and Tankard, A. J., eds., Sedimentary basins and basin-forming mechanisms: Canadian Society of Petroleum Geologists Memoir 12, p. 393–402.

Stockmal, G. S., Beaumont, C., and Boutilier, R., 1986, Geodynamic models of convergent margin tectonics—transition from rifted margin to overthrust belt and consequences for foreland-basin development: American Association of Petroleum Geologists Bulletin, v. 70, p. 181–190.

Stott, D. F., and Aitken, J. D., eds., 1989, Sedimentary cover of the craton; Canada: Geological Survey of Canada, v. 5 (also Geological Society of America, Geology of North America, v. D-1) (in press).

Stott, D. F., and 7 others, 1989, Cretaceous, *in* Stott, D. F., and Aitken, J. D., eds., Sedimentary cover of the craton; Canada: Geological Survey of Canada, Geology of Canada, v. 5 (also, Geological Society of America, Geology of North America, v. D-1) (in press).

Struik, L. C., 1988, Crustal evolution of the eastern Canadian Cordillera: Tectonics, v. 7, no. 4, p. 727–748.

Summerhayes, C. P., 1986, Sea-level curves based on seismic stratigraphy—their chronostratigraphic significance: Palaeogeography, Palaeoclimatology, Palaeoecology, v. 57, no. 1, p. 27–42.

Sutherland, P. K., 1988, Arkoma basin, *in* Sloss, L. L., ed., Sedimentary cover–North American craton, U.S.: Boulder, Colorado, Geological Society of America, Geology of North America, v. D-2, p. 331–340.

Tankard, A. J., 1986, On the depositional response to thrusting and lithospheric flexure—Examples from the Appalachian and Rocky Mountain basins, *in*

Allen, P., and Homewood, P., eds., Foreland basins: International Association of Sedimentologists Special Publication 8, p. 369–392.
Thomas, W. A., 1977, Evolution of Appalachian–Ouachita salients, and recesses from reentrants and promontories in the continental margin: American Journal of Science, v. 277, p. 1233–1278.
Vail, P. R., 1987, Seismic stratigraphy interpretation using sequence stratigraphy, *in* Bally, A. W., ed., Atlas of seismic stratigraphy: American Association of Petroleum Geologists Studies in Geology, v. 27, p. 11–14.
Vail, P. R., Mitchum, R. M., Jr., and Thompson, S., III, 1977, Global Cycles of Relative Changes of Sea Level, *in* Payton, C. E., ed., Seismic stratigraphy—applications to hydrocarbon exploration: American Association of Petroleum Geologists Memoir 26, p. 83–97.
Vail, P. R., and 5 others, 1987, La stratigraphie séquentielle et son application aux corrélations chronostratigraphiques dans le Jurassique du basin de Paris: Bulletin de la Société Geologique de France, v. 7, p. 1301–1322.
Van der Voo, R., and Watts, D. R., 1978, Paleomagnetic results from igneous and sedimentary rocks from the Michigan basin borehole: Journal of Geophysical Research, v. 83, p. 5844–5848.
van Hinte, J. E., 1978, Geohistory analyses—applications of micropaleontology in exploration geology: American Association of Petroleum Geologists Bulletin, v. 62, p. 201–222.
Van Wagoner, J. C., Mitchum, R. M., Jr., Posamentier, H. W., and Vail, P. R., 1987, Seismic stratigraphy interpretation using sequence stratigraphy, *in* Bally, A. W., ed., Atlas of seismic stratigraphy: American Association of Petroleum Geologists Studies in Geology, v. 27, p. 11–14.
Vogt, P. R., and Tucholke, B. E., eds., 1986, The western North Atlantic region: Boulder, Colorado, Geological Society of America, Geology of North America, v. M, 696 p.
Wade, J. A., and MacLean, B. C., 1989, Aspects of the geology of the Scotian basins from recent seismic and well data, *in* Keen, M. J., and Williams, G. L., eds., Geology of the continental margin of eastern Canada: Geological Survey of Canada, Geology of Canada, v. 2 (also, Geological Society of America, Geology of North America, No. I-1) (in press).
Walcott, R., 1972, Gravity, flexure, and the growth of sedimentary basins at a continental edge: Geological Society of America Bulletin, v. 83, p. 1845–1848.
Wanless, H. R., and Shepard, F. P., 1936, Sea level and climatic changes related to Late Paleozoic cycles: Geological Society of America Bulletin, v. 47, p. 1177–1206.
Watts, A. B., and Ryan, W.B.R., 1976, Flexure of the lithosphere at continental margins: Tectonophysics, v. 36, p. 25–44.
Watts, A. B., and Steckler, M. S., 1979, Subsidence and eustacy at the continental margin of eastern North America: American Geophysical Union, M. Ewing Series, v. 3, p. 218–234.
Watts, A. B., and Thorne, J., 1984, Tectonics, global changes in sea level and their relationship to stratigraphic sequences at the United States Atlantic continental Margin: Marine and Petroleum Geology, v. 1, p. 319–339.
Watts, A. B., Karner, C. D., and Steckler, M. S., 1982, Lithospheric flexure and the evolution of sedimentary basins, *in* Kent, P., and others, eds., The evolution of sedimentary basins: Philosophical Transactions of the Royal Society of London, v. 305A, p. 249–282.
Weimer, R. J., 1983, Relation of unconformities, tectonics, and sea-level changes—Cretaceous of the Denver Basin and adjacent areas, *in* Reynolds, M. W., and Dolly, E. D., eds., Mesozoic paleogeography of the west-central United States, Rocky Mountain Paleogeography Symposium 2: Rocky Mountain Section, Society of Economic Paleontologists and Mineralogists, p. 359–376.
——, 1986, Relationship of unconformities, tectonics, and sea-level changes in the Cretaceous of the western interior, U.S., *in* Peterson, J. A., ed., Paleotectonics and sedimentation in the Rocky Mountain region, United States: American Association of Petroleum Geologists Memoir 41, p. 397–422.
Welsink, H. J., and Tankard, A., 1988, Structural and stratigraphic framework of the Jeanne D'Arc Basin, Grand Banks, *in* Bally, A. W., ed., Atlas of seismic stratigraphy, v. 2: American Association of Petroleum Geologists Studies in Geology, v. 27, p. 14–21.
Wernicke, B., 1985, Uniform-sense normal simple shear of the continental lithosphere: Canadian Journal of Earth Sciences, v. 22, p. 108–125.
Wheeler, H. E., 1963, Post-Sauk and pre-Absaroka Paleozoic stratigraphic patterns in North America: American Association of Petroleum Geologists Bulletin, v. 47, p. 1497–1526.
White, D. A., 1980, Assessing oil and gas plays in facies cycle wedges: American Association of Petroleum Geologists Bulletin, v. 64, p. 1158–1178.
Winker, C. D., 1982, Cenozoic shelf margins, Northwestern Gulf of Mexico basin: Gulf Coast Association of Geological Societies Transactions, v. 32, p. 427–448.
Ziegler, P., 1988, Evolution of the Arctic–North Atlantic and western Tethys: American Association of Petroleum Geologists Memoir 43, 198 p.
Zoback, M. D., Hamilton, R. M., Crone, A. J., Russ, D. P., McKeown, F. A., and Brockman, S. R., 1980, Recurrent intraplate tectonism in the New Madrid seismic zone: Science, v. 209, p. 971–976.

Manuscript Accepted by the Society December 22, 1988

ACKNOWLEDGMENTS

This type of an overview chapter cannot possibly be a one-man show. Many key authors are credited in my reference list. I ask forgiveness from authors whose views should have been mentioned but were overlooked. Because much of my stratigraphic background was obtained during my Shell days, let me specifically thank my former Canadian colleagues P. F. Moore, J. Stout, G. Bassett, and P. Ziegler; and my former United States colleagues T. D. Cook and R. E. Farmer. This chapter was reviewed by L. Sloss, P. Vail, J. Wheeler, and A. R. Palmer. I thank all of them for their prompt and constructive reviews. Most of their suggestions I accepted, but on occasion I agreed to disagree. I am most grateful to Ms. Chingju Liu, my cheerful assistant, for preparing most of the figures and recalculating the accumulation maps. Finally thank you Ms. Edie Scott for so patiently typing this manuscript. As is customary, all the above-mentioned people are responsible for any mistakes the reader may find!

Printed in U.S.A.

The Geology of North America
Vol. A, The Geology of North America—An overview
The Geological Society of America, 1989

Chapter 16

Precambrian geology and tectonic history of North America

Paul F. Hoffman
Geological Survey of Canada, Ottawa, Ontario K1A 0E4, Canada

INTRODUCTION: TECTONIC ELEMENTS AND EVOLUTION

North America is an old continent. Whereas South America and Africa were not assembled until 0.7 Ga, and the assembly of Eurasia began at 0.3 Ga, most of the North American craton has been coherent since 1.7 Ga. This craton, known as Laurentia, included Greenland and northwest Scotland until their partial separation in the Late Cretaceous. This chapter describes the constituents of Laurentia, their aggregation in the Early Proterozoic (Table 1), and subsequent adventures of the craton until the rifting events at the end of the Proterozoic, which gave the continent approximately its present shape.

Radiogenic isotopic data from the Precambrian shield, and from inliers and subsurface samples on the platform indicate that about 55 percent of the area of the craton separated from the mantle in the Archean and about 45 percent in the Proterozoic (Fig. 1). In this regard, the shield is not representative of the craton as a whole, being strongly biased in favor of Archean crust (Fig. 2). Conversely, most of the Proterozoic crust underlies the Phanerozoic sedimentary veneer of the southern interior platform.

The Archean protocraton of Laurentia is an aggregate of seven former microcontinents (Fig. 1): the familiar Superior, Wyoming, Slave, and Nain (North Atlantic) provinces, and the newly recognized Hearne, Rae, and Burwell provinces (formerly parts of the composite Churchill province). The Rae province includes northern, southwestern, and southeastern prongs. Each province is a Late Archean crustal aggregate and contains variable proportions of Early and/or Middle Archean crust. Early Proterozoic rifting and subsequent collisional deformation govern the dimensions of the provinces. Some of the provinces may have had common ancestry prior to Early Proterozoic rifting, but this is speculative.

The Archean provinces are welded by Early Proterozoic collisional orogens (Fig. 3). The orogens are characterized by deformed passive-margin and foredeep sedimentary prisms, and foreland thrust-fold belts. Their hinterlands, bordered by Andean-type magmatic arcs, have regions of basement reactivation, thrusting, and transcurrent shearing accommodating collisional foreland indentation. Only the Trans-Hudson orogen, which separates the Superior province from the Wyoming and Hearne provinces, preserves a significant width (up to 400 km) of juvenile Proterozoic crust, including relics of island arcs and obducted oceanic crust. The Thelon orogen tightly welds the Slave and Rae provinces, the Snowbird orogen, the Hearne and Rae provinces, and the New Quebec orogen the Superior and Rae provinces. The Nain and Rae provinces are separated by a branching system of orogens (Torngat, Foxe, Rinkian, and Nagssugtoqidian orogens), which enclose the small Burwell province. The Wyoming and Hearne provinces are welded in the subsurface by the Great Falls orogen. U-Pb isotopic ages for the orogenic events show that the protocraton was assembled between 1.98 and 1.83 Ga (Fig. 4).

TABLE 1. GEOLOGIC TIME DIVISIONS

Age	Division
0 Ga	
	Phanerozoic
0.57 Ga	
	Late Proterozoic
0.90 Ga	
	Middle Proterozoic
1.60 Ga	
	Early Proterozoic
2.50 Ga	
	Late Arechean
3.00 Ga	
	Middle Archean
3.40 Ga	
	Early Archean
3.80 Ga	
	Hadean
4.6 Ga	

The Archean protocraton is flanked to the west, south, and southeast by crust that was accreted in the Early Proterozoic and contains little or no Archean material (Fig. 1). In the Wopmay orogen and its subsurface extensions, terranes having apparent crust-formation ages of 2.4 to 2.1 Ga were accreted onto the western margin of the protocraton between 1.91 and about 1.7 Ga. Juvenile crust was accreted between about 1.86 and 1.80 Ga onto the southern and southeastern margins of the protocontinent in the Penokean and Ketilidian-Makkovik orogens respectively. Between 1.80 and 1.65 Ga, more than 1,200 km of juvenile crust was accreted in the southern and southwestern United States

Hoffman, P. F., 1989, Precambrian geology and tectonic history of North America, *in* Bally, A. W., and Palmer, A. R., eds., The Geology of North America—An overview: Boulder, Colorado, Geological Society of America, The Geology of North America, v. A.

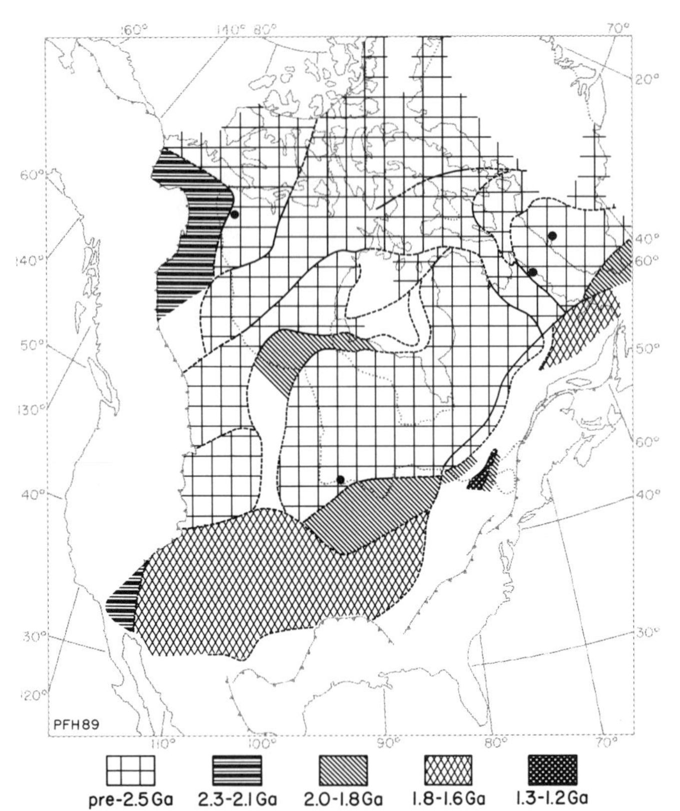

Figure 1. Distribution of crust by age of formation for the North American shield and platforms. Pre-drift restoration of Greenland after *Rowley and Lottes (1988)*. Dotted lines indicate edge of shield. Areas of uncertain crust-formation age are unpatterned. Heavy dots locate crust over 3.5 Ga. Inferred Proterozoic sutures between areas of Archean (pre-2.5 Ga) crust are indicated by pattern offsets.

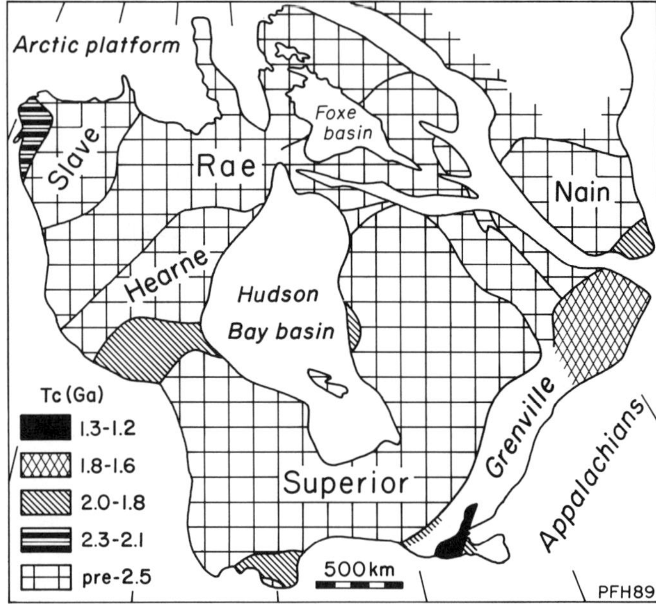

Figure 2. Distribution of crust by age of formation in the Canadian shield and Greenland in pre-drift restoration. Inferred Proterozoic sutures indicated as in Figure 1. Note bias in favor of Archean crust in shield relative to craton. Uplift of Proterozoic crust in southeastern shield may manifest mantle upwelling responsible for Atlantic geoid high.

(Central Plains and Yavapai-Mazatzal orogens respectively). Extensions of the same age occur in the Great Lakes area (Killarney belt) and southern Labrador (Labrador orogen), where they were reworked by the 1.2- to 1.0-Ga Grenvillian orogeny. Except for the more internal zones of the Grenville orogen, the Laurentian craton was assembled by 1.65 Ga.

A variety of sedimentary basins and igneous suites ranging in age from 1.8 to 1.2 Ga compose postorogenic overlap assemblages on the craton. The oldest (1.85 to 1.65 Ga) formed in the interior of the Archean protocraton while tectonic accretion was ongoing at its margins. They include 1.85-Ga alkaline and 1.75-Ga subalkaline igneous suites and 1.7-Ga cratonic basins west of Hudson Bay. Between 1.5 and 1.3 Ga, anorogenic gabbro-anorthosite-granite suites were intruded in the eastern part of the Archean protocraton, and widespread syenogranite-rhyolite suites were emplaced in the southern and southwestern parts of the Early Proterozoic accreted terranes. Between 1.3 and 1.1 Ga, scattered alkaline igneous complexes and extensive mafic dike swarms penetrated the craton, the latter feeding plateau lava fields. Deep localized sedimentary basins, most poorly dated, formed along the western and northern margins of the craton between 1.6 and 0.8 Ga.

The Grenville orogen, extending from southern Sweden to southern Mexico, was a zone of northwest-directed crustal-scale thrusting between 1.2 and 1.0 Ga. Its southeastern part includes terranes accreted during the Grenvillian orogeny, but its northwestern part reworked terranes already accreted in the Early Proterozoic and impinged on the Archean protocraton. The Midcontinent rift (1.11 to 1.09 Ga), containing 15 to 20 km of basalt, formed contemporaneously with the Grenvillian orogeny. Meanwhile, the Racklan orogeny was affecting rocks older than 1.27 Ga in the northern Cordillera and western Arctic platform, where seismic reflection profiling reveals a southeast-directed thrust belt in the subsurface.

Between 0.8 and 0.5 Ga, polyphase rifting created the continental margins, which would evolve into the Paleozoic orogens bordering the continent. During the Paleozoic, Late Proterozoic arc terranes of Gondwanide ancestry were accreted in the Appalachians, and Grenvillian terranes in the Franklinides and Ouachitas.

ARCHEAN PROVINCES

An Archean province, as here defined, is (or was, in the case of three provinces split by the separation of Greenland) a contiguous area of Archean continental lithosphere framed by Proterozoic orogens inferred to be suture zones. The seven Archean provinces recognized differ from each other in the ages and arrangement of their internal constituent terranes. The Superior and

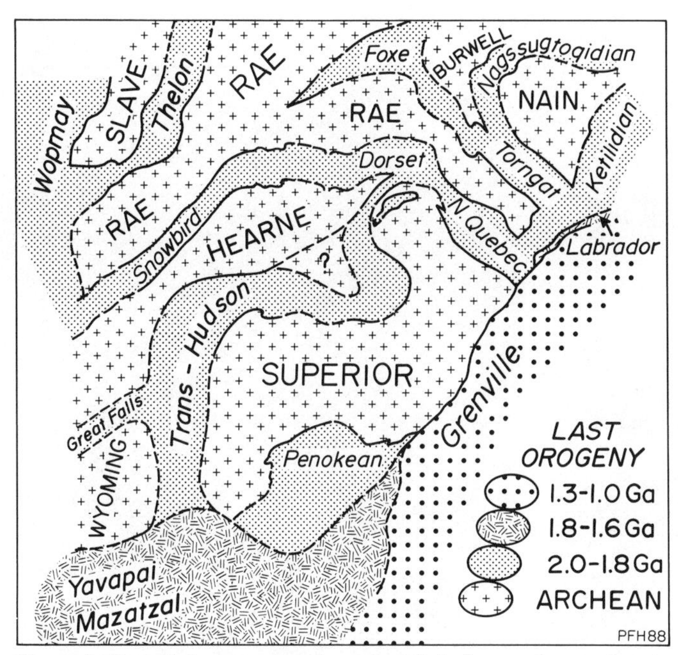

Figure 3. Exploded craton showing inferred Archean microcontinents (upper case names) and bounding Proterozoic orogens (italic lower case names). Separation of Archean provinces is arbitrary and not meant to imply a particular paleogeography.

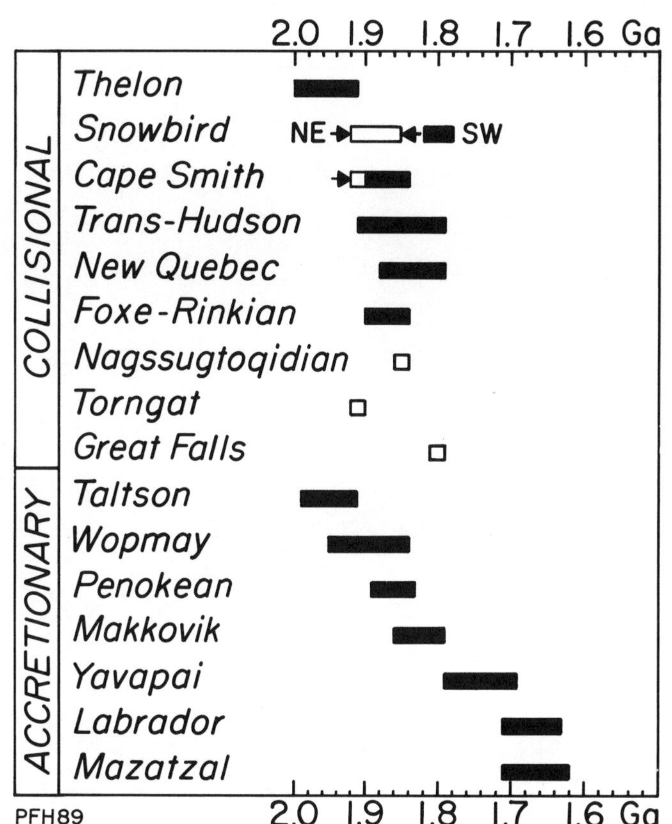

Figure 4. Age spans for Early Proterozoic orogens as indicated by U-Pb ages for orogenic igneous and/or metamorphic suites. Igneous suites represent foredeep, island arc, continental arc, and collisional anatectic magmatism; metamorphic ages are based on zircon and monazite, but not titanite, dating. Open boxes represent single ages and arrows indicate minimum or maximum limits based on pre- or post-orogenic rocks. For the Snowbird orogen, age spans for the shield (NE) and platform (SW) are shown.

Slave provinces, for example, contain small areas of pre–3.5 Ga crust but are largely composed of crust formed after 3.0 Ga. Large areas of the Superior province formed at 2.8 to 2.7 Ga, and of the Slave province at 2.7 to 2.6 Ga. The Wyoming and Nain provinces, in contrast, are composed mainly of terranes formed before 3.1 and 2.9 Ga respectively, although they were not finally assembled until about 2.7 Ga. In fact, all the provinces experienced strong compressional deformation with attendant plutonism and metamorphism between 2.8 and 2.6 Ga.

Superior province

Having an exposed area of 1.6 million km^2, the Superior province (Fig. 5) is by far the largest Archean province and thereby offers an unrivalled perspective on early crustal genesis. In common with other Archean provinces, the rocks exposed are compositionally similar to those formed at younger subduction zones, with differences attributable to higher mean mantle temperature and possibly greater crustal (slab?) melting at mantle depths in the Archean. The similarity in composition has led to the suggestion that Archean crust formed by the successive accretion of Archean equivalents of island arcs. This scenario predicts that Archean crust should be aggregated from belts of relatively uniform age along strike but incrementally varying age across strike (*Krogh and Davis, 1971*). More than 250 precise U-Pb zircon ages, mainly determined by T. E. Krogh and his associates, have confirmed this prediction.

The Superior province provides a valuable perspective on another long-standing question in Archean tectonics: Are high-grade gneiss terrains and low-grade volcanic-plutonic terrains fundamentally different crustal types, or do they merely represent different erosion levels? The latter view is supported by studies (Percival, 1989a) of three linear terranes in the Superior province that grade from low grade to high grade along strike (Wawa to Kapuskasing, Sachigo to Pikwitonei, James Bay to Ashuanipi).

The Superior province is composed of subparallel east-northeast–trending belts of contrasting lithology, age, and/or metamorphic grade (*Card, 1989*). As the belted structure is truncated at the western margin of the province by the Trans-Hudson orogen and at the eastern margin by the Grenville and New Quebec orogens (Fig. 5), the province must be a rifted fragment of a larger Late Archean crustal assembly.

There are four types of belts (*Card, 1989*): (1) volcanic-plutonic terranes, which resemble island arcs; (2) metasedimentary belts, which resemble accretionary prisms; (3) plutonic

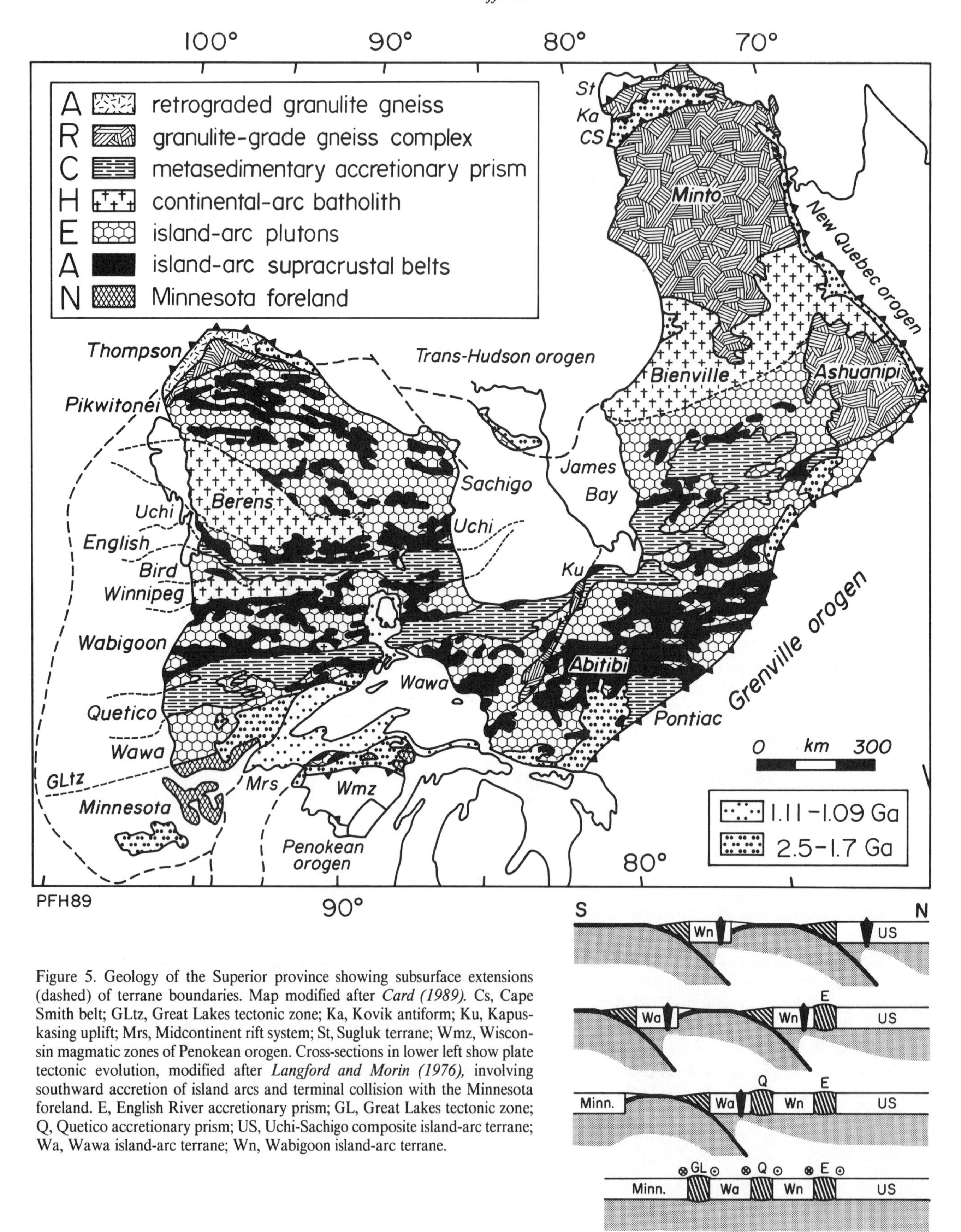

Figure 5. Geology of the Superior province showing subsurface extensions (dashed) of terrane boundaries. Map modified after *Card (1989).* Cs, Cape Smith belt; GLtz, Great Lakes tectonic zone; Ka, Kovik antiform; Ku, Kapuskasing uplift; Mrs, Midcontinent rift system; St, Sugluk terrane; Wmz, Wisconsin magmatic zones of Penokean orogen. Cross-sections in lower left show plate tectonic evolution, modified after *Langford and Morin (1976),* involving southward accretion of island arcs and terminal collision with the Minnesota foreland. E, English River accretionary prism; GL, Great Lakes tectonic zone; Q, Quetico accretionary prism; US, Uchi-Sachigo composite island-arc terrane; Wa, Wawa island-arc terrane; Wn, Wabigoon island-arc terrane.

complexes, which may have formed continental slivers within island arcs; and (4) high-grade gneiss complexes, most of which are simply deeper erosion levels of the other belt types (Percival, 1989a). One gneiss belt (Minnesota) is part of an older (3.6 Ga) foreland against which the younger terranes to the north were accreted. Isotopically, the southernmost island-arc terrane (Wawa-Abitibi) appears to be composed mainly of juvenile crust (*Arth and Hanson, 1975*; *Corfu and Grunsky, 1987*), whereas terranes to the north preserve multiple generations of arc construction back to 3.0 Ga. The main terminal orogeny occurred about 2.725 Ga in the Uchi-Sachigo terrane, about 2.705 Ga in the Wabigoon terrane, and about 2.695 Ga in the Wawa-Abitibi terrane (*Card, 1989*). Thus, the arc terranes appear to have been assembled progressively from north to south (*Krogh and Davis, 1971*; Langford and Morin, 1976) before finally colliding collectively with the foreland. The metasedimentary belts and southern arc terranes were deformed in a dextral transpressive regime (*Poulsen, 1986*; *Hudleston and others, 1988*), suggesting an oblique dextral component of plate convergence between the arcs and the foreland.

Minnesota foreland. Tonalitic to granodioritic orthogneisses of Early Archean age occur with amphibolites in the southwest corner of the Superior province (*Morey and Hanson, 1980*). Protoliths of the tonalitic gneisses crystallized at 3.66 Ga and were first deformed about 3.6 Ga (*Goldich and Fischer, 1986*). They were subsequently deformed, metamorphosed, and intruded by granite at about 3.05 and 2.7 Ga. The ancient gneiss complex is separated from the 2.7-Ga Wawa terrane by the Great Lakes tectonic zone (Fig. 5), a seismically reflective layer dipping about 30° to the north-northwest (*Gibbs and others, 1984*) and partly overprinted by south-southeast–dipping Penokean (1.85 Ga) thrusts (Southwick and others, 1988). The Great Lakes tectonic zone is currently viewed as a 2.7-Ga suture along which the amalgamated island-arc terranes to the north were thrust onto the 3.6-Ga Minnesota foreland. Precise ages are required to determine if the Late Archean granites south of the suture formed during the arc-continent collision or manifest an earlier Andean-type arc in the foreland.

Wawa island-arc terrane. Flanked by the Great Lakes tectonic zone and the Quetico metasedimentary belt, the Wawa terrane (*Card, 1989*) exposes volcanic and sedimentary rocks and subvolcanic plutons, deformed by late open upright-plunging folds imposed on early tight recumbent folds and related shear zones (*Hooper and Ojakangas, 1971*; *Bauer, 1985*), metamorphosed to greenschist or amphibolite grade, and cut by post-tectonic 2.68-Ga granites. The deformation involves rocks as young as 2.69 Ga and records early transverse shortening with progressively increasing dextral transcurrent and north-side-up components of displacement (*Hudleston and others, 1988*). The volcanic rocks consist of mafic tholeiites intercalated with iron-formation and mixed mafic-felsic calc-alkaline suites (2.75 to 2.71 Ga) intruded by coeval tonalitic plutons, and are overlain unconformably by terrestrial and marine epiclastic sediments derived from the underlying volcanics and tonalites (*Sims, 1976*; *Schulz, 1980*; *Shegelski, 1980*; *Turek and others, 1984*; *Corfu and Stott, 1986*; *Sylvester and others, 1987*). The sediments contain tonalite clasts as young as 2.70 Ga and are interspersed with mixed mafic-felsic calc-alkaline to shoshonitic 2.69-Ga volcanic complexes. Unrecognized early structural telescoping may account for some apparent stratigraphic repetitions, but distinctly older (2.88 Ga) felsic volcanics have been documented locally (*Turek and others, 1988*).

Kapuskasing uplift. The Wawa and Abitibi are correlative colinear terranes interrupted by a crustal-scale southeast-vergent thrust of Early Proterozoic age (*Percival and Card, 1985*; Percival and McGrath, 1986; *Anonymous, 1988*; *Boland and others, 1988*). The hanging wall of the thrust uplift exposes an oblique cross section 20 km deep through the Wawa-Abitibi terrane (Fig. 6). The deepest levels consist of planar mylonitic para- and orthogneisses, including stratiform anorthosite-gabbro-ultramafic intrusions, metamorphosed to upper amphibolite or granulite grade at 7 to 9 kbar. To the west is an intermediate level composed of gneissic tonalite, granodiorite, and granite having domal and ductile extensional structures, and amphibolite-grade metamorphic enclaves equilibrated at 4 to 6 kbar. The highest level corresponds to the greenschist to lower amphibolite-grade Wawa volcanic-plutonic terrane, metamorphosed at 2 to 3 kbar. The basic thrust structure is complicated by northwest-side-down hanging-wall normal faults.

Thrusting must have occurred before 1.87 Ga, when the highest grade gneisses were pierced by high-level alkaline complexes (*Bell and others, 1987*). Progressive younging of all radiometric systems with increasing paleodepth (U-Pb zircon, 2.70 to 2.62 Ga; U-Pb titanite, 2.69 to 2.49 Ga; K-Ar hornblende, 2.69 to 2.48 Ga; Rb-Sr biotite, 2.50 to 1.93 Ga) suggests slow (nearly isobaric) conductive cooling following crust formation at 2.7 Ga, and later thrusting at about 1.9 Ga (*Percival and others, 1988*). The inferred age and orientation of the uplift implies a genetic relation to convergence at the Thompson segment of the Trans-Hudson orogen, or alternatively to that part of the Penokean orogen later incorporated in the Grenville orogen. As a crustal-scale intracontinental thrust, the Kapuskasing uplift resembles the Laramide uplifts of the western United States and the active Tien Shan uplifts in central Asia.

Abitibi island-arc terrane. An unusually shallow erosion level accounts for the relatively high proportion of supracrustal rocks (MERQ-OGS, 1983), and the large areas of prehnite-pumpellyite and lower greenschist metamorphic grades in this richly mineralized terrane (*Jolly, 1978*). Amphibolite-grade rocks are limited to aureoles of plutons and the transition with the Pontiac belt. The oldest rocks in the terrane are extensive submarine platforms of tholeiitic and komatiitic flows with thin pelagic chemical horizons (*Dimroth and others, 1982*). Although not dated directly, a mafic platform in the extreme northeast of the terrane is overlain by a 2.80-Ga rhyolite (*Allard and others, 1985*; J. K. Mortensen, personal communication, 1988). Throughout the terrane, the tholeiitic-komatiitic platforms are overlain by mixed tholeiitic and calcalkaline, submarine to emer-

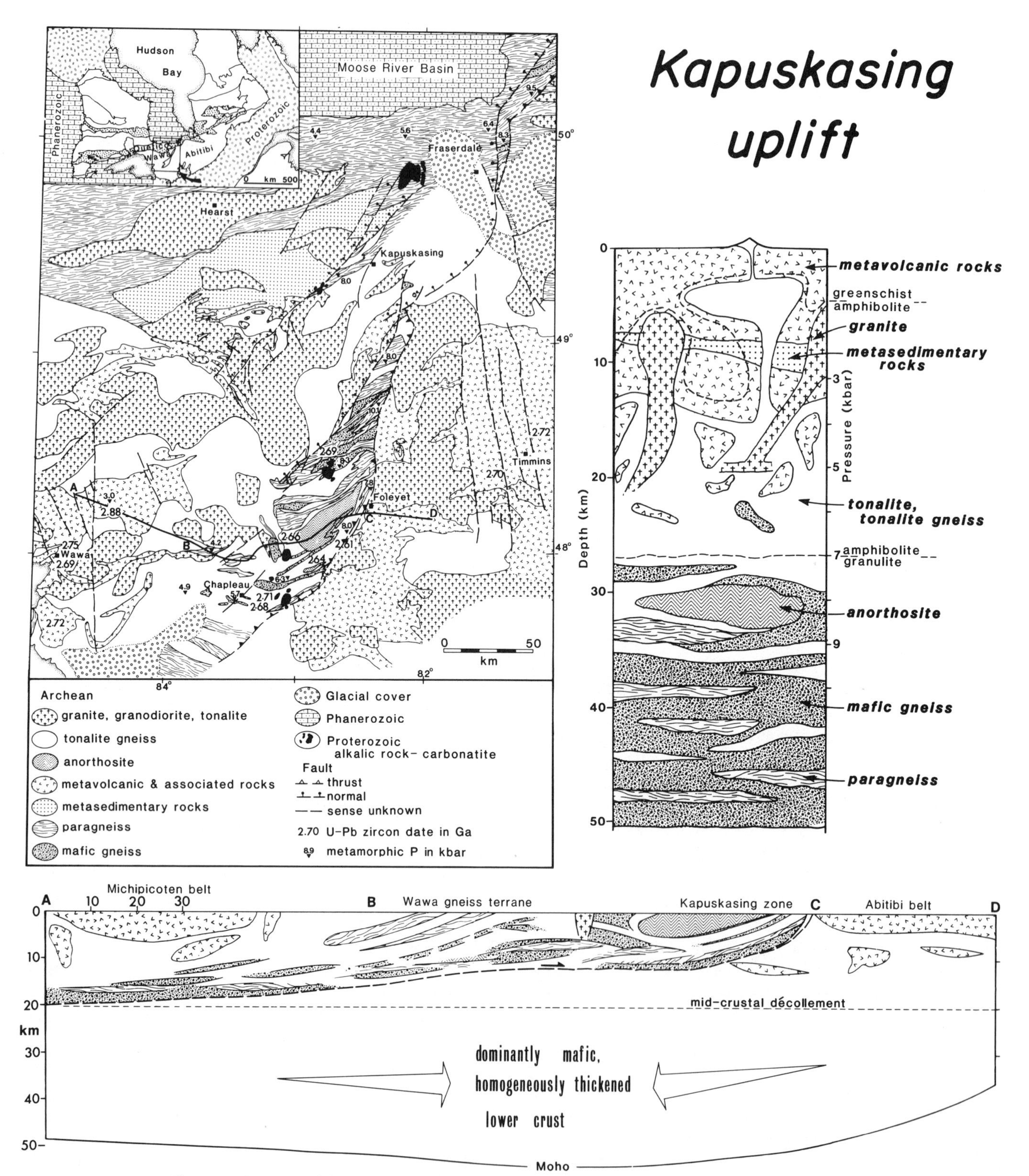

Figure 6. Geology of Kapuskasing uplift, south-central Superior province, according to *Percival (1989a)*. Crustal cross-section (below) consistent with metamorphic geobarometry is based on LITHOPROBE seismic refraction and reflection profiling. Crustal column (upper right) is inferred from oblique cross-section exposed at surface.

gent, centered volcanic complexes and derived turbidites, ranging from 2.73 to 2.70 Ga in age (*Dimroth and others, 1985*; *Mortensen, 1987*; *Corfu and Grunsky, 1987*; *Corfu and others, 1988*). They are intruded by coeval layered gabbro-anorthosite-ultramafic complexes and zoned diorite-tonalite-granodiorite plutons (*Dimroth and others, 1983b*; *Card, 1989*). Unconformably overlying alluvial-fluvial sediments (*Hyde, 1980*) postdate early folds and enclose 2.70- to 2.68-Ga alkalic volcanic rocks chemically similar to those of mature island arcs (*Ujike, 1985*). Major north–south shortening was accompanied by intrusion of 2.70- to 2.68-Ga porphyries and monzogranite plutons, yet deformation and attendent metamorphism were largely complete when syenite-diorite stocks were emplaced at 2.68 to 2.67 Ga (*Card, 1989*). Although direct evidence of older continental crust is lacking, lead isotopic data for syntectonic granitoids are consistent with partial melting of juvenile crust and "non-negligible amounts of earlier formed sialic material" (*Gariépy and Allegre, 1985*).

Contrasting scenarios for the Abitibi terrane have been postulated. Some envision magmatism evolving above a north-dipping subduction zone terminated by orthogonal collision with a southern foreland (*Dimroth and others, 1983b*), while others attribute the magmatism and deformation to a sinistral-oblique south-dipping subduction zone (*Ludden and others, 1986*). Analogy with the Wawa terrane would favor collision at a dextral-oblique north-dipping subduction zone. This would be consistent with north-dipping seismic reflections observed beneath the southern Abitibi terrane and the adjacent Pontiac belt (*Ludden and others, 1988*), and with the observed south-facing folds and north-dipping thrusts in the Abitibi terrane (*Dimroth and others, 1983a*). The role of transcurrent faults and associated en echelon folds is contentious—the suggestion that they manifest regional (sinstral) simple shear (*Hubert and others, 1984*) is challenged by those (*Dimroth and others, 1984*; *Archambault, 1985*) who favor a conjugate system of northwesterly dextral and northeasterly sinistral faults compatible with regional pure shear (north-south shortening). If cogenetic, the observed northerly faults should have dextral slip in the simple-shear model and normal slip in the pure-shear model. Northeast-trending thrusts (including back thrusts) of presumed Grenvillian age occur near the Grenville front.

Pontiac accretionary prism. A dominantly metasedimentary belt characterized by south-facing folds and south-vergent thrusts lies south of the central Abitibi terrane, from which it is separated by a regional north-dipping thrust, the Larder-Cadillac fault (*Dimroth and others, 1983a*; MERQ-OGS, 1983). Most of the sediments are turbidites containing 2.73- to 2.70-Ga detrital zircons, presumably derived from calc-alkaline rocks of the Abitibi terrane, and a subordinate population derived from an unknown source exceeding 2.94 Ga (*Gariépy and others, 1984*). A south-facing syncline of terrestrial conglomeratic sediments overlies turbidites in the footwall of the Larder-Cadillac thrust. Metamorphic grade increases in a Barrovian-facies series from greenschist at the flanks of the Pontiac belt to a central paragneiss domain containing synkinematic 2.695-Ga tonalites and peraluminous pegmatites (*Van de Walle, 1978*; *Mortensen and others, 1988*). Post-kinematic 2.68-Ga syenite plugs prove the contemporaneity of major deformation in the Pontiac and Abitibi belts, but the higher metamorphic grade and depth of erosion in the Pontiac is reflected by more protracted uplift and cooling (J. K. Mortensen, personal communication, 1988). In the south, Pontiac metaturbidites are in tectonic(?) contact with undated greenschist-grade tholeiitic basalt flows and subordinate felsic tuffs. The change along strike from Pontiac metasediments to the southwestern Abitibi terrane is hidden by Early Proterozoic cover.

Quetico accretionary prism. A metasedimentary prism analogous to the Pontiac flanks the Wawa-Abitibi terrane to the north (Fig. 5). The Quetico-Opatica prism (Percival, 1989b; *Card, 1989*) is a symmetrically metamorphosed belt of deformed turbidites of mixed felsic-mafic igneous provenance (*Wood, 1980*; *Ojakangas, 1985*; *Sawyer, 1986*; *Devaney and Williams, 1989*). Detrital zircon populations range from 3.3 to 2.7 Ga (*Percival and Williams, 1989*). The weakly metamorphosed margins of the prism are characterized by stratigraphically northward facing panels and steep easterly (S2) foliations, which are refolded in the high-grade axial zone into upright easterly folds with gently plunging stretching lineations (*Bauer, 1985*; *Kehlenbeck, 1986*; *Williams, 1986*; *Borradaile and others, 1988*; Percival, 1989b). In the axial zone, migmatite and local granulite-grade paragneiss of post-D2 metamorphic age (*Pirie and Mackasey, 1978*; *Sawyer, 1983*) are intruded by discrete suites of peraluminous and magnetite-bearing granite, and subordinate pre- or syn-D2 tonalite and alkaline syenite-diorite suites (Percival, 1989b). Major granitic magmatism occurred at 2.67 to 2.65 Ga, postdating plutonism in the Wabigoon terrane and accretion of the prism by at least 15 m.y. (*Percival and Sullivan, 1986*). The boundaries of the prism are marked by steep, long-lived shear zones, containing abundant mafic material that evolved progressively from north-side-up to dextral slip (*Devaney and Williams, 1989*). Fluviatile conglomerates, localized at the northern margin, have been interpreted alternatively as dextral rhombochasm (*Poulsen, 1986*) or proximal fore-arc deposits (*Devaney and Williams, 1989*). The Quetico prism is viewed as having been constructed largely of trench turbidites accreted to the Wabigoon fore arc during dextral-oblique northward subduction terminated by collision with the back of the Wawa arc (*Percival and Williams, 1989*). The late-stage high-temperature/low-pressure metamorphism and attendant generation of granites in the prism may signify asthenospheric upwelling in the Wawa back arc, collapse of the subducting slab, and rapid thickening and erosion of the prism following arc-arc collision.

Wabigoon island-arc terrane. Langford and Morin (1976) suggested that the Wabigoon terrane originated as a south-facing island arc that backed up against the Uchi-Sachigo arc before being sandwiched by the back of the Wawa arc, the three arcs being separated by the English River and Quetico accretionary prisms (Fig. 5). Initially disregarded, this model makes predictions that stand up well in light of current data. Lithologically, the Wabigoon is similar to the other island-arc terranes of the Superior Province, but the age of major deformation (2.71 to 2.70 Ga) is about 20 m.y. younger than in the Uchi-Sachigo, and about 10 m.y. older than in the Wawa-Abitibi terrane (*Davis and others, 1982, 1985, 1988*; *Davis and Edwards, 1986*).

Supracrustal belts, best exposed in the west part of the terrane (Blackburn and others, 1985; Trowell and Johns, 1986), contain extensive basal units (2.78 to 2.73 Ga) of tholeiitic basalt and komatiitic basalt flows with pelagic (cherty iron-formation) interlayers and local felsic flows, intruded by gabbro-anorthosite layered complexes. They are overlain by emergent buildups (2.74 to 2.71 Ga) of tholeiitic and calc-alkaline, mafic through felsic, fragmental rocks, flows, and derived sediments. The volcanic buildups are coeval with diorite-tonalite-granodiorite plutons. They intertongue with and are overlain by turbidites containing 2.7- and 3.0-Ga detrital zircon populations. These rocks were subjected to strong subhorizontal north-south shortening, manifested by early thrusts and recumbent folds that were compressed into open to tight upright subhorizontal folds, and late systems of ductile to brittle shear zones compatible with north-south shortening and east-west extension in the interior of the terrane, and dextral simple shear at its margins (*Poulsen and others, 1980*). The late-stage deformation (2.70 to 2.68 Ga) was accompanied by deposition of alluvial fanglomerate (*Turner and Walker, 1973*) and intrusion of discordant granodiorite and granite plutons.

Unlike the Wawa-Abitibi terrane, several areas in the Wabigoon expose rocks that predate the main stage of arc construction (2.74 to 2.71 Ga). Arc magmas were erupted through some of the older rocks, while others were structurally juxtaposed. In the southeast, a 3.00-Ga tonalite (Marmion batholith), having a metamorphic (titanite) age of 2.81 Ga, is flanked by a belt of mainly mafic to felsic metavolcanic rocks of the same (3.00 Ga) age (*Davis and Jackson, 1988*). At its southwest end, the tonalite is overlain unconformably by a sedimentary sequence (Steep Rock Group) comprising conglomerate, stromatolitic carbonate (up to 0.5 km thick) with an upper karstic surface, manganese-iron-formation, and magnesian ashrock (*Wilks and Nisbet, 1988*). A thick mass of relatively tectonized mafic flows, sills, and (downward-facing) clastic metasediments structurally overlies the ashrock (*Joliffe, 1966*). A possible scenario is that the karst and overlying chemical sediments record the passage of a flexural forebulge and starved foredeep outer slope, respectively (cf., Hoffman, 1987), during thrusting of the tectonized mafic rocks onto a 3.00-Ga microcontinent and its carbonate platform. Neither the platform sequence nor the mafic allochthon have been dated, and the age of thrusting is poorly constrained (3.0 to 2.7 Ga).

Along the northwestern margin of the Wabigoon terrane, the Winnipeg plutonic complex (Fig. 5) contains widely scattered occurrences of mainly tonalitic gneisses ranging in age from 3.17 to 2.84 Ga (*Krogh and others, 1976*; *Beakhouse, 1985*; *Corfu, 1988*; *Davis and others, 1988*). The pre–2.8-Ga gneisses are intruded by dioritic to granitic plutons similar in age (2.76 to 2.69 Ga) to the Wabigoon island arc (*Card, 1989*), signifying that the older gneisses of the complex formed a microcontinental core within the arc (typical of island arcs split off continental margins by back-arc spreading). However, isotopic data indicate that the older rocks contributed relatively little to magmas of crustal origin in the main central part of the Wabigoon island arc (*Birk and McNutt, 1981*; *Shirey and Hanson, 1986*). The Winnipeg plutonic complex experienced tectonothermal events (*Gower and Clifford, 1981*; *Corfu, 1988*) at about 2.79 Ga (penecontemporaneous with metamorphism of the Marmion tonalite), 2.71 to 2.70 Ga (coeval with major compression of the Wabigoon arc), and 2.68 Ga (coeval with peak metamorphism in the English River metasedimentary belt).

A small, low-grade volcano-plutonic belt northwest of the Winnipeg complex contains 2.74-Ga mafic and felsic volcanic rocks, coeval with a mafic-ultramafic layered complex (Bird River sill), and conglomeratic sediments unconformably overlying the volcanics (*Card, 1989*). Plutonic rocks include presumed synvolcanic diorites and granodiorites, and a large 2.66-Ga post-tectonic granite. The belt is included within the greater Wabigoon island-arc terrane, which may be a composite of two or more arcs and/or remnant arcs.

English River accretionary prism. The belt of metasedimentary and plutonic rocks (*Breaks and others, 1978*; *Thurston and Breaks, 1978*) between the greater Wabigoon and Uchi-Sachigo island-arc terranes (Fig. 5) is analogous to the Pontiac and Quetico accretionary prisms (*Card, 1989*). The metasediments are mainly turbidites derived from igneous sources of dacitic mean composition (*van de Kamp and Beakhouse, 1979*). Relatively proximal turbidites associated with subordinate conglomerate, crossbedded sandstone, iron-formation, and mafic rocks are concentrated near the northern margin of the belt (*Meyn and Palonen, 1980*). A zone of dextral south-side-up faulting occurs along the north boundary, telescoping what may have been a north-to-south facies transition from volcanic arc rocks to fore-arc sediments. Within the belt, the turbidites form tight subhorizontal upright synmetamorphic folds, variably refolded about steeply plunging axes. Metamorphic grade increases, in a low- to intermediate-pressure facies-series, from greenschist at the margins of the belt to amphibolite or granulite (700° to 750°C and 5 kbar) in the interior (*Chipera and Perkins, 1988*). The belt contains numerous pre- to synmetamorphic tonalite and granodiorite intrusions, and late- to postkinematic granites and pegmatites (*Breaks and others, 1978*). A 2.68-Ga leucosome in paragneiss provides an age estimate for anatexis, and a 2.66-Ga granite gives a minimum age for ductile deformation of the prism (*Krogh and others, 1976*).

Uchi-Sachigo island-arc terrane. This composite terrane comprises the relatively high-grade Berens plutonic complex and flanking lower grade volcanic-plutonic zones, the Sachigo zone to the north and Uchi to the south (Fig. 5). It has a more complex history than the terranes to the south. Three distinct episodes of volcanism and plutonism (ending at about 2.93, 2.83, and 2.73 Ga) occurred in both the Uchi and Sachigo zones. Major ductile deformation occurred at 2.73 to 2.72 Ga, about 20 and 30 m.y. earlier than in the Wabigoon and Wawa-Abitibi terranes (*Card, 1989*). This implies that the Uchi-Sachigo terrane was assembled prior to successive accretion of the Wabigoon and Wawa-Abitibi terranes (Langford and Morin, 1976).

Volcanic belts in the Uchi zone preserve three mafic-intermediate-felsic cycles (*Nunes and Thurston, 1980*; *Corfu and Wallace, 1986*; Wallace and others, 1986; *Corfu and Andrews, 1987*). Felsic rocks in each cycle are 2.99 to 2.93 Ga, 2.89 to 2.83 Ga, and 2.75 to 2.73 Ga. Xenocrystic zircon cores indicate that the oldest felsic volcanics were erupted through still older sialic crust. Each cycle has coeval intrusions of gabbro, diorite, tonalite, and/or granodiorite. In the oldest cycle, repeated units of komatiitic and tholeiitic basalt, separated by iron-formation, are overlain by intermediate and/or felsic volcanics intercalated with stromatolitic carbonate (*Hofmann and others, 1985*) and clastic sediments. The unconformably overlying middle cycle contains alternations of tholeiitic and komatiitic basalt, and intermediate to felsic volcanics, capped by carbonate. The upper cycle is composed of tholeiitic and calc-alkaline basalt, and intermediate to felsic volcanics intercalated with clastic sediments. In places the three cycles appear structurally conformable; elsewhere they are separated by unconformities or faults (Wallace and others, 1986).

Three mafic-felsic volcanic cycles (3.02 to 2.95, 2.88 to 2.83, and 2.74 to 2.73 Ga) and related intrusions have also been documented in the Sachigo zone (*Corfu and others, 1985*; *Corfu and Wood, 1986*; *Turek and others, 1986*; D. W. Davis, personal communication, 1988). The oldest cycle contains komatiitic flows and is capped by stromatolites, pure quartzite, and/or conglomerate containing homogeneous 3.00- to 2.99-Ga detrital zircon suites and coeval tonalite clasts. The youngest cycle, comprising tholeiitic and calc-alkaline volcanics, and relatively thick immature clastic sediments (*Wood, 1980*), is intruded by zoned diorite-tonalite-granodiorite plutons. Gabbro-peridotite-anorthosite layered complexes (*Raudsepp and Ayres, 1982*) intrude rocks possibly belonging to this cycle.

Three intrusive suites are recognized in the Berens plutonic complex (*Ermanovics and others, 1979*; *Krogh and others, 1974*). Early dioritic to granodioritic gneisses (3.0 to 2.9 Ga) correlate with the oldest volcanic cycle in the Uchi and Sachigo zones. Foliated sodic plutons (2.77 to 2.73 Ga) correlate with the youngest volcanic cycle, and nonfoliated potassic plutons (2.71 to 2.69 Ga) correlate with intrusions that postdate the main ductile deformation and peak of metamorphism. It is not known whether the Berens complex represents a microcontinental core within the composite arc terrane, or simply a more deeply eroded part of the arc (*Ayres, 1978*).

The entire terrane experienced strong north-south shortening between 2.73 and about 2.70 Ga (*Card, 1989*). Early thrusts and recumbent folds were squeezed into upright subhorizontal folds with subvertical stretching lineations, and then rotated around subvertical axes adjacent to steep northwest dextral and northeast sinistral shear zones (*Fyson and others, 1978*; *Thurston and Breaks, 1978*; *Park, 1981*). Peak metamorphism coincided with formation of the upright folds, and was accompanied by zircon growth at 2.73 to 2.715 Ga, and intrusion of granodiorite and granite bodies (*Corfu and Ayres, 1984*), around which the upright folds are deflected. Terrestrial coarse clastic sediments eroded from synmetamorphic (2.72 Ga) plutons and older rocks (*Corkery, 1983*; *Corkery and Cameron, 1987*) are preserved along, and may be related to, the oblique transcurrent shear zones. The sediments are intercalated with 2.71-Ga shoshonitic mafic-felsic volcanics (*Brooks and others, 1982*). Late granites and pegmatites (2.70 to 2.65 Ga) are coeval with small-scale retrograde shear zones. The regional strain is recorded as an azimuthal seismic anisotropy in the lithospheric mantle beneath the Uchi zone (*Silver and Chan, 1988*).

Pikwitonei uplift and Thompson belt. In the northwest corner of the Superior province, Archean granulites (Pikwitonei uplift) and retrogressed granulites (Thompson belt) border a syntaxis of the Trans-Hudson orogen (Fig. 5) dated at 1.9 to 1.8 Ga. The high-grade rocks represent a relatively deeply eroded section of the Sachigo terrane. The orthopyroxene isograd defining the eastern limit of the Pikwitonei uplift cuts diagonally through the Sachigo metavolcanic and plutonic belts (*Hubregtse, 1980*; *Weber and Scoates, 1978*). The uplift is dominated by tonalitic orthogneiss interspersed with steep meridional layers of mafic and metasedimentary gneiss, trondhjemite, and anorthosite. The range of peak metamorphic conditions was 630 to 800°C and 6.4 to 7.6 kbar (*Mezger and others, 1986*). U-Pb zircon and garnet dating (*Mezger and others, 1988*) reveals thermal events at 2.96 Ga (first Sachigo volcanic cycle), 2.74 Ga (third Sachigo volcanic cycle), 2.70 Ga (magmatism following major Sachigo deformation). 2.64 Ga (post-tectonic Sachigo granites and pegmatites), and 2.60 Ga. The granulites were unroofed prior to intrusion of the 1.88-Ga Molson dikes, which have chilled margins and are unmetamorphosed (*Heaman and others, 1986*).

The Thompson belt is underlain by Archean gneisses, with infolded remnants of Early Proterozoic metasediments (Ospwagan Group), discordantly intruded by 1.82-Ga granite and 1.77-Ga pegmatites (*Machado and others, 1987*). The Pikwitonei-Thompson boundary is drawn where the Archean granulites have been retrograded, coincident with ductile deformation and amphibolite-grade metamorphism of the Molson dikes. The Early Proterozoic deformation involves southeast-directed ductile thrusting that both predates and postdates Molson dikes (the latter deformation coeval with peak metamorphism of the Ospwagan Group), followed by upright en echelon folding related to sinistral transpression of the Thompson belt, and several subsequent lesser strain events (Bleeker, 1989). Antiformal windows of unretrogressed Archean granulites within the Thompson belt may represent structural culminations in the footwall of a décollement within the basement (W. Bleeker, personal communication, 1988). While events in the Trans-Hudson orogen are evidently responsible for prograde metamorphism of the Ospwagan Group and retrogression of the basement, it is not known if they also caused the initial (pre-Molson dikes) unroofing of the granulites. Alternatively, rifting of the Early Proterozoic margin may have caused the granulites to be unroofed.

Terranes east of James Bay. The northeastern prong of the Superior province is far less well known than the northwestern prong. While there are several hundred U-Pb age determinations in Ontario and Manitoba, there are only a handful north of the Abitibi terrane in Quebec, an area largely mapped only in broad reconnaissance. Nd and Sr isotopic ratios of samples representing a north-south transect of nearly the entire region indicate a mean crust formation age (T_{DM} model) of 2.8 Ga (*McCulloch and Wasserburg, 1978*).

East of James Bay is a broad zone containing narrow meridional metavolcanic belts and broad anastomosing metasedimentary domains, perforated and separated by granitoid plutons and orthogneisses (*Avramtchev, 1985*). The zone lies on strike with the Quetico, Wabigoon, English River, and Uchi-Sachigo terranes to the west (Fig. 5). The metavolcanic belts are composed of mafic to felsic and subordinate ultramafic eruptive and related intrusive rocks (*Eade, 1966*; *Franconi, 1974*; *Hocq, 1976*; *Sharma, 1975*; *Skulski and others, 1984*). Intercalated metasediments include iron-formation, carbonate, pure quartzite and uranium-bearing quartz-pebble conglomerate (*Roscoe and Donaldson, 1988*), and ultramafic turbidites (*Stametelopoulou-Seymour and Francis, 1980*), as well as aluminous semipelites that constitute the bulk of the metasedimentary domains (*Valiquette, 1975*). Strata are mainly exposed in tight, doubly plunging meridional folds with subvertical stretching lineations. Magmatic evolution in the northern metavolcanic belt is interpreted in terms of progressive rifting of continental crust, but the existence of preexisting crust is hypothetical as contacts between the metavolcanics and adjacent "basement gneiss" are intrusive (*St. Seymour and Francis, 1988*; *Skulski and others, 1988*). In the area of the metavolcanic belt, tonalitic gneiss and a nonfoliated granodiorite are 2.81 and 2.71 Ga, respectively (*Mortensen and Ciesielski, 1987*), but the age of volcanism is unknown.

Ashuanipi gneiss complex. Eastward, the relatively low-grade metavolcanic, metasedimentary, and plutonic rocks described above pass into the Ashuanipi granulite gneiss complex (Fig. 5). It consists of older paragneiss interlayered with tonalite and minor ultramafic-mafic sheets, and a voluminous younger suite of anatectic granodiorite-granite plutons with pegmatite and minor nepheline syenite (*Percival and Girard, 1988*). All rocks have been metamorphosed in the granulite facies at pressures of 5 to 6 kbar. Deformation and migmatization of the older rocks preceded intrusion of anatectic granodiorites and granites, which are involved in broad, doubly plunging folds. Both generations of structures formed during granulite-facies metamorphism. Zircon and monazite chronology indicates that an older tonalite was emplaced at 2.69 Ga and that major plutonism under granulite-facies conditions occurred at 2.67 to 2.65 Ga (*Mortensen and Percival, 1987*). The ages of plutonism and metamorphism in the Ashuanipi complex are therefore indistinguishable from the lithologically similar Quetico accretionary prism. The ultimate cause of the relatively high heat flux and/or uplift of the Ashuanipi complex relative to areas to the west is unknown, but the complex was unroofed prior to deposition of the 1.88-Ga foredeep sediments (Ferriman Group) of the New Quebec orogen.

Bienville plutonic and Minto gneiss complexes. A vast area east of Hudson Bay is underlain by Archean plutonic and high-grade gneissic rocks (*Eade, 1966*; *Stevenson, 1968*; *Herd, 1978*; *Taylor, 1982*). Little studied, the area is provisionally divided into two domains (Fig. 5) on the basis of prevailing lithology and structural trend (*Card, 1989*). The Bienville plutonic complex consists mainly of easterly trending tonalitic and granodioritic orthogneisses with mafic xenoliths, cut discordantly by relatively massive granodiorite and granite plutons (*Ciesielski, 1984*). There are patches of orthopyroxene-bearing gneiss and vestiges of amphibolite and paragneiss. In the southwestern part of the complex, orthogneisses and a discordant granodiorite pluton date from 2.8 and 2.71 Ga, respectively (*Mortensen and Ciesielski, 1987*). The Minto gneiss complex consists of northwesterly trending granulite and amphibolite-facies orthogneiss, paragneiss, and mafic gneiss, with abundant anatectic granodiorite-granite, foliated granodioritic and charnockitic plutons, and minor postkinematic granites. A granodiorite pluton at the eastern margin of the complex is 2.72 Ga (*Machado and others, 1988*). There is a southward increase in meridional discontinuities that disrupt the prevailing northwesterly structural grain of the complex (Committee for the Magnetic Anomaly Map of North America, 1987). A broad positive gravity anomaly trending northeasterly across the central part of the complex is interpreted as a residual forebulge related to the northern Quebec segment of the Trans-Hudson orogen (*Hoffman, 1985*). Accordingly, uplift of the complex might be partly caused by lithospheric flexure at 1.9 Ga. However, the northern and eastern margins of the complex must have been unroofed prior to deposition of autochthonous strata bordering the Cape Smith belt and New Quebec orogen, respectively. Between the Cape Smith belt and the Sugluk suture, the Kovik antiform exposes 2.9 to 2.6 Ga (Rb-Sr) gneisses (*Doig, 1987*) that are structurally continuous with the Minto complex and were overridden by the ophiolitic Cape Smith allochthon (St-Onge and Lucas, 1989).

Nain province

The Nain (North Atlantic) province is a triangular Archean block bounded by the Early Proterozoic Torngat orogen to the west, the Ketilidian orogen to the southeast, and the Nagssugtoqidian orogen to the northeast (Fig. 3). The province is exposed on the coasts of southwest and southeast Greenland, and central and northern Labrador (Bridgwater and others, 1976; *Andrews and others, 1973*; Taylor, 1979). The Nuuk (formerly Godthåb) region of southwest Greenland (Fig. 7) is the most studied part of the province because it contains relics of Early Archean (3.8 to 3.6 Ga) rocks—among the oldest on earth. The methodology of *McGregor* (*1973*) and his evolutionary scheme for the region have become models for other parts of the province. Recent work

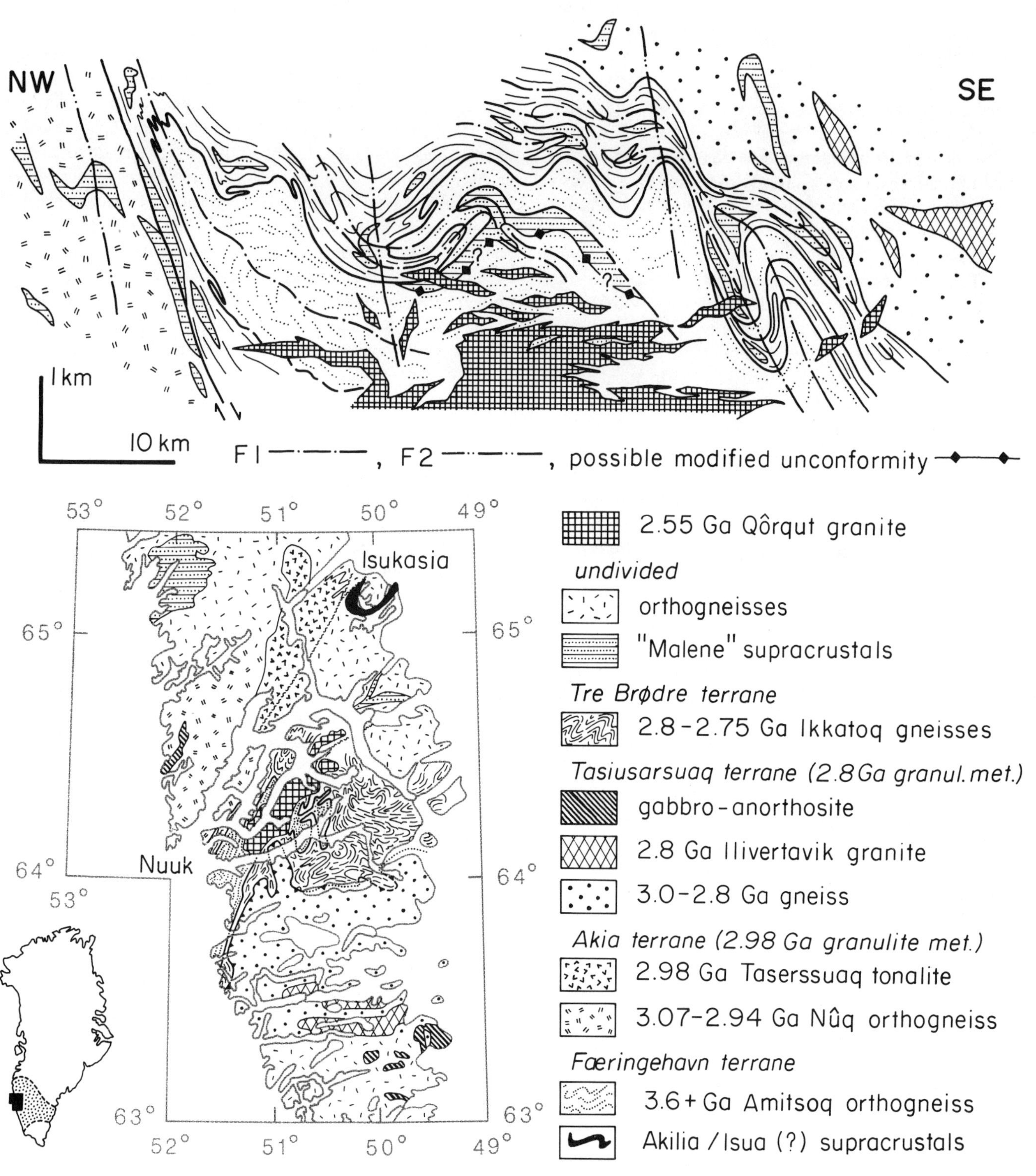

Figure 7. Geology and generalized cross-section of Archean terranes near Nuuk, southwest Greenland (central Nain province), modified after *Nutman and others (1989).*

suggests that the region contains a collage of terranes having independent histories before their aggregation in the Late Archean (*Friend and others, 1988*).

McGregor (*1973*; *McGregor and others, 1986*) distinguished two generations of para- and orthogneisses separated by the emplacement of mafic (Ameralik) dikes between 3.4 and 3.1 Ga. The older gneisses comprise the Akilia association of supracrustal and basic to ultrabasic intrusive rocks, and the much more voluminous Amitsoq gneisses that intrude them. The Akilia association contains interlayered amphibolite, iron-formation, and felsic paragneiss, intruded by leucogabbros and layered ultramafic rocks. The best-preserved equivalents of the Akilia association occur at Isukasia (Fig. 7) and include epiclastic, calcareous, and cherty sediments in addition to amphibolite and iron-formation (*Nutman, 1984; Jacobsen and Dymek, 1988*). The Amitsoq gneisses include a calc-alkaline series of early tonalitic and younger syntectonic granitic gneisses, intruded by geochemically distinct ferrodioritic augen gneisses. Protoliths of the tonalitic gneisses are as old as 3.82 Ga, a minimum age for the Akilia association and similar in age to zircons in the Isua supracrustal belt; zircons in the Akilia rocks were reset by granulite-grade metamorphism of Barrovian type accompanied by the generation of granitic gneisses at about 3.63 Ga (*Griffin and others, 1980*; *Baadsgaard and others, 1984*; *Dymek, 1984*; *Kinny, 1986*). Minor 3.4-Ga pegmatites predate the Ameralik dikes.

The post-Ameralik gneisses include the Malene supracrustals, layered anorthositic complexes, and the voluminous Nuk gneisses that intrude them. The Malene supracrustals comprise amphibolites of submarine volcanic origin and associated epiclastic metasediments. Depositional contacts between Malene supracrustals and Amitsoq gneisses are reported, but most contacts between them are tectonic (Nutman and others, 1989). The anorthosite-gabbro complexes may be petrogenetically related to the Malene metabasalt (*Myers, 1984*). The Nuk gneisses include a 3.08 to 2.94 Ga calc-alkaline diorite-tonalite-granodiorite-trondhjemite suite and a subordinate suite of trondhjemitic and granitic dikes dated at 2.7 to 2.6 Ga (*McGregor and others, 1986*). The former were emplaced during major subhorizontal shortening that preceded metamorphism to granulite grade at about 2.8 Ga (*Myers, 1984*). Although the Malene supracrustals are intruded by Nuk gneisses, detrital zircon dating shows some of the epiclastic sediments were deposited after 2.9 Ga, possibly after 2.8 Ga (*Schiøtte* and others, 1988). The basic evolutionary scheme proposed by *McGregor* (*1973*)—two generations of supracrustal rocks, each invaded by syntectonic granitoids and subjected to high-grade metamorphism, separated in time by the intrusion of mafic dikes—has been extended to northern and central Labrador (*Collerson and others, 1981*; *Korstgård and Ermanovics, 1985*). In southeast Greenland, amphibolite to granulite-grade gneisses and gabbroic to granitic intrusions appear to contain correlatives of only the younger (Nuk) gneisses of the Nuuk region (*Andrews and others, 1973*; *Escher and others, 1986*).

Recent work in the Nuuk region suggests a more complex scenario, involving at least four distinct terranes that had independent histories before being assembled by thrusting and wrench faulting between 2.75 and 2.65 Ga (*Friend and others, 1988*; Nutman and others, 1989). Aggregation was complete prior to emplacement of the overlapping post-tectonic Qorqut granite at 2.53 Ga. This concept suggests that some of the previous relationships and geochronological calibrations, which include rocks situated in separate terranes, need to be reconsidered. On the other hand, the new view strengthens the comparison between Phanerozoic processes of crustal accretion and those inferred to have operated in forming the Archean gneiss complex.

The youngest structures in the Nuuk region are a set of northeasterly trending dextral shear zones (*Smith and Dymek, 1983*) that are kinematically incompatible with parallel sinistral shear zones of Nagssuqtoqidian age to the north.

Slave province

The well-exposed Slave province is a 2.7- to 2.5-Ga plutonic-metamorphic terrane with older gneissic inliers and is bounded by the Thelon orogen (2.0 to 1.9 Ga) to the east and the Wopmay orogen (1.9 to 1.8 Ga) to the west (Fig. 8). The province is characterized by tightly folded metasediments, mostly turbidites of plutonic and felsic volcanic provenance, perforated by pre, syn-, and post-deformational plutons ranging in composition from gabbro to granite (*Henderson, 1975,* 1985; *Frith, 1987*; *King and others, 1988*). Subordinate volcanic sequences occur as folded complexes overlain by turbidites or as inward-facing homoclines bordering turbidite belts. Deformation is primarily the result of subhorizontal regional shortening and secondarily of diapiric plutonism (Fyson and Helmstaedt, 1988). Metamorphism reflects advective heating by plutonism and uplift driven by crustal thickening (*Thompson, 1978*). The Slave province differs from other Archean provinces in having a high proportion of turbidites relative to volcanic rocks (*Padgham, 1985*).

There are several differences between the southwestern and northeastern parts of the province, although there is no obvious structural break between them. First-order structural trends are northerly in the southwest but northwesterly in the northeast. The volcanic sequences are mostly bimodal in the southwest and resemble those erupted in back-arc basins (*Helmstaedt and others, 1986*; *St. Seymour and others, 1988*); intermediate and felsic arc-like volcanics prevail in the northeast (*Lambert, 1978*; *Ewing, 1979*). Felsic volcanism peaked at 2.67 to 2.66 Ga in the southwest but about 30 m.y. earlier in the northeast (*Padgham, 1987*; *Mortensen and others, 1988*; *van Breemen and Henderson, 1988*). Both areas experienced plutonism coeval with felsic volcanism and more voluminous synmetamorphic plutonism at 2.63 to 2.58 Ga (Fig. 9). There are inliers of 3.8- to 2.8-Ga gneiss in the southwest that predate the metavolcanics (*Easton, 1985*; *Henderson and others, 1987*; *Bowring and others, 1989*); none have been found in the northeast (*van Breemen and others, 1987*). In Exmouth antiform, an autochthonous structural culmination in central Wopmay orogen (Fig. 8), a tonalite-amphibolite gneiss complex contains zircons as old as 3.84 Ga (minimum $^{207}Pb/^{206}Pb$ age), and Nd isotopic ratios indicate a crustal protolith older than 4.0 Ga (*Bowring and others, 1989*).

Although the interpretation of the metavolcanic-turbidite belts as collapsed ensialic rifts (*Henderson, 1981*; *Easton, 1985*) has long held sway, there has recently been a revival of an earlier view that they represent island arcs (*Folinsbee and others, 1968*). The belts lack the typical lithologies of continental rifts, such as alkalic volcanics, alluvial-fan deposits, and evaporites. Rifting does not account for the observed tectonic shortening or the fact that younger plutons are far more areally extensive than the older basement. Rifting sidesteps the problem of crust formation, especially in the eastern Slave province where there is little or no evidence of older crust and Nd isotopic data indicate a mean crust-formation age of 2.7 Ga (E. Hegner, personal communication, 1988). In the western Slave province, contacts between volcanics and older gneisses are shear zones containing ultramafic slivers, suggesting that the volcanics are allochthonous with re-

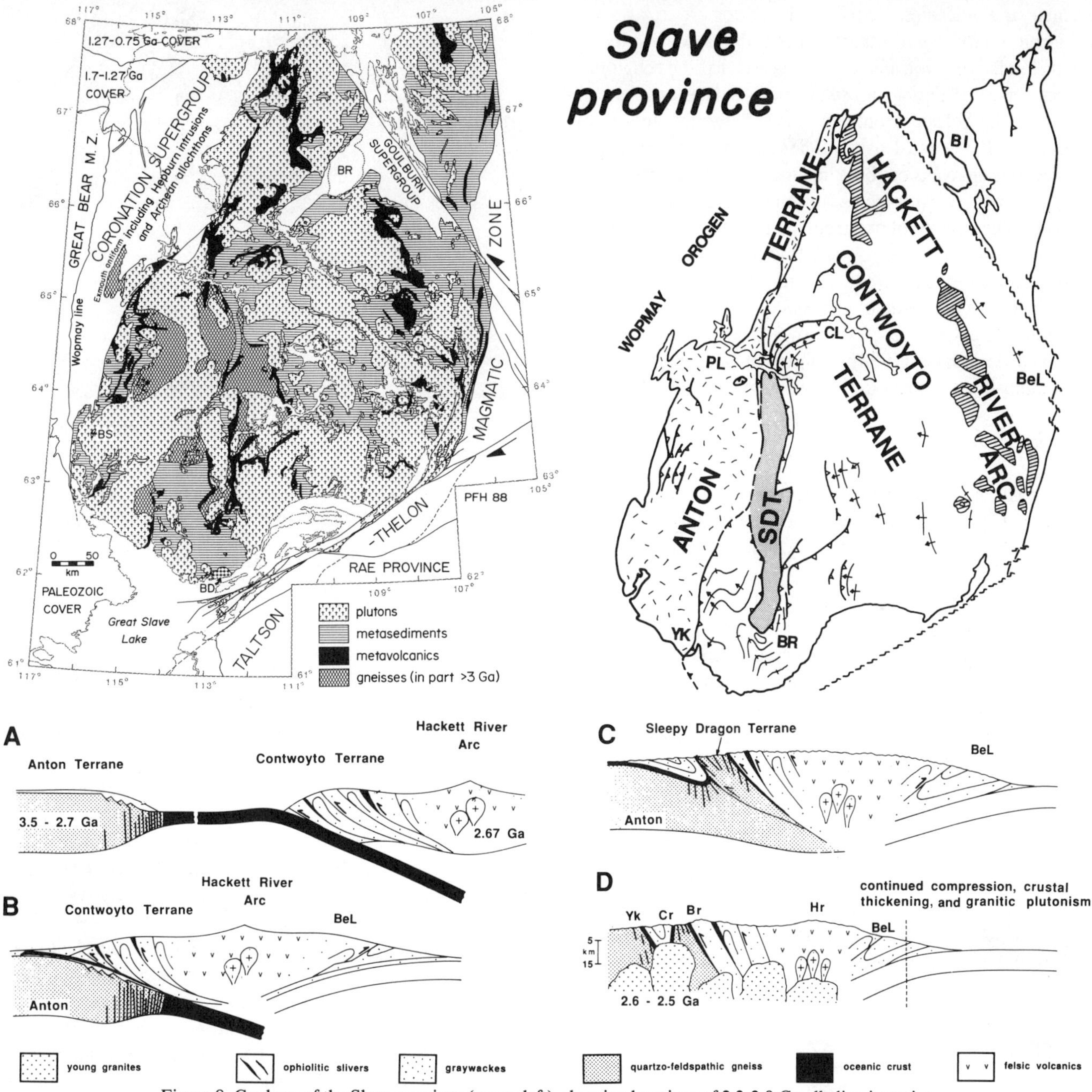

Figure 8. Geology of the Slave province (upper left), showing locations of 2.2-2.0 Ga alkaline intrusive complexes, BD, Blachford; BR, Booth River; BS, Bigspruce. Archean terranes (upper right) and plate tectonic evolution (below) according to *Kusky (1989b)*. BeL, Beechey Lake domain; CR, Cameron River; BR, Beaulieu River; Hr, Hackett River arc; PL, Point Lake; SDT, Sleepy Dragon terrane; Yk, Yellowknife. Dashed vertical line in panel D indicates present eastern margin of Slave province.

spect to the gneisses (*Kusky, 1988a*; *Lambert, 1988*). At Point Lake (Fig. 10), an erosional unconformity separating conglomerate and turbidites from 3.15-Ga granite has been cited as evidence that the volcanic and sedimentary rocks were deposited during rifting of the basement (*Henderson, 1981,* 1985; *Easton, 1985*). However, the volcanics lie below the unconformity, and their contact with the basement is a shear zone containing ultramafic slivers (T. Kusky, personal communication, 1988). A set of what appears to be west-directed thrusts and related folds imbricate the basement and volcanics. Certain of the thrusts are truncated by the unconformity, while others displace the unconformity less than the underlying volcanics. This suggests that the conglomerate was deposited during thrusting, and postdates apparent obduction of the volcanics onto the older basement. Fyson and Helmstaedt (1988) and Kusky (*1988b*) propose that obduction occurred during collision of a microcontinent (western Slave province) with a west-facing magmatic arc (eastern Slave province). The absence of basement in the eastern Slave province favors an island arc (*Kusky, 1988b*) rather than an Andean arc (Fyson and Helmstaedt, 1988). The magmatic gap in the eastern Slave (Fig. 9) is compatible with Kusky's (*1988b*) scenario invoking an arc-polarity reversal following the collision, whereas Fyson and Helmstaedt (1988) surmise that east-dipping subduction continued but stepped to the west following the collision.

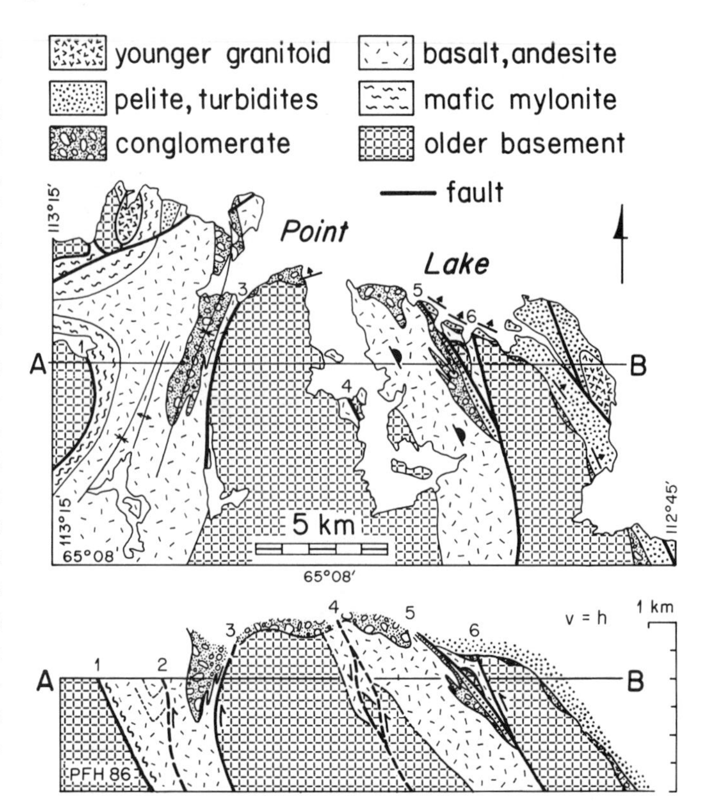

Figure 10. Map (above) and cross-section (below) of basement-cover relations at Point Lake (see Figure 8 for location). Note that sediments truncate or are relatively little displaced by thrusts that imbricate basement and volcanic rocks, implying that sediments were deposited during tectonic shortening. Basement-cover contact 1 is tectonic; others are equivocal. Note that conglomerate which unconformably overlies basement at Point Lake is younger than mafic volcanics.

Wyoming province

The Laramide ranges of Wyoming and southwestern Montana (Fig. 11) expose Archean rocks constituting less than 4 percent of the inferred area of the Wyoming province. The only exposed margin of the province is the Cheyenne belt of southeastern Wyoming, south of which juvenile 1.8- to 1.6-Ga terranes were accreted. Archean rocks near the margin are cut by swarms of amphibolite dikes, presumably rift related, bracketed by 2.05- and 1.98-Ga granites. The eastern and northern margins of the province are bounded, mainly in the subsurface, by the approximately 1.8-Ga Trans-Hudson orogen and Great Falls tectonic zone, respectively (Fig. 3). Archean rocks extend westward beneath the Snake River Plain in south-central Idaho (*Leeman and others, 1985*) and into the Great Basin as far as northeastern Nevada (*Lush and others, 1988*).

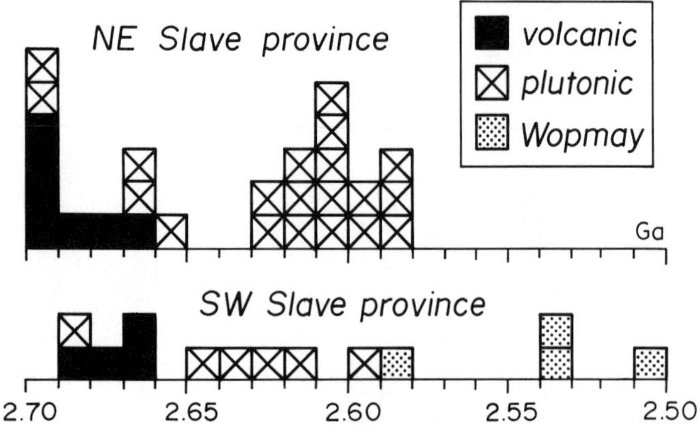

Figure 9. U-Pb ages for Late Archean volcanic and plutonic rocks in Slave province and Wopmay orogen. NE Slave province corresponds to Hackett River arc, SW Slave province to Anton and Contwoyto terranes of Figure 8.

The Wyoming province differs from the Superior province in having abundant shelf-type metasedimentary rocks and isotopic evidence for widespread continental crust older than 3.1 Ga (*Peterman and Futa, 1988*; *Wooden and Mueller, 1988*). The ancient crust is represented by more or less retrogressed granulite-grade ortho- and paragneisses (*Koesterer and others, 1987*). They form high-grade equivalents of, and/or basement to, shelf-facies successions of quartzite, marble, and pelite, with minor amphibolite and iron-formation, best developed in southwest Montana and southeast Wyoming (*Houston and Karlstrom, 1979*; *Erslev, 1983*; *Gibbs and others, 1986*). Two units of stromatolitic dolomite, having a combined thickness of 1 to 2 km, occur in the Hartville uplift in southeast Wyoming (*Hofmann and Snyder, 1985*). Tight polyphase folding and shearing makes it difficult to establish age relations between the gneisses and metasediments. In contrast to the shelf-facies metasediments, the protoliths of

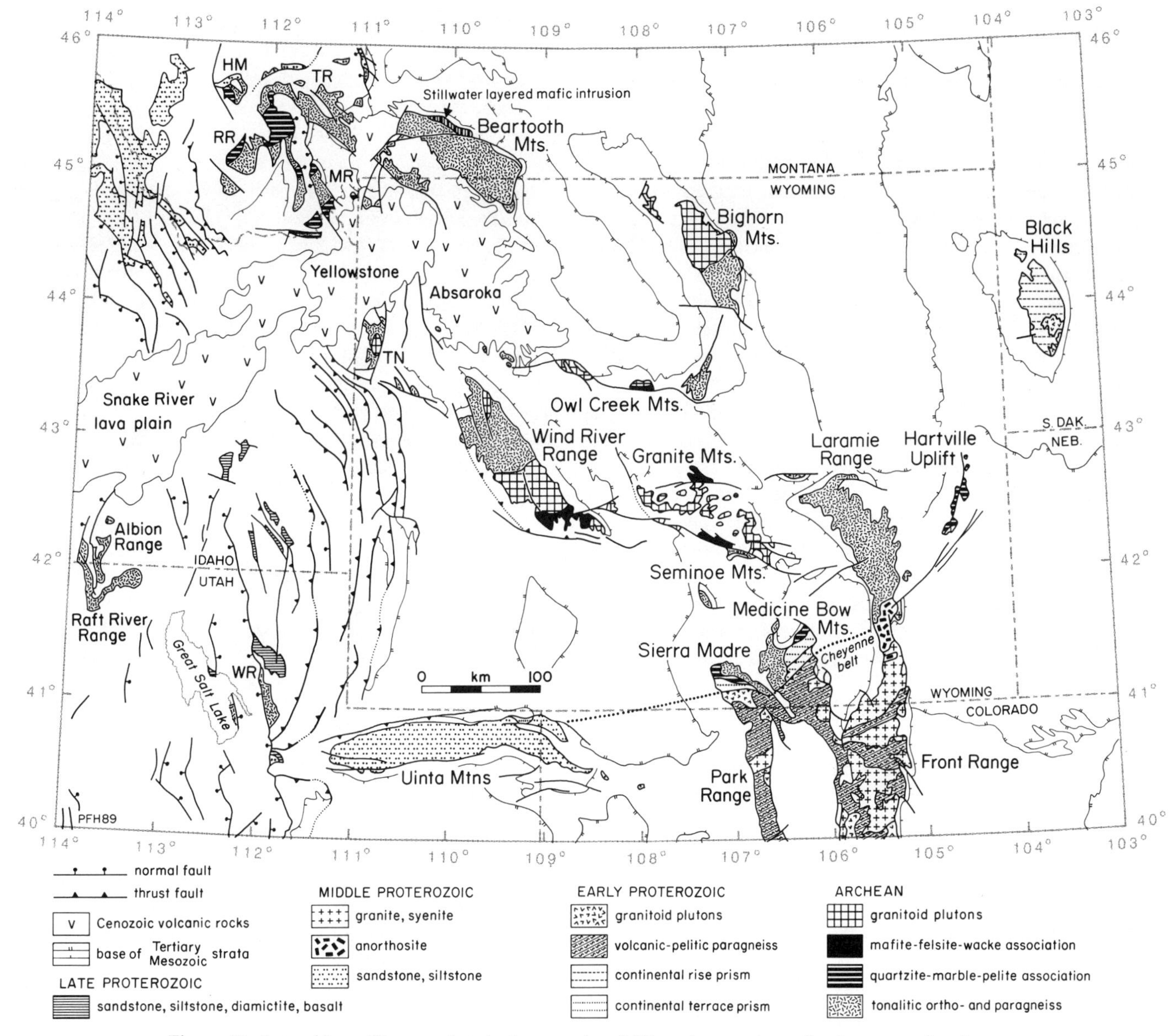

Figure 11. Laramide uplifts exposing Archean rocks of Wyoming province. Southeast margin of Wyoming province is exposed in Cheyenne belt. Deformation related to northwest margin (Great Falls tectnoic zone) increases toward Highland Mountains (HM), implying reactivation to form southeast margin of Belt basin defined by LaHood conglomerate (see Figure 36). MR, Madison Ranges; RR, Ruby Range; TN, Teton Range; TR, Tobacco Root Mountains.

metamorphic belts in central Wyoming were subaqueous basalt, graywacke-pelite, and subordinate intermediate to felsic volcanics (*Bayley and others, 1973*; *Mueller and others, 1985*). The 2.9- to 2.7-Ga volcanics are intruded by relatively undeformed 2.7- to 2.6-Ga granite-granodiorite batholiths (*Stuckless and others, 1985*), which are broadly coeval with the Stillwater layered mafic intrusion (2.71 Ga) in Montana (*Czamanske and Zientek, 1985*). Although Nd crust-formation ages of 3.6 to 3.1 Ga are found throughout most of the Wyoming province, it is not yet clear whether the province has been coherent since that time or represents a tectonic collage assembled about 2.9 to 2.6 Ga. The province may be transected by a latitudinal Late Archean suture zone exposed at the south end of the Wind River Range (*Condie, 1972*; *Harper, 1985*). A northeasterly mylonite zone that crosses the South Madison and northwestern Beartooth ranges is also postulated to be a Late Archean suture zone (*Erslev, 1983*; *Mogk and others, 1986*), based on purported lithologic contrasts between the adjacent crustal blocks.

Wyoming/Hearne province boundary

Nd crust-formation ages for the buried southern part of the Hearne province are about 2.8 Ga (*Frost and Burwash, 1986*), whereas those of the Wyoming province exceed 3.1 Ga (*Peterman and Futa, 1988*). The boundary between them (Fig. 3) may correspond to the Great Falls tectonic zone, a subsurface crustal discontinuity that extends from central Idaho to southwestern Saskatchewan (O'Neill and Lopez, 1985). In the Tobacco Root and Ruby Ranges of southwestern Montana (Fig. 11), Archean rocks of the Wyoming province become progressively overprinted toward the northwest, approaching the Great Falls tectonic zone, by northeasterly oriented ductile flattening and metamorphism imposed at about 1.8 Ga (*O'Neill and others, 1988*). The Great Falls tectonic zone forms the southern boundary of the Medicine Hat block (Fig. 12), a distinctive terrane characterized by northwesterly trending geopotential anomalies bounded to the north by a discontinuity in southern Alberta known as the Vulcan low (Ross and others, 1989). Hoffman (*1988*) interpreted the Vulcan low as a south-dipping suture between the Wyoming and Hearne provinces, based on gravimetric and seismic reflection profiles, but Nd data shows that the Medicine Hat block has 2.9- to 2.8-Ga crust-formation ages more like those of the Hearne province. Furthermore, if a parallel magnetic high north of the Vulcan low is inferred to be a related magmatic arc, then a north-dipping suture is implied (Ross and others, 1989). A 2.7- to 2.6-Ga age for the suture is implied by dating of basement cores from the magnetic high, the Vulcan low, and the northern rim of the Medicine Hat block (Ross and others, 1989). Therefore, the best current interpretation is that the Great Falls tectonic zone represents an approximately 1.8-Ga boundary between the Wyoming and Hearne provinces, and that the Vulcan low is a 2.7- to 2.6-Ga suture within the southern Hearne province. The Great Falls tectonic zones appears to be truncated by, and therefore older than, the 1.8-Ga Trans-Hudson orogen (Thomas and others, 1987).

Hearne province

The Hearne province (*Hoffman, 1989b*) is a juvenile Late Archean terrane flanked by the Early Proterozoic Snowbird and Trans-Hudson orogens (Fig. 3). It preserves infolded remnants of platform cover and foreland basins (Hurwitz and Kiyuk groups) of Early Proterozoic age (Eade and Chandler, 1975; *Aspler and others, 1989*). The Hearne province may extend beneath the Paleozoic Hudson Bay basin and merge with the Middle Archean Sugluk terrane of northern Quebec (Fig. 13). Alternatively, Hudson Bay may be underlain by an independent terrane of Archean or Early Proterozoic age (Roksandic, 1987).

The Hearne province contains a central core of greenschist-grade Archean rocks in the southern District of Keewatin, increasing outward in metamorphic grade and state of strain toward the bounding orogens (Fraser and Heywood, 1978; Fraser and others, 1978). Rocks of granulite grade prevail in Saskatchewan, northern Manitoba, and southern Keewatin bordering the Trans-Hudson orogen. Crustal shortening normal to the bounding orogens is evidenced by thrusts and open to tight, horizontal upright folds affecting the basement and Early Proterozoic cover (*Eade, 1974*; *Aspler and others, 1989*). The variation in metamorphic grade reflects an outward increase in Early Proterozoic crustal shortening and consequent depth of erosion in the Archean basement, plus increased heat advected during Early Proterozoic plutonism (*Loveridge and others, 1988*).

The low-grade core of the province is underlain by folded mafic-intermediate-felsic submarine volcanic and volcanic-derived turbiditic rocks, penetrated by plutons of gabbro, diorite, tonalite, and granite (*Mortensen and Thorpe, 1987*). Felsic volcanism occurred at 2.70 to 2.68 Ga over a minimum strike length of 550 km. No basement is observed beneath the volcanic piles, but 3.2- to 3.1-Ga zircons occur in orthogneisses in the high-grade zones (*Loveridge and others, 1988*). A post-tectonic nepheline syenite-carbonatite complex intruded the low-grade rocks at about 2.54 Ga (*Mortensen and Thorpe, 1987*). Swarms of mafic dikes trending north-northeast and west-northwest were intruded between 2.54 and about 2.4 Ga (Fahrig and West, 1986).

Rae province

The Rae province (*Hoffman, 1989b*) is that area of Archean crust bounded by the Thelon orogen to the northwest, by the Snowbird and New Quebec orogens to the south, and by the Torngat orogen to the east (Fig. 3). The province is dominated by felsic gneisses of poorly known age and origin, but composite samples representing transects across the province in northwestern Saskatchewan and northern Baffin Island have Nd crust-formation ages (T_{DM} model) of about 2.8 Ga (*McCulloch and Wasserburg, 1978*). Between the Thelon basin and Baffin Island, the gneisses surround narrow, northeasterly trending belts (Woodburn, Prince Albert, and Mary River groups) composed of komatiitic, tholeiitic, and felsic metavolcanic rocks, intercalated and overlain by quartzite, iron-formation, and graywacke-pelite of upper greenschist–lower amphibolite grade (*Schau, 1982*; *Frisch, 1982*; *Taylor, 1985*). The majority of dated orthogneisses in the province are coeval or younger (2.6 Ga) than the felsic volcanic rocks (2.9 to 2.8 Ga), but there are relics of older gneiss (3.1 to 2.9 Ga) and remnants of subaerial rhyolite coeval with the 2.6-Ga granites.

The southeast arm of the province is exposed discontinuously on the islands at the mouth of Hudson Bay (*Heywood and Sanford, 1976*), on southern Baffin Island where Archean(?) gneisses underlie shelf-type metasediments (Lake Harbour Group) of the Dorset fold belt (*Blackadar, 1967a, b*), and in northeastern Quebec between the Torngat, New Quebec, and Grenville orogens (Taylor, 1979; *Ashwal and others, 1986*). Very scanty isotopic evidence suggests that the Quebec segment evolved contemporaneously (2.9 to 2.7 Ga) with the main body of the province (*Wooden and others, 1987*; *Machado and others, 1988*).

The presence of linear Early Proterozoic calc-alkaline plutonic belts along its margins indicates that the Rae province was part of the overriding plate (hinterland) of the Thelon, Torngat, and New Quebec orogens. During the subsequent collision

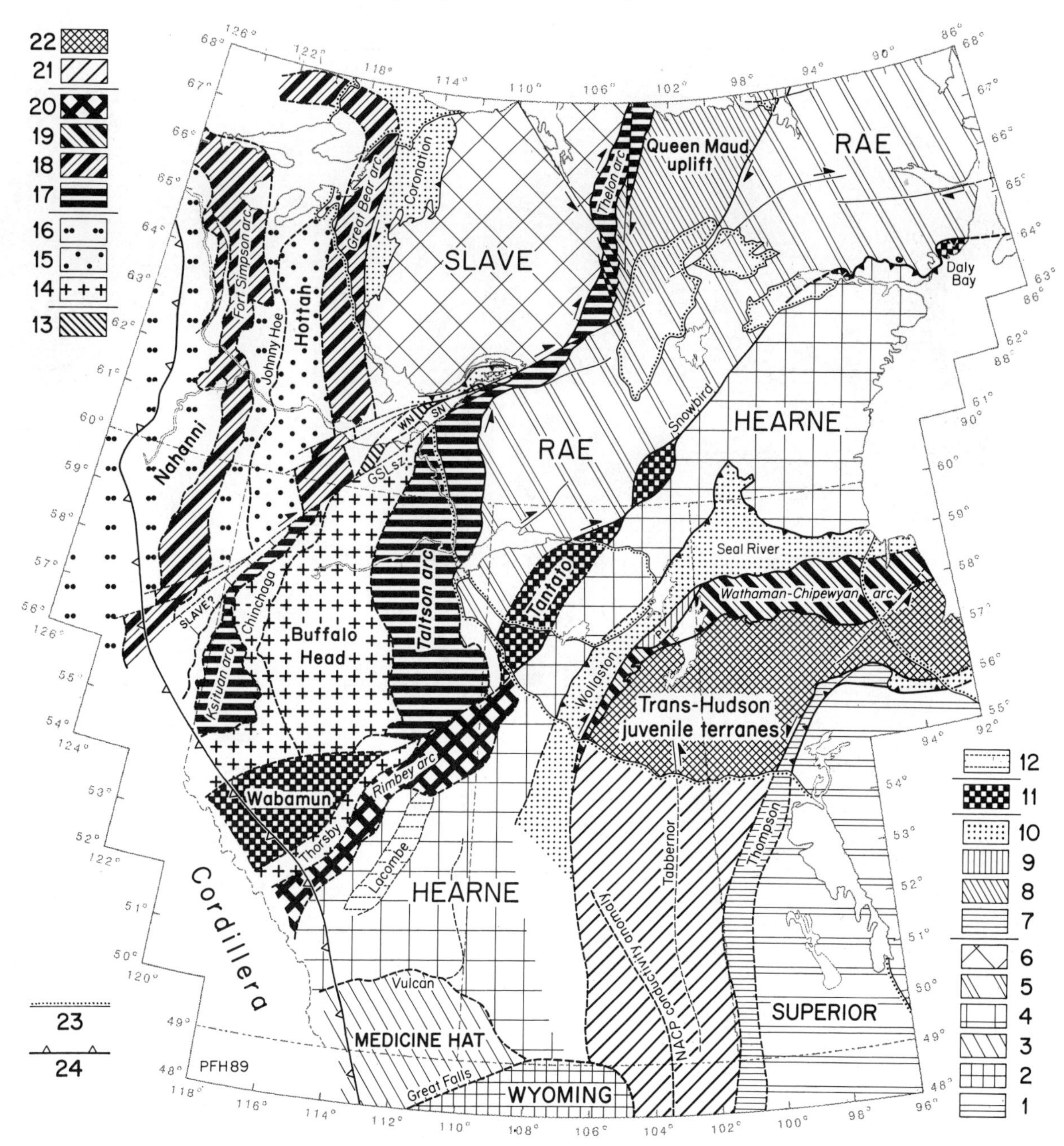

Figure 12. Major tectonic elements of western Canadian shield and basement of western Canadian platform (modified and extended from *Ross and others, 1989* in preparation). Archean provinces (1-6): 1, Superior; 2, Wyoming; 3, Medicine Hat; 4, Hearne; 5, Rae; 6, Slave, including Simpson Islands terrane (SN). Zones of Archean crustal reactivation (7-10): 7, Thompson; 8, Queen Maud; 9, Peter Lake; 10, thrust-fold belts involving Early Proterozoic cover. 11, mylonitic mafic-felsic granulites of uncertain age occurring within Snowbird orogen. 12, Metasedimentary-volcanic rocks of unknown age in Lacombe zone of Hearne province. 13, volcanic (1.93 Ga) and sedimentary rocks of Wilson Island terrane (WN) within and adjacent to Great Slave Lake shear zone (GSLsz). Early Proterozoic terranes (14-16): 14, Buffalo Head, Chinchaga, and Thorsby (all 2.3 to 2.1 Ga); 15, Hottah (1.95 to 1.90 Ga arc built on 2.3 to 2.1 Ga crust); 16, Nahanni (age unknown, possibly equivalent to 2.3 to 2.1 Ga Yukon-Tanana terrane of northern Cordillera). Early Proterozoic continental magmatic arcs (17-20): 17, Taltson-Thelon and Ksituan (both 2.00 to 1.90 Ga); 18, Great Bear (1.88 to 1.84 Ga) and Fort Simpson (ca. 1.85 Ga); 19, Wathaman-Chipewyan (1.86 to 1.84 Ga); 20, Rimbey (1.82 to 1.78 Ga). Internal zones of Trans-Hudson orogen (21-22): 21, subsurface extension underlain by North American central plains conductivity anomaly (NACP) and Archean subcrops; 22, juvenile crust exposing 1.91 to 1.85 Ga island arcs and interarc metasediments. 23, edge of platform (including Middle-Late Proterozoic) cover. 24, edge of Cordilleran deformation.

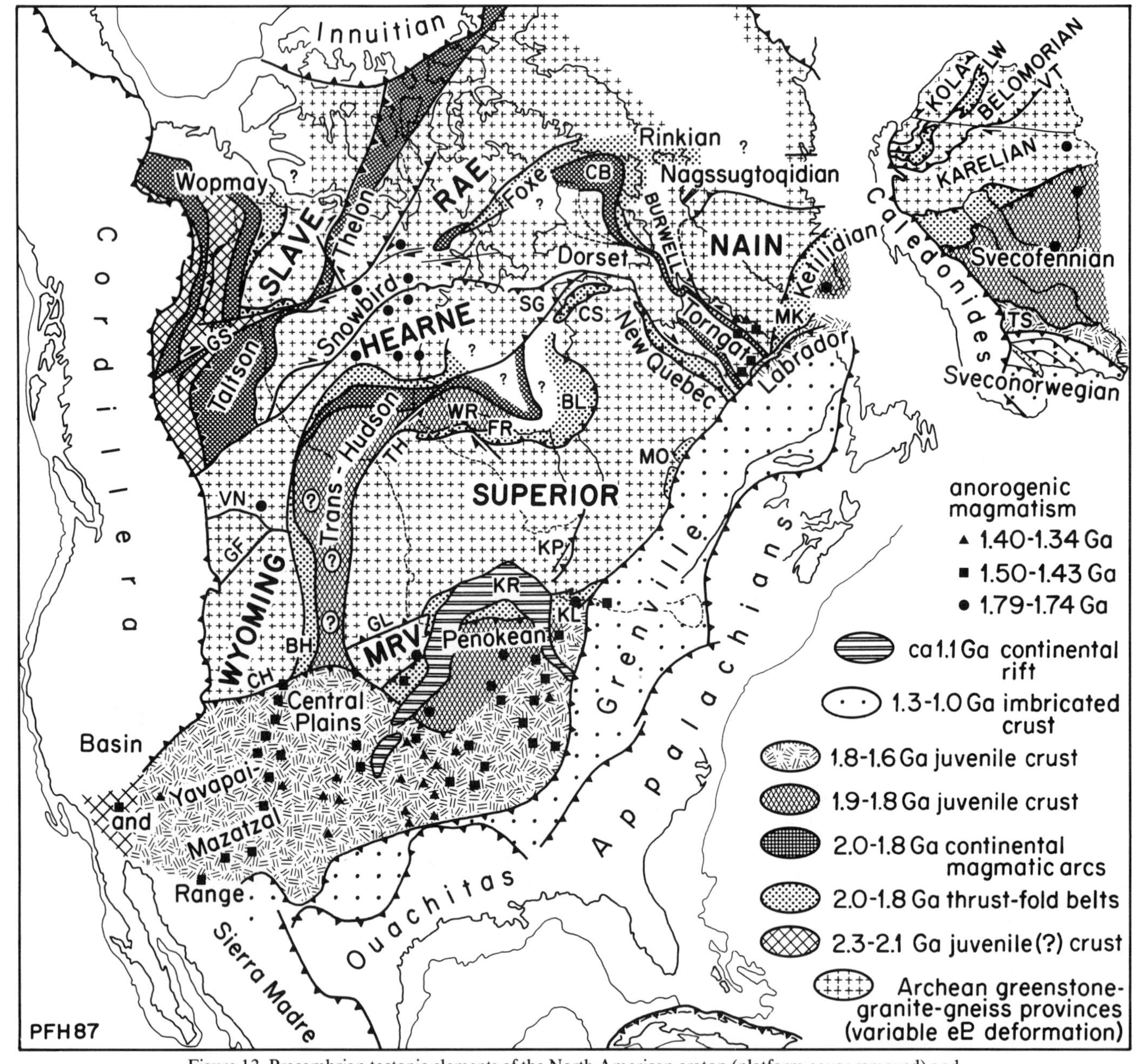

Figure 13. Precambrian tectonic elements of the North American craton (platform cover removed) and Baltic shield. Upper case names are Archean provinces; lower case names are Proterozoic and Phanerozoic orogens. BH, Black Hills inlier; BL, Belcher fold belt; CB, Cumberland batholith; CH, Cheyenne belt; CS, Cape Smith belt; FR, Fox River belt; GF, Great Falls tectonic zone; GL, Great Lakes tectonic zone; GS, Great Slave Lake shear zone; KL, Killarney magmatic zone; KP, Kapuskasing uplift; KR, Keweenawan rift; LW, Lapland-White Sea tectonic zone; MK, Makkovik orogen; MO, Mistassini and Otish basins; MRV, Minnesota foreland; SG, Sugluk terrane; TH, Thompson belt; TS, Trans-Scandinavian magmatic zone; VN, Vulcan tectonic zone; VT, Vetrenny tectonic zone; WR, Winisk River fault.

events, the Archean basement was tectonically thickened and folded, along with its Early Proterozoic cover (*Thomas and Gibb, 1985*; *Patterson, 1986*). Transcurrent shear zones developed to accommodate postcollisional indentation by the Slave and northeastern Superior provinces (Fig. 14; *Thomas and Gibb, 1983*).

Burwell province

Toward the northern tip of Labrador, the Early Proterozoic Torngat orogen (Fig. 3) bifurcates into a pair of major shear zones, between which lies the Burwell province, composed

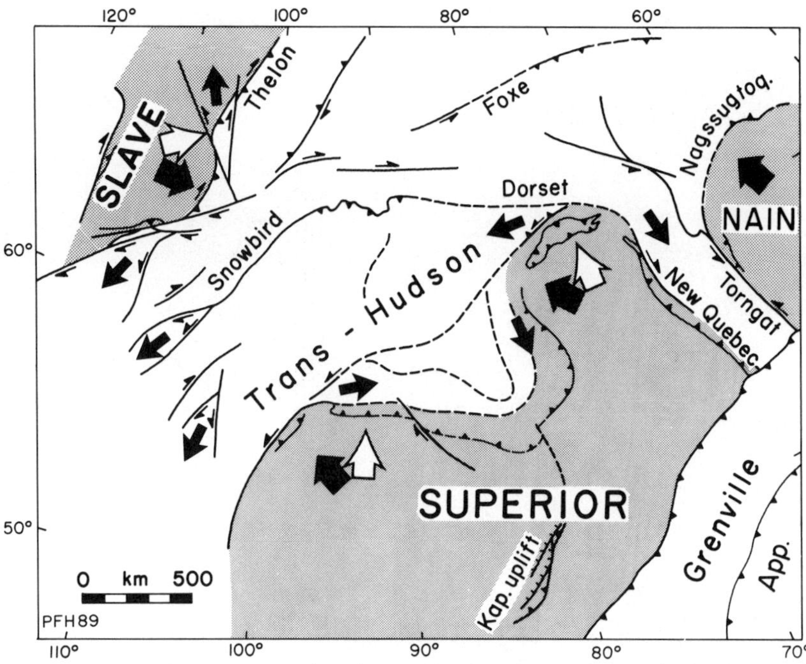

Figure 14. Transcurrent faults and extrusion of crustal blocks related to indentation by the Superior and Slave provinces, modified after *Gibb (1983)*. Kinematic evolution was complex: Slave province may have first moved northeast (present coordinates), then east; Superior province may have first moved north, then northwest. Role of Nain province is uncertain pending geochronology of Torngat orogen.

mainly of granulite-grade granitoid gneiss, mafic gneiss, and paragneiss (Taylor, 1979; Korstgård and others, 1988). The more easterly Komaktorvik shear zone may have been coextensive with the Nagssugtoqidian orogen prior to opening of Davis Strait. The more westerly Abloviak shear zone extends northward across eastern Hudson Strait (Committee for the Magnetic Anomaly Map of North America, 1987) and the base of Hall Peninsula toward the Foxe fold belt of central Baffin Island (*Hoffman, 1989b*). In central West Greenland, a relatively undeformed 2.8-Ga granite occurs between the Early Proterozoic Nagssugtoqidian and Rinkian orogens (*Kalsbeek and others, 1988*), the latter being coextensive with the Foxe fold belt. Accordingly, the granite may belong to a northward extension of the Burwell province. The province is therefore interpreted as a microcontinental Archean terrane bounded by three Early Proterozoic suture zones, the Abloviak to the west, the Komaktorvik-Nagssugtoqidian to the southeast, and the Foxe-Rinkian to the north (Fig. 3).

EARLY PROTEROZOIC COLLISIONAL OROGENS

The Laurentian protocraton is an aggregate of seven Archean provinces welded by orogenic belts (Fig. 13) representing collision zones that were active between 2.0 and 1.8 Ga (Hoffman, 1988). A list of the collision zones and their vital statistics are given in Table 2. The Superior, Nain, and Slave provinces belonged to subducting plates during convergence and were forelands during collisional orogeny. The other provinces belonged to overriding plates and were hinterlands during orogeny at one or more of their margins. The forelands are characterized by passive-margin and foredeep sedimentary prisms and foreland thrust-fold belts. The hinterlands are bordered by pre- and syncollisional magmatic zones, and by extensive basement reactivation. Oblique convergence is manifested by pre- and syncollisional transcurrent shearing concentrated in the magmatic zones bordering the hinterlands. The orogenic age ranges are based on times of hinterland magmatism and associated high-grade metamorphism, and foredeep volcanism, deformation, and metamorphism.

Trans-Hudson orogen

The Trans-Hudson orogen (Hoffman, 1988) is the collision zone between the Superior province and Archean provinces to the north and west (Fig. 3). The orogen is divisible into segments—the Hudson Bay and northern Quebec segments to the northeast, the Manitoba-Saskatchewan and Dakota segments to the southwest. At its southern terminus, the orogen is truncated by the Central Plains orogen (Fig. 13). In the extreme northeast, the orogen may merge with the Snowbird orogen in Hudson Strait, from whence it turns southeast and is exposed as the New Quebec orogen welding the Superior and southeastern arm of the Rae province.

Northern Quebec segment. This segment comprises three tectonic elements (*Hoffman, 1985*): Sugluk terrane, Kovik antiform, and Cape Smith klippe (Fig. 15A). The Sugluk terrane consists of granulite-grade ortho- and paragneisses, older than 3.0

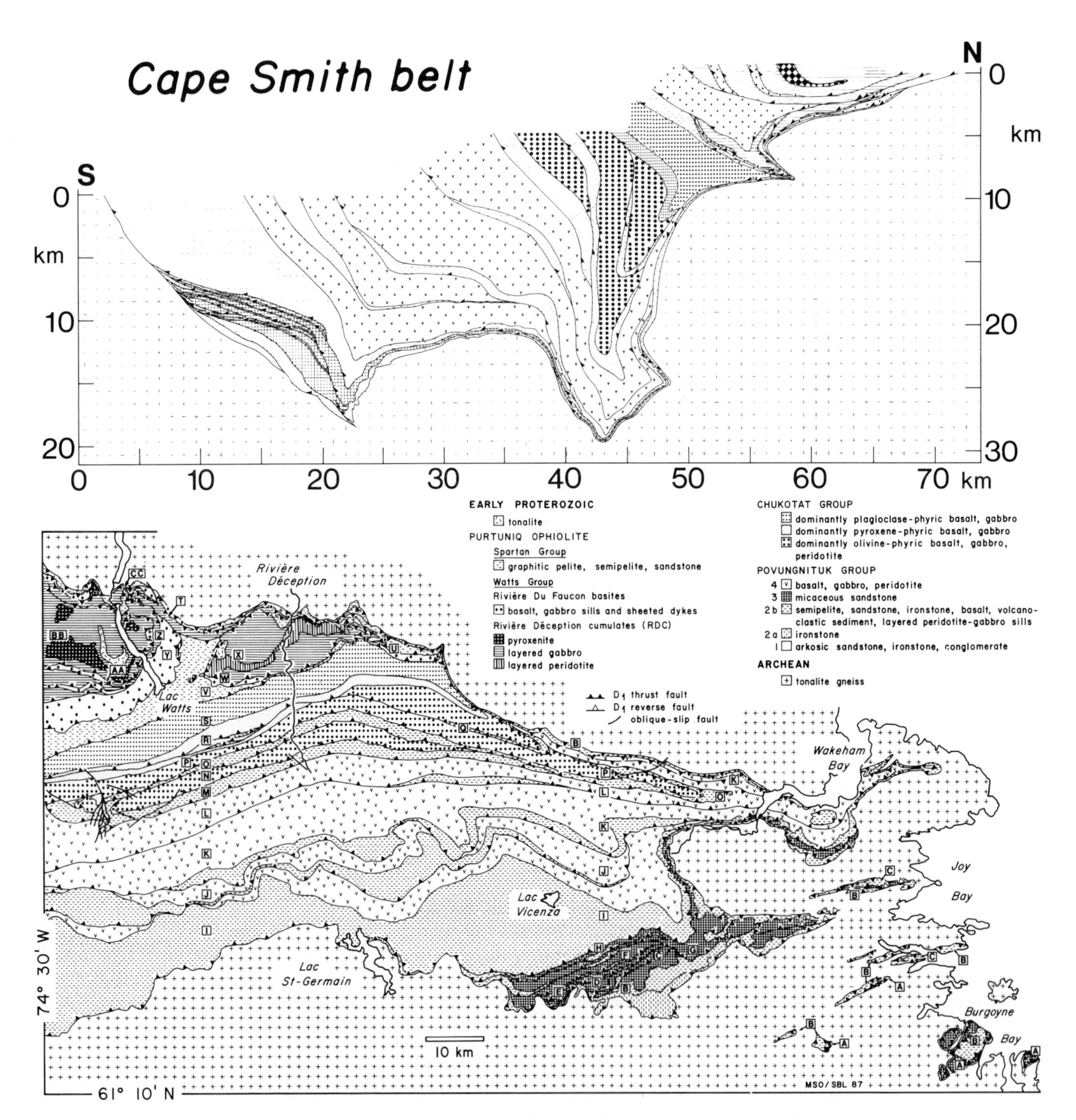

Figure 15. Geologic (this page) and metamorphic (facing page) maps and cross-sections of eastern end of Cape Smith belt, northern Quebec (see Figure 16 for location), after *St-Onge and Lucas (1989)*. Cross-sections were constructed from over 50 independent axial projections of surface geology in domains of statistically uniform plunge.

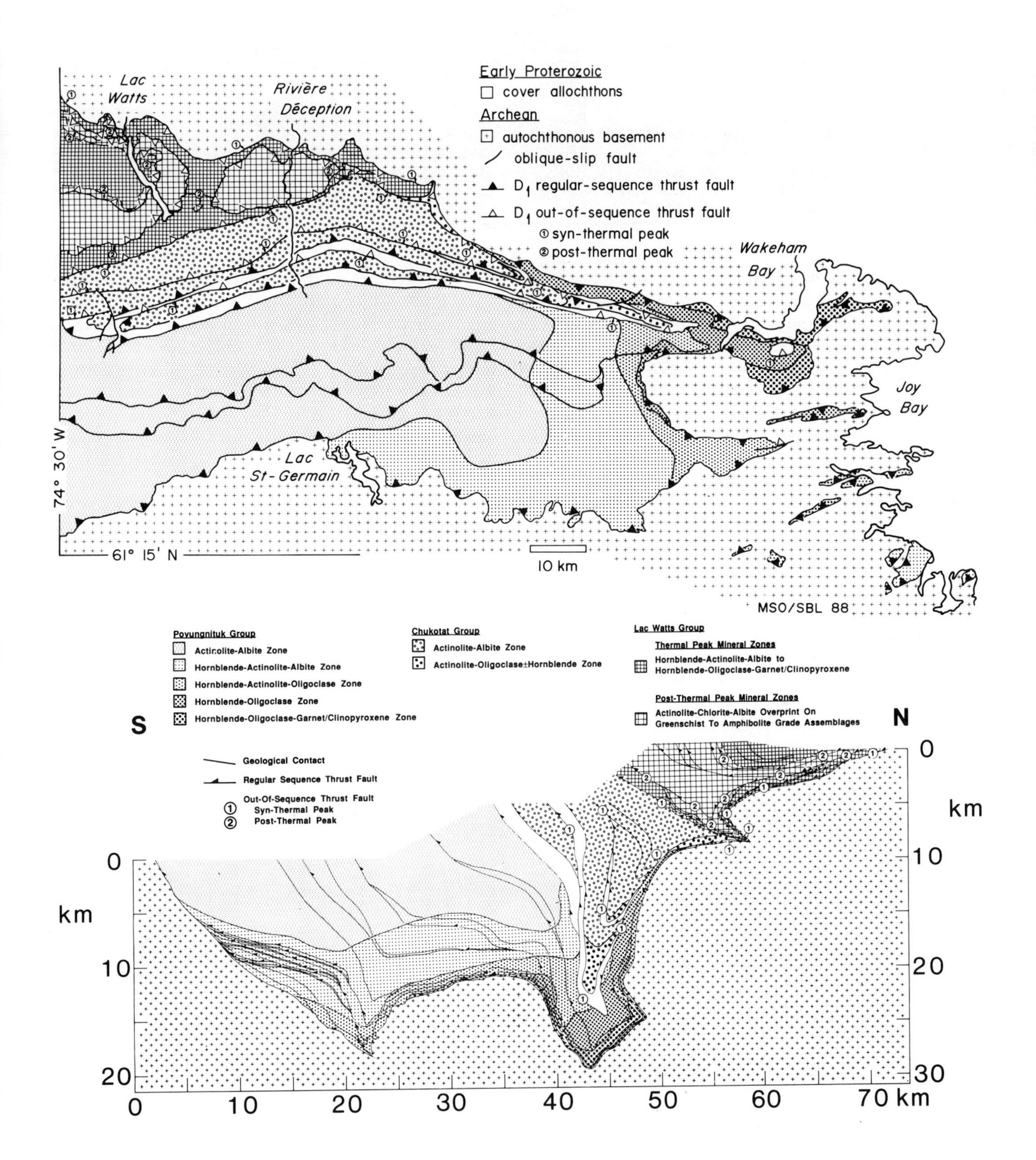

Lac Watts
Rivière Déception
Early Proterozoic
cover allochthons
Archean
autochthonous basement
oblique-slip fault
D1 regular-sequence thrust fault
D1 out-of-sequence thrust fault
① syn-thermal peak
② post-thermal peak
Wakeham Bay
Joy Bay
Lac St-Germain
74° 30' W
61° 15' N
10 km
MSO/SBL 88
Povungnituk Group
Actinolite-Albite Zone
Hornblende-Actinolite-Albite Zone
Hornblende-Actinolite-Oligoclase Zone
Hornblende-Oligoclase Zone
Hornblende-Oligoclase-Garnet/Clinopyroxene Zone
Chukotat Group
Actinolite-Albite Zone
Actinolite-Oligoclase±Hornblende Zone
Lac Watts Group
Thermal Peak Mineral Zones
Hornblende-Actinolite-Albite to Hornblende-Oligoclase-Garnet/Clinopyroxene
Post-Thermal Peak Mineral Zones
Actinolite-Chlorite-Albite Overprint On Greenschist To Amphibolite Grade Assemblages
S
N
Geological Contact
Regular Sequence Thrust Fault
Out-Of-Sequence Thrust Fault
① Syn-Thermal Peak
② Post-Thermal Peak
km
0
10
20
30
0 10 20 30 40 50 60 70 km

TABLE 2. COLLISION OROGENS BETWEEN ARCHEAN PROVINCES

Orogen	Foreland	Hinterland	Obliquity	Orogenic U-Pb ages
Trans-Hudson	Superior	Hearne	Left	1.91–1.79 Ga
New Quebec	Superior	Rae	None	1.87–1.79 Ga
Torngat	Nain	Rae	Left	Post-2.4/pre-1.65 Ga
Nagssugtoqidian	Nain	Burwell	Left	1.87 Ga
Foxe/Rinkian	Rae	Burwell	Right(?)	1.90–1.84 Ga
Abloviak	Burwell	Rae	Left(?)	(?)
Snowbird	Hearne(?)	Rae(?)	(?)	Post-1.92/pre-1.85 Ga
Thelon	Slave	Rae	Right	2.02–1.91 Ga

Ga (Rb-Sr), cut by dioritic to granitic plutons (*Taylor, 1982*; *Doig, 1987*). The 2.7-Ga (Rb-Sr) amphibolite-grade gneisses of Kovik antiform, representing parautochthonous basement of the Superior province, dip beneath the Sugluk terrane on a moderately northwest-dipping granulite-grade mylonite zone (Sugluk suture). The suture is the inferred root zone for the Cape Smith belt, an infolded imbricate thrust belt (Fig. 15B) containing sedimentary and igneous rocks of the rifted margin of the Superior province and the vanished ocean to the north (St-Onge and Lucas, 1989). The structural evolution of the belt (*Lucas, 1989*) involved (D1a) "piggy-back" imbrication and translation of the belt onto the Superior province along a sole thrust at the basement-cover interface, (D1b) "out-of-sequence" thrusting, which reimbricated the cover and carried thin basement slices, (D2) folding of basement and cover parallel to the thrust belt, producing lobate antiforms and cuspate synforms, and (D3) crossfolding of basement and cover about northerly trending axes, possibly related to shortening in the New Quebec orogen. Heating of the belt in response to D1a thrusting peaked early in D1b. The crossfolds enable cross sections of the belt (Fig. 15B and C) to be constructed by axial projection.

Three groups of supracrustal rocks are preserved in the Cape Smith belt. Coarse to fine clastic sediments and bimodal volcanics of the southern and structurally lowest part of the belt (Povungnituk Group) are interpreted as a rift facies. A central set of thrust sheets comprise sediment-free tholeiitic basalt up to 6 km thick (Chukotat Group), interpreted as transitional oceanic crust. The northern and structurally highest part of the belt comprises, in ascending structural sequence, graphitic pelite, pillow basalt, a complex of sheeted dikes and sills, and mafic to ultramafic cumulates (Purtuniq ophiolite) interpreted as true oceanic crust. Rhyolite in the Povungnituk Group dates rifting at 1.96 Ga, and a differentiated sill related to Chukotat volcanism dates the generation of transitional crust at 1.92 Ga (R. R. Parrish, personal communication, 1988). Synmetamorphic plutonism at 1.87 Ga provides a minimum constraint on the age of D1a thrusting. The Purtuniq ophiolite, at 2.00 Ga, is about 40 m.y. older than the inferred rifting event at the Superior margin, implying an ocean to the north of substantial size and longevity.

Hudson Bay segment. The external parts of this arcuate segment (Fig. 16) are exposed on the coast and islands of eastern Hudson Bay, and inliers on the southern mainland; the internal parts are covered by the Paleozoic Hudson Bay basin, and their nature is inferred from seismic and geopotential data. The segment comprises the autochthonous Nastapoka homocline, the Belcher thrust and fold belt, the Winisk trough, and the central Hudson Bay hinterland (Roksandic, 1987). The oldest autochthonous sequence (Richmond Gulf Group) is preserved in a meridional 70-km-wide graben and consists of westerly derived fluvial sandstone and basalt (*Chandler, 1988a*). Diagenetic apatite gives a minimum age of 2.02 Ga for the basal sandstone. The unconformably overlying marine strata are more complete on the Belcher Islands, which expose the structural culmination of a train of large-scale doubly plunging décollement folds of northerly trend (*Jackson, 1960*). A sequence of marine shelf sediments with a thin basalt unit is overlain disconformably by a foredeep succession, consisting in ascending order, of quartzarenite, ironstone, tholeiitic basalt, euxinic pelite, graywacke turbidite, and fluvial molasse shed southeastward (Ricketts and Donaldson, 1981). The décollement folds pass northward, based on seismic reflection data, into an east-vergent imbricate thrust belt intermediate in degree of shortening between the Belcher Islands and the Cape Smith belt (Roksandic, 1987). The Ottawa Islands in the west-central part of the thrust belt expose tholeiitic and komatiitic flows similar to those in the Cape Smith belt (*Arndt and others, 1987*; *Baragar and Scoates, 1987*). The arcuate 100-km-wide Winisk trough, bounded by high-angle faults(?), is characterized by broad, open upright folds developed in well-stratified Proterozoic strata at least 6 km thick (Roksandic, 1987). The trough may be an episutural basin separating the thrust belt from the hinterland to the northwest, which is bordered by a prominent linear magnetic high, possibly delineating a magmatic arc generated above a northwest-dipping subduction zone. The hinterland appears to be continuous with the Sugluk terrane of northern Quebec, but its relation to the Hearne province hinges on the nature of a discontinuity in the gravity and magnetic fields parallel to the coast of western Hudson Bay.

Manitoba-Saskatchewan segment. This 500-km-wide dogleg has four composite tectonic zones (Fig. 17): a southeastern foreland belt, an internal zone composed of juvenile Proterozoic crust, an Andean-type (Wathaman-Chipewyan) batholith, and a northwestern hinterland belt. The foreland is segmented into the Fox River belt, a steep north-dipping thrust stack of semipelite and tholeiitic to komatiitic flows and sills (*Scoates, 1981*); the

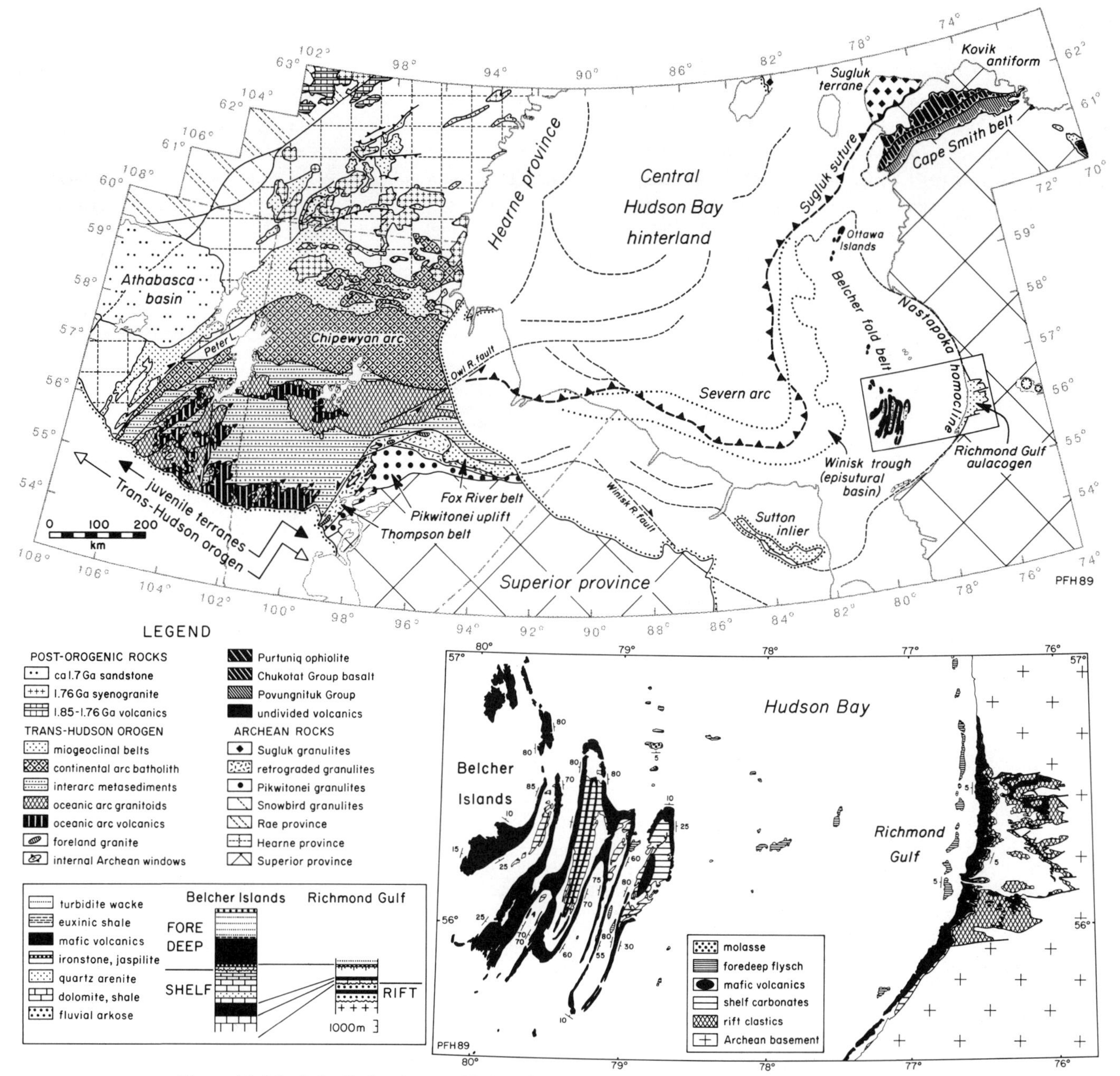

Figure 16. Manitoba-Saskatchewan, Hudson Bay, and northern Quebec segments of Trans-Hudson orogen. Dotted line in southern Hudson Bay outlines inferred episutural Winisk basin after *Roksandic (1987)*. Geology (lower right) and stratigraphy (lower left) of Richmond Gulf aulacogen and Belcher fold belt.

Orr Lake and Spilt Lake blocks, in which Archean Pikwitonei granulites of the Superior province have been retrograded to amphibolite grade; and the Thompson nickel belt, in which similarly retrograded basement and Early Proterozoic cover (Ospwagan Group) were thrust southeastward onto the Superior province, then (following peak metamorphism) sinistrally transpressed into upright en echelon folds transected by steep mylonite zones having southeast-side-up reverse shear, and finally cut by conjugate transcurrent faults related to northwest-southeast shortening (Bleeker, 1989). The 2-km-thick Fox River mafic-ultramafic sill and related northeast-trending Molson dikes were intruded at 1.88 Ga into the Fox River belt and the Thompson belt, respectively (*Heaman and others, 1986*), during progressive deformation of the Ospwagan Group (W. Bleeker, personal communication, 1988).

The internal zone, up to 400 km wide, was long thought to

be a typical Archean "granite-greenstone-gneiss" terrain until isotopic data showed that it consists of essentially juvenile 1.9-Ga crust (*Sangster, 1978*; *Chauvel and others, 1987*; *Van Schmus and others, 1987a*). Subdivisions based on prevailing lithologies and metamorphic grades include low-grade volcanic-plutonic belts, high-grade para- and orthogneiss belts, and plutonic belts (Fig. 17). The 1.91- to 1.88-Ga volcanic and associated 1.89- to 1.84-Ga plutonic rocks closely resemble those of island arcs (*Gaskarth and Parslow, 1987*; *Watters and Pearce, 1987*; Syme, 1989; *Thom and others, 1989*), and the paragneiss belts may have evolved from inter-arc basins. Deformation involved major thrust stacking (mainly south- to southeast-vergent), possibly coeval with 1.83-Ga fluvial sedimentation, followed by large-scale upright folding of northeast trend contemporaneous with peak metamorphism at 1.82 to 1.81 Ga (Hoffman, 1988; Lewry and others, 1989). This is attributed to accretion of island arcs and sediments due to north- to northwestward subduction, followed by oblique sinistral collision between the Hearne and Superior provinces. Archean rocks in the internal zone are exposed only in small tectonic windows in the Hanson and Glennie domains (Fig. 17), and their subsurface extent beneath allochthonous Proterozoic crust is unknown.

The Wathaman-Chipewyan batholith (1.86 to 1.85 Ga) is a composite calc-alkaline intrusion, up to 100 km wide, constituting an eroded Andean-type magmatic arc developed on Archean crust, against which the internal zone was accreted (*Meyer,*

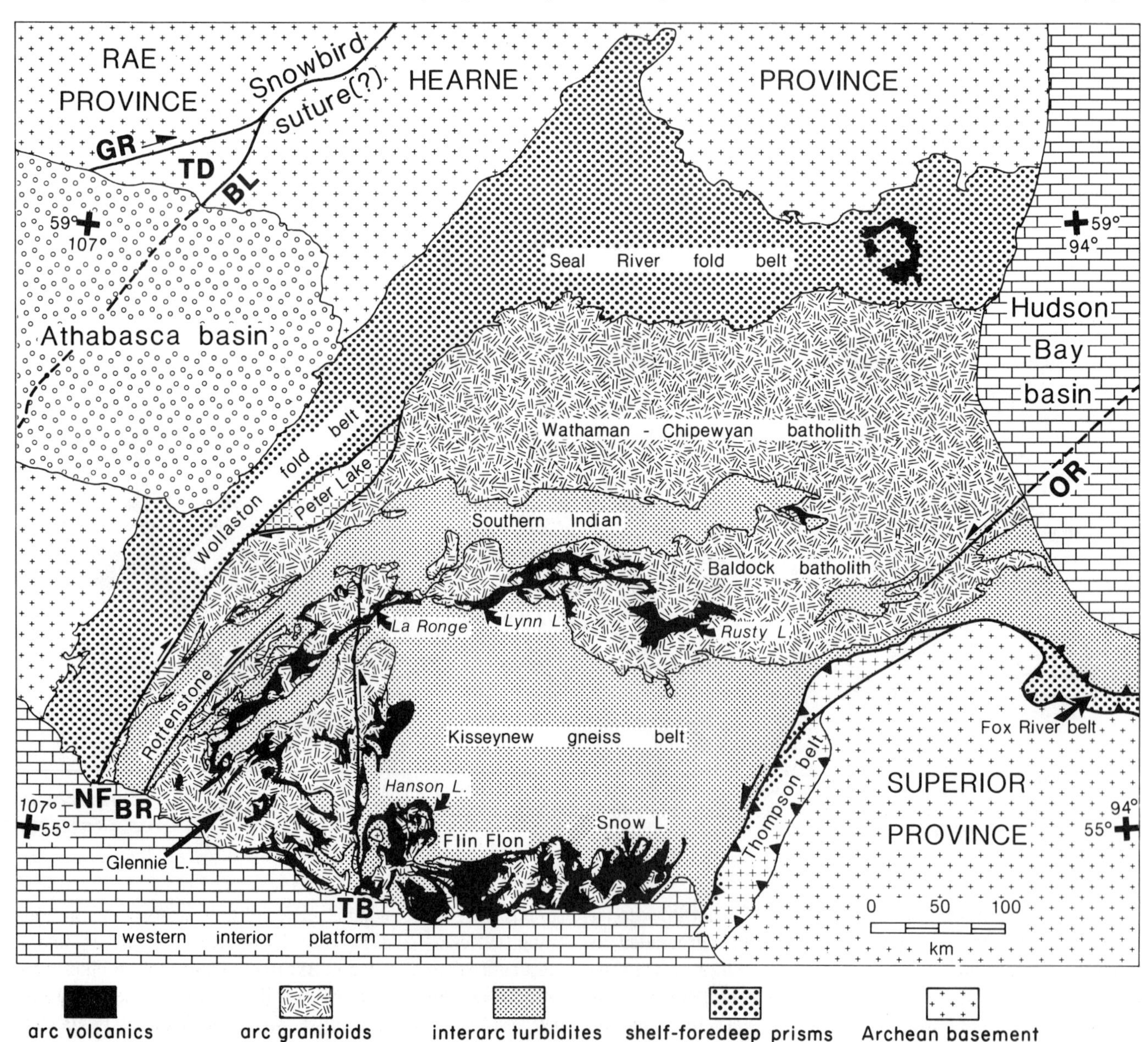

Figure 17. Manitoba-Saskatchewan segment of Trans-Hudson orogen. Major shear zones: BL, Black Lake; BR, Birch Rapids; GR, Grease River; NF, Needle Falls; OR, Owl River; TB, Tabbernor; TD, Tantato granulite domain.

1987). The Archean Peter Lake terrane (Fig. 17), of unknown heritage, locally intervenes between the batholith and the Wollaston–Seal River fold belt of the Hearne province hinterland. The fold belt exposes strongly deformed and metamorphosed Early Proterozoic sediments of rift, shelf, and foredeep aspect, as well as Archean basement antiforms, intrusions related to the Wathaman-Chipewyan batholith, and 1.76-Ga anorogenic syenogranites.

Dakota segment. The extent of the orogen beneath the western interior platform (Fig. 13) is based on gravity, magnetic, and electrical conductivity anomalies (Thomas and others, 1987); there are many basement cores but few U-Pb ages. The only exposures are in the Black Hills of South Dakota near the western margin of the orogen. There, metamorphosed shale and graywacke overlie shelf and rift sediments that locally rest on Archean basement (*DeWitt and others, 1986*). Ages of associated sills and tuffs are 2.17 Ga (initial rifting), 1.97 Ga (shelf collapse), and 1.88 Ga (youngest turbidites), and major north-vergent folds (related to the Central Plains orogen?) predate the 1.72-Ga Harney Peak granite (*Redden and others, 1987*). Nd isotopes (*Walker and others, 1986*) show that the basement is akin to the Wyoming rather than the Superior province, and that the metasediments were derived neither from entirely juvenile crust nor from an exclusively Archean terrain.

New Quebec orogen

The New Quebec orogen (in part formerly known as the Labrador trough) is the collision zone between the Superior province and the eastern Rae province (Hoffman, 1988). It trends southeast for 1,200 km from west of Ungava Bay in the north to within the Grenville parautochthon in the south (Fig. 18), where it turns southwest toward the Otish and Mistassini basins (Fig. 13). The orogen comprises autochthonous foreland strata, a southwest-vergent thrust and fold belt, and an Archean hinterland intruded by synorogenic plutons (Wardle, 1982; *Boone and Hynes, 1989*; Poirier and others, 1989; *van der Leeden and others, 1989*). A flexural forebulge related to the northern Quebec segment of the Trans-Hudson orogen produces a structural culmination in the New Quebec orogen in which Archean basement is exposed beyond and structurally beneath the northern preserved limit of the thrust and fold belt (Fig. 18).

The autochthon preserves three unconformity-bounded sequences (*Wardle and Bailey, 1981*; Le Gallais and Lavoie, 1982; *Clark, 1984*). The oldest sequence, which is overstepped by the middle sequence except in the Cambrian Lake aulacogen, comprises basal fluvial red beds (Seward Subgroup), marine-shelf quartzite and dolomite (Pistolet Subgroup), euxinic shale and turbidites of an intrashelf basin or foredeep (Swampy Bay Subgroup), and a progradational dolomite reef complex (Denault Formation). The middle sequence begins with a transgressive marine-ramp triad (Wishart Quartzite, Ruth Shale, Sokoman Ironstone) overlain by foredeep shale and turbidites (Menihek Formation). The upper sequence is a fluvial molasse—the Tamarack River Formation in the south and the southwesterly derived Chioak Formation in the north. Tentative correlatives in the Otish/Mistassini basin are, in ascending order: fluvial sediments (Seward = Indicator/Papaskwasati), marine-shelf quartzite and dolomite (Pistolet = Peribonca/Cheno), quartzite-ironstone couplet (Wishart-Sokoman = Temiscamie), and foredeep shale and turbidites (Menihek = Kallio).

To the northeast, the autochthon is overridden by a stack of extensive, thin-skinned, internally imbricated thrust sheets of large relative displacement, which have been locally disrupted by younger basement-involved folds and high-angle faults (Wardle, 1982; *Boone and Hynes, 1989*). In the north, high-angle longitudinal faults record late dextral strike-slip between the thrust belt and the hinterland; in the south, the thin-skinned thrusts are refolded in north-trending, basement-involved shear zones having reverse slip. Confident stratigraphic identifications are possible only for the more external thrust sheets, which differ from the autochthon mainly in having volcanic flows and related sills of at least three ages. Alkalic basalt in the initial rift sequence (Seward Subgroup) is undated; rhyolite associated with tholeiitic mafic flows and sills correlated with the Swampy Bay Subgroup is dated at 2.14 Ga, and gabbro sills in the Menihek foredeep and highly alkalic volcanics in the underlying Sokoman ironstone are dated at 1.87 to 1.88 Ga, providing a maximum age for thrusting (*Machado and others, 1988*; *Chevé and Machado, 1988*). Successively more internal and structurally higher thrust sheets are composed of undated mafic-ultramafic sill complexes and associated volcanics, and arkosic semipelite of the Laporte Group (*Clark, 1988*; *van der Leeden and others, 1989*). Archean basement antiforms veneered by quartzite and marble structurally overlie the Laporte Schist, but structural continuity between the schist and the basement antiforms, or between the antiforms and the Superior province, is uncertain (Poirier and others, 1989). Barrovian metamorphism postdates thin-skinned thrusting and increases in grade toward the hinterland; its age of 1.79 Ga is a minimum for thin-skinned thrusting.

Near Kuujjuaq (Fig. 18), the proximal hinterland of the thrust belt consists of Archean gneisses and Early Proterozoic(?) metasediments and metavolcanics, cut by 1.84- to 1.83-Ga tonalites and granites associated with granulite-grade metamorphism that peaked at 1.83 Ga (Poirier and others, 1989). Contemporaneous cooling of the hinterland and adjacent thrust and fold belt (1.79-Ga monazites; 1.77-Ga titanites; 1.74-Ga rutiles) implies that accretion of the hinterland occurred before 1.79 Ga and perhaps as early as 1.83 Ga (*Machado and others, 1988*). The 1.84- to 1.81-Ga De Pas batholith is a linear calc-alkaline plutonic belt east of the thrust and fold belt, coincident with a granulite-grade, pre- to synplutonic, dextral shear zone involving Early Proterozoic (Laporte Group) and Archean rocks (*van der Leeden and others, 1989*). Based on mainly reconnaissance studies, the hinterland is tentatively viewed as an extension of the Rae province that overrode the northeast margin of the Superior province in a dextral oblique collision event between 1.87 and 1.79 Ga. This is compatible with clockwise rotation of the southeastern arm of the Rae province as a consequence of northward

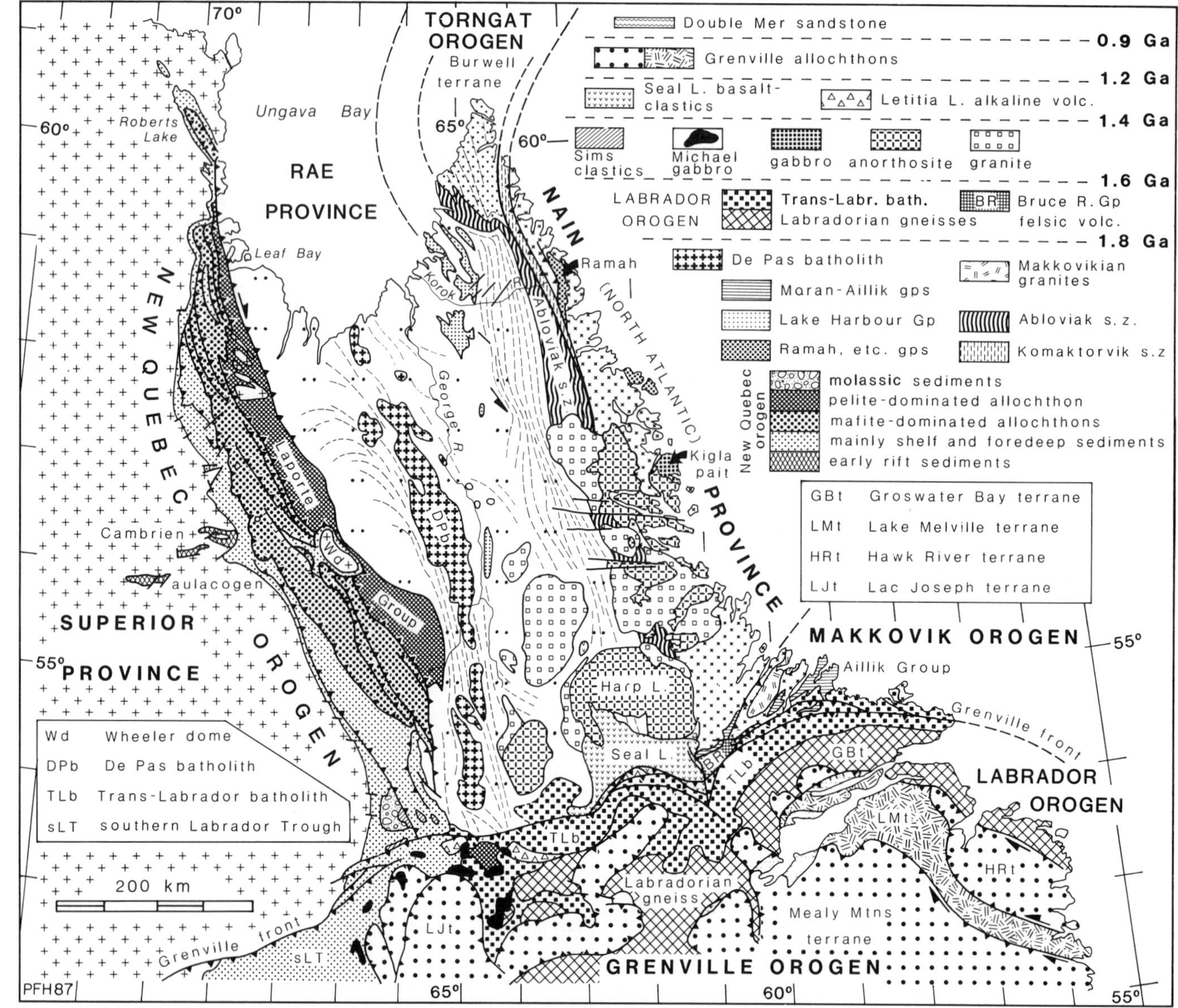

Figure 18. Geology of northeastern Quebec and Labrador showing collision zones between Superior and Rae provinces (New Quebec orogen) and between Rae and Nain provinces (Torngat orogen). Makkovik and Labrador orogens involved accretion of Early Proterozoic juvenile crust onto Nain province and the Rae-Nain assembly, respectively. Middle Proterozoic anorogenic igneous suites intrude Rae and Nain provinces and Torngat orogen. All crustal elements were telescoped by northwest-directed thrusting in Grenville orogen.

indentation by the Superior province following initial collision in the northern Quebec segment of the Trans-Hudson orogen (Gibb, 1983).

Torngat and related orogens between the Rae and Nain provinces

A branching system of orogens separates the Rae and Nain provinces and encloses the Burwell province (Fig. 3). In northern Labrador (Fig. 18), the Torngat orogen (Hoffman, 1988) is a zone of oblique sinistral convergence between the Nain foreland and Rae hinterland (*Ermanovics and others, 1989*). An east-vergent foreland thrust-fold belt involves Archean basement and Early Proterozoic shelf and foredeep strata of the Ramah Group (Knight and Morgan, 1981). To the west is a composite shear zone that bifurcates at the southern tip of the Burwell terrane (Korstgård and others, 1988). The eastern branch (Komaktorvik shear zone) is characterized by Archean anorthosite bodies enclosed by amphibolite- to granulite-grade mylonite produced by Early Proterozoic sinistral transpression. Before the opening of Davis Strait, it was apparently coextensive with the 1.85-Ga Nagssugtoqidian suture zone (Fig. 19), which also combines sinis-

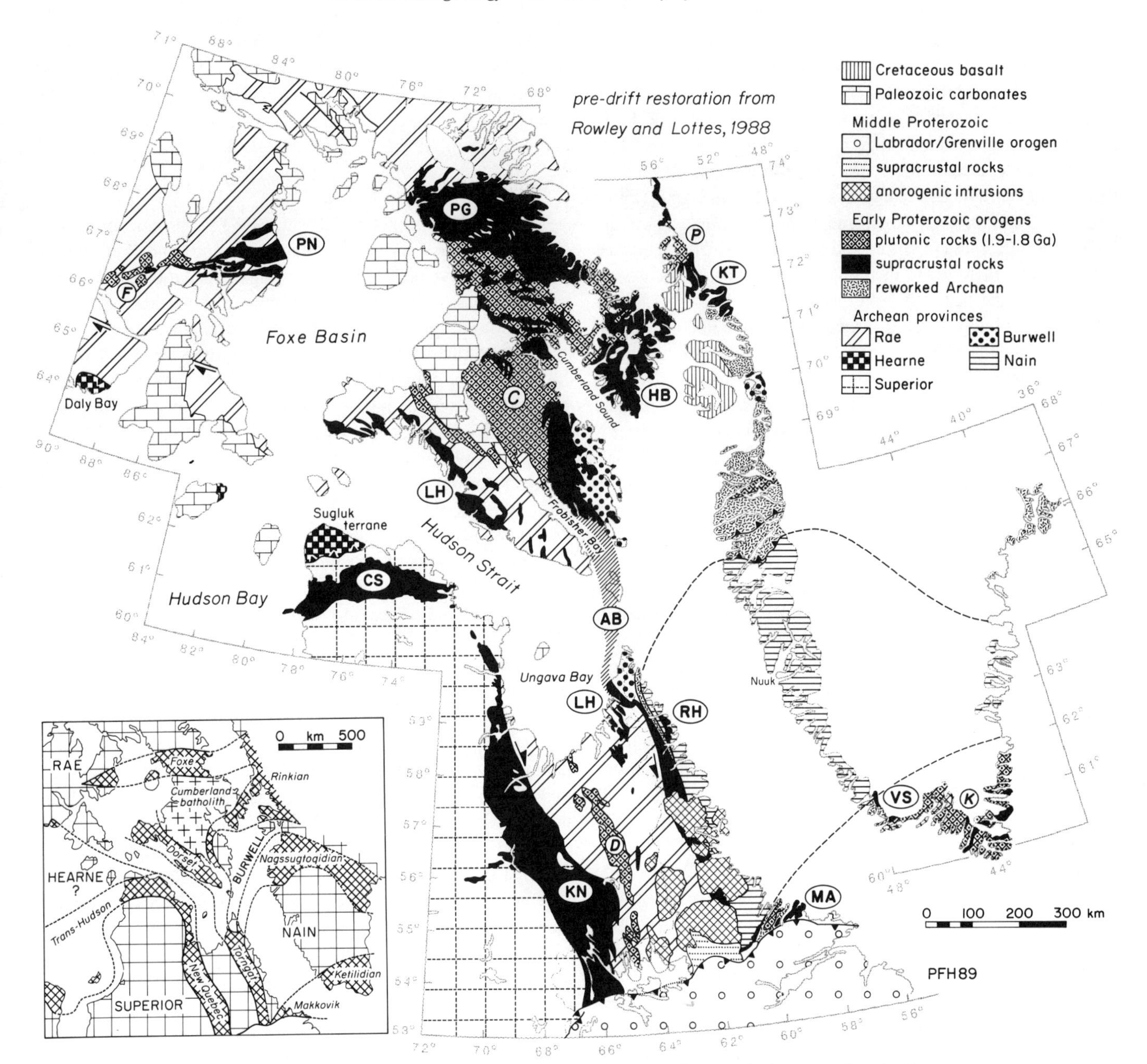

Figure 19. Geology of parts of eastern Canada and southern Greenland, showing inferred relations (inset) between various Archean provinces and Early Proterozoic orogens in pre-drift restoration of *Rowley and Lottes (1988).* Supracrustal sequences: AB, Tasiyuak gneiss (partly locus of Abloviak shear zone); CS, Cape Smith belt; HB, Hoare Bay Group; KN, Kaniapiskau Supergroup; KT, Karrat Group; LH, Lake Harbour Group; MA, Moran and Aillik Groups; PG, Piling Group; PN, Penrhyn Group; RH, Ramah Group; VS, Vallen, Sortis, Qipisarqo, and Ilordleq Groups.

tral transcurrent shear with thrusting toward the Nain province (Escher and others, 1976; *Kalsbeek and others, 1987*). The western branch (Abloviak shear zone) consists of distinctive graphitic garnetiferous mylonite (*Blackadar, 1967a*; Taylor, 1979) resulting from sinistral transpression of a pelitic protolith. It is identified with a pronounced negative magnetic anomaly and can be traced for 1,300 km from the Grenville front to Cumberland Sound on Baffin Island (Fig. 19). In Labrador, the proximal hinterland comprises Archean and/or Early Proterozoic orthogneiss with infolds of quartzite, marble, rusty pelite, and metagraywacke (Lake Harbour Group) of presumed Early Proterozoic age (Taylor, 1979). These rocks are coextensive with the Dorset fold belt of southern Baffin Island (*Jackson and Taylor, 1972*), which is separated from the northern extension of the Abloviak shear zone by the enormous Cumberland charnockite-granite batholith (Fig. 19).

The Foxe-Rinkian fold belt (Fig. 19) is defined by the presence of a relatively thin unit of quartzite and/or marble, resting on Archean basement, overlain by a thick sequence of flysch that locally contains sheets of mafic rock near the base. The Early Proterozoic strata, which range from greenschist to upper amphibolite grade, extend in a predrift reconstruction from Melville Peninsula (Penrhyn Group), across central Baffin Island (Piling Group), to central west Greenland (Karrat Group). There are significant differences in setting and structural evolution between the segments. In Melville Peninsula, Archean basement lies on both sides of the belt, but a cozonal string of 1.83- to 1.82-Ga calc-alkaline plutons extends beyond the termination of the belt to the southwest (*LeCheminant and others, 1987b*). An eastward-fanning system of upright folds, deforming earlier recumbent folds of basement and cover, is associated with strike-parallel extension and sheath-fold development attributed to westward-tapering sinistral transpression (Henderson, 1983, *1984*). In Baffin Island, Archean basement lies to the north, and the south margin is intruded by the 1.90- to 1.84-Ga Cumberland charnockite-granite batholith. Synmetamorphic deformation involved north-vergent folding and thrusting with basement-cover imbrication, succeeded by upright basement-involved folding in response to continued north-south compression. In Greenland, Archean basement lies to the south, and the belt is intruded by the 1.86-Ga (Rb-Sr) Proven charnockite-granite batholith. Early northeast-vergent premetamorphic folds are strongly overprinted by northwest-directed ductile thrust ramps that climb upward from the basement into the cover in the direction of tectonic transport (Grocott and Pulvertaft, 1989). Studies of extensions of the Rinkian and/or Nagssugtoqidian belts in southeast Greenland are in progress (*Chadwick and others, 1989*).

Snowbird tectonic zone

The Snowbird tectonic zone (Hoffman, 1988) is a 2,800-km-long boundary between the Hearne province and the southwest arm of the Rae province evident as a crustal break on horizontal gravity gradient and magnetic anomaly maps (Sharpton and others, 1987; Committee for the Magnetic Anomaly Map of North America, 1987). Where exposed (Fig. 20), it forms a braided system of granulite-grade mylonites (e.g., *Hanmer, 1987*) enclosing a string of crustal-scale augen up to tens of kilometers wide, composed of layered mafic and felsic granulite and anorthosite (e.g., *Gordon, 1988*) containing mineral assemblages equilibrated at pressures up to 11 kbar (*Tella and Eade, 1986*). The Snowbird tectonic zone is a major structure in the subsurface of Alberta (Fig. 12), where it truncates the Taltson magmatic zone, implying an age younger than about 1.95 Ga (Ross and others, 1989). A minimum age of about 1.85 Ga is inferred from lamprophyre dikes and related syenites and alkalic volcanics of the Baker basin (*LeCheminant and others, 1987a*), which form an overlap assemblage in the central District of Keewatin (Fig. 20). However, a younger age (1.84 to 1.78 Ga) is inferred for convergence across the Snowbird zone in Alberta (Ross and others, 1989). This suggests either diachronous suturing or, alternatively, that the Snowbird zone was reactivated as a boundary zone of southwest-directed crustal extrusion from the Slave-Superior vise (Fig. 14), leading to a cycle of limited oblique divergence and convergence in Alberta (cf., *Tapponnier and others, 1982*).

Thelon orogen

The Thelon orogen (Hoffman, 1988) is a product of dextral oblique collision between the Slave (foreland) and Rae (hinterland) provinces (Fig. 21). Postcollisional indentation by the Slave province was accommodated by oblique shortening across the Queen Maud uplift concurrent with dextral shear on the Great Slave Lake transform, and by younger conjugate strike-slip on the McDonald and Bathurst faults and related escape structures. The orogen has a minimum strike length of 3,200 km, extending from central Alberta to central Ellesmere Island (Fig. 13). With an estimated collision age of 1.97 to 1.92 Ga, it is the oldest of the Early Proterozoic suture zones welding Archean provinces.

The exposed segment of the orogen (Fig. 22) is a miniature analogue of the active India-Eurasia collision zone. It comprises erosional remnants of an autochthonous foredeep (Bear Creek Group) and foreland thrust-fold belt, a belt of sheared Archean rocks of the Slave province margin, a pre- to syncollisional plutonic-metamorphic belt (Thelon magmatic zone), and an eroded hinterland plateau (Queen Maud uplift). The Bear Creek foredeep (Fig. 23A) is a westward-tapering, upward-shoaling wedge of turbiditic to fluvial detritus of southeasterly derivation that overlies relatively thin shelf strata (Kimerot platform), apparently deposited on a short-lived east-facing shelf (*Grotzinger and McCormick, 1988*). The frontal part of a thin-skinned, northwest-vergent thrust-fold belt is preserved and exposed in cross section (Fig. 23B) as a result of bulk rotation related to the Bathurst transcurrent fault (*Tirrul, 1985*). To the east, Archean basement and Early Proterozoic mafic dikes of the Slave province have undergone increasing degrees of dextral shear toward their common boundary (inferred suture) with the Thelon magmatic zone, which consists of an older (2.02 to 1.95 Ga) suite of granodioritic plutons intruded into country rocks that underwent coeval granulite-grade metamorphism, and a younger (1.92 to 1.91 Ga) suite of peraluminous granites emplaced during uplift (*van Breemen and others, 1987*). Steeply dipping mylonites within the magmatic zone resolve dextral and reverse components of shear. The mainly granulite-grade rocks of the Queen Maud uplift are juxtaposed against less deeply eroded parts of the Rae province along oblique east-vergent reverse faults. A 1.97- to 1.92-Ga collision is inferred from tuff beds in the Bear Creek foredeep (*Grotzinger and others, 1989*; S. A. Bowring, personal communication, 1988), and from the onset of uplift and change from arc- to collision-type magmatism in the Thelon magmatic zone.

The distinctive magnetic anomaly signatures of the Thelon magmatic zone and Queen Maud uplift can be traced northward across the Arctic platform toward exposures in Boothia uplift. On eastern Somerset Island, a diatreme cutting Paleozoic strata contains xenocrystic zircons of Thelonian (1.935 Ga) age (*Reichen-*

bach and Parrish, 1988). Farther north, Archean granulite-grade gneisses on eastern Devon Island pass northward into 1.97- to 1.95-Ga charnockitic orthogneiss and 1.91-Ga anatectic granite on southern Ellesmere Island (*Frisch, 1988*), representing possible extensions of the Queen Maud uplift and Thelon magmatic zone respectively.

The Thelon and Taltson magmatic zones (Fig. 21) are linked by the Great Slave Lake shear zone (Hoffman, 1987), a 25-km-wide zone of progressive granulite- to greenschist-grade mylonites recording dextral and subordinate northwest-vergent reverse components of shear (Hanmer, 1988a; *Hanmer and Needham, 1988*). Synkinematic intrusions have a minimum age range of 2.05 to 1.92 Ga (S. A. Bowring, personal communication, 1987). The basin in the east arm of Great Slave Lake north of the shear zone (Fig. 22) experienced a complex history of dextral transtension and transpression, and received detritus from the Thelon orogen and the slightly younger Wopmay orogen to the west (Hoffman, 1988). To the south, the nonmarine Nonacho basin evolved in a sinistral shear zone (Aspler and Donaldson, 1985), which bounds a wedge that "escaped" southwestward from the Slave province indentor (Fig. 14). This segment of the orogen is geometrically analogous to the intracontinental transform segment of the India-Eurasia plate boundary in Burma (Hoffman, 1987).

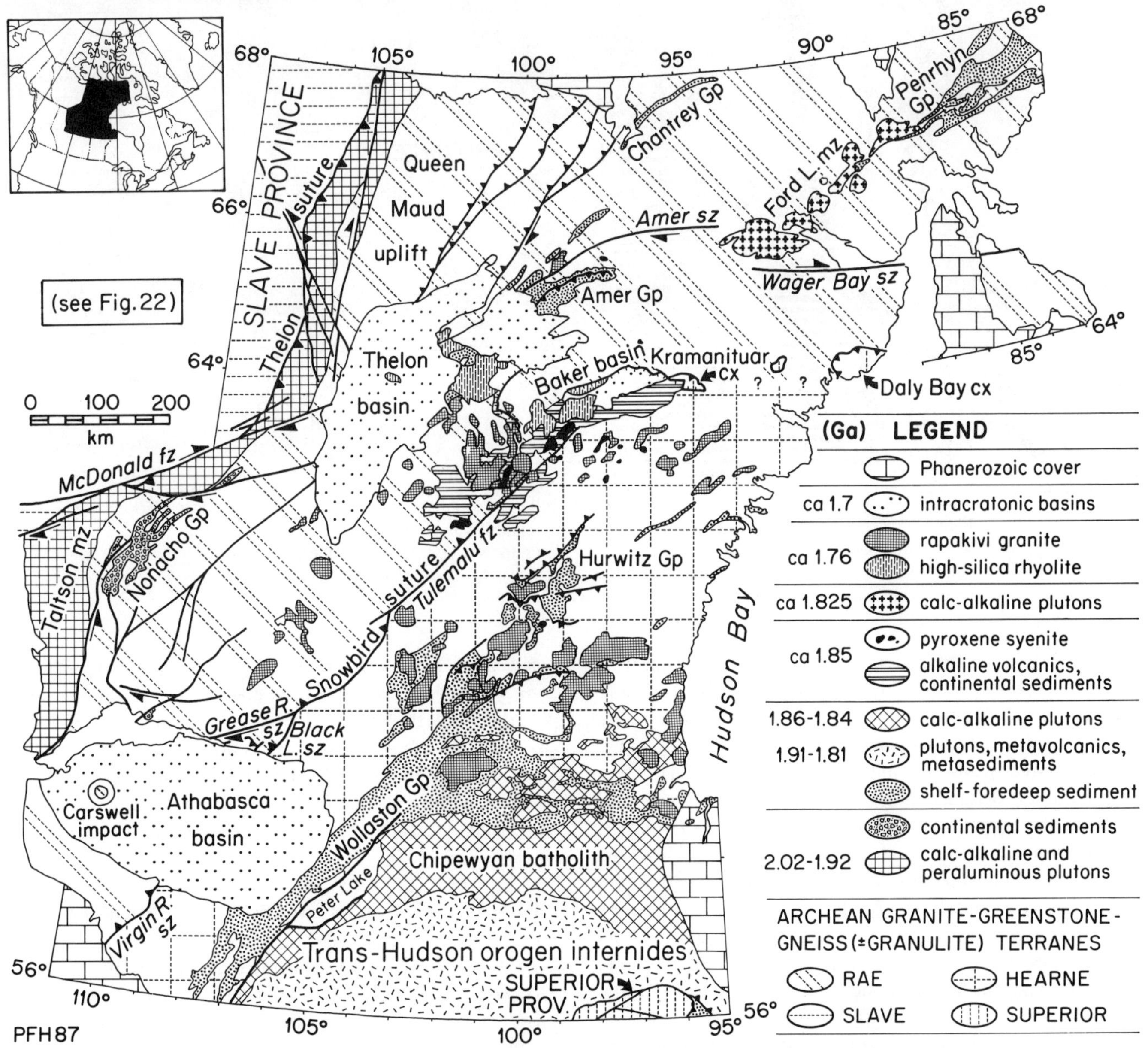

Figure 20. Geology of parts of Rae and Hearne provinces framed by Thelon orogen in the west, Trans-Hudson orogen in the south, Hudson Bay in the east, and Arctic platform in the north. Note overlap of Hearne and Rae provinces by Baker basin, providing minimum age of 1.85 Ga for segment of Snowbird suture(?).

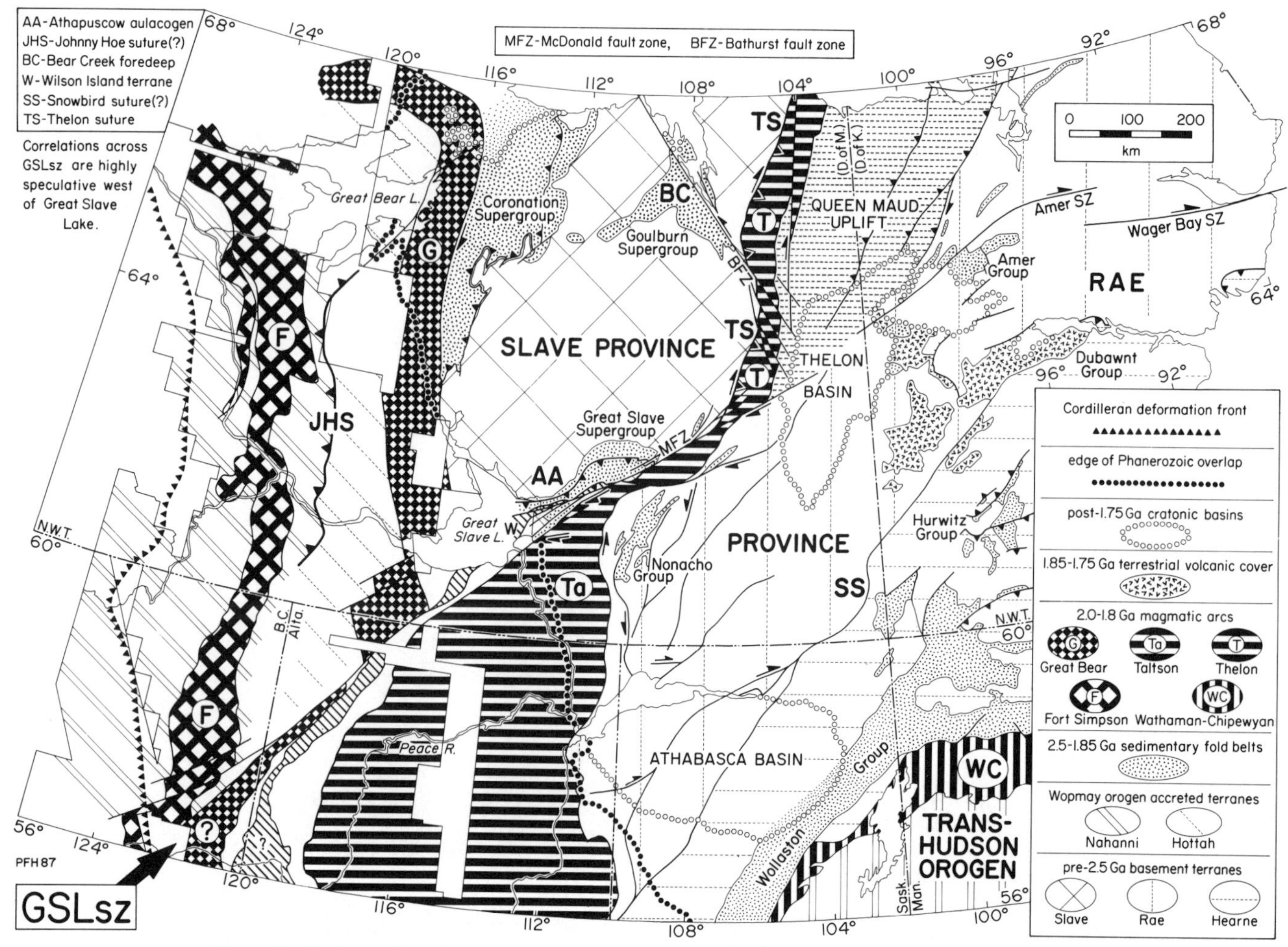

Figure 21. Geology of northwest Canadian shield and adjacent basement of western platform. Great Slave Lake shear zone (GSLsz) is interpreted as a continental transform developed during post-collisional indentation of Slave and Rae provinces. Recent geochronology has reduced westerly subsurface extent of inferred Taltson magmatic arc (Ta), as indicated in Figure 12.

The Taltson magmatic zone (Fig. 22), like the Thelon magmatic zone, is a belt of 1.99 to 1.95-Ga dioritic to granitic plutons and 1.93- to 1.91-Ga peraluminous granites (*Bostock and others, 1987*). Extensive granulites comparable to the Queen Maud uplift are apparently absent south of the Great Slave Lake shear zone, suggesting that the location of the shear zone was governed by the southern limit of the Slave province indentor (Hoffman, 1987). This inference is supported by subsurface dating (Ross and others, 1989), which shows that the area west of the Taltson magmatic zone is underlain by 2.3- to 1.9-Ga terranes rather than an Archean foreland (Fig. 12). Ross and others (1989) interpret these terranes as having been accreted to the Rae province both before and after the arrival of the Slave province to the north. This is supported by 2.3- to 2.1-Ga Nd model ages for the Hottah terrane (Fig. 12), which was accreted to the west margin of the Slave province at about 1.91 Ga (*Bowring and Podosek, 1989*). The presence of 2.44- to 1.99-Ga granites intrusive into Archean rocks of the Rae province east of the Taltson magmatic zone (*Van Schmus and others, 1986*; *Bostock and Loveridge, 1988*) suggests that there may have been episodes of east-dipping subduction beneath the Rae province before the arrival of the Slave Province. The only granitoids of this age in the Slave province belong to the 2.19- to 2.02-Ga alkaline-peralkaline Blachford, Bigspruce, and Booth River (Fig. 8) intrusive complexes (*Bowring and others, 1984*; *Cavell and Baadsgaard, 1986*; Roscoe and others, 1987).

EARLY PROTEROZOIC ACCRETED TERRANES

Flanking the Archean protocraton are Early Proterozoic accreted terranes (Fig. 1) that contain little or no Archean crust (*Nelson and DePaolo, 1985*; *Kalsbeek and Taylor, 1985*; *Barovich and others, 1988*; *Bowring and Podosek, 1989*). They imply rapid continental growth between 1.80 and 1.65 Ga, immediately following the aggregation of Archean microcontinents between 1.95 and 1.80 Ga (Hoffman, 1988). The terranes are best exposed

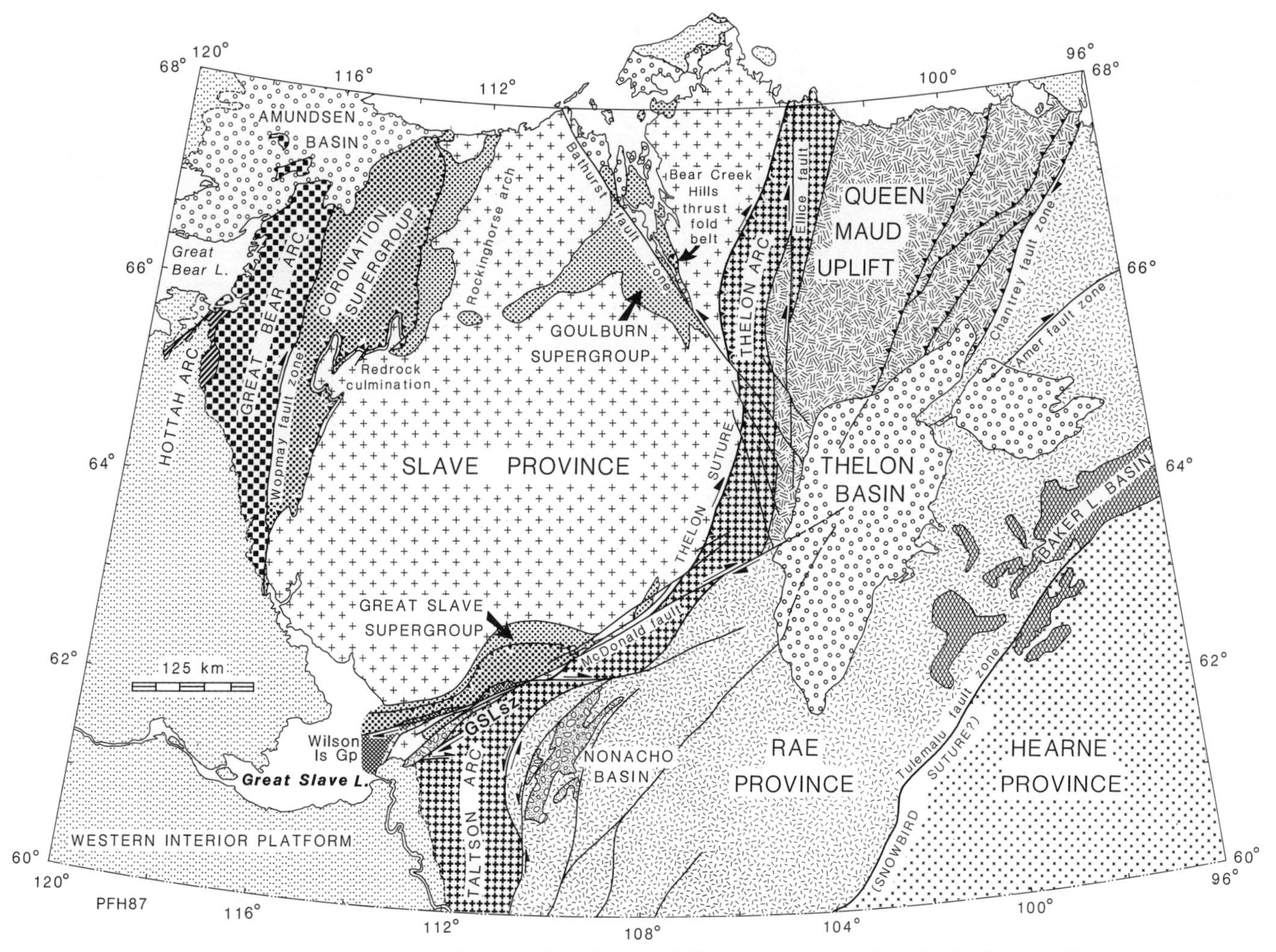

Figure 22. Geology of the northwestern Canadian shield. The Slave province is bounded by elements of the collisional Thelon orogen to the east and the accretionary Wopmay orogen to the west, and onlapped by the Middle Proterozoic Amundsen basin to the northwest. GSLsz, Great Slave Lake shear zone.

in the southwestern United States, south of Lake Superior, in southern Greenland and Labrador, and in the northwestern Canadian shield (Fig. 2). They also underlie most of the southern midcontinent platform and the Grenville orogen.

Wopmay orogen and northwestern Canada

Much of the interior platform and eastern Cordillera of northwestern Canada is underlain by 2.4- to 2.0-Ga crust that was accreted to the Archean protocraton between 1.9 and 1.7 Ga (*Bowring and Podosek, 1989*). The western limit of Archean crust in the Canadian shield is the median tectonic line of the Wopman orogen (Fig. 24). To the east is the tectonically foreshortened Coronation Supergroup, a shelf-rise and succeeding foredeep prism (Fig. 25A) deposited across the rifted western margin of the Slave province (Hoffman and others, 1988). Dating of volcanic-ash beds on the autochthonous equivalents of the passive-margin sequence indicates that the shelf began to subside at about 1.97 Ga (S. A. Bowring, personal communication, 1988). Destruction of the margin, possibly resulting from collision with the Hottah arc terrane at about 1.91 Ga, involved (1) flexure of the shelf and deposition of foredeep sediments (euxinic pelite, feldspathic turbidites, fluvial red beds); (2) invasion of the (mainly off-shelf) sediments by 1.90- to 1.88-Ga mafic through felsic magmas (Akaitcho felsic sills, Morel mafic sills, Hepburn plutonic suite); and (3) eastward translation and imbrication of the prism and the still-hot Hepburn plutons onto the Slave province (Fig. 25B).

West of the median line are the Hottah and Great Bear magmatic arcs (Hildebrand and others, 1987), which were generated on cryptic 2.4 to 2.0 Ga crust, according to xenocrystic and detrital zircon dating and Pb and Nd isotopic data (*Housh and Bowring, 1988*; *Bowring and Podosek, 1989*). The older (1.95 to 1.91 Ga) Hottah arc was strongly deformed between 1.91 and 1.90 Ga, possibly due to collision with the Slave province. Establishment of an east-dipping dextral-oblique subduction zone following the Hottah-Slave collision led to generation of the 1.88 to

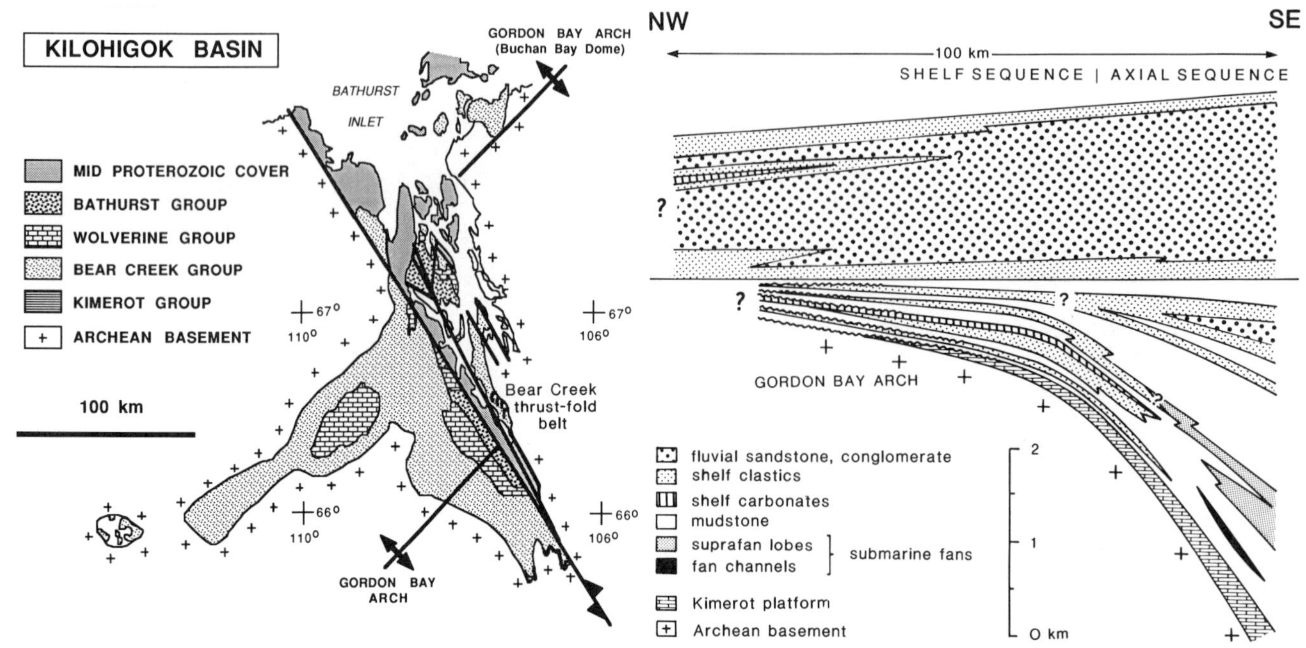

Figure 23. Geology of Kilohigok basin (Goulburn Supergroup) from *Grotzinger and McCormick (1988).* Stratigraphic cross-section of Bear Creek Group foredeep shows multiple disconformities over Gordon Bay arch, a syndepositional forebulge manifesting lithospheric flexure presumably caused by tectonic loading by Thelon arc (see Figure 22) and Bear Creek thrust-fold belt.

1.86 Ga Great Bear arc, a 100- by 1,000-km zone of calc-alkaline, mainly intermediate, subaerial volcanic and plutonic rocks developed mainly on top of the Hottah arc but onlapping and intruding (Bishop Suite) rocks of the deformed continental margin to the east. Cessation of arc magmatism, possibly due to ridge subduction, was followed by (1) oblique en echelon folding, signifying dextral shearing of the Great Bear arc and adjacent parts of the deformed continental margin; (2) intrusion of large, tabular, 1.86- to 1.84-Ga syenogranites and associated diorite plugs in the folded zone; and (3) transection of the entire orogen by a system of conjugate transcurrent faults manifesting irrotational east-west shortening and north-south extension, regionally exceeding 20 percent.

The conjugate faulting event (post-1.84, pre-1.66 Ga) is tentatively ascribed to docking of the Nahanni terrane (Fig. 21), the leading edge of which is delineated in the subsurface by the Johnny Hoe gravity high, a possible suture, and the Fort Simpson magnetic high, a possible magmatic arc from which a 1.86-Ga hornblende granodiorite core has been obtained (S. A. Bowring, personal communication, 1985). The crust-formation age of the Nahanni terrane is not yet determined, but there is widespread evidence of 2.4- to 2.0-Ga crustal inheritance in the eastern Cordillera (*Dusel-Bacon and Aleinikoff, 1985*; *Aleinikoff and others, 1986*), similar to that in the exposed arcs of western Wopmay orogen.

Penokean orogen and the Great Lakes region

Juvenile Early Proterozoic crust accreted to the southern margin of the Superior province is exposed in the Penokean orogen south of Lake Superior (*Barovich and others, 1988*). The southern limit of exposed Archean crust continuous with the Superior province is the Niagara fault zone (Fig. 26). To the south are the Wisconsin magmatic terranes, interpreted as accreted island arcs and/or closed back-arc basins; to the north is a deformed continental margin prism, the Marquette Range Supergroup and its equivalents.

The Wisconsin magmatic terranes (Fig. 26) consist of a northern Pembine-Wausau terrane and a southern Marshfield terrane, separated by the Eau Pleine suture zone (Sims and others, 1989). The Pembine-Wausau terrane consists of deformed volcanic and derived sedimentary rocks, and coeval 1.89- to 1.84-Ga gabbroic through granitic plutons. Nd isotopic data indicate derivation of the terrane from Early Proterozoic (2.3 to 1.85 Ga) crust or, alternatively, from juvenile crust with a minor Archean component that decreases from north to south. In the northern and southern regions, 1.88- to 1.86-Ga arc tholeiites are overlain by 1.85- to 1.84-Ga calc-alkaline andesite-dacite-rhyolite suites; in the central region, a bimodal association of high-alumina basalt and dacite-rhyolite with massive-sulphide deposits resembles an intra-arc rift. Serpentinite, sheeted dikes and plagiorhyolite are associated with tholeiitic basalt near the Niagara suture zone. The suture zone is steeply dipping and has a steeply plunging stretching fabric bracketed in age between 1.86 and 1.835 Ga. In Wisconsin, the terrane is interpreted as an island arc that converged with the Superior province above a south-dipping subduction zone, but equivalents of its northern part in Minnesota are thought to represent an obducted back-arc basin developed above a north-dipping subduction zone (Southwick and others,

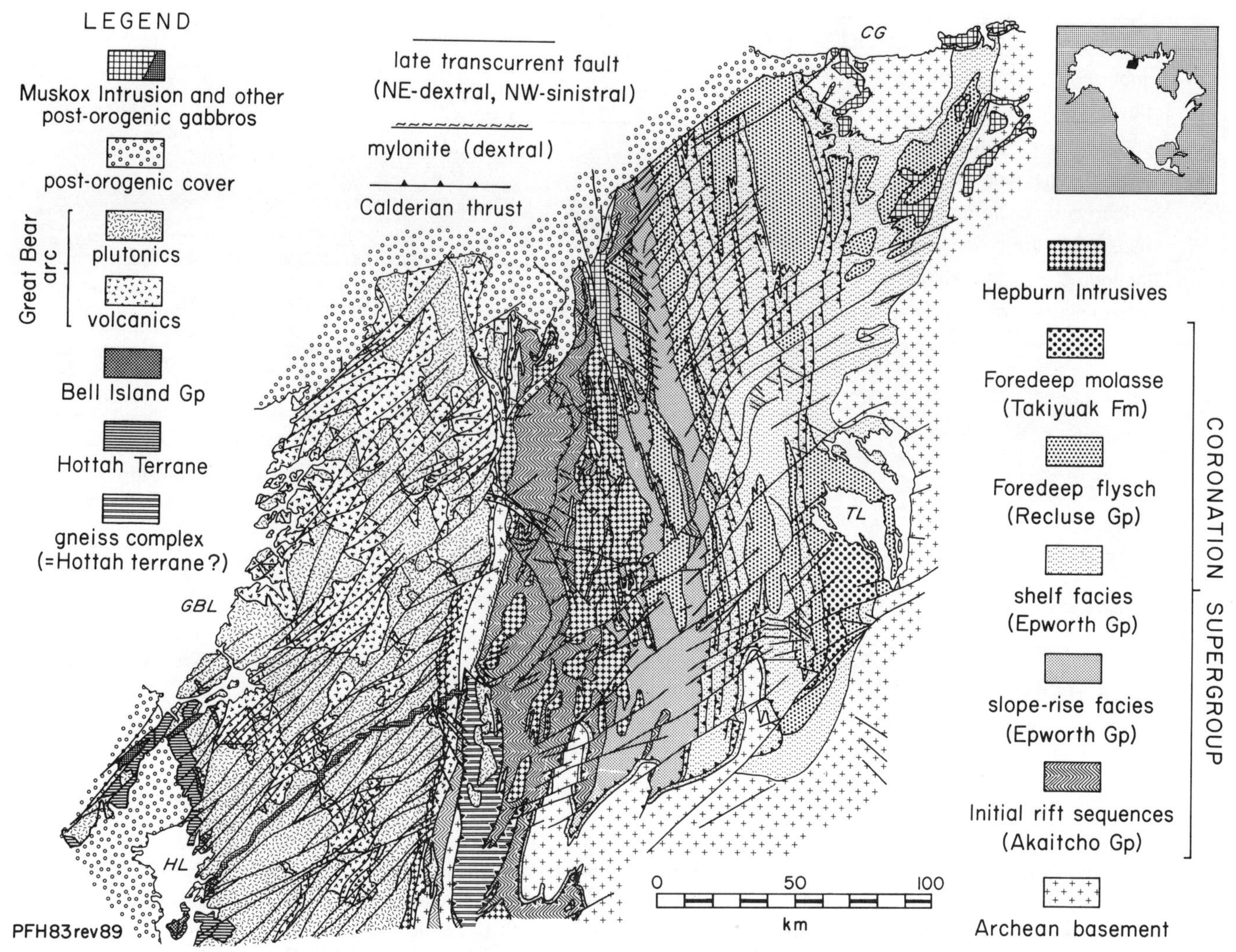

Figure 24. Geology of northern Wopmay orogen, based on mapping by the author, M. R. St-Onge and R. S. Hildebrand. Hottah terrane is an inferred 1.95 to 1.90 Ga island arc built on 2.3 to 2.1 Ga crust that collided with Slave province, deforming the Coronation Supergroup. Subsequently, the Great Bear continental arc developed above a dextral-oblique east-dipping subduction zone, obscuring inferred Hottah-Slave suture. CG, Coronation Gulf; GBL, Great Bear Lake; HL, Hottah Lake; TL, Takujuq Lake.

1988). A subsurface extension of the suture zone, the Spirit Lake trend, cuts across the northwest corner of Iowa (*Van Schmus and others, 1987c*).

Unlike the Pembine-Wausau terrane, the Marshfield terrane has an Archean (3.0 to 2.5 Ga) basement, which is overlain by terrigenous sediments and 1.86-Ga felsic to mafic volcanics, and intruded by 1.89- to 1.84-Ga tonalitic, mafic, and granitic plutons. Like the Niagara suture zone, the Eau Pleine suture zone (Fig. 26) is steeply dipping, has a down-dip stretching lineation, and is bracketed between 1.86 and 1.835 Ga. The latter is the age of relatively undeformed alkali-feldspar granites and comagmatic rhyolites that overlap the two terranes and pin the suture. Sims and others (1989) suggest that the Eau Pleine suture evolved from a north-dipping subduction zone above which the 1.85- to 1.84-Ga calc-alkaline rocks of the Pembine-Wausau terrane were generated following deformation related to the arc-continent collision at the Niagara suture at about 1.85 Ga.

In addition to the 2.2- to 1.7-Ga Marquette Range Supergroup and equivalents, the southern margin of the Superior province is also the site of the 1.850-Ga Sudbury impact structure and a distinctly older sedimentary prism, the 2.48- to 2.22-Ga Huron Supergroup (Fig. 27). The southern extremities of both sedimentary prisms were foreshortened and metamorphosed during the docking of the Pembine-Wausau terrane at 1.85 Ga (Penokean orogeny). The Sudbury intrusion (Pye and others, 1984) is an elliptical norite-granophyre lopolith that was emplaced into extensively brecciated country rock and cradles a basin filled by fallback breccia, euxinic pelite, and turbidites. A leading producer of nickel, copper, cobalt, and platinum group elements, the intrusion was generated from Archean crustal rocks according to Nd

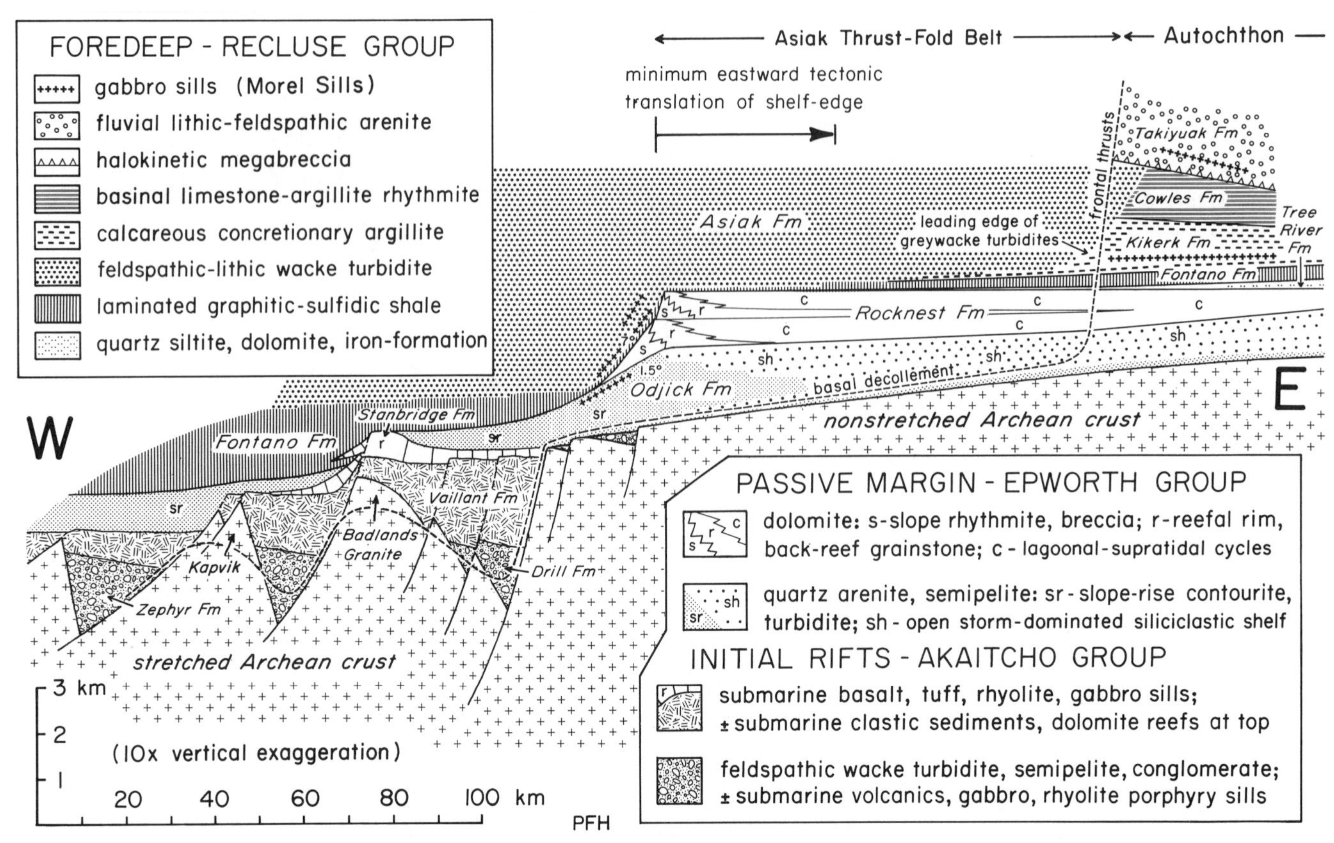

Figure 25A. Stratigraphic restoration of Coronation Supergroup, a continental margin prism exposed in eastern Wopmay orogen.

isotopic data, not from the contemporaneous mantle, supporting the long-contentious meteorite impact model for its origin (*Faggart and others, 1985*). Deformation and metamorphism (lower greenschist to lower amphibolite grade) of the intrusion, decreasing northward, is attributed to the penecontemporaneous Penokean orogeny.

The Marquette Range Supergroup (Fig. 26) and equivalents consist of a rifted passive-margin sequence (Mille Lacs and Chocolay Groups), overstepped northward by a synorogenic foredeep sequence (Animikie and equivalent groups). The rift rocks are 2.20-Ga (Sm-Nd) mafic volcanics and immature terrigenous sediments; the shelf rocks are quartzarenite and dolomite. The foredeep contains a basal transgressive marine quartzite overlain by ironstone (of variable thickness due to syndepositional normal faulting), euxinic shale with buildups of tholeiitic basalt, and thick graywacke turbidites derived from the Early Proterozoic arc terrane to the south (*Barovich and others, 1988*). Early Penokean deformation involved detachment and northward-directed thrusting and related folding of cover strata, and tectonic inversion of basement normal faults. Metamorphism in response to crustal thickening softened the basement, enabling the formation of large-scale doubly plunging lobate-cuspate folds and/or basement thrusts (*Ueng and Larue, 1988*; *Holm and others, 1988*).

The Huron Supergroup (Fig. 27) contains four unconformity-bounded, siliciclastic prisms of northerly provenance, three of which include glaciogenic intervals. The prisms taper northward and have an aggregate maximum thickness exceeding 12 km. The thickness and facies variations reflect syndepositional down-to-the-south normal faulting that controlled the accumulation and preservation of the three lower prisms. They are overlapped northward by the youngest prism, an extensive sheet of clastic sediments recording post-rift regional subsidence (*Zolnai and others, 1984*). Gabbro-anorthosite intrusions and related basalt and rhyolite beneath the oldest prism date initial rifting at 2.49 to 2.45 Ga (Pye and others, 1984). Granites intruded the oldest prism (at least) at 2.39 Ga, and the entire supergroup was cut by Nipissing diabase at 2.22 Ga (*Corfu and Andrews, 1986*). Although initial folding occurred before 2.22 Ga (*Card, 1978*), major shortening, north-directed thrusting, and metamorphism occurred during the Penokean orogeny (*Zolnai and others, 1984*).

Southern Greenland and Labrador

Accretion of Early Proterozoic terranes to the southeastern margin of the Nain province is recorded in the ca. 1.80-Ga Ketilidian orogen of southern Greenland (Fig. 28) and its equivalent, the Makkovik orogen of Labrador (Fig. 29). Following amalgamation of the Nain and southeastern Rae provinces, the Makkovik orogen was truncated by the ca. 1.65 Ga Labrador orogen.

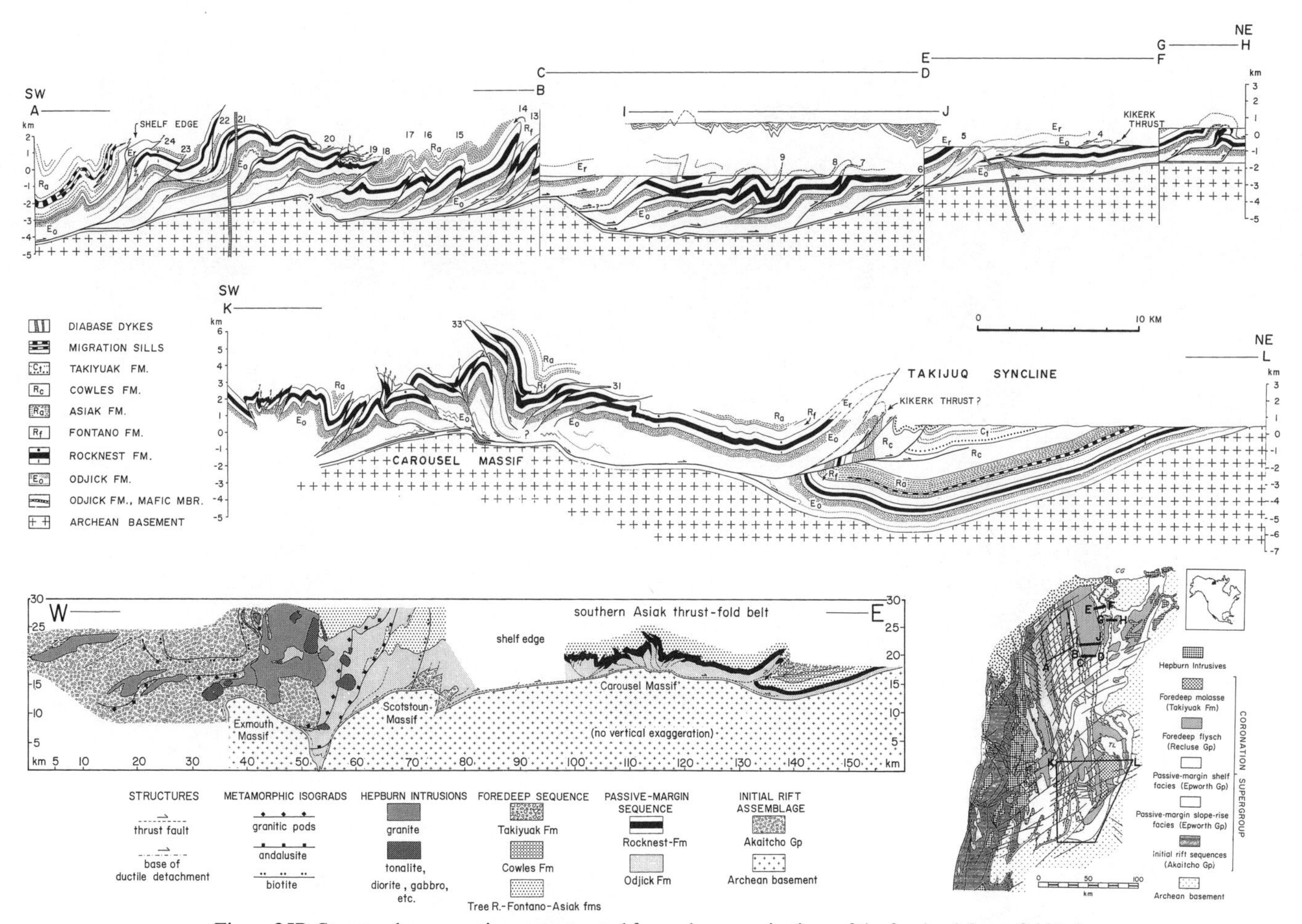

Figure 25B. Structural cross-sections, constructed from plunge projections of the foreland thrust-fold belt exposed in eastern Wopmay orogen, after *Hoffman and others (1988).* Imbrication of Epworth Group (Odjick and Rocknest Formations) accommodates a minimum of 42% east-west shortening; comparable shortening is accomplished by chevron-type folding in overlying foredeep flysch. Piggy-back thrust sequence is indicated by refolding of structurally higher thrusts. An active wedge of low taper is suggested by high step-up angles, prevalence of back-thrusts (southern cross-section K-L), and lack of overall increase in exposed structural depth from east to west. Relatively large displacements on frontal thrust ramps may record subaerial emergence of belt and onset of erosional unloading of active thrust sheets. Note that autochthon is broadly folded but not faulted, and that thin autochthonous cover persists westward beneath allochthons for 100 km from frontal thrust ramp to Exmouth massif (lower panel). Note also rootless Hepburn intrusions (lower panel) and inverted metamorphic isograds between Exmouth and Scotstoun massifs, caused by thrusting of hot plutonic-metamorphic complex onto cold autochthon, rapidly unroofed.

Makkovik-Ketilidian orogen. Whereas the absence of Penokean granites in the Archean autochthon of the Great Lakes region is consistent with an arc-continent collision, the converse situation in the Makkovik-Ketilidian orogen favors an Andean-type model. In Greenland, the orogen includes a northwestern border zone, a medial batholith, and an internal migmatite zone (Allaart, 1976; *Kalsbeek and Taylor, 1985*). In Labrador, only the border zone is preserved, but studies are relatively advanced (Schärer and others, 1988). In both areas, the border zone exposes reworked Archean basement, infolded remnants of Early Proterozoic cover increasing southeastward in metamorphic grade from lower greenschist to middle amphibolite, and granodioritic intrusions. The cover comprises a lower sequence of quartzite, graywacke-semipelite, and subaqueous metabasalt (Labrador: Moran Lake and lower Aillik Groups; Greenland: Vallen and Sortis Groups). It is overlain tectonically by an upper sequence of feldspathic epiclastic rocks and subaerial rhyolitic, dacitic, and andesitic tuffs and flows (Labrador: upper Aillik Group; Greenland: Qipisarqo and Ilordleq Groups). The mafic volcanics of the lower sequence may be related to the 2.13-Ga dikes (Rb-Sr) in the Archean foreland (Greenland) and are intruded by a 1.91-Ga granodiorite (Labrador). The upper Aillik Group felsic volcanism occurred from 1.86 to 1.81 Ga, and was followed by northwest-directed (D1) thrusting of the basement

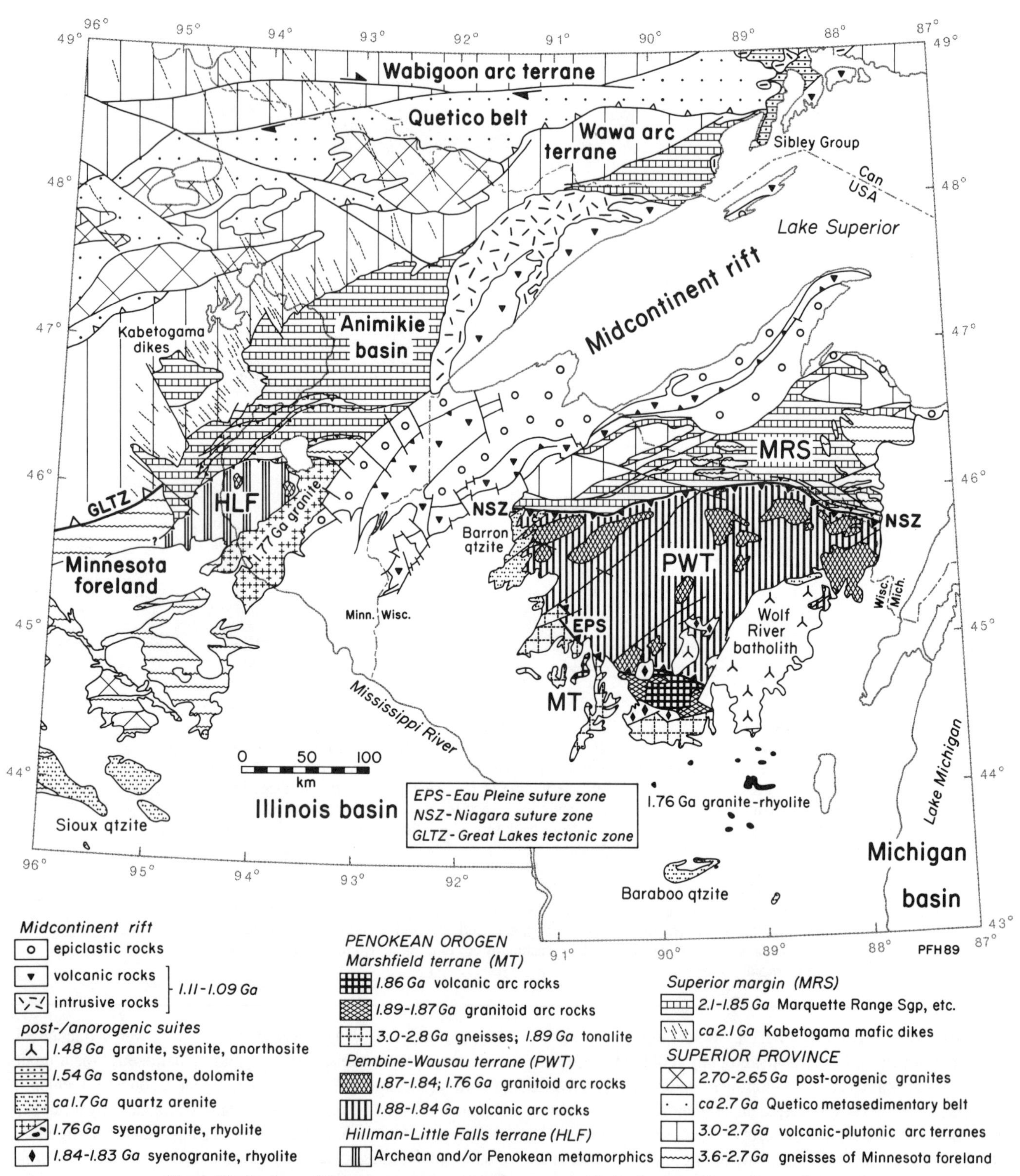

Figure 26. Geology of Penokean orogen and environs around Lake Superior. According to *Sims and others (1989),* the Pembine-Wausau terrane (PWT) is a juvenile oceanic arc accreted to the Superior province margin (MRS) at 1.85 Ga along the Niagara suture zone (NSZ), and bounded along the Eau Pleine suture zone (EPS) by the Marshfield terrane (MT), an inferred island arc cored by Archean crust. The Eau Pleine suture zone is stitched by 1.84 to 1.83 Ga granite plutons. An outstanding problem is whether the Niagara suture zone extends north or south of the Hillman-Little Falls terrane (HLF) west of the Midcontinent rift (*Southwick and others, 1988*).

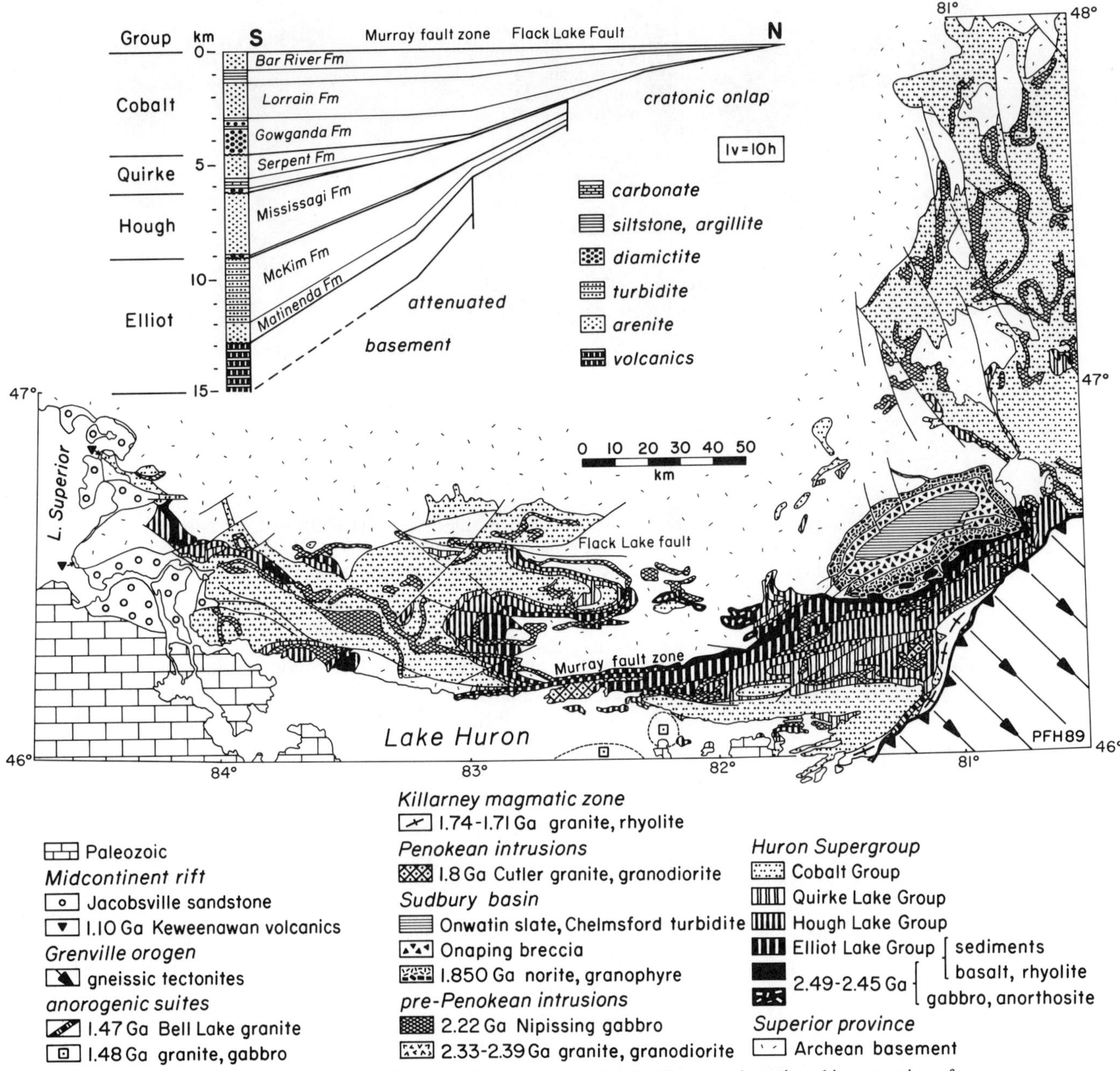

Figure 27. Geology of the Penokean fold belt north of Lake Huron and stratigraphic restoration of Huron Supergroup (modified after *Zolnai and others, 1984*). Sudbury basin (1.85 Ga) is a probable impact structure coeval with the Penokean orogeny. According to *Card (1978),* Penokean shortening exceeded older (pre-Nipissing, 2.4 to 2.2 Ga) or younger (Grenvillian, 1.2 to 1.0 Ga) deformation of the fold belt.

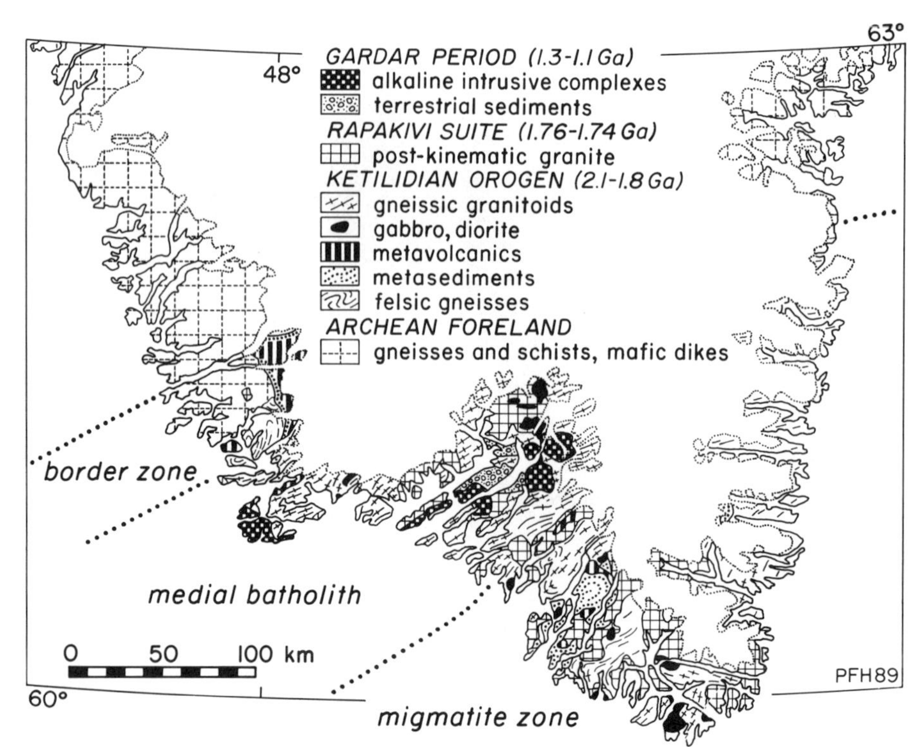

Figure 28. Geology of Ketilidian orogen, south Greenland, modified after *Allaart (1976)*. Coextensive with Makkovik orogen of Labrador and Svecofennian orogen of Baltic shield, Ketilidian orogen contains juvenile Early Proterozoic crust accreted against southern margin of Nain province (*Kalsbeek and Taylor, 1985*).

and cover. Continued northwest shortening produced large-scale (D2) basement-cover folds contemporaneous with the intrusion of 1.81- to 1.80-Ga granodioritic masses in the border zone, and northeast-trending shear zones developed during postmetamorphic cooling, recorded by monazite and titanite ages of 1.79 and 1.76 Ga respectively (Labrador). In Greenland, the medial batholith consists of a subordinate older suite of foliated tonalites and granodiorites, and a dominant suite of more weakly foliated granites. The migmatite zone consists of semipelitic and mafic paragneisses (upper amphibolite to granulite grade), granodioritic orthogneiss, and sheets of synmetamorphic 1.80-Ga granite. It hosts post-tectonic 1.76-Ga rapakivi granites. Nd, Pb, and Sr isotopic systematics indicate that the medial batholith and migmatite zones are composed of essentially juvenile Early Proterozoic crust (*Kalsbeek and Taylor, 1985*).

Labrador orogen. A broad east-northeasterly belt of 1.71- to 1.63-Ga plutonic and low- to high-grade metamorphic rocks underlies most of the northeastern Grenville orogen, locally extending north of the Grenville front (Schärer and Gower, 1988). The Labradorian orogeny culminated at 1.65 Ga (about 600 m.y. before Grenvillian reworking), and was penecontemporaneous with the Mazatzal orogeny of the southwestern United States. Labradorian rocks overlie, intrude, or truncate, from east to west, the Makkovik orogen, the Nain province, the Torngat orogen, the southeastern Rae province, and the New Quebec orogen (Fig. 18).

The zonation of the orogen, similar to the Makkovik-Ketilidian orogen, consists of a northern volcanic and sedimentary belt (Bruce River Group), a medial Trans-Labrador batholith, and a zone of para- and orthogeniss, the southern limit of which has yet to be established (Fig. 29). The 1.65-Ga Bruce River Group lies unconformably on Makkovikian rocks to the north and is invaded by its intrusive equivalent, the Trans-Labrador batholith, to the south (Ryan, 1984; Schärer and others, 1988). Lower fluvial sediments and bimodal lava flows are overlain by rhyolitic-dacitic-andesitic-basaltic ash and lava flows of potassic calc-alkaline character, derived sediments, and intrusive porphyries. The 1.65-Ga batholith, which intrudes Makkovikian rocks along its northern contact in eastern Labrador, consists mainly of syn- to post-tectonic granite and granodiorite, and small bodies of diorite and gabbro. To the south, the batholith intrudes amphibolite-grade paragneiss in the parautochthonous Groswater Bay terrane of the Grenville orogen. Farther south, the structurally overriding Hawke River, Lake Melville, and Mealy Mountains terranes are composed of granulite-grade para- and orthogneiss, including layered gabbro-anorthosite-monzonite complexes. U-Pb zircon ages for both para- and orthogneiss in all the terranes range only from 1.71 to 1.63 Ga, and the virtual absence of older inheritance suggests that the Labradorian was a time of major crust formation (Schärer and Gower, 1988). Labradorian titanite (U-Pb) ages in granulite-grade gneisses of the structurally highest Hawke River and Mealy Mountains terranes

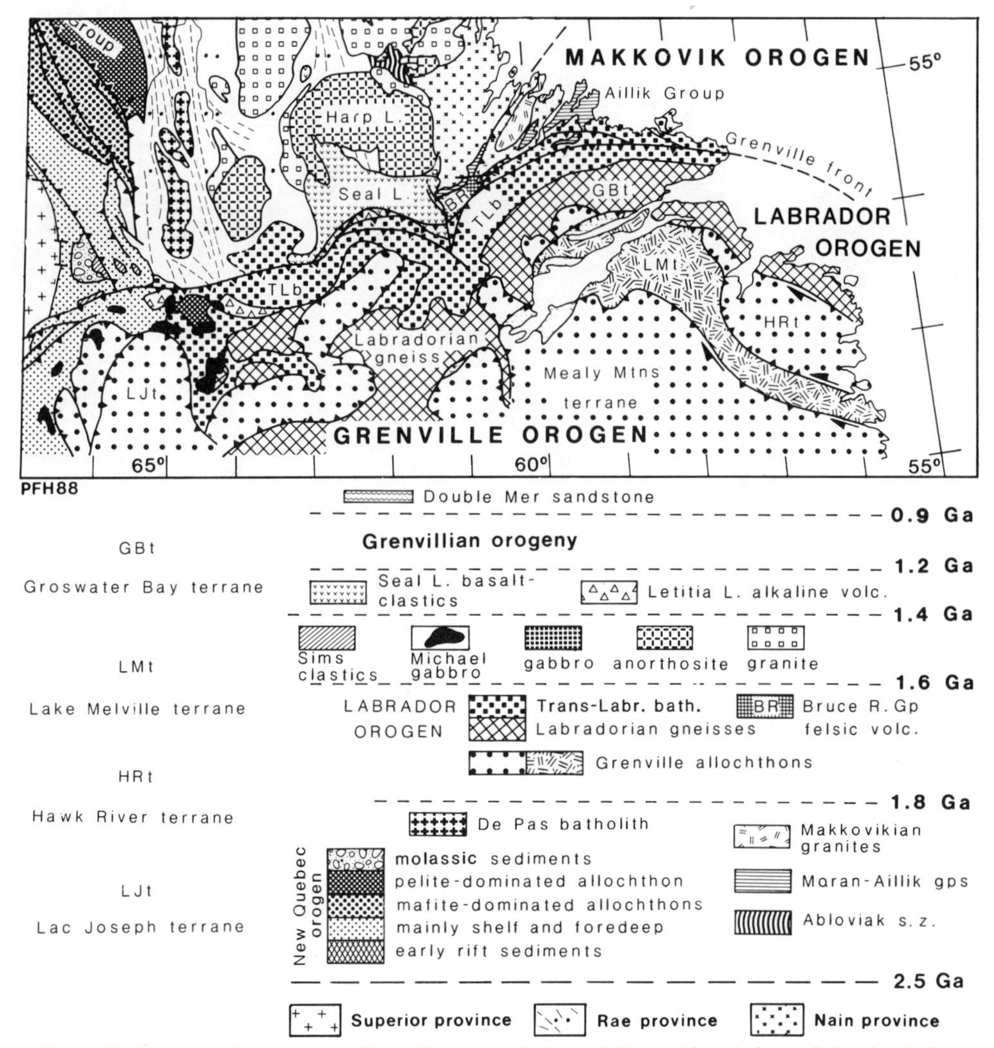

Figure 29. Geology of northeastern Grenville orogen (1.2 to 1.0 Ga) and its relation to Labrador (1.7 to 1.6 Ga), and New Quebec and Makkovik (both 1.9 to 1.8 Ga) orogens. Makkovik orogen is coextensive with Ketilidian orogen of southern Greenland (see Figure 19 for regional setting). Labrador orogen is essentially coeval and possibly coextensive with Mazatzal orogen of southwestern United States (see Figure 30).

intimate that their exhumation occurred long before the Grenvillian orogeny.

Southwestern United States and the southern Midcontinent

A vast area, from the south margin of the Wyoming province to Sonora in northern Mexico, and from the Front Ranges of Colorado to the San Andreas fault in southern California (Fig. 30), is underlain by a 1.79- to 1.63-Ga metamorphic-plutonic complex cut by Middle Proterozoic anorogenic intrusions (Condie, 1981, 1986; Hoffman, 1988). Pb, Nd, and Sr isotopic data indicate mean crust-formation ages of 2.3 to 2.0 Ga for southern California, eastern Nevada, and northwestern Utah, and 2.0 to 1.7 Ga for the area to the east, including most of the southern Midcontinent (*Nelson and DePaolo, 1985*; Bennet and DePaolo, 1987; *Wooden and others, 1988*). A significant Archean contribution is possible (but not required) in the western area, but to the east at least 1,300 km of essentially juvenile crust was accreted to the southern margin of the protocraton in less than 160 m.y.

Cheyenne belt. The northern border of the accreted terranes is exposed in the Cheyenne belt (Karlstrom and Houston, 1984; *Duebendorfer and Houston, 1987*) at the southern margin of the Wyoming province (Fig. 31). To the east, the accreted terranes (Central Plains orogen) are inferred to truncate the Trans-Hudson and Penokean orogens and the Superior province in the subsurface (Sims and others, 1987). In the Cheyenne belt, a southeast-dipping suture separates an imbricated sedimentary prism (Snowy Pass Supergroup) from an overthrust 1.79- to 1.74-Ga metamorphic-plutonic assemblage interpreted as an accreted island arc. In the Medicine Bow Mountains, the sedimen-

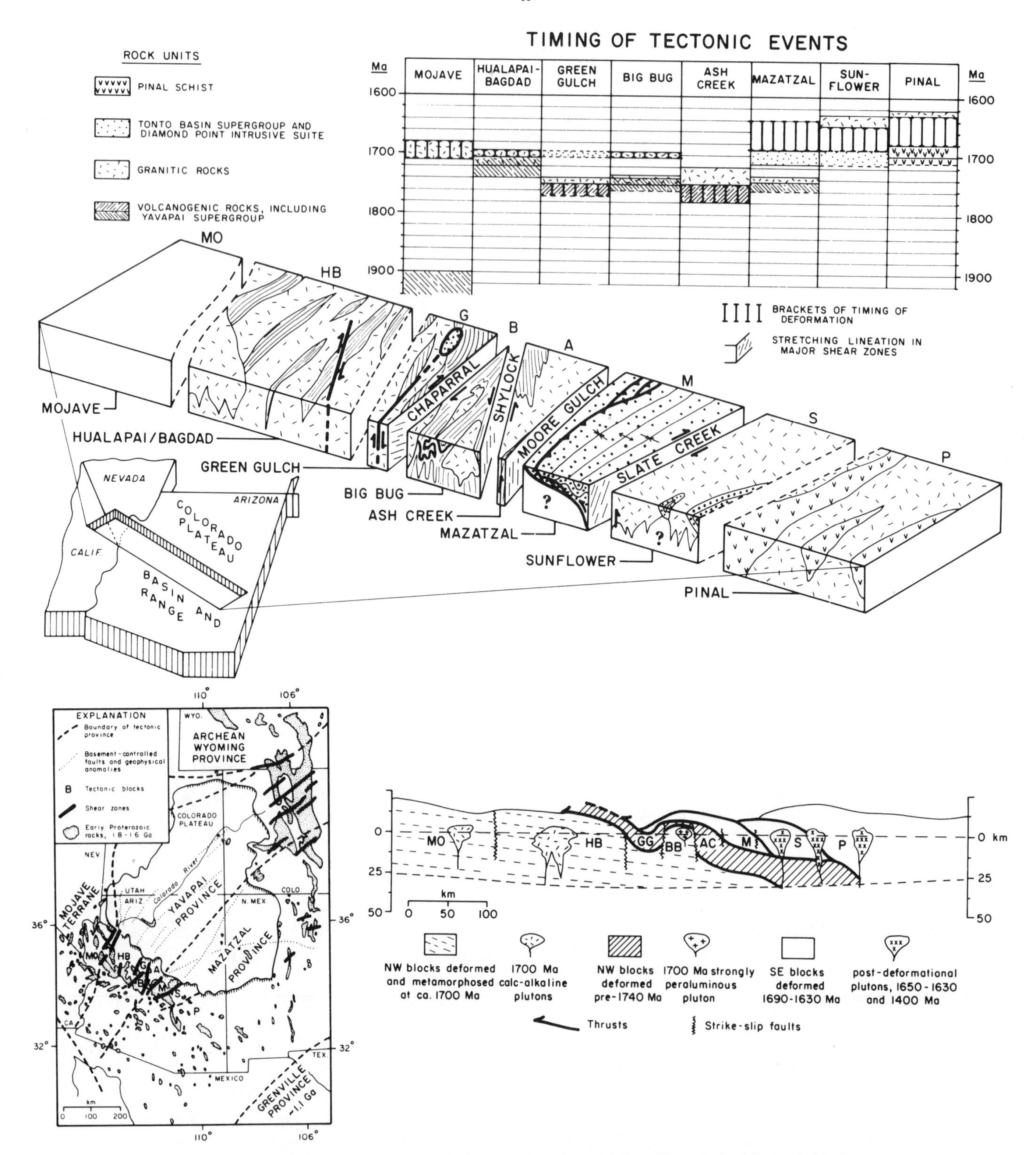

Figure 30. (Lower left) Exposures of Early Proterozoic rocks and inferred boundaries of tectonic blocks, according to *Karlstrom and Bowring, 1989.* (Above) Block diagram showing tectonostratigraphic blocks in Arizona and adjacent regions proposed by *Karlstrom and Bowring, 1988.* Moore Gulch fault separated composite northwestern region (5 blocks) from composite southeastern region (3 blocks). Timing of tectonic events based on U-Pb geochronology. (Lower right) Schematic NW-SE cross-section through central Arizona, from *Karlstrom and Bowring (1988),* showing minimum complexity of assembled blocks. At least three major terranes seem to be required by data on timing of deformation.

tary prism is exposed in three structural units—a lower thrust sheet and autochthon composed of quartzite, phyllite, and diamictite, and an upper thrust sheet in which nearly 2 km of stromatolitic dolomite are overlain by a thin mafic unit and a ferruginous pelite, signifying a passive-margin to foredeep transition. All the sediments are cut by gabbro sheets that predate thrusting, but the one that is dated (minimum 2.0 Ga) occurs in the lower thrust sheet and therefore does not constrain the age of foredeep subsidence. Inverted metamorphic isograds in the upward-facing ferruginous pelite may record thrusting of a hot allochthon, composed of mafic-intermediate-felsic metavolcanics and derived metasediments, intruded by dioritic to granitic plutons. The intervening braided system of mylonites has southeast-side-up and subordinate dextral components of shear.

Accreted terranes in Colorado, New Mexico, and Arizona. Although inherently complex, the Early Proterozoic crust of central Arizona, northern New Mexico, and southern Colorado appears to have evolved in two generalized stages (Karlstrom and Bowring, 1988; Grambling and others, 1988; Bickford, 1988). In the first stage, a collage of 1.79- to 1.71-Ga calc-alkaline volcano-plutonic terranes, interpreted as former island arcs and inter-arc sedimentary basins were amalgamated by about 1.70 Ga. The resulting deformation, metamorphism, and plutonism is referred to as the Yavapai orogeny. In the second stage, subaerial 1.70-Ga felsic volcanism and succeeding fluvial to shelf-facies sedimentation preceded northwest-vergent brittle thrusting and/or ductile shearing of regional extent (Mazatzal orogeny). This was followed by high-angle strike-, oblique-, and dip-slip faulting of northerly to northeasterly trend, and emplacement of post-tectonic 1.64- to 1.62-Ga granites. A zone dominated by turbiditic metasediments and granites in central and northern Colorado has been interpreted as a collapsed inter-arc basin, and a similar zone in southern New Mexico, southeastern Arizona, and Sonora has been proposed as a fore-arc basin and/or accretionary prism developed above a northwest-dipping slab. Metamorphism reached lower granulite grade in southern California and westernmost Arizona, but only greenschist or amphibolite grades were attained to the east. Rocks now exposed over wide areas experienced slow isobaric cooling (*Grambling, 1986*), suggesting that their unroofing did not immediately follow tectonic thickening but occurred later, possibly as a result of magmatic underplating associated with Middle Proterozoic anorogenic magmatism. Perhaps the outstanding regional problem is the cause of the Mazatzal orogeny, which seems to imply collision with a large unknown terrane to the southeast between 1.69 and 1.64 Ga.

MIDDLE PROTEROZOIC OVERLAP ASSEMBLAGES

A variety of little-deformed sedimentary and volcanic strata and intrusive igneous suites overlap the Archean protocraton and the Early Proterozoic accreted terranes (Fig. 32). Although mainly of Middle Proterozoic age, the overlap assemblages began forming about 1.8 Ga, immediately following aggregation of the protocraton.

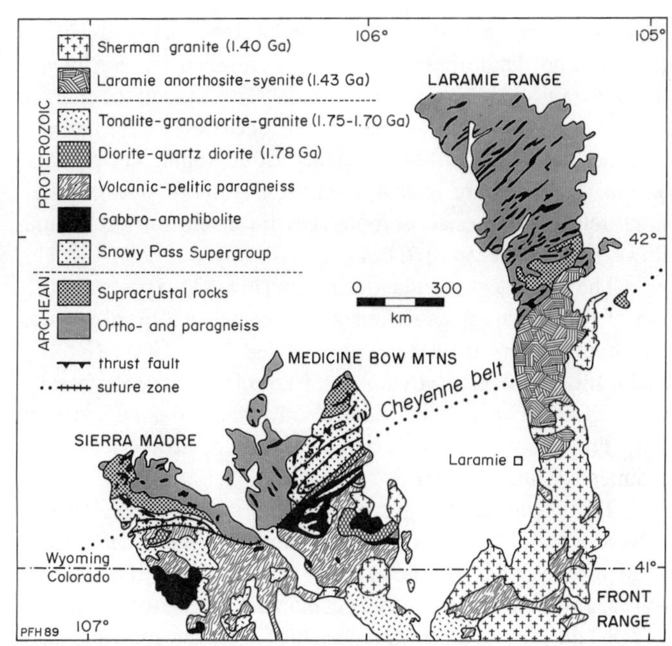

Figure 31. Geology of Cheyenne belt and environs (modified after *Karlstrom and Houston, 1984*), southeastern Wyoming (see Figure 11 for regional setting). Snowy Pass Supergroup is inferred continental margin prism deformed during accretion of juvenile 1.8 to 1.7 Ga crust against southern margin of Wyoming province. There is stratigraphic and geochronologic evidence that the margin experienced repeated Early Proterozoic rifting and suturing events.

Western Canadian shield

Four contrasting assemblages overlap the Snowbird orogen and the western Rae and Hearne provinces (Fig. 20). Youngest is the northwest-trending 1.27-Ga Mackenzie dike swarm (LeCheminant and Heaman, 1989). It cuts sediments of the Athabasca and Thelon basins, which are mainly quartzarenites of fluvial, aeolian, and paralic origin having easterly to southeasterly provenance (Ramaekers, 1981). Deposition began before 1.72 Ga (*Miller and others, 1988*) but after 1.75 Ga, the age of an extensive suite of epizonal syenogranites and comagmatic ash-flow tuffs associated with fluvial sediments. Predating the subalkaline granite-rhyolite suite is a 1.85-Ga potassic alkaline suite comprising subaerial trachyandesite and trachyte flows, associated with fluvial sediments, pyroxene-syenite stocks, and easterly trending lamprophyre dikes (*Blake, 1980*; LeCheminant and others, 1987a).

Northern Greenland and eastern arctic Canada

A series of Middle Proterozoic basins overlap the northern Rae province between Baffin Island and northeast Greenland

(Fig. 33). The present configuration of the Fury and Hecla, Borden, and Thule basins is largely controlled by northwest-trending faults (Jackson and Iannelli, 1981), although the characterization of the basins as rifts or aulacogens may overstate the evidence for syndepositional faulting. Stratigraphic correlations within the basins are relatively secure, but interbasinal correlations rely on imprecise isotopic ages for mafic intrusions and flows, which occur in each basin.

The northeast Greenland platform (Fig. 33) exposes up to 2 km of basal arenaceous sediments (Independence Fjord Group, Rb-Sr minimum age 1.38 Ga), intruded by 1.23-Ga (Rb-Sr) mafic sills and overlain by up to 1.3 km of related flood basalts (Zig-zag Dal Formation), which are overstepped southward by Late Proterozoic sediments and westward by lower Paleozoic sediments (Higgins, 1986).

The Thule basin at the head of Baffin Bay (Fig. 33) preserves up to 4.5 km of arenaceous sediments, rhythmically interbedded with carbonate near the top (*Dawes, 1976*; *Dawes and others, 1982*). There are three ages of mafic magmatism: 1.65-Ga (Rb-Sr) dikes trend northwest along the Greenland coast and pass beneath the Tule basin, 1.2-Ga (K-Ar) sills and flows occur within the lower Thule Group sediments, and 0.7-Ga (K-Ar) northwesterly dikes and sills intrude the entire Thule Group (*Nielsen, 1987*).

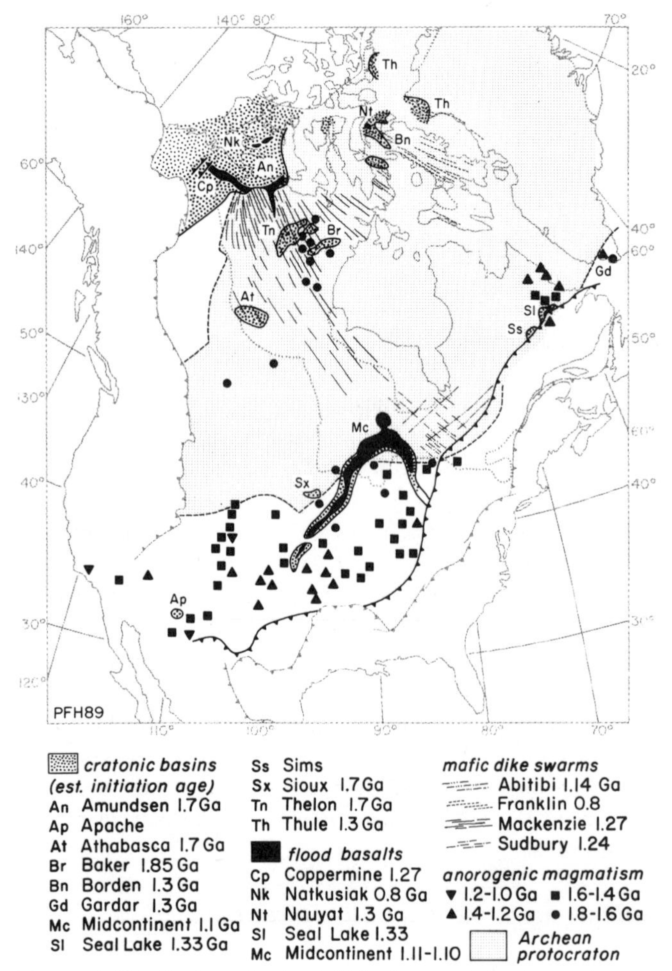

Figure 32. Distribution of major Middle Proterozoic basins and igneous suites in North America.

The Borden basin (Fig. 33) preserves up to 6 km of sediments divided into three groups of subequal thickness separated by local unconformities (Jackson and Iannelli, 1981). The lower (Eqalulik) group comprises quartzarenite, interrupted by 1.2-Ga (K-Ar) basalt flows, that grades upward into finer grained terrigenous sediments and carbonates. The middle (Uluksan) group is a carbonate platform sequence. The upper (Nunatsiaq) group consists of drowned carbonate reefs overlain by dark shales and turbidites, locally with carbonate-clast debris-flows related to active faulting, which grade upward into shallow-water sandstones. Eqalulik sands were shed northwestward, and Nunatsiaq sands southeastward (*Jackson and others, 1985*), suggesting a possible passive margin (Eqalulik and Uluksan) to foredeep (Nunatsiaq) transition, consistent with the hypothesis that the basin records the opening and closing of a Middle Proterozoic (Poseidon) ocean to the northwest (Jackson and Iannelli, 1981). K-Ar ages reach 1.22 Ga for the near-basal Eqalulik basalt flows and 0.82 Ga for northwesterly trending dikes that cut the entire sequence, corresponding to the Mackenzie and Franklin mafic magmatic episodes, respectively (Fahrig, 1987). As in the upper Thule Group, a conspicuous small-scale (1 to 10 m thick) rhythmic motif suggests the dominant influence of Milankovitch band climatic forcing (*Grotzinger, 1986*) on sedimentation throughout the sequence. Assuming an average cycle thickness of 6 m and period of 100 k.y., the Borden basin would represent 100 m.y.

The Fury and Hecla basin (Fig. 33) contains over 6 km of fluvial to shallow marine, mainly arenaceous sediments shed from the northeast (*Chandler, 1988b*). Basalt flows about 0.5 km above the base have Mackenzie (1.1 Ga) K-Ar ages, and sills cutting the entire sequence have Franklin (0.75 Ga) K-Ar ages. Although thrice the thickness, the Fury and Hecla arenites are correlated with the Eqalukik Group of the Borden basin; a capping carbonate unit preserved along the southern boundary fault is equated with the lower Uluksan Group (*Chandler, 1988b*).

In the northern Boothia uplift (Fig. 33), basement granulites of the Thelon orogen are locally separated from Paleozoic cover by thrust slices of Proterozoic sediments cut by mafic sills and dikes (*Okulitch and others, 1986*). There are two disconformable sedimentary units: an older arenaceous Aston Formation (over 0.8 km thick) and a younger dolomitic Hunting Formation (1.4 km thick). Two ages (1.1 and 0.7 Ga, K-Ar) of mafic intrusions are present, the older of which intrudes only the Aston Formation. Accordingly, the Aston and Hunting Formations may correlate respectively with the Eqalulik and Uluksan Groups of the Borden basin.

Western Arctic platform

Overlapping the Wopmay orogen, the Amundsen basin (Fig. 34) was an intermittent depocenter and locus of magmatism during the Middle and Late(?) Proterozoic, and is a key to correlations with the northern Cordillera (Young and others, 1979).

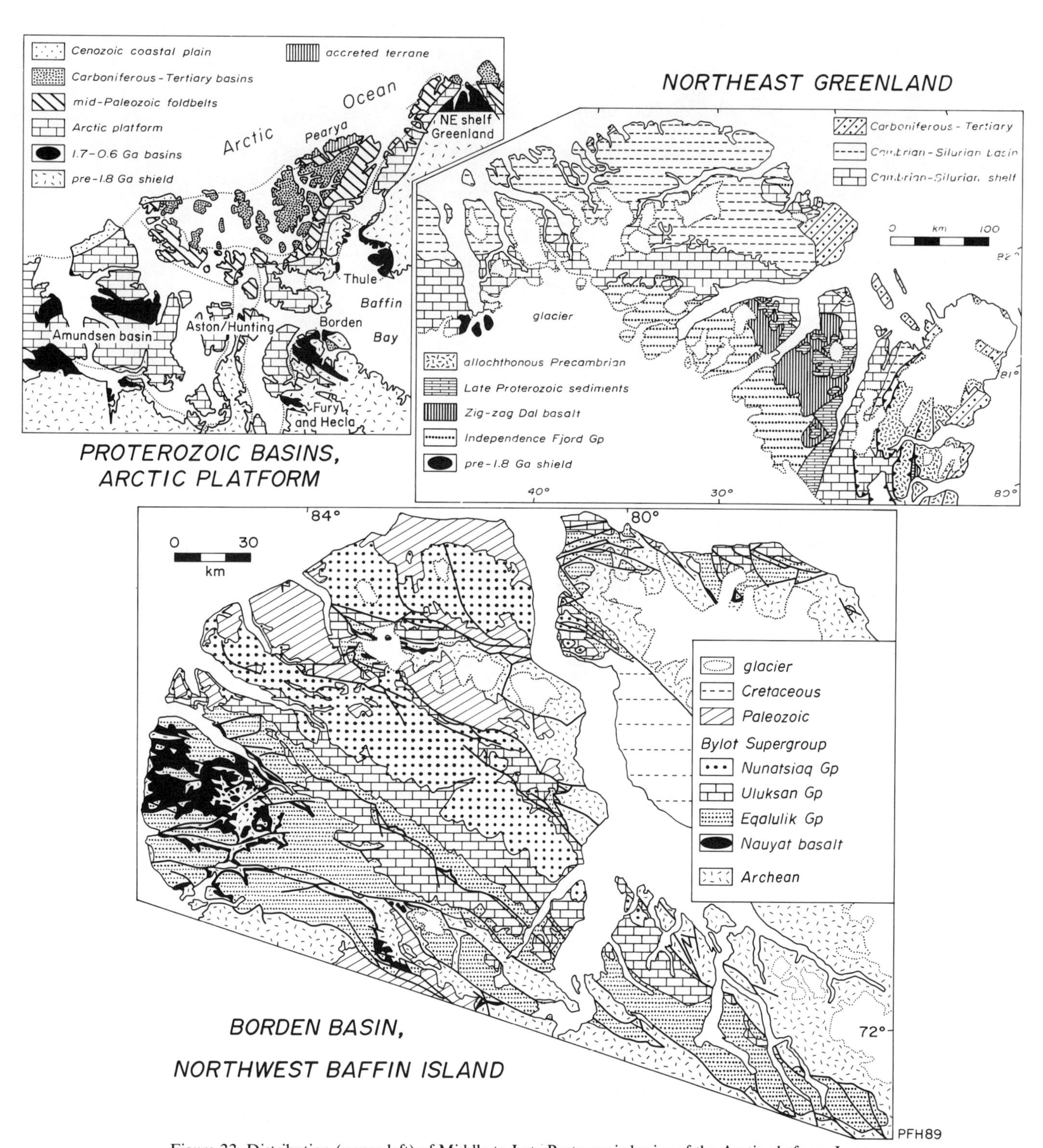

Figure 33. Distribution (upper left) of Middle to Late Proterozoic basins of the Arctic platform. Inset maps show stratigraphic relations of northeast Greenland shelf (modified after *Higgins, 1986*) and Borden basin of northern Baffin Island (modified after *Jackson and Iannelli, 1981*).

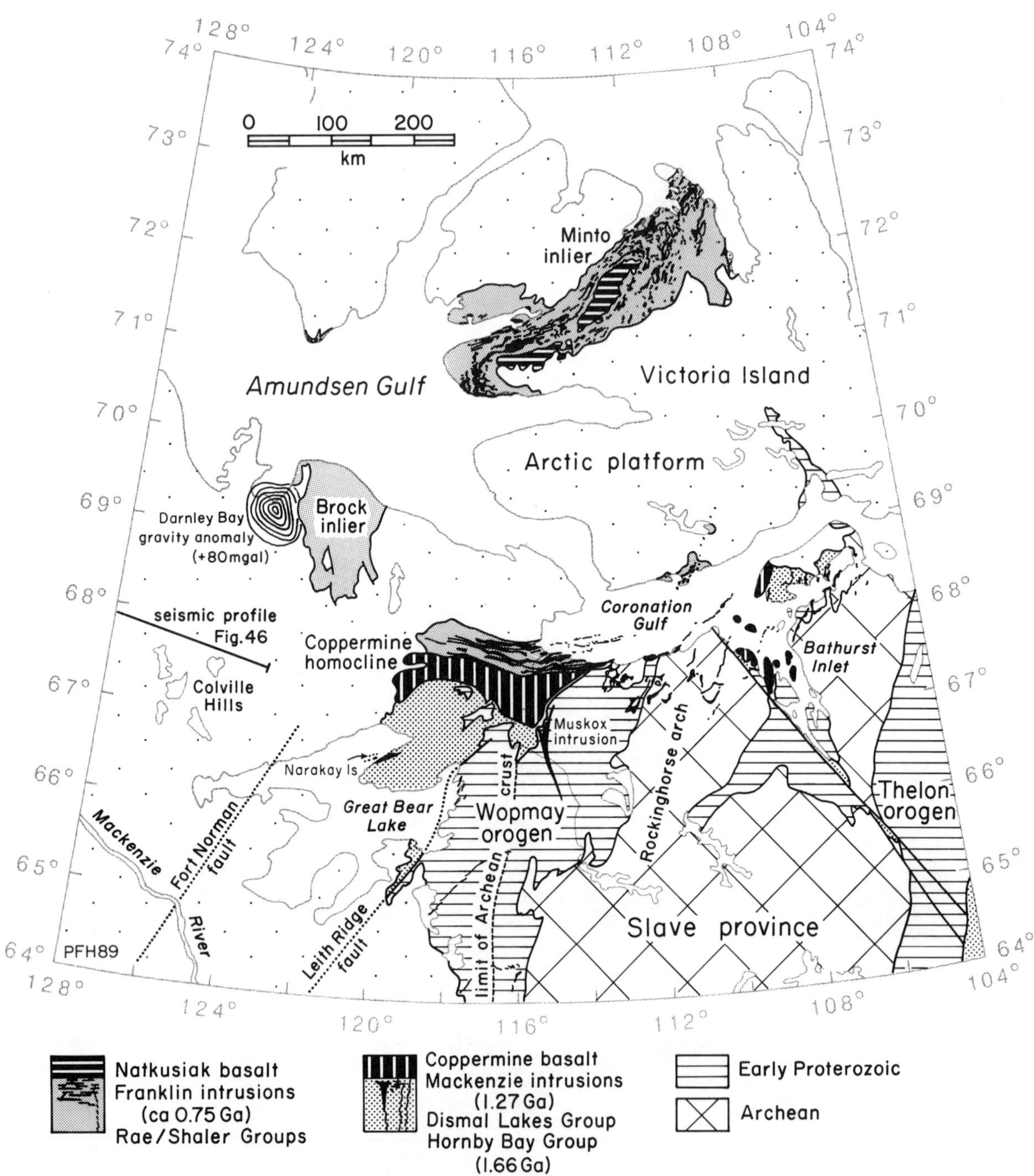

Figure 34. Geology of Amundsen basin and environs, western Arctic platform.

The youngest rocks are those of the 0.75-Ga Franklin tholeiite suite (Fahrig, 1987), including the Natkusiak plateau basalts (*Dostal and others, 1986*), the Coronation sills, and northeasterly to northwesterly trending dikes. An unconformity-bounded sequence (Shaler/Rae Group) up to 4 km thick underlies the Natkusiak basalts and overlies the 1.27-Ga Coppermine basalts (*Young, 1981a*). It is composed of marginal marine carbonate, terrigenous and evaporitic sediments, and hosts the Coronation sills. A southeast-directed thin-skinned thrusting event (Racklan orogeny?) occurred after 1.27 Ga but before Rae/Shaler deposition (Cook, 1988). The thrust front is located in the subsurface northwest of Great Bear Lake (minor compressional structures occur in the exposed homocline to the east), but a coeval basement uplift (Rockinghorse high) separates pre–Rae/Shaler strata preserved in the Coppermine and Bathurst Inlet areas (Fig. 34). The 1.27-Ga Mackenzie tholeiite suite includes the Coppermine plateau basalts (*Dostal and others, 1983*) and associated fluvial sediments, the Muskox layered ultramafic intrusion (*Irvine,*

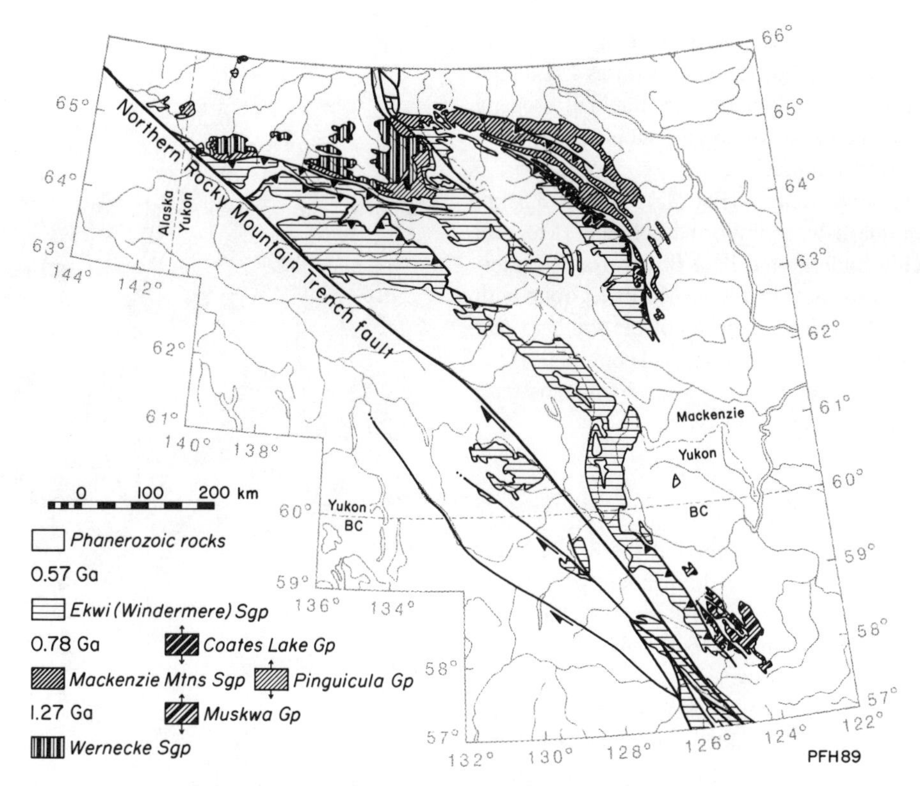

Figure 35. Distribution of Proterozoic strata of northern Canadian Cordillera.

1980), and northwest-trending dikes that extend across the entire western Canadian shield (Fahrig, 1987). The dikes were emplaced in less than 4 m.y. (LeCheminant and Heaman, 1989) and appear to radiate from an area around Amundsen Gulf, the site of a cluster of subcircular gravity anomalies rising as much as 130 milligals above background levels. Two sequences, each about 1.5-km thick, underlie the plateau basalts on both sides of the Rockinghorse high. A karstic surface is developed in dolomite of the younger sequence less than 50 m below the conformable base of the basalt flows, which reach an aggregate thickness of 4 km. The younger sequence (Dismal Lakes Group) is dominantly dolomitic but grades downward into paralic quartzarenite and shale; the older sequence (Hornby Bay Group) is dominantly fluvial, in part controlled by reactivated faults, but grades upward into marginal marine dolomite (Kerans and others, 1981). In the Coppermine homocline, both sequences thicken and become more basinal westward. The 1.66-Ga bimodal Narakay volcanic center dates the middle part of the Hornby Bay Group (*Bowring and Ross, 1985*) and may be related to gently dipping dikes of northeasterly trend (Western Channel diabase) in the lower Hornby Bay Group. Northwesterly trending dikes (Cleaver diabase) are truncated by the Hornby Bay Group but cut the transcurrent faults of Wopmay orogen and constitute the oldest postorogenic suite. In the subsurface southwest of the Coppermine homocline (Fig. 34), the Fort Norman and Leith Ridge faults approximate the southeastern limits of the Rae/Shaler Group and the Hornby Bay-Dismal Lakes groups, respectively (*Aitken and Pugh, 1984*).

Northern Canadian Cordillera

In the northern Canadian Cordillera (Fig. 35), strata related to Late Proterozoic rifting along the Cordillera (Ekwi/Windermere Supergroup) are underlain by sequences correlative with those of the western Arctic platform (Young, 1981b). The latter are divided by the Racklan orogeny (Young and others, 1979) into a younger Mackenzie Mountains Supergroup (correlative with Rae/Shaler Group) and an older Wernecke Supergroup (correlative with Hornby Bay and/or Dismal Lakes Groups). The Ekwi and Mackenzie Mountains Supergroups are locally separated by an unconformity-bounded package (Coates Lake Group), deposited during active faulting, that consists of red mudstone, evaporite, shallow and redeposited carbonate, and stratabound copper deposits (*Jefferson and Ruelle, 1986*). The Mackenzie Mountains Supergroup consists of terrigenous, carbonate, and evaporitic shelf sediments, which thicken to 5 km and become more basinal southwestward (*Aitken, 1981*). It is inferred to postdate 1.10- to 1.17-Ga granite clasts in an Ordovician diatreme and predate a 0.78-Ga quartz diorite plug (*Jefferson and Parrish, 1988*). The Wernecke Supergroup, limited to areas west of the Richardson fault zone, contains over 11 km (base not exposed) of terrigenous deep-water sediment of northerly provenance, gradationally overlain by a 1.5-km-thick dolomite shelf (Delaney, 1981). It is intruded by mafic dikes and 1.27 ± .04 Ga mineralized megabreccias (*Parrish and Bell, 1987*). The megabreccias postdate a weak tectonic fabric and greenschist-grade metamorphism (G. H. Eisbacher, personal communication, 1988), attributed to the Racklan orogeny. This raises a potential conflict in that deformation attributed to the Racklan orogeny predates 1.27 Ga in the Wernecke Mountains but postdates 1.27-Ga lavas in the Coppermine homocline.

In the central Muskwa Ranges (Fig. 35), at least 3.5 km (base not exposed) of quartzite, argillite, and dolomite (Muskwa Group) unconformably underlie the Late Proterozoic Windermere Supergroup. *Bell (1968)* compares the Muskwa Group with the Middle Proterozoic Purcell Supergroup of the southern Canadian Cordillera, but G. H. Eisbacher (personal communication, 1988) suggests a correlation with the southwestern (more basinal) facies of the Mackenzie Mountains Supergroup.

Middle Cordillera

Between southern British Columbia and the Snake River plain (Fig. 36), the eastern Cordillera is dominated by the 10- to 20-km-thick Belt/Purcell Supergroup, which is exposed in a fan-shaped area opening westward from the Helena Embayment (Hobbs, 1984; Roberts, 1986). In the southern half of the embayment, the Belt rocks are metamorphosed or cut out by the Idaho batholith (Cretaceous) and related intrusions. The only exposed basal unconformity is at the terminus of the embayment, where Belt strata lie on Archean rocks of the Wyoming province. The depositional axis trends northwest from the embayment, and the basin was apparently landlocked to the southwest, southeast, and northeast (*Winston and others, 1984*). The bulk of the sediment is argillaceous, but intercalated lithosomes define an overall stratigraphic sequence of lower turbidites (Prichard/Aldrich Formation), middle quartzite (Ravalli/Creston Group), middle carbonate (Helena/Wallace Formation), and upper quartzite (Missoula Group). Conglomerate is limited to the southern fringe of the embayment (*McMannis, 1963*), and shallow-water deposits prevail except for the lower turbidites, which are 6 to 10 km thick in the basin axis. Most of the quartzite occurs toward the southwestern margin, and the carbonate toward the northeastern margin of the basin; the turbidites were deposited by flows directed to the north or northwest. Based on Nd isotopic data, most of the terrigenous sediments have crustal residence ages of 2.2 to 1.6 Ga; only the localized southern conglomerate and a basal(?) orthoquartzite below the turbidites have Archean sources (*Frost and Winston, 1987*; *Burwash and others, 1988*). This virtually rules out the Archean basement to the northeast and southeast (Hearne and Wyoming provinces) as sources for most of the terrigenous sediment, consistent with evidence of westerly provenance from sedimentary facies.

There are few igneous rocks with which to date the Belt/Purcell Supergroup (*Evans, 1986*). Ductile shearing predating Belt sedimentation provides a maximum age of 1.8 Ga, and basaltic flows and sills near the base of the upper quartzites have minimum ages of 1.1 Ga (K-Ar). The lower turbidites were intruded by mafic sills at 1.43 Ga, felsic intrusions at 1.37 Ga, and weakly metamorphosed at 1.35 to 1.30 Ga (K-Ar, Rb-Sr).

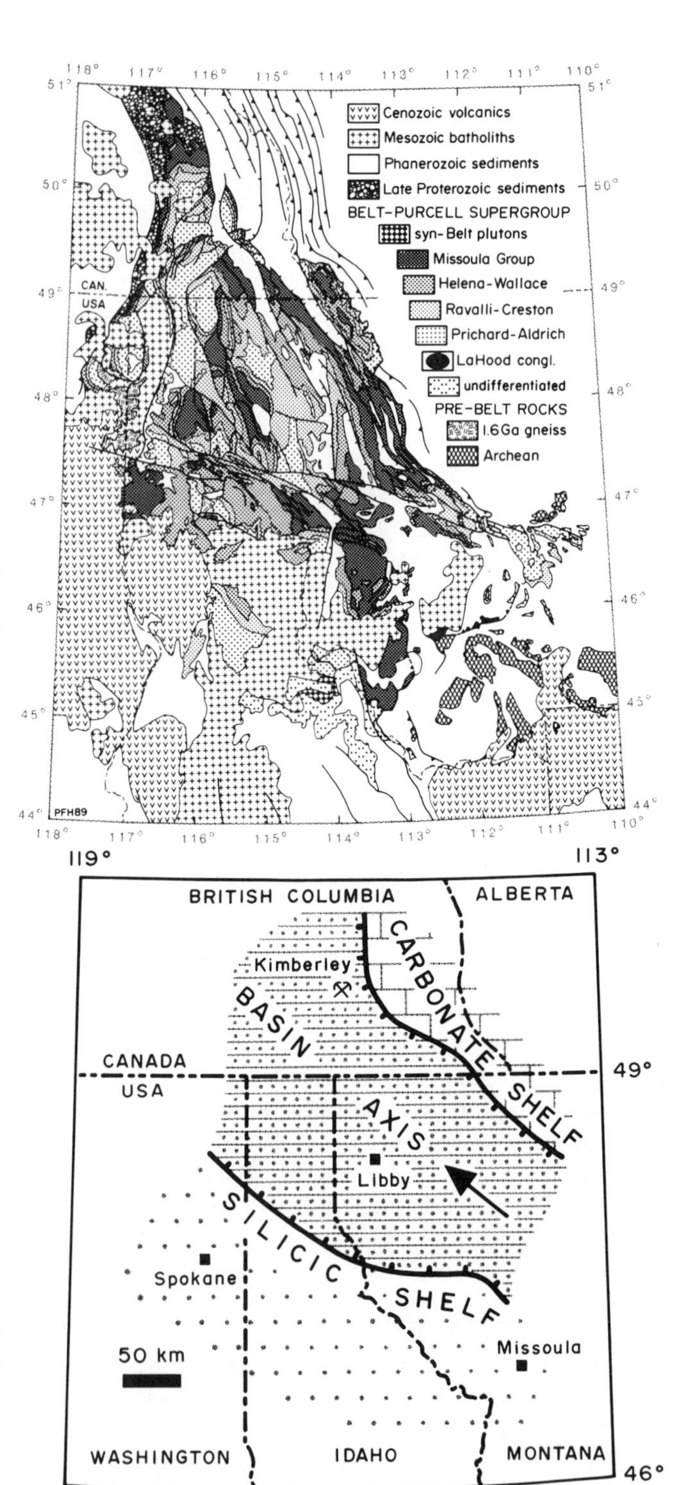

Figure 36. (Above) Geology of the Belt-Purcell Supergroup and environs (modified after compilation by D. Winston in *Roberts, 1986*). (Below) Paleogeographic restoration for lower Belt strata.

McMechan and Price (1982) infer that the lower greenschist-grade metamorphism and weak synmetamorphic cleavage (East Kootenay orogeny) postdate Belt/Purcell sedimentation.

The tectonic-setting of the Belt/Purcell basin is problematic—opinions are polarized between a passive continental margin (*McMechan, 1981*) and intracratonic rift (*Winston and others, 1984*). The following observations are pertinent: (1) sediment thickness of 15 to 20 km implies axial deposition on oceanic or extremely attenuated continental crust; (2) lack of significant pre-Mesozoic compressional deformation is improbable for a precarious passive margin; (3) western terrigenous source implies a basin closed on both sides for most of its history; (4) sedimentological and stable isotopic evidence indicates a stagnant, stratified water column evolving within an increasingly isolated basin (*Winston and others, 1984*); (5) episodic intrusion of mafic, intermediate, and felsic magmas; and (6) lower turbidites host stratiform lead-zinc sulphide deposits (e.g., 1.44-Ga Sullivan orebody). These considerations suggest a remnant back-arc basin trapped within a continent (e.g., south Caspian, Black Seas).

Southern Cordillera

Middle(?) Proterozoic sediments are preserved beneath Late Proterozoic strata of the southern Cordilleran miogeocline only in the Wasatch Mountains of northern Utah, and in the Death Valley region of eastern California (Fig. 32). In the Wasatch Mountains, a 4.8-km-thick shoaling-upward sequence (Big Cottonwood Formation) composed of shale and subfeldspathic arenite of easterly derivation was deposited on Archean basement of the Wyoming province (*Crittenden and Wallace, 1973*) following high-grade metamorphism at 1.79 Ga (*Hedge and others, 1983*). To the east, the correlative Uinta Mountain Group comprises at least 8 km of arenaceous sediments, which grade from marine in the south and west to fluvial in the north and east, where they lie unconformably on Early Proterozoic metasediments deposited on the southern margin of the Wyoming province (*Wallace and Crittenden, 1969*). Other Cordilleran sequences have little in common with those in Utah, and correlations cannot be justified with existing age constraints (1.8 to 0.8 Ga).

In the Death Valley region, Late Proterozoic sediments, including diamictites (Kingston Peak and younger formations), are unconformably overlain by 0 to 1.3 km of terrigenous and dolomitic shelf sediments (Crystal Spring and Beck Spring Formations) of northeasterly provenance that were deposited on 1.7-Ga basement gneisses and are preserved in a northwesterly trending belt (Wright and others, 1976; *Roberts, 1976*). The original extent of the shelf sediments is conjectural—to the south they are obscured by Mesozoic plutons and Tertiary volcanics; to the north they are limited by faults active during Late Proterozoic sedimentation. The shelf sediments are cut by mafic sills and dikes, but the proposed correlation with 1.13-Ga mafic intrusions in similar sediments in southern Arizona (Shride, 1967) has yet to be verified.

Both the Utah and California sequences were once interpreted as aulacogens that opened westward onto a hypothetical proto-Cordilleran margin. However, the Pacific continental margin probably did not exist before about 0.6 Ga (*Armin and Mayer, 1983*; *Bond and Kominz, 1984*).

Southwestern United States

The Early Proterozoic accreted terranes south of the Wyoming province (Fig. 32) are perforated by epizonal anorogenic granites, most of which cluster between 1.46 and 1.41 Ga, with a secondary mode between 1.40 and 1.36 Ga (Anderson, 1983; Condie, 1981). Most are subalkalic (or peraluminous where hosted by metasediment) and are enriched in potash and iron relative to calc-alkaline suites. They are associated with subordinate anorthositic, gabbroic, and syenitic intrusions, and originated by anhydrous partial melting of Early Proterozoic lower crust, probably in response to mantle upwelling and consequent invasion of the crust by mafic magma.

In Arizona, the anorogenic granites and their metamorphic host rocks are overlain by little-deformed Middle Proterozoic shelf strata. In southern Arizona, up to 850 m of sediments—including an upper Troy quartzite and a lower terrigenous and dolomitic Apache Group, separated by a few basalt flows and a low-angle unconformity—are intruded by 1.13-Ga diabase sills (Shride, 1967). Up to 3 km of strata containing at least five internal unconformities occur in the Grand Canyon of northern Arizona (*Elston and McKee, 1982*). A lower arenaceous Unkar Group is capped by 1.07-Ga (Rb-Sr) Cardenas basalt flows, which are separated by a thin, unconformity-bounded sandstone (Nankoweap Formation) from an upper argillaceous and dolomitic Chuar Group. The sequence is capped by sandstone and conglomerate (Sixtymile Formation) deposited during block faulting and gentle folding of the underlying sequence, inferred from K-Ar ages of altered Cardenas lavas to have occurred at about 0.82 Ga.

The youngest major Precambrian intrusions in the southwestern United States are the 1.20-Ga San Gabriel anorthosite-syenite complex of southern California (Carter and Silver, 1972) and the 1.02-Ga (Rb-Sr) Pikes Peak batholith of central Colorado, which comprises a cogenetic suite of subalkalic to alkalic granites, syenites, and gabbros (Tweto, 1987).

Midcontinent platform and southern Canadian shield

The Early Proterozoic accreted terranes between the Superior province and the Grenville orogen (Fig. 32) are overlapped by recurrent (1.51 to 1.43 and 1.41 to 1.32 Ga) anorogenic granite-rhyolite-gabbro suites and by the 1.11 to 1.09-Ga Midcontinent rift system. In addition, a 1.77- to 1.74-Ga granite-rhyolite-basalt suite and overlying arenaceous cover overlap the Penokean orogen (1.88 to 1.84 Ga). They are coeval with tectonic accretion to the south, and their deformation may be related to the 1.65-Ga Mazatzal/Labradorian orogeny. Deformed and metamorphosed equivalents of the Midcontinent anorogenic suites occur in the northwestern Grenville orogen.

The Penokean orogen was locally the site of 1.77- to 1.74-Ga granite and rhyolite magmatism (Figs. 26, 27). Although coeval with calc-alkaline rocks of the Central Plains orogen, they chemically resemble the 1.5- to 1.3-Ga anorogenic granites of the Midcontinent (*Smith, 1983*). Their deformation predates 1.4 Ga (*van Breemen and Davidson, 1989*) and may be related to regional Rb-Sr isotopic resetting at about 1.63 Ga, coeval with the end of the Mazatzal and Labradorian orogenies (Hoffman, 1988).

The Penokean orogen and adjacent Superior province are overlapped by remnants, up to 1.8 km thick, of red quartzarenite of northerly provenance that predate the Midcontinent rift (Fig. 32). The Sioux and Baraboo Quartzites apparently overlie 1.76-Ga rhyolites, and their deformation may have occurred at about 1.63 Ga (Mazatzal orogeny?), a time of regional Rb-Sr isotopic resetting (*Dott, 1983; Greenberg and Brown, 1984*). These more southerly outliers, including the Barron Quartzite, may be older than similar pre-rift sediments near Lake Superior, including the Bessemer and Puckwunge Quartzites and the 1.54-Ga Sibley Group (*Davis and Sutcliffe, 1985*).

In the southern and eastern parts of the Midcontinent, Paleozoic sediments are underlain by up to 6.5 km of rocks exhibiting semicontinuous subhorizontal seismic layering (*Pratt and others, 1988*). Basement inliers in southeastern Missouri (St. Francois Mountains) consist of rhyolite ash-flow tuffs and comagmatic epizonal syenogranites, and subordinate gabbroic sills and layered plutons (Denison and others, 1984; Sims and others, 1987; Van Schmus and others, 1987b). Like the anorogenic granites in the southwest, they are potassic and iron-enriched subalkalic rocks generated by anhydrous partial melting of Early and (underplated?) Middle Proterozoic lower crust (Anderson, 1983; *Nelson and DePaolo, 1985*). There are two age clusters (Fig. 37): 1.51- to 1.43-Ga granites and rhyolites are widespread across the eastern and southern Midcontinent, and occur as isolated plutons in the Penokean and Central Plains orogens to the north and west; 1.41- to 1.32-Ga granites and rhyolites are limited to the western midcontinent.

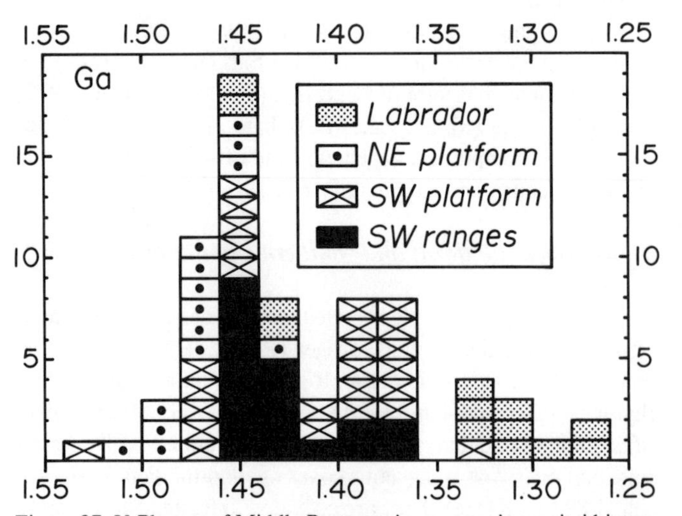

Figure 37. U-Pb ages of Middle Proterozoic anorogenic granitoid intrusions in Labrador, northeastern and southwestern parts of midcontinent platform, and southwestern United States.

The Midcontinent rift (Fig. 38) is a system of linked half-grabens of alternating polarity, containing up to 20 km of basaltic flows. It is characterized by late-stage synformal flexure and tectonic inversion (reverse slip on synrift normal faults), concurrent with axial and peripheral terrigenous sedimentation (*Wallace, 1981; Wold and Hinze, 1982; Green, 1983;* Van Schmus and Hinze, 1985; *Dickas, 1986;* Cannon and others, 1989; *Peterman and Sims, 1988*). Rift volcanism occurred between 1.109 and 1.094 Ga (*Davis and Sutcliffe, 1985; Paces and Davis, 1988*), but was preceded by alkaline intrusions and diabase dikes (e.g., 1.19-Ga Coldwell complex, 1.14-Ga Abitibi swarm). Rifting occurred contemporaneously with northwest-directed crustal-scale thrusting in the Grenville orogen of Ontario (1.10-Ga syntectonic pegmatite in the Moon River/Parry Sound boundary shear zone; O. van Breemen, personal communication, 1988), implying a mechanical linkage between crustal thickening in the orogen and thinning in the foreland in response to regional northwest shortening.

Labrador

Profuse Middle Proterozoic (1.46 to 1.27 Ga) anorogenic intrusions of anorthosite, subalkaline to peralkaline granite, and gabbro overlap the Archean Rae and Nain provinces, and the Early Proterozoic Torngat and Labrador orogens (Fig. 39). The larger intrusions are tabular bodies several kilometers thick and up to 125 km in diameter, and were emplaced at depths of less than 12 km. Subordinate associated volcanic and sedimentary rocks serve to document contemporaneous unroofing of the intrusions. Metamorphosed Middle Proterozoic gabbros and peralkaline rocks occur in the Grenville orogen of southern Labrador.

Monzogranites and gabbros, intrusive into anorthosites and followed by peralkaline granites and rhyolites, were emplaced in central and northern Labrador (and adjacent Quebec) at about 1.45 and 1.30 Ga, respectively. In central Labrador, the Michikamau and Harp Lake anorthosites are believed to be close in age to their peripheral intrusive monzogranites (Emslie, 1980), which along with the Mistastin monzogranite batholith, date from 1.46 to 1.44 Ga. To the southeast and southwest, mainly within the parautochthonous Grenville orogen, are the 1.43-Ga Michale and 1.38-Ga (Sm-Nd) Shabogamo gabbro suites and related northeast trending diabase dikes (*Emslie and others, 1984*). The Shabagamo gabbros cut the arenaceous Sims Formation, which was shed from the southeast and lies unconformably on the Early Proterozoic thrust-fold belt of the New Quebec orogen (*Ware and Hiscott, 1985*). The youngest pre-Grenvillian rocks in central Labrador are the 1.33-Ga peralkaline volcanic and intrusive rocks of the Letitia Lake Group and Red Wine complex, respectively (*Hill and Thomas, 1983*), and the overlying continental red beds, plateau basalts, and gabbro sills of the 1.32-Ga (Rb-Sr) Seal Lake Group (*Baragar, 1981*). The Seal Lake Group erosionally

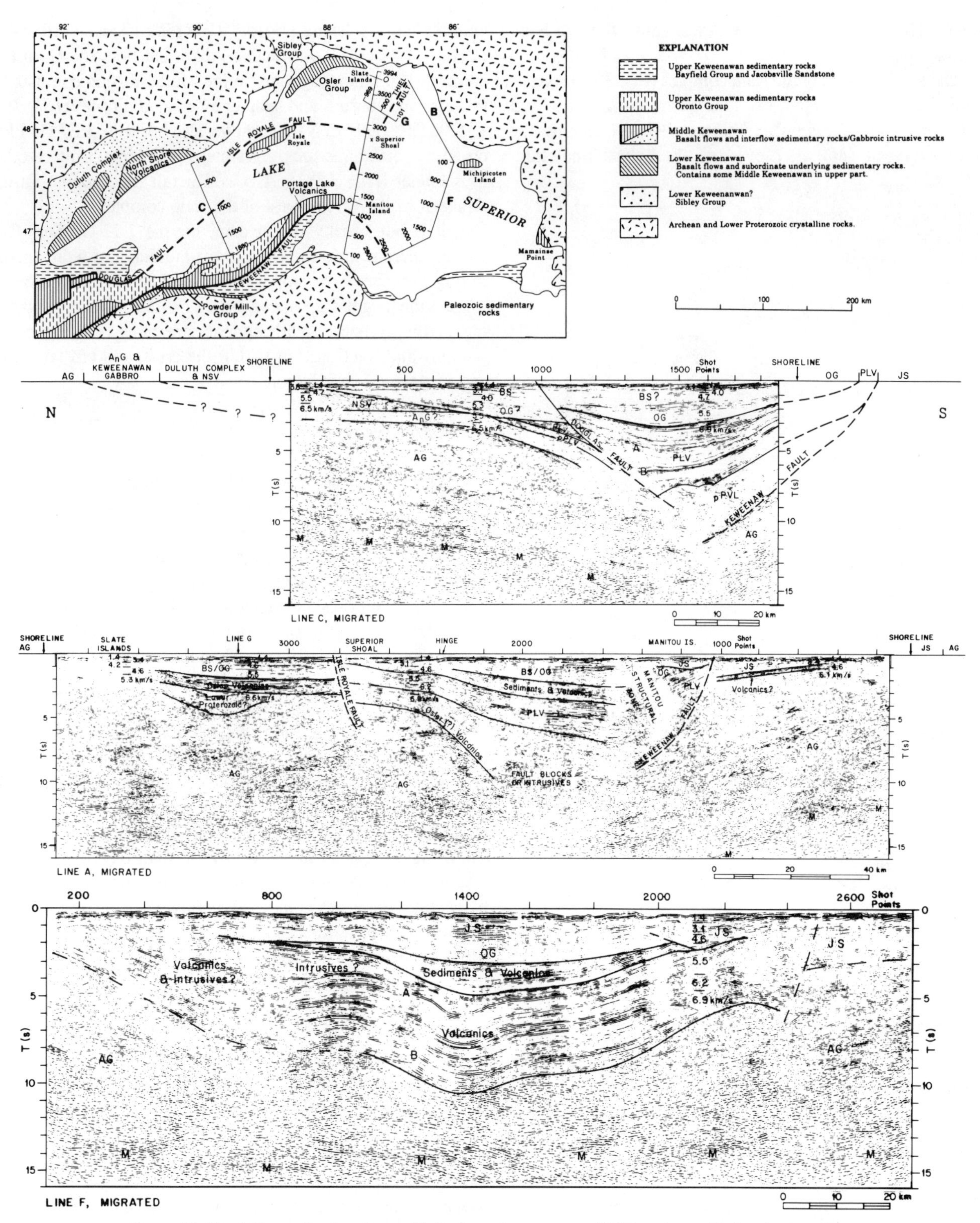

Figure 38. (Top) Generalized geology of Lake Superior segment of Midcontinent rift showing locations of GLIMPCE seismic reflection profiles. (Below) Migrated reflection profiles from *Cannon and others, 1989.* Vertical exaggeration is 1:1 for average velocity of 6 km/sec. Inferred subsurface units are projected updip to exposed extensions on land. AG, Archean gneiss; AnG, Animikie Group (Early Proterozoic); BS, Bayfield Group sediments; JS, Jacobsville sandstone; M, Moho (approximate depth); NSV, North Shore volcanics; OG, Oronto Group sediments; PLV, Portage Lake volcanics; pPLV, pre-Portage Lake sediments.

overlies the Harp Lake anorthosite, which straddles the Rae-Nain suture zone (Fig. 18).

In the northern part of the Nain complex (Fig. 39), anorthosite batholiths are intruded by 1.30-Ga monzogranites and layered complexes (*Simmons and others, 1986*), including the gabbroic Kiglapait (*Morse, 1969*) and the hybrid troctolitic-granitic Newark Island (*Wiebe, 1988*) intrusions. Northeasterly trending 1.32-Ga (K-Ar) diabase dikes cut both the Harp Lake complex and a monzogranite in the southern Nain complex that intrudes anorthosites and smaller associated diorites (*Hill, 1982, 1988*). The southern Nain complex also hosts the 1.27-Ga Flowers River peralkaline suite, a granite-rhyolite ring complex 60 km in diameter (*Hill, 1982*). A coeval peralkaline granite intrudes Archean rocks 200 km west of the Nain complex.

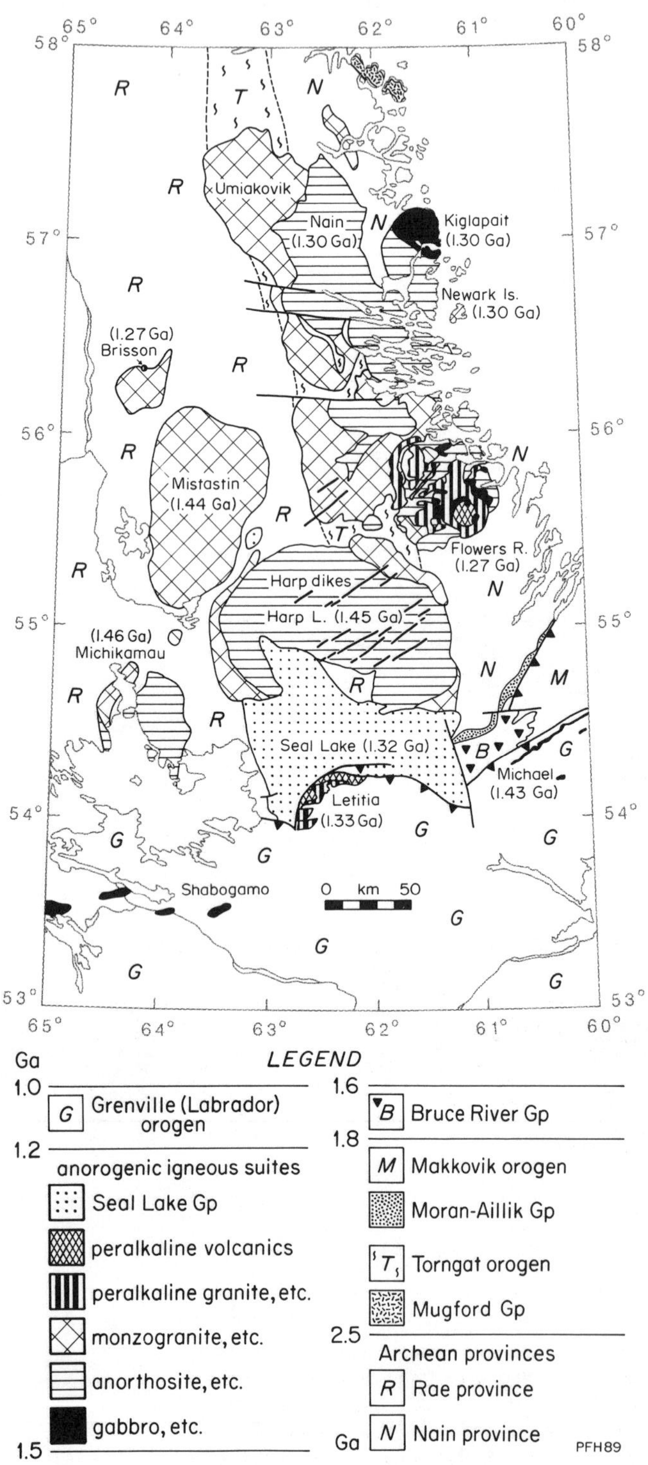

Figure 39. Distribution of Middle Proterozoic anorogenic igneous suites in Labrador and adjacent Quebec.

It is noteworthy that, except for the 1.32-Ga Seal River Group, there is little evidence of rift faulting and sedimentation during anorogenic magmatism in Labrador. Emslie (1980) attributes the magmatism to convective mantle upwelling and melting in the absence of lithospheric stretching, causing magma ponding and fractionation within the crust, and crustal melting and magmatic hybridization.

Southern Greenland

The Early Proterozoic Ketilidian orogen of southern Greenland hosts two suites of pre-Mesozoic anorogenic intrusions—the alkaline Gardar intrusions and related sediments and volcanics (Emeleus and Upton, 1976; *Upton and Emeleus, 1987*), and the rapakivi granite suite (*Bridgwater and others, 1974*). The rapakivi suite comprises post-tectonic elongate mushroom-shaped batholiths of monzogranite and quartz monzonite, and small bodies of norite and diorite, confined to the southern "migmatite" zone of the orogen (Fig. 28). The 1.76- to 1.74-Ga rapakivi suite postdates the peak of Ketilidian metamorphism by about 60 m.y. (*Kalsbeek and Taylor, 1985*) and is coeval with similar suites in the Penokean orogen and the Hearne and western Rae provinces.

The Gardar suite overlaps the central "granite" zone of the Ketilidian orogen (Fig. 28). Up to 3 km of gently dipping continental sediments, basaltic to trachytic lavas, and local rhyolitic ash flows are cut by northeasterly trending olivine gabbro and alkaline felsic dikes (characterized by anorthositic xenoliths), and by central complexes composed mainly of augite and nepheline syenite, gabbro, and peralkaline granite. Rb-Sr ages for the central complexes and dikes range from 1.33 to 1.15 Ga, overlapping temporally with the Seal Lake Group, the gabbroic and granitic plutons of the Nain complex, and both of the peralkaline suites in Labrador.

MIDDLE PROTEROZOIC GRENVILLE AND RACKLAN OROGENS

The youngest Precambrian orogens indigenous to Laurentia developed along its southeastern and northwestern margins between 1.3 and 1.0 Ga, following an orogenic hiatus of at least 350 m.y. Both the Grenville and Racklan orogens are characterized by thrusting directed toward the interior of Laurentia.

The Grenville orogen extends from southern Sweden to southern Mexico but is exposed principally in the southeast part of the Canadian shield (Fig. 40; Moore and others, 1986; Rivers and others, 1989). The most complete cross section (675 km) of

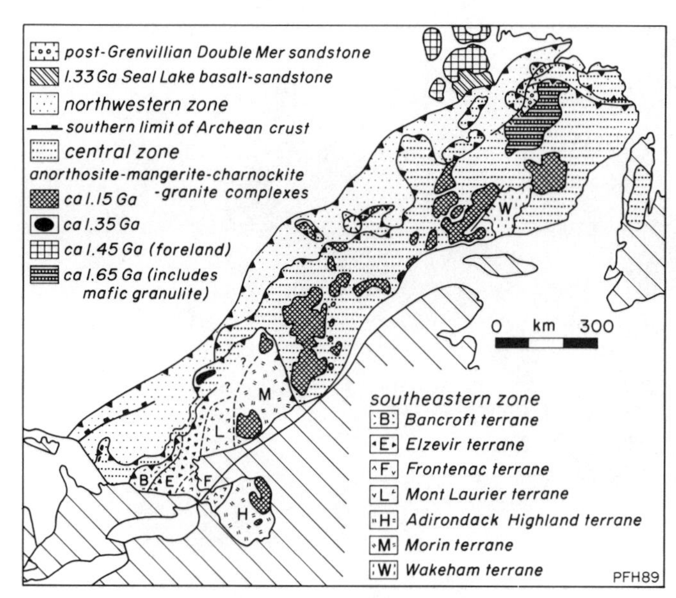

Figure 40. Geology of Grenville orogen in southeastern Canadian shield.

the orogen lies between Georgian Bay on Lake Huron and the Adirondack Mountains of New York (Fig. 41). The fine coastal outcrops of Georgian Bay and southeastern Labrador are currently being studied in detail. Seismic reflection profiling documents Grenvillian crustal imbrication in Georgian Bay (Green and others, 1988) and Ohio (*Culotta and others, 1988*), and information bearing on the extent of the orogen in the subsurface of the eastern United States is reviewed in Denison and others (1984). Grenvillian inliers occur along the length of the Appalachians, in west Texas, and in eastern and southern Mexico.

The definition and extent of the Racklan orogeny (sensu Young and others, 1979) are far more uncertain. Thrusting on the western Arctic platform involved strata as young as 1.27 Ga (Cook, 1988), but deformation and low-grade metamorphism in the northern Cordillera predate 1.27 Ga, implying either distinct or diachronous events. While the Grenville orogen mainly exposes crystalline rocks that were deformed and metamorphosed at midcrustal depths, the Racklan orogen affects thick Middle Proterozoic strata of low metamorphic grade.

Grenville orogen

In the Canadian shield, the Grenville orogen is notable for the following prevailing characteristics: (1) high metamorphic grade and ductile deformation; (2) northwest-directed tectonic transport; (3) retrogressive sequence of thrusting, younging to the southeast; (4) extensive reworking of older crust; and (5) absence of preserved foredeep sediments. The orogen has been divided into three composite zones (Rivers and others, 1989): a northwestern (parautochthonous) zone, a central (allochthonous polycyclic) zone, and a southeastern (allochthonous monocyclic) zone. The northwestern zone is composed of rocks directly related to those in the adjacent foreland but bearing a Grenvillian structural and (greenschist- to granulite-grade) metamorphic overprint. The central zone contains amphibolite- to granulite-grade gneisses that cannot be directly linked with rocks to the northwest but have protoliths that include rocks similar in age to the foreland of Labrador and the southern Midcontinent (Fig. 38). Along much of its length, the boundary between the northwestern and central zones is defined by an abrupt change from low to high magnetic and gravity anomalies corresponding to the leading edge of granulite-grade allochthons overriding lower grade rocks to the northwest. The southeastern zone contains belts of juvenile Grenvillian crust (e.g., Elzevir terrane) and belts of older crust (e.g., Frontenac terrane) probably accreted during the Grenvillian orogeny (*Dickin and others, 1988*). The boundary between the central and southeastern belts is a southeast-dipping mylonite zone having early high-grade reverse and late low-grade normal slip.

Northwestern zone. A deep seismic reflection profile in Lake Huron (Green and others, 1988) shows this zone to be underlain by strong reflectors, dipping 25° to 35° to the southeast and extending to depths of at least 30 km (9 s), that sharply truncate the subhorizontal crustal layering of the foreland at the Grenville front (Fig. 42). Rocks at the surface have undergone ductile deformation typified by southeast-plunging stretching lineations coaxial with open upright folds of foliation, formed during Grenvillian metamorphism that increased in grade from greenschist near the Grenville front to upper amphibolite over granulite palimpsest throughout most of the zone (*Davidson and Bethune, 1988; Culshaw and others, 1988*). Metamorphic pressures of 8 to 10 kbar were attained within 30 km of the Grenville front (*Anovitz, 1987*). The front is the most external of a set of northwest-directed thrusts that transect the Archean provinces and Early Proterozoic orogens of the foreland, and truncate the various Early and Middle Proterozoic foreland cover units (Fig. 40).

Recent isotopic studies are beginning to resolve the ages of rocks, structures, and metamorphic events. In Labrador (Figs. 18, 29, 40), the zone consists mainly of 1.71- to 1.63-Ga granites (Trans-Labrador batholith) coextensive with those of the Labrador orogen, and Early Proterozoic paragneisses related the New Quebec orogen in the west and the Labrador orogen in the east. Following the widespread invasion of gabbros at 1.43 Ga, Grenvillian metamorphism is documented by 1.02- to 0.98-Ga whole-rock, hornblende, muscovite, and biotite $^{40}Ar/^{39}Ar$ plateau ages (*Dallmeyer, 1987*), and cooling ages of 0.98 to 0.97 and 0.93 to 0.92 Ga for titanite and rutile, respectively (Schärer and others, 1986). In Ontario (Fig. 41), rocks with crust-formation (T_{DM} model) ages of 2.7 to 2.4 Ga extend 50 to 60 km southeast of the Grenville front, where they are abruptly juxtaposed with rocks having crust-formation ages of 1.9 to 1.7 Ga (*Dickin and McNutt, 1989*). The contact is interpreted as an extension of the Penokean suture (Niagara suture, Fig. 26) between the Superior province and an accreted island-arc terrane. This suture is tentatively identified as the Manitoulin Island discontinuity in the Grenville fore-

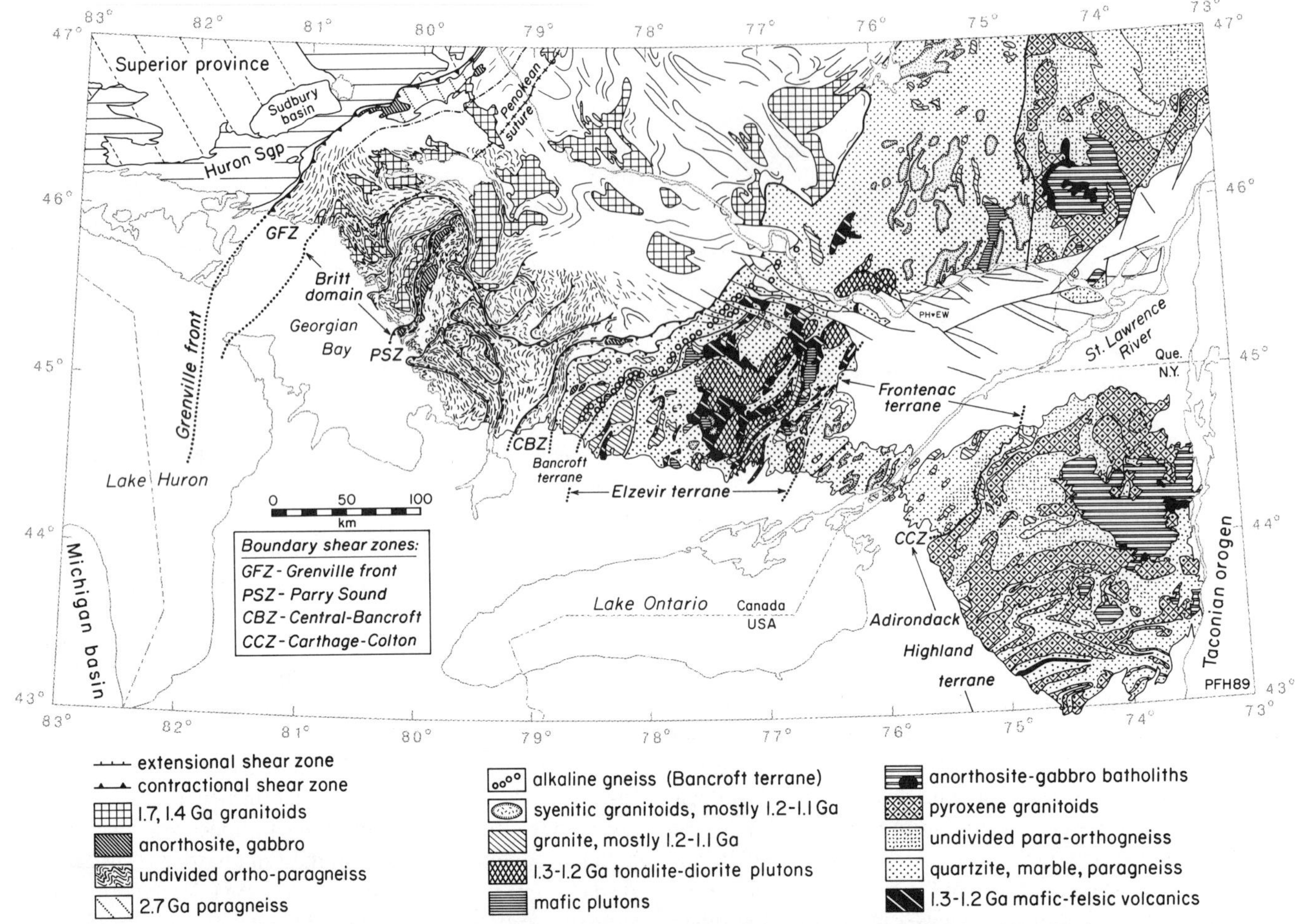

Figure 41. Grenville orogen between Georgian Bay, Ontario, and Adirondack Highlands, New York. Parautochthonous northwestern zone comprises GFZ and Britt domain; central zone lies between northwest margins of PSZ and CBZ; southeastern zone includes juvenile 1.3 to 1.2 Ga crust (Elzevir terrane) and accreted terranes containing older rocks (Frontenac terrane). The dominant structural style throughout much of the transect is northwest-directed ductile thrusting exposed at midcrustal depths.

land of northern Lake Huron (Fig. 42). In the northwestern zone south of the Penokean suture, one of many large bodies of megacrystic granodioritic orthogneiss has a primary crystallization age of 1.46 Ga, coeval with anorogenic granites in the southern Midcontinent (*van Breemen and others, 1986*). Early Grenvillian deformation began at the front during emplacement of the 1.24-Ga Sudbury dikes (*Bethune and Davidson, 1988*), but in the southeastern part of the zone, Grenvillian metamorphism peaked around 1.16 and 1.03 Ga, contemporaneous with overthrusting of the central and southeastern zones, respectively (*van Breemen and others, 1986*).

Central zone. The central zone was transported northwestward on a granulite-grade mylonite zone (Davidson, 1984) that undulates around southeasterly and northeasterly axes and has an apparent minimum displacement of 200 km (Figs. 40, 41). Metamorphic pressures in excess of 11 kbar are typical for granulites within and structurally beneath the central zone (*Anovitz, 1987*), but metamorphic grade decreases upward from the structural base of the zone. In Labrador, the zone comprises 1.68- to 1.63-Ga (Labradorian) granulites and granitic orthogneisses, paragneisses possibly related to the Labrador and New Quebec orogens, a 1.30-Ga syenite-granite complex, and scattered Grenvillian (1.08, 0.99, 0.97 Ga) granites (Schärer and Gower, 1988; *Gower and Loveridge, 1987*). The lower structural levels of the zone have Grenvillian monazite and titanite ages of 1.04 to 1.03 Ga, but Labradorian titanite ages (1.65 to 1.63 Ga) are retained at higher structural levels. In Ontario, the basal (Parry Sound) mylonite contains sheared bodies of 1.35-Ga gabbro and anorthosite, and granitic orthogneiss in a higher thrust sheet is 1.45 Ga, suggesting that the Midcontinent bimodal anorogenic suites extend into the central zone. Therefore, geochronology in both Labrador and Ontario is consistent with the central zone having been contiguous with the protocraton since about 1.65 Ga. A retrogradational sequence of thrusting in the central zone is indicated by synkinematic pegmatite ages of 1.16 Ga in the basal mylonite zone, 1.10 Ga in a structurally higher shear zone sepa-

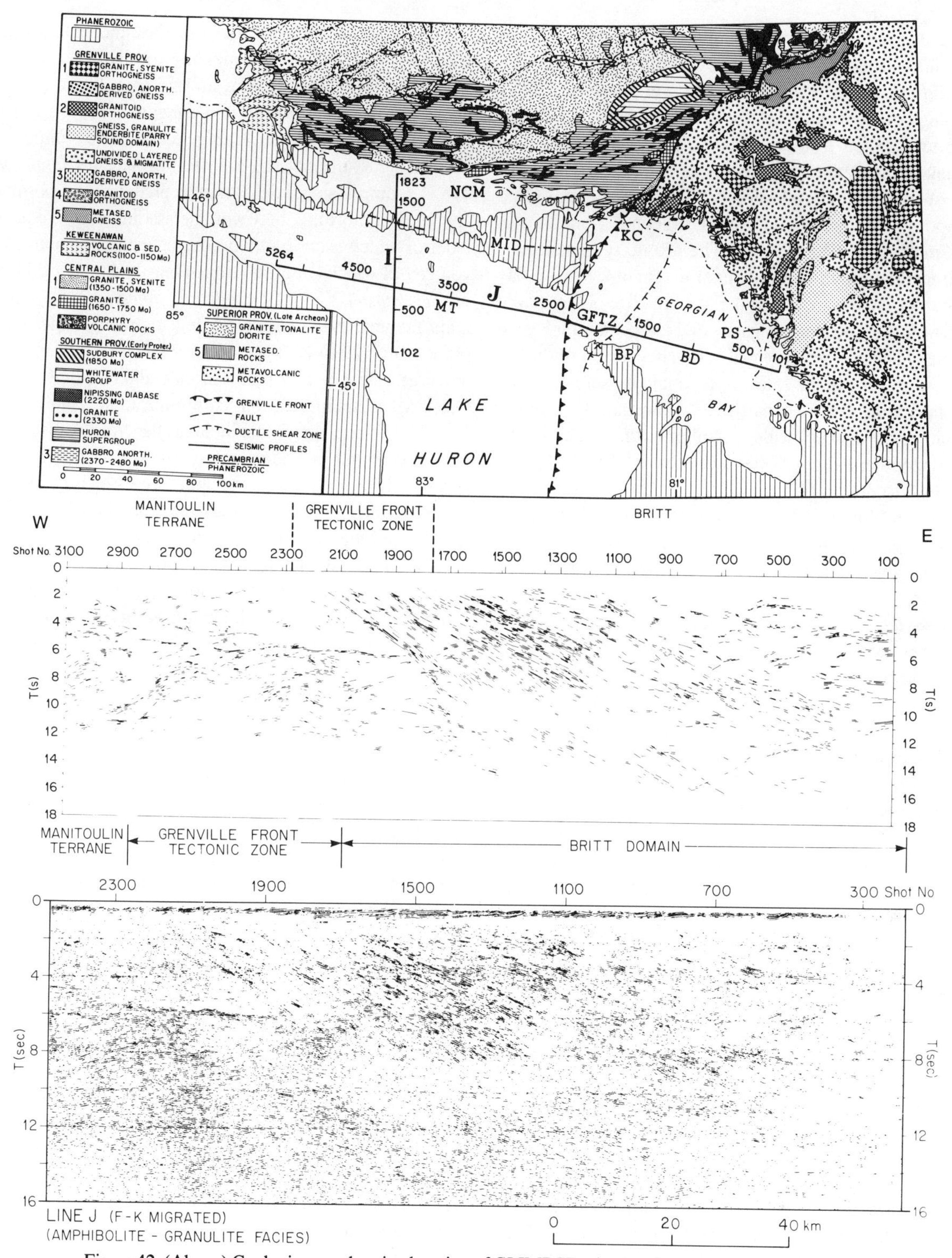

Figure 42. (Above) Geologic map showing location of GLIMPCE seismic reflection profiles after *Green and others, 1988).* Numbers 1-5 in legend match rock units in Grenville front tectonic zone (GFTZ) with correlative units in foreland. BD, Britt domain; BP, Bruce Peninsula; KC, Killarney magmatic zone; MID, Manitoulin Island discontinuity (Penokean suture?); MT, Manitoulin terrane; NCM, North Channel magnetic low; PS, Parry Sound shear zone. (Middle) Line diagram showing reflections recorded along part of seismic line J, based on migrated section, part of which is shown below. Vertical scale is two-way travel time in seconds. M, reflection Moho. (Below) Migrated seismic reflection data for part of line J across Grenville front tectonic zone. Data were obtained using marine seismic reflection surveying techniques.

rating granulite-grade from amphibolite-grade domains, and 1.06 to 1.03 Ga in the shear zone basal to the southeastern zone (*van Breemen and others, 1986; van Breemen and Hanmer, 1986*). The age of high-grade metamorphism in the central zone, inferred to be 1.06 to 1.03 Ga from secondary zircons, correlates with overthrusting of the southeastern zone.

An east-west seismic reflection profile across central Ohio reveals important differences in crustal structural from that in Ontario (*Culotta and others, 1988*). The geometry of reflectors near the Grenville front in Ohio is similar to that in Georgian Bay (Fig. 42), but the front is located at the western edge of the central zone, as identified by positive magnetic and gravity anomalies. In Ohio, a zone of negative geopotential anomalies corresponding to the northwestern zone in the shield is underlain by subhorizontal reflectors, indicating that it is part of the foreland. The central zone in Ohio, about 150 km wide, is flanked to the east by a zone of negative geopotential anomalies and a band of west-dipping reflectors at 14 to 30 km (4.5 to 9 s) depth. These west-dipping reflectors have no known counterpart at the surface in Ontario, indicating a reversal in structural polarity with depth or latitude. This discovery gives high priority to a reflection profile in Lake Erie.

Southeastern terranes. The southeastern zone consists of diverse terranes lacking evidence of pre-Grenvillian contact with the protocraton (Rivers and others, 1989). The Bancroft, Elzevir, and Frontenac–Mont Laurier terranes (Figs. 40, 41) constitute the "central metasedimentary belt" of *Wynne-Edwards* (*1972*). Pb and Nd isotopic ratios indicate that the Bancroft and Elzevir terranes are composed of juvenile 1.3- to 1.2-Ga crust (*Fletcher and Farquhar, 1982; Dickin and others, 1988*), implying that the boundary between the southeastern and central zones represents a pre-Grenvillian continental margin against which the southeastern terranes were accreted. In Ontario, this boundary is a broadly folded, southeast-dipping set of amphibolite-grade, northwest-directed ductile thrusts, the oldest and structurally lowest of which contains syntectonic 1.06-Ga pegmatites (*van Breemen and Hanmer, 1986;* Hanmer, 1988b). Younger, greenschist-grade mylonites parallel to the boundary have top-side-down-to-the-southeast kinematics. The juvenile crustal terranes are bounded to the southeast by the Frontenac terrane, for which Nd isotopic data indicate crust-formation ages of 2.0 to 1.6 Ga (*Dickin and others, 1988*).

The Bancroft terrane consists of middle to upper amphibolite-grade marble and siliciclastic metasediments, intruded by granodioritic orthogneiss and 1.09- to 1.05-Ga bodies of nepheline syenite and carbonatite (*Heaman and others, 1988*). These bodies, which distinguish the terrane, overlap in age with thrusting at the structural base of the southeastern zone and with high-grade metamorphism of the underlying central zone.

The Elzevir terrane is characterized by greenschist- and amphibolite-grade metavolcanic rocks, intercalated with and overlain by marble and siliciclastic metasediments similar to those in the adjacent terranes. The main crust-forming episode involved the eruption of mafic and felsic, tholeiitic and calc-alkaline volcanics, and related tonalites and granites at 1.29 to 1.27 Ga, followed by calc-alkaline to alkaline and peralkaline volcanics and related plutons at 1.25 to 1.23 Ga (*Heaman and others, 1987; van Breemen and Davidson, 1989*). The tholeiitic and calc-alkaline metavolcanic rocks have immobile trace-element signatures of intra-arc rift magmatism (*Smith and Holm, 1987*). Compressional deformation predated and postdated a regional unconformity between metasedimentary sequences, the older of which is cut by numerous calc-alkaline plutons, and the younger of which (Flinton Group) may be about 1.23 Ga (*Moore and Thompson, 1980; Connelly and others, 1987*). Although the main magmatic and structural development of the terrane took place from 1.29 to 1.22 Ga, minor tonalite-trondjhemite relics are dated at 1.35 Ga, and renewed calc-alkaline plutonism at 1.17 Ga (L.M. Heaman, personal communication, 1988).

The Frontenac terrane includes the "northwest lowlands" of New York and is equivalent to the Mont Laurier terrane in Quebec. It lacks the metavolcanics and tonalites of the Elzevir terrane, but contains a similar association of marble and siliciclastic metasediments. Metamorphic grade increases inward from amphibolite at the margins of the terrane to low-pressure (4 to 6 kbar) granulite in the median. Southeast-dipping foliations (with northwest-vergent thrust kinematics) in the northwest rotate through vertical to northwest-dipping in the southeast. Two ages of gabbro-granite-syenite plutonism are well established at 1.18 to 1.16 and 1.08 Ga, the younger being the same as titanite cooling ages throughout the Frontenac and Elzevir terranes (*Heaman and others, 1987; van Breemen and Davidson, 1989*). In New York, older granites were intruded at 1.30 and 1.42 Ga (*McLelland, 1988*).

The Adirondack ("highlands") terrane (Morin terrane in Quebec) is in contact with the Frontenac terrane along a steep, northwest-dipping (Carthage-Colton) mylonite zone having top-side-down-to-the-northwest kinematics. Whether it is an extensional or a folded contractional structure is unknown (Rivers and others, 1989). The terrane is distinguished by large anorthosite-gabbro-charnockite-mangerite complexes, intrusive into siliciclastic, carbonate, and possible evaporitic metasediments, and felsic metavolcanics (*Wiener and others, 1984*). All are involved in early west- to northwest-vergent recumbent folds, refolded by northeasterly and southeasterly upright folds, and metamorphosed to granulite grade at 6 to 8 kbar (McLelland and Isachsen, 1986). The oldest dated intrusion is a 1.32-Ga tonalite; the anorthosites are probably coeval with 1.15- to 1.13-Ga mangerites and charnockites, and 1.05- to 1.00-Ga zircons in gabbro and anorthosite probably date the high-grade metamorphism (*McLelland, 1988*).

The isolated Wakeham terrane (Fig. 40) in northeastern Quebec (*Martignole and others, 1987*; *Bourne, 1986*; *Loveridge, 1986*) overlies 1.66-Ga (Labradorian) gneisses of the central belt along a tectonic contact that locally has top-down-to-the-southeast extensional kinematics. The terrane is composed of two unconformable groups of greenschist-grade peralkaline rhyolites, basalts, gabbros, and terrestrial sediments, intruded by post-

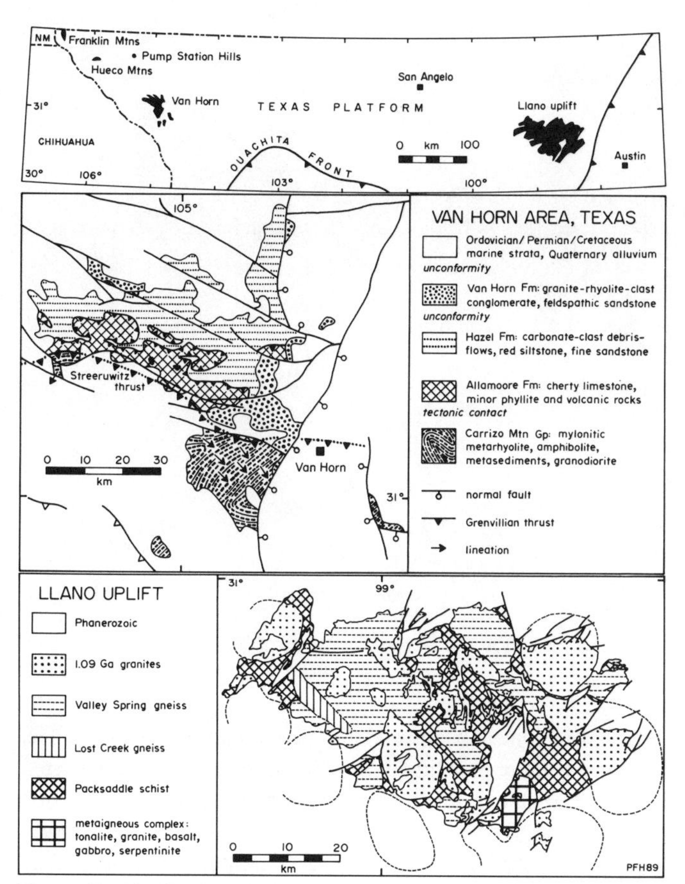

Figure 43. Distribution of Grenvillian inliers in Texas. Map of Grenville front (Streeruwitz thrust) near Van Horn modified from *King and Flawn (1953)*; map of Llano uplift modified from *Garrison (1981)*.

tectonic 0.99-Ga granites. Northwesterly upright folds in both groups refold northwest-vergent recumbent folds observed only in the older group. Rhyolite in the older group is 1.27 Ga, and the younger group must be older than 1.08 Ga, the age of granite associated with anorthosite that intrudes the western margin of the terrane. The dated peralkaline magmatism (continental rift-like) is therefore coeval with the main calc-alkaline magmatism (island arc–like) in the Elzevir terrane.

Texas and Mexico. Grenvillian island-arc terranes accreted onto a foreland characterized by late Grenvillian alkalic felsic magmatism are exposed in Texas (Fig. 43). Near Van Horn, metamorphic rocks (Carrizo Mountain Group) were thrust northwestward onto autochthonous foreland strata (*King and Flawn, 1953*). The greenschist- to amphibolite-grade allochthon includes rhyolite porphyry (1.35 Ga; S. A. Bowring, personal communications, 1988), amphibolite, and psammitic, pelitic, and minor calcareous metasediments. The foreland sequence comprises three formations separated by unconformities: a lower shelf carbonate unit with minor volcanics, a middle foredeep unit of red beds and proximal carbonate-clast conglomerate, and an upper postorogenic unit of arkose and conglomerate containing clasts of rhyolite and granite. In the Franklin Mountains to the northwest, correlatives of the shelf and foredeep units are overlain by alkalic rhyolite intruded by epizonal granite (*Thomann, 1980*), a likely source for the Van Horn Conglomerate. Correlative 1.15- to 1.13-Ga granite and rhyolite outcrop in the intervening Hueco Mountains and Pump Station Hills, respectively (*Copeland and Bowring, 1988*).

In the Llano uplift (Fig. 43), distinct metamorphic suites are perforated by large equant plutons of undeformed 1.09-Ga syenogranite (*Garrison, 1981*; *Walker, 1988*). The quartzofeldspathic Valley Spring Gneiss of uncertain protolith is structurally overlain by the more mafic Packsaddle Schist, which is intruded by syntectonic serpentinite, metabasalt, tonalite, granodiorite, and granite. The schist is interpreted as an arc-flank deposit, and its contact with the underlying gneiss contains relicts of eclogite (minimum pressure 15 kbar) that survived the prevailing low-pressure metamorphism related to the late granites (*Wilkerson and others, 1988*). Ages of 1.23 Ga for the Valley Spring Gneiss, 1.24 Ga (revised) for the structurally overlying Packsaddle Schist, and 1.30 Ga for a granite that supposedly intrudes the schist (*Walker, 1988*) reveal problems with existing interpretations and the need for systematic reinvestigation of this key area on the doorstep of a major university department.

A Grenvillian meta-igneous complex composed of granite, gabbro, and diorite, cut by diabase and trondhjemite dikes and minor postmetamorphic pegmatite, is exposed near Chihuahua in northern Mexico (*Blount and others, 1988*; *Ruiz and others, 1988*). The complex resembles a continental margin back-arc basin geochemically, consistent with its Nd crust-formation age (1.5 to 1.4 Ga) being significantly older than its range of igneous crystallization ages (1.33 Ga for a diorite and 1.27 Ga for a granite). The latter ages are comparable to ages of premetamorphic rocks in the Llano uplift and Carrizo Mountains, with which the complex may be coextensive in the subsurface.

Appalachians and Caledonides. High-grade Grenvillian ortho- and paragneisses are exposed all along the Blue Ridge–Green Mountain–Long Range system of external massifs of the Appalachians (Fig. 44), and in the cores of internal gneiss domes to the southeast (*Williams, 1978*; Powell and others, 1988; *Bartholomew, 1984*).

Equivocal evidence of Grenvillian metamorphism occurs in the southwestern part of the East Greenland Caledonides (Fig. 45). The classic view of a Caledonian infrastructure (*Haller, 1971*) was challenged by isotopic data interpreted as indicating Grenvillian metamorphism of Early Proterozoic sediments (Krummedal sequence) later involved in Caledonian thrusting (*Steiger and others, 1979*). A neoclassical interpretation is that the metasediments are Late Proterozoic (lower Eleonore Bay Group) and locally preserve Grenvillian detrital ages despite Caledonian metamorphism (*Peucat and others, 1985*).

Racklan orogen

In the northern Canadian Cordillera, open folding and greenschist-grade metamorphism, which affects the Middle Prot-

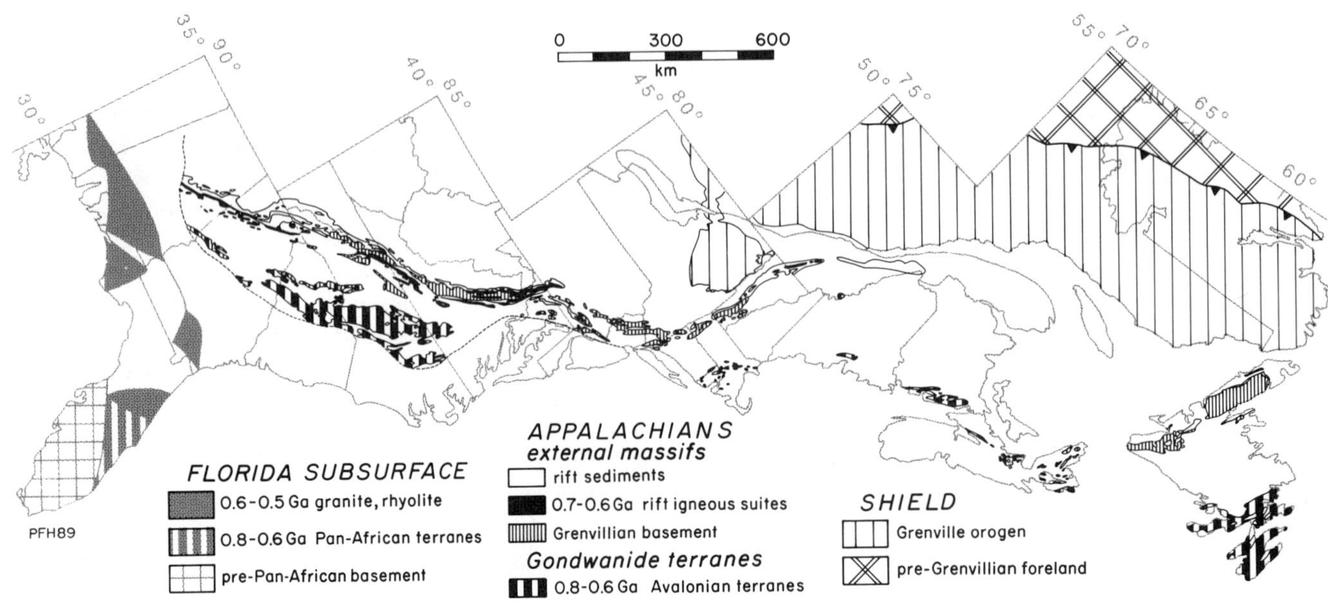

Figure 44. Distribution of Middle and Late Proterozoic rocks in the Appalachians.

erozoic Wernecke Supergroup (Delaney, 1981) but not the younger Mackenzie Mountains Supergroup, is attributed to the Racklan orogeny (Young and others, 1979). Mineralized (U-Cu-Ba-Co-Fe) intrusive megabreccias (1.27 ± .04 Ga; *Parrish and Bell, 1987*) postdate the orogeny (G. H. Eisbacher, personal communication, 1988). Cook (1988) provisionally correlates the orogeny with an east- to southeast-vergent, thin-skinned, thrust-fold belt in the subsurface between the Beaufort Sea and Great Bear Lake (Fig. 46). The thrusting appears to predate the Rae Group, a platformal correlative of the Mackenzie Mountains Supergroup, but deforms strata as young as the Coppermine River flood basalt, which is cogenetic with the 1.27-Ga Muskox intrusion and Mackenzie dikes (LeCheminant and Heaman, 1989). Northerly trending folds in the Dismal Lakes Group in western exposures of the Coppermine homocline (Fig. 34) may also manifest this event (G. M. Ross, personal communication, 1986). It is not known whether the conflicting age relations between the Cordillera and the Arctic platform (pre- or post-1.27 Ga) imply distinct or diachronous events. However, the subsurface thrust belt signifies that the northwest margin of the craton experienced a major compressional event sometime after 1.27 Ga and well before 0.78 Ga (perhaps at 1.17 to 1.10 Ga; *Jefferson and Parrish, 1988*).

LATE PROTEROZOIC RIFTING: CREATING THE MARGINS OF LAURENTIA

Subsidence analysis of the early Paleozoic passive margin prisms bordering Laurentia indicates that continental breakup occurred more or less simultaneously at about 0.6 Ga along the Appalachian and Cordilleran margins (*Bond and others, 1984*). However, breakup was the end result of episodic rifting events recorded in Late Proterozoic strata beginning at about 0.8 Ga. Unlike the discrete Middle Proterozoic basins, the rift-related Late Proterozoic deposits appear to have encircled Laurentia (Stewart, 1976). The latter are mainly immature clastic sediments, with subordinate volcanic rocks, and are characterized by glaciogenic deposits.

A number of failed rift arms, or aulacogens, developed contemporaneously with continental breakup (Fig. 47). The Southern Oklahoma, Reelfoot, St. Lawrence, and Lake Melville aulacogens extend far into the craton (*Keller and others, 1983*; *Larson and others, 1985*; *Gower and others, 1986*). Alkaline intrusions and dike swarms associated with rifting are mostly Early Cambrian in age, although fertile mantle frozen into the lithosphere as a consequence of rifting remained susceptible to subsequent melting (Phipps, 1988).

Appalachians

The allochthonous Blue Ridge–Green Mountains–Long Range anticlinorium (Fig. 44) corresponds to a hinge line separating Late Proterozoic rift-related igneous and sedimentary rocks that are subaqueous and relatively thick to the southeast, and mainly subaerial and thin or absent to the northwest (*Rankin and others, 1988*). The sediments are dominantly immature epiclastic deposits, including glaciogenic diamictites, for which fault-controlled basins are inferred from variability in thickness and grain size. The underlying Grenvillian basement is intruded by swarms of alkalic to tholeiitic mafic dikes, and alkalic to peralkaline granite plutons. Volcanic equivalents overlie most of the rift-related sediments and are succeeded by the onlapping quartzarenite-pelite blanket (Chilhowee Group) of the early Paleozoic continental terrace prism. The felsic volcanics are local-

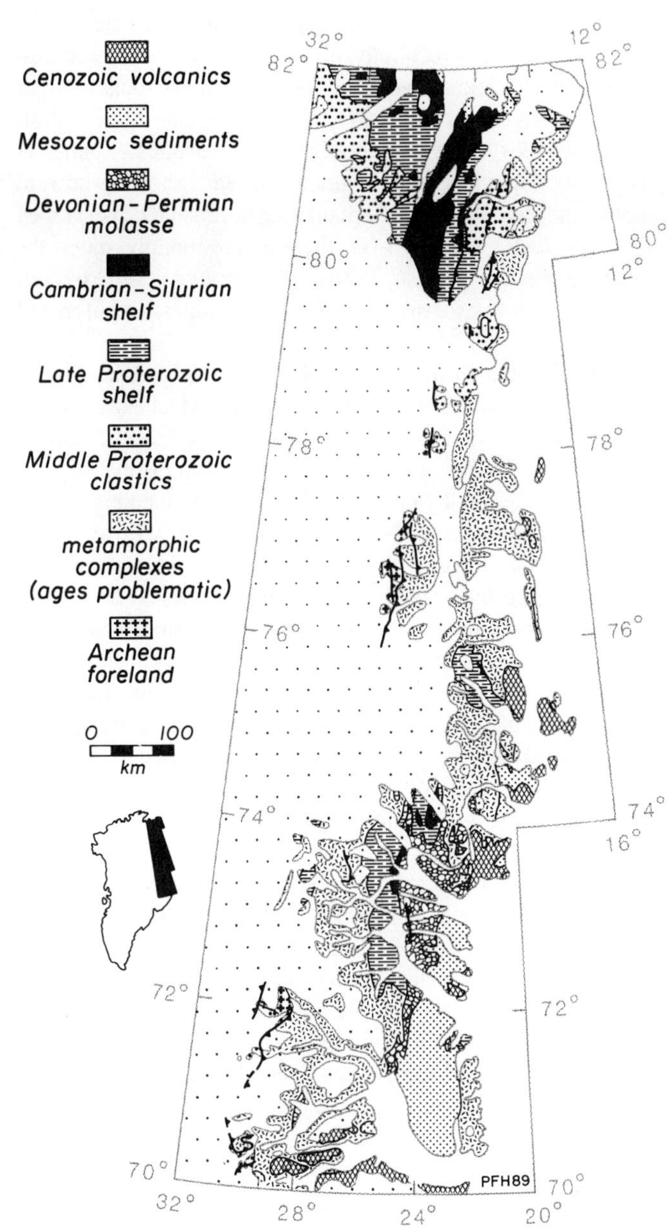

Figure 45. Proterozoic rocks of the east Greenland Caledonides.

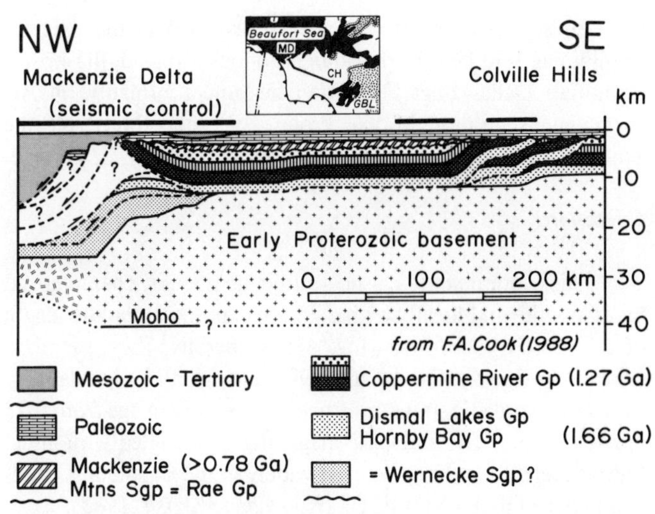

Figure 46. Interpretation of subsurface thrust structure (post-1.27 Ga, pre-0.78 Ga), according to *Cook (1988),* based on seismic reflection profiling between Mackenzie Delta (MD) and Colville Hills (CH) near Great Bear Lake (GBL). Inferred root zone of thrust system was reactivated to form rifted margin of Beaufort Sea.

ized at reentrants (at the southern boundaries of Virginia, Pennsylvania, and Quebec), which are interpreted as triple junctions linking the failed rifts of the eastern craton to the ancestral Appalachian rift system (Figs. 44, 47). Variation in rift deposits along strike—thick sediments (Ocoee Supergroup) lacking volcanics in Tennessee to thin sediments with abundant volcanics (Catoctin Formation) in Virginia—may reflect segmentation of a rift system dominated by master faults of alternating polarity (i.e., dipping southeast in Tennessee, northwest in Virginia).

Geochronology has been a stumbling block in efforts to erect a comprehensive model for Appalachian rifting. In Newfoundland, mafic dikes and rift-related granites are both 0.60 Ga ($^{39}Ar/^{40}Ar$ and U-Pb respectively). In the central and southern Appalachians, 0.73-Ga ages have been obtained for mafic dikes (Rb-Sr), 0.69 Ga (U-Pb) for felsic volcanics, 0.64 Ga (U-Pb) for peralkaline granites, and 0.57 Ga (Rb-Sr) for the Catoctin Basalt, the latter age being the most easily reconciled with the early Cambrian biota of the conformably overlying Chilhowee Group (*Badger and Sinha, 1988*). Stratigraphic and radiometric evidence indicates protracted or repeated episodes of rifting prior to continental breakup in the earliest Cambrian (*Williams and Hiscott, 1987*).

Caledonides and Franklinides

The East Greenland Caledonides contain thick Late Proterozoic sediments in which uniform shelf facies prevail, unlike the rift facies sediments and volcanics of the Appalachians. In the central part of the East Greenland Caledonides (Fig. 45), an allochthonous sequence at least 12 km thick of interlayered quartzite, pelite, and carbonate (Eleonore Bay Group) is spectacularly exposed (Henriksen and Higgins, 1976). It is separated from lower Paleozoic shelf sediments by a relatively thin interval (Tillite Group) of clastic and evaporitic sediments containing two diamictite units. In the foreland of the Caledonides in northeastern Greenland (Fig. 33), shelf sediments with a local basal diamictite occur disconformably between Middle Proterozoic and lower Paleozoic sequences (Higgins, 1986). Their equivalents in the Caledonian thrust belt to the east are up to 5 km thick and contain, in their lower part, the only Late Proterozoic turbidite facies in the East Greenland Caledonides.

Although rifting of the Franklinian continental margin of northern Canada and Greenland probably occurred in the Late

Proterozoic, no rocks of that age are exposed in the external Franklinian fold belt. In the autochthonous foreland, the Lower Cambrian Dallas Bugt Formation lies unconformably on Archean gneisses or on Middle Proterozoic strata bordering the Thule basin (Fig. 33).

Cordillera

Thick, dominantly clastic sedimentary rocks, characterized by diamictite and locally by basalt, are exposed along the length of the eastern Cordillera (Fig. 48). Generally, they are overstepped by Lower Cambrian shelf quartzite and underlain by Middle Proterozoic strata or by gneisses ranging in age from 0.73 to over 2 Ga. Mafic and felsic magmatism associated with initial Late Proterozoic rifting occurred widely in the Canadian Cordillera between 0.78 and 0.73 Ga (*Roots and Parrish, 1988*).

In the Tatonduk River area, straddling the Alaska-Yukon boundary, about 2 km of Late Proterozoic strata (upper Tindir Group) underlie Lower Cambrian carbonates and overlie a pair of kilometer-thick, shoaling-upward (shale-carbonate-quartzite and shale-carbonate) sequences (lower Tindir Group), possibly equivalent to Middle Proterozoic strata to the east (*Young, 1982*). The upper Tindir Group consists of basal basalt, overlain by ferruginous mudstone, diamictite, westward-directed turbidites, and an upper mixed carbonate-siliciclastic unit that grades eastward from slope to shelf facies (*Young, 1982*).

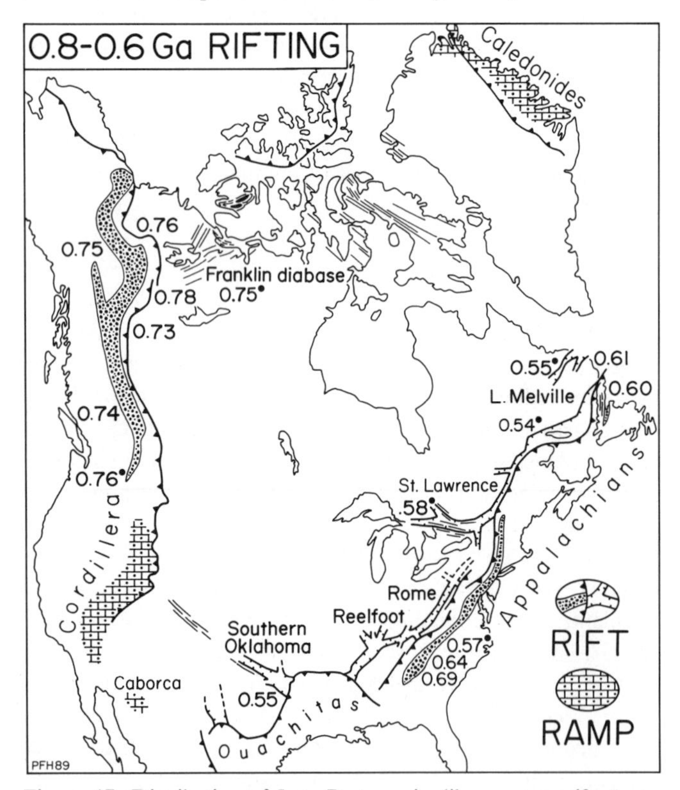

Figure 47. Distribution of Late Proterozoic dike swarms, rifts (autochthonous and allochthonous), and shelf-ramps in North America. Numbers give U-Pb ages (Rb-Sr, K-Ar ages are dotted) in gigayears of rift-related magmatism.

In the Ogilvie Mountains, Yukon Territory, a Late Proterozoic half-graben, structurally inverted by Mesozoic compression, preserves 1.8 km of volcanic and sedimentary rocks (Harper Group) separated unconformably from underlying Middle Proterozoic and overlying Lower Cambrian carbonate units. A wedge of dolomite-clast conglomerate and shoaling-upward basaltic and rhyolitic volcanics flanks the north-side-down graben boundary fault. The 0.75-Ga rhyolite presumably dates the graben (Roots and Parrish, 1988). The volcanic complex is onlapped by a more extensive sequence of turbidites, argillites, and limestones.

The Rapitan Group, which unconformably overlies Middle Proterozoic dolomites in the Wernecke and Mackenzie Mountains, comprises four formations of highly variable thickness (*Eisbacher, 1981; Yeo, 1981*). The basal Sayunei Formation consists of turbidites cut by channels of conglomerate and is capped by nodular and/or banded cherty iron-formation with abundant dropstones. The Sayunei and the succeeding Shezal diamictite were influenced by a fanning system of northeast to northwest-trending normal faults, and were deposited on a southwest-dipping submarine slope. The overlying Twitya and Keele Formations consist of turbidites, locally with channelized conglomerates and diamictites, overlain by shoaling-upward dolomite-quartzite cycles, capped by an extensive peritidal dolomite. Dark shales of the Sheepbed Formation separate the Rapitan Group from shelf quartzites containing Lower Cambrian fauna.

Late Proterozoic strata of the Windermere Supergroup flank the Northern Rocky Mountain Trench (*Evenchick, 1988*). They consist of up to 4 km of mainly deep-water feldspathic grit, quartzite, semipelite, pelite, marble, diamictite, and mafic sheets. From north to south, they are referred to the Hyland, Misinchinka, and Miette Groups northeast of the Trench, and the Ingenika Group southwest of the Trench. The latter overlies a 1.85-Ga granitic orthogneiss, and the Misinchinka Group overlies a foliated 0.73-Ga leucogranite, providing a local maximum age for the Windermere Supergroup (*Evenchick and others, 1984*).

In southern British Columbia and adjacent Washington, the Late Proterozoic Windermere Supergroup thickens southwestward from the Rocky Mountains to the Columbia Mountains (Fig. 48). Unconformities separate the Windermere Supergroup from the Middle Proterozoic Belt–Purcell Supergroup and the Lower Cambrian Hamill Group and equivalents. A maximum age for the Windermere Supergroup may be given by a 0.74-Ga granite cutting the Early Proterozoic Malton Gneiss (*Evenchick and others, 1984*). Regional correlations have traditionally inferred a simple four-fold succession for the Windermere Supergroup, comprising (1) conglomerate (in part glaciogenic) and feldspathic grit (with intercalated basalt near the 49th parallel), (2) turbiditic semipelite with mafic sheets and lenses, (3) interlayered carbonate and pelite, and (4) interlayered quartzite, semipelite, and pelite. However, Pell and Simony (1987) suggest that the succession in the northern Columbia Mountains (Kaza and Caribou Groups) is gradational with, but largely overlies, the

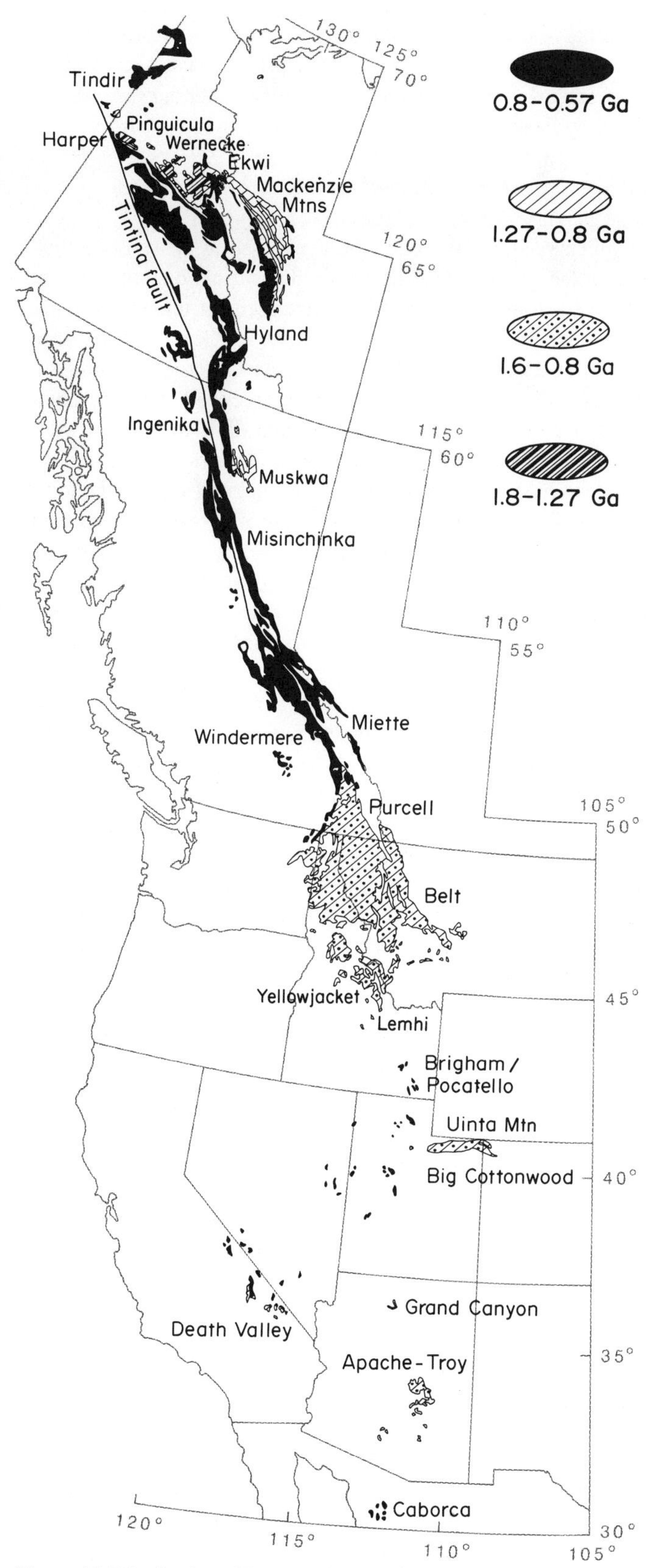

Figure 48. Distribution of Proterozoic strata in the Cordillera and correlative strata in Arizona.

succession to the south (Horsethief Creek Group), consistent with the regional structural plunge. This implies two distinct episodes of rifting and offlapping grit-pelite-carbonate–upper clastic successions, each over 5 km thick. Alternatively, the superimposed successions may be the result of structural duplication (*Struik, 1986*). Devlin and Bond (1988) present lithologic and stratigraphic evidence, including local basaltic volcanism, for a final episode of rifting during Hamill Group sedimentation.

Late Proterozoic strata at least 7 km thick in northwestern Utah and adjacent parts of Idaho and Nevada are divided into a lower Sheeprock or Pocatello Group, and an upper Brigham Group (Christie-Blick, 1982). The older group is dominated by two intervals of glaciogenic sediments separated by up to 1 km of quartzite and, in Idaho, contains synsedimentary normal faults and up to 350 m of basalt (*Link, 1983*). The younger group comprises four sequences, bounded by subaerial exposure surfaces, of fluvial and/or shallow-marine quartzite and siltstone, the youngest of which contains Lower Cambrian fossils (*Link and others, 1987*). Evidence for rifting concurrent with the younger group is contentious.

In the Death Valley region of southeastern California and southern Nevada, Middle Proterozoic strata of the Pahrump Group, intruded by gabbro sheets, are overlain by over 2 km of Late Proterozoic sediments (*Wright and others, 1976*). Rifting and minor basaltic volcanism accompanied deposition of the mainly glaciogenic Kingston Peak Formation (*Miller, 1985*) at the base of the Late Proterozoic sequence. The overlying Noonday Dolomite comprises a stromatolitic shallow-water platform and correlative mixed carbonate-siliclastic basinal facies (*Williams and others, 1976*). The succeeding Johnnie and Stirling Formations consist mainly of quartzite with subordinate siltstone and dolomite, and are separated disconformably from fossiliferous Lower Cambrian quartzite of the Wood Canyon Formation (*Stewart, 1970*).

Near Caborca in northwestern Mexico, 1.11- and 1.40-Ga granites intruding a 1.75- to 1.60-Ga plutonic-metamorphic complex are overlain nonconformably by nearly 1.3 km of shelf dolomite and quartzite, which pass upward into similar shelf strata containing Lower Cambrian fossils (*Stewart and others, 1984*). *Stewart* (*1988*) considers the Caborca shelf sequence to have been deposited on a west-facing Cordilleran passive margin, truncated by Early Cambrian rifting along the south-facing margin coextensive with the Ouachitas (Fig. 47).

EXOTIC PRECAMBRIAN TERRANES ACCRETED IN THE PHANEROZOIC

Gondwanide terranes of the Appalachians

The eastern Appalachians contain Proterozoic terranes of Gondwanide affinity (Fig. 44) that were accreted to Laurentia in the Paleozoic (Van der Voo, 1988). All are characterized by Late Proterozoic volcanic and plutonic rocks that experienced the Avalonian (= Cadomian) orogeny at about 0.6 Ga, and are overlain by earliest Paleozoic shelf sediments containing an Avalonian fauna (*Morris and Rushton, 1988*) distinct from that in coeval cofacial strata indigenous to Laurentia. Controversy concerns their time(s) of accretion to Laurentia, whether they are relics of a single or a composite Proterozoic terrane, and the age(s) and heritage of their basement.

The Avalon terranes of eastern Canada (*Nance, 1986; Krogh and others, 1988*; *King, 1988*) were accreted in the mid-Paleozoic (Acadian orogeny) and are exposed in eastern Newfoundland (and underlie most of the Grand Banks), southeastern Cape Breton Island, the Antigonish and Cobequid Highlands of mainland Nova Scotia, southern New Brunswick, and adjacent coastal Maine. The oldest rocks comprise a quartzite-carbonate shelf sequence and vestiges of basement(?) gneiss containing detrital(?) zircons at least as old as 1.6 Ga. Collapse of the shelf at 0.80 to 0.76 Ga led to deposition of megabreccias and turbidites, mafic magmatism, and metamorphism of the underlying gneiss. This probable rifting event is separated by a prolonged hiatus from widespread plutonism and volcanism, mainly terrestrial, at 0.63 to 0.60 Ga. The magmatism is believed to be subduction-related, and its variable tholeiitic and calc-alkaline to peralkaline character is attributed to oblique intra-arc rifting, consistent with the local development of contemporaneous dike swarms and transcurrent mylonite zones. The arc volcanics are locally overlain by thick deep-water sediments containing diamictites and abundant mafic intrusions. The basinal sediments grade upward into fluvial facies correlative with 0.59- to 0.58-Ga felsic magmatism. Open folding and low-grade metamorphism (Avalonian orogeny) occurred prior to deposition of Cambro-Ordovician shelf sediments containing minor volanics. The Avalon terranes did not experience the early Paleozoic Taconic orogeny.

Southeastern New England is underlain by a terrane like the Avalon comprising a 0.62- to 0.60-Ga calc-alkaline plutonic-volcanic suite succeeded by latest Proterozoic basin-filling sediments containing diamictites. The overlying Cambrian strata have the same exotic fauna as other Gondwanide terranes, but in New England they were not accreted to Laurentia until the late Paleozoic (Zen, 1983).

The Carolina terrane (Carolina Slate Belt and the equivalent but more highly metamorphosed Charlotte belt) of the southeastern Appalachian Piedmont (Harris and Glover, 1988) comprise a thickness of 3 to 4 km of calc-alkaline volcanic (0.65 to 0.62 Ga) and overlying epiclastic deposits, which were folded and faulted at about 0.60 Ga (Virgilina deformation), prior to bimodal volcanism and related plutonism at 0.59 to 0.57 Ga, and deposition of early Paleozoic sediments containing an Avalonian fauna. Unlike the Gondwanide terranes to the north, however, the Carolina terrane experienced strong Ordovician deformation (Taconic orogeny), believed to record its accretion to Laurentia at that time.

Areas of Late Proterozoic felsic volcanic and plutonic rocks in the subcrop of northern Florida and adjacent states lie south of the inferred late Paleozoic (Alleghanian) suture between Africa and Laurentia (*Tauvers and Muehlburger, 1987*). The difficulties of suture searching are well illustrated here—the terrane of African ancestry accreted in the late Paleozoic is juxtaposed against the Carolina terrane of similar lithology and heritage accreted in the early Paleozoic.

Pearya terrane of the Franklinides

Pearya is a composite terrane exposed in the most internal part of the Franklinian orogen (Fig. 33), mainly on northwestern Ellesmere Island (Trettin, 1987). Its basement underwent high-grade metamorphism and/or plutonism at 1.1 to 1.0 Ga, and is overlain by shallow and deep-water Late Proterozoic sediments, including diamictite, and an early Paleozoic shelf sequence. Fault contacts between the shelf sediments and Early to Middle Ordovician volcano-plutonic arc and ophiolite suites are overstepped by Late Ordovician calc-alkaline volcanics and Late Ordovician to Late Silurian sediments. In contrast to Pearya, the Franklinian margin of Laurentia and the Arctic platform have an Archean–Early Proterozoic basement and lack evidence of Middle Ordovician orogenesis. Pearya was likely accreted in the Late Silurian and appears to have affinities with the northern Caledonides.

Grenvillian terranes in Mexico

Inliers of amphibolite- and granulite-grade gneisses in eastern and southern Mexico, respectively (*Ortega-Gutierrez, 1981*), have Grenvillian metamorphic and igneous ages, and Nd crust-formation ages of 1.60 to 1.35 Ga (*Ruiz and others, 1988*). Although previously considered to be part of the autochthonous foreland of the Ouachitas, *Stewart (1988)* considers the Grenvillian inliers to represent terranes rifted from the southern margin of Laurentia in the Cambrian and reattached in the late Paleozoic and perhaps Triassic.

SYNTHESIS: PRECAMBRIAN OF NORTH AMERICA IN A GLOBAL CONTEXT

The long-term geologic record is governed by the repeated aggregation and fragmentation of continents, modulated by secular cooling of the mantle and net growth of continental crust. Accordingly, the Precambrian history of North America is effectively summarized in the form of a cladogram (Fig. 49). As the mean age of the extant continental crust is about 2.0 Ga, a knowledge of Precambrian crustal history is a prerequisite for understanding how continents originate and evolve.

Archean. The exposed Precambrian shield is strongly biased in favor of Archean crust—it makes up 84 percent of the shield (including ice-covered areas of Greenland) but only 55 percent of the Precambrian craton as a whole. This bias contributed to the earlier view that most Precambrian crust formed in the Archean, and that the Proterozoic was a time of crustal reworking but little or no crustal growth. To some this implied that a form of plate tectonics operated in the Archean but not during the Early and Middle Proterozoic. These ideas have receded with the discoveries of 2.0-Ga ophiolites in the Baltic and Canadian

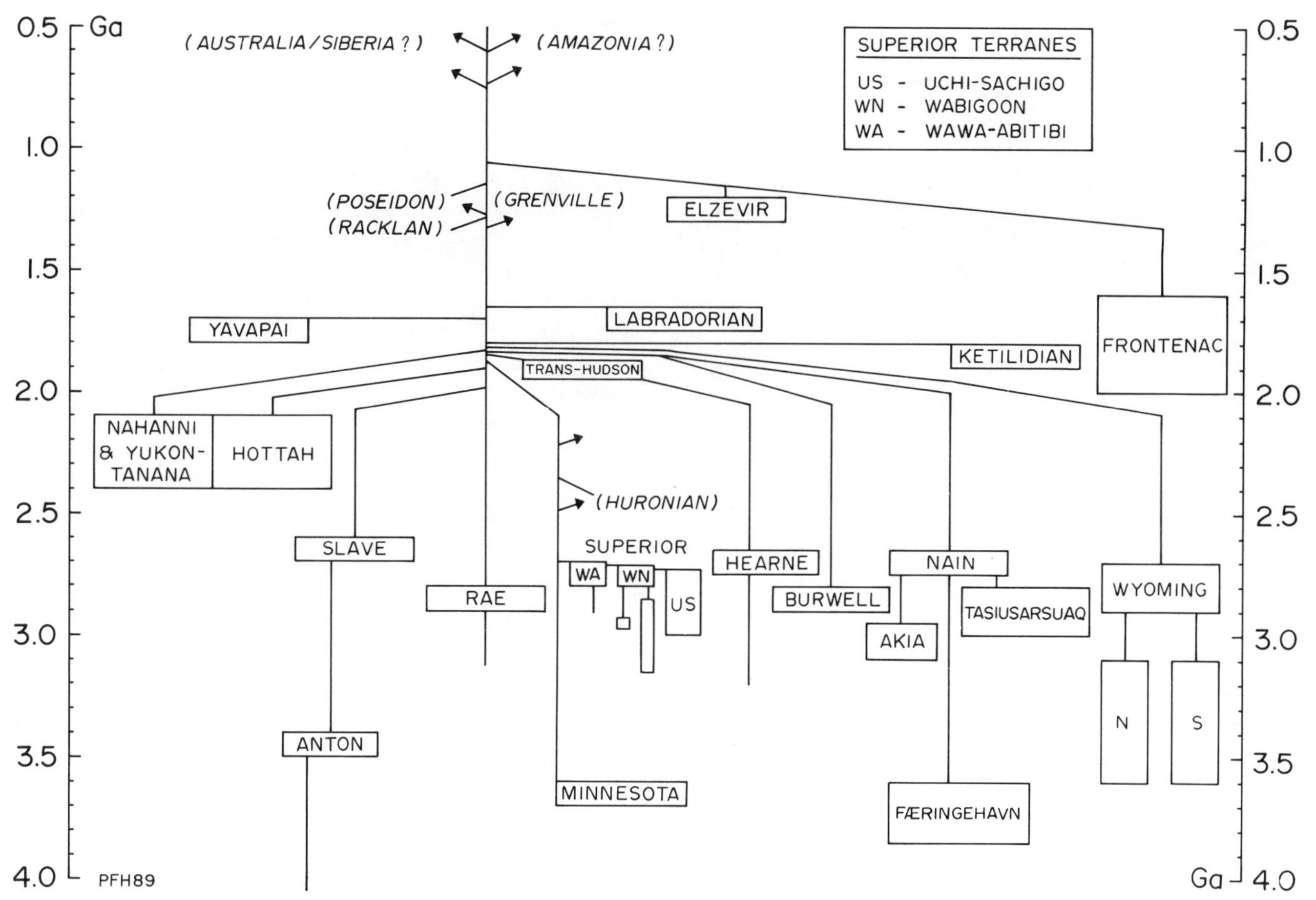

Figure 49. Cladogram (*Young, 1986*) summarizing accretion of North American craton. Boxes indicate times of crust formation of specific terranes. Merging of lines gives age of collision of respective terranes. Splitting of lines gives age of separation of terranes (bracketed names locate sites of separation; bracketed names with question marks identify terranes postulated to have separated). Note major episode of crust formation at 2.9 to 2.7 Ga, important confluence of Archean terranes at 2.0 to 1.8 Ga, accretion of juvenile crust at 1.9 to 1.7 Ga, and lack of convergent tectonism during 1.6 to 1.2 Ga period of anorogenic magmatism.

shields, and the realization that vast areas of juvenile Early Proterozoic crust underlie the sedimentary veneer of the platform.

The observation that the raised shield is centered on the Archean protocraton seems to imply that the Archean lithosphere is more buoyant than Proterozoic lithosphere. This is consistent with geophysical and geochemical evidence that a refractory low-density mantle root (tectosphere), depleted in basaltic melt fraction, is stabilized beneath the Archean cratons and moves coherently with the lithospheric plates (*Jordan, 1981*). The shear-velocity structure beneath North America suggests that tectospheric roots extend about 150 km deeper (to 400 km) beneath the Archean provinces as compared with the Proterozoic crust (*Grand, 1987*). The correlation of tectospheric thickness with lithospheric age could result from progressive growth of the root over geologic time (*Oxburgh and Parmentier, 1978*), or secular change in the tectonics of continental accretion. Support for the latter alternative comes from isotopic and seismological evidence implying that mantle roots beneath the Archean provinces formed in the Archean (*Bell and Blenkinsop, 1987; Silver and Chan, 1988*). The suggestion that the roots result from tectonic thickening of the lithosphere during continental aggregation (*Jordan, 1981*) is not supported by the present study, which reveals no apparent difference in structure between Archean and Proterozoic juvenile crust in North America. Rather, the secular decrease in tectospheric thickness may be inherited from changes in the oceanic lithosphere, in which extreme depletion in the Archean would be complementary to the greatly increased thickness of oceanic crust inferred as a consequence of higher asthenospheric temperatures (*Bickle, 1986*).

How did the Archean continental crust evolve from the mantle? Did the tectonic processes involved differ greatly from those at later times? Chemically, Archean igneous suites differ subtly from younger ones in ways attributable to the presumed higher mean mantle temperature—ultramafic (komatiitic) suites that crystallized from magmas approaching mantle compositions were more common, as were felsic (trondhjemite-tonalite-granodiorite) suites, which are inferred from their enrichment in light rare-earth elements to be products of partial melting of subducted oceanic crust. However, the bulk composition of Archean crust does not differ much from that of younger crust believed to have formed by the aggregation of oceanic island arcs. The comparison is reinforced by integrated geological and geochronological investigations recently undertaken, particularly in the Superior province. They show that the province is constituted of alternating linear belts of volcanic-plutonic and sedimentary protoliths. The construction and evolution of the volcanic-plutonic belts resemble those of island arcs, and the sedimentary belts those of accretionary prisms incorporating arc-flank basins. Furthermore, the belts have age ranges that are remarkably consistent along strike but vary incrementally across strike (Card, 1989), consistent with the lateral accretion of island arcs.

A problem for the island-arc model for crustal genesis is the fact that the mean composition of continental crust is more silicic than the primary magmas in oceanic island arcs, which are fundamentally basaltic. This implies the systematic recycling of a mafic-ultramafic fraction of island-arc crust back to the mantle. It has been postulated that island arcs delaminate during collision events, the more felsic upper crust "floating" at the surface but the more mafic lower crust and lithospheric mantle sinking into the asthenosphere (*Kay and Kay, 1988*). Geological observations may support this scenario. Although the volcanic-plutonic terranes have undergone severe horizontal shortening and vertical thickening, most are not deeply eroded, nor do they have excessively thick crust. This would be consistent with detachment and removal of the lower crust during tectonic shortening such that deformation of the former upper crust alone achieved a total crustal thickness requiring little subsequent isostatic uplift. Conversely, the metasedimentary belts of the Superior province responded to tectonic thickening with substantially greater and more protracted uplift.

Archean low-grade volcanic-plutonic belts, commonly called "granite-greenstone" terrains, have often been viewed as unique to the Archean. This is a myth. What emerges strongly from this study is the similarity in lithology, structure, and evolutionary development of Archean and Proterozoic juvenile crust. In fact, volcanic-plutonic belts within the Trans-Hudson orogen (1.9 to 1.8 Ga) and the southwestern United States (1.8 to 1.7 Ga) were long assumed to be Archean granite-greenstone terrains until radiometric dating proved otherwise. North America is impoverished in Middle and Later Proterozoic juvenile crust, but the record of crust formation in the Elzevir terrane (1.28 to 1.22 Ga) of the Grenville orogen bears comparison with Archean and Early Proterozoic volcanic-plutonic belts.

A puzzling phenomenon is that many of the Archean provinces, despite their disparate early histories, record major crustal growth between 2.8 and 2.6 Ga, and all experienced important tectonothermal events at that time. As the provinces are rifted fragments of a larger crustal aggregate, one wonders if they have a common ancestry as part of a single Late Archean continent that fragmented in the Early Proterozoic. This question becomes more acute with the knowledge that 2.8- to 2.6-Ga events are also important in many shields outside of North America, giving rise to the notion of a Late Archean global episode of accelerated crustal growth. It is important to determine if such an episode is real, or is a product of biased exposure or preservation.

Early Proterozoic. Complementary to the concept of accelerated Late Archean crustal growth is the apparent lull in crust formation between 2.5 and 2.0 Ga. Until recently, crust of this age was believed to be absent in North America, but recent isotopic studies in the Wopmay orogen and the subsurface of western Canada have dramatically altered this perception (*Bowring and Podosek, 1988*). It now appears that a large part of western Canada is underlain by crust formed in this interval. This finding has implications for the northern Canadian Cordillera. It was previously thought that the vast Yukon-Tanana terrane might be exotic to North America because of evidence that it is underlain by 2.4- to 2.1-Ga crust, thought not to be represented in the craton to the east. Conversely, the crust-formation age of the Yukon-Tanana terrane now provides the strongest argument that it is indigenous to North America, and greatly extends the area inferred to be underlain by crust of this age. These discoveries reduce the apparent episodicity in crustal growth and emphasize the dangers in drawing inferences from the incomplete sample of Precambrian crust that has so far been well characterized isotopically.

The cladogram (Fig. 49) graphically shows that most of the North American craton was assembled between 1.98 and 1.65 Ga. The confluence of Archean provinces occurred between 1.98 and 1.84 Ga, while at the same time Early Proterozoic crust began to be accreted at their margins. In the west, 2.4- to 2.1-Ga crust was accreted to the western margins of the Slave and Rae provinces. In the south and southeast, juvenile crust was accreted to the Superior province at 1.85 Ga (Penokean orogen) and the Nain province at 1.80 Ga (Ketilidian orogen). A vast area of juvenile crust was accreted south of the Wyoming province between 1.8 and 1.7 Ga, and much of the northeastern Grenville orogen involves crust originally accreted to the protocraton at about 1.65 Ga (Labrador orogen). Except for the southeastern terranes of the Grenville orogen, the entire North American craton was consolidated by 1.65 Ga.

The relatively rapid aggregation of Archean and juvenile crust between 1.95 and 1.65 Ga may have been driven by asthenospheric flow converging on a large-scale mantle downwelling (Hoffman, 1989a). Because the mantle would be relatively cold in a downwelling region, continents aggregated there would stand low relative to sea level. The widespread deposition of platformal sediments during this interval, including the 1.7-Ga (Athabasca, Thelon, Sioux) cratonic basins, is consistent with such a hypothesis. As the interval from 1.9 to 1.7 Ga was one of intense orogenic activity and crust formation on other continents, it is conceivable that a supercontinent analogous to Pangea may have been assembled at that time.

Middle Proterozoic. The concept of a mid-Proterozoic supercontinent has implications for the origin of anorogenic magmatism extensively represented in North America between 1.5 and 1.3 Ga. Stationary supercontinents insulate the subjacent mantle, inducing asthenospheric upwellings to form beneath them (*Holmes, 1931*; *Anderson, 1982*). Such upwellings cause mantle melting and crustal underplating, resulting in uplift and crustal melting. These effects will be manifested at the surface by extensive bimodal anorogenic magmatism similar to that observed. The anorthosite batholiths characteristic of the period may be products of fractionation of magma ponded near the base of the crust. Eventually, mantle flow diverging from the head of the upwelling may promote rifting and continental breakup. In North America, the change from predominantly felsic to predominantly mafic anorogenic magmatism at about 1.3 Ga may signify the onset of continental breakup. Rifting along the southeastern and northwestern margins of the craton may have defined the new continental margins that became the sites of collisional events during the Grenvillian and Racklan orogenies. Accordingly, the 1.32-Ga (Seal Lake Group) flood basalts in Labrador may be related to rifting at a margin destroyed in the Grenvillian orogenies, and the 1.27-Ga (Coppermine) flood basalts and related dikes (Mackenzie swarm) may relate to rifting at a northwestern (Poseidon) margin whose evolution is best recorded stratigraphically in the Borden basin of Baffin Island and structurally in the subsurface thrust belt bordering the Beaufort Sea (Fahrig, 1987; LeCheminant and Heaman, 1989).

Late Proterozoic. It has been postulated that the episodic rifting events at the margins of Laurentia between 0.8 and about 0.55 Ga record the breakup of a Late Proterozoic supercontinent (*Bond and others, 1984*). However, continental reconstructions are highly uncertain, and much of Gondwana was being aggregated at that time (Pan-African and Brasiliano orogenies). There is no consensus as to the identities of crustal fragments presumed to have rifted from Laurentia. It has been suggested that Siberia (*Sears and Price, 1978*) and/or Australia (*Bell and Jefferson, 1987*) were separated from western North America, but alternatively, rifting may have occurred in a back-arc setting, implying a more venerable Pacific Ocean basin. It has also been suggested that northwest Africa (*Morel and Irving, 1978*) or western South America (*Bond and others, 1984*) formed the Grenvillian hinterland that rifted from eastern North America. Faunal arguments (*Donovan, 1987*) have been mounted against the latter reconstruction, but the existence of Grenvillian orogens in the west of the Amazonian craton (Rondonian/Sunsas) and in southwestern Africa (Namaqua) enhance the appeal of the *Bond and others* (*1984*) reconstruction. It seems unlikely that the mysterious happenings of the Proterozoic/Phanerozoic transition, including marine geochemical anomalies, paleoclimatic crises, and the inception of skeletal metazoa, can be understood so long as basic continental reconstructions remain so poorly defined.

Concluding remarks. Stirring progress in unravelling the Precambrian tectonic history of North America is being made through the integration of geophysical, geological, and geochemical studies of the shield and the subsurface. The progress is beginning to be commensurate with the importance of the subject. A measure of the progress is the ability to recognize and define the big problems that remain, some of which are outlined in the preceding paragraphs. What links these problems is the growing realization that the Precambrian history of North America can only be understood in the context of the global Precambrian record.

REFERENCES CITED

Allaart, J. H., 1976, Ketilidian mobile belt in South Greenland, *in* Escher, A., and Watt, W. S., eds., Geology of Greenland: Copenhagen, Denmark, Geological Survey of Greenland, p. 120–151.

Anderson, J. L., 1983, Proterozoic anorogenic granite plutonism of North America, *in* Medaris, L. G., Jr., Byers, C. W., Mickelson, D. M., and Shanks, W. C., eds., Proterozoic geology; Selected papers from an international Proterozoic symposium: Geological Society of America Memoir 161, p. 133–154.

Bennett, V. C., and DePaolo, D. J., 1987, Proterozoic crustal history of the western United States as determined by neodymium isotopic mapping: Geological Society of America Bulletin, v. 99, p. 674–685.

Bickford, M. E., 1988, The accretion of Proterozoic crust in Colorado; Igneous, sedimentary, deformational, and metamorphic history, *in* Ernst, W. G., ed., Metamorphic and crustal evolution of the western United States: Englewood Cliffs, New Jersey, Prentice-Hall, p. 411–430.

Blackburn, C. E., and 7 others, 1985, Evolution of Archean volcanic-sedimentary sequences of the western Wabigoon subprovince and its margins; A review, *in* Ayres, L. D., Thurston, P. C., Card, K. D., and Weber, W., eds., Evolution of Archean supracrustal sequences: Geological Association of Canada Special Paper 28, p. 89–116.

Bleeker, W., 1989, New structural-metamorphic constraints on Early Proterozoic oblique collision along the Thompson nickel belt, northern Manitoba, *in* Lewry, J. F., and Stauffer, M. R., eds., The Early Proterozoic trans-Hudson orogen of North America: Geological Association of Canada Special Paper (in press).

Bridgwater, D., Keto, L., McGregor, V. R., and Myers, J. S., 1976, Archaean gneiss complex of Greenland, *in* Escher, A., and Watt, W. S., eds., Geology of Greenland: Copenhagen, Denmark, Geological Survey of Greenland, p. 18–75.

Cannon, W. F., and 11 others, 1989, The North American midcontinent rift beneath Lake Superior from GLIMPCE seismic reflection profiling: Tectonics (in press).

Christie-Blick, N., 1982, Upper Proterozoic and Lower Cambrian rocks of the Sheeprock Mountains, Utah; Regional correlation and significance: Geological Society of America Bulletin, v. 93, p. 735–750.

Committee for the Magnetic Anomaly Map of North America, 1987, Magnetic anomaly map of North America: Boulder, Colorado, Geological Society of America, Continent-Scale Map-003, 4 sheets, scale 1:5,000,000.

Condie, 1981, Precambrian rocks of the southwestern United States and adjacent areas of Mexico: New Mexico Bureau of Mines and Mineral Resources Map 13, 2 sheets, scale 1:1,500,000.

—— , 1986, Geochemistry and tectonic setting of Early Proterozoic supracrustal rocks in the southwestern United States: Journal of Geology, v. 94, p. 845–864.

Cook, F. A., 1988, Middle Proterozoic compressional orogen in northwestern Canada: Journal of Geophysical Research, v. 93, p. 8985–9006.

Davidson, A., 1984, Identification of ductile shear zones in the southwestern Grenville Province of the Canadian Shield, *in* Kröner, A., and Greiling, R., eds., Precambrian tectonics illustrated: Stuttgart, Schweitzerbart'sche, p. 263–279.

Delaney, G. D., 1981, The mid-Proterozoic Wernecke Supergroup, Wernecke Mountains, Yukon Territory, *in* Campbell, F.H.A., ed., Proterozoic basins of Canada: Geological Survey of Canada Paper 81-10, p. 1–23.

Denison, R. E., Lidiak, E. G., Bickford, M. E., and Kisvarsanyi, E. B., 1984, Geology and geochronology of Precambrian rocks in the central interior region of the United States: U.S. Geological Survey Professional Paper 1241-C, 20 p.

Eade, K. E., and Chandler, F. W., 1975, Geology of Watterson Lake (west half) map area, District of Keewatin: Geological Survey of Canada 74-64, 10 p.

Emeleus, C. H., and Upton, B.G.J., 1976, The Gardar period in southern Greenland, *in* Escher, A., and Watt, W. S., eds., Geology of Greenland: Copenhagen, Denmark, Geological Survey of Greenland, p. 150–181.

Emslie, R. F., 1980, Geology and petrology of the Harp Lake complex, central Labrador; An example of Elsonian magmatism: Geological Survey of Canada Bulletin 293, 136 p.

Escher, A., Sørensen, K., and Zeck, H. P., 1976, Nagssugtoqidian mobile belt in East Greenland, *in* Escher, A., and Watt, W. S., eds., Geology of Greenland: Copenhagen, Denmark, Geological Survey of Greenland, p. 76–95.

Fahrig, W. F., 1987, The tectonic settings of continental mafic dyke swarms; Failed arm and early passive margin, *in* Halls, H. C., and Fahrig, W. F., eds., Mafic dyke swarms: Geological Association of Canada Special Paper 34, p. 331–348.

Fahrig, W. F., and West, T. D., 1986, Diabase dyke swarms in the Canadian shield: Geological Survey of Canada Map 1627A, scale 1:4,873,900.

Fraser, J. A., and Heywood, W. W., eds., 1978, Metamorphism in the Canadian shield: Geological Survey of Canada Paper 78-10, 367 p.

Fraser, J. A., Heywood, W. W., and Mazurski, M. A., 1978, Metamorphic map of the Canadian shield: Geological Survey of Canada Map 1475A, scale 1:3,500,000.

Fyson, W. K., and Helmstaedt, H., 1988, Structural patterns and tectonic evolution of supracrustal domains in the Archean Slave province, Canada: Canadian Journal of Earth Sciences, v. 25, p. 301–315.

Gibb, R. A., 1983, Model for suturing of Superior and Churchill plates; An example of double indentation tectonics: Geology, v. 11, p. 413–417.

Grambling, J. A., Williams, M. L., and Mawer, C. K., 1988, Proterozoic tectonic assembly of New Mexico: Geology, v. 16, p. 724–727.

Green, A. G., and 9 others, 1988, Crustal structure of the Grenville front and adjacent terranes: Geology, v. 16, p. 788–792.

Grocott, J., and Pulvertaft, T.C.R., 1989, The Early Proterozoic Rinkian belt of central West Greenland, *in* Lewry, J. F., and Stauffer, M. R., eds., The Early Proterozoic Trans-Hudson orogen of North America: Geological Association of Canada Special Paper (in press).

Hanmer, S. K., 1988a, Great Slave Lake shear zone, Canadian shield; Reconstructed vertical profile of a crustal-scale fault zone: Tectonophysics, v. 149, p. 245–264.

——, 1988b, Ductile thrusting at midcrustal level, southwestern Grenville province: Canadian Journal of Earth Sciences, v. 25, p. 1049–1059.

Harris, C. W., and Glover, L., III, 1988, The regional extent of the ca. 600 Ma Virgilina deformation; Implications for stratigraphic correlation in the Carolina terrane: Geological Society of America Bulletin, v. 100, p. 200–217.

Henderson, J. B., 1985, Geology of the Yellowknife–Hearne Lake area, District of Mackenzie; A segment across an Archean basin: Geological Survey of Canada Memoir 414, 135 p.

Henderson, J. R., 1983, Structure and metamorphism of the Aphebian Penrhyn Group and its Archean basement complex in the Lyon Inlet area, Melville Peninsula, District of Franklin: Geological Survey of Canada Bulletin 324, 50 p.

Henriksen, N., and Higgins, A. K., 1976, East Greenland Caledonian fold belt, *in* Escher, A., and Watt, W. S., eds., Geology of Greenland: Copenhagen, Denmark, Geological Survey of Greenland, p. 182–246.

Higgins, A. K., 1986, Geology of central and eastern North Greenland: Geological Survey of Greenland Report 128, p. 37–54.

Hildebrand, R. S., Hoffman, P. F., and Bowring, S. A., 1987, Tectonomagmatic evolution of the 1.9-Ga Great Bear magmatic zone, Wopmay orogen, northwestern Canada: Journal of Volcanology and Geothermal Research, v. 32, p. 99–118.

Hobbs, S. W., ed., 1984, The Belt: Montana Bureau of Mines and Geology Special Publication 90, 117 p.

Hoffman, P. F., 1987, Continental transform tectonics; Great Slave Lake shear zone (1.9 Ga), northwest Canada: Geology, v. 15, p. 785–788.

——, 1988, United plates of America, the birth of a craton; Early Proterozoic assembly and growth of Laurentia: Annual Reviews of Earth and Planetary Sciences, v. 16, p. 543–603.

——, 1989a, Speculations on Laurentia's first gigayear (2.0 to 1.0 Ga): Geology (in press).

Hoffman, P. F., Tirrul, R., King, J. E., St-Onge, M. R., and Lucas, S. B., 1988, Axial projections and modes of crustal thickening, eastern Wopmay orogen, northwest Canadian shield, *in* Clark, S. P., Jr., Burchfiel, B. C., and Suppe, J., eds., Processes in continental lithospheric deformation: Geological Society of America Special Paper 218, p. 1–19.

Jackson, G. D., and Iannelli, T. R., 1981, Rift-related cyclic sedimentation in the Neohelikian Borden basin, northeastern Baffin Island, *in* Campbell, F.H.A., ed., Proterozoic basins of Canada: Geological Survey of Canada Paper 81-10, p. 269–302.

Karlstrom, K. E., and Bowring, S. A., 1988, Early Proterozoic assembly of tectonostratigraphic terranes in southwestern North America: Journal of Geology, v. 96, p. 561–576.

Karlstrom, K. E., and Houston, R. S., 1984, The Cheyenne belt; Analysis of a Proterozoic suture in southern Wyoming: Precambrian Research, v. 25, p. 415–446.

Kerans, C., Ross, G. M., Donaldson, J. A., and Geldsetzer, H. J., 1981, Tectonism and depositional history of the Helikian Hornby Bay and Dismal Lakes groups, District of Mackenzie, *in* Campbell, F.H.A., ed., Proterozoic basins of Canada: Geological Survey of Canada Paper 81-10, p. 157–182.

Knight, I., and Morgan, W. C., 1981, The Aphebian Ramah Group, northern Labrador, *in* Campbell, F.H.A., ed., Proterozoic basins of Canada: Geological Survey of Canada Paper 81-10, p. 313–330.

Korstgard, J., Ryan, B., and Wardel, R. J., 1988, The boundary between Proterozoic and Archaean crustal blocks in central West Greenland and northern Labrador, *in* Park, R. G., and Tarney, J., eds., Evolution of the Lewisian and comparable Precambrian high-grade terrains: Geological Society of London Special Paper 27, p. 247–259.

Langford, F. F., and Morin, J. A., 1976, The development of the Superior province of northwestern Ontario by merging island arcs: American Journal of Science, v. 276, p. 1023–1034.

Le Cheminant, A. N., and Heaman, L. M., 1989, Mackenzie igneous events, Canada; Middle Proterozoic hotspot magmatism associated with ocean opening: (in preparation).

Le Gallais, C. J., and Lavoie, S., 1982, Basin evolution of the Lower Proterozoic Kaniapiskau Supergroup, central Labrador miogeocline (Trough), Quebec: Bulletin of Canadian Petroleum Geology, v. 30, p. 150–166.

Lewry, J. F., Thomas, D. J., MacDonald, R., and Chiarenzelli, J., 1989, Structural relations in accreted terranes of the Trans-Hudson orogen, Saskatchewan; Telescoping in a collisional regime?, *in* Lewry, J. F., and Stauffer, M. R., eds., The Trans-Hudson orogen of North America: Geological Association of Canada Special Paper (in press).

McLelland, J. M., and Isachsen, Y. W., 1986, Synthesis of geology of the Adirondack Mountains, New York, and their tectonic setting within the southwestern Grenville Province, *in* Moore, J. M., Davidson, A., and Baer, A. J., eds., The Grenville Province: Geological Association of Canada Special Paper 31, p. 75–94.

MERQ-OGS, 1983, Lithostratigraphic map of the Abitibi subprovince: Ontario Geological Survey Map 2484/Ministere de l'Énergie et des Ressources, Québec, DV 83-16, scale 1:500,000.

Moore, J. M., Davidson, A., and Baer, A. J., eds., 1986, The Grenville province: Geological Association of Canada Special Paper 31, 358 p.

Nance, R. D., 1986, Precambrian evolution of the Avalon terrane in the northern Appalachians; A review: Maritime Sediments and Atlantic Geology, v. 22,

p. 214–238.

Nutman, A. P., Friend, C.R.L., and Baadsgaard, H., 1989, Evolution and assembly of Archean gneiss terranes in the Godthåb region, southern West Greenland—Structural, metamorphic, and isotopic evidence: Tectonics (in press).

O'Neill, J. M., and Lopez, D. A., 1985, Character and regional significance of Great Falls tectonic zone, east-central Idaho and west-central Montana: American Association of Petroleum Geologists Bulletin, v. 69, p. 437–447.

Oxburgh, E. R., and Parmentier, E. M., 1978, Thermal processes in the formation of continental lithosphere: Philosophical Transactions of the Royal Society of London, Series A, v. 288, p. 415–429.

Pell, J., and Simony, P. S., 1987, New correlations of Hadrynian strata, south-central British Columbia: Canadian Journal of Earth Sciences, v. 24, p. 302–313.

Percival, J. A., 1989a, Archean tectonic settings in the Superior province, Canada; A view from the bottom, *in* Granulites and crustal deformation: NATO Advanced Study Institute Series, Dordrecht, Kluver (in press).

——, 1989b, A regional perspective of the Quetico metasedimentary belt, Superior Province, Canada: Canadian Journal of Earth Sciences (in press).

Percival, J. A., and McGrath, P. H., 1986, Deep crustal structure and tectonic history of the northern Kapuskasing uplift of Ontario; An integrated petrological-geophysical study: Geotectonics, v. 5, p. 553–572.

Phipps, S. P., 1988, Deep rifts as sources for alkaline intraplate magmatism in eastern North America: Nature, v. 334, p. 27–31.

Poirier, G., Perreault, S., and Hynes, A., 1989, The nature of the eastern boundary of the Labrador trough near Kuujjuaq, Quebec, *in* Lewry, J. F., and Stauffer, M. R., eds., The Early Proterozoic Trans-Hudson orogen of North America: Geological Association of Canada Special Paper (in press).

Powell, D., Anderson, T. B., Drake, A. A., Jr., Hall, L., and Keppie, D., 1988, The age and distribution of basement rocks in the Caledonide orogen of the N. Atlantic, *in* Harris, A. L., and Fettes, D. J., eds., The Caledonide-Appalachian orogen: Geological Society of London Special Publication 38, p. 63–74.

Pye, E. G., Naldrett, A. J., and Giblin, P. E., eds., 1984, The geology and ore deposits of the Sudbury structure: Ontario Geological Survey Special Volume 1, 603 p.

Ramaekers, P., 1981, Hudsonian and Helikian basins of the Athabasca region, northern Saskatchewan, *in* Campbell, F.H.A., ed., Proterozoic basins of Canada: Geological Survey of Canada Paper 81-10, p. 219–233.

Rankin, D. W., and 6 others, 1988, Plutonism and volcanism related to the pre-Arenig evolution of the Caledonide-Appalachian orogen: Geological Society of London Special Publication 38, Oxford, Blackwell, p. 149–183.

Ricketts, B. D., and Donaldson, J. A., 1981, Sedimentary history of the Belcher Group of Hudson Bay, *in* Campbell, F.H.A., ed., Proterozoic basins of Canada: Geological Survey of Canada Paper 81-10, p. 235–254.

Rivers, T., Martignole, J., Gower, C. F., and Davidson, A., 1989, New tectonic divisions of the Grenville province, southeast Canadian shield: Tectonics, v. 8, p. 63–84.

Roberts, S. M., ed., 1986, Belt Supergroup; A guide to Proterozoic rocks of western Montana and adjacent areas: Montana Bureau of Mines and Geology Special Publication 94, 311 p.

Roksandic, M. M., 1987, The tectonics and evolution of the Hudson Bay region, *in* Beaumont, C., and Tankard, A. J., eds., Sedimentary basins and basin-forming mechanisms: Canadian Society of Petroleum Geologists Memoir 12, p. 507–518.

Ryan, B., 1984, Regional geology of the central part of the Central Mineral Belt, Labrador: Newfoundland Mineral Development Division Memoir 3, 185 p.

Schärer, U., and Gower, C. F., 1988, Crustal evolution in eastern Labrador; Constraints from precise U-Pb ages: Precambrian Research, v. 38, p. 405–421.

Schärer, U., Krogh, T. E., Wardle, R. J., Ryan, B., and Gandhi, S. S., 1988, U-Pb ages of Lower and Middle Proterozoic volcanism and metamorphism in the Makkovik orogen, Labrador: Canadian Journal of Earth Sciences, v. 25, p. 1098–1107.

Sharpton, V. L., Grieve, R.A.F., Thomas, M. D., and Halpenny, J. F., 1987, Horizontal gravity gradient; An aid to the definition of crustal structure in North America: Geophysical Research Letters, v. 14, p. 808–811.

Shride, A. F., 1967, Younger Precambrian geology in southern Arizona: U.S. Geological Survey Professional Paper 566, 89 p.

Sims, P. K., Kisvarsanyi, E. B., and Morey, G. B., 1987, Geology and metallogeny of Archean and Proterozoic basement terranes in the northern midcontinent, U.S.A.; An overview: U.S. Geological Survey Bulletin 1815, 51 p.

Sims, P. K., Van Schmus, W. R., Schulz, K. J., and Peterman, Z. E., 1989, Tectonostratigraphic evolution of the Early Proterozoic Wisconsin magmatic terrane of the Penokean orogen: Canadian Journal of Earth Sciences (in press).

Southwick, D. L., Morey, G. B., and McSwiggen, P. L., 1988, Geologic map of the Penokean orogen, central and eastern Minnesota, and accompanying text: Minnesota Geological Survey Report of Investigations 37, scale 1:250,000.

St-Onge, M. R., and Lucas, S. B., 1989, Evolution of the Cape Smith belt; Early Proterozoic continental underthrusting, ophiolite obduction, and thick-skinned folding, *in* Lewry, J. F., and Stauffer, M. R., eds., The Trans-Hudson orogen of North America: Geological Association of Canada Special Paper (in press).

Syme, E. C., 1989, Stratigraphy and geochemistry of the Lynn Lake and Flin Flon metavolcanic belts, Manitoba, *in* Lewry, J. F., and Stauffer, M. R., eds., The Trans-Hudson orogen of North America: Geological Association of Canada Special Paper (in press).

Taylor, F. C., 1979, Reconnaissance geology of a part of the Precambrian shield, northeastern Quebec, northern Labrador and Northwest Territories: Geological Survey of Canada Memoir 393, 99 p.

Thomas, M. D., Sharpton, V. L., and Grieve, R.A.F., 1987, Gravity patterns and Precambrian structure in the North American central plains: Geology, v. 15, p. 489–492.

Trettin, H. P., 1987, Pearya; A composite terrane with Caledonian affinities in northern Ellesmere Island: Canadian Journal of Earth Sciences, v. 24, p. 224–245.

Trowell, N. F., and Johns, G. W., 1986, Stratigraphic correlation of the western Wabigoon subprovince, northwestern Ontario, *in* Wood, J., and Wallace, H., eds., Volcanology and mineral deposits: Ontario Geological Survey Miscellaneous Paper 129, p. 50–61.

Tweto, O., 1987, Rock units of the Precambrian basement in Colorado: U.S. Geological Survey Professional Paper 1321, 54 p.

Van der Voo, R., 1988, Paleozoic paleogeography of North America, Gondwana, and intervening displaced terranes; Comparisons of paleomagnetism with paleoclimatology and biogeographical patterns: Geological Society of America Bulletin, v. 100, p. 311–324.

Van Schmus, W. R., and Hinze, W. J., 1985, The midcontinent rift system: Annual Reviews of Earth and Planetary Sciences, v. 13, p. 345–383.

Van Schmus, W. R., Bickford, M. E., Lewry, J. F., and Macdonald, R., 1987a, U-Pb geochronology in the Trans-Hudson orogen, northern Saskatchewan, Canada: Canadian Journal of Earth Sciences, v. 24, p. 407–424.

Van Schmus, W. R., Bickford, M. E., and Zietz, I., 1987b, Early and Middle Proterozoic provinces in the central United States, *in* Kröner, A., ed., Proterozoic lithospheric evolution: American Geophysical Union Geodynamics Series, v. 17, p. 43–68.

Wallace, H., Thurston, P. C., and Corfu, F., 1986, Developments in stratigraphic correlation; Western Uchi subprovince, *in* Wood, J., and Wallace, H., eds., Volcanology and mineral deposits: Ontario Geological Survey Miscellaneous Paper 129, p. 88–102.

Wardle, R. J., 1982, Geology of the south-central Labrador trough: Newfoundland Mineral Development Division Maps 82-5 and 82-6, scale 1:100,000.

Wright, L. A., Troxel, B. W., Williams, E. G., Roberts, M. T., and Diehl, P. E., 1976, Precambrian sedimentary environments of the Death Valley region, eastern California: California Division of Mines and Geology Special Report 106, p. 7–15.

Young, G. M., 1981b, Upper Proterozoic supracrustal rocks of North America; A brief review: Precambrian Research, v. 15, p. 305–330.

Young, G. M., Jefferson, C. W., Delaney, G. D., and Yeo, G. M., 1979, Middle and late Proterozoic evolution of the northern Canadian Cordillera and Shield: Geology, v. 7, p. 125–128.

Zen, E., 1983, Exotic terranes in the New England Appalachians; Limits, candidates, and ages; A speculative essay, *in* Hatcher, R. D., Jr., Williams, H., and Zietz, I., eds., Contributions to the tectonics and geophysics of mountain chains: Geological Society of America Memoir 158, p. 55–83

Zolnai, A. I., Price, R. A., and Helmstaedt, H., 1984, Regional cross section of the Southern Province adjacent to Lake Huron, Ontario; Implications for the tectonic significance of the Murray Fault Zone: Canadian Journal of Earth Sciences, v. 21, p. 447–456.

Manuscript Accepted by the Society January 31, 1989

Note added in proof: On page 468, the source for the age of 2.02 Ga for diagenetic apatite from the basal sandstone of the Richmond Gulf Group was inadvertently omitted. It is from Chandler, F. W., and Parrish, R. R., 1989, Age of the Richmond Gulf Group and implications for rifting in the Trans-Hudson Orogen, Canada: Precambrian Research (in press).

ACKNOWLEDGMENTS

U-Pb geochronology, refined primarily by T. E. Krogh, underpins nearly every interpretation in this chapter, and unless otherwise stated, all ages cited are based on this method. Space precludes references to all of the hundreds of reports and maps from which the information given was culled. I have tried to compensate by citing recent papers that contain relatively complete bibliographies. I am grateful to all those who supplied preprints, especially Ken Card for his synthesis of the Superior province. Elizabeth Hurdle assisted with the figures. This is Geological Survey of Canada Contribution No. 43488.

Printed in U.S.A.

The Geology of North America
Vol. A, The Geology of North America—An overview
The Geological Society of America, 1989

Chapter 17

The Quaternary

H. E. Wright, Jr.
Limnological Research Center, University of Minnesota, Minneapolis, Minnesota 55455

INTRODUCTION

In designing the contents of this chapter I adopted a personal view, for the subject is highly diversified and seems to be too large for a systematic or comprehensive review. I focus on facets of the subject that have stimulated my curiosity and sense of history and have reinforced my holistic view of environmental change, but I also deal with facets that have prompted specific questions by thoughtful students and colleagues—or, more directly, the more cynical question, "What's so great about the Quaternary?"

Quaternary research involves in one way or another virtually all of the disciplines within the physical sciences, as well as certain aspects of biology, archaeology, and documentary history. Its vigor during the past two decades is illustrated by the introduction of four international journals—Quaternary Research (U.S.) in 1970, Boreas (Nordic countries) in 1972, Journal of Quaternary Science (Britain) in 1982, and Quaternary Science Reviews (London) in 1982—and by the organization of national associations in the United States, Canada, Britain, and several other countries, to say nothing of regional groups like the Friends of the Pleistocene.

But first the source of the strange term Quaternary should be clarified, and why it is spelled with only two r's. In the early nineteenth century the hypothetical geologic time scale was subdivided into four parts, the Primary being represented by the primordial crystalline rocks of the Earth's origin, the Secondary by fossiliferous marine rocks derived from the Primary and then consolidated and commonly deformed, the Tertiary by sediments derived from preexisting rocks and containing some extant fossil groups, and the Quaternary by materials derived from preexisting rocks but not consolidated. When it was acknowledged that crystalline rocks formed at many times in Earth history, the terms Primary and Secondary were used for Paleozoic and Mesozoic and then abandoned. Tertiary has been retained and subdivided on biostratigraphic grounds. The Quaternary includes the Pleistocene and Holocene, and discussion about proper biostratigraphic or chronostratigraphic definitions of boundaries has subsided in the last few years with the realization that radiometric dating may be the most practical basis, at least for the Pleistocene/Holocene boundary, now set by committee at 10,000 radiocarbon years before the present. Many nonstratigraphic geologists (e.g., Quaternary paleoecologists) do not concern themselves with such details (see Watson and Wright, 1980).

As for the spelling, the extra r is retained in Germany (Quartär) and Scandinavia (Kvartär), where a slightly different Latin root is used.

In any case the concept of the Quaternary as an important segment of geologic time worthy of formal designation has come a long way since Flint (1957), long the dean of American glacial geologists, recommended that the term be dropped from stratigraphic nomenclature—but then quietly adopted the term in the title of his next book (1971).

The rapid pace of Quaternary research today reveals new relationships that deserve highlighting. At least half of the references I use in this commentary are less than three years old. It is difficult to follow all of the diversified lines of investigation, especially those developed by paleoceanographers and geochemists. They bring us ever closer to a goal of understanding the complex processes and history of the geosphere/biosphere under changing environmental conditions. One advantage of the Quaternary over older times is that the global geographic relations were much the same as today or can be readily reconstructed—the continents and oceans have not altered their locations much, nor have mountains and plains. The last deglaciation covers the time when many environmental changes were swift and pronounced, and when chronological control is provided by radiocarbon dating. A world dominated by continental ice sheets and a climate and biota greatly different from today's, even far from the ice sheets, changed to one in which environmental changes have been more modest in most areas, albeit significant in revealing the past operation of natural processes. The details available from the study of the last deglaciation provide a framework for considering earlier deglacial phases as well as for understanding how variations in causal factors affect the dynamics of ice sheet/ocean/atmosphere relations and of the biosphere. Therefore I lean heavily on the contents of the recent volume on *North America and Adjacent Oceans during the Last Deglaciation* (Ruddiman and Wright, 1987), but I use an approach different from that used in the synthesis chapters of that book.

As the most recent segment of geologic time, the Quaternary can be approached in a myriad of ways, and all of these involve the accumulated knowledge of the natural and cultural processes

Wright, H. E., Jr., 1989, The Quaternary, *in* Bally, A. W., and Palmer, A. R., eds., The Geology of North America—An overview: Boulder, Colorado Geological Society of America, The Geology of North America, v. A.

of the modern world as a starting point to reconstruct past environments. The present *is* the key to the past, at least as a first approximation. But this is not true unless one understands all the controlling environmental factors affecting a given physical or biological process. For example, in the field of pollen analysis it was usually assumed that every fossil pollen assemblage could be matched by a modern assemblage somewhere, thus providing the basis for reconstructing past climatic conditions. But diligent collecting of surface samples throughout much of North America has shown that modern pollen analogues cannot be found for late-glacial pollen assemblages, leading to the conclusion that certain past combinations of climatic variables are not present today (e.g., different seasonality brought about by differences in the distribution of solar radiation, a factor not previously recognized). Numerical modeling of past climates has helped to explain the apparent anomalies. But more of this later.

I first focus on the importance of establishing a chronology to control regional and global reconstructions of Quaternary history. Then I consider the outstanding stratigraphic records contained in ocean cores and ice cores, especially for the insights they provide with respect to the causes for multiple continental glaciation and its inception in the late Cenozoic. The terrestrial glacial record cannot match the duration nor the detail provided by ocean cores; the loess of China has the greatest potential. Otherwise the terrestrial record is most instructive in suggesting some of the complex dynamics of the Laurentide ice sheet, especially during deglaciation. It also illustrates the dynamic biotic responses to the changing climate as driven by variations in the distributional patterns of solar radiation, modified during deglaciation by the waning influence of the retreating ice sheet. The climatic reconstructions are better understood through numerical paleoclimate models that incorporate both the long-term astronomic and glaciological factors. Such models have not yet explained the shorter term events like the Little Ice Age, but they provide possible tested analogues for the global conditions of the next century—if the human disturbance to the climate regime has the magnitude predicted.

CHRONOLOGY

The geologic record of surficial processes on the earth is fragmentary, for it is largely limited to sedimentary deposits in a few specialized environments (especially those containing fossils) or to landforms produced by erosional processes. Quaternary studies progressed slowly during the first half of the present century, as glacial stratigraphers and geomorphologists interpreted exposures, mapped landforms, and correlated them with one another by extrapolation and interpolation, there being no independent means of dating. Pollen stratigraphers and archaeologists developed correlations on the same basis, and altogether the paleoenvironmental reconstructions were rather loosely founded. The state of the science during these times was effectively summarized by Flint in his first two textbooks (1947 and 1957).

But the essence of history is chronology, and here the late Quaternary in particular has the advantage over all other segments of geologic time. The introduction of radiocarbon dating revolutionized the field; it became possible to relate what happened here to what happened there at the very same time, and it was no longer necessary to use such crude chronologic controls as biologic evolution, which forms the basis for subdividing earlier segments of geologic time through the introduction or extinction of species—processes that inherently take a certain amount of time and therefore provide only an imprecise chronology. Plants hardly evolved at all during the entire Quaternary, as far as the fossil record shows. Even mammalian evolution, which is more rapid, forms the basis of only four land-mammal ages for the entire Quaternary, and the last one may have been initiated by special human intervention at the end of the Pleistocene. Radiometric dating—not only by the carbon-14 method but by the potassium/argon and uranium-series techniques—provides a better basis for chronological correlations. The impact of this technology on the field is apparent in Flint's third general book (1971)—the last American textbook on the Quaternary and all of its ramifications.

Perfection of the radiocarbon dating technique has provided a reliable chronology for the last 40,000 yr for all kinds of geologic, biologic, and archaeologic events. Tens of thousands of radiocarbon dates from dozens of laboratories around the world are now available, many of them reported in the journal *Radiocarbon*. The recent development of accelerator mass spectrometry for radiocarbon dating permits the use of very small samples, thereby enhancing its application to special problems not previously tractable. Continued research reveals certain limitations in its application (e.g., the radiocarbon time scale differs significantly from calendar time as recorded by tree rings or glacial varves). But reliable regional and even global environmental histories can now be compiled, at least for this time range. The award of a Nobel prize to W. F. Libby in 1960 for the introduction of radiocarbon dating was an early recognition of the significance of this development.

Although other radiometric and geochemical methods of dating are used, as recently summarized by Rosholt and others (1989), none has proven as practical as radiocarbon dating for the last Quaternary. The latest radiometric innovation with strong potential for Quaternary time spans ranging from a few years to hundreds of thousands of years, at least for marine corals, is uranium-thorium dating of very small samples, not by the radioactive-decay method but by high-precision mass spectrometry (Edwards and others, 1987). First results, for example, show that the Barbados marine terrace recording the last interglacial maximum (stage 5e) is dated 122,000 to 130,000 B.P., very close to the insolation maximum of 126,000 B.P. calculated from the Milankovitch orbital variations—and an estimate 5 to 10 times more precise than that made by the decay method.

OCEAN CORES

A second breakthrough in Quaternary studies came with detailed analyses of microfossils in ocean-sediment cores, involving both oxygen-isotope ratios as records of paleotemperature and ice-sheet volume, a technique developed by Emiliani (1955), and the mapping of faunal assemblages reflecting past temperature and salinity of ocean waters, an approach perfected by Imbrie and colleagues in the CLIMAP program (1981). Hundreds of cores have subsequently been analyzed to reveal the global signal of continental ice volume and the regional signals of ocean temperature (Mix, 1987).

The ice-volume component of the oxygen-isotope curves depends on the process by which the water molecules with ^{16}O evaporate preferentially over those with the heavier ^{18}O isotope. Although this process is accentuated with higher sea-surface temperatures, the principal effect during glacial periods is the long-time extraction of the isotopically light water from the ocean, with storage in the ice sheets. As the air masses travel to higher latitudes and lower temperatures, the rain and snow that precipitates contains preferentially the heavier molecule. If snow is then stored in ice sheets, the ocean water becomes depleted in ^{16}O, and its resulting isotopic composition shows up in the carbonate shells of foraminifera and other marine microfossils recovered from sediment cores. The isotopic composition of the shells, expressed as the per mil departure from a standard ($\delta^{18}O$), therefore is largely a proxy for the volume of continental ice sheets, so the oxygen-isotope profiles from cores from all the world's oceans have a great similarity. Emiliani's numbering of the glacier intervals (even numbers) and interglacial or major interstadial intervals (odd numbers) is still retained in modern stratigraphic studies.

Because ocean sedimentation is reasonably constant, unlike sedimentation in most land areas, the time scale for ocean cores can be extrapolated beyond the 40,000-yr limit of radiocarbon dating, especially with controls provided by independent time markers. Specifically, uranium-series dating of corals in uplifted marine terraces in Barbados, which are believed to represent the last-interglacial high stands of sea level, are generally dated as about 125,000 B.P., 105,000 B.P., and 85,000 B.P. and correlated with three minima on the oxygen-isotope curves for ice-sheet volume (stages 5e, 5c, and 5a). Further, the last major paleomagnetic polarity reversal in ocean-sediment cores, known from radiometric dates on terrestrial lava flows to be 730,000 B.P., provides another time marker deeper in the cores. With interpolation and extrapolation controlled by these markers, and with assumptions about the duration of lags in ice-sheet growth and wastage, Imbrie and others (1984) in their SPECMAP program tuned the chronology of the oxygen-isotope record of ice-sheet volume to match the prominent variations in the distribution of solar radiation as controlled by temporal changes in the inclination of the earth's axis, the precession of the equinoxes, and the eccentricity of the earth's orbit—the Milankovitch cycles (Fig. 1). Before the era of radiocarbon dating, these orbital variations had been used as a basis for correlating and dating Quaternary geologic and archaeologic events in Europe, especially by Zeuner, whose two books *The Pleistocene Period* (1945) and *Dating the Past* (1952) presented an integrated explanation of Quaternary paleoclimatic history. But these concepts were rejected in detail by Flint as late as 1971 in his textbooks. Zeuner's role has not been recognized adequately in the more recent resuscitation of the theory, perhaps because of his archaeological orientation.

Because the oxygen-isotope profiles of ocean cores convincingly demonstrate that about seven major phases of continental glaciation have occurred during the last 700,000 years (and many more during the earlier parts of the Pleistocene), the continental record of four glaciations in North America and Europe is far from complete. Glacial geologists in the Great Lakes region are confident about the extent and chronology of only the last two—the Wisconsin and the Illinoian. In the most recent compilation the terms Kansan and Nebraskan were dropped in favor of the noncommittal term pre-Illinoian (Richmond and Fullerton, 1986).

The incomplete continental record of glaciation may have resulted not just from the erosion of older tills and interglacial materials by younger ice sheets in the Middle West, where the stratigraphy is best studied, but rather it may be a reflection of the smaller extent of the Laurentide ice sheet at certain times. Such an explanation is supported by the ocean-core record itself, which shows the strongest $\delta^{18}O$ values for the last 700,000 yr (and thus the largest ice sheets) for isotope stages 2, 6, 12, and 16 but much weaker values for isotope stages 8, 10, and 14 (Fig. 2). Thus the Laurentide ice sheet may have been moving back and forth on the Canadian Shield without leaving a record in the Great Lakes region. Alpine glaciation, on the other hand, may contain a more detailed record: for example, the tills of the Yellowstone Plateau, which are closely associated with volcanic deposits dated by the potassium-argon method, have been correlated almost one for one with the marine isotope chronology back to more than 900,000 B.P. (Richmond and Fullerton, 1986, chart 1).

With this interpretation the major continental glaciations culminated at 20,000 B.P. (stage 2, Wisconsin), 150,000 B.P. (stage 6, Illinoian), 430,000 B.P. (stage 12), and 630,000 B.P. (stage 16). If the two older phases represented the Kansas and Nebraskan glaciations, we'd be back to the concept of four major intervals of continental glaciation in the central United States, with the major break between the second and third suggested by the deep weathering and erosion commonly described for the surface of Kansan tills, as well as the shift in orientation of major ice lobes from west of the Mississippi Valley to east.

Independent dating of these older glacial periods is possible only through paleomagnetic chronology and the ages of "Pearlette" volcanic ashes associated with the tills. One ash dated as about 600,000 B.P. is consistent with the stage 16 glaciation (Nebraskan), but another ash is dated about 2 Ma. Kukla (1989) suggests that the sediment associated with the older ash may not be a till but rather a locally derived nonglacial deposit. If it is a till, Kukla goes on to suggest that it may correlate with an anomalously large $\delta^{18}O$ oscillation in North Atlantic core 552A record at about 2.4 Ma and that it constitutes an undifferentiated unit of the Nebraskan till.

If the magnitude of the $\delta^{18}O$ values is a measure of the

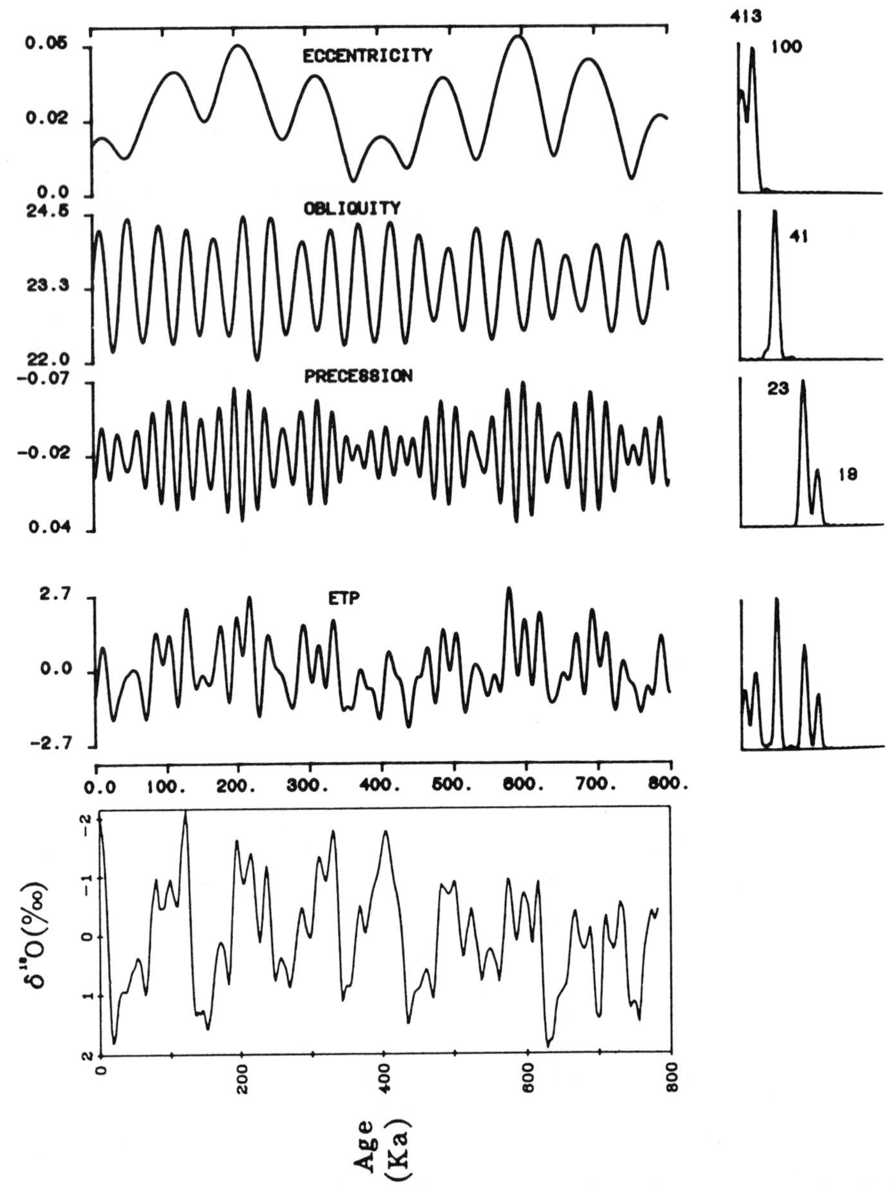

Figure 1. Variations in the three major components of the earth's orbit around the sun for the last 800,000 years, plotted separately and then combined in units of standard deviation (ETP). On the right are variance spectra, with peaks indicated in thousands of years. Below is the composite global oxygen-isotope SPECMAP record combined from multiple records and smoothed, with units of standard deviations from the mean. From Imbrie and others (1984).

extent of continental glaciation, then before about 700,000 B.P. the ice sheets may have been generally much smaller than at any time since (Fig. 2). Periodic expansions every 41,000 years or so reflected primarily the obliquity cycle of insolation, which is stronger at high latitudes (Ruddiman and others, 1986; Ruddiman and Wright, 1987). After about 700,000 B.P. the ice sheets expanded to lower latitudes, where the higher summer insolation of the 23,000 and 19,000 yr precessional cycles had a stronger effect on the glacial regime. The particularly abrupt terminations for stages 2 and 6 may reflect this sensitivity of distended ice sheets. The major uncertainty in the Milankovitch explanations for continental glaciations is the great strength of the 100,000-yr rhythm of glaciation, despite the minimal climatic effects calculated for the eccentricity cycle of this frequency (Ruddiman and Wright, 1987).

With the focus on Milankovitch radiation cycles as the driving force in Quaternary climatic change and continental glaciation (Hays and others, 1976), one may reasonably ask, "What happened to Milankovitch cycles before the Quaternary, and how and when was continental glaciation initiated?" Because Milankovitch cycles are astronomic in origin, it is certain that they have existed in some form throughout geologic time, although

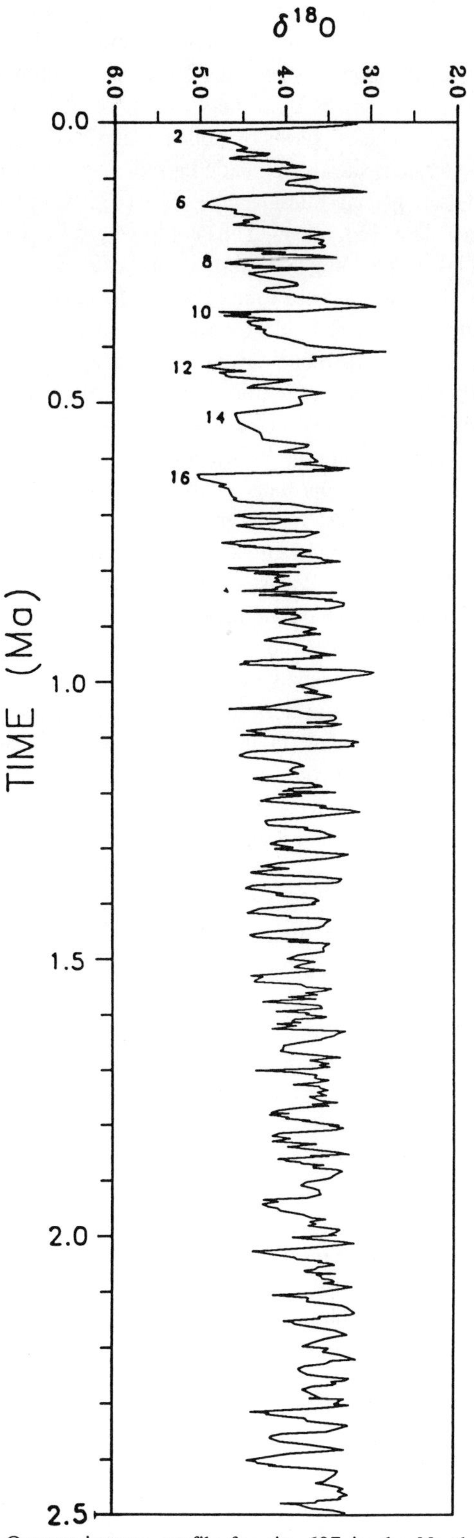

Figure 2. Oxygen-isotope profile for site 607 in the North Atlantic showing the dominance of the 41,000-yr frequency before about 700,000 years ago, and the 100,000-yr frequency after. Note the higher $\delta^{18}O$ values (and thus larger ice volumes) for stages 2, 6, 12, and 16, perhaps representing times when the Laurentide ice sheet extended into the Great Lakes region and beyond. (Unpublished compilation provided by W. F. Ruddiman and M. Raymo.)

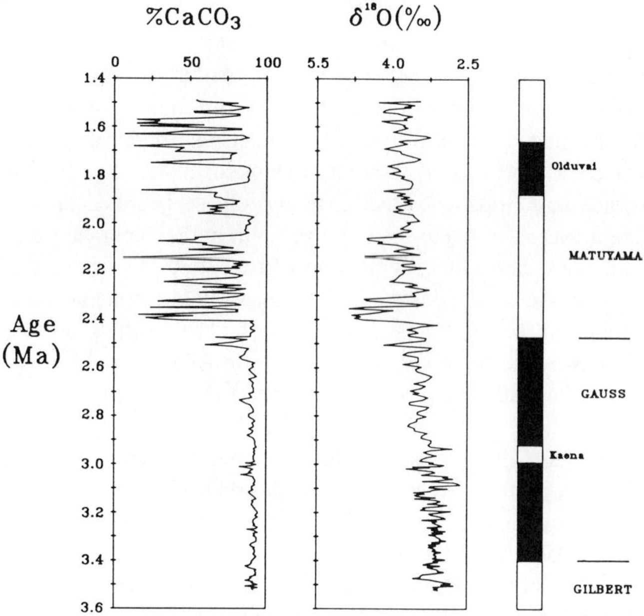

Figure 3. Comparison of oxygen-isotope stratigraphy for benthic foraminifera with carbonate content on the paleomagnetic time scale for core 552A from the North Atlantic. The low levels of carbonate after about 2.5 Ma signal the influx of ice-rafted particles derived from continental ice sheets, which apparently did not border the North Atlantic before this time and probably were very limited elsewhere, according to the small range of the isotope fluctuations. These minor fluctuations may therefore record only ocean temperatures rather than ice volume. From Shackleton and others (1984).

any calculation of their chronology and magnitude is less accurate before a few million years ago. They have been implicated as the explanation for cyclic stratigraphic features in many pre-Quaternary rocks. Where the sedimentary record seems to contain annual laminations, the obliquity, precession, and eccentricity cycles have all been identified (Berger and others, 1984). The existence of geologic evidence for a 100,000-yr cycle in the distant past before the presence of continental ice sheets does not support the attribution of continental glaciation at this rhythm to isostatic depression and delayed recoil of the Earth's crust under the load of ice sheets, as proposed by Peltier (1987).

The inception of Quaternary continental glaciation probably came about in response to hemispheric tectonic factors and associated changes in ocean circulation (e.g., the inception of circum-Antarctic oceanic and atmospheric circulation, the emergence of the Panama isthmus, and the uplift of certain mountain masses and continental interiors). It is best documented not by isotope dating of old tills but by the carbonate stratigraphic record of a core from the North Atlantic Ocean (Fig. 3). This shows that starting about 2.5 Ma the previously high levels of $CaCO_3$ became periodically diluted with ice-rafted noncarbonate components. The marked subsequent fluctuations in carbonate match the oxygen-isotope stratigraphy, and the two types of profile provide independent records of ice-sheet volume (Shackleton and others, 1984; Ruddiman and Wright, 1987). The inferred enlargement of ice sheets about 700,000 B.P. and the shift in emphasis from the 41,000-yr to the 100,000-yr cycle may likewise be a consequence of changes in the pattern of storm tracks that are guided by the course of the jet stream. These changes in turn could be brought about by mountain uplifts (e.g., Sierra Nevada and Himalaya; Ruddiman and others, 1986). If the jet stream was anchored to the north by uplift of the Sierra Nevada, modeling suggests that it would bow to the south across the rest of North America (Manabe and Terpstra, 1974), bringing cool summers to promote ice-sheet expansion. The resulting downstream wave to the north across the North Atlantic could bring warm moist air to nourish the ice sheets on both sides of the Atlantic.

Kuhle (1987) proposes that the uplift of the Himalaya-Tibetan region was the trigger that initiated Quaternary continental glaciation in the Northern Hemisphere. The hypothesis states that the subtropical latitudes receive three times as much radiation as subpolar latitudes, and that at the high altitudes of the Tibetan region the thin atmosphere is highly transparent and thus more sensitive to changes in albedo. Where the area was uplifted to a certain height, the Milankovitch radiational changes lowered the equilibrium line just enough to produce an ice sheet over the entire area, which is larger than Greenland. The consequent reduction in albedo from 20 percent to the 75 to 95 percent characteristic of snow-covered surfaces reduced the energy balance of the earth's atmosphere enough to cool the subpolar areas of the Northern Hemisphere, where the major ice sheets then developed. The validity of the hypothesis depends in part on the great extent of glaciation of the Tibetan Plateau, which heretofore had not been recognized.

The relation of tectonics to the inception of continental glaciation is supported by the increased flux of dissolved salts in ocean sediments during the last 5 m.y. (Raymo and others, 1988). Such an increase can be attributed to the rise in the Himalayas, Tibetan Plateau, and the Andes, which together today deliver much of the dissolved salts to the ocean because of accelerated weathering rates in areas of high topographic relief. Weathering consumes atmospheric CO_2. Also, the calcium released by increased weathering could result in the observed increase in deposition of marine carbonates, further depleting atmospheric CO_2 and thus perhaps explaining the global climatic cooling and the consequent onset of continental glaciation (Raymo and others, 1988). This process, however, does not account for the abrupt increase in atmospheric CO_2 at the end of the Pleistocene recorded in ice cores, for the mountains are still rising.

THE TERRESTRIAL RECORD IN NONGLACIATED AREAS

The failure of continental glacial stratigraphy to match the oceanic record with complete satisfaction has prompted the search for long and continuous stratigraphic sequences in nonglaciated areas. The tectonic basins of the western United States have potential, but results so far have been disappointing, for dry climatic intervals have resulted in nondeposition of sediment or in destruction of the previous record. Quaternary tectonism may also disrupt the record. Even in very long cores it is difficult to distinguish climatic oscillations by pollen analysis (King, 1989).

A few western sites have yielded a sequence covering most of the last two glacial/interglacial cycles (e.g., Clear Lake in California; Adam and others, 1981). Elsewhere in the United States, old lakes providing continuity do not exist. The exception is Pittsburg Basin in southern Illinois, which covers the time from the late Illinoian glaciation to the present (Grüger, 1972).

Long records are more common in Europe. For the late Quaternary, the peat site of Grand Pile in eastern France extends back to the last interglaciation and provides detail that matches the ocean record (Woillard, 1978). Such a sequence is also reported from northern Germany (Behre and Lade, 1986). The tectonic stability of western Europe precludes the existence of deep depositional basins. In Greece, however, the long sequence from Tenaghi Pillippon covers several climatic cycles, although close correlation with the ocean record is inhibited by the absence of radiometrically dated time markers (van der Hammen and others, 1971). What is needed is a long lacustrine record from the monsoonal areas of the northern subtropics (e.g., southern Asia or northern Africa), for here might be the clearest signal of the Milankovitch insolation changes with only a subdued influence of shifts in the mid-latitude jet stream caused by the Northern Hemisphere ice sheets (Prell and Kutzbach, 1987).

The most impressive continental pollen sequence comes from the Bogotá plain in the Columbian Andes, where a 360-m core reveals repeated altitudinal shifts in vegetational zones (Hooghiemstra, 1984). Chronological control by paleomagnetic reversals and by fission-track and K/Ar dating of volcanic ashes permits correlation with the isotopic record of ocean cores back to 3.5 Ma. The sequence is of particular interest because it records the progressive immigration of North American plants to the area after the formation of the Isthmus of Panama; for example, oak, which is dominant in the hills adjacent to the plain, apparently arrived in the area at about 1 Ma.

Loess stratigraphy in nonglaciated areas provides a further opportunity for correlation with the ocean record, not so much in North America as in central Europe, southern USSR, and especially China, where composite sections reaching a thickness of 200 m contain alternating loess and paleosols that match almost one for one the oceanic isotope sequence (Fig. 4), with chronological control provided by paleomagnetic reversals (Kukla, 1989). The inception of continental glaciation at about 2.5 Ma is recorded, as well as the increase in intensity after about 0.7 Ma and the stronger episodes of isotope stages 2, 6, 12, and 16, just as in the marine sequence. The loess was blown from the semidesert regions of northern China and Mongolia, even as it is today in minor amounts. China had no continental ice sheet, so it would seem that the strong winds and arid conditions favoring loess deposition must be attributed to climatic factors related directly to Milankovitch variations, rather than indirectly to the perigla-

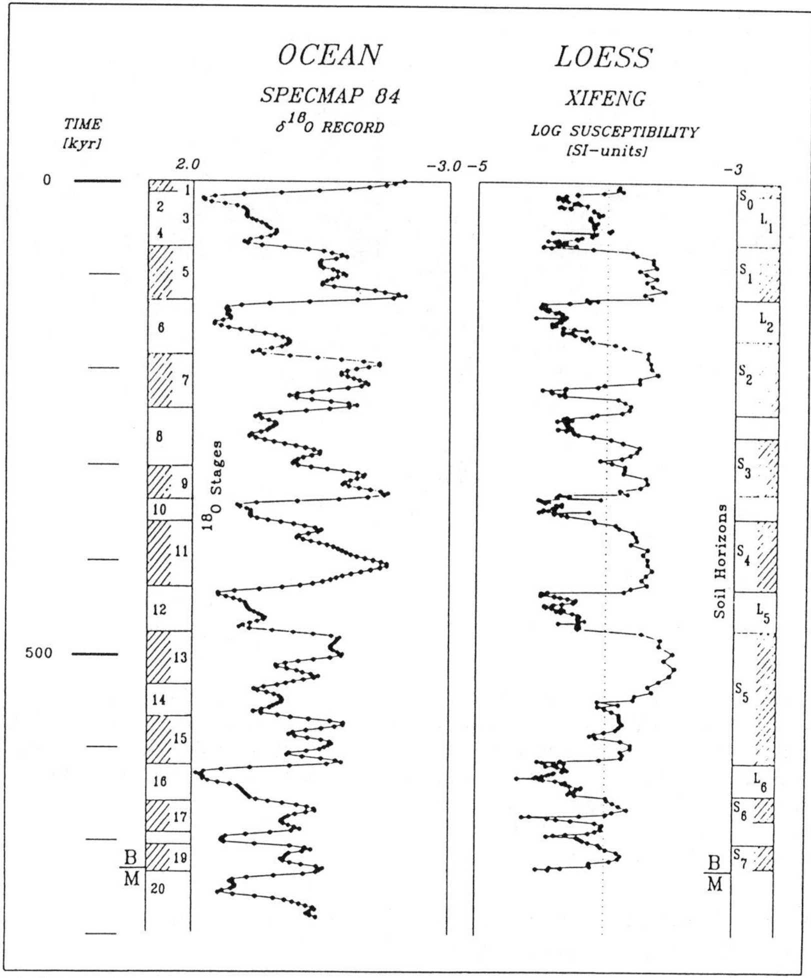

Figure 4. Comparison of the SPECMAP oxygen-isotope ocean record with the magnetic susceptibility of loess (L) and soil (S) at the Xifeng site in China. The SPECMAP time scale, with standard stage numbers, is adjusted to the astronomic frequency. The time scale for the loess stratigraphy is based on thickness weighted by susceptibility. B/M indicates the Brunhes/Matuyama paleomagnetic polarity boundary. From Kukla (1987).

cial effects of an ice sheet, as is assumed to be the case for North American loess, unless the modifications of the waves on the jet stream by North American ice sheets were transmitted to the other side of the world.

ICE CORES

The success of stratigraphic analyses of ocean-sediment cores in the reconstruction of Quaternary climates can be attributed in part to continuous sedimentary records, and thus the possibility of establishing reasonable time scales by interpolation between radiometrically dated marker horizons. It can also be attributed to innovative interpretations of the microfossil or geochemical stratigraphy. Even more impressive global reconstructions are now coming from another type of continuous sedimentation—cores from the interior parts of existing ice sheets, where no ice is lost by melting. This approach, summarized by Paterson and Hammer (1987), dates back to analyses of the Camp Century core in northwestern Greenland. The oxygen-isotope profile was interpreted as a temperature profile, on the basis of Dansgaard's (1964) latitudinal transect of precipitation for North Atlantic coastal stations, which showed a nearly linear increase in $\delta^{18}O$ values with latitude as a measure of atmospheric temperatures. Thus, in the core the abrupt upward change in $\delta^{18}O$ 250 m above the base implied a shift from colder to warmer climate. Because of the difficulty of radiometric dating of glacial ice, the time scale for the ice core was estimated by applying an equation that involves the rate of ice accumulation (snowfall) and an exponential rate of flow as the ice moves downward and outward toward the margin. Results placed the isotope change at about 11,000 B.P., and fluctuations in the isotope stratigraphy were correlated with the Younger Dryas oscillation and with older isotope stages in the ocean-core record, going back to the last interglaciation.

Since then, other ice cores have been obtained in Greenland and in northeastern Canada, showing that the lower parts of these

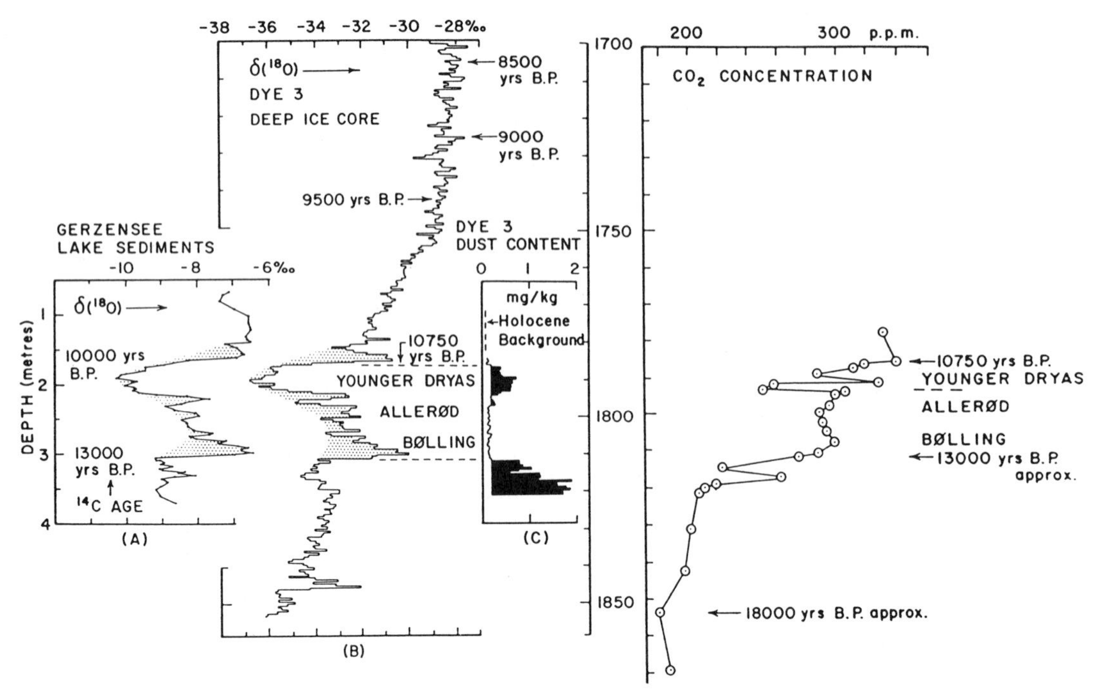

Figure 5. Oxygen-isotope stratigraphy (left) of a portion of the Dye 3 ice core from southern Greenland. The time scale down to 10,750 B.P. is determined from annual layers measured by seasonal variations in oxygen-isotope ratios, acidity, and dust content. Below this level the higher dust content neutralized the acidity variations, and the isotope laminations were obscured by diffusion. The Younger Dryas oscillation is correlated with the oxygen-isotope stratigraphy for a Swiss lake sediment, which is dated by radiocarbon. On the right is a plot of the CO_2 concentrations for the lower portion of the sequence. From Paterson and Hammer (1987).

ice cores were subject to so much lateral flow and deformation that only the upper parts can yield a reliable chronology. However, close-interval analyses of the Dye 3 core from interior southern Greenland for oxygen isotopes, acidity, and dust content reveal annual layers that can be counted back to 10,750 years ago, marking the end of the Younger Dryas interval and the beginning of the Holocene (Fig. 5). The isotopic record of the laminations is obscure below the 8,000-B.P. level because of diffusion, and the acidity values (attributed to aerosols of volcanic origin) were neutralized below the 10,750-yr level because of the higher dust content of the Pleistocene ice—attributed to stronger atmospheric circulation. The Alleröd/Younger Dryas climatic fluctuation so well known in northern Europe and the North Atlantic from glacial and paleoecological evidence is clearly documented, and its termination was abrupt, lasting only an estimated 100 yr (Paterson and Hammer, 1987). The date of 10,750 yr for its termination closely matches the revised figure for this event in the Swedish varve chronology (Stromberg, 1985). The radiocarbon date for the end of the Younger Dryas, on the other hand, is about 10,400 B.P., although this apparent 350-yr discrepancy between the two dating methods probably diminishes to zero by about 12,500 years ago (Björck and others, 1987).

The Dye 3 core also shows an increase from 200 to 300 ppm in the CO_2 content of air bubbles in the ice coincident with the initial warming at 13,000 B.P., with a fluctuation recording the Younger Dryas interval (Fig. 5). This result adds support for the link between climate and atmospheric CO_2—of important concern if CO_2 is doubled in the next century from the present level of 340 ppm.

Whereas the chronology of the Greenland ice cores is reliable only since the last glacial maximum, the stratigraphic analyses by French groups of the 2,083-m core from the Soviet Vostok station in interior Antarctica offers a record covering the last 160,000 yr (Lorius and others, 1988). The chronology is based on rates of snow accumulation and ice flow—in this case the ice is not subject to severe deformation because the site is located in the deep interior of Antarctica, and because the core covers only the upper part of the ice sheet, where the horizontal flow and deformation are limited. The sequence extends back to the penultimate glaciation. Deuterium analyses ($^3H/^2H$) yield the same kind of temperature data as oxygen isotopes. The deuterium content of snow in a transect of decreasing atmospheric temperature from the Antarctic coast to the interior provides the basis for inferring from detailed analyses of the Vostok core a 9°C temperature increase from the last glacial maximum to the Holocene (Jouzel and others, 1987).

The deuterium profile for Vostok (Fig. 6) closely matches the oxygen-isotope profile in a core from the subpolar Indian Ocean (Martinson and others, 1987), as well as cores from the Northern Hemisphere oceans, at least back to 110,000 B.P. Before this time the two chronologies diverge: the last interglacial stage 5e has a duration from 140,000 to 116,000 B.P. in the

Vostok core but from 128,000 to 122,000 B.P. in the ocean-core chronology (Jouzel and others, 1987). These discrepancies cast more doubt on the Vostok ice-accumulation chronology than on the ocean-core chronology, which is closely controlled by the new mass-spectrometric thorium dates for the Barbados marine terraces and is closely matched by the form of the Milankovitch curves. The isotope fluctuations in ocean cores are attributed primarily to ice-volume changes in the Northern Hemisphere rather than to local ocean-temperature changes, so the similarity of the profiles merely demonstrates that the major climatic changes in the two hemispheres are synchronous.

The microfossil assemblages for the Southern Ocean cores imply for the last glacial maximum a temperature depression of generally only 2° to 4°C at the edge of the sea ice (CLIMAP, 1981). The discrepancy between these low values for the Southern Ocean and the 9°C change on the Antarctic continental interior resembles a general dilemma identified for low-latitude regions: CLIMAP (1981) reconstructions show a depression of less than 2°C for sea-surface temperatures during the last glacial maximum, whereas the high mountains in these regions (Andes, New Guinea, New Zealand, Hawaii, East Africa) were so heavily glaciated that a much greater temperature depression is implied. The independent evidence for dry conditions in some of these areas indicates that increased precipitation cannot account for the inferred snowline depression of 800 to 1,000 m. The discrepancy prompted a modeling experiment for the last glacial maximum in which a greater temperature depression was assumed for the tropical ocean surface; results showed an improvement in the comparison, but a substantial discrepancy remains (Rind and Peteet, 1985). This difference between tropical oceanic and high-mountain temperature reconstructions remains a problem.

The CO_2 content of entrapped air in the Vostok core (Fig. 6) provides further evidence for climatic change; its stratigraphy closely matches that for deuterium (Barnola and others, 1987). Northern Hemisphere insolation changes are apparently reinforced by CO_2 changes and transferred by some mechanism to Antarctica, although it is still not clear whether the CO_2 changes are the cause or the effect of climatic changes. The CO_2 content of the atmosphere clearly is related to climate, but the CO_2 reservoir in the ocean is much larger than that in the atmosphere, so the ocean must be implicated in global climatic change. Ocean circulation in turn may be affected by the extent of Northern Hemisphere ice sheets, which themselves owe their initiation to insolational changes in high northern latitudes. The interactions and feedbacks are admittedly complex and incompletely understood, but the stratigraphy of the Vostok core provides an opportunity to place these large-scale forcings in a global model of ice-age development.

GLACIATION

It was formerly believed that the Laurentide ice sheet originated on the highlands of eastern Labrador (actually not highlands but rather a plateau with a scarp on the east) and that it spread in the direction of the moisture source (Flint, 1971). Eastward expansion was prevented by the deep water of the Labrador Sea. Instead the ice spread to the south and west, ultimately filling the Hudson Bay lowland to a height of more than 3,000 m and forming a great dome with radial ice flow, resembling the Greenland ice sheet.

A better explanation for the inception of the ice sheet involves "instant glacierization" (Ives and others, 1975) on both the Labrador and Keewatin areas, as the summers cooled in response to insolation changes. The Hudson Bay area between them may have been covered with perennial snow fields as well, for it was presumably dry land prior to glaciation. The increased albedo over this vast snow-covered area across Canada might be enough to reinforce the cooling trend and lead to ice-sheet growth. The process may almost have started again during the Little Ice Age,

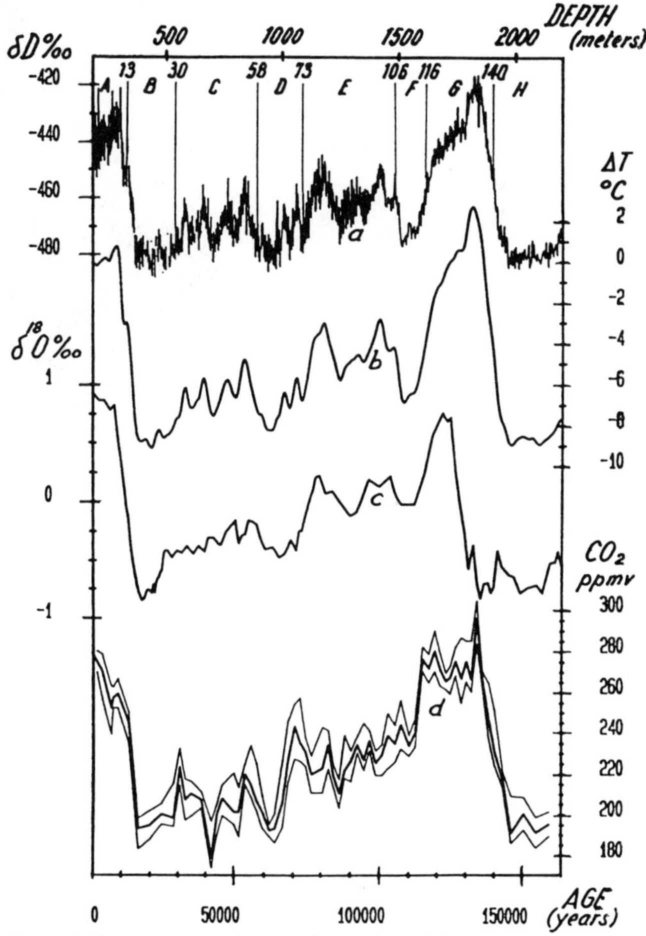

Figure 6. Vostok ice core, interior Antarctica, with time scale determined by a model of ice accumulation. (a) Deuterium profile for 1,500 samples. Climatic stages are lettered, and their ages are indicated in thousands of years. (b) Paleotemperature curve smoothed from deuterium profile. Temperature scale is based on temperature and isotopic ratios for modern snow samples on a transect from the edge to the center of Antarctica (from Jouzel and others, 1987). (c) Marine oxygen-isotope profile, which represents primarily the global ice volume (from Martinson and others, 1987). (d) CO_2 concentrations with uncertainty bands (from Barnola and others, 1987). From Lorius and others (1988).

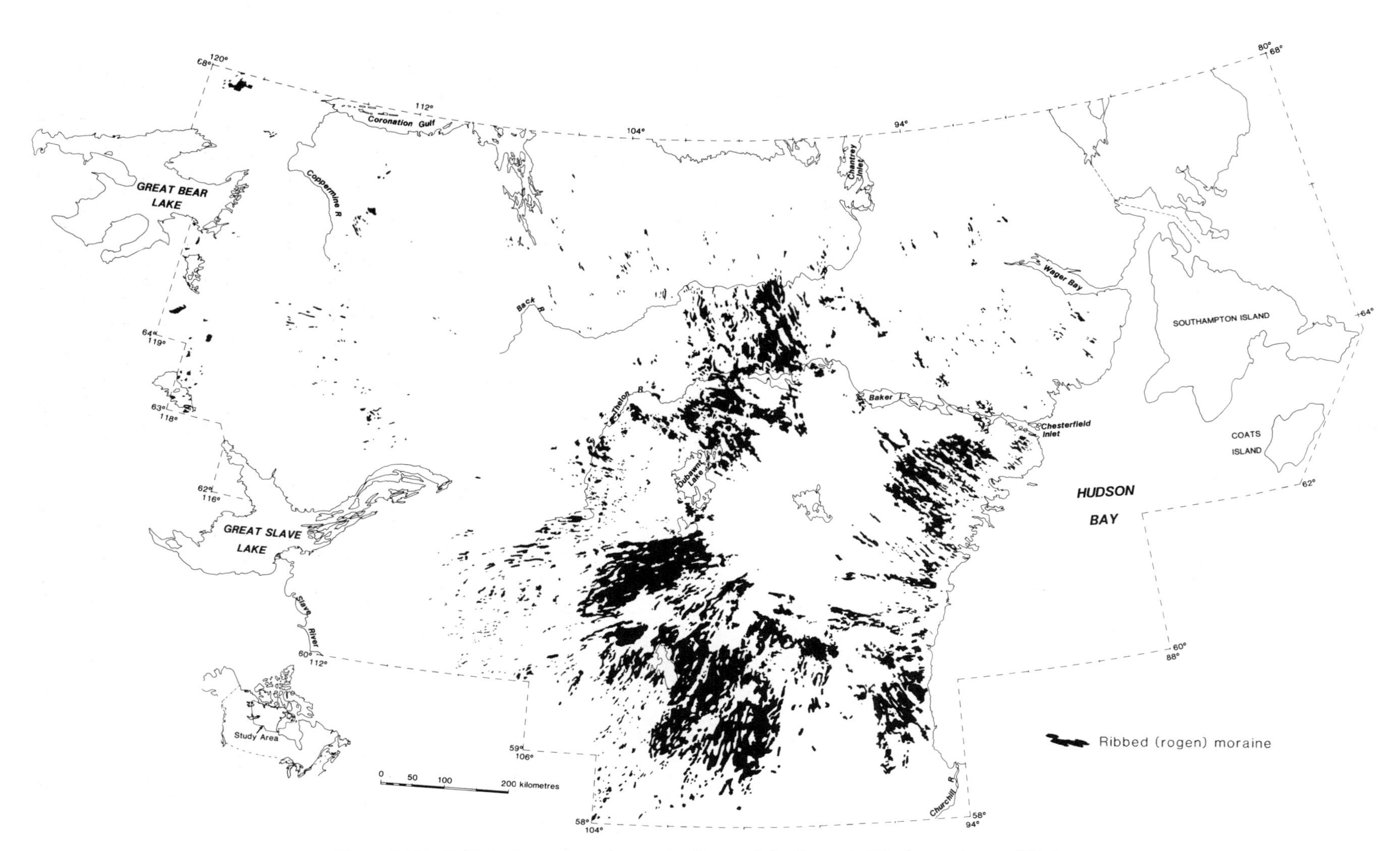

Figure 7. Distribution of rogen moraines centered around the Keewatin District northwest of Hudson Bay, indicating the existence of a separate ice dome in this area. From Shilts and Aylsworth (1987).

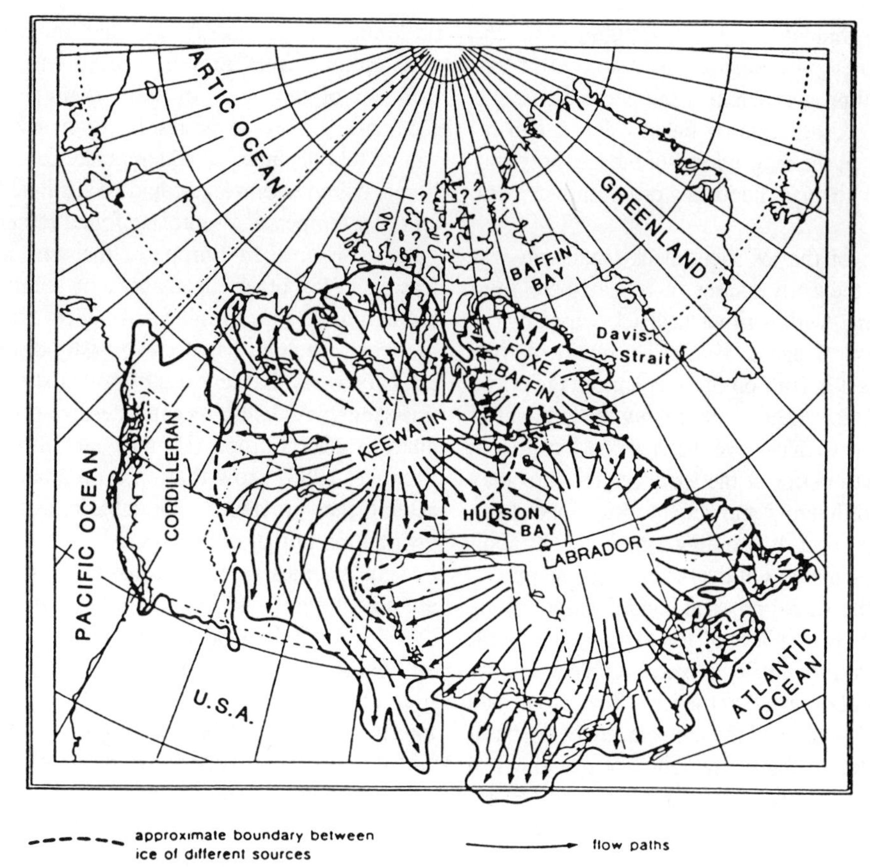

Figure 8. Morphology of the North American ice sheets at their last glacial maximum (Prest, 1984, as simplified by Andrews, 1987).

when perennial snow fields expanded over Baffin Island (Ives, 1962). Was this an "abortive glaciation" (Lamb and Woodroffe, 1970) arrested by the onset of greenhouse warming caused by CO_2 emissions accompanying industrialization of the Western World?

The hypothetical dome centered over the Hudson Bay area implies radial ice flow. But evidence from stone counts and landforms (Fig. 7) shows that ice flowed eastward from the Keewatin district toward Hudson Bay rather than in the reverse direction (Shilts and Aylsworth, 1987). A recent reconstruction recognizes several separate ice domes, especially during deglaciation (Fig. 8). The major discharge was at the southern and western periphery, where the great series of lake basins were excavated near the margin—the Laurentian Great Lakes, Lake Agassiz, Lake Athabaska, Great Slave Lake, and Great Bear Lake (Andrews, 1987). These basins may have been located beneath what was the equilibrium-line altitude on the ice sheet—the boundary on the ice surface between net accumulation and net ablation—where the maximum flux of ice and thus the maximum excavation might be expected, providing that the ice sheet was thawed at its bed and thus able to erode. The massive accumulation of rock debris in the numerous moraines down-glacier from these basins, especially in the Great Lakes area, indicates the magnitude of this process.

The last global glacial maximum is generally dated at about 18,000 B.P.—a figure based on the approximate date for the highest values of the $\delta^{18}O$ curve for ocean-sediment cores, representing the time when the greatest volume of ocean water was stored on the land as glacier ice. This indirect evidence for the timing of the last glacial maximum is more or less supported by radiocarbon dates for the outermost moraines of the Laurentide ice sheet—dates range from about 21,000 to 14,000 B.P. on different ice lobes along the southern margin of the ice sheet (Mickelson and others, 1983). The dynamic nature of the southern margin is shown by the numerous recessional moraines in the Great Lakes area, some of which were formed by readvancing ice after substantial recession and the formation of proglacial lakes. Although these recessional moraines have been correlated at roughly 1,000-yr intervals across the Middle West (Mickelson and others, 1983), asynchroneity in the behavior of adjacent ice lobes can be demonstrated in some cases, notably by the Des Moines lobe in Iowa, which reached its maximum about 14,000 B.P. when the adjacent Superior lobe was withdrawn far to the north. These two ice lobes emanated from the Keewatin and Labrador sectors of the ice sheet, respectively, and the relations illustrate the increasing importance of the Keewatin ice during the late Wisconsin. The instability of the southern ice margin has been attributed by some investigators to glacial surges (Clayton and others, 1985; Dyke and others, 1989) resulting from the buildup of subglacial water pressure over a substratum of low permeability (e.g., clays of proglacial lakes), but the mechanism is difficult to demonstrate on this scale by field evidence, and regional or local variations in the mass budget of the ice sheet may instead reflect changes in air-mass frequency or in other climatic variables.

The eastern margin of the ice sheet at its maximum was fronted in the sea, and the early phases of retreat there were dominated by rapid calving, with positive feedback caused by the attendant rise in sea level (Hughes, 1987). The major marine embayment that developed in Hudson Strait enhanced the draw-down of the center of the ice sheet by steepening the gradient of the ice surface. This process may have affected the location of domes and saddles in the interior of the ice sheet and thus may have accounted for the differential movement of ice lobes from adjacent sectors of the ice sheet. It also may explain the instabilities that led to multiple oscillations of the southern ice margin.

Reconstruction of the varied physical conditions prevailing during recessional phases of the several ice lobes in the Great Lakes region constitutes a difficult glaciological problem. Ice dynamics depend a great deal on whether the ice is frozen to its bed or slides on a thin film of water, and the temperature of the basal ice is controlled by virtually the entire range of glaciological processes and factors—the atmospheric temperature at the ice surface and beyond the ice front, the geothermal flux, the heat generated by the friction of flow, the flow velocity as controlled by sediment load and by ice thickness and rate of accumulation, and the entire hydrologic system. Although bottom conditions can be inferred in some cases from the nature of the erosional and depositional features, estimation of ice thickness and of the elevational profile of the ice sheet during the maximum and recessional phases is highly speculative.

Bed temperatures at the very margin of the ice are particularly critical in the formation of moraines and fluvioglacial features and should be consistent with paleoecological or geomorphic indicators of ground temperature adjacent to the ice front. For example, if the toe of the ice sheet is frozen to the base, the basal ice flow is inhibited, and the internal flow should be upward toward the margin, bringing rock debris to the ice surface and accounting for the buildup of large moraines and stagnant-ice features, as well as for the paucity of subglacial fluvial features. At the same time the mean annual temperatures should be below freezing in the immediate periglacial area, and permafrost features and tundra vegetation should be evident. This is in fact the case in much of the Great Lakes region, where the moraines are generally massive and hummocky and where permafrost features and tundra vegetation indicate a narrow zone of low temperatures.

PALEOECOLOGY

One of the puzzles that developed in the early days of Quaternary paleoecology was the pollen and faunal evidence suggesting that certain late-glacial floral and faunal assemblages cannot be found today—assemblages that are often called disharmonious, although they may have been harmonious with the environment of the day. An early example in pollen analysis in Denmark seemed to be resolved when Iversen (1936) demonstrated that the unexpected temperate component in an otherwise boreal pollen assemblage could be attributed to redeposition from an older temperate assemblage found in nearby till, eroded from older sediments. In Europe at the time it was not considered feasible to test other explanations by searching systematically for modern analogues for all fossil pollen assemblages, because the modern vegetation has been so vastly disturbed for many thousands of years that any use of pollen surface samples would be misleading. Actually, recent extensive compilations of core-top analyses over Europe (Huntley and Birks, 1983; Huntley and Prentice, 1988) show that on a broad scale the modern pollen assemblages provide a reasonable representation of the natural distribution of major tree types.

In America an even stronger mixture of boreal and temperate pollen types was found in a study in Michigan by Andersen (1954), and following Iversen he opted also for redeposition, without searching for evidence from the till. But other explanations are possible (viz., distant transport of pollen from temperate forests, or vegetation associations not seen today).

I remember that John Hack, who has always been given to critical thinking, suggested to me that it wasn't very scientific to reconstruct past climate from pollen diagrams without at least searching for modern analogues. So in a small way I attempted this in a project in New Mexico and failed to find the anticipated analogues (Bent and Wright, 1963). In the Near East I was somewhat more successful (Wright and others, 1967; Wright, 1967). At about the same time it was pointed out in New England that the pollen assemblage in a core-top sample of lake sediments had only a slight resemblance to the vegetation of the immediate area, so that if the relations were applied to the pollen assemblage of the early Holocene pine zone, any climatic interpretation would be "without substance" (Davis, 1963). It was clear, however, that a large network of surface samples over much of the continent would be necessary to resolve any questions about modern analogues or about representivity.

The problem of agricultural disturbance perceived in Europe was much less critical in North America, where significant land settlement has been limited to the last 100 to 250 years. In any case, in the central and eastern parts of the continent the disturbance level is readily recognized in pollen diagrams by the increase in ragweed, as McAndrews (1966) convincingly demonstrated in Minnesota. Thousands of surface samples have since been analyzed for North America, principally from lakes (for a better comparison with lake-sediment pollen diagrams) but also from moss polsters and soil surfaces where lakes are not available. Transfer functions and response surfaces have been calculated in attempts to quantify the climatic reconstructions (Webb and others, 1987). The results show that late-glacial pollen assemblages in particular have no modern analogues. With no positive evidence for redeposition nor for distant transport of pollen from other vegetation regions, paleoecologists have been forced to recognize either that past climates must have been different in certain respects to permit the mixed combinations, or that the severe disruptions and distant migrations during glacial times resulted in fortuitous assemblages of early successional species, with slower immigrants arriving later to make up the modern vegetation—the hypothesis termed migrational lag.

Perhaps the most striking example of a pollen assemblage that has no modern analogue is the late-glacial spruce pollen zone of the Middle West, which lacks pine pollen (except for the minor amount that can be attributed to distant transport from the east) but contains temperate types like ash, oak, and ironwood as well as some prairie types like *Artemisia* and *Ambrosia* (Amundson and Wright, 1979; Overpeck and others, 1985). The boreal spruce forest of today contains jackpine except in Labrador and Alaska where, however, the temperate trees and prairie herbs do not occur.

To explain the mixed assemblages in climatic terms I expanded a suggestion of Bryson and Wendland (1967) that the strong seasonal contrasts existing today in the Middle West were actually subdued during the glacial period by the presence of the massive ice sheet in the northern half of the continent—a great white highland generating a cold air mass in summer that cooled the periglacial region and inhibited the invasion of moist maritime air from the southeast (Wright, 1984a). In winter the ice sheet, which terminated in the north at the Arctic coast and in its center may have been 3,000 m high, provided a substantial barrier to the southward spread of Arctic air generated in the polar regions. Today, without the ice sheet, such air frequently breaks out across the western Canadian interior to bring cold blizzards to the Great Plains. In glacial times the Arctic air that came off the ice sheet may have been warmed adiabatically as it descended, just as is the case with Chinook winds of the modern Rocky Mountains, bringing moderate temperatures and dry conditions to the adjacent plains. The cool summers could account for the expansion of spruce to the southern states, and at the same time keep the mean annual temperatures in the periglacial area low enough to account for permafrost features on the Wyoming plains and in North Dakota and Wisconsin (Péwé, 1983). The absence of extremely low winter temperatures could account for the northerly distribution of ash and the other hardwoods, which are limited today by such extreme cold. This explanation could be applied to the mixed assemblages of fossil vertebrates, which contain components that today have separate eastern, boreal, and prairie ranges (Graham and Mead, 1987). Redeposition in these cases does not seem to be possible, and migrational lag seems unreasonable. Difference in the seasonality of climate is a feasible explanation.

A corollary to this explanation comes with a consideration of what might happen to the cold winter air trapped north of the ice sheet. It could escape eastward and then south into the North Atlantic area, thereby helping to explain the cold waters documented by the foraminiferal evidence of ocean sediment cores during the glacial maximum. It could also escape across the plains of Siberia, and even of Europe, for permafrost in Eurasia extended far to the south during the glacial period. Numerical modeling of climate at the glacial maximum supports the concept of the eastward spread of cold Arctic air, because a branch of the westerly jet stream was located north of the ice sheet, thereby displacing the polar easterlies that prevail there today (Kutzbach, 1987). This westerly air flow was also intensified by a strong anticyclonic circulation that developed around the ice sheet.

MEGAFAUNAL EXTINCTIONS

One of the consequences of the rapid climatic and vegetational change of 12,000 to 10,000 years ago may have been the extinction of much of the Pleistocene megafauna in North and South America—at least in one view. The other view is that the withdrawal of the Laurentide ice sheet from the Rocky Mountain front allowed the immigration of human hunters to the area south of the ice sheet—in fact rapidly all the way to the southern end of South America—to decimate the large herbivores, which previously had no such an efficient predator. This subject has been debated widely since Paul Martin defined the issue at a symposium in the 1965 INQUA Congress (Martin and Wright, 1967), and it was enlarged and debated more broadly in a subsequent volume (Martin and Klein, 1984).

In some respects the issue has reached an impasse, because the same argument is made in the defense of both viewpoints (viz., the close temporal correlation among extinction, climatic change, and human immigration). Considering the errors inherent in radiocarbon dating and the difficulty in finding datable material in just the right context, this dilemma may not be solved. The timing for the opening of the Alberta corridor is only vaguely set, although it is clear that human populations south of the ice front virtually exploded about 12,000 B.P. with the advent of the Clovis culture (Bonnichsen and others, 1987), which terminated about 1,000 year later, about the same time as the major extinction of the megafauna and the most rapid environmental change.

Numerous mechanisms for both scenarios have been offered. Proponents of the cultural side offer several arguments: the lack of defensive behavior by game animals genetically unfamiliar with human hunters, the evidence for game drives and other massive kills, the lack of major extinctions associated with previous glacial terminations, and the demonstrated association of extinctions with human immigration elsewhere in the world, particularly on islands (e.g., New Zealand, Hawaii, Madagascar). On the environmental side are the equally persuasive arguments that the large herbivores in question had slow rates of reproduction and were unable to adjust genetically to rapid changes in the nature of their food supply, as the more highly diversified and more open "disharmonious" vegetational mosaic changed to the Holocene structure of more discrete zones including closed forests. One might say with some cynicism that most of the arguments are strong because they are basically untestable with field evidence and therefore are likely to survive. Nonetheless, the extent of research and of ecological and archaeological imagination that has been devoted to this subject in the two decades between the two extinction volumes stimulated by Martin demonstrates the vitality and challenge of one of the more perplexing problems in Quaternary studies.

PALEOCLIMATE MODELS AND THE GEOLOGIC RECORD

A recent development in Quaternary studies is the application of numerical models of the general atmospheric circulation, of the type used in long-range weather forecasting and adapted to such problems as predicting the climate of the next century if atmospheric CO_2 is doubled. Global boundary conditions used in the model for different times in the past are based on the insolation values calculated from the Milankovitch orbital variations and on the geologic evidence for the area and height of the ice sheets, the sea-surface temperatures, the areas of continents under conditions of lowered sea level, albedo values inferred for the ice sheets or vegetation cover, and the CO_2 content of the atmosphere. Results are expressed for July and January for temperature, precipitation, atmospheric pressure, and wind strength and direction, and the patterns provide an impression of the global influence of the two main driving forces—insolation changes and the shifting size of the ice sheets, the latter a manifestation of prior insolation changes (Kutzbach, 1987).

The mechanism for many Quaternary environmental changes is becoming apparent through the results of these model experiments (COHMAP, 1988). Not much is known of the details of ice-sheet initiation and expansion to its maximum, because the geologic evidence on the continents is obscured by later events. But it is clear from the long-range similarity of the glaciation/interglaciation patterns to the Milankovitch cycles that the last glaciation was initiated as a result of reduction of summer insolation at high northern latitudes. The ice sheets reached their maxima around 20,000 to 18,000 B.P. The combined Laurentide/Cordilleran ice sheet in North America was probably at least 3,000 m high, and it provided a substantial barrier to the eastward course of the upper-atmosphere westerly jet stream, which today enters the continent in the Pacific Northwest. The result was a bifurcation of the jet stream, with the northern branch circumventing the ice sheet in Arctic Canada and returning south into the North Atlantic, where expanded sea ice was the manifestation (Fig. 9). The southern branch of the jet stream was displaced to the south of its present course and guided storms over what is now the desert Southwest, causing the well-documented expansion of pluvial lakes. Although increased winter rains were probably the primary cause for lake expansion, a reduction in summer evaporation occasioned by increased cloudiness may have been a contributing factor. In any case, summer temperatures were certainly lower, permitting the expansion of scrub vegetation and even trees in the arid basins (Van Devender and others, 1987).

While the American Southwest was wet during the last glacial maximum, the Pacific Northwest was dry and cold. Evidence comes primarily from the nature of the vegetation, which was characterized by spruce parkland rather than the modern type of closed forest of mixed conifers (Barnosky and others, 1987). Lake levels were low at this time rather than high. Apparently the development of anticyclonic circulation around the North American ice sheet brought easterly flow of air across the Great Plains to the Pacific Northwest, in contrast to the moist on-shore winds that prevail there today in the Cascade Mountains (Fig. 9). The existence of strong anticyclonic winds at a later date during ice wastage is shown by the occurrence of parabolic dunes in northern Alberta (David, 1981) and also in southern Quebec (Filion, 1987). During the glacial maximum these winds were apparently not so strong, although they were common enough to produce the observed vegetation patterns. Instead, the strong winds came from the north-northwest, perhaps funneled down the sag between the Laurentide and Cordilleran ice sheets at the Rocky Mountain front; they produced the ubiquitous (although poorly dated) deflation landforms, sand dunes, and loess deposits of the northern and central Great Plains (Kutzbach and Wright, 1985).

The northern plains were also cold during the glacial maximum, according to evidence from permafrost features in the Wyoming plains and North Dakota; the low mean annual temperature may have been a manifestation of low summer temperatures rather than especially cold winters, according to the paleontological evidence (see above).

The pervading influence of the North American ice sheet on the climate, vegetation, hydrology, and landforms of the area to the south during the glacial maximum diminished as the ice receded in response to increasing summer insolation, which was to culminate about 10,000 years ago. But the climatic response was somewhat delayed because of the vast amount of ice to be melted. The conflicting forces of periglacial summer cooling and insolational summer warming resulted in climatic patterns that produced the disharmonious flora and fauna of the late-glacial phase and perhaps contributed to the great extinctions of the mammalian megafauna. Supporting evidence comes from the fact that the late-glacial transformation to temperate vegetation occurred first in the Pacific Northwest (and Alaska), "upwind" of the ice sheets, as early as 12,000 B.P., whereas the periglacial climatic influence persisted in the Great Lakes region as late as 8,000 B.P., because the Laurentide ice sheet still covered central Canada and influenced the summer climate to the south.

Overall, most of the paleoecological action on the continent was between 12,000 and 10,000 B.P. (Fig. 10). Prior to this time the southern ice front had been retreating for several thousand years; the fluctuations in the retreat represented by numerous recessional moraines may have been a result of thinning of the ice and its greater sensitivity to changes in the mass budget. By 12,000 B.P. the retreat accelerated, and the marginal fluctuations were more pronounced, perhaps involving surging. The vegetation began to shift more rapidly as the spruce forest was replaced by oak and other hardwoods in the central United States and by pine closer to the retreating ice margin. The precipitous transformation of spruce forest to pine forest in the Minnesota/Wisconsin area 10,000 years ago occurred over an interval that may have been as short as 50 yr (Amundson and Wright, 1979), prompting the hypothesis that this was a time of great conflagrations precipitated by increased lightning ignitions accompanying a change in climatic patterns, specifically the increased incidence of westerly air flow characteristic of subsequent time. The contrast in vegetation patterns between 12,000 and 10,000 B.P. for the eastern half of the continent is clearly illustrated by the sequential maps for major pollen types (Fig. 10) and by related maps of pollen assemblages (Jacobson and others, 1987). In the Great Lakes area the zonal late-glacial pattern, controlled largely by the periglacial climatic influences, shifted gradually to a meridional Holocene pattern reflecting the increased flow of dry westerly air, which reached its maximum expression about 7,000 years ago, when the prairie/forest border was located at least 150 km east of its present position.

On a global scale the patterns of insolation controlled by the Milankovitch curves can best be seen in the monsoonal areas of Africa and southwest Asia, where now-desert basins were occupied by lakes between 12,000 and 6,000 B.P. and where the vegetation and animal life were more abundant than they are today (Fig. 8). These conditions are the reverse of those in most desert basins in the American Southwest, where pluvial lakes prevailed during the glacial maximum prior to 11,000 B.P. (Fig. 11). This difference was a conundrum in paleoclimatic reconstructions until numerical model experiments for 9,000 B.P., close to the time of maximum insolation at middle latitudes of the Northern Hemisphere, showed that interior Asia and Africa had summer temperatures several degrees warmer than today, causing enhanced monsoonal rainfall in southern Asia and North Africa (Kutzbach and Otto-Bliesner, 1982; COHMAP, 1988). Just why the pluvial conditions there were not temporally symmetrical around the insolation maximum at about 10,500 B.P. is unclear—there may be some distant effect of Northern Hemisphere periglacial circulation conditions (Prell and Kutzbach, 1987), or perhaps the global influence of a different atmospheric CO_2 content.

In the American Southwest, plant fossils from radiocarbon-dated packrat middens provide more detailed evidence for past climatic conditions than do expanded lakes (Spaulding and Graumlich, 1986). In the Sonoran Desert area of southern Arizona and adjacent Mexico the full-glacial pluvial conditions with winter rains supported woodland vegetation as well as expanded lakes. Farther north in the Mohave Desert area, in the shadow of the Sierra Nevada, conditions were less wet and were colder than those in the Sonoran Desert area, and as the storm tracks shifted north in late-glacial times the pluvial lakes and diagnostic steppe shrubs (supported by winter rains) diminished in extent as early as 15,000 B.P., leading to Holocene desert conditions. In the Sonoran Desert area, however, the full-glacial winter rains were replaced by late-glacial summer rains as the radiation maximum was approached, with moisture both from the Gulf of California and the Gulf of Mexico.

However, this reconstruction for the Southwest is not accepted by Van Devender and others (1987), who suggest that the periglacial climatic influence persisted well into the Holocene. Earlier controversies on Southwestern climatic history, concerned with whether pluvial lakes resulted from increased precipitation or decreased temperature, have been settled in favor of precipitation, in part because of the mechanism shown by climate modeling. The present controversy, however, although based on different interpretations of the wealth of paleoecological data provided by packrat middens, is not aided by existing paleoclimate models, which have a grid spacing too coarse to resolve all the climatic conditions for this topographically diverse area.

A direct response of vegetation to radiational changes is also suggested for eastern North America after the complete wastage of the ice sheet. As summers cooled in the Middle West following the period of high summer radiation, the prairie/forest border retreated westward, lake levels rose, spruce expanded southward, and the great peatlands of northern Minnesota began to form. At the same time in the Southeast, as winter temperatures rose, southern pines expanded at the expense of oaks. The temperature responses to radiation changes in these regions seem to be more conspicuous than the monsoonal moisture signal.

SHORT-TERM CLIMATIC CHANGES

A major emphasis in Quaternary paleoclimatic studies has been on the larger glacial/interglacial cycles, because of the wealth of stratigraphic data from ocean and ice cores as well as from glacial and paleoecological studies on land, and because of efforts to elucidate or document the Milankovitch radiation cycles. Any climatic fluctuation of a duration shorter than the precession cycle of about 20,000 years cannot be easily explained by Milankovitch processes. One such phenomenon that is currently under intense study is the so-called Younger Dryas oscillation. It can be viewed as a 1,000-yr interruption of the late-glacial warming trend that had begun by 13,000 B.P.—called the Bölling/Alleröd interval in western Europe, where colonization of the deglaciated terrain by trees was interrupted by the return of tundra at the same time as the Scandinavian and Scottish glaciers readvanced (Björck and Hakansson, 1982; Watts, 1980). The Younger Dryas is manifested in the oxygen-isotope stratigraphy of lake sediments in Switzerland and the Dye-3 ice core from southern Greenland (Fig. 5). Polar foraminifera once again dominated in the North Atlantic almost to their full-glacial distribution (Ruddiman and McIntyre, 1981). Tundra returned to maritime Canada (Mott and others, 1986), and spruce and other boreal conifers increased in Ohio after their temporary replacement by hardwoods like ash, ironwood, and oak (Shane, 1987).

The dating of the Younger Dryas episode varies from one area to another, probably more as a result of normal errors in radiocarbon dating and the selection of the particular stratigraphic horizons to be dated than a result of asynchroneity in the inception or termination of the event. The interval 11,000 to 10,000 B.P. encompasses most estimates.

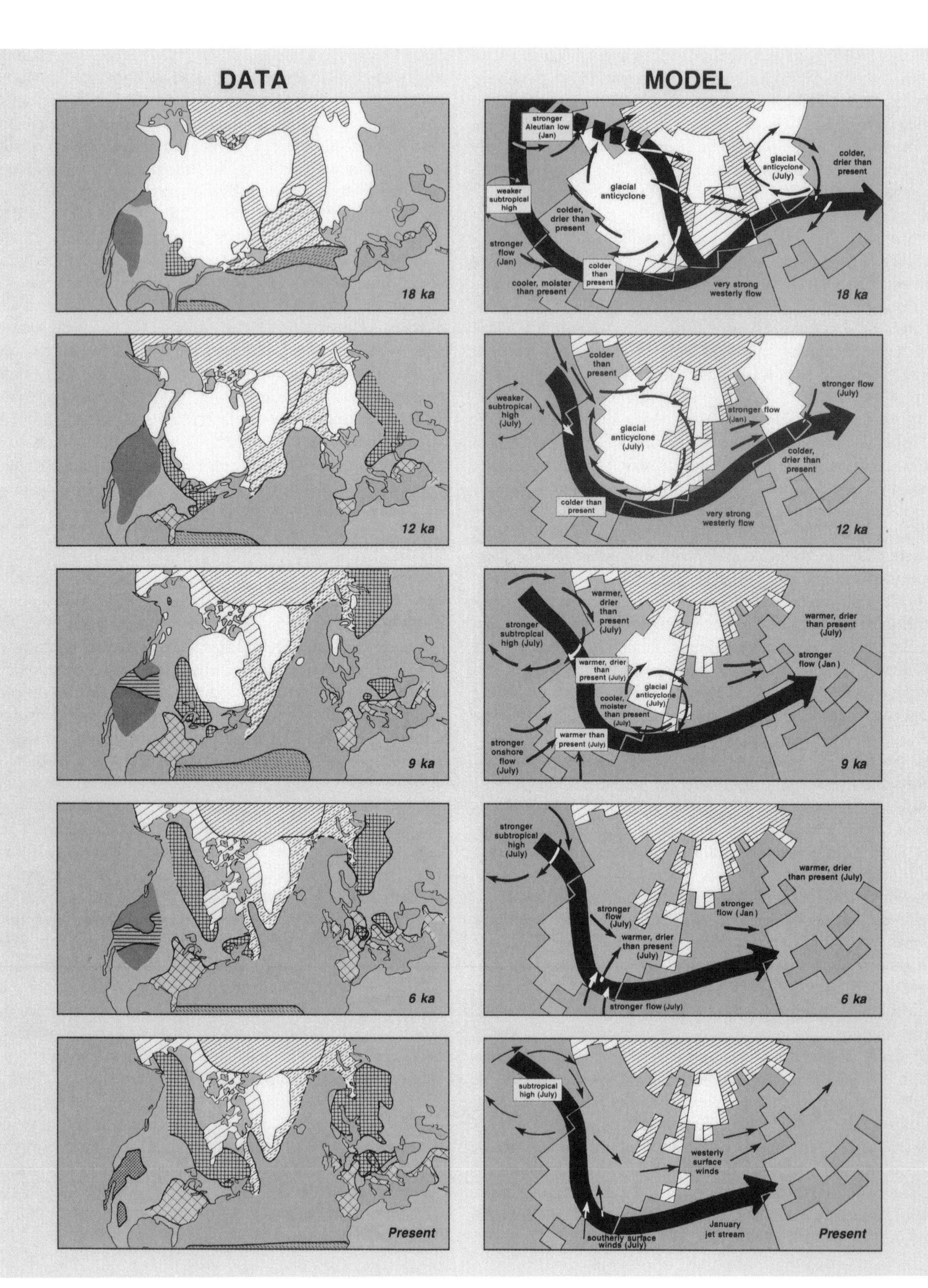

DATA
MODEL
18 ka
stronger Aleutian low (Jan)
weaker subtropical high
glacial anticyclone
colder, drier than present
stronger flow (Jan)
cooler, moister than present
colder than present
very strong westerly flow
glacial anticyclone (July)
colder, drier than present
18 ka
12 ka
colder than present
weaker subtropical high (July)
glacial anticyclone (July)
stronger flow (Jan)
stronger flow (July)
colder, drier than present
colder than present
very strong westerly flow
12 ka
9 ka
stronger subtropical high (July)
warmer, drier than present (July)
warmer, drier than present (July)
glacial anticyclone (July)
cooler, moister than present (July)
warmer than present (July)
stronger onshore flow (July)
warmer, drier than present (July)
stronger flow (Jan)
9 ka
6 ka
stronger subtropical high (July)
stronger flow (July)
warmer, drier than present (July)
stronger flow (Jan)
warmer, drier than present (July)
stronger flow (July)
6 ka
Present
subtropical high (July)
westerly surface winds
southerly surface winds (July)
January jet stream
Present

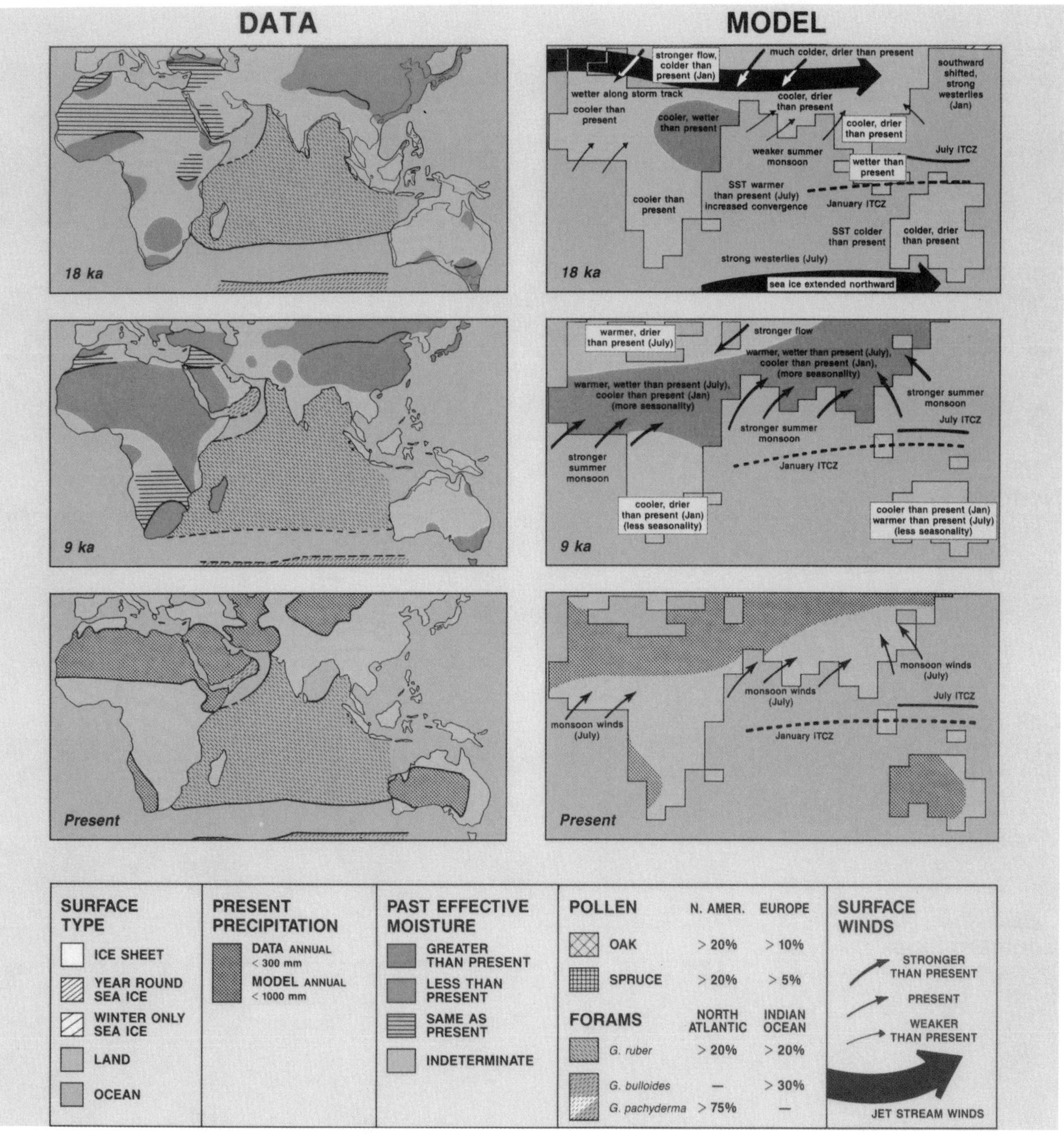

Figure 9. Comparison of field data with results of paleoclimatic simulations for certain time intervals from 18,000 years ago (18 ka) to the present. The data maps show the diminishing extent of the ice sheets and sea ice during deglaciation, the expansion of spruce and oak forests (based on pollen evidence), the distribution of diagnostic foraminifera in the oceans, and the extent of relatively dry and moist areas compared to the present. The model maps show the shifting position of the jet stream and surface winds for summer or winter, as well as areas of enhanced monsoonal rains in Africa and southern Asia. During the glacial maximum the jet stream split around the North American ice sheet; the southern branch brought rains and high lake levels to the American Southwest, and the northern branch brought cold air to the North Atlantic at the same time that the glacial-anticyclonic circulation caused cold dry air to prevail in the Pacific Northwest. From COHMAP (1988).

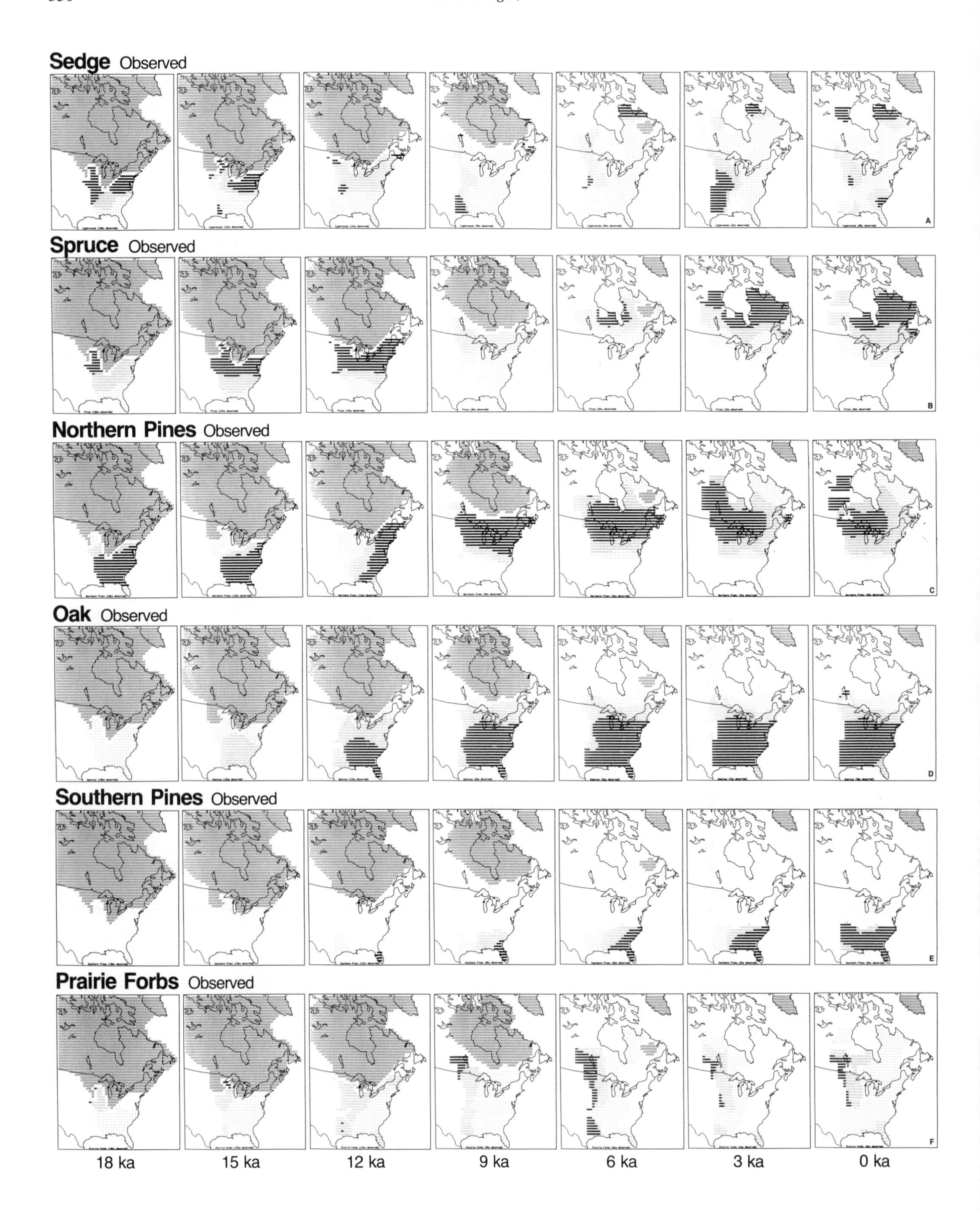

Sedge Observed
Spruce Observed
Northern Pines Observed
Oak Observed
Southern Pines Observed
Prairie Forbs Observed
A
B
C
D
E
F
18 ka
15 ka
12 ka
9 ka
6 ka
3 ka
0 ka

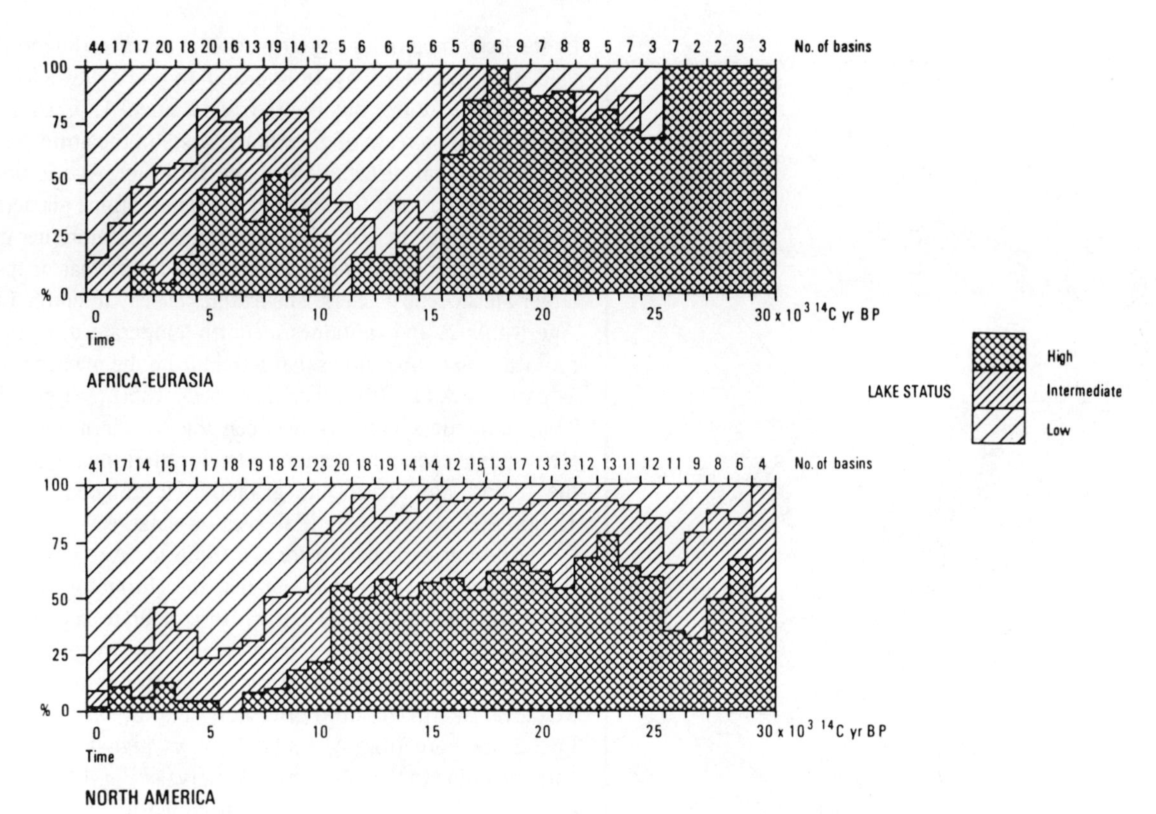

Figure 11. Frequency of high, intermediate, and low lake levels since 30,000 years ago for tropical areas (mostly Africa) and North America (mostly in the Southwest). High tropical lake levels in the early Holocene are attributed to enhanced monsoonal rains related to the insolation maximum at about 10,000 years ago, but it is not clear why the distribution is not symmetrical around that time. The North American high lake levels reflect the southward displacement of the jet stream during the glacial period. From Street-Perrott and Harrison (1984).

Because the area of conspicuous display of the Younger Dryas event is located largely in and around the North Atlantic, the explanation for this episode is sought in some special aspect of North Atlantic climate. No comparable event can be identified in the pollen or ocean-core stratigraphy for the termination of the preceding glaciation, implying some unique manifestation of the last deglaciation in the North Atlantic area. Paleoclimatic model experiments of the general circulation suggest that the event could have been the direct result of expansion of North Atlantic sea ice and not an indirect effect of different radiation distributions or of the presence of the ice sheets (Rind and others, 1986).

One explanation involves the abrupt and temporary diversion of drainage of the vast expanse of southern Canadian proglacial lakes from the Mississippi River to the St. Lawrence and thus to the North Atlantic (Fig. 12), diverting the Gulf Stream or providing a cap of fresh water effective in permitting the southward spread of sea ice and of icebergs released from the wasting ice sheets to the north (Wright, 1987). The timing is just right. Indirect evidence for sea-ice expansion comes from the temporary interruption in the production of North Atlantic Deep Water (Broecker and others, 1988).

Although it was suggested above that the Younger Dryas event was too brief to be explained by any Milankovitch mechanism, a recent finding from three cores in the northeast Atlantic shows that a sharp maximum in the occurence of ice-rafted quartz grains occurred about every 10,000 years back to about 70,000 B.P., with lesser peaks back to about 130,000 B.P., correlating with each maximum and each minimum in the precession cycle (Heinrich, 1988). Maximum summer warmth should enhance delivery of icebergs, and minimum winter warmth should result in buildup of the ice margin and the slightly delayed production of more icebergs.

A climatic episode correlative with the Younger Dryas elsewhere in the world has commonly been claimed. The most recent suggestion comes from the Antarctic Vostok core, where a distinct fluctuation in the deuterium paleotemperature curve is dated at 12,000 to 11,000 years ago according to the ice-flow

Figure 10. Maps showing the relative percentages of key pollen types to illustrate the changing vegetation of central and eastern North America for certain times from the last glacial maximum at 18,000 years ago (18 ka) to the present. Light to dark shading indicates isopolls of 1, 5 and 20 percent. The extent of the Laurentide ice sheet is also shown. Note the changing patterns between 12 ka and 9 ka, resulting from a combination of accelerated ice-sheet retreat and the maximum of summer insolation. From Webb and others (1987).

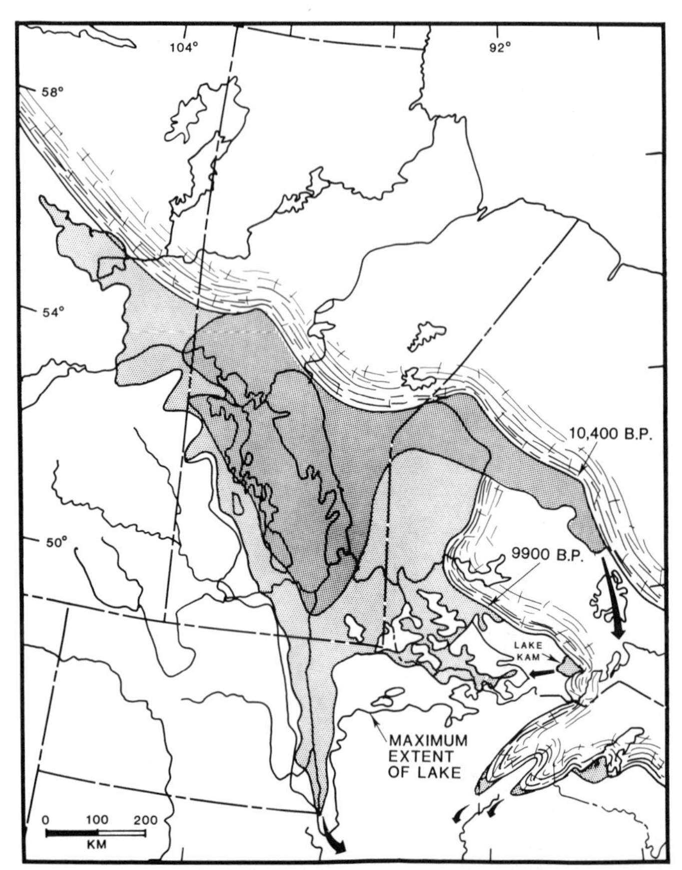

Figure 12. Extent of Glacial Lake Agassiz in Manitoba and western Ontario in the Moorhead phase about 10,400 years ago, when a temporary withdrawal of the Superior lobe of the Laurentide ice sheet permitted diversion of drainage from the Mississippi River to the eastern Great Lakes and thence to the Gulf of St. Lawrence and the North Atlantic, perhaps diverting the Gulf Stream and setting the stage for southward expansion of sea ice and for the Younger Dryas cool period. Readvance of the Superior lobe about 9,900 years ago restored the southern outlet, coincident with the termination of the Younger Dryas event. From Teller (1987).

method used for the chronology—thus 1,000 years older than North Atlantic event. If the dating discrepancy could be resolved, the global significance of the Younger Dryas would have more support.

Another well-documented short-term episode is the Little Ice Age, from about A.D. 1200 to 1850. During this interval, most north-temperate alpine glaciers advanced to limits not attained since the late Pleistocene. In other temperate regions the Little Ice Age is manifested by recent trends in pollen profiles that can be attributed to cooler or moister climatic conditions (Grimm, 1983). A compilation of well-dated pollen diagrams from the central and eastern United States (Fig. 13) indicates that the vegetation was changing more rapidly during the last 1,000 years than at any time since the end of the Pleistocene (Jacobson and others, 1987). The Little Ice Age could owe its origin to the Heinrich mechanism mentioned above. At the same time it could be the beginning of a long-term cooling trend leading to the next glaciation, predicted by Imbrie and Imbrie (1980) for 23,000 years in the future, but now arrested since A.D. 1850 by the effects of the increase of greenhouse gases in the atmosphere.

The global distribution of the Little Ice Age is not easily established. Around the small ice caps and alpine glaciers of the Peruvian Andes are conspicuous trimlines and moraines marking the most conspicuous ice advance since the retreat of the much larger Pleistocene glaciers. The features closely resemble Little Ice Age trimlines and moraines in north-temperate mountains, but radiocarbon dating shows that retreat from the maximum started as early as A.D. 600 rather than A.D. 1850 (Wright, 1984b). Thus, climatic synchrony between the Northern and Southern Hemisphere cannot be demonstrated for this time range, although the major late Pleistocene glaciation terminated there about 12,000 B.P., as elsewhere in tropical mountains.

Another explanation for the Little Ice Age is defended by Porter (1981), who points out that the chronologies of ice advances in glaciers of several north-temperate regions (Rocky Mountains, Alps, Scandinavia, Asia) all show roughly concurrent advanced positions, preceded by the recessions of the so-called Medieval Warm Period. Porter notes that the annual laminated Dye 3 ice core from Greenland shows high levels of acidity corresponding to the inferred cold intervals (Fig. 14). Because the acidity in Greenalnd snowfall is attributed to sulfate aerosols of volcanic origin—as documented by especially high acidity levels for the years of historically dated volcanic eruptions—Porter attributes the cold intervals to the long-range climatic effects of repeated volcanic eruptions. For the Alps he was able to correlate seven well-dated moraines since A.D. 1600 with seven acidity peaks, assuming a lag of 10 to 15 years in the response of the glaciers to the presumed climatic change. On the other hand, the few major volcanic eruptions within historic time did not produce significant changes in the weather for more than a very few years.

CONCLUSIONS

In the late Pliocene before about 2.5 Ma, ice sheets were present in Antarctica, but the Northern Hemisphere was apparently without continental ice sheets, although ocean temperatures (and presumably the climate) fluctuated in response to Milankovitch radiation cycles, particularly the 41,000-yr obliquity rhythm. Then, at about the same time as the change from normal magnetic polarity (Gauss) to reversed (Matuyama), continental ice sheets developed around the North Atlantic and fed ice-rafted detritus into the previously dominant carbonate sediments. The inception of these Northern Hemisphere ice sheets was presumably related to basic changes in ocean and atmospheric circulation arising from the formation of the Panama isthmus and other tectonic events.

During the million and a half years that followed, these small ice sheets fluctuated back and forth with this 41,000-yr rhythm, and in a North Atlantic core some 40 cycles can be identified by the carbonate content, oxygen-isotope ratios, and

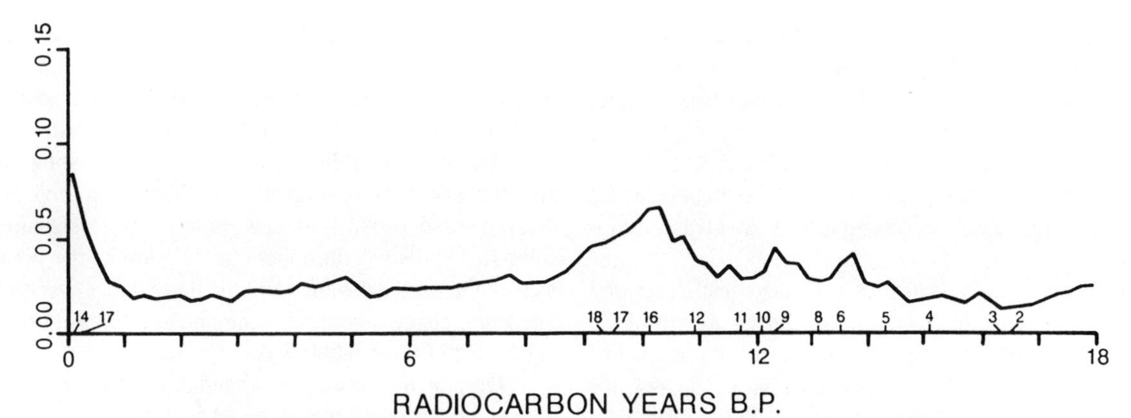

Figure 13. Rates of change of vegetation inferred from a compilation of 18 well-dated pollen diagrams from central and eastern North America, showing principal maxima at about 10,000 years ago and during the last 1,000 years. Small numbers above the time axis indicate the number of sites averaged for those times. From Jacobson and others (1987).

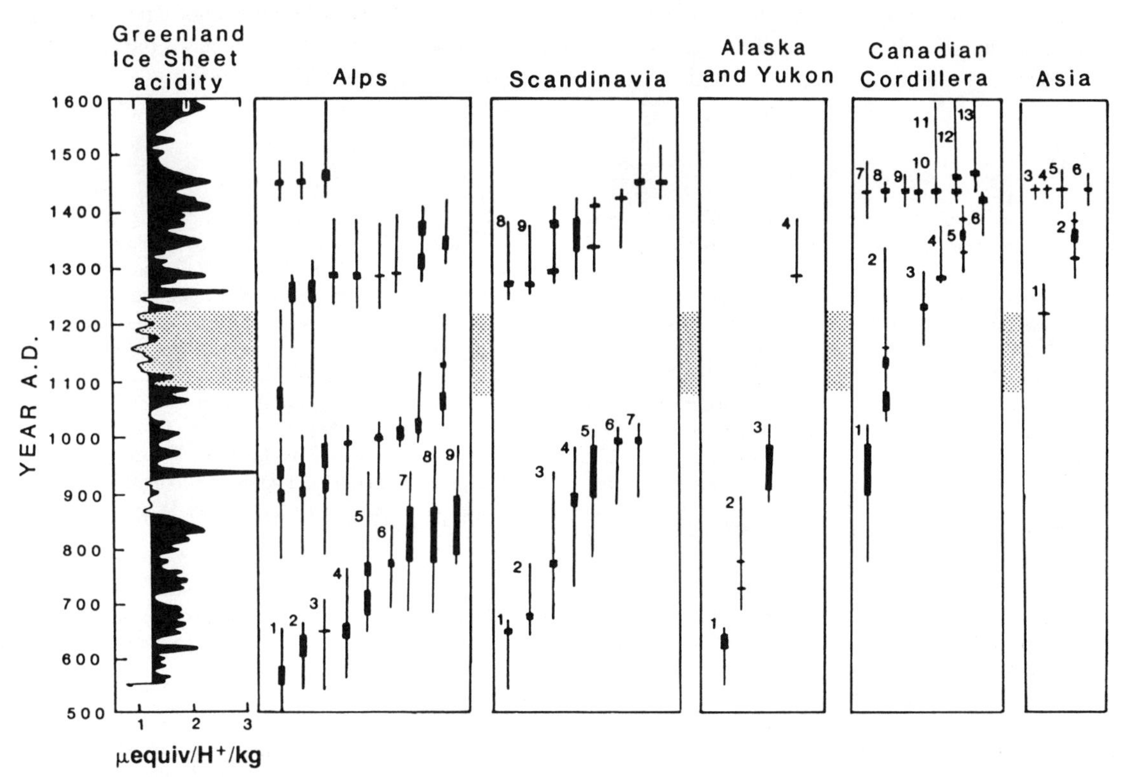

Figure 14. Comparison of glacial chronologies of Northern Hemisphere alpine areas with the acidity record for the Dye-3 core of Greenland. The shaded area between A.D. 1090 and 1230 marks the Medieval warm period preceding the Little Ice Age. From Porter (1986).

sea-surface temperature records (Ruddiman and others, 1986). Then about 700,000 years ago, about the time of the change to the Brunhes normal magnetic polarity epoch, the ice sheets became about twice as large and at times expanded into the Great Lakes region. Thereafter, these greater periodic expansions followed the 100,000-yr eccentricity cycles, and as the ice sheets reached lower latitudes the 23,000/19,000-yr precession cycles had a greater effect on the ice regime. The major glaciations as recorded in the Middle West (and in Europe) may correlate with those eccentricity cycles that show the strongest isotopic record of ice-volume change (stages 2, 6, 12, and 16), whereas during other stages the ice sheets may not have reached so far south.

No question is raised about the general nature of the last glacial/interglacial cycle, because of the broad accessibility of the deposits and the availability of radiocarbon dating for the last 40,000 years. The replication of the isotope stratigraphy throughout the world's oceans is impressive even in the details of the 20,000-yr precession cycle as superimposed on the 100,000-yr eccentricity cycle. The Vostok Antarctic ice-core records of temperature and CO_2 closely match the marine ice-volume record as well as the Northern Hemisphere summer insolation curve. Thus, changes in insolation in the Northern Hemisphere seem to be responsible for the growth of northern ice sheets, and both radiation and ice sheet subsequently affected the global climate by some interhemispheric process—perhaps involving atmospheric CO_2.

Although the isotopic records of both the ocean cores and the Vostok ice core indicate several phases during growth of the last ice sheet, the terrestrial record is deficient in this regard. The opposite relation exists with the deglacial phase. The isotopic record shows a precipitous "termination," possibly with two or three ill-defined steps (Mix, 1987), whereas the ice lobes on the southern margin of the Laurentide ice sheet were unstable during its wastage and experienced numerous fluctuations, which became more pronounced as the ice thinned. Proglacial lakes with fine-grained sediments of low permeability may have facilitated periodic surging of certain ice lobes over a well-lubricated bed.

The total global environmental picture during deglaciation can be brought together through model simulations that illustrate how the North American ice sheet at its maximum caused the westerly jet stream to bifurcate, with the northern branch fringing the Arctic coast and bringing cold air to the North Atlantic, and the southern branch displaced to the south to bring rains to the American Southwest. Vegetational changes inferred from pollen diagrams and packrat-midden studies can be explained by the simulated shifts in atmospheric circulation as the periglacial effects of the ice sheet waned and the more direct effects of seasonal insolation changes became dominant, especially during the interval from 12,000 to 6,000 B.P.

Despite the increasing abundance of field and analytical data and the effectiveness of model simulations to suggest climatic mechanisms, many problems remain in deciphering the interactions and feedbacks among solar-radiation distributions, seasonal climatic trends, atmospheric CO_2 contents, ocean temperatures and isotopic composition, ice-sheet dynamics, and the vegetation and fauna on the world's continents. The Quaternary remains a field of study that requires ever more interdisciplinary imagination and methodological innovation.

REFERENCES

Adam, D. P., Sims, J. D., and Throckmorton, C. K., 1981, 130,000-year continuous pollen record from Clear Lake, Lake County, California: Geology, v. 9, p. 373–377.

Amundson, D. C., and Wright, H. E., Jr., 1979, Forest changes in Minnesota at the end of the Pleistocene: Ecological Monographs, v. 49, p. 153–164.

Andersen, S. -T., 1954, A late-glacial pollen diagram from southern Michigan: Danmarks Geologiske Undersogelse, II Raekke, no. 80, p. 140–155.

Andrews, J. T., 1987, The late Wisconsin glaciation and deglaciation of the Laurentide Ice Sheet, *in* Ruddiman, W. F., and Wright, H. E., Jr., eds., North America and Adjacent Oceans during the Last Deglaciation: Boulder, Colorado, Geological Society of America, The Geology of North America, v. K-3, p. 13–38.

Barnola, J. M., Raynaud, D., Korotkevich, Y. S., and Lorius, C., 1987, Vostok ice core provides 160,000-year record of atmospheric CO_2: Nature, v. 329, p. 408–412.

Barnosky, C. W., Anderson, P. M., and Bartlein, P. J., 1987, The northwestern U.S. during deglaciation; Vegetational history and paleoclimatic implications, *in* Ruddiman, W. F., and Wright, H. E., Jr., eds., North America and Adjacent Oceans during the Last Deglaciation: Boulder, Colorado, Geological Society of America, The Geology of North America, v. K-3, p. 13–38.

Behre, K.-E., and Lade, U., 1986, Eine Folge von Eem und 4 Weichsel-Interstadialen in Oerel/Niedersachsen und ihr Vegetationsablauf: Eiszeitalter und Gegenwart, v. 36, p. 11–56.

Bent, A. M., and Wright, H. E., Jr., 1963, Pollen analyses of surface materials and lake sediments from the Chuska Mountains, New Mexico: Geological Society of America Bulletin, v. 74, p. 491–500.

Berger, A., Imbrie, J., Hays, J., Kukla, G., and Saltzman, B., eds., 1984, Milankovitch and climate; Understanding the response to astronomical forcing: Dordrecht, D. Reidel, 894 p.

Björck, S., and Håkansson, S., 1982, Radiocarbon dates from Late Weichselian lake sediments in south Sweden as a basis for chronostratigraphic subdivision: Boreas, v. 11, p. 125–180.

Björck, S., Sandgren, P., and Holmquist, B., 1987, A magnetostratigraphic comparison between ^{14}C years and varve years during the Late Weichselian, indicating significant differences between time scales: Journal of Quaternary Science, v. 2, p. 133–140.

Bonnichsen, R., Stanford, D., and Fastook, J. L., 1987, Environmental change and developmental history of human adaptive patterns; The Paleoindian case, *in* Ruddiman, W. F. and Wright, H. E., Jr., eds., North America and Adjacent Oceans during the Last Deglaciation: Boulder, Colorado, Geological Society of America, The Geology of North America, v. K-3, p. 403–424.

Broecker, W. S., and 6 others, 1988, The chronology of the last deglaciation; Implications to the cause of the Younger Dryas event: Paleoceanography, v. 3, p. 1–20.

Bryson, R. A., and Wendland, W. M., 1967, Tentative climatic patterns for some late-glacial and postglacial episodes in central North America, *in* Mayer-Oakes, W. J., ed., Life, land, and water: Winnipeg, University of Manitoba Press, p. 271–298.

Clayton, L., Teller, J. T., and Attig, J. W., 1985, Surging of the southwestern part of the Laurentide ice sheet: Boreas, v. 14, p. 235–241.

CLIMAP Project Members, 1981, Seasonal reconstructions of the Earth's surface at the last glacial maximum: Geological Society of America Map and Chart series MC-36.

COHMAP Members, 1988, Climatic changes of the last 18,000 years. Observations and model simulations: Science, v. 241, p. 1043–1052.

Dansgaard, W., 1964, Stable isotopes in precipitation: Tellus, v. 16, p. 436–468.

David, P. P., 1981, Stabilized dune ridges in northern Saskatchewan: Canadian Journal of Earth Sciences, v. 18, p. 286–310.

Davis, M. B., 1963, On the theory of pollen analysis: American Journal of Science, v. 261, p. 897–912.

Dyke, A. S., Vincent, J.-S., Andrews, J. T., Dredge, L. A., and Cowan, W. R., 1989, The Laurentide Ice Sheet and an introduction to the Quaternary geology of the Canadian Shield, *in* Fulton, R. J., ed., Quaternary geology of Canada and Greenland: Geological Survey of Canada, Geology of Canada, No. 1 (also Geological Society of America, The Geology of North America, v. K-1) (in press).

Edwards, R. L., Chen, J. H., Ku, T.-L., and Wasserburg, G. J., 1987, Precise timing of the last interglacial period from mass spectrometric determinations of Thorium-230 in corals: Science, v. 236, p. 1547–1583.

Emiliani, C., 1955, Pleistocene temperatures: Journal of Geology, v. 63, p. 538–578.

Filion, L., 1987, Holocene development of parabolic dunes in the central St. Lawrence Lowland, Quebec: Quaternary Research, v. 28, p. 196–209.

Flint, R. F., 1947, Glacial geology and the Pleistocene epoch: New York, Wiley, 589 p.

—— , 1957, Glacial and Pleistocene geology: New York, Wiley, 553 p.

—— , 1971, Glacial and Quaternary geology: New York, Wiley, 892 p.

Graham, R. W., and Mead, J. I., 1987, Environmental fluctuations and evolution of mammalian faunas during the last deglaciation of North America, *in* Ruddiman, W. F., and Wright, H. E., Jr., eds., North America and Adjacent Oceans during the Last Deglaciation: Boulder, Colorado, Geological Society of America, The Geology of North America, v. K-3, p. 371–402.

Grimm, E. C., 1983, Chronology and dynamics of vegetation change in the prairie-woodland region of southern Minnesota: New Phytologist, v. 93, p. 311–350.

Grüger, E., 1972, Late Quaternary vegetation development in south-central Illinois: Quaternary Research, v. 2, p. 217–231.

Hays, J. D., Imbrie, J., and Shackleton, N. J., 1976, Variations in the Earth's orbit; Pacemaker of the ice ages: Science, v. 194, p. 1121–1132.

Heinrich, H., 1988, Origin and consequences of cyclic ice rafting in the North Atlantic Ocean during the past 130,000 years: Quaternary Research, v. 29, p. 142–152.

Hooghiemstra, H., 1984, Vegetational and climatic history of the High Plain of Bogata, Colombia; A continuous record of the last 3.5 million years: Dissertationes Botanicae, v. 79: Vaduz, The Netherlands, J. Cramer Verlag, 368 p.

Hughes, T., 1987, Ice dynamics and deglaciation models when the ice sheets collapsed, *in* Ruddiman, W. F., and Wright, H. E., Jr., eds., North America and Adjacent Oceans during the Last Deglaciation: Boulder, Colorado, Geological Society of America, The Geology of North America, v. K-3, p. 183–220.

Huntley, B., and Birks, H.J.B., 1983, An atlas of past and present pollen maps for Europe; 0–13,000 years ago: Cambridge, Cambridge University Press, 667 p.

Huntley, B., and Prentice, I. C., 1988, July temperatures in Europe from pollen data, 6,000 years before present: Science, v. 241, p. 687–690.

Imbrie, J., and Imbrie, J. Z., 1980, Modeling the climatic response to orbital variations: Science, v. 207, p. 943–953.

Imbrie, J., and 8 others, 1984, The ortibal theory of Pleistocene climate; Support from a revised chronology of the marine $\delta^{18}O$ record, *in* Berger, A., Imbrie, J., Hays, J., Kukla, G., and Saltzman, B., eds., Milankovitch and climate: Understanding the response to astronomical forcing: Dordrecht, D. Reidel, p. 269–305.

Iversen, J., 1936, Sekondäres Pollen als Fehlerquelle: Danmarks Geologiske Undersøgelse, IV Reike, v. 2, p. 3–24.

Ives, J. D., 1962, Indications of recent extensive glacierization in north-central Baffin Island, Northwest Territories: Journal of Glaciology, v. 4, p. 197–205.

Ives, J. D., Andrews, J. T., and Barry, R. G., 1975, Growth and decay of the Laurentide Ice Sheet and comparisons with Fenno-Scandinavia: Naturwissenschaften, v. 62, p. 118–125.

Jacobson, G. L., Jr., Webb, T., III, and Grimm, E. C., 1987, Patterns and rates of vegetation change during the deglaciation of eastern North America, *in* Ruddiman, W. F., and Wright, H. E., Jr., eds., North America and Adjacent Oceans during the Last Deglaciation: Boulder, Colorado, Geological Society of America, The Geology of North America, v. K-3, p. 277–288.

Jouzel, J., Lorius, C., Petit, J. R., Genthon, C., Barkov, N. I., Kotlyakov, V. M., and Petrov, V. M., 1987, Vostok ice core; A continuous isotope temperature record over the last climatic cycle (160,000 years): Nature, v. 329, p. 403–407.

King, J. E., 1989, Early and Middle Quaternary vegetation, *in* Morrison, R. B., ed., Quaternary Non-glacial Geology: Boulder, Colorado, Geological Society of America, The Geology of North America, v. K-2 (in press).

Kuhle, M., 1987, Subtropical mountain- and highland-glaciation as ice age triggers and the waning of the glacial periods in the Pleistocene: GeoJournal, v. 14, p. 393–421.

Kukla, G. J., 1987, Loess stratigraphy in central China: Quaternary Science Reviews, v. 6, p. 191–219.

—— , 1989, Pleistocene stratigraphy of deep-sea sediments and loess, *in* Smiley, T. C., Bryson, R. A., King, J. E., Kukla, G. J., and Smith, G. I., eds., Quaternary paleoclimate, *in* Morrison, R. B., ed., Quaternary Non-glacial Geology: Boulder, Colorado, Geological Society of America, The Geology of North America, v. K-2 (in press).

Kutzbach, J. E., 1987, Model simulations of the climatic patterns during the deglaciation of North America, *in* Ruddiman, R. F., and Wright, H. E., Jr., eds., North America and Adjacent Oceans during the Last Deglaciation: Boulder, Colorado, Geological Society of America, The Geology of North America, v. K-3, p. 425–446.

Kutzbach, J. E., and Otto-Bliesner, B. L., 1982, The sensitivity of the African–Asian monsoonal climate to orbital parameter changes for 9,000 years B.P. in a low-resolution general circulation model: Journal of Atmospheric Sciences, v. 39, p. 1177–1188.

Kutzbach, J. E., and Wright, H. E., Jr., 1985, Simulation of the climate of 18,000 years BP—Results for the North American/North Atlantic/European sector and comparison with the geologic record of North America Quaternary Science Reviews, v. 4, p. 147–187.

Lamb, H. H., and Woodroffe, A., 1970, Atmospheric circulation during the last ice-age: Quaternary Research, v. 1, p. 29–58.

Lorius, C., Barkov, N. I., Jouzel, J., Korotkevich, Y. S., Kotlyakov, V. M., and Raynaud, D., 1988, Antarctic ice core; CO_2 and climatic change over the last climatic cycle: EOS Transactions of the American Geophysical Union, June 18, 1988, p. 681–684.

Manabe, S., and Terpstra, T. B., 1974, The effects of mountains on the general circulation of the atmosphere as identified by numerical experiments: Journal of the Atmospheric Sciences, v. 31, p. 3–42.

Martin, P. S., and Klein, R. G., eds., 1984, Quaternary extinctions; A prehistoric revolution: Tucson, University of Arizona Press, 892 p. See also Wright, H. E., Jr., 1986, Faunal extinctions at the end of the Pleistocene: Reviews in Anthropology, v. 13, p. 223–235.

Martin, P. S., and Wright, H. E., Jr., 1967, Pleistocene extinctions; The search for a cause: New Haven, Connecticut, Yale University Press, 453 p.

Martinson, D. G., Pisias, N. G., Hays, J. D., Imbrie, J., Moore, T. C., Jr., and Shackleton, N. J., 1987, Age dating and the orbital theory of the ice ages; Development of a high-resolution 0 to 300,000 year chronostratigraphy: Quaternary Research, v. 27, p. 1–29.

McAndrews, J. H., 1966, Postglacial history of prairie, savanna, and forest in northwestern Minnesota: Torrey Botanical Club Memoirs, v. 22, p. 1–72.

Mickelson, D. M., Clayton, L., Fullerton, D. S., and Borns, H. W., Jr., 1983, The Late Wisconsin glacial record of the Laurentide ice sheet in the United States, *in* Porter, S. C., ed., Late-Quaternary environments of the United States; v. 1, The late Pleistocene: Minneapolis, University of Minnesota Press, p. 3–37.

Mix, A. C., 1987, The oxygen-isotope record of glaciation, *in* Ruddiman, W. F., and Wright, H. E., Jr., eds., North America and Adjacent Oceans during the Last Deglaciation: Boulder, Colorado, Geological Society of America, The Geology of North America, v. K-3, p. 111–136.

Mott, R. J., Grant, D. R., Stea, R., and Ochietti, S., 1986, Late-glacial climatic oscillation in Atlantic Canada equivalent to the Alleröd/Younger Dryas event: Nature, v. 123, p. 247–250.

Overpeck, J. T., Webb, T., III, and Prentice, I. C., 1985, Quantitative interpretation of fossil pollen spectra; Dissimilarity coefficients and the method of modern analogs: Quaternary Research, v. 23, p. 87–108.

Paterson, W.S.B., and Hammer, C. U., 1987, Ice core and other glaciological data, *in* Ruddiman, W. F., and Wright, H. E., Jr., eds., North America and Adjacent Oceans during the Last Deglaciation: Boulder, Colorado, Geological Society of America, The Geology of North America, v. K-3, p. 91–110.

Peltier, W. R., 1987, Glacial isostasy, mantle viscosity, and Pleistocene climatic change, *in* Ruddiman, W. F., and Wright, H. E., Jr., eds., North America and Adjacent Oceans during the Last Deglaciation: Boulder, Colorado, Geological Society of America, The Geology of North America, v. K-3, p. 155–182.

Péwé, T. L., 1983, The periglacial environment in North America during Wisconsin time, *in* Porter, S. C., ed., Late-Quaternary environments of the United States; v. 11, The late Pleistocene: Minneapolis, University of Minnesota Press, p. 157–189.

Porter, S. C., 1986, Pattern and forcing of Northern Hemisphere glacier fluctuations during the last millennium: Quaternary Research, v. 26, p. 27–48.

Prell, W. L., and Kutzbach, J. E., 1987, Monsoon variability over the past 150,000 years: Journal of Geophysical Research, v. 92D, p. 8411–8425.

Prest, V. K., 1984, The Late Wisconsin glacier complex, *in* Fulton, R. J., ed., Quaternary stratigraphy of Canada; A Canadian contribution of IGCP Project 24: Geological Survey of Canada Paper 84–10, p. 21–38, map 1584A.

Raymo, M. E., Ruddiman, W. F., and Froelich, P. N., 1988, Influence of late Cenozoic mountain building on ocean geochemical cycles: Geology, v. 16, p. 649–653.

Richmond, G. M., and Fullerton, D. S., 1986, Summation of Quaternary glaciations in the United States of America: Quaternary Science Reviews, v. 5, p. 183–196.

Rind, D., and Peteet, D., 1985, Terrestrial conditions at the last glacial maximum and CLIMAP sea-surface temperature estimates—are they consistent?: Quaternary Research, v. 24, p. 1–22.

Rind, D., Peteet, D., Broecker, W. S., McIntyre, A., and Ruddiman, W., 1986, The impact of cold North Atlantic sea surface temperatures in climate—Implications for the Younger Dryas cooling (11–10k): Climate Dynamics, v. 1, p. 3–33.

Rosholt, J. N., and 7 others, 1989, Dating methods applicable to the Quaternary, *in* Morrison, R. B., ed., Quaternary Non-glacial Geology; Conterminous US.: Boulder, Colorado, Geological Society of America, Geology of North America, v. K-2 (in press).

Ruddiman, W. F., and McIntyre, A., 1981, The North Atlantic during the last deglaciation: Palaeogeography, Palaeoclimatology, Palaeoecology, v. 35, p. 145–214.

Ruddiman, W. F., and Wright, H. E., Jr., 1987, Introduction, *in* Ruddiman, W. F., and Wright, H. E., Jr., eds., North America and Adjacent Oceans during the Last Deglaciation: Boulder, Colorado, Geological Society of America, The Geology of North America, v. K-3, p. 1–12.

Ruddiman, W. F., Raymo, M., and McIntyre, A., 1986, Matuyama 41,000-year cycles; North Atlantic and Northern Hemisphere ice sheets: Earth and Planetary Science Letters, v. 80, p. 117–129.

Shackleton, N. J., and 16 others, 1984, Oxygen isotope calibration of the onset of ice-rafting and history of glaciation in the North Atlantic region: Nature, v. 307, p. 216–219.

Shane, L.C.K., 1987, Late-glacial climatic and vegetational history of the Allegheny Plateau and till plains of Ohio and Indiana, U.S.A.: Boreas, v. 15, p. 1–20.

Shilts, W. W., and Aylsworth, J. M., 1987, Glacial geomorphology of northwestern Canadian Shield, *in* Graf, W. L., ed., Geomorphic Systems of North America: Boulder, Colorado, Geological Society of America, Centennial Special Volume 2, p. 126–142.

Spaulding, W. G., and Graumlich, L. J., 1986, The last pluvial climatic episodes in the deserts of southwestern North America: Nature, v. 320, p. 441–444.

Street-Perrott, F. A., and Harrison, S., 1985, Temporal variations in lake levels since 30,000 yr B.P.—an index of the global hydrological cycle, *in* Hansen, J. E., and Takahashi, T., eds., Climate processes and climate sensitivity: American Geophysical Union Geophysical Monograph 29, p. 118–129.

Stromberg, B., 1985, Revision of the late-glacial Swedish varve chronology: Boreas, v. 14, p. 101–105.

Teller, J. T., 1987, Proglacial lakes and the southern margin of the Laurentide Ice Sheet, *in* Ruddiman, W. F., and Wright, H. E., Jr., eds., North America and Adjacent Oceans during the Last Deglaciation: Boulder, Colorado, Geological Society of America, The Geology of North America, v. K-3, p. 39–70.

van der Hammen, T., Wijmstra, T. A., and Zagwijn, W. H., 1971, The floral record of the late Cenozoic of Europe, *in* Turekian, K. K., ed., The late Cenozoic glacial ages: New Haven, Yale University Press, p. 391–424.

Van Devender, T. R., Thompson, R. S., and Betancourt, J. L., 1987, Vegetation history of the deserts of southwestern North America; The nature and timing of the Late Wisconsin–Holocene transition, *in* Ruddiman, W. F., and Wright, H. E., Jr., eds., North America and Adjacent Oceans during the Last Deglaciation: Boulder, Colorado, Geological Society of America, The Geology of North America, v. K-3, p. 323–352.

Watson, R. A., and Wright, H. E., Jr., 1980, The end of the Pleistocene—a general critique of chronostratigraphic classification: Boreas, v. 9, p. 159–164.

Watts, W. A., 1980, Regional variations in the response of vegetation to Late glacial climatic events in Europe, *in* Lowe, J. J., Gray, J. M., and Robinson, J. E., eds., The Late glacial of north-west Europe: New York, Pergamon Press, p. 1–22.

Webb, T., III, Bartlein, P. J., and Kutzbach, J. E., 1987, Climatic change in eastern North America during the last 18,000 years: Comparisons of pollen data with model results, *in* Ruddiman, W. F., and Wright, H. E., Jr., eds., North America and Adjacent Oceans during the Last Deglaciation: Boulder, Colorado, Geological Society of America, The Geology of North America, v. K-3, p. 447–463.

Woillard, G., 1978, Grande Pile peat bog—A continuous pollen record for the last 140,000 years: Quaternary Research, v. 9, p. 1–21, p. 373–377.

Wright, H. E., Jr., 1967, The use of surface samples in Quaternary pollen analysis: Review of Palaeobotany and Palynology, v. 2, no. 9, p. 321–330.

—— , 1984a, Sensitivity and response time of natural systems to climatic change in the late Quaternary: Quaternary Science Reviews, v. 3, p. 91–132.

—— , 1984b, Late-glacial and late-Holocene moraines in the Cerros Chuchpanga, central Peru: Quaternary Research, v. 21, p. 275–285.

—— , 1987, Synthesis; Land south of the ice sheets, *in* Ruddiman, W. F., and Wright, H. E., Jr., eds., North America and Adjacent Oceans during the Last Deglaciation: Boulder, Colorado, Geological Society of America, The Geology of North America, v. K-3, p. 479–488.

Wright, H. E., McAndrews, J. H. and van Zeist, W., 1967, Modern pollen rain in western Iran and its relation to plant geography and Quaternary vegetational history: Journal of Ecology, v. 55, p. 415–443.

Zeuner, F. E., 1945, The Pleistocene period; Its climate, chronology, and faunal successions: London, Ray Society, 322 p.

—— , 1952, Dating the past; An introduction to geochronology: London, Methuen, 3rd. ed., 495 p.

ACKNOWLEDGMENTS

I appreciate the perceptive reviews of a draft of this chapter by C. W. Barnosky, G. L. Jacobson, Jr., W. F. Ruddiman, and T. Webb III, as well as discussions over the years with these persons and with J. E. Kutzbach, P. J. Bartlein, and other COHMAP colleagues, as facilitated by NSF grant ATM-871422. Contributions 375, Limnological Research Center.

Printed in U.S.A.

The Geology of North America
Vol. A, The Geology of North America—An overview
The Geological Society of America, 1989

Chapter 18

Fresh water of the North American continent; A profile

Gerald Meyer
15107 Interlachen Drive, No. 908, Silver Spring, Maryland 20906

INTRODUCTION

The eminent global hydrologist R. L. Nace (1969, p. 11) noted that "the story of the growth of civilization and science could be written largely in terms of human concern with water." That quotation applies fittingly to the North American continent, whose economic and social development are intimately tied to its natural water supply. Demographic, agricultural, and industrial expansion have evolved largely around opportunities proffered by the continent's surface, ground, and soil water.

Cultural and economic gains attributable to water development have been aided by coincident advances in knowledge of the hydrology and geology of the continent, accompanied by parallel progress in understanding of basic principles of the science of geohydrology. North American scientists have exercised leadership in both applied and basic geohydrological investigation. The significant roles of water in the continent's geophysical and geochemical processes are only now being more fully recognized and integrated into the earth sciences, with both scientific and pragmatic benefits. It is now understood that water, whether in its liquid, vapor, or solid (ice) form, fulfills many fundamentally important physical and chemical functions in virtually all Earth environments.

This overview chapter is concerned primarily with the geohydrology of North America, and most particularly with the natural occurrence of fresh surface and ground water of the continent, with less attention to practical water-supply and water-use aspects. This is true also for Wolman and Riggs (1989) and Back and others (1988) of this series of volumes. Those two volumes provide, respectively, comprehensive descriptions of the surface and ground-water hydrology of the continent.

Scientific water problems and pragmatic problems share many common information needs, and applied and scientific aspects are so intertwined and mutually supportive that they lack a distinct boundary. Utilitarian water investigations in the countries of North America have always contributed prominently to hydrogeological understanding, and the reverse is true as well. North American scientists exercise leadership in both practical and basic geohydrology, and the science has evolved to its present high status through an effective union of applied and basic elements.

Water problems and resolution efforts

There is little complacency among the nations of North America about its water from either of the standpoints discussed above—satisfying utilitarian requirements or searching for better understanding of the functioning of hydrologic systems. Government and public recognition of mankind's dependence on water for survival and progress has risen markedly during the past three or four decades, stemming from widening understanding of water's broad, basic societal, economic, biologic, and environmental influences.

The nature of occurrence of water and its hazards and benefits are matters of systematic surveillance and investigation by many scientific governmental agencies of North American nations. In addition, educational institutions, various scientific organizations, and many other formal and lay organizations together reflect the extensive awareness and study directed to the water of the continent.

Increasing investigative and managerial efforts devoted to the continent's water reflect the growing number of serious water problems. They are many, but the principal ones concern water quality (contamination, disposal of wastes), shortages and excesses (drought, floods), water supply (distribution, development), water-related hazards (earthquakes, landslides), and environmental issues that involve water (virtually all do).

Most of these problems are of local extent and can be addressed locally. Others are of regional, national, or international dimensions, generally necessitating more extensive political and technological attention. Regional and interregional transfer of water over great distances, already heavily employed internally within Canada and the United States, continues to attract interest as a means of satisfying major deficiencies as described in example 1 below.

Meyer, G., 1989, Fresh water of the North American continent; A profile, *in* Bally, A. W., and Palmer, A. R., eds., The Geology of North America—An overview: Boulder, Colorado, Geological Society of America, The Geology of North America, v. A.

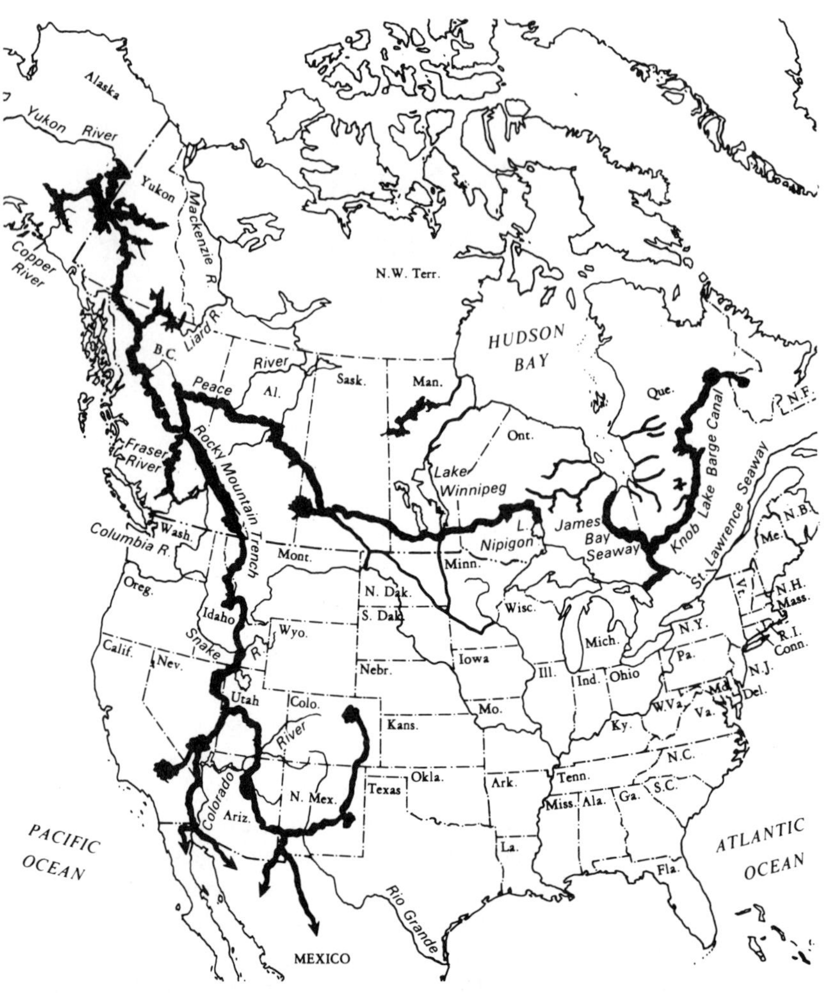

Figure 1. Proposed distribution system, North American Water and Power Alliance. (From Howe and Easter, 1971, Fig. 3. Reprinted with permission of the publisher.)

Continuing development and economic expansion of the largest North American nations is generating water problems of continental proportions, and extending beyond single environments to involve the surface-water regime, ground-water systems, the atmosphere together. One prominent example, "acid rain," is described in example 2.

Example 1: Redistribution of water by regional transfer

Transferring water from areas of excess supply to areas of deficiency by means of engineering works is common in Canada, mainly to facilitate regional power generation, and in the United States, mainly for irrigation and power generation. Approximately 60 interbasin water-transfer projects in Canada redistribute 4,450 m^3/s, which is about 4.5 percent of the nation's total mean streamflow. Canadian water transfer exceeds the combined transfer flow of the next two leading countries, the United States and the USSR. Hirsch and others (1989, Tables 3 to 6, Fig. 27) identify and provide quantitative data for operational and proposed water-transfer projects in Canada and the United States.

The continent's grandest water-redistribution plan, the North American Water and Power Alliance (NAWAPA), as first proposed nearly three decades ago, would distribute western Canadian river water among three nations—7 provinces of Canada, 35 states of the United States, and 3 states in Mexico. The vast system of dams and waterways is illustrated somewhat schematically in Figure 1. Increasing demand for agricultural water in the western United States and in northern and central Mexico from time to time stimulates further interest in the NAWAPA plan or adaptations of it. However, its economic feasibility, environmental impacts, and political acceptance in both the contributing and receiving nations are yet to be resolved.

Example 2: Acidic precipitation—Sources and control measures

The acidity of precipitation and the detrimental effects that this water of low pH, deposited on the land and in water bodies, may have on aquatic animals, plants, buildings, and other structures, and indirectly on human health, are major concerns in

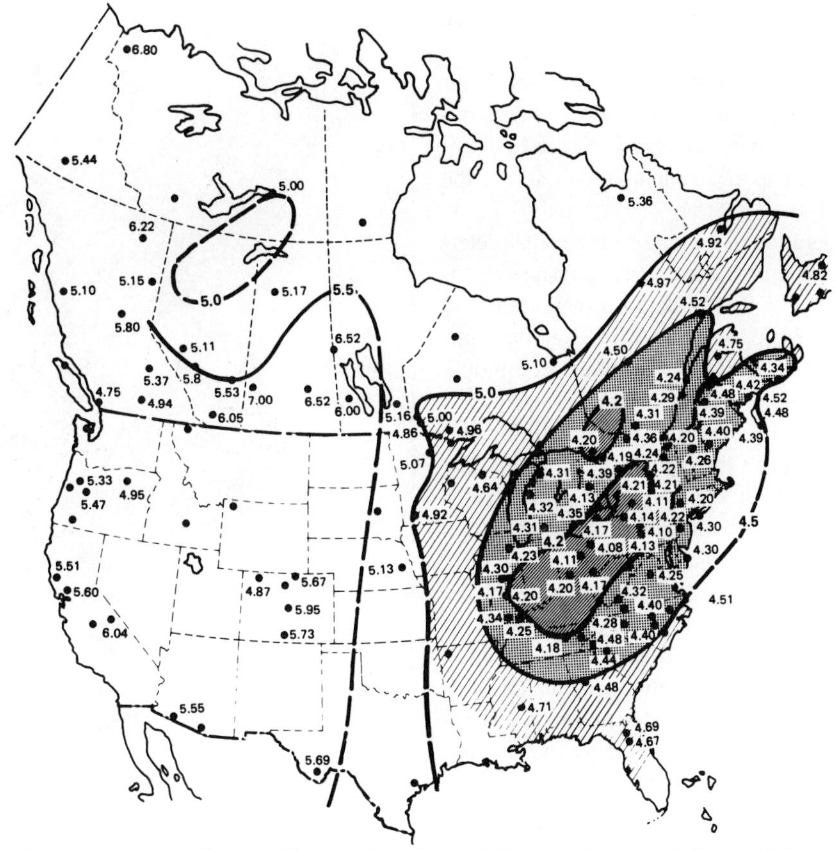

Figure 2. Annual mean values of pH in precipitation, weighted by the amount of precipitation on the United States and Canada during 1980. (From United States–Canada Work Group 2, 1982.)

North America. The eastern regions of the continent defined by the contours in Figure 2, which include parts of Canada and the United States, are the areas of greatest concern. Acidic precipitation occurs locally in other parts of North America, as indicated by the pH values of samples collected throughout the continent, also included on the map, but problem areas are more isolated and less defined.

Acidic gases carried by air masses are derived from natural sources, such as volcanoes and forest fires, but more significantly from certain activities of man, including discharges to the atmosphere from the burning of coal and other fossil fuels in industrial and power plants and from motor-vehicle exhaust. Through complex physical-chemical interactions with sunlight, water, and dust particles, these gases may be altered to strong acids, including sulfuric and nitric acids (U.S. Geological Survey, 1984, p. 61–63). Acidic precipitation in areas comparatively unaffected by industrial emissions generally has a minimum (most acidic) pH of about 5.0, ranging upward to 6 or higher. In the eastern United States and Canada, however, measurements average less than 5.0. Some areas in the northeastern United States and nearby areas of southeastern Canada receive precipitation with an average pH of 4.2, which is nearly 10 times more acidic than unaffected, natural precipitation measured throughout the continent.

Acidic precipitation poses difficult scientific problems and creates sensitive international issues. Canadian and U.S. agencies, with the assistance of specially formulated task forces, are collaborating in the search for viable options through the examination of scientific, political, economic, ecological, and health aspects. Present technical focus is on reduction of certain industrial sulfur-dioxide and nitrogen-oxide emissions thought to be important ingredients of acidic precipitation.

CONTINENTAL MOISTURE DISTRIBUTION

Fresh water of the North American continent is constantly replenished by precipitation of rain, snow, sleet, and hail. Precipitation, in turn, is dependent on airborne moisture (water vapor) transport and condensation. On a regional scale the patterns of distribution of precipitation are a function of interdynamics of the atmosphere with major bodies of water and land areas. Air masses sweeping across North America generally take form over the surrounding oceans, Gulf of Mexico, Caribbean Sea, and Arctic region, where they absorb marine moisture and move inland, carrying water vapor to be condensed and deposited as water in liquid or frozen state.

The behavior of air masses is complex, being controlled by internal dynamics, topographic conditions encountered in transit, physical features of other air masses encountered, topographic influences on altitude, and temperature and other physical influences of water bodies and land areas with which the flowing air comes in contact. These phenomena also are principal determinants of moisture capacity of the air masses and rates and quantities of precipitation triggered as the systems move across the continent.

Principal paths of migration of major air masses that determine North America's climate and atmospheric moisture distribution in winter months are illustrated in generalized and schematic form in Figure 3. Major terrainal features of the continent control the directions of flow. Air masses are commonly designated by their source regions. The letter symbols in Figure 3 refer to the continental-arctic air mass (cA), the maritime-polar air mass (mP), and the maritime-tropical air mass (mT). The north-south trend of the high Cordilleran ranges of western North America effectively limits deep inland flow of moist maritime polar air from the Pacific Ocean, which is dry and warm after crossing the mountains. Much of the eastern two-thirds of the continent experiences winter Arctic air-mass inflow, on occasion bringing snow and frigid weather to the southern United States and northern Gulf of Mexico. Moist maritime polar air originating in the Atlantic Ocean flows onto the continent only occasionally. When it does, it affects the climate and increases moisture of only the maritime regions of eastern Canada, and the United States east of the Appalachian Mountains.

Marine moisture inflow bypasses the extensive arid region of the southwestern United States and northwestern Mexico, but narrowing of the continent southward somewhat progressively increases areal influence of the Pacific, Gulf, and Caribbean seas on climate and moisture. Tropical-equatorial climate, the marine environment, and high mountain ranges of the narrow southern isthmus of Central America combine to produce mountain rainfall amounts that are among the highest measured throughout the continent.

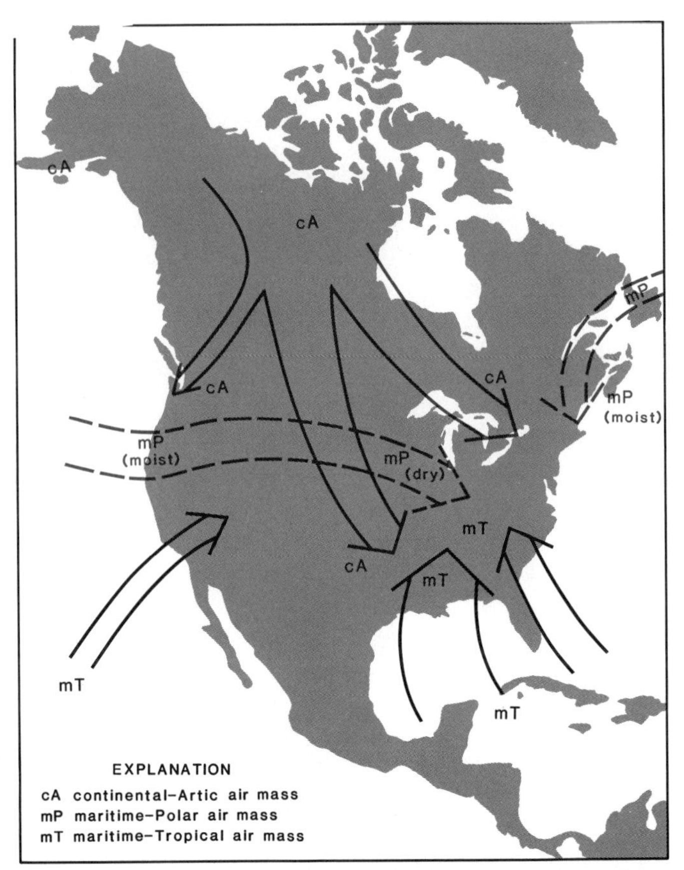

Figure 3. Common winter-season paths of air masses that bring moisture to Canada and the United States. (After Trewartha and Horn, 1980, Fig. 6.3a.)

The tracks of air masses shift direction through the seasons with changes in the relative positions of the Earth and sun. Summer flow patterns (see Trewartha and Horn, 1980, Fig. 6.3B) differ from the winter tracks shown in Figure 3, and the regimens of physical interactions that govern moisture content and precipitation are altered as well.

Inasmuch as precipitation is the continent's sole source of natural fresh water, air-moisture flow regimes and their control of the distribution of this vital natural resource are of fundamental importance to the welfare of each of its nations. Climatic conditions and related airborne water-vapor transport and precipitation among the nations of North America are summarized in the following paragraphs.

Airborne moisture of Canada and Alaska

Canada is predominantly a humid country with abundant surface water attributable to substantial rainfall and snowmelt. In addition, rates of evaporation and transpiration are less than in the other nations of the continent lying at lower, warmer latitudes where dissipation of water by those phenomena is favored. Frozen ground further reduces these "losses." Riggs and Wolman (1989, Fig. 5) delineated regions of continuous, discontinuous, and scattered permafrost in northern Arctic Canada and neighboring Alaska. Approximately half the nation's precipitation is returned to the atmosphere by evapotranspiration and by ablation of snow and ice.

The average annual precipitation on Canada is about 600 mm, but it ranges from only 100 mm in the Arctic region to over 3,500 mm in the marine coastal environment of southwestern British Columbia. Over one-third of the total precipitation of the country is in the form of snow, and precipitation data in this chapter are adjusted where appropriate to include the water equivalent of snow. Inasmuch as most of the snow, particularly in upland and mountain regions, remains frozen until spring, at which time snowmelt contributes a large share of stream runoff, snowpack accumulation and melting are well timed to the growing season and irrigation-water requirements of Canada's agricultural regions.

Polar maritime air masses originating in the north Pacific Ocean region bring a generous supply of moisture to the west coast of Canada, but orographic precipitation induced by flow over the Cordilleran range effectively blocks inland flow of the marine moisture. Arctic air flowing southward through central Canada brings with it cold air but little moisture or precipitation. Interior Canada, from the Rocky Mountains to the Great Lakes, has a continental climate and scant precipitation. The Atlantic provinces have a more humid continental climate. Atlantic marine polar air influences the climate and brings moderately heavy precipitation to the extreme eastern part of the country, the Nova Scotia area.

The Alaskan peninsula, jutting northwestward into the Pacific Ocean, Arctic Ocean, and Bering Sea, has climate similar to that of adjacent regions of northern Canada, but with some marked differences significant to the supply of atmospheric moisture and precipitation to the state. Moisture and temperature conditions range from wet and fairly mild along the southern coast to cold and dry on the Arctic Slope and high mountain ranges. The narrow coastal reach just north of the Yukon Territory is mild compared to the rest of the state, with precipitation of rain and snow totaling about 500 mm a year.

In interior regions of Alaska, much of the precipitation, which varies from about 125 to 500 mm annually, is in the form of snow. Winters are long and cold, and the frost-free period lasts only two or three months. The Brooks Range and Arctic Slope regions have an Arctic climate with precipitation of less than 125 mm a year, most all of it snow. However, snowmelt runoff is substantial in these regions during the brief summers, but with virtually no infiltration to ground-water reservoirs, owing to widespread continuous permafrost.

Airborne moisture of the conterminous United States

An average of about 760 mm of precipitation each year on the conterminous United States constitutes a substantial basic source of fresh-water supply for the nation as a whole. About 90 percent falls as rain, and the remainder as ice in the forms of snow and lesser amounts of hail and sleet, but the precipitation is unevenly distributed. Less than 100 mm falls in arid parts of the Great Basin and lower Colorado River regions of the southwestern United States, whereas more than 5,000 mm falls in the humid Pacific coastal belt of Oregon and Washington.

Air masses governing the climate and airborne moisture of middle and northern latitudes of the United States commonly move inland from the Pacific Ocean and from the broad plains regions of Canada to the north. Incoming Pacific air masses release large amounts of water on coastal belts of the northwestern states of Washington and Oregon and then move over the Cascades, Sierra Nevada, and Rocky Mountains, where they release still more water, much of it snow. These mountain regions are the principal sources of water for power generation, irrigation, and public supply for much of the western United States. As in Canada, winter snowpack in the northern and midlatitude mountain ranges becomes a primary source of regional and interregional water supply during spring thaw.

Air masses moving farther eastward from the Rocky Mountains carry little moisture; much of the western plains region of the United States lies in "rain shadow," and precipitation is small compared to most of the country. Heavy reliance is placed on surface storage reservoirs and aquifers. Climate of the midcontinent region of the country is determined predominantly by airflow from central Canada, bringing cold temperatures and moderate precipitation, accompanied by dry air inflow from the plains region to the west (Fig. 3). In addition, moisture inflow to the region between May and October from the Gulf of Mexico spawns warm-weather rainstorms, which generally provide about twice as much water to the region as occurs during the remainder of the year.

Farther east, in the Atlantic coastal region of the United States, the proximity of major water bodies, including the Atlantic Ocean, Chesapeake Bay, and Great Lakes, moderates air temperature and increases precipitation of both rain and snow. Contributions of the Great Lakes to atmospheric moisture in their vicinity, coupled with cold air inflow from central Canada, generates heavy winter snow in the Great Lakes region, accounting for a sizable share of its annual precipitation of about 1,000 mm.

Tropical-maritime environments of the Gulf of Mexico, Caribbean Sea, and equatorial latitudes of the Atlantic Ocean control the climate and moisture levels of much of the southeastern United States, including moderating effects on temperature, increased atmospheric moisture, and corresponding increase in rainfall. Frequent thunderstorms and seasonal hurricanes convey storm water to coastal states and, on occasion, to states farther inland.

Airborne moisture of Mexico and Central America

Much of Mexico and Central America is mountainous or upland terrain, which exerts strong influence on the region's climate, moisture flow, and surface-water distribution. The Cordilleran belt of mountain ranges continues southward through Mexico, the nations of Central America, and beyond into South America. Mountain ranges parallel the two coasts, and an intermontane plateau occupies most of the intervening area. Lowlands and discontinuous coastal plains extend along the Gulf Coast from the Rio Grande to the Yucatan Peninsula.

The climate of Mexico is varied, ranging from extensive desert lands in the northwest to very humid climate and substantian rainfall in mountain areas of southernmost tropical Mexico. Tropical latitude, wet maritime storms, and moisture-condensing orographic effects of coastal ranges are the principal controls of rainfall generation and distribution. Much of the country is warm or hot, with only moderate or slight rain; large regions amounting to almost two-thirds of its land area are arid or semi-arid, and in those areas, fresh water—both surface water and ground water—is of limited supply. The Sonoran Desert, bordering on companion desert land of the southwest United States, receives less than 100 mm of rain annually on the average, and that average includes some years in which no measurable rain falls.

Rainfall generated in high mountain regions and upland

humid areas, however, is substantial. Rainfall is heaviest in the mountainous area of extreme southern Mexico near Guatemala, where annual rainfall on the order of 5,000 mm has been recorded. Wet tropical storms sweep across Mexico from both the Pacific Ocean on the west and the Gulf on the east during the hot summer and fall seasons. Cyclonic depressions deposit rain with less intensity but longer duration over large regions of both coasts during the winter months. These phenomena elevate the average annual rainfall on the country to about 700 mm. Rates of evapotranspiration in Mexico are much larger than in cooler regions to the north; the rate is estimated to amount to about 75 percent of Mexico's total rainfall.

Most of Mexico's rain falls between May and September. Rainfall is minimal and erratic between February and April, which happens to be the period of greatest demand for crop water. Thus, irrigation is practiced somewhat extensively in major agricultural regions with sufficient sources of supply.

Central America has a wet, tropical-equatorial climate. It is largely a mountainous region, bordered by the Pacific Ocean on the south and the Caribbean Sea on the north. Both the high land elevations and proximity to large water bodies bring cyclonic and storm moisture to the region. Rain is much heavier on the northern slopes, facing the warm, unstable climate of the Caribbean Sea. Sedimentary flatlands and narrow, discontinuous coastal plains flank the mountain chain on both the northern and southern coasts. Rainfall exceeds 1,500 mm annually nearly everywhere, and some areas of high altitude receive more than 3,000 mm a year.

The heavy rainfall yields abundant surface water, but in some areas, surface-reservoir capacity is inadequate to accommodate extended dry spells that occur from time to time. The predominance of metamorphic and volcanic rocks is not favorable to productive aquifers, but development of ground water has proceeded rapidly in recent decades for public and rural water supply and for seasonal crop irrigation.

FRESH-WATER GEOHYDROLOGY

Precipitation reaching the land is distributed among surface and subsurface environments in accordance with their hydrologic and geologic characteristics. Hydrology encompasses all natural water reservoirs and the physical and chemical fluxes operating within them. Geology engineers the framework: it influences the architecture of topographic features and surface drainage systems, it provides the shallow subsurface zone for storage of soil moisture and for downward transmission of water to the zone of saturation (ground water), and it forms the ubiquitous groundwater systems that enable underground storage and flow of water.

Major physiographic features of North America are surficial expressions of broad, regional aspects of its geology and hydrology. The continental land mass consists of huge crystalline-rock complexes, extensive sedimentary basins underlain by folded or flat-lying layered rocks, unconsolidated surficial deposits of alluvial and glacial origin, large bodies of fresh and saline water, and in the northern regions, vast areas of snow, ice sheets, and sea ice. Viewed at high altitude (say from the perspective of an Earth satellite), these different geologic settings are revealed as contrasting terrains, the most prominent of which are the Cordilleran range extending the full length of the continent on the west, the eastern Appalachian Mountains range of lesser proportions, the flat Atlantic and Gulf Coastal Plains, the broad plains region and Canadian Shield in the middle regions of the continent, and the extensive, featureless, snow- and ice-covered tracts of northern Canada and Greenland.

These grand features reflect the hydrogeologic framework for the myriad water settings and drainage networks of the continent. Surface water of North America flowing through these terranes discharges ultimately to the three bounding oceans or to internal closed drainage basins ("sinks"; see Riggs and Wolman, 1989, Fig. 1). General ground-water characteristics and patterns of subsurface flow are also controlled by regional terrane conditions. Broad aspects of hydrogeology can be deduced from regional features of the terrain and geology, surface-water flow patterns, and other surficial indicators (Heath, 1988, Tables 1 and 2).

Surface-water and ground-water characteristics receive only brief discussion here, limited to aspects of greatest significance. Liberal references are made to the two hydrological volumes of this series (Back and others, 1988; Wolman and Riggs, 1989) where appropriate for elaboration.

The reception given rainwater at the land surface may be likened to rain falling on a house having both a leaky roof and leaky cellar (the soil and rocks). Part of the water runs off the roof (surface-water runoff); part moves downward, wetting the walls and floors (unsaturated zone; soil moisture); some is evaporated back to the atmosphere from the roof and living quarters (evapotranspiration); and the part escaping these diversions migrates farther downward to the cellar where it ponds and seeps away (saturated zone; ground water).

This elementary domestic analogy for what is in reality a complex system of geohydrologic events illustrates the associations of land, rocks, and water in an area receiving precipitation, at which point surface- and ground-water flow begin. Figure 4 depicts the flow system schematically and identifies terminology for components of the system.

Surface water

A sizable portion of North America is covered by water in its liquid or frozen forms, even disregarding the vast submerged coastal margins. Major inland water bodies are most prevalent in the northern and middle regions of the continent; it has been estimated that nearly one-seventh of the fresh surface water of the world lies within Canada's borders (Department of Energy, Mines, and Resources, 1972, p. 4).

Most extensive is the vast, and in many areas perennial, snow and ice cover extending across Arctic regions of northern Canada, Alaska, and Greenland, followed by the Great Lakes, Hudson and Chesapeake Bays, Lake Okeechobee, and numerous other bodies of surface water of lesser areal dimensions. Surface water of the continent also occupies stream channels and floodlands; swamps, marshes, and other wetlands; and numerous manmade reservoirs that account for a small but economically significant portion of the total surface water. Snow and ice, particularly where subject to melting and runoff in stream channels, are generally considered part of the surface-water inventory.

Though appearing simple on casual observation of streams and lakes, the hydrology and geochemistry of surface water of the continent are intricate and complex. Water in storage in these many different surface settings is constantly in a state of flux owing to fluctuating rates of replenishment, runoff, and evaporation, and inflow to and outflow from neighboring soil and ground-water environments. Drainage characteristics of the river basins of North America vary widely (Riggs and Wolman, 1989, Figs. 1, 2, and 4, and Plates 3A and 3B).

Climatic factors, including precipitation, temperature, wind, and solar radiation, in company with the geologic and topographic framework, control the rates and magnitude of these surficial processes, which in turn govern the quantity and distribution of surface-water supply throughout the continent.

Runoff. Runoff—the volume of flow during a specified period of time—differs throughout North America in accordance with variations in climatological, physiographic, and hydrologic conditions (Fig. 5). Runoff at any point in the flow system consists of the collective, integrated inflow from upstream reaches and tributaries, each with its suite of hydrologic and chemical features. Magnitude of runoff ranges from only a few millimeters annually in desert lands of western United States and Mexico to maximum values on the order of 4,000 mm along the middle and upper Pacific Coast and in mountain areas of eastern Costa Rica.

Figure 5 charts the annual runoff of the continent in generalized, regional patterns. It reveals that high runoff (over 300 mm a year) occurs in eastern humid regions, along the continent's midwestern and northwestern coast and adjacent Cordilleran ranges, in the Rocky Mountains of the United States, and in a southernmost segment of the Cordilleran range extending through most of Central America. Smaller rates of runoff (10 to 300 mm) occur in a wide longitudinal swath of lesser precipitation extending southward from eastern Alaska, through the central plains regions of Canada and the United States, and throughout much of Mexico.

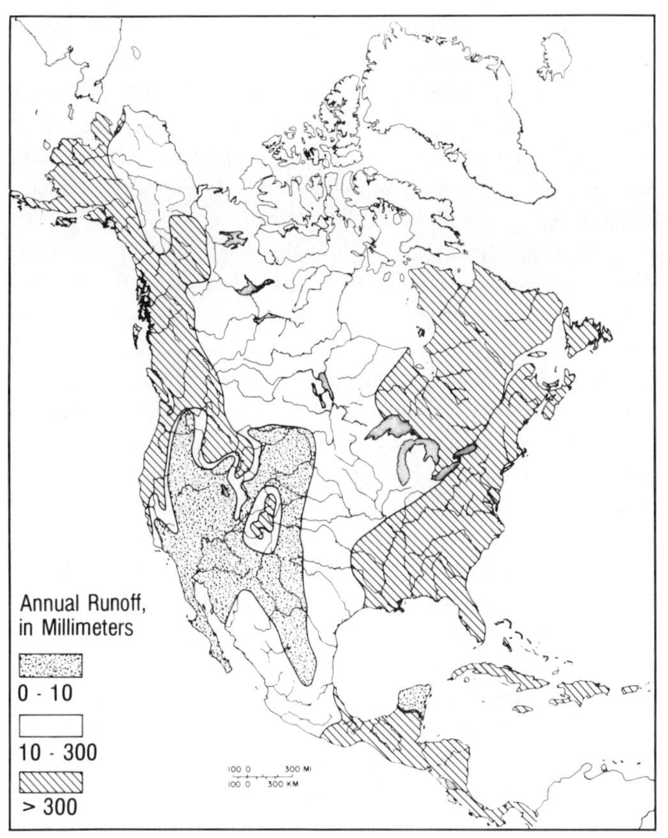

Figure 5. Generalized map showing annual average runoff in North America, in millimeters. (From Riggs and Wolman, 1989, Fig. 4.)

Least runoff (0 to 10 mm) occurs in arid and semiarid regions of the western United States and central and northwestern Mexico. Runoff from Greenland and the northern Canadian islands is as yet not fully measured and charted. Factors that determine the temporal and spatial variability of streamflow of the continent are addressed by Riggs and Harvey (1989).

Plates 3A and 3B in Wolman and Riggs (1989) show, respectively, runoff from North America in much greater areal detail than Figure 5, and areal flow regimes throughout the continent. Flow regimes identify the variation of runoff throughout an average year at given points in stream systems. When areally integrated, as in Plate 3B, flow-regime maps are useful for hydrological comparisons and quantitative analysis of river basins.

The total annual runoff of water averaged over a period of many years constitutes approximately the overall water supply of a continent. The concluding section of this chapter provides a quantitative assessment of the total runoff (water supply) of North America, and quantitative comparisons of the magnitude of its water supply with that of the six other continents, and with the total water supply of all the world's land masses.

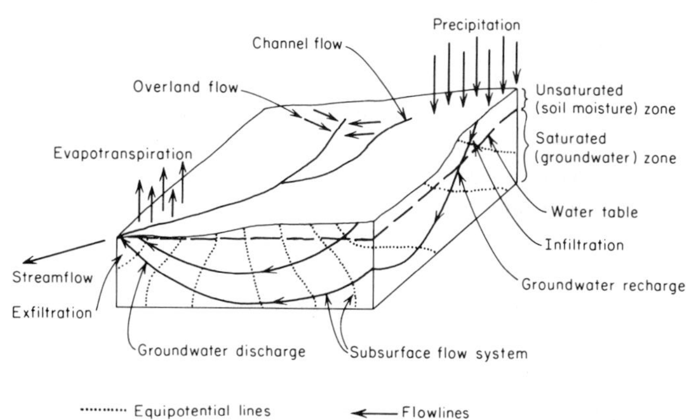

Figure 4. Schematic flow system and terminology. (After Freeze and Cherry, 1979, p. 3. Reprinted with permission of the publisher.)

Low flow and drought. Droughts and floods represent the two extremes of surface-water occurrence. Normal or average flow lies between these generally infrequent endpoints. The smallest rate of flow of a stream commonly occurs in the same season each year, and for many streams in approximately the same month each year, in relation to regularly repeating climatic conditions.

Measured flow regimes show that over much of the United States and southern Canada the smallest flows (low flow) generally occur in late summer when temperature and evapotranspiration rates are highest and snowmelt runoff has ceased. Two such low-flow periods occur annually in some colder areas of the northern United States and southern Canada, one at the usual time elsewhere during the late summer, and a second one during winter when much of the surface moisture accumulates as snowpack. In the far north the minimum flow always occurs in late winter or early spring as the result of lengthy periods of Arctic temperature that restrict both surface-water flow (frozen surface water) and ground-water discharge (permafrost).

Minimum streamflow in Mexico, Central America, and the Caribbean Islands commonly occurs in the spring, the season of lowest precipitation in those regions.

Under natural drainage conditions, without man-made surface storage reservoirs, streamflow during periods of minimal or no precipitation commonly is maintained by discharge of ground water. Except for cold regions in which a hard freeze may immobilize water, cessation of streamflow can occur only when ground-water storage is depleted, either by natural discharge or by pumping. In regions of heavy pumping, such as the irrigated farmlands of the western United States and parts of Mexico, and along alluvial valleys of large streams, extraction of ground water may reverse hydraulic gradients and induce stream water to flow into ground-water reservoirs. During periods of minimal streamflow, the amount of water diverted in this manner may be sufficient to "dry up" the streams.

Annual low flow and variability of low flow are expressed in a number of statistical and graphical ways, each having its merits for particular purposes. Most methods involve probability analysis of annual low-flow records for a period of many years, utilizing selected data representative of the low-flow characteristics. Rogers and Armbruster (1989) employ a number of graphical illustrations to describe these methods and their applications in surface-water hydrology.

All regions of North America incur infrequent drought, with resultant human and ecological detrimental consequences. Minimal streamflow or absence of flow over an extended period of time is symptomatic of hydrologic drought conditions. Hydrologic drought usually is attributable to a pronounced deficiency of precipitation extending over an abnormally long period of time. Severity of the drought may be aggravated by accompanying decreased ground-water storage and base-flow discharge to streams, and by abnormally high air temperature with associated increase in rates of evaporation.

In addition to hydrologic drought, many other forms of drought have been identified, some for scientific usage and others for practical purposes. The World Meteorological Organization (Subrahmanyan, 1967) has defined six types of drought:

1. *Meteorological drought.* Defined in terms of deficiencies in precipitation in absolute amounts and for specified duration.

2. *Climatological drought.* Also defined in terms of deficiencies in precipitation, but expressed as a ratio to mean or normal values rather than in absolute amounts.

3. *Atmospheric drought.* Defined in terms of atmospheric moisture and precipitation, but including temperature, humidity, wind velocity, and other pertinent atmospheric phenomena.

4. *Agricultural drought.* Defined, usually for a specific crop or group of related crops, in terms of the amount of soil moisture and plant behavior (i.e., wilting) under prolonged soil-moisture deficiency.

5. *Hydrologic drought.* Defined mainly in terms of deficiency in surface- and ground-water storage and flow as a result of natural moisture shortage.

6. *Water-management drought.* Serious water shortages attributable to inadequate preparations to cope with any of the previous five natural types of drought.

In any of these drought events, water is the principal factor, and for that reason the classification is an overlapping one. Most droughts will have at least several characteristics of the six types. Natural drought of regional proportions is largely beyond man's control, although advance planning and preparations may ease the impact. Water-management drought is the most amenable to alleviation by means of advance planning, engineering, and management preparations. Where irrigation is practicable and feasible, agricultural drought also may be subject to amelioration.

Floods. Floods, like drought occurrences, are natural, recurring hydrologic events. The primary natural function of flood plains is to store and convey intermittent uncommonly large volumes and high stages of runoff that exceed the capacity of defined stream channels. Flood plains become hazards only after man inhabits and develops them. Virtually all major population centers of North America, and many minor ones, lie adjacent to rivers, lakes, bays and estuaries, and oceans, all of which are subject to overbank flow of water of one form or another.

Floods occur in great variety throughout the continent, wherever water is deposited on the land at rates in excess of the capacity of normal flow routes to accommodate it. They may occur during any season or month of the year. Tidal waves and storm surges inundate ocean, estuary, and bay-shore areas. In humid regions, heavy and prolonged rainfall, aggravated by snowmelt at times, generates flood runoff in river basins. Thunderstorms produce flash floods, especially throughout mountain regions and in arid regions of the southwestern United States and Mexico. Spring thaw in areas of heavy snowpack accumulation generates flood runoff, most commonly in mountainous areas and lower borderlands of the northwestern United States, Canada, and Alaska. In summer and early fall, hurricanes and tropical storms release large quantities of water on the Atlantic and Gulf Coasts of the United States, inland regions adjacent to the coastal states, and the Caribbean islands, often with widespread inundation and flood damage.

Magnitude of flooding is dependent on the physiographic setting and the coincidence of climatological events and the state of water storage in surface- and ground-water systems. In river basins the primary factors that generate storm-derived flooding include the amount and intensity of precipitation, ability of lakes, the soil, and ground-water reservoirs to store some of the rain water, topography, and the level of development of the basin (i.e., paved areas, storm drains). Inasmuch as moisture content of the soil, ground-water storage, and land development vary with time, similar rainfall events may generate different flood responses. Snowmelt alone may produce floods, but more commonly it exacerbates flooding produced by rainfall. Coastal flooding is subject to the influences of all these factors, and additionally, the flooding effects of tropical storms and hurricanes can be aggravated by strong landward wind, which raises coastal tide levels and "piles" seawater on shorelands.

Major flooding also may be precipitated by channel blockage created by ice jams, volcanic flows, landslides and mud flows, drainage blockages by glaciers, and the failure of reservoir dams.

The economic attractiveness of flood plains is readily apparent: level ground, fertile soil, ease of access, scenic settings, and ready availability of water supplies. However, flooding is one of the most destructive natural hazards in North America. Floods in the United States cause ten times as many deaths as any other geologic hazard (Robinson and Spieker, 1978), and damage and fatality rates are continuing to rise. About 6 percent of the land area of the United States is prone to stream flooding. That percentage does not include low-lying coastal areas subject to flooding from hurricanes and coastal storms.

Government programs alert citizens to the hazards inherent in floodplain usage and attempt to restrain inappropriate development and losses through zoning efforts, flood-forecasting and warning systems, Federally sponsored flood insurance in areas approved for development, and denial of that protection or other financial assistance in areas heavily prone to flooding such as most coastal barrier islands.

In addition, major engineering approaches are employed in efforts to manage flooding. Many dams and reservoirs are built solely or primarily for the purpose of flood control. River-bank levees help to confine floodwater to channels. Rerouting of river flow bypasses developed areas prone to flooding. Many of these flood-wall or redirecting efforts may alleviate flooding along the targeted reaches of a river while exacerbating the intensity of flooding downstream.

Complete protection from floods by engineering works is never achieved, and these measures may create a false sense of security that encourages further development and increases risk.

Lakes and wetlands. Lakes and wetlands are major components of the surface-water regimen in several parts of North America, most particularly the broad regions of glacial terrane of Canada and the north-central United States (Winter and Woo, 1989). Lakes occupy about 8 percent of the surface area of Canada, and much smaller fractions of the rest of the continent. They are most numerous in the subarctic region, Canadian Shield, Atlantic provinces of Canada, northeastern and north-central United States, and the state of Florida.

Wetlands occur locally throughout much of the continent, but large wetland areas are most prevalent in the subarctic, the north-central plains region, and the Atlantic and Gulf coastal zone. Wetlands cover about 18 percent of Canada, but less than 4 percent of the United States. They include bogs, fens, swamps, marshes, muskegs, and sloughs.

Lakes and wetlands are dynamic water systems, continuously receiving and releasing water though interchange with the atmosphere, streams, and ground water. Lakes and wetlands of North America have some general hydrologic and ecological similarities, but commonly they are unlike in many respects owing to differences in mode of origin, physical and hydrologic settings, and biology. Hydrologically they may differ in many aspects of water inflow, storage, outflow, evapotranspirative release of water to the atmosphere, and thermal and chemical chararacteristics of the water. Integrated physical, chemical, and biologic processes, many of which are as yet only poorly understood, are operative in both lake and wetland environments.

All lakes and many wetlands occur in topographic depressions. The scouring action of moving glaciers created many lake basins of Canada and the northern United States. Gouging of bedrock joints, faults, and bedding planes removed large blocks of rock to form depressions. Lakes occupying these basins characteristically have irregular shorelines that reflect the structural features of the area. Glacial scour created a large percentage of the world's lakes, including the greatest number of its largest lakes. Some shallow lakes created in this manner subsequently were filled with inflowing sediment; they remain saturated, however, and sustain wetlands referred to as muskeg.

Virtually all the thousands of lakes occurring on surficial glacial sediments of Canada and the northern United States were initially formed in kettle holes, which are depressions created by the melting of ice masses buried in the glacial deposits. Kettle-hole lakes are commonplace on glacial terrane skirting the southern rim of the Canadian Shield. They also occur in mountainous areas that have experienced glacial deposition.

Lake basins also are formed by glacial damming of valleys. Active glaciers may create impoundments when the flowing ice dams a valley or lowland. Fluvial processes stemming from glacial melting may form lakes in river valleys, such as by discharge of sediment from a tributary stream to form a fan and impoundment in the receiving stream channel. In reverse manner, buildup of glacial outwash deposits in the main stream of a drainage system may create lakes in dammed tributary valleys. Geologic evidence indicates that this occurred along the Mississippi River during late Pleistocene time.

Landslides and tectonic activity form many lake basins. Landslide dams are created by rock slumps, mud flows, and rock and debris avalanches. Earthquakes and abnormally heavy rainfall are the most common triggering mechanisms. Most landslide dams are breached and fail in a short time, but some large lakes formed by this process have persisted for many years—Hebgen Lake, Montana, is an example. Down-throw or tilting of fault blocks may create geologic dams in active tectonic regions. Lakes of this origin are common in the Basin and Range Province of the western United States. Grabens have formed lake basins in many tectonically active regions of North America. Among the largest are Lake Tahoe (California and Nevada), Pyramid Lake (Nevada), and Great Salt Lake (Utah), in the United States, and Lake Nicaragua in Nicaragua.

Land subsidence from natural geologic causes can create depressions, which may form lake basins or wetland areas. Dolines (sinkholes), commonly circular in outline, are formed by collapse of surficial soil and rock overburden into caverns produced by the dissolution of carbonate rocks. Many of Florida's numerous lakes originated in this way. The subsidence of volcanic craters produces calderas, which when filled with water, form steep-sided, circular lakes. Crater Lake, Oregon, is a familiar example.

Ground-water discharge in low-lying land areas may create wetlands. The constant supply of water keeps the soil saturated and may permit growth of aquatic vegetation. A similar wetland setting may be created by impediments to ground-water flow in the subsurface that generate upward flow of ground water and discharge at the land surface to form ponds, lakes, or wetlands. Freeze (1969) and Winter (1976) cite several examples in Canada and the United States.

Permafrost terrane underlying northern Canada and Alaska inhibits or prevents ground-water circulation; this impervious substrate impedes infiltration of surface water, which may fill depressions in the land surface to form lakes and wetlands. Intermittent thaw of the shallow permafrost may create subsidence depressions in the land surface favorable to ponding as lakes or wetlands.

Influences of man on surface-water systems. Significant alterations of North America's surface-water flow systems and water chemistry result from the actions of man (Hirsch and others, 1989). Principal among these are (1) diversions of water from one basin to another or one region to another; (2) imposition of reservoir storage on flow regimens; (3) pollution; (4) modifications of wetlands (elimination, reduction in area, expansion, or alteration of water chemistry); and (5) hydrologic and chemical changes associated with land development (stimulation of erosion and sedimentation, alteration of runoff and infiltration characteristics, and changes in rates of evapotranspiration).

Ramifications of man's disturbances of terrain and natural water systems extend beyond stream environments to affect the biosphere in intricate and numerous ways not yet fully understood. Direct, measurable streamflow effects of man's activities include: alternation of long-term average flow, changes in low-flow and flood-flow magnitude, and changes in chemistry and sediment load of streams.

Streamflow changes caused by undertakings that involved damming of streams, urbanization, interbasin transfer of water, or the diversion of water from streams for usage have been documented with some certitude. Williams and Wolman (1984) compared the magnitude of average annual floods below 29 selected dams in the central and western United States with flood records collected prior to their existence; floods with the dams in place ranged from about 3 to 90 percent of pre-dam flood magnitudes, with an average reduction of 40 percent. Less clearly demonstrated are the comparatively subtle effects on streamflow of man-initiated changes in vegetation, alteration of channel configuration, land disturbances by mining, and land drainage operations. Their evolution is gradual, and their impacts on runoff and water quality are more diffuse.

Ground water

Unlike surface water, which can be observed, measured, and studied directly, ground water is hidden from view and direct access, and investigation necessitates indirect methods and much subjective interpretation. It may be said that ground-water science is both old and new—its present practice encompasses both its century-old emphasis on resource aspects of ground water (water supply) and its broadened application in the past three or four decades to the wide assortment of chemical and physical functions of ground water in the biosphere (the environment) and in geologic processes (see Meyer and others, 1988).

A major share of the early, fundamental groundwork in hydrogeology was laid by North American scientists, but with certain important contributions by Europeans as well. Though born of a merger of geology and hydrology (hency, *hydrogeology*), it is now a much broader multidisciplinary science that addresses the manifold functions of ground water as an active liquid component of the environment and a participant in many geologic processes.

Water-supply needs continue to motivate ground-water investigation, but these concerns have been somewhat subordinated by more complicated, multidisciplinary hydrogeological problems relating to environmental protection, water quality and waste management, and geotechnical engineering endeavors involving ground water.

Hydrogeology. A ground-water regime is a dynamic system in which water is continuously in motion, flowing from areas of recharge to the system to areas of discharge from it (Fig. 4), and fluctuating in the quantity in storage with changes in rates of replenishment and outflow. In a typical ground-water flow system, movement of water takes place through an extensive, heterogeneous geologic framework containing interconnected openings.

The framework generally consists of permeable units, the water-bearing zones or aquifers, and adjacent, less permeable units commonly referred to as aquitards, which retard flow but are not thought to be capable of fully preventing it.

Fresh-water aquifer systems underlie virtually all of North America and generally extend to depths of several hundred to several thousand feet. The systems may be differentiated and

Figure 6. Approximate depth to saline ground water (base of fresh ground water) in the United States. (After Feth and others, 1965.)

mapped on the basis of their water-bearing characteristics—most particularly the nature and distribution of openings in the rocks and the thickness and geometry of permeable and less permeable units composing each system. The openings consist of pores, fractures (joints, shear zones, and faults), lava tubes, and caverns and other such solution-derived voids, some of which were formed contemporaneously with the rock and others by subsequent geologic processes.

Using criteria formulated on those differentiating characteristics, Heath (in Back and others, 1988, Plates 2 and 3) prepared two hydrogeologic maps of the continent showing (A) consolidated-rock (bedrock) ground-water systems, and (B) surficial unconsolidated or semiconsolidated deposits that form widespread shallow to deep ground-water systems underlying the land surface. They are reproduced as Plates 11 and 12, respectively, in this volume.

As shown on Plate 11, consolidated rocks form the basement or bedrock of North America. In extensive areas of the continent, they are exposed at the land surface as well, cropping out most prominently in rugged mountain areas devoid of overburden. Shallow unconsolidated and semiconsolidated deposits that overlie the bedrock in many areas have been omitted in order to reveal the consolidated rocks fully for identification and comparison of their water-bearing properties. Consolidated rocks contain important, productive aquifers throughout much of North America; yet in some regions their water-bearing capacity is relatively small and may be overshadowed by overlying permeable unconsolidated rocks.

Plate 12 shows the distribution of overlying unconsolidated to semiconsolidated materials. In the main, they include: glacial deposits blanketing much of north-central and northeastern North America, coastal plains of the Atlantic, Gulf, and Caribbean regions, intermontane valley fill of the western mountain and Basin-and-Range regions, bolsons and other broad deposits of alluvium, and alluvium flanking major rivers. Where saturated, highly permeable sandy beds commonly occurring in all these deposits transmit huge quantities of ground water and are productive sources of water supply.

Saline ground water generally lies beneath the fresh ground-water systems, demarcating the lower boundary of fresh-water occurrence. Saline ground water has little or no utilitarian value. Deep-lying saline ground-water reservoirs are candidate environments for disposal of liquid wastes by deep-well injection. Figure 6 shows the approximate depth to saline ground water in the United States, and accordingly the thickness of overlying fresh ground-water systems. Under certain hydrogeologic conditions, fresh water may occur beneath saline aquifers.

Ground-water regions. The same hydrogeologic characteristics and criteria on which Plates 11 and 12 were prepared provide a basis for division of North America into distinctive ground-water regions, as shown on Figure 7. Classification of the myriad ground-water settings into differentiated regions is a useful and concise means of synthesizing and displaying the complex hydrogeology of the continent.

Figure 7, reproduced from Heath (in Back and others, 1988), delineates 28 regions, differentiated primarily on the basis

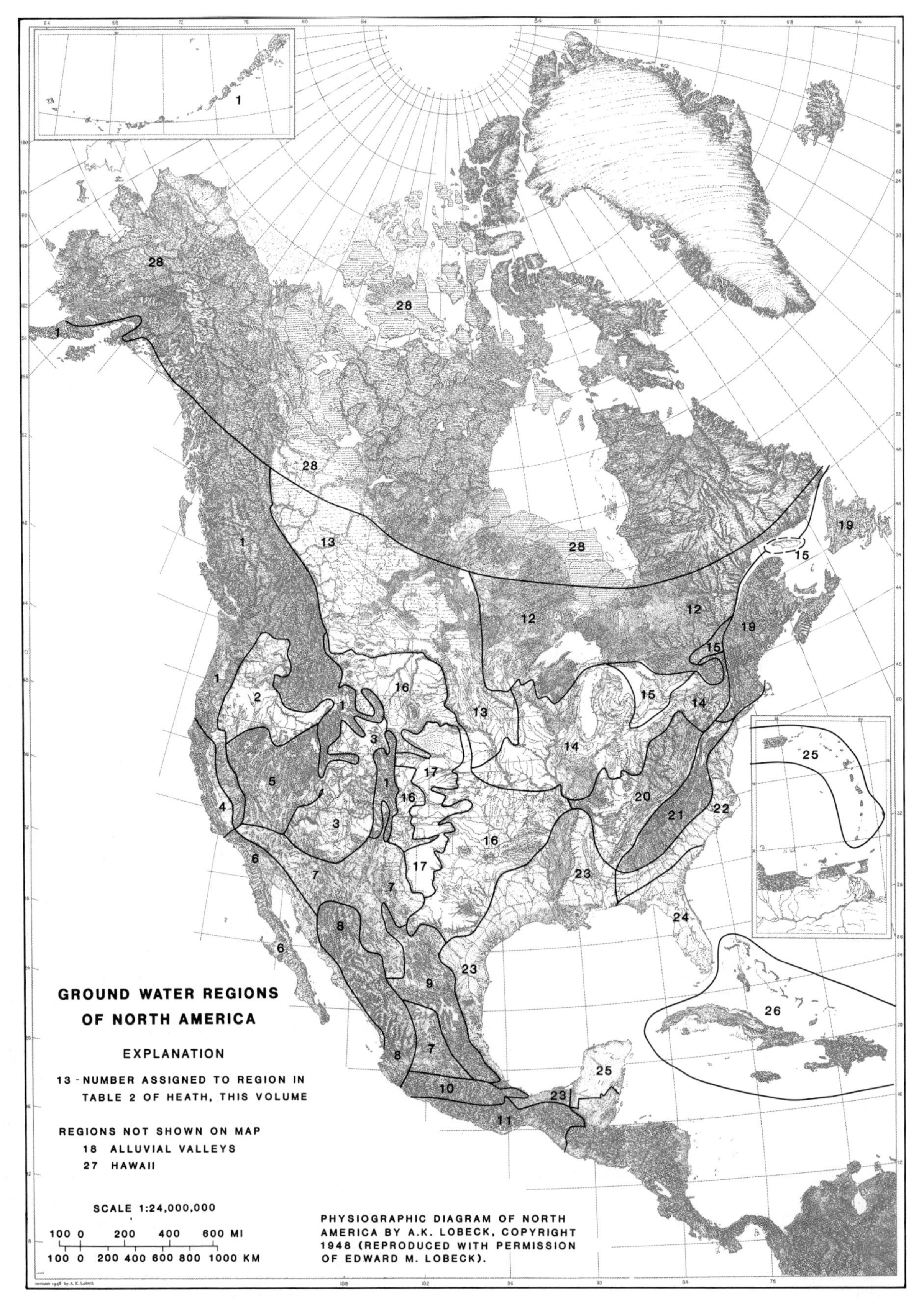

Figure 7. Ground-water regions of North America. (From Heath, 1988, Fig. 3.)

TABLE 1. GROUND-WATER REGIONS OF NORTH AMERICA AND THEIR HYDROGEOLOGIC SETTINGS*

Region	Hydrogeologic Setting
1. Western Mountain Ranges	Mountains with thin soils over fractured rocks of Precambrian to Cenozoic age alternating with valleys underlain by alluvial and glacial deposits of Pleistocene age. Includes the Puget-Willamette Trough of Washington and Oregon.
2. Columbia Lava Plateau	Low mountains to undissected plains underlain by discontinuous alluvial deposits and thin soils over a thick, complex sequence of lava flows irregularly interbedded with unconsolidated deposits. The lava flows and sediments range in age from Miocene to Holocene.
3. Colorado Plateau and Wyoming Basin	A region of canyons, cliffs, and plains underlain by thin residuum and colluvium over horizontal to gently dipping consolidated sedimentary rocks of Paleozoic to Cenozoic age.
4. Central Valley and Pacific Coast Ranges	Broad, relatively flat valleys underlain by thick alluvial deposits bordered along the coast by low mountains composed of semiconsolidated sedimentary rocks and volcanic deposits of Mesozoic and Cenozoic age.
5. Great Basin	Alternating wide, relatively flat-floored basins underlain by thick alluvial deposits and short, subparallel mountain ranges composed, in part, of crystalline and sedimentary rocks of Paleozoic and Mesozoic age and, in part, of volcanic rocks of Cenozoic age.
6. Coastal Alluvial Basins	Relatively flat valleys underlain by thick alluvial deposits separated by mountain ranges composed of metamorphic and sedimentary rocks of Mesozoic age and volcanic rocks of Cenozoic age.
7. Central Alluvial Basins	Relatively flat valleys underlain by thick alluvial deposits separated by elongated, discontinuous mountain ranges composed, in part, of sedimentary rocks of Paleozoic and Mesozoic age and, in part, of volcanic rocks of Cenozoic age.
8. Sierra Madre Occidental	A relatively high, dissected region of thin regolith over a complex sequence of volcanic rocks of Cenozoic age.
9. Sierra Madre Oriental	A relatively high area of anticlinal mountain ranges and synclinal valleys underlain by thin regolith over sedimentary rocks of Mesozoic age.
10. Faja Volcanica Trans-mexicana	A high, mountainous area underlain by thin regolith over a complex sequence of volcanic rocks of Cenozoic age.
11. Sierra Madre Del Sur	A highly dissected mountainous area underlain by thin regolith over metamorphic rocks of Precambrian and Paleozoic age, sedimentary rocks of Mesozoic age, and volcanic rocks of Mesozoic and Cenozoic age.
12. Precambrian Shield	A hilly terrane underlain by glacial deposits over complexly folded to flat-lying metamorphic rocks of Precambrian age. Along the southwest side of James Bay, the bedrock consists of relatively flat-lying consolidated sedimentary rocks mostly of Paleozoic age, which overlap the metamorphic rocks of the Precambrian Shield.
13. Western Glaciated Plains	Hills and relatively undissected plains underlain by glacial deposits over relatively flat-lying consolidated sedimentary rocks of Mesozoic and Cenozoic age.
14. Central Glaciated Plains	An area of diverse topography, ranging from the plains of Iowa to the Catskill Mountains of New York, underlain by glacial deposits over flat-lying consolidated sedimentary rocks of Paleozoic age.
15. St. Lawrence Lowlands	A hilly area underlain by glacial deposits over flat-lying consolidated sedimentary rocks of Paleozoic age.
16. Central Non-Glaciated Plains	Relatively undissected plains underlain by thin regolith over flat-lying consolidated sedimentary rocks of Paleozoic to Cenozoic age. Includes the Black Hills, where metamorphic rocks of Precambrian age are exposed in a dome structure surrounded by the upturned truncated edges of the sedimentary rock layers.
17. High Plains	A relatively undissected, eastward-sloping tableland underlain by thick alluvial deposits over consolidated sedimentary rocks of Paleozoic to Cenozoic age.
18. Alluvial Valleys	Thick deposits of sand and gravel, in places, interbedded with silt and clay of Pleistocene and Holocene age, underlying flood plains and terraces of streams.
19. Northeastern Appalachians	Hilly to mountainous area underlain by glacial deposits over folded metamorphic rocks of Paleozoic age complexly intruded by igneous rocks.
20. Appalachian Plateaus and Valley and Ridge	Hilly to mountainous area underlain by thin regolith over flat-lying to folded consolidated sedimentary rocks of Paleozoic age. The folded rocks of the Valley and Ridge province differ somewhat in their water-bearing characteristics from the flat-lying rocks of the Appalachian Plateaus but not enough to warrant including them in a separate region.
21. Piedmont and Blue Ridge	Hilly to mountainous area underlain by thick regolith over folded metamorphic rocks of Paleozoic age complexly intruded by igneous rocks. Includes downfaulted basins containing rocks of early Mesozoic age.
22. Atlantic and Eastern Gulf Coastal Plain	A relatively undissected low-lying plain underlain by complexly interbedded sand, silt, and clay that thicken progressively toward the east and south. The coastal plain deposits are of Mesozoic and Cenozoic age and overlie truncated crystalline rocks similar in composition and structure to the bedrock in region 20.
23. Gulf of Mexico Coastal Plain	A relatively undissected low-lying plain underlain by complexly interbedded sand, silt, and clay of Mesozoic and Cenozoic age that thicken progressively toward the coast and the center of the Mississippi Embayment.
24. Southeastern Coastal Plain	A relatively low-lying area underlain by thick layers of sand and clay over semiconsolidated carbonate rocks of Cenozoic age.
25. Yucatan Peninsula	A flat, low-lying area underlain by thin regolith over semiconsolidated carbonate rocks of Cenozoic age.
26. West Indies	Mostly hilly and mountainous islands underlain by intrusive igneous and volcanic rocks of Mesozoic and Cenozoic age, which are overlain by thin regolith and bordered, in part, by semiconsolidated carbonates and unconsolidated alluvial deposits of Cenozoic age.
27. Hawaiian Islands	Mountainous islands underlain by thin regolith and discontinuous alluvial deposits over a complex sequence of lava flows of Cenozoic age.
28. Permafrost Region	A topographically diverse area ranging from the highest mountains in North America eastward across the tundra plains of northern Canada. Commonly underlain by unconsolidated deposits, partly of glacial origin, overlying fractured igneous, metamorphic, and consolidated sedimentary rocks of Precambrian to Cenozoic age. Hydrogeologic conditions are dominated by continuous permafrost in the northern part of the region and discontinuous permafrost in the southern part.

*Adapted from Heath (1988).

of physiography, geology, water-bearing characteristics, mineral composition of the host rocks, hydraulic characteristics of aquifer materials, and the nature of inflow and outflow of water.

Table 1, a listing of the ground-water regions of North America, supplements Figure 7. It characterizes briefly the hydrogeology of ground-water regions identified by name on the figure. The names given to the regions generally reflect their geologic features and provide a first clue to their hydrogeologic characteristics (i.e., *Columbia Lava Plateau*). More detailed information for each region is provided by Heath (1988), including quantitative data on the hydraulic properties of principal aquifers.

Water-bearing rocks. Plates 11 and 12, Figure 7, and Table 1 reflect the wide variety of rocks that make up the ground-water systems of the continent. In general, sedimentary rocks whose intergranular pore spaces provide porosity and permeability far exceed igneous and metamorphic rocks in terms of storage and transmission capacity for ground water. There are exceptions, however; a principal one is basalt and certain other volcanic rock. During their origination, volcanic rocks may develop extensive systems of connected voids, which when saturated, are among the most productive water-bearing materials. Basalt underlying the Snake River Plain of the northwestern United States is an example.

The rock types most favorable for ground-water storage and development have received intensive study in regions of the continent in which ground water is an important segment of water supply, or a candidate or adopted environment for storage of liquid or solid wastes. These rocks include alluvium, glacial deposits, coastal plain sediments, limestone and other carbonate rocks, basalt and various other volcanic rocks, and in certain regions, plutonic and metamorphic crystalline rocks. Several chapters in Back and others (1988) describe in detail the principal water-bearing rocks of North America and the physical and chemical characteristics of hydrogeologic terranes formed by these rocks.

Hydrogeochemistry

Water quality and its protection are major concerns among the nations of North America. Hydrogeochemical information is most plentiful for the United States and Canada, with generally less density of investigation and fewer data being available for other nations.

The chemical characteristics and constituents of water govern its usefulness for the varied industrial, agricultural, and domestic needs of North American nations. Either high or low content of dissolved minerals may impair its utility for particular purposes, while the species of its chemical constituents and its physical characteristics (temperature, color, etc.) further delimit its usefulness. Chemical and biologic conditions of surface- and ground-water systems are key factors in management of disposal of industrial, agricultural, and domestic effluents and solid wastes, a uniform concern among North American nations.

The chemical character of water is also a controlling factor in fundamental natural processes of much broader significance than human usage alone. Water and solutes in rainfall reaching the Earth engage in chemical reactions with minerals, gases, and organic materials of soils and rocks. These reactions are the major source of solutes in surface and ground water. Chemical, physical, and biochemical activity within stream and lake water are the primary influences on ecological conditions supporting aquatic plant and animal life.

Streams and ground water perform geologic work through processes of erosion, dissolution, and transport. Rivers continuously convey large quantities of dissolved minerals, organic matter, and eroded sediment from the continents to the oceans. By this process they lower land elevations, create new land by sedimentation, strip and export nature's organic wastes, and shape stream-channel geometry, patterns of drainage systems, and topography.

In a somewhat analogous manner, ground water flowing through rock materials dissolves, transports, and redeposits mineral matter underground, or discharges it to a surface-water body for conveyance out of the area. Underground hydrogeochemical processes dissolve rocks unevenly, the differing rates of solution being determined by the chemical makeup of the rock minerals and the water in contact with them. Flowing ground water may enlarge or plug openings in rocks, respectively by dissolution or deposition of mineral matter, which in turn may increase or decrease the permeability of the rocks. Underground solutional activity may weaken rocks; the loss of structural strength may precipitate subsidence or collapse of the overlying land, and over geologic time may cause major regional geomorphic changes.

Surface and subsurface hydrogeochemical phenomena also carry a high order of engineering and economic significance. Their influences on the bearing strength and slope stability of land and rocks are fundamental considerations in the design of dams and other major engineering works. Sediment-laden rivers build deposits of construction sand and gravel. In a parallel sense, transport and precipitation of mineral solutes by ground water enable concentration of metallic and nonmetallic minerals in deposits of economically valuable quantities in the subsurface. Similar processes alter the configuration, size, and degree of interconnection of underground void spaces, and thereby influence their water-bearing and well-yielding capacity.

Chemical and biological characteristics of surface- and ground-water systems are key concerns in weighing the impacts of disposal of agricultural, industrial, and domestic wastes and treated effluents in those environments, now a common problem among the countries of North America and the world.

Chemical characteristics of fresh surface water. Hem and others (1989) describe the inorganic chemistry and geochemistry of rivers and lakes of North America, and the various physical and chemical processes responsible for these characteristics. Biochemical processes active in river and lake environments influence the chemical composition of the water greatly, and these effects are also covered by Hem and others (1989). Physical, chemical, and biological processes governing the chemical char-

TABLE 2. MAJOR CHEMICAL FEATURES OF RIVERS OF NORTH AMERICA

Constituent or Property	Range in Concentration of Major Ions and Related Properties*		
	CANADA†	UNITED STATES§	MEXICO, CENTRAL AMERICA, AND CARIBBEAN REGION**
Silica (SiO_2)	0.0 - 14	1.3 - 31	11.5 - 29.5
Calcium (Ca)	1.1 - 70	2.9 - 690	3.3 - 136
Magnesium (Mg)	0.4 - 28	0.5 - 400	1.0 - 34
Socium (Na)	0.5 - 59	2.0 - 7,100	1.5 - 44
Potassium (K)	<0.1 - 6.3	0.6 - 280	0.0 - 7.3
Bicarbonate (HCO_3)	0.6 - 232	7.3 - 475	11 - 271
Sulfate (SO_4)	1.7 - 100	1.1 - 2,800	3.4 - 340
Chloride (Cl)	0.2 - 84	0.7 - 11,000	2.9 - 38
Fluoride (F)	0.0 - 2.6	0.0 - 0.9	<0.1 - 0.1
Nitrate (NO_3)	0.00 - 7.0	0.00 - 43	0.04 - 24
Dissolved Solids	34 - 474	24 - 22,400	29.7 - 130
Specific Conductance (µS cm^{-1}, 25°C)	12 - 805	44 - 30,800	81 - 1,131
pH	5.1 - 8.9	6.4 - 8.7	7.4 - 8.4

*Data in mg L^{-1} except for specific conductance and pH.
†Maximum and minimum measurements among samples collected at 20 selected river sites.
§Maximum and minimum measurements among samples collected at 29 selected river sites.
**Maximum and minimum measurements among samples collected at 5 selected river sites. Includes two sites in Venezuela and Colombia, S.A.
Adapted from tables of chemical analyses in Hem and others (1989).

acter of water in lakes and wetlands of North America are described by Winter and Woo (1989). Biochemical processes and certain physical conditions (temperature, for instance) commonly are more active in lake and wetland environments, where water velocity is slower and surface exposure to the atmosphere and sunlight more extensive than in streams.

Table 2, adapted from extensive chemical data in Hem and others (1989), illustrates major constituents of rivers in North America. In a general way, the concentration of dissolved elements in fresh surface water reflects the proportionate abundance of those elements in nearby surficial and near-surface rocks of the crust. That broad generalization applies best to the four major cations of most natural water: calcium (Ca^{2+}), magnesium (Mg^{2+}), sodium (Na^+), and potassium (K^+), and to dissolved silica (silicon combined with oxygen; Hem, and others, 1989). After oxygen, these five elements are among the seven most abundant in igneous and sedimentary rocks. Aluminum (Al) and iron (Fe) are the other two of the seven prevalent elements, but in river and lake water they normally occur mainly in combined form (oxides or hydroxides).

Anions, which are present in the water in electrochemical balance with the cations, characteristically tend to reflect various chemical, biochemical, and physical processes taking place in the region. They include chemical breakdown of rock minerals by weathering and solution, aquatic biochemical activity, and various other phenomena taking place in and around water bodies that add dissolved and undissolved constituents to them. As an example, the dominant concentration of bicarbonate anions (HCO_3^-) in most surface water is attributed to carbon dioxide obtained from the atmosphere and biochemical processes taking place in the soil.

As reflected by the concentrations of chemical constituents in the analyses given in Table 2, these common cationic and anionic elements are among the principal constituents of river water of North America.

Chemical characteristics of fresh ground water. The chemical characteristics of fresh ground water, as indicated in the introduction to this section, are intimately tied to its geologic environments. The constituents of ground water are determined primarily by chemical interactions of the flowing water and the rock minerals with which it comes in contact. In most hydrogeologic settings, other sources—precipitation, surface-water bodies, and soil—are only secondary contributors to the chemical content of ground water. Because of close physical and chemical association, therefore, flow characteristics and hydrochemistry of the continent's ground-water systems are addressed jointly in the set of chapters in Back and others (1988) describing its ground-water provinces.

Chemical composition of ground water of the extensive glacial deposits at shallow depths throughout parts of central and north-central North America is difficult to generalize because of the heterogeneity of these deposits and the resultant varied chemistry of the ground water. Pyritic shale and carbonate occurring in many till deposits are the sources of the calcium, sulfate, and bicarbonate ions common to till ground water. Stephenson and others (1988) provide additional information on the chemical character of ground water in glacial deposits of North America.

Limestone and other carbonate rocks are highly soluble compared to most other rocks, and the flow of ground water through them may increase pore space and permeability. Flow, dissolution, and solute transport together create the systems of connected openings favoring development as aquifers. Precipitation of mineral matter has the reverse effect of reducing the dimensions of subsurface openings. Many additional important geochemical processes function in carbonate ground-water systems, creating a broad diversity of hydrogeologic settings. More complete description of principles and processes is provided in chapters 38 and 43 of Back and others (1988). Geochemical details for specific hydrogeologic regions of North America are covered in chapters 3, 19, and 23 through 29 of Back and others (1988). (See Appendix A, this volume.)

Unconsolidated deposits of fluvial and aeolian origin generally are more uniform in geochemical properties than those of glacial origin. This is true also of many areas of sedimentary rock. However, much of the sedimentary cover of the continent, both consolidated and unconsolidated, consists of interlayered rock sequences containing assorted assemblages of rock particles derived from varied sources, which impart differing chemical characteristics to the ground water and distinctive characteristics to the water chemistry. Sequences of sandstone, siltstone, shale, limestone, and dolomite are common in the sedimentary provinces of North America. Many of the geochemical principles covered above for other hydrogeologic settings apply to these stratified sedimentary rocks as well, including for instance, the strong contribution of carbonate minerals to the major-ion makeup by processes of dissolution.

Chemical principles and processes as they apply to sedimentary rocks of North America are described in detail in chapters 36, 44, and to lesser extent, in several other chapters of Back and others (1988).

As the results of their geodynamic origin and subsequent geologic influences, volcanic rocks of North America occur in diverse petrologic and formational settings, each having special hydrogeologic characteristics, including varied geochemical characteristics of the ground water. Solute concentrations in ground water of volcanic rocks range from less than 10 to more than 100,000 mg/l; concentrations as high as 100,000 mg/l are unusual. A large sampling of concentrations of major solutes in ground water from basalt, rhyolite, and tuff of the northwestern United States indicated a range in total dissolved solids of 264 to 477 mg/l (Wood and Fernandez, 1988).

The plutonic and metamorphic rocks that constitute the "basement" of the continent were formed at great depths, pressure, and temperature. Through uplift and erosion, large masses of these rock bodies subsequently were brought to or near the land surface where they have been subjected to ground-water flow, chemical and physical alteration, and processes of weathering and dissolution under the influence of dissolved CO_2. Being composed largely of quartz and aluminosilicate minerals (feldspar and mica), the rocks normally release the cations Na^+, K^+, Mg^{2+}, and Ca^{2+} and the anion HCO_3^- to the ground water, and these are the common constituents of water in the plutonic and metamorphic rocks of North America. These hydrochemical characteristics are discussed more comprehensively in chapter 40 of Back and others (1988), which describes the hydrogeological principles and processes active in the crystalline rocks of the continent, and in chapters 5, 14, 15, and 23, which contain specific hydrogeochemical information on crystalline-rock regions in the Canadian Shield, Appalachian, and Cordilleran provinces.

CONCLUSION—MAGNITUDE OF THE CONTINENT'S FRESH-WATER SUPPLY

North America receives nearly its equitable share of the world's precipitation: the continent constitutes 15 percent of the Earth's land area, and it receives approximately 12 percent of total precipitation on the world's land masses.

As described in this chapter, precipitation is the initial bulk source of fresh-water supply for the continents, providing the sole replenishment for surface- and underground-water systems. The standard water-budget expression $P = ET + R$ equates precipitation to evapotranspiration plus runoff. Of these three components, stream discharge as runoff is the most easily and accurately measured, and comprehensive networks of streamflow gaging stations are in operation throughout much of North America.

The average of runoff measured over many years is considered to be a reasonably good approximation of the overall rate of replenishment to, flow through, and discharge from a natural water system consisting of surface- and ground-water components. For that reason, average long-term runoff is also considered to be the long-term dependable water supply. Adjustments may be required for certain circuits in the system by which some water may escape measurement. For instance, consumptive diversions by man, or the discharge of ground water directly to an ocean or to the atmosphere by evaporation, may bypass stream gaging stations. Measured runoff, therefore, is considered to be a conservative estimate of the total stream discharge and dependable natural water supply.

Comparison of runoff among the continents indicates the magnitude of North America's fresh-water supply relative to the rest of the world. Table 3 ranks the continents by total mean annual discharge and compares their land area. North America ranks third among the continents in magnitude of runoff, although it is fourth in land area. Appreciable snowmelt runoff and only moderate "losses" by evapotranspiration in the vast middle

TABLE 3. ESTIMATED AVAILABLE WATER SUPPLY FOR THE WORLD AND CONTINENTS

CONTINENT	MEAN ANNUAL DISCHARGE (WATER SUPPLY)* KM^3/YR	RANK	LAND AREA* KM^2/YR	RANK
Asia	12,200	1	44,100	1
South America	11,100	2	17,900	4
North America	5,900	3	24,100	3
Africa	3,400	4	29,800	2
Europe	2,800	5	10,000	6
Australia and Oceana	2,400	6	8,900	7
Antarctica	2,000	7	14,100	5
All continents	39,800	-	134,000	-

*Source: Baumgartner and Reichel (1975).

and northern regions of the continent account for much of the disproportionately large runoff compared to land area.

Over the long term, North America's replenished supply of fresh water (computed as runoff) of streams, lakes, wetlands, snowmelt, and aquifer systems is estimated to total about 5,900 km^3 a year, or 16.5 trillion liters a day (Baumgartner and Reichel, 1975).

That rate of replenishment is about ten times the present total annual withdrawal rate for usage throughout the continent of approximately 551 km^3. Thus, for the continent as a whole, the water supply is abundant. What is more, the large, favorable ratio of renewal to withdrawals for use does not take into account many practices that, in effect, compound the supply manyfold. Instream usage of surface water—that is, usage without diversion from stream channels or lakes—for industrial cooling and power generation exceeds withdrawal usage many times over, and potential remains for additional such nondiversionary usage.

Repeated diversion and return of stream water by successive downstream users extends the supply significantly beyond its "once through" usage. However, its quality may be progressively diminished downstream by repeated use. Even though some North American stream systems are virtually fully developed and allocated in regions of heavy water demand, a number of river basins still have sizable further water-supply potential, through further successive downstream treatment and reuse. Many ground-water reservoirs are not fully developed and can provide additional supply; under suitable hydrogeologic conditions they also are amenable to recycling for repetitive usage to extend the supply.

Additionally, conjunctive management of snowpack, surface-water, and ground-water systems for maximum combined yield may effectively increase the supply beyond the total capacity of the three sources if developed individually. This practice, too, has unrealized potential in North America, and includes opportunities for transfer of water from localities of excess supply to those in need (see earlier discussion).

The water data in Table 3, indicating the gross global and continental magnitude of natural water supply, are of general and scientific interest, but these bulk data hide differences in intracontinental and regional distribution of water of greater economic significance. Runoff tallied by nations, as follows, reveals sharp differences in water distribution between the northern and southern countries:

Canada	2,685
United States (including Alaska)	2,340
Central American Nations	549
Mexico	330

Even these national totals blur regional and areal distribution of water within countries, variations that are important to hydrological understanding and water-related enterprise. Differences in natural water supply exercise strong influence on cultural and economic development and, hence, on the public welfare. An effort was made to identify these differences in this chapter through description of airborne moisture transport, its release as precipitation, and the surface and subsurface geohydrology of the continent.

REFERENCES CITED

Back, W., Rosenshein, J. S., and Seaber, P. R., eds., 1988, Hydrogeology: Boulder, Colorado, Geological Society of America, The Geology of North America, v. O-2, 509 p.

Baumgartner, A., and Reichel, E., 1975, The world water balance—Mean annual global, continental, and maritime precipitation, evaporation, and run-off: Amsterdam, The Netherlands, Elsevier, 179 p.

Department of Energy, Mines and Resources, 1972, Facts from Canadian maps; A geographical handbook: Ottawa, Canada, Surveys and Mapping Branch, 62 p.

Feth, J. H., and others, 1965, Preliminary map of the conterminous United States showing depth to and quality of shallowest ground water containing more than 1,000 parts per million dissolved solids: U.S. Geological Survey Hydrology Inventory Atlas HA-199, scale 1:3,168,000.

Freeze, R. A., 1969, Theoretical analysis of regional ground-water flow: Canadian Department of Energy, Mines, and Resources, Inland Waters Branch Scientific Series no. 3, 147 p.

Freeze, R. A., and Cherry, J. A., 1979, Groundwater: Englewood Cliffs, New Jersey, Prentice-Hall, Inc., 604 p.

Heath, R. C., 1988, Hydrogeologic setting of regions, *in* Back, W., Rosenshein, J. S., and Seaber, P. R., eds., Hydrogeology: Boulder, Colorado, Geological Society of America, The Geology of North America, v. O-2, p. 15–24.

Hem, J. D., Demayo, A., and Smith, R. A., 1989, Hydrogeochemistry of rivers and lakes, *in* Wolman, M. G., and Riggs, H. C., eds., Surface water hydrology: Boulder, Colorado, Geological Society of America, The Geology of North America, v. O-1, (in press).

Hirsch, R. M., Walker, J. F., Day, J. C., and Kallio, R., 1989, The influence of man on hydrologic systems, *in* Wolman, M. G., and Riggs, H. C., eds., Surface water hydrology: Boulder, Colorado, Geological Society of America, The Geology of North America, v. O-1 (in press).

Howe, C. W., and Easter, K. W., 1971, Interbasin transfers of water; economic issues and impacts: Baltimore, Maryland, Johns Hopkins Press (for Resources for the Future), 196 p.

Meyer, G., Davis, G., and LaMoreaux, P. E., 1988, Historical perspective, *in* Back, W., Rosenshein, J. S., and Seaber, P., Hydrogeology: Boulder, Colorado, Geological Society of America, The Geology of North America, v. O-2, p. 1–8.

Nace, R. L., 1969, Water and man—a world view: Paris, UNESCO, 46 p.

Riggs, H. C., and Harvey, K. D., 1989, Temporal and spatial variability of streamflow, *in* Wolman, M. G., and Riggs, H. C., eds., Surface water hydrology: Boulder, Colorado, Geological Society of America, The Geology of North America, v. O-1 (in press).

Riggs, H. C., and Wolman, M. G., 1989, Introduction, *in* Wolman, M. G., and Riggs, H. C., eds., Surface water hydrology: Boulder, Colorado, Geological Society of America, The Geology of North America, v. O-1 (in press).

Robinson, G. D., and Speiker, A. M., 1978, Nature to be commanded: U.S. Geological Survey Professional Paper 950, 97 p.

Rogers, J. D., and Armbruster, J. T., 1989, Low flows and hydrologic droughts, *in* Wolman, M. G., and Riggs, H. C., eds., Surface Water Hydrology: Boulder, Colorado, Geological Society of America, The Geology of North America, v. O-1 (in press).

Stephenson, D. A., Fleming, A. H., and Mickelson, D. M., 1988, The hydrogeology of glacial deposits, *in* Back, W., Rosenshein, J. S., and Seaber, P. R., eds., Hydrogeology: Boulder, Colorado, Geological Society of America, The Geology of North America, v. O-2, p. 301–314.

Subrahmanyam, V. P., 1967, Incidence and spread of continental drought: Geneva, Switzerland, World Meteorological Organization, International Hydrological Decade Reports on WHO/IHD Projects, no. 2, 52 p.

Trewartha, G. T., and Horn, H. H., 1980, An introduction to climate, 5th ed.: New York, McGraw Hill Book Company, 416 p.

United States–Canada Work Group 2, 1982, Atmospheric Sciences and analysis—Final report: Washington, D.C., U.S. Environmental Protection Agency, 181 p.

United States Geological Survey, 1984, Acidic precipitation, *in* National water summary 1983—hydrologic events and issues: U.S. Geological Survey Water Supply Paper 2250, p. 61–63.

Williams, G. P., and Wolman, M. G., 1984, Downstream effects of dams on alluvial rivers: U.S. Geological Survey Professional Paper 1286, 83 p.

Winter, T. C., 1976, Numerical simulation analysis of the interaction of lakes and ground water: U.S. Geological Survey Professional Paper 1001, 45 p.

Winter, T. C., and Woo, M. K., 1989, Hydrology of lakes and wetlands, *in* Wolman, M. G., and Riggs, H. C., eds., Surface water hydrology: Boulder, Colorado, Geological Society of America, The Geology of North America, v. O-1 (in press).

Wolman, M. G., and Riggs, H. C., eds., 1989, Surface water hydrology: Boulder, Colorado, Geological Society of America, The Geology of North America, v. O-1 (in press).

Wood, W. W., and Fernandez, L. A., 1988, Volcanic rocks, *in* Back, W., Rosenshein, J. S., and Seaber, P. R., eds., Hydrogeology: Boulder, Colorado, Geological Society of America, The Geology of North America, v. O-2, p. 353–366.

Manuscript Accepted by the Society February 6, 1989

Printed in U.S.A.

The Geology of North America
Vol. A, The Geology of North America—An overview
The Geological Society of America, 1989

Chapter 19

North American fossil fuels

Kenneth J. Bird
U.S. Geological Survey, 345 Middlefield Road, Menlo Park, California 94025

INTRODUCTION

Fossil fuels (oil, gas, coal, uranium, and thorium) are found in considerable abundance in widely distributed sedimentary basins on North America (Bally, this volume, Fig. 1); uranium and thorium occur in hardrock, nonbasin areas as well. For the past 100 years, North America's energy requirements have been met primarily by fossil fuels, and this will probably be true well into the next century. Although one or more of the fossil fuels have predominated at various times, the trend is toward the fuels with greater concentrations of energy per unit volume. This chapter provides an overview of North America's fossil fuels, including their geographic and geologic distribution, resource volumes, associated problems, and future research related to solving these problems. Various aspects of these fuels are covered in greater detail in other volumes of this series.

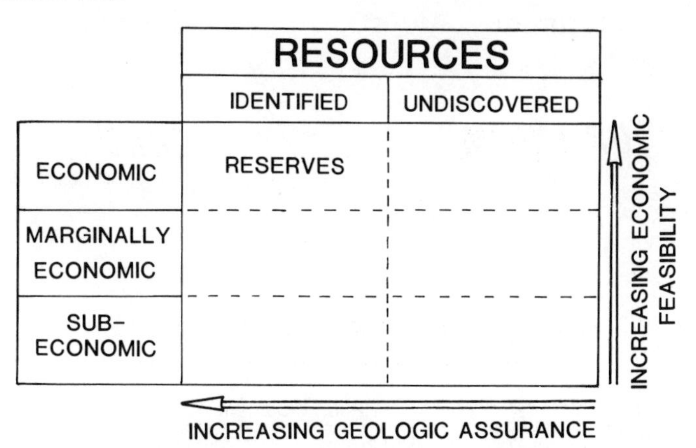

Figure 1. Simplified resource classification scheme illustrating resource categories reported in this paper (modified from U.S. Bureau of Mines and U.S. Geological Survey, 1980).

Fossil fuel volumes are described in this chapter as identified resources, reserves, and undiscovered resources. Identified resources are those whose location, characteristics, and quantity are known from specific geologic evidence. This category includes resources that could be economically extracted—reserves—and those that are currently uneconomic to extract. Undiscovered resources are those postulated to exist separate from identified resources. The interrelations of these terms are illustrated on Figure 1, a simplified version of the classification and nomenclature scheme designed for all minerals, developed by the U.S. Bureau of Mines and the U.S. Geological Survey (1980). Unconventional resources, a separate resource category not included in Figure 1, but of possible future importance, require extraction techniques different from conventional extraction techniques. Although the volume of unconventional resources may be extremely large (e.g., oil shale), most are not of economic value at the present time.

Note that resources are described from the standpoints of (1) purely geologic or physical/chemical characteristics of the material in place (e.g., grade, quality, quantity, thickness, and depth); and (2) profitability analyses based on costs of extracting and marketing the material in a given economy at a given time. A resource estimate represents an attempt to "freeze" in an instant of time a dynamic situation that is actually constantly changing and has resulted from the interplay of mineral production, new geological information, and changing economic/technological conditions.

Because differences in the geologic occurrence of fossil fuels can affect the reliability of resource estimates, the actual process of estimating resources involves uncertainty. The more reliable estimates, as noted by Averitt (1975), are for those resources that occur in stratified deposits near the Earth's surface and are often visible in outcrop or readily outlined by shallow drilling. These resources include coal, oil shale, natural bitumen (tar), and some heavy oil and uranium accumulations. In contrast, estimates of undiscovered petroleum have a greater degree of uncertainty because oil and gas are highly mobile substances that can occur in a great variety of structural and stratigraphic traps hidden deep below the surface.

Resource estimates are obviously concerned with the volume of the accumulations in question, but the energy content of fossil fuels is also an important consideration. Table 1, which compares heat-energy content, demonstrates the million-fold greater energy concentration of uranium to oil or coal. This dramatic difference in energy content is illustrated in a comparison (Fig. 2) showing the volume of each fuel required to produce the same amount of energy. For the past 150 years, the trend in the United States has been toward utilization of fuels with ever-increasing concentrations of energy—wood → coal → petroleum → nuclear (Fig. 3).

Bird, K. J., 1989, North American fossil fuels, *in* Bally, A. W., and Palmer, A. R., eds., The Geology of North America—An overview: Boulder, Colorado, Geological Society of America, The Geology of North America, v. A.

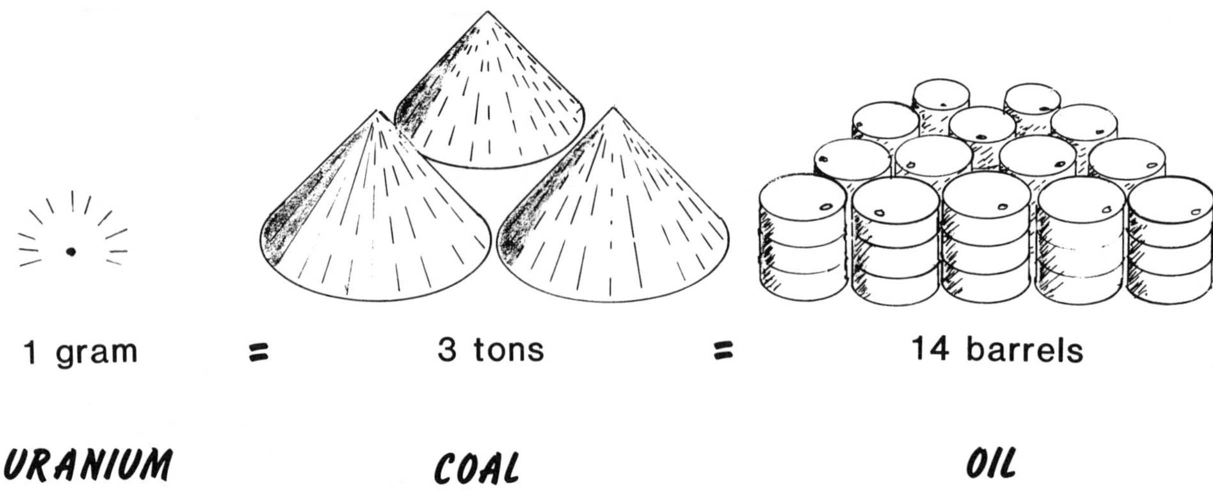

Figure 2. Comparison of fossil fuels in terms of equal energy content.

TABLE 1. ENERGY CONTENT OF FOSSIL FUELS

Fossil Fuel	Energy Content (Btu/lb)	(MJ/kg)
Coal	5 to 15 x 10^3	12 to 35
Oil	19.5 x 10^3	45
Uranium	35 x 10^9	81 x 10^6

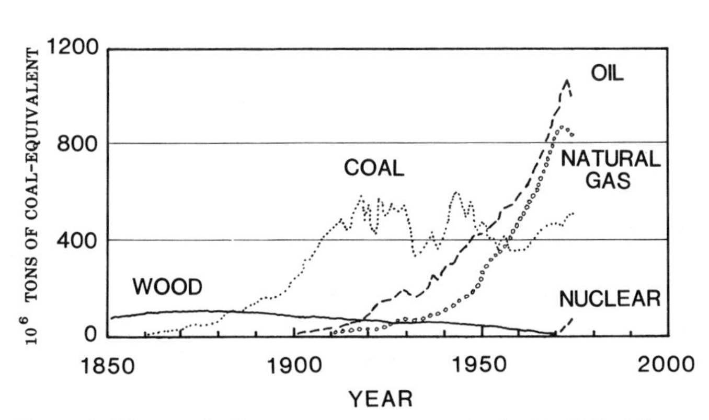

Figure 3. History of primary energy consumption in the United States (from Marchetti and Nakicenovic, 1979).

PETROLEUM

Petroleum, from the Latin meaning *rock oil,* is a form of bitumen composed principally of the elements carbon and hydrogen (hydrocarbons) that exists in a gaseous or liquid state in its natural reservoir (Hunt, 1979). The elements sulfur, nitrogen, and oxygen constitute less than 3 percent of most petroleum, but they largely account for the color and odor of the crude oil. Traces of phosphorus and heavy metals, such as vanadium and nickel, are also present. Petroleum occurs in three principal forms: (1) natural gas, which does not condense at standard temperature and pressure; (2) condensate, which is gaseous in the ground but condenses at the surface (also known as natural gas liquids or NGL); and (3) crude oil, the liquid part of petroleum. The differences in physical and chemical properties of petroleum are due to the variations in the distribution of the different sizes and types of hydrocarbon molecules.

There are two basic hypotheses of the origin of petroleum: the biogenic hypothesis and the abiogenic hypothesis. Geochemical and geological evidence clearly shows that most petroleum originated from organic matter buried with the sediments in a sedimentary basin (Hunt, 1979). The abiogenic hypothesis assumes oil forms from the reduction of primordial carbon or its oxidized form at elevated temperatures deep in the Earth. In 1987, the first significant test of this hypothesis was conducted at a location in Sweden. Here, a well was drilled on an ancient meteor impact crater; the well penetrated 6 km of granite without encountering significant hydrocarbons.

Petroleum resources are classified as conventional and unconventional. The former class includes oil, condensate, and natural gas that are recovered by conventional means (flowing or pumping). The unconventional-oil class consists of extra-heavy oil, natural bitumen (tar sands), and oil shale. Unconventional natural gas is that found in very low-permeability (<0.1 md) reservoirs ("tight" gas sands), dissolved in high-pressure hot waters associated with coal beds (coal-bed methane), or frozen in a hydrate state. Each material requires its own special extraction techniques.

North America's abundant petroleum resources are found from the Arctic to the Caribbean (Fig. 4), and are estimated to

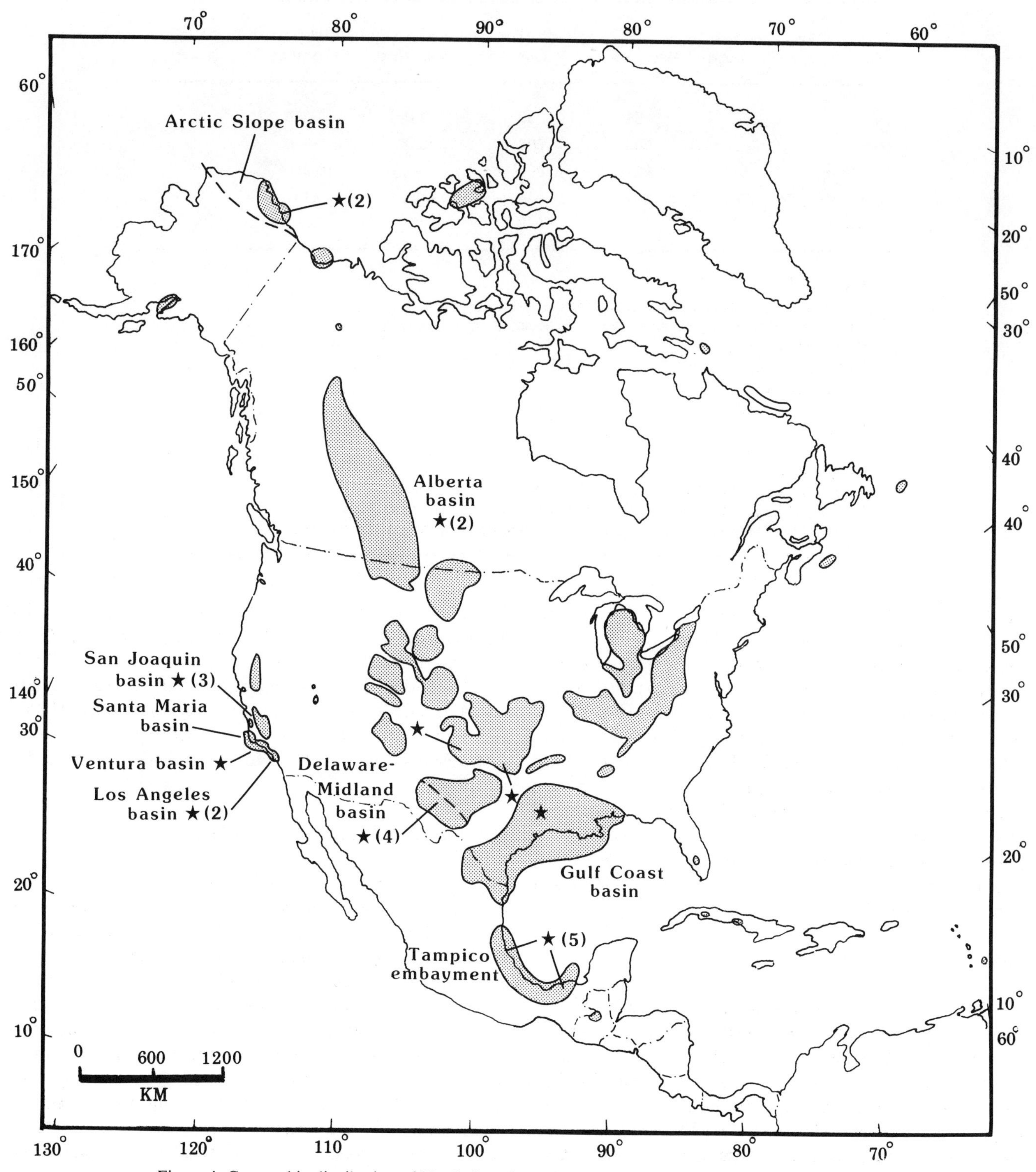

Figure 4. Geographic distribution of North American oil and gas accumulations (shaded). Compare with distribution of sedimentary basins (Bally, this volume, Fig. 1). ★ , at least one oil accumulation of more than 10^9 barrels (if more than one, total number in parentheses).

TABLE 2. SUMMARY OF CONVENTIONAL FOSSIL FUEL RESOURCES OF NORTH AMERICA

Fossil Fuel	Produced	Reserves	Identified Resources	Undiscovered Resources	Ultimate Resources*	Data Source
Oil†	186	98	98	101	385	1
Gas §	708	503	503	697	1908	1
Coal**	67	2721‡	10,892‡	——	10,959‡	2
Uranium§§	479	291	918	2751	4147	3
Thorium§§	?	——	266	301***	>567	3

Notes:

*Produced plus identified and undiscovered resources.
†10^9 barrels of oil, heavy oil, and natural gas liquids (1 m^3 = 6.29 bbl).
§10^{12} ft^3 (1 m^3 = 35.31 ft^3).
**10^9 metric tons.
‡In-place resources.
§§10^3 metric tons of U or Th.
***Includes some identified resources.

Data Sources:

1. Masters and others (1987), Masters (1989, personal communication)
2. Ridley (1982), Smith (1989), Ferm and Muthig (1982), Drummond (1986)
3. OECD Nuclear Energy Agency and International Atomic Energy Agency (1986)

represent nearly 20 percent of the world's conventional oil and gas. It is thought that roughly one-half of these resources have already been produced, one-quarter are reserves, and one-quarter remain to be discovered. Petroleum has been the predominant energy source in North America since the 1940s (Fig. 3), and North American daily production during 1987 was about 12 million (159l; 42 gal) barrels (1.77×10^6 metric tons) of oil and 1.68×10^9 m^3 (60 billion ft^3) of gas. Large amounts of unconventional oil and gas are also present. Problems associated with oil and gas include decreasing discovery rates, dwindling supplies, concerns about environmental disturbance by petroleum exploration and production activities, and pollution resulting from poor combustion of petroleum.

Resource volumes

The ultimate recoverable resources of conventional petroleum, as of January 1985, were estimated by Masters and others (1987) to total about 385 billion barrels of oil and natural gas liquids and 1,908 trillion ft^3 of gas (Table 2). Combining these conventional resources on an energy-equivalent basis (6 trillion ft^3 gas = 1 billion barrels of oil equivalent, BBOE; Fig. 5), shows that about 43 percent has already been produced (304 BBOE), that reserves constitute about 26 percent of the total (182 BBOE), and that undiscovered petroleum amounts to about 31 percent (217 BBOE). Geographically, about two-thirds of all conventional petroleum resources occur in the United States. The remaining one-third is distributed between Canada (14 percent oil, 23 percent gas) and Mexico (20 percent oil, 11 percent gas). Small amounts (<1 percent) of oil and gas are present in Cuba, Guatemala, and Barbados (Fig. 4).

Unconventional oil resources in North America are estimated to total about 6 trillion barrels of oil in place (Masters and others, 1987). Most of this resource (94 percent) is oil shale. Natural bitumen (tar sands or oil sands) constitutes the remainder.

Geographic and geologic distribution

One of the more remarkable facts about petroleum is its occurrence as a few large accumulations in a relatively small number of basins. For example, more than three-fourths of the world's oil and natural bitumen occurs in the largest 1 percent of all accumulations, and one basin (Arabian-Iranian) accounts for 42 percent of the world's total original oil reserves. Similar concentrations exist, although not in the same basins, for natural gas as well as unconventional petroleum resources. In North America, six basins account for 61 percent of the continent's original oil reserves (Table 3). These basins are the Gulf Coast, Tampico Embayment, Delaware-Midland, Alberta, San Joaquin, and Arctic Slope. The petroleum geology of these basins is summarized below.

The Gulf Coast basin (Fig. 4) developed in a post-Paleozoic passive margin setting on the Paleozoic Ouachita fold belt. Subsidence of the Gulf Coast basin took place along an arcuate zone of faults overlying and extending seaward of the

Ouachita orogenic belt. Basin fill consists of Triassic and Lower Jurassic red beds, Middle Jurassic evaporite deposits, Upper Jurassic to Upper Cretaceous carbonate and clastic sequences, and uppermost Cretaceous to Holocene clastic deposits. Some 75 percent of the oil and gas occurs in Cenozoic sandstone reservoirs trapped in structures related to salt domes, deep-seated anticlines, and rollover anticlines. Surprisingly, source rocks for Cenozoic hydrocarbons have not been identified. Oil and gas in Mesozoic rocks occur in sandstone and carbonate reservoirs trapped by faults, anticlines, permeability and truncation traps, and salt domes. Source rocks are Jurassic and Cretaceous marine shales (Curtis, 1987). The Gulf Coast basin is the largest basinal accumulation of oil and gas in the United States; yet only one field (East Texas) greater than one billion barrels is present.

The Tampico Embayment (Fig. 4) of Mexico is an extension of the Gulf Coast basin. In this part of the basin, the sedimentary fill consists of Jurassic and Cretaceous carbonate rocks and Tertiary clastic sedimentary rocks. Most oil and gas production comes from Jurassic and Cretaceous carbonate reservoirs. Source rocks are identified as marine shales of Jurassic and Cretaceous age. Petroleum accumulations in the northern part of the Tampico Embayment occur in anticlinal structures formed in response to the early Tertiary formation of the Sierra Madre, in a Cretaceous barrier reef and flanking beds (the famous Golden Lane fields), or in Upper Cretaceous to Lower Tertiary sandstones. Petroleum accumulations in the southern part of the embayment, in the Reforma area (onshore) and the Campeche Sound (offshore), occur in Jurassic and Cretaceous carbonate reservoirs in faulted, domal structures formed largely in response to salt tectonics. According to Roadifer (1987), ten fields or areas with original oil reserves exceeding one billion barrels are present in the Tampico Embayment: Arenque, Bermudez, Cactus-Nispero, Cantarell, Chicontepec, Ebano-Panuco, Giraldes, Naranjos–Cerro Azul, Poza Rica, and Samaria-Cunduacan.

The Delaware-Midland basin (Fig. 4), also known as the Permian basin, began to develop during the time of formation of the late Paleozoic ancestral Rocky Mountains. An early Paleozoic carbonate shelf was structurally segmented in Pennsylvanian time, resulting in the formation of carbonate platforms flanked by depressions, the sites of source-rock deposition. Subsidence of the basin was accentuated in Permian time, and major carbonate deposits with reefs prograded into the basins. Here, all elements of petroleum occurrence are found in optimum development, resulting in the second largest basinal accumulation of oil and gas in the United States. Reservoir rocks, mostly carbonates, are associated with a variety of traps, including stratigraphic pinchouts, reefs, and anticlines. Fields with greater than one billion barrels of recoverable oil include Slaughter-Levelland, Yates, Kelly-Snyder, and Wasson.

TABLE 3. ORIGINAL RESERVES OF OIL IN THE SIX MOST PROLIFIC PETROLEUM BASINS IN NORTH AMERICA*

Basin or Area	Original Reserves of Oil (BBO)	Number of Fields >1 BBO†
Gulf Coast, U.S.§	39	1
Tampico, Mexico	38	10
Delaware-Midland, Texas	31	4
Alberta, Canada	16	2
San Joaquin, California	13	3
Arctic Slope, Alaska	11	2
Total	148	22

*Adapted from Masters and others (1987). See Figure 4 for basin locations. Reserves in billions (10^9) of barrels oil (BBO). (1 m^3 = 6.29 bbl).

†See Figure 4 for locations of fields.

§Includes East Texas basin of some authors.

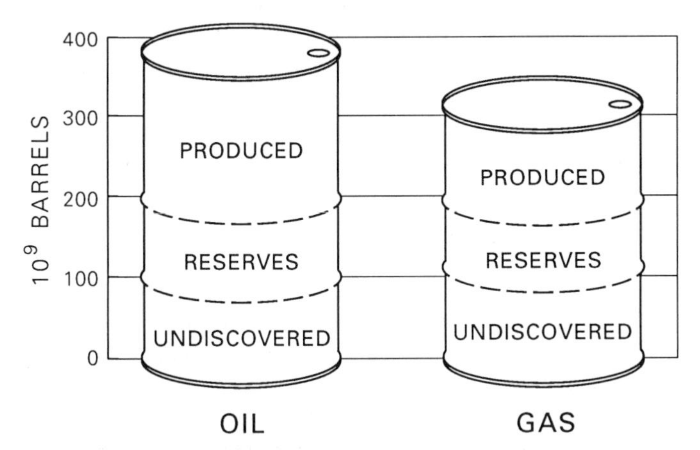

Figure 5. Estimated ultimate conventional petroleum resource volumes of North America according to Masters and others (1987). Gas converted to oil-equivalent basis (6,000 ft^3 [168 m^3] of gas per barrel of oil).

The Alberta basin (Fig. 4) is a composite entity of two major westward-thickening depositional wedges. As described by Procter and others (1984), the older wedge of late Proterozoic to early Mesozoic age is a passive margin deposit composed of clastic and carbonate rocks deposited on, and outboard of, the ancient North American craton. The second wedge of late Mesozoic and Tertiary age is a foredeep deposit composed of clastic rocks that record the change from a passive margin tectonic setting to one of active subduction, resulting in the formation of the Rocky Mountains. Petroleum source rocks are primarily marine shales of Devonian, Carboniferous, and Mesozoic age. Most oil reserves are concentrated in Devonian carbonate reservoirs (>60 percent) and Cretaceous clastic reservoirs (25 percent). Almost half of the gas reserves occur in Cretaceous reservoirs, with Devonian and Carboniferous fields accounting for about 20 percent each. Two accumulations with greater than one billion barrels of recoverable oil occur in this basin—Swan Hills and Pembina. The shallow eastern flank of the basin contains the four largest deposits of heavy oil and natural bitumen in North America, with total in-place volume of 1.35 trillion barrels (Fig. 6; Roadifer, 1987).

The San Joaquin basin (Fig. 4) located in the southern part of the Great Valley of California, is a Cenozoic basin that developed on a preexisting Jurassic and Cretaceous fore-arc basin. This Cenozoic basin, filled predominantly with marine sediments of Neogene age, is the product of the complex tectonic interaction of the North American Plate and plates in the Pacific Ocean. The most important petroleum source rocks in the San Joaquin basin are marine shales of Eocene and Miocene age. Reservoir rocks are primarily sandstones of shallow- to deep-marine origin. Some heavy oil deposits occur in diatomite reservoirs. Structural traps predominate along the west and south margins, whereas stratigraphic and combination traps predominate along the homoclinal east flank of the basin. Much of the oil in this basin is low gravity and high in sulfur content. Three accumulations with greater than one billion barrels of oil are known—Midway-Sunset, Kern River, and Elk Hills. Nearby California coastal basins (Los Angeles, Ventura, and Santa Maria) are prolific oil producers (>12 billion barrels) that have many similarities to the San Joaquin basin.

The Arctic Slope basin of northern Alaska (Fig. 4) is a composite basin composed of two wedges of sedimentary rocks, similar to the Alberta basin. The older wedge consists of upper Paleozoic and Mesozoic carbonate and clastic sedimentary rocks derived from a northern cratonic source, now tectonically removed. The younger wedge consists of upper Mesozoic and Cenozoic clastic sedimentary rocks derived from an orogenic landmass to the south, the ancestral Brooks Range. An episode of rifting, generally synchronous with subduction at the south margin of the Brooks Range, occurred near the northern margin of the basin and resulted in the formation of the Canada basin of the Arctic Ocean. Important petroleum source rocks are marine shales deposited during Late Triassic to Cretaceous time. The most important reservoirs are shallow marine to nonmarine sandstones of Triassic and Cretaceous age. The prograding clastic wedges derived from the mountains filled the foredeep basin and provided the deep burial necessary for the generation of petroleum. Most of the oil in the Arctic Slope basin is located in large, combination structural-stratigraphic traps located along the buried rift margin. Two fields with more than one billion barrels of oil are located in this basin—Prudhoe Bay and Kuparuk. Major deposits of heavy oil (20 to 40 billion barrels) occur at shallow depths in this area, as do natural gas hydrates (Werner, 1987; Collett and others, 1988).

Resource problems and future research

A most important problem related to petroleum in North America is the declining discovery rate of new oil and gas. Because this rate is less than the rate of production, reserves of oil and gas are dwindling. The decreasing discovery rate is a function of the fact that in unexplored (frontier) basins the largest fields (with a disproportionately large share of the total resource), if present, are generally found early in the exploration history, and North America has few unexplored basins or parts of basins. The United States, for example, is the most maturely explored country in the world; more than three million wells have been drilled, and in 1986, two-thirds of a world total (excluding Eastern Europe and the USSR) of 60,000 wells were drilled in the United States.

Although there are unexplored or lightly explored offshore areas and promising onshore areas (such as the Arctic National Wildlife Refuge of northern Alaska) with potential for large accumulations, the remaining undiscovered oil and gas resources of North America are expected to be found mainly in numerous small fields. It is estimated that as many as 100,000 smaller fields, each with less than 10 million barrels of in-place resources, remain to be discovered. To find these accumulations, special techniques and a better understanding of the petroleum geology of basins may be required. Various papers in Magoon (1988) provide a concise summary of the status of current research in petroleum geology, including some papers on unconventional petroleum resources.

Given that the finding rate of new fields in North America is likely to remain low (currently less than 3 barrels of oil per meter of exploratory drilling in the United States), that petroleum imports will continue to meet the demand, and that conservation efforts will continue, solutions to the problem of dwindling petroleum reserves are: (1) to recover more oil and gas from known deposits (enhanced recovery) or (2) to exploit unconventional petroleum resources. Both solutions have the common characteristics of lower production rates and higher costs compared with conventional petroleum extraction methods.

Enhanced oil recovery strategies focus on a large resource that results from another remarkable fact about petroleum: on average, only about one-third of the original oil in place is recoverable by conventional techniques. It is the two-thirds of the original oil remaining in the ground that is targeted for enhanced oil recovery. As described by Tyler (1988), this resource consists of two parts: (1) residual immobile oil, that which is held in the pore spaces of the reservoir rock by physical and chemical forces, and (2) mobile oil, that which is left in inefficiently drained reservoirs. Tyler postulates that mobile oil constitutes about 25 percent of this resource and that the key to recovery of the mobile oil fraction is better understanding of the architecture of the enclosing reservoirs and quantification of paths of fluid movement. Enhanced recovery of immobile oil involves the introduction of heat or chemicals into the reservoir to destroy constraining forces holding this oil in place. Production of heavy oil by various recovery techniques is currently underway in a number of areas of North America. Most of heavy-oil production (81%) in the United States comes from California, where 830,000 barrels per day are produced.

Although unconventional petroleum resource volumes are large, the amounts that are recoverable are limited by recovery efficiency, economics, and environmental constraints. The locations of some of the more important unconventional petroleum

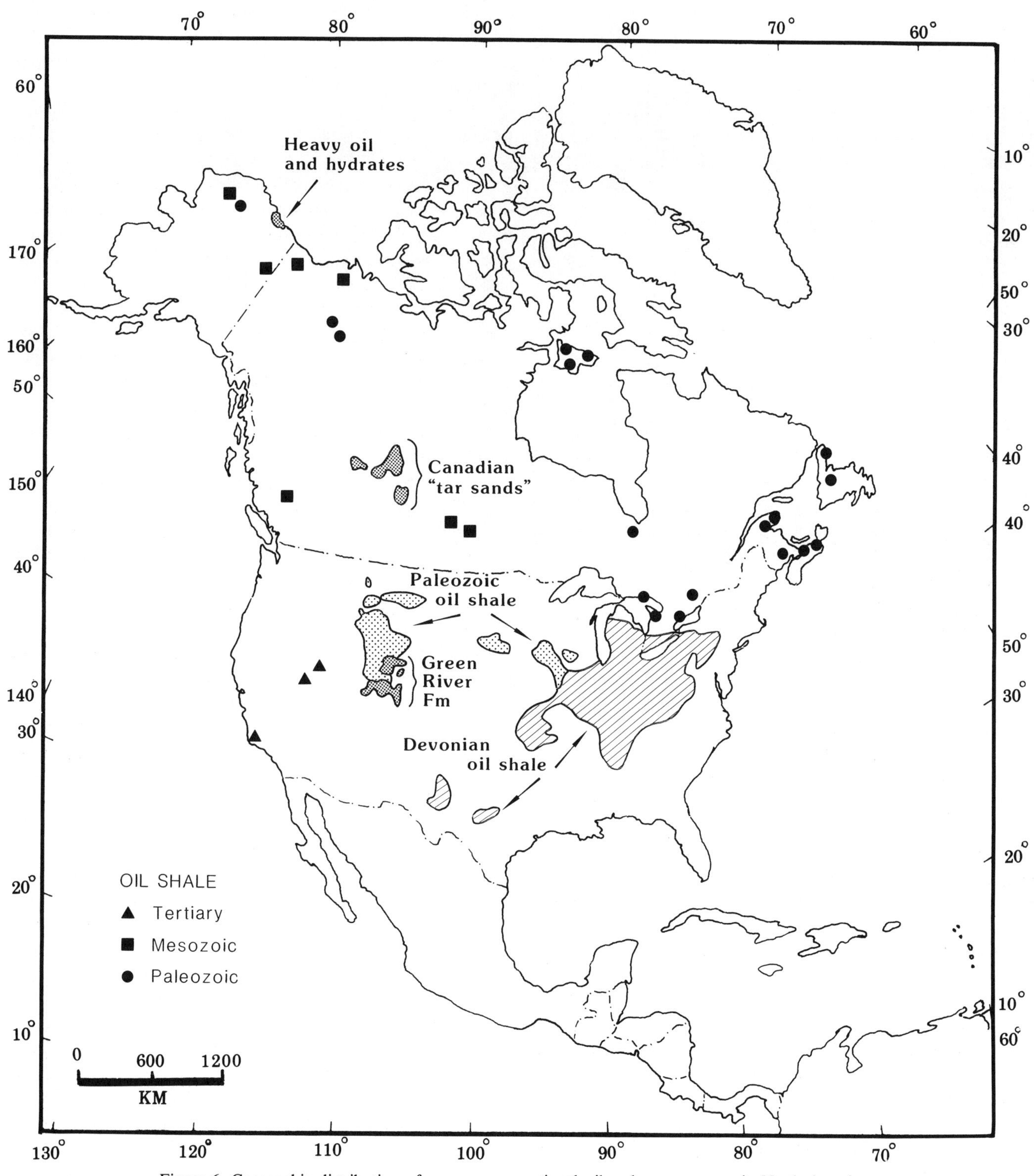

Figure 6. Geographic distribution of some unconventional oil and gas resources in North America. Compare with distribution of sedimentary basins (Bally, this volume, Fig. 1).

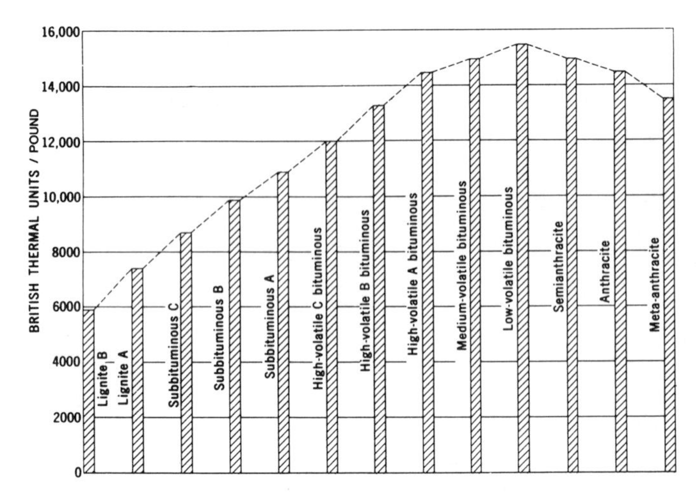

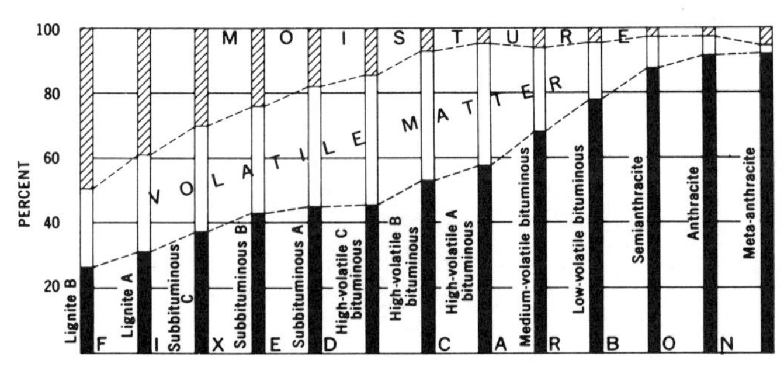

Figure 7. Comparison of heat values (on moist, mineral-matter-free basis) and proximate analyses of coal of different ranks (from Averitt, 1975).

resources are shown in Figure 6. In 1985, about 20 percent of Canadian crude-oil production (290,000 barrels/day) came from natural bitumen (tar sands) and heavy-oil deposits in the Alberta basin. Three commercial projects (two surface mining and one in-situ recovery project) and 65 experimental in-situ projects were in operation on these, the largest deposits in North America. Low permeability (tight) gas reservoirs in the United States are estimated to have potential recoverable resources approximately equal to those of undiscovered conventional gas (about 16.8 trillion m^3); about 28 million m^3 of gas per year is produced from these reservoirs. Coal-bed methane resources in the United States are estimated at 2 to 24 trillion m^3; coal-bed methane is commercially produced in the San Juan and Black Warrior Basins in the United States. The largest and richest oil shale deposit in the United States (Green River Formation) has received much study, and several pilot projects have been devoted to recovery of oil. However, there is as yet no commercial means of extracting this oil. For additional information on unconventional petroleum resources in North America, the reader is directed to publications by Masters and others (1987), Procter and others (1984), Choate and McCord (1986), Cox and Baughman (1980), Meyer (1987), Smith (1980), and U.S. Geological Survey (1988).

Other problems include concern about the environmental disturbances caused by petroleum exploration and development, especially in offshore and wilderness areas, and pollution from petroleum combustion adding to the greenhouse effect and acid rain. Environmental problems similar to those encountered in surface coal mining are also associated with development of some unconventional petroleum resources (e.g., oil shale and natural bitumen).

COAL

Coal is a complex material made up mainly of consolidated organic residues from vegetation that grew, died, and partially decomposed. The precursor of coal is peat. However, most coal that is mined includes not only mineral matter from the original vegetation, but also mineral matter carried into the swampy basins by wind and water. This mineral matter occurs in the form of noncoal interbeds or partings (volcanic ash, sandstone, mudstone, or limestone), diagenetically formed minerals (such as pyrite), and small quantities of virtually all metallic and nonmetallic elements.

Because coal has different uses and values depending on its impurities and heat content, a rigorous classification scheme has been developed by the U.S. Geological Survey (Wood and others, 1983). Coal is commonly classified by both rank and grade. Coal rank, an expression of the progressive metamorphism of coal, is based on fixed carbon content in higher rank coal and on calorific value in lower rank coal. Both increase with increasing rank. Values for fixed carbon, moisture, volatile matter, and calorific content over the entire range of coal rank are illustrated in Figure 7. Grade, a measure of coal quality, is determined according to the content of deleterious constituents. The most commonly reported parameters of coal quality are sulfur and ash content. Sulfur content of North American coals varies by region and age. It averages 1 to 2 percent but may range as high as 10 percent. Ash content of mined coal may range as high as 30 percent, but averages about 10 percent (Averitt, 1975).

Coal is widespread and abundant in North America (Fig. 8). It is found from the Arctic to the tropics, but occurs most abundantly in the United States, where it underlies about 13 percent of the land area (Averitt, 1975). Most coal in North America is Pennsylvanian, Cretaceous, and early Tertiary in age. An estimated 30 percent of the world's coal resources occur in North America where, for about 70 years (1880 to 1950), coal was the primary fuel (Fig. 3). North America currently produces more than 850 million metric tons of coal per year, of which about 10 percent is exported, primarily to Japan and Europe. Of the coal consumed in North America, about 85 percent is used in the production of electric power, while industrial uses, including steelmaking, account for the remaining 15 percent (Energy Information Administration, 1986). Problems associated with coal are primarily pollution from coal combustion and disruption of the environment in coal mining.

Resource volumes

North American coal resources (original in-place tonnage) are estimated to total about 11 trillion metric tons (Fig. 9; Table

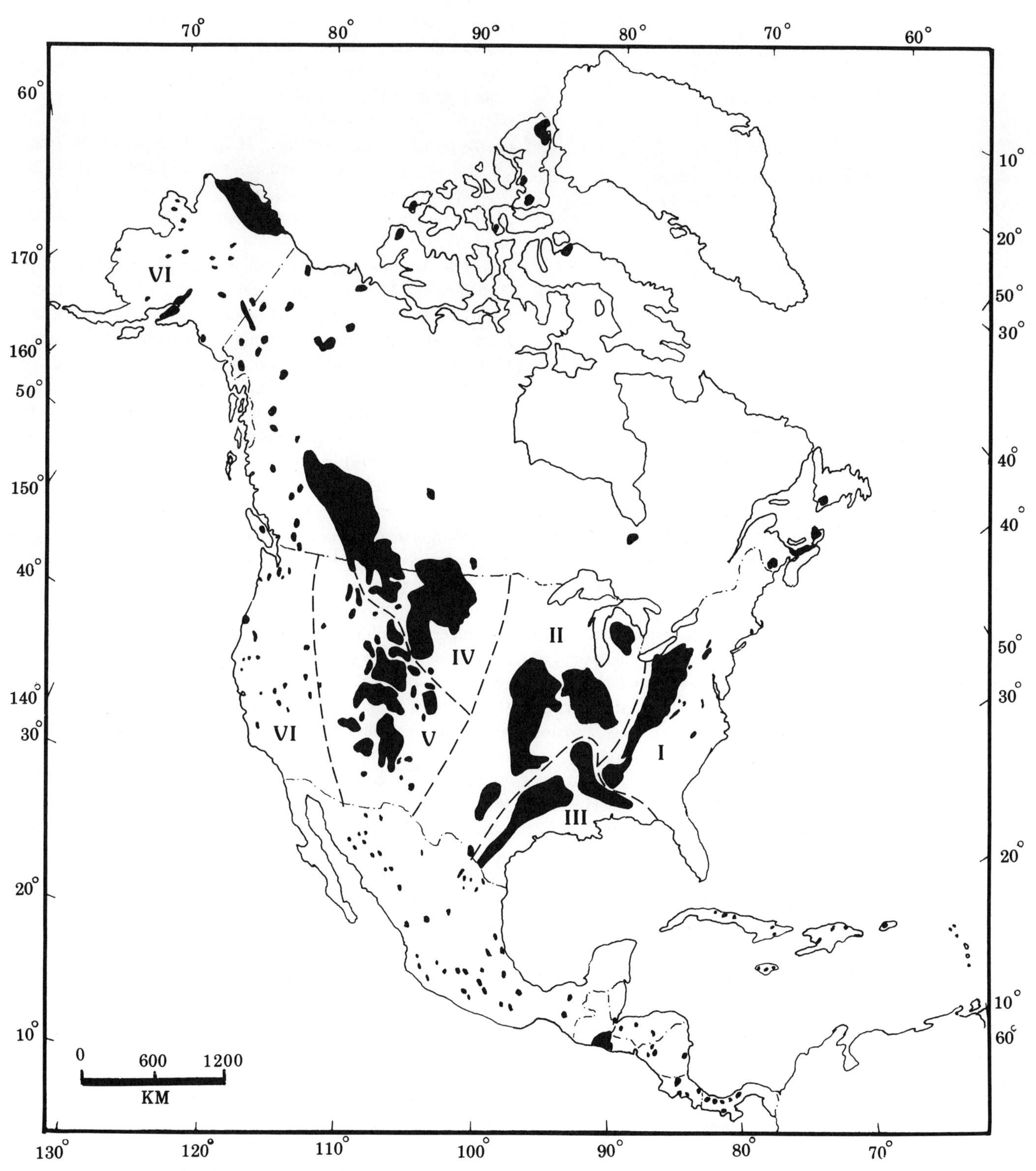

Figure 8. North American coal-bearing areas (shaded) and United States coal provinces. I, Appalachian Province; II, Interior Province; III, Gulf Coastal Province; IV, Northern Great Plains Province; V, Rocky Mountain Province; VI, Pacific Coast Province. Adapted from Smith (1989), Nelson (1987), and Drummond (1986). Compare with distribution of sedimentary basins (Bally, this volume, Fig. 1).

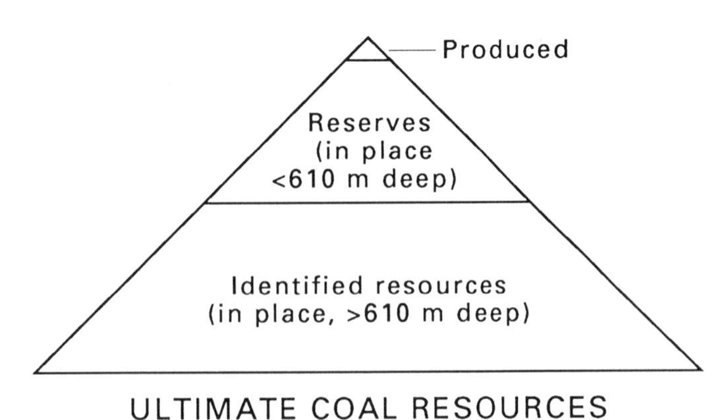

Figure 9. North American coal resources from data sources listed in Table 2.

2). These resources are found primarily in the United States (97 percent) and Canada (3 percent). A comparatively small amount (>1 percent) of North American coal resources occur in Mexico (Ridley, 1982), Guatemala, Honduras, Nicaragua, Costa Rica, El Salvador, Panama, Cuba, Jamaica, Dominican Republic, Haiti, and Puerto Rico (Drummond, 1986). Estimates from different countries are not strictly comparable because criteria for making estimates differ. Canadian estimates are conservative in that they employ geographic limits on extrapolation of the resource data control points (Smith, 1989); United States estimates are not dependent on such constraints, but rely on the establishment of approximately homogeneous coal-facies blocks, which permit larger areas to be included in the estimates (Ferm and Muthig, 1982). These estimates, in spite of their shortcomings, provide ample evidence that North American coal resources are enormous.

The amount of economically recoverable coal (reserves) is a small fraction (about 1/20th or less) of total resources and is affected by many factors, which are illustrated in Figure 10. The method of mining is one important factor. The amount of coal recovered from underground mines averages about 50 percent of the in-place coal, whereas in surface mines the recovery averages about 80 percent. North American coal reserves (in place) amount to nearly 3 trillion metric tons (Table 2). These reserves generally represent identified resources that lie less than 610 m deep—the lower limit of underground coal mining as practiced in North America. The Gulf Coast and northern Great Plains lignite deposits at depths greater than 150 m are excluded from reserves because underground mining is considered impractical in those unconsolidated deposits (Ferm and Muthig, 1982).

Geographic and geologic distribution

Most significant coal deposits and coal production in North America are associated with interior basins and bordering foreland basins of Pennsylvanian, Cretaceous, and early Tertiary age. Numerous deposits, representing relatively minor amounts of coal, occur in Pacific margin basins of Mesozoic and Cenozoic age. Coal fields of the United States have been divided into six provinces by the U.S. Geological Survey on the basis of geology, coal quality, or mining conditions. These provinces can be extended with some degree of confidence into adjacent areas outside of the United States (Fig. 8). The provinces are (1) Appalachian, (2) Interior, (3) Gulf Coastal, (4) Northern Great Plains, (5) Rocky Mountains, and (6) Pacific Coast. Their geologic settings, coal characteristics, and mining practices are summarized in the following paragraphs, taken largely from Nelson (1987).

The Appalachian Province includes the coal fields of the Appalachian Mountains and plateaus, and several disconnected basins farther east. This province can be extended northeastward to encompass coal deposits of similar age and character in eastern Canada. This is the oldest and most extensively developed coal province in the United States, and it contains about 40 percent of the bituminous coal plus nearly all of the anthracite. The minable coal is dominantly of Pennsylvanian age. Coal rank increases from west (high-volatile bituminous) to east (low-volatile bituminous through graphite) across this province, a reflection of progressively greater heating associated with greater burial depth.

Most coal reserves and most of the current mining are in high- and medium-volatile bituminous coal that is used mostly for electrical generation. Much Appalachian coal is low enough in sulfur to comply with current environmental regulations. Some coal higher in sulfur (1 to 4 percent) is present, but generally not so high as most coal from the Interior Province. Eastern coal seams may be more than 3.6 m thick, but most beds mined are 0.9 to 2.4 m thick. Through most of the province the coal beds are nearly flat-lying, but moderate to strong folding is encountered in the eastern part of the province. The rugged terrain and multiplicity of coal beds favor small operations. Most larger mines are underground operations, below drainage. Surface mining (contour-mining and/or mountain-top removal) is widespread, but consists mostly of small operations because of limited strippable reserves.

The Interior Province comprises several separate basins containing bituminous coal of Pennsylvanian age, extending from Texas to Michigan. Nearly half the United States bituminous reserves occur here. Coal in this province was mostly deposited far from the mountainous uplifts, and the peat swamps were invaded more often by the sea than in the Appalachian Province. The high sulfur content of most Interior Province coal (3 to 5 percent) is largely attributed to influx of sulfate-bearing sea water into the peat swamps. Low-sulfur coal is present in the Arkoma Basin and in certain localities in the Illinois Basin where coal is overlain by nonmarine rock. Coal seams mined in this province are relatively thin (0.45 to 2.4 m) but laterally extensive. In the eastern part of the province, about half of the coal is surface mined and half underground mined, whereas in the western part of the province the coal is mined exclusively by stripping.

The Gulf Coastal Province includes the area underlain by Cretaceous and Tertiary sedimentary rocks of the Gulf Coast

Basin (Fig. 4). Most of the coal in this province is low-sulfur lignite in nearly flat-lying Eocene rocks. About one-third of U.S. lignite reserves are located in this province. Coal rank decreases from older to younger rocks, as reflected in their calorific values of 7,500 to 5,000 Btu/lb. In this province, coal is mined only in Texas where seams generally range from 0.9 to 3 m thick, but locally may reach 7.5 m thick. Most coal is mined from large pits and utilized in large mine-mouth electrical generating plants. Maximum mining depth is currently about 36 m, but this may be extended to 75 m where multiple coal seams are present. The loosely consolidated overburden is easy to excavate, and the gentle topography is easy to reclaim after mining.

The Northern Great Plains Province includes coal deposits of Cretaceous and early Tertiary age, largely in the Williston and Powder River basins, east of the Rocky Mountains in Montana, Wyoming, and the Dakotas. These coal deposits extend across the border into Canada (Fig. 8). Most of the coal resources in this province are subbituminous and lignitic. The Upper Cretaceous and Paleocene Fort Union Formation is the most prolific coal-bearing unit in this province, with some of the world's thickest coal beds, 30 to 60 m thick. Rank increases gradually from east to west, toward the mountains: lignite in the Williston basin, subbituminous in the Powder River basin and Tertiary basins of Montana, and bituminous in Cretaceous rocks of Montana. Most of the coal is low in sulfur content (<1.5 percent). Mining in this province is primarily open pit, a method preferred because of the great thickness of the coal seams, their gentle dip, and the slightly rolling terrain. In 1982, eight of the ten largest mines in the United States were in the Powder River basin. Mining problems in this province include spontaneous combustion of the coal, and land reclamation. Because of the great thicknesses of coal that are removed, restoration of the land to grade is difficult. Revegetation is made difficult by the arid climate and thin, alkaline topsoil.

The Rocky Mountain Province includes those coal deposits found in the numerous intermontane basins of the Rocky Mountains. Much coal in this province is low-sulfur (<1 percent), subbituminous and bituminous rank of Cretaceous age. The seams are thick; many are more than 3 m, and some are as thick as 10 m. This province ranks third among U.S. coal provinces in abundance of bituminous coal, and second in abundance of subbituminous coal. Mining practice varies depending on geology and topography. Open-pit mining is practiced in broad open basins, and underground mines operate in the rugged plateau and mesa country.

The Pacific Coast Province lies west of the Rocky Mountains and includes all of Alaska. Coal deposits of northern Alaska constitute an enormous subeconomic resource that has been estimated to contain, in place, anywhere from 400 billion to 5 trillion tons of low-sulfur, bituminous to lignitic coal. These deposits occur in a Cretaceous and early Tertiary foreland basin setting,

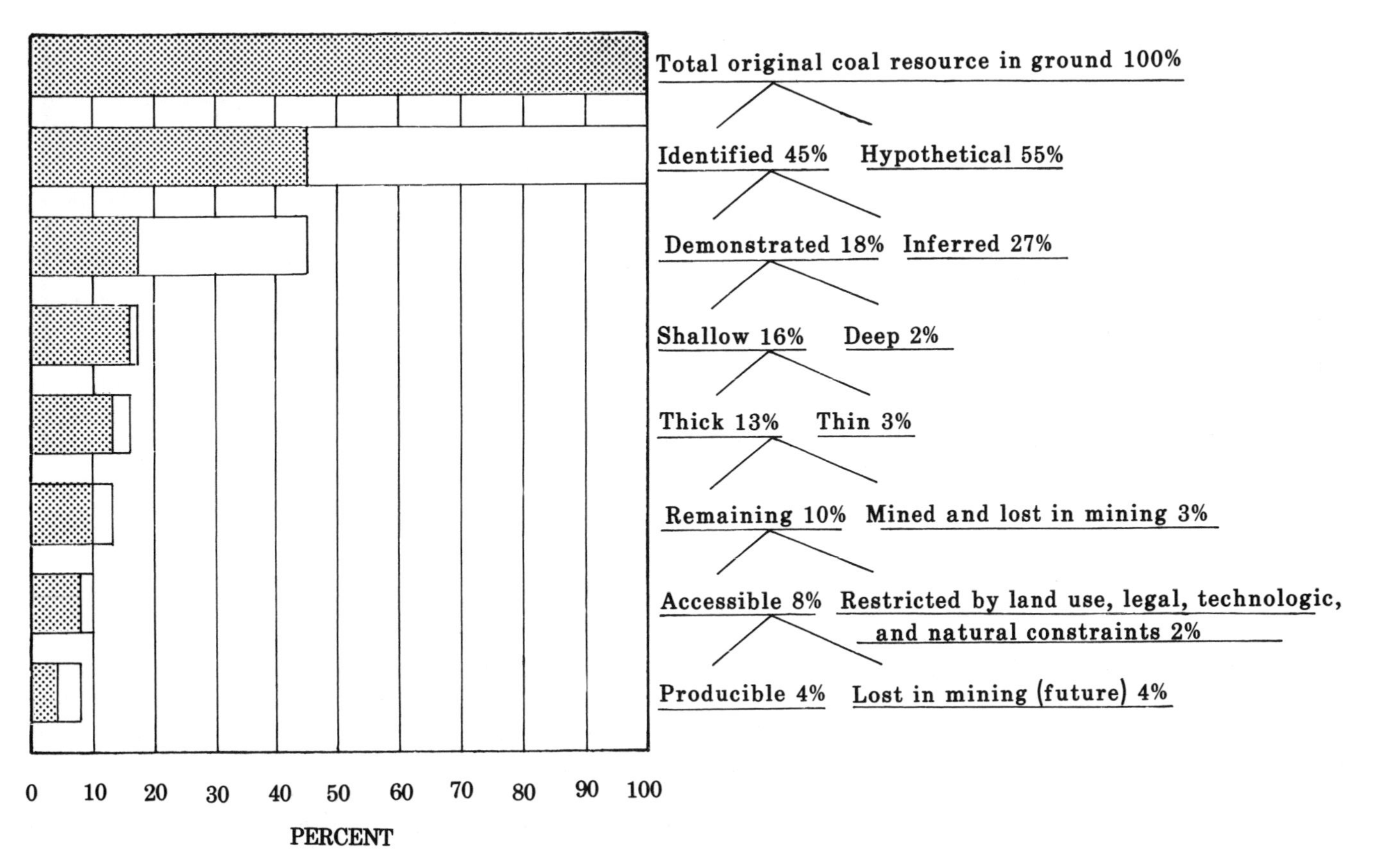

Figure 10. Components of the estimated coal resources of the United States. Modified from M. D. Carter (in U.S. Geological Survey, 1988).

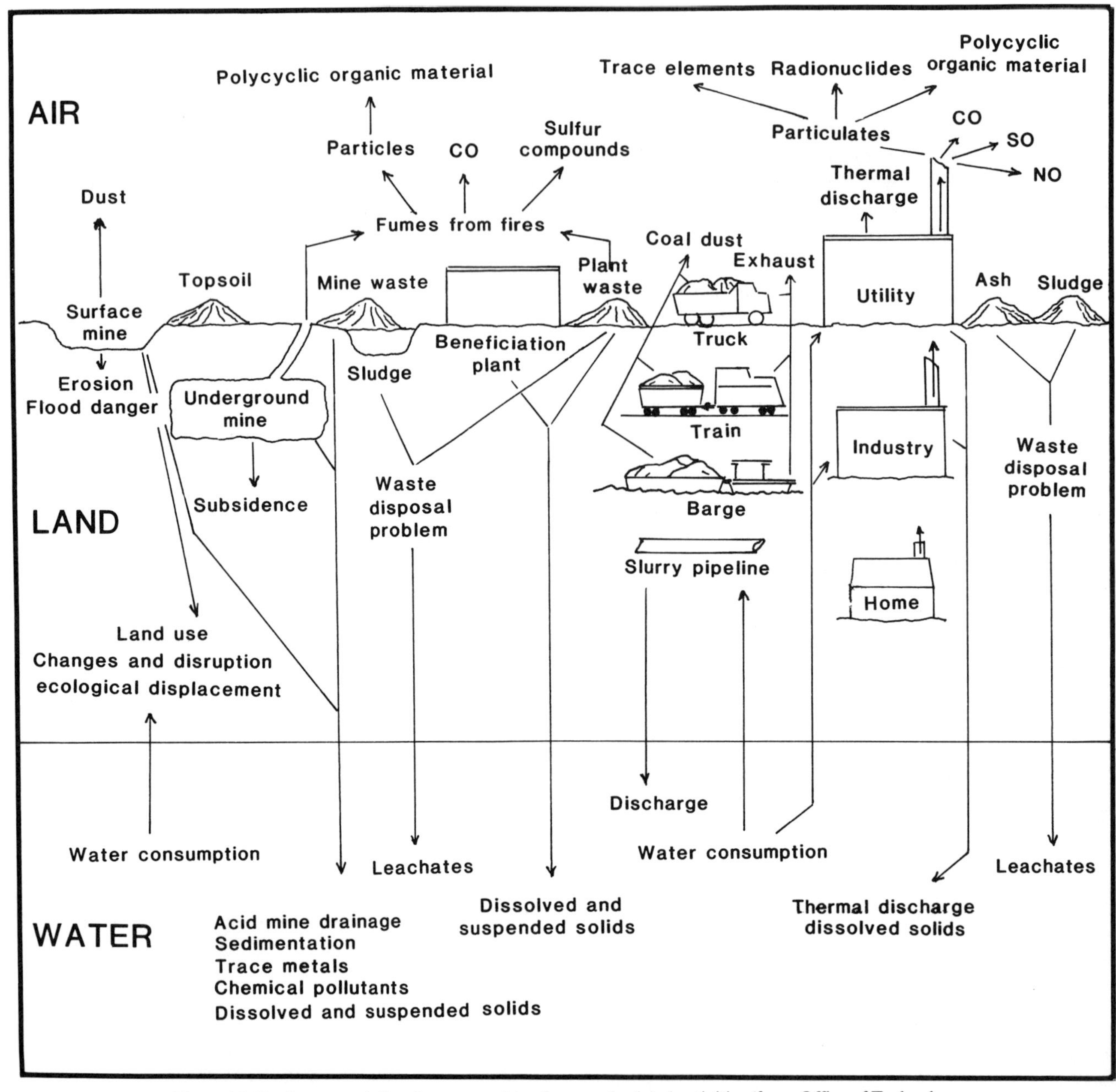

Figure 11. Environmental disturbances resulting from coal-related activities (from Office of Technology Assessment, 1979).

similar to Rocky Mountain and Northern Great Plains Province coals. Except for the northern Alaskan deposits, coal in this province occurs in numerous small basins, mostly of Tertiary age. Similar types of coal deposits occur in the western Cordillera of Canada and Mexico as well as in Central America and the Caribbean. In general, these are small deposits of low-sulfur, bituminous to lignitic coal that range from Triassic to Tertiary in age (Drummond, 1986). Mining is mostly by open pit, and only a few mines are active. Compared with the rest of North America, coal resources and production are insignificant.

Resource problems and future research

Coal mining and coal burning have given rise to an array of problems and issues. These include problems with mining, transportation, combustion, and pollution from exhaust and wastes. The wide range of environmental problems associated with coal mining and utilization are illustrated in Figure 11. As summarized by the U.S. Geological Survey (1988), coal mining disturbs the environment; coal transport is expensive and may adversely affect communities along transport routes; coal burned by utilities may necessarily be cleaned before burning; flue gases commonly must be scrubbed of sulfur and other noxious components after burning; and even after those expensive treatments, coal combustion remains a major contributor of CO_2 and acid-forming SO_2. Waste materials resulting from coal combustion, spoil piles, and disrupted ground of coal mines are sources of noxious chemical elements that may be mobilized by rainwater and leach to contaminate surface and ground water.

Research on a great variety of fronts is being directed at solving or reducing these problems: (1) An important question of how much of the remaining coal resources may be recovered given the problems of land-use restrictions is being addressed in a detailed study of a mature mining area in the Central Appalachian coal field (U.S. Geological Survey, 1988). (2) Because variations in the coal-forming process commonly result in variations in physical character, chemistry, and mineralogy, modern studies of coal typically attempt to decipher the setting and depositional environment of the original peat deposit, including its paleobotanical and paleoclimatic aspects. Analog studies of present-day peat swamps (e.g., Cecil and others, 1988; Neuzil and others, 1988) are also part of this approach. (3) An integration of research activities provides a basis for modeling coal-bearing areas to predict occurrence and quality of coal beyond current exploration boundaries in an attempt to determine both tomorrow's reserves and the problems that producing those reserves might bring. (4) The National Coal Resources Data System a large computerized data bank of information on coal and its enclosing rocks, has been used in a variety of studies, including a study of the nature of the occurrence of sulfur in coal. These and other recent research directions in coal are summarized in various publications (e.g., U.S. Geological Survey, 1988; Carter, 1988; Kuellmer, 1988; and Cobb, 1987).

URANIUM AND THORIUM

The crust of the earth contains 2 to 4 ppm uranium and 6 to 13 ppm thorium. In spite of its lower crustal abundance, uranium occurs in a great variety of minerals, many of which form richer, and more economically attractive concentrations of higher grade than does thorium. This is because uranium, a silvery-white metal, is readily oxidized. In its oxidized state, uranium is very mobile in ground and meteoric water systems and reconstitutes into a variety of minerals, which may form deposits in many kinds of rocks and environments. In contrast, thorium, a heavy silver-gray metal, occurs in minerals that are generally resistant to oxidation. Thus, thorium minerals occur as primary vein or disseminated minerals or as placer deposits. Primary uranium minerals seldom form placer deposits, except for those deposits of early Precambrian age that are believed to have formed under nearly oxygen-free reducing atmospheric conditions at that time (Finch and others, 1973).

Natural uranium consists of three semistable radioactive isotopes U^{238}, U^{235}, and U^{234}. It is an important energy source because the fission of isotope U^{235} releases large amounts of energy. However, this readily fissionable nuclide constitutes only about 0.7 percent of natural uranium. The isotope U^{238} makes up most of the remaining 99.3 percent, and the third, U^{234}, only about 0.005 percent. U^{238} is not fissionable. It is, however, recognized as *fertile* material, that under neutron bombardment converts to fissionable plutonium-239. Thorium is also fertile material that converts to fissionable U^{233} upon neutron bombardment.

Resource volumes

The total ultimate nuclear fuel resource of North America as of January 1985 was estimated to be about 4.7×10^6 metric tons of uranium and thorium at prices up to \$130/kg U and Th (Table 2; OECD Nuclear Energy Agency and International Atomic Energy Agency, 1986). Uranium constitutes nearly 90 percent of this resource, an estimated 4.15×10^6 tonnes of U (Fig. 12). Of this amount, 12 percent has been produced, 7 percent is classified as reserves, 22 percent is classified as identified resources (includes reserves), and 66 percent is classified as undiscovered resources. These figures may be conservative in light of a doubling of previous uranium estimates in a recent study of the highly productive Grants uranium region in the San Juan basin of New Mexico (McCammon and others, 1986). Thorium constitutes about 12 percent of North America's nuclear fuel resource, an estimated 0.57×10^6 tonnes of Th (Fig. 12; Table 2). Because of limited demand for thorium, its information base for resource estimates is considerably smaller than that for uranium. North American thorium resource estimates are relatively sketchy and

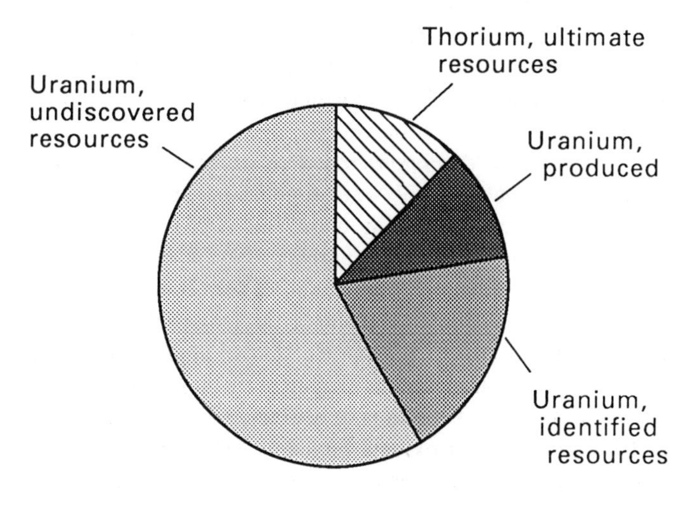

Figure 12. North American uranium and thorium resources as of January 1985 at costs up to \$130/kg U and Th. Not included are unconventional resources (from phosphoric-acid production from marine-phosphate deposits), which are estimated to total about 120×10^3 tonnes U in Mexico and the United States. Data from OECD Nuclear Energy Agency and International Atomic Energy Agency (1986). Compare with distribution of sedimentary basins (Bally, this volume, Fig. 1).

are available only for Canada and the United States (OECD Nuclear Energy Agency and International Atomic Energy Agency, 1986; Staatz and Olsen, 1973; Staatz and others, 1979, 1980).

Geographic and geologic distribution

Many parts of North America are considered favorable for the occurrence of uranium and thorium mineralization (Fig. 13). Most uranium and thorium resources in North America occur in Canada and in the United States; small conventional uranium resources are estimated for Mexico, and no resources are estimated for Central America or the Caribbean region. This distribution of resources is partly a function of the amount of exploration or the number of systematic surveys, such as the United States' National Uranium Resource Evaluation program (U.S. Department of Energy, 1980) and Canada's Uranium Reconnaissance Program. Only limited surveys for uranium have been conducted in Costa Rica, El Salvador, Jamaica, and Panama—countries with no known uranium or thorium resources.

Uranium

Three types of uranium deposits account for most of North American production and resources. These are (1) Proterozoic placer deposits, known as quartz-pebble conglomerate deposits; (2) Proterozoic vein and disseminated deposits, known as unconformity-related deposits; and (3) Mesozoic and Cenozoic uranium-impregnated sandstone deposits. Lesser, but significant, amounts of uranium are estimated to occur in North America in vein, volcanogenic, disseminated collapse-breccia pipe, and surficial types of deposits. Uranium is also derived as a by-product from the mining of phosphate deposits and copper deposits. In recent years, as much as 20 percent of total U.S. uranium production has come from these sources.

Quartz-pebble conglomerate deposits are restricted to the Precambrian Shield area of North America in early Proterozoic strata situated unconformably above an Archaean basement composed of igneous and metamorphic rocks. The uranium occurs as detrital brannerite and uraninite, associated with other heavy minerals containing uranium or thorium, in the matrix of fluvial conglomerates. The presence of detrital uranium minerals, pyrite, and carbonaceous material in these conglomerates is interpreted as indicating deposition at a time when the atmosphere contained little or no oxygen. Similar conglomerates younger than 2.3 Ga are not considered prospective for this type of uranium deposit because of deposition under oxidizing conditions. A substantial proportion of Canada's uranium resources occur in these types of deposits in the Elliot Lake and Agnew Lake areas of southern Ontario. Quartz-pebble conglomerate deposits are among the lowest grade uranium deposits mined in Canada, ranging from 0.05 to 0.15 percent U_3O_8.

Proterozoic unconformity-related uranium deposits are confined to Precambrian shield areas containing Archean basement rocks and early Proterozoic metasedimentary rocks that are unconformably overlain by flat-lying middle Proterozoic quartzose sandstone, conglomerate, and shale. The known deposits are located in the early Proterozoic rocks, usually within a few hundred meters below the unconformity, but in a few places mineralization is found in the middle Proterozoic sedimentary rocks above the unconformity. The ore consists chiefly of pitchblende in both disseminated and massive form in host rocks of pelitic schists, dolomitic-calcareous metasediments, breccias, and graphitic quartzose and pelitic gneisses. The ore control is structural, related to faulting, fracturing, and brecciation. These deposits are the largest and richest of the world's uranium deposits and occur primarily in the Athabasca basin of northern Saskatchewan (Ruzicka and LeCheminant, 1985), where average grade ranges from 0.3 to 5 percent U_3O_8. These deposits, together with quartz-pebble conglomerate deposits, account for nearly all of Canada's uranium reserves and about 60 percent of its undiscovered uranium resources; the remaining 40 percent are estimated to occur (in about equal amounts) in vein deposits, pegmatite deposits, and sandstone deposits.

Sandstone-hosted uranium deposits are the source of most uranium production in the United States. This type of deposit is known in Alaska, Canada, and Mexico, and the potential for this type of deposit occurs in Honduras and Jamaica (Joint Steering Group on Uranium Resources, 1980). Sandstone beds containing the uranium ores were deposited in fluvial, beach, and offshore-bar environments and are commonly interlayered with mudstone. The principal, original uranium minerals in sandstone-ore deposits are uraninite and coffinite. Oxidation of these ores produces a number of other minerals, most commonly carnotite. The ore minerals mainly occupy pore spaces in the sandstones, but in places they replace sand grains and carbonaceous plant debris. The uranium minerals in these deposits are thought to have precipitated from oxidizing ground water at the interface with the reducing environments. In the most important U.S. uranium-producing area, the San Juan basin of New Mexico, the primary ore control is organic material (humate); the primary uranium ore occurs as a unique pore-filling uranium/organic-matter mixture (Turner-Peterson and Fishman, 1986). Uranium deposits in sandstone are of two main types: roll bodies and tabular bodies. Roll bodies are elongated deposits, crescent-shaped in cross section, that are scattered along kilometers-long interfaces between altered (oxidized) sandstone updip and unaltered (reduced) sandstone downdip. These deposits occur chiefly in Cretaceous and Tertiary beds in Wyoming, South Dakota, and south Texas. Tabular bodies are discrete masses, enveloped by chemically reduced sandstone that is surrounded by oxidized sandstone: these deposits occur chiefly in Triassic and Jurassic beds in Colorado, Utah, Arizona, and New Mexico. Sandstone ore bodies range in size from a meter or two across, containing a few tons of ore, to several hundred meters across (rarely more than a kilometer), containing more than 10 million tons of ore. The average grade of ore mined ranges from 0.1 to 0.3 percent U_3O_8.

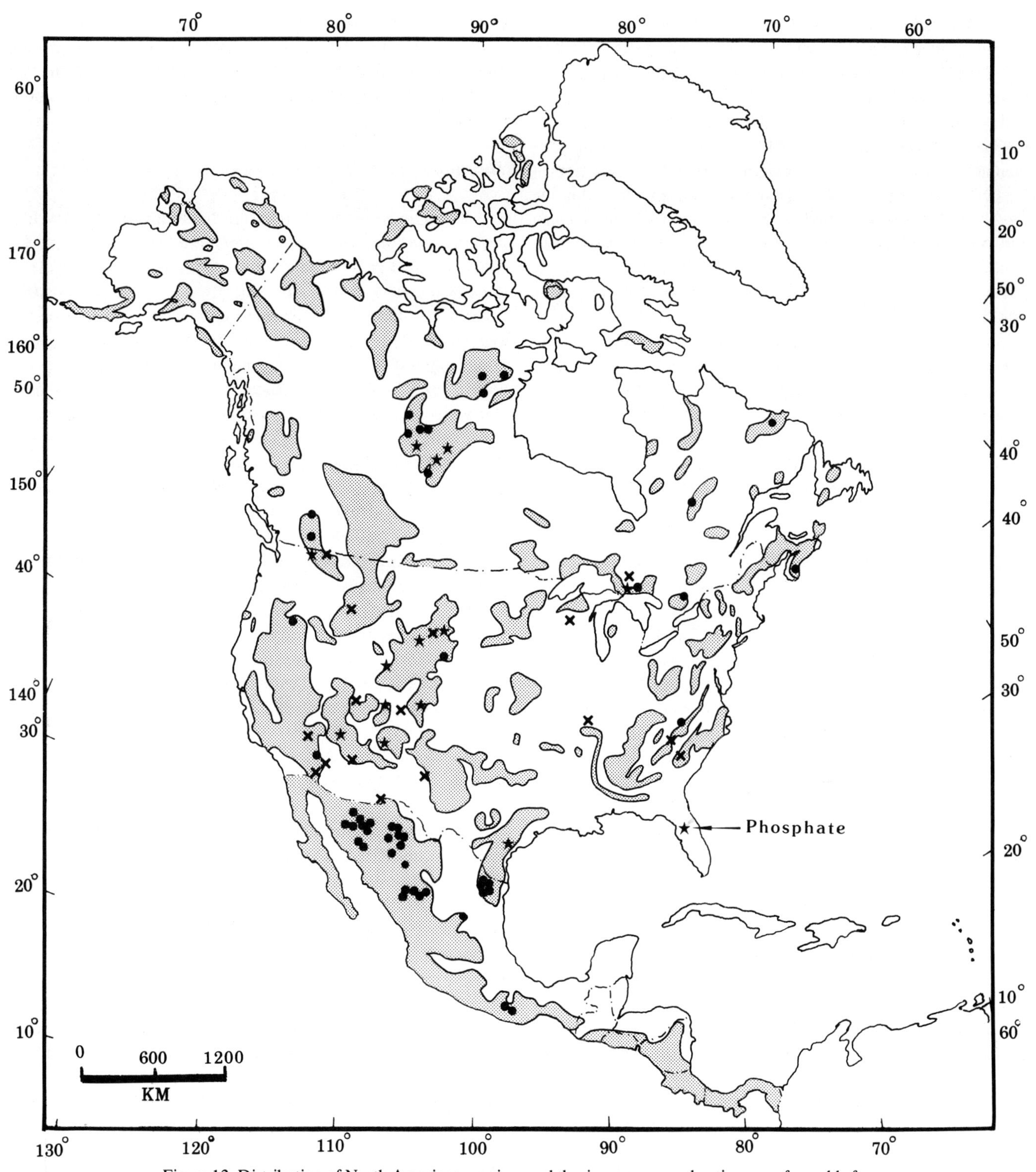

Figure 13. Distribution of North American uranium and thorium resources showing areas favorable for the occurrence of uranium deposits (shaded), areas of uranium mineralization (dot), uranium deposits with production history (star), and thorium deposits (x). Shading in Mexico and Central America shows areas of volcanic rock. Adapted from OECD Nuclear Energy Agency and International Atomic Energy Agency (1986), Joint Steering Group on Uranium Resources (1980), Staatz and others (1979), and U.S. Geological Survey (1988).

Collapse-breccia pipe deposit. This type of uranium deposit is of increasing importance in the United States. Found in the Grand Canyon region of the Colorado Plateau, these high-grade uranium deposits are the targets of intensive exploration and development (Chenoweth, 1987). The host pipes, which tend to occur in clusters, were formed by collapse of overlying sedimentary rocks into solution caverns within the Mississippian Redwall Limestone. Most of the uranium ore occurs within the sandy breccia matrix formed by comminution of Pennsylvanian and Permian sedimentary rocks. Uranium occurs in these deposits along with base metals (Co, Cu, Zn, and Pb), precious metals (Au, Ag), and rare earths (Ge and Ga) (Wenrich and others, 1987).

Surficial uranium deposit. A new type of uranium deposit, recognized only within the last few years, is the surficial uranium deposit (Otton, 1984). One variety occurs in wetland environments and consists of uranium in organic matter. The origin of this variety of deposit is related to ground water or surficial water transport and deposition of uranium in peat accumulations. These deposits are generally so young (<12 ka) that they are not detectable using normal gamma-ray radiometric surveys and must be located by identifying favorable terranes, sampling, and chemical analysis. They are commonly found in terranes containing granitic rocks from which surface waters can leach uranium and redeposit it nearby in organic materials along small stream drainages in boggy meadows, swamps, and floodplains. One wetlands surficial deposit has been mined along Flodelle Creek in northeastern Washington State. This deposit is estimated to contain half a million kilograms of uranium oxide with an average grade of 0.08 percent. Surficial uranium deposits of the wetlands variety are known to occur in north-central Idaho, the Sierra Nevada of California, the Colorado Front Range, and Maine (U.S. Geological Survey, 1988). Other areas where conditions are favorable for these deposits include large parts of the Canadian Shield, the Appalachian Mountains, and the Cordilleran region of North America. Another variety of surficial uranium deposit, the calcrete deposit, is related to evaporation of ground water in arid climates. Deposits of this variety are known in Africa and Australia; they may also occur in the Basin and Range Province and in parts of southern Canada and northern Mexico.

Numerous other types of uranium deposits occur in North America, or conditions favorable for their occurrence are known (Joint Steering Group on Uranium Resources, 1980). Veins of uranium minerals associated with complex faults in metamorphosed sedimentary and igneous rocks of Precambrian age are mined in the Front Range of Colorado (Chenoweth, 1987). Other uranium vein deposits are known from Canada, Virginia, and Honduras. The largest occurrences of uranium in Mexico are of the volcanogenic type and are found in Tertiary volcanic rocks and underlying sedimentary rocks in the Peña Blanca Mountains of north-central Mexico. Volcanogenic-type deposits are also present at Marysvale, Utah; and McDermott, along the Nevada-Oregon border (International Atomic Energy Agency, 1985). Occurrences of disseminated uranium deposits in igneous and metamorphic rocks (including carbonatites and pegmatites) are known from southeastern Alaska, throughout the Canadian Shield area, British Columbia, northeastern Washington, Honduras, and Guatemala.

Thorium

Thorium is commonly associated with rare earths as well as with uranium, and nearly all thorium produced in North America is a co-product or by-product in the recovery of one or more of these elements. The chief ore minerals of thorium are monazite (phosphate), thorite and uranothorite (silicates), and thorianite and brannerite (oxides). Thorium concentrations of future economic interest in the United States occur in veins, chiefly in metamorphic and igneous rocks, and as modern and ancient placer deposits. Most of the identified thorium resources in the United States are in high-grade veins—those containing more than 0.1 percent ThO_2. Thorium veins are known in more than a dozen areas of the western United States (Fig. 13). In at least half of these areas, alkalic igneous rocks have been found; consequently areas of alkalic rocks are considered favorable for thorium prospecting. Monazite-bearing sand has been found in many parts of the country, including the Carolinas, Idaho, Florida, and Georgia (Staatz and Olson, 1973; Staatz and others, 1979, 1980). In Canada, large thorium resources are associated with uranium in quartz-pebble conglomerate deposits in southern Ontario. Thorium is also associated with uranium minerals in granitic and syenitic rocks, alkalic carbonatite intrusions, and in uranium-free environments.

Resource problems and future research

Problems associated with uranium and thorium resources include those related to mining, the variable demand for nuclear power, and nuclear waste disposal. The problems associated with uranium and thorium mining are those common to underground or open-pit mining operations. Uranium-mining operations have an additional hazard in the form of radon, a highly radioactive gaseous product resulting from the decay of uranium that may cause lung cancer when inhaled over a long period of time.

In the long term, demand for uranium and thorium depends on the types of nuclear power reactors employed and the fuel-reprocessing strategies followed. Most power reactors in use today are converter reactors, those that yield less fissionable material than is consumed. These reactors utilize only about 1.5 percent of the potential energy in the uranium fuel. Reprocessing of spent reactor fuel elements for the recovery and reuse of unused uranium and plutonium increases the energy yield. The breeder reactor is a type in which the yield of fissionable material is more than is consumed. These reactors utilize about 80 percent of the potential energy in the uranium fuel. Future uranium requirements would be greatest by following the present nuclear power strategy: converter reactors and no reprocessing. Future

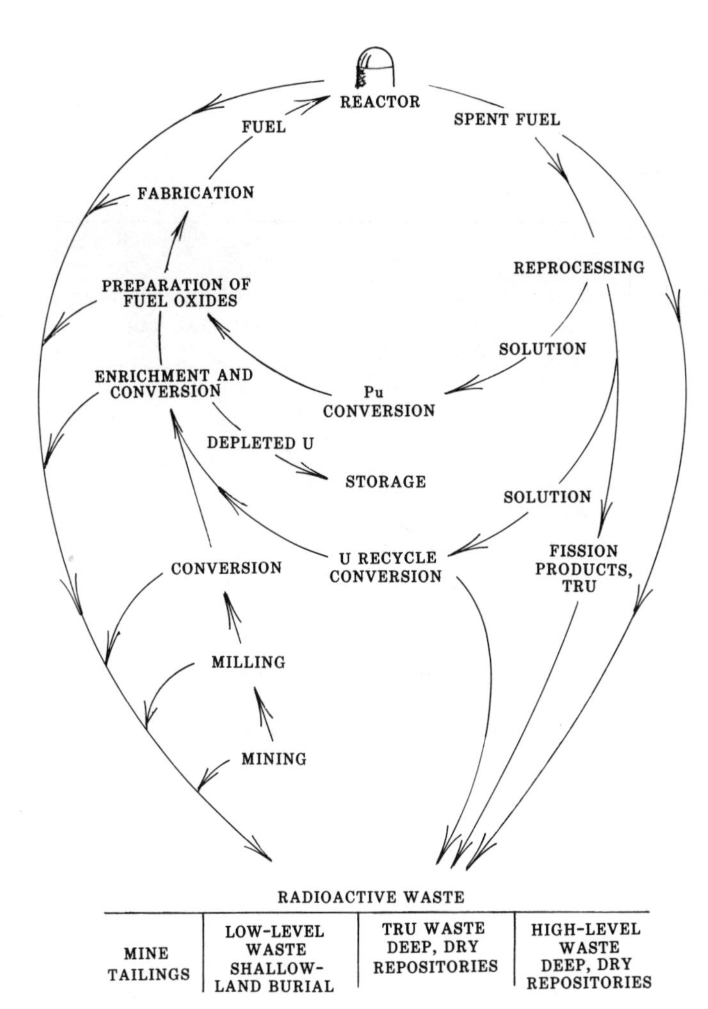

Figure 14. Sources of radioactive waste in the light-water fuel cycle (from DeBuchananne, 1978).

uranium requirements would be least, and would in fact decrease, with replacement of converter reactors by breeder reactors.

The task of disposing of the radioactive wastes produced by nuclear power plants is often cited as one of the principal drawbacks to the continued expansion of the capacity to generate electricity by means of the nuclear fission process. Radioactive wastes are generated at different stages in the uranium fuel cycle, as illustrated in Figure 14. As described by Cohen (1977), the task is not as difficult or uncertain as generally thought; it is more a problem of perception.

Cohen (1977) notes that the volume of waste from a nuclear power reactor is millions of times smaller than that from a similar-sized coal-burning power plant, and the price of the power produced makes it practical to use highly sophisticated waste-management procedures. For example, the amount of radioactive waste produced annually from a 1,000 megawatt nuclear reactor is about 2 m^3, and the value of the power produced is about $200 million. The effects of radiation on the human body are far better understood than the effects of chemicals such as air pollutants, food additives, and pesticides. Radiation is easy to measure accurately with inexpensive but highly sensitive instruments. Processed nuclear reactor wastes produce heat and radiation, the amount of which declines by nearly an order of magnitude between years 1 and 10. Health hazards presented by high-level radioactive waste from nuclear reactors after 10 years are on a par with, or less than, those of other poisonous substances routinely used in large quantities (such as barium, arsenic, chlorine, and ammonia). This comparison demonstrates that there is nothing unprecedented or uniquely dangerous about nuclear wastes. Further, other poisonous substances do not decrease in toxicity with time, yet they are not carefully buried. Some, such as arsenic, are scattered around on the ground as pesticides in regions where food is grown.

The basic requirement for a safe repository is the long-term isolation of the nuclear wastes from mankind and the biologic environment; especially important is limiting their exposure to circulating ground water. Since 1957, when the National Academy of Sciences committee proposed underground burial of radioactive wastes, many sites in many different rock types and geologic settings have been evaluated. In late 1987, the U.S. Congress selected a disposal site in volcanic rock at Yucca Mountain, Nevada (Marshall, 1988).

FOSSIL FUELS IN THE FUTURE

What is the future of fossil fuel consumption in North America likely to be? Many predictions have been offered, and these usually involve various economic assumptions. One method of analysis that appears to offer the promise of valuable prediction and that has received relatively little attention is logistic substitution analysis. This method involves no economic assumptions; it utilizes only the historic record of amounts of energy sources as technologies competing for a market.

Research in marketing reveals a surprisingly consistent pattern in the way a new product penetrates a market and displaces its competing predecessor. Marchetti and Nakicenovic (1979) applied this method of analysis, known as logistic substitution, to primary energy sources in more than 300 cases, including the entire world and individual countries. Their analysis shows a remarkably consistent pattern of energy substitutions over the last 100 years, a pattern that is insensitive to political or economic perturbations. This analysis shows only market share through time. It does not address the total amount of energy consumed, the origin of the energy consumed (domestic or foreign sources), nor the introduction of new energy sources. Projections, based on segments of the historical data set, agree well with the entire data set. Because of these features, the method appears to be a powerful predictive tool.

In analyzing the energy consumption of the United States (Fig. 15), this analysis shows that about 100 years are required for an energy source to increase from 1 percent to 50 percent share, and that peaks of maximum energy share have occurred at about 50-year intervals: wood in the mid-1800s, coal in 1910 to

1920, and oil in 1960s. For the future, this analysis predicts that the share of wood, coal, and oil in the total United States primary energy budget will continue to decline and that natural gas will become the dominant energy source near the end of this century and will probably be displaced by nuclear power in the middle of the twenty-first century. Furthermore, a negligible role is postulated for new sources such as geothermal, solar, and fusion energy during the next 50 years because of the very long lead times intrinsic to the system.

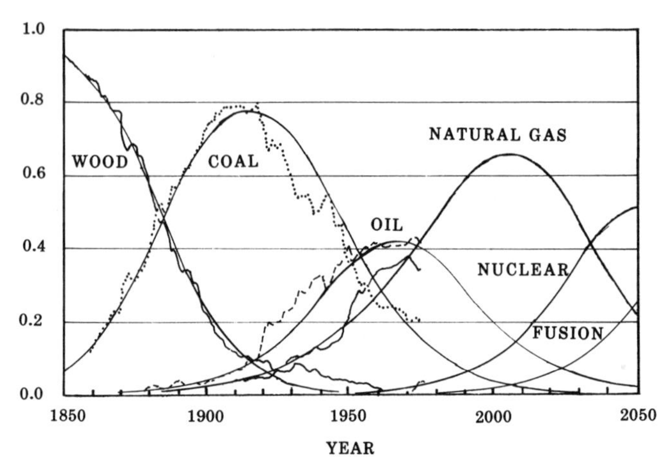

Figure 15. Logistic analysis of primary energy consumption in the United States illustrating patterns of substitution of one energy source over another through time (from Marchetti and Nakicenovic, 1979).

SUMMARY

Fossil fuels (oil, gas, coal, uranium, and thorium) provide nearly all of North America's energy needs at present, and they will probably continue to do so well into the next century. These fuels are abundant in North America. Because these fuels are primarily related to the formation of sedimentary basins, their abundance and distribution in North America is similar to that of sedimentary basins. Although these resources (and others) are nonrenewable and finite, the amount consumed relative to the total endowment is still rather small. To speak of "running out" or "using the last drop" of such resources is a gross oversimplification. What is true is that much of the cheap, readily extractable resources have been consumed. The future will face us with higher costs for extraction of these resources and choices between environmental disruption and the need for these fuels.

REFERENCES

Averitt, P., 1975, Coal resources of the United States, January 1, 1974: U.S. Geological Survey Bulletin 1412, 131 p.

Carter, L.M.H., ed., 1988, USGS research on energy resources; 1988 Program and Abstracts: U.S. Geological Survey Circular 1025, 70 p.

Cecil, C. B., Dulong, F. T., Cobb, J. C., Supardi, and Turnbull, P., 1988, Allogenic processes in the Central Sumatra Basin—A modern analog for the origin of Lower Pennsylvanian coal-bearing strata in the eastern United States [abs.], *in* Carter, L.M.H., ed., USGS research on energy resources; 1988 Program and Abstracts: U.S. Geological Survey Circular 1025, p. 8.

Chenoweth, W. L., 1987, Developments in uranium in 1986: American Association of Petroleum Geologists Bulletin, v. 71, no. 10B, p. 384–389.

Choate, R., and McCord, J. P., 1986, Assessment of natural gas from coalbeds by geologic characterization and production evaluation, *in* Rice, D. D., ed., Oil and gas assessment: American Association of Petroleum Geologists Studies in Geology, no. 21, p. 223–245.

Cobb, J. C., 1987, Coal: Geotimes, v. 32, no. 2, p. 11–12.

Cohen, B. L., 1977, The disposal of radioactive wastes from fission reactors: Scientific American, v. 236, no. 6, p. 21–31.

Collett, T. S., Bird, K. J., Kvenvolden, K. A., and Magoon, L. B., 1988, Geologic interrelations relative to gas hydrates within the North Slope of Alaska (DOE Task 6 final report): U.S. Geological Survey Open File-Report 88-389, 150 p.

Cox, C. H., and Baughman, G. L., 1980, Oil sands—resource, recovery, and industry: Mineral and Energy Resources, v. 23, no. 4, p. 1–12.

Curtis, D. M., 1987, The northern Gulf of Mexico basin: Episodes, v. 10, no. 4, p. 267–270.

DeBuchananne, G. D., 1978, The role of earth sciences in the disposal of radioactive waste: U.S. Geological Survey Yearbook, Fiscal Year 1977, p. 15–21.

Drummond, K. J., 1986, Explanatory notes for the Energy-Resources Map of the Circum-Pacific region, northeast Quadrant: American Association of Petroleum Geologists, 72 p.

Energy Information Administration, 1986, Annual outlook for U.S. coal 1986: Washington, D.C., U.S. Department of Energy Report DOE/EIA-0333(86), 58 p.

Ferm, J. C., and Muthig, P. J., 1982, A study of the United States coal resources: Pasadena, California, California Institute of Technology, Jet Propulsion Laboratory Publication 82-14, 213 p.

Finch, W. I., Butler, A. P., Jr., Armstrong, F. C., Weissenborn, A. E., Staatz, M. H., and Olson, J. C., 1973, Nuclear fuels, *in* Brobst, D. A., and Pratt, W. P., eds., United States mineral resources: U.S. Geological Survey Professional Paper 820, p. 455–468.

Hunt, J. M., 1979, Petroleum geochemistry and geology: San Francisco, W. H. Freeman and Company, 617 p.

International Atomic Energy Agency, 1985, Uranium deposits in volcanic rocks; Proceedings of a technical committee meeting, 2–5 April, 1984: Vienna, Austria, International Atomic Energy Agency, 468 p.

Joint Steering Group on Uranium Resources, 1980, World uranium; Geology and resource potential: San Francisco, Miller Freeman Publications, 524 p.

Kuellmer, F. J., 1988, Coal geology: Geotimes, v. 33, no. 2, p. 14–15.

Magoon, L. B., 1988, Petroleum systems of the United States: U.S. Geological Survey Bulletin 1870, 68 p.

Marchetti, C., and Nakicenovic, N., 1979, The dynamics of energy systems and the logistic substitution model: Laxenburg, Austria, International Institute of Applied Systems Analysis Report RR-79-13, 73 p.

Marshall, E., 1988, Nevada wins the nuclear waste lottery: Science, v. 239, p. 15.

Masters, C. D., Attanasi, E. D., Dietzman, W. D., Meyer, R. F., Mitchell, R. W., and Root, D. H., 1987, World resources of crude oil, natural gas, natural bitumen, and shale oil: World Petroleum Congress Proceedings, 12th, v. 5, p. 3–27.

McCammon, R. B., Finch, W. I., Kork, J. O., and Bridges, N. J., 1986, Estimation of uranium endowment in the Westwater Canyon Member, Morrison Formation, San Juan Basin, using a data-directed numerical method, *in* Turner-Peterson, C. E., Santos, E. S., and Fishman, N. S., eds., A basin analysis case study—the Morrison Formation Grants uranium region, New Mexico: American Association of Petroleum Geologists Studies in Geology 22, p. 331–355.

Meyer, R. F., ed., 1987, Exploration for heavy crude oil and natural bitumen: American Association of Petroleum Geologists Studies in Geology No. 25, 731 p.

Nelson, W. J., 1987, Coal deposits of the United States: International Journal of Coal Geology, v. 8, p. 355–365.

Neuzil, S. G., and six others, 1988, Peat deposits on coastal Sumatra—a modern analog of coal formaion [abs.], *in* Carter, L.M.H., ed., USGS research on energy resources—1988 Program and Abstracts: U.S. Geological Survey Circular 1025, p. 37–38.

OECD Nuclear Energy Agency and International Atomic Energy Agency, 1986, Uranium resources, production, and demand: Paris, France, Organization for Economic Cooperation and Development Publications, 413 p.

Office of Technology Assessment, 1979, The direct use of coal—Prospects and problems of production and combustion: Washington, D.C., Office of Technology Assessment, 411 p.

Otten, J. K., 1984, Surficial uranium deposits in the United States of America, *in* International Atomic Energy Agency, Surficial uranium deposits—Report of the working group on uranium geology: Vienna, Austria, International Atomic Energy Agency Technical Document 322, p. 237–242.

Procter, R. M., Taylor, G. C., and Wade, J. A., 1984, Oil and gas resources of Canada, 1983: Geological Survey of Canada Paper 83–31, 59 p.

Ridley, R. S., 1982, Growth in world coal trade slows in 1981: World Coal, v. 8, no. 6, p. 57–64.

Roadifer, R. E., 1987, Size distributions of the world's largest known oil and tar accumulations, *in* Meyer, R. F., ed., Exploration for heavy crude oil and natural bitumen: American Association of Petroleum Geologists Studies in Geology, no. 25, p. 3–23.

Ruzicka, V., and LeCheminant, G. M., 1985, Summary on uranium in Canada, 1984, *in* Current Research, Part A, Geological Survey of Canada Paper 85–1A, p. 15–22.

Smith, G. G., 1989, Coal resources of Canada: Geological Survey of Canada Paper 89–4 (in press).

Smith, J. W., 1980, Oil shale resources of the United States: Mineral and Energy Resources, v. 23, no. 6, p. 1–20.

Staatz, M. H., and Olson, J. C., 1973, Thorium, *in* Brobst, D. A., and Pratt, W. P., eds., United States mineral resources: U.S. Geological Survey Professional Paper 820, p. 468–476.

Staatz, M. H., and seven others, 1979, Principal thorium resources in the United States: U.S. Geological Survey Circular 805, 42 p.

Staatz, M. H., Hall, R. B., Macke, D. L., Armbrustmacher, T. J., and Brownfield, I. K., 1980, Thorium resources of selected regions in the United States: U.S. Geological Survey Circular 824, 32 p.

Turner-Peterson, C. E., and Fishman, N. S., 1986, Geologic synthesis and genetic models for uranium mineralization in the Morrison Formation, Grants uranium region, New Mexico, *in* Turner-Peterson, C. E., Santos, E. S., and Fishman, N. S., eds., A basin analysis case study—the Morrison Formation, Grants uranium region, New Mexico: American Association of Petroleum Geologists Studies in Geology No. 22, p. 357–388.

Tyler, N., 1988, New oil from old fields: Geotimes, v. 33, no. 7, p. 8–10.

U.S. Bureau of Mines and U.S. Geological Survey, 1980, Principles of a resource/reserve classification for minerals: U.S. Geological Survey Circular 831, 5 p.

U.S. Department of Energy, 1980, An assessment report on uranium in the United States of America: U.S. Department of Energy GJO–111(80), 150 p.

U.S. Geological Survey, 1988, National energy resource issues, geologic perspective and the role of geologic information: U.S. Geological Survey Bulletin 1850, 79 p.

Wenrich, K. J., Verbeek, E. R., Sutphin, H. B., Van Gosen, B. S., and Modreski, P. J., 1987, The Apex mine, Utah—Colorado Plateau-type solution-collapse breccia pipe [abs.], *in* Sachs, J. S., ed., USGS research on mineral resources 1987: U.S. Geological Survey Circular 995, p. 73–74.

Werner, M. R., 1987, Tertiary and Upper Cretaceous heavy-oil sands, Kuparuk River Unit area, Alaskan North Slope, *in* Meyer, R. F., ed., Exploration for heavy crude oil and natural bitumen: American Association of Petroleum Geologists Studies in Geology No. 25, p. 537–547.

Wood, G. H., Jr., Kehn, T. M., Carter, M. D., and Culbertson, W. C., 1983, Coal resource classification system of the U.S. Geological Survey: U.S. Geological Survey Circular 891, 65 p.

MANUSCRIPT ACCEPTED BY THE SOCIETY FEBRUARY 1, 1989

Printed in U.S.A.

The Geology of North America
Vol. A, The Geology of North America—An overview
The Geological Society of America, 1989

Chapter 20

Mineral resources of North America

Brian J. Skinner
Department of Geology and Geophysics, Yale University, New Haven, Connecticut 06520

INTRODUCTION

The number of mineral deposits, large and small, discovered in North America over the last half millennium has not been tallied, but it must be in the hundreds of thousands. Most discoveries are small and of no more than local importance, but some are giants. As a result, Canada, Mexico, the Caribbean region, and the United States have at one time or another each been the world's leading producer of one or more mineral resources. The complex diversity and the remarkable plenty of the deposits played a vital role in the development of North America's vibrant societies. From the time of the first European settlers to the present, our use of, and dependence on, mineral resources has grown steadily larger.

Mineral consumption in North America has now reached enormous proportions. For the region as a whole, the mass of mineral resources used directly or indirectly in 1988, by every man, woman, and child, weighed 14 metric tons. There are approximately 360 million people in the region. In Canada and the United States, annual per capita consumption is approximately 16 metric tons; in Mexico and the Caribbean, per capita consumption is lower—closer to 10 metric tons—but still considerable. Nonmetallic resources, such as crushed stone, sand, gravel, clay, cement, and plaster, account for a significant fraction of the consumed mass. Such materials tend to be locally produced, and the sources are so large and widespread that there does not seem to be any reason to suspect that supply limitations lie ahead. But even though supply problems may not be cause for concern, continued massive use of mineral resources does raise environmental concerns. The magnitude of mineral products mined each year now exceeds the magnitude of the sediment transported annually to the sea by streams. Inevitably, use of mineral resources is changing the global environment.

The mass of metallic mineral resources consumed is considerably smaller than the mass of nonmetallics, but in many respects the metals are more important. Metals are the enzymes of industry. They are needed for machines, and machines are the means through which sources of energy are turned to useful purposes. The human body can do useful work at a rate of about 100 watts. By using machines the supplemental energy-use rate in North America is about 10,000 watts. Our complex industrial civilization is totally dependent on our use of supplemental energy, and hence on metals, just as the human body is totally dependent on its enzymes. If a sufficiency of metals is not available, then civilization will inevitably suffer. The balance of this chapter, therefore, is focused on metallic mineral resources.

A HISTORIC VIEW OF MINING

It has sometimes been argued that mineral production has determined the course of history. Mineral deposits have finite sizes and are not replenished after exploitation. The same mineral wealth that leads a country to power may, upon exhaustion of the mines, lead to increasing dependence on imports, and ultimately national decline. That is a pessimistic viewpoint, but those who espouse it point to examples such as the decline of Athens when the silver mines of Larium were exhausted, the decline of the economic power of Britain as its 19th-century mining industry withered, and even the demise of the Roman Empire. The optimistic view is that a sufficiency of all mineral resources exists because advancing technology will always find a way to satisfy requirements, and that global transportation systems expand questions of mineral supply to global questions, not national ones. The truth probably lies somewhere between the two extremes. National concerns will certainly be important for the foreseeable future, and a true global community that shares its resources impartially may never arise.

A paper published in 1929 by the late D. F. Hewett provides a basis through which the changing fortunes of national mineral production and use can be viewed. Hewett analyzed the mining histories of a number of European countries and pointed out that production and use go through cycles. An example of Hewett cycles, as refined by Lovering in 1943, is shown in Figure 1. As a country is explored and prospected, deposits are found and new mines are opened. Eventually, as the discovery rate declines, the number of mine closings due to exhaustion exceeds the discovery rate. When all deposits have been found and exploited, the number of working mines returns to zero. Similar curves record the amount of metal produced and the quantity exported. Note that exports decline much sooner than metal production does. This is so in an industrial country because internal demand grows and eventually exceeds the supply. To make up the growing

Skinner, B. J., 1989, Mineral resources of North America, *in* Bally, A. W., and Palmer, A. R., eds., The Geology of North America—An overview: Boulder, Colorado, Geological Society of America, The Geology of North America, v. A.

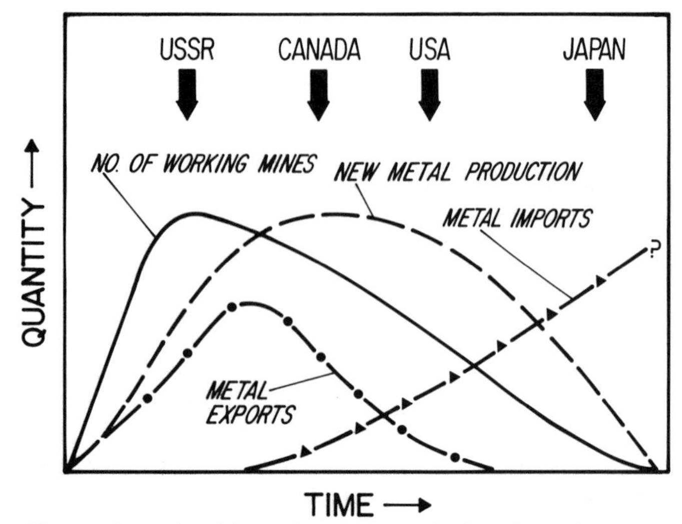

Figure 1. Stages in mining and metal production in an industrial country as deduced by Hewett (1929) and refined by Lovering (1943). As time passes, a country moves from left to right. A country starting a cycle today would complete it in about a century due to the intensity of modern resource exploitation. The estimated positions of several countries are indicated.

deficit, imports must rise. Because one axis in Figure 1 is time, the position of a country moves from left to right as time passes. An indication of where some industrial countries lie today with respect to the Hewett cycles is shown in Figure 1, based on data gleaned from the fraction of important mineral resources that must be imported in order to satisfy their needs (Fig. 2).

A continuously growing population on a finite globe must eventually consume all resources. There is a good deal of optimistic evidence to suggest that continued growth of the global population is not only unlikely, but that growth will cease within a century. Demographic projections based on age-sex distribution around the world lead to the conclusion that by the year 2100 the global population will be constant at no more than 12 billion. For North America, constancy is predicted somewhat earlier, about 2050, at a total population of about 550 million (Demeny, 1984).

As the world population has grown over the past century, an increasing number of people (but not necessarily an increasing percentage of the population) has enjoyed a high standard of living. If the growth pattern holds into the future, a leveling of the global population will not necessarily lead to an immediate reduction of the stress on supplies of mineral resources. Therefore, prediction of Hewett curves into the future is not straightforward. What does seem certain, however, is that a huge global population will require that all countries develop their resources if demands are to be met. For the countries of North America, which are already far advanced in their Hewett cycles, new finds will only happen if technological advances open new territory to prospecting. That new territory will be the deeper and covered parts of the North American crust that are inaccessible to current geophysical and geological prospecting techniques. At least half of North America falls into this category, and the percentage is higher still if the continental shelves are included.

Background mapping of the North American crust has already commenced through programs such as COCORP, LITHOPROBE, and DOSECC. It seems certain that in 2088, when the Geological Society of America celebrates its bicentennial, North America will be a very different place from North America today. It is likely that one of the differences will be that mining will be active throughout the region and that a new Hewett cycle will be underway (Fig. 3). When that new cycle will commence is an open question, but the first programs designed to define and map covered basement rocks in the central plains of the United States and Canada are already underway (see for example Sims and others, 1987). Such programs are probably preludes to a new era of mineral exploration. I believe that a new era of prospecting in North America may start within two decades. It is instructive, therefore, to briefly examine the state of knowledge concerning the genesis of ore deposits, and metallogenesis, on which such prospecting will be based, and to consider the parts of the continent most likely to be fertile sites for prospecting.

A PERSPECTIVE ON MINERAL DEPOSITS

The number of mineral deposits of all kinds discovered around the world is in the millions. The pool of data describing the deposits is thus enormous. Certain features, such as the kinds of minerals present, types of host rocks, and tectonic settings of ores, can be observed again and again, and hence must be characteristic features of a given type of deposit. The set of features characteristic of a class of deposits is called a deposit model. Two recent publications, one by Eckstrand (1984) giving the Canadian viewpoint, and one by Cox and Singer (1986) with the U.S. opinion, summarize current thinking regarding deposit models in North America. The most recent of the two publications, Cox and Singer (1986), groups deposits in terms of four family lines (or logic trees, as they call them). The family lines, as shown in Table 1, are drawn on the basis of the gross geologic settings in which the deposits occur. The family lines are divided into fourteen geologic environments, and these in turn contain one or more deposit models. Each of the 39 models describes a class of deposit, but each may also be divided into two or more subclasses. Cox and Singer list 99 subclasses of the 39 deposit models.

Deposit models serve many purposes, classification being one of them. The models are not based on presumed genetic processes, as were most previous classification schemes of mineral deposits, such as the famous classification of Lindgren (1913). Rather, the models are empirical groupings of observations from the global data bank. The models readily lend themselves to testing and thus are expected to be important in the future as prospecting guides for hidden ores.

Deposit models may not be based on genetic concepts, but they are proving to be powerful guides to thinking about the genesis of mineral deposits. One very important point concerning

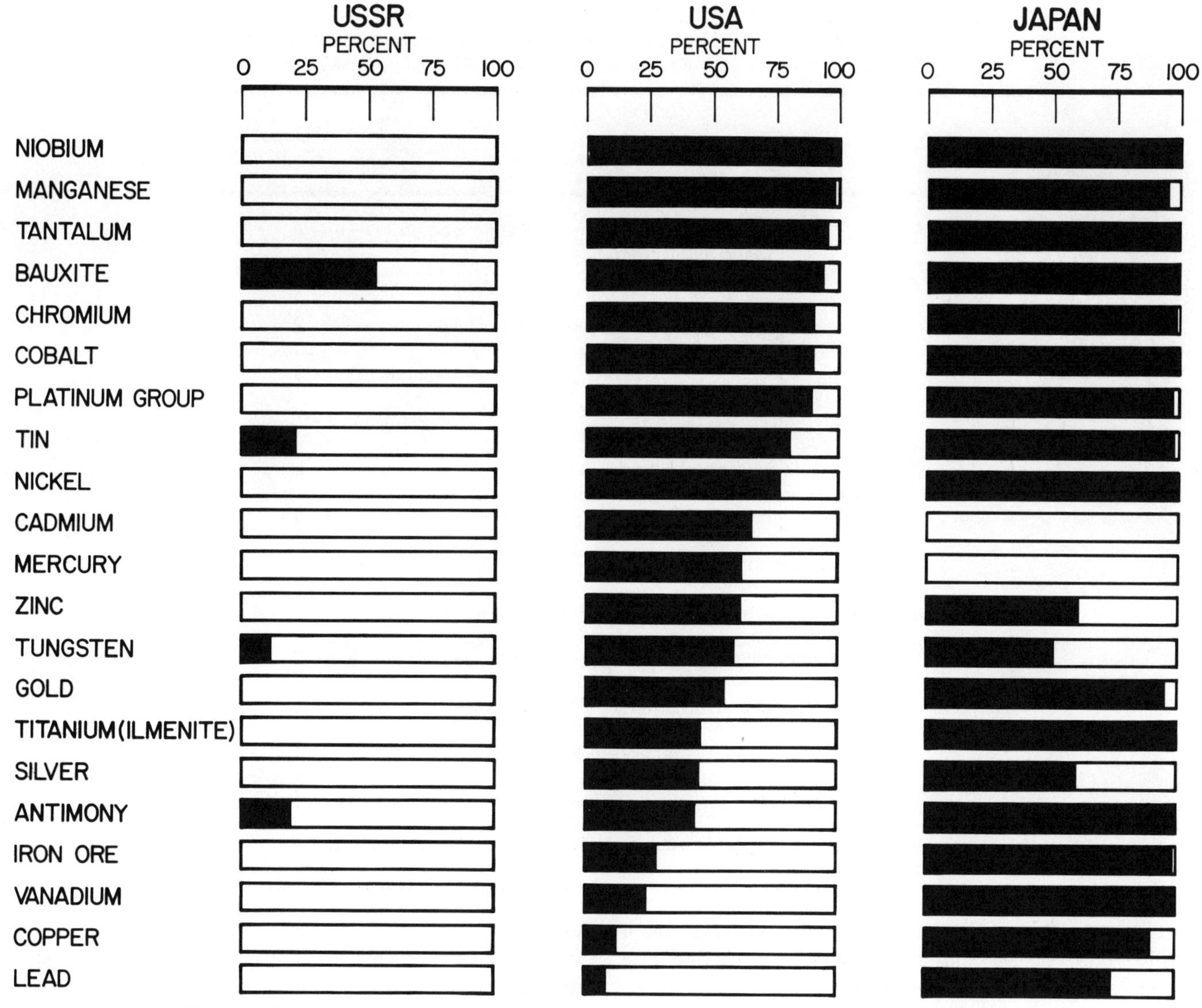

Figure 2. The percentage of selected mineral resources that three industrial countries had to import during 1984. The positions of countries with respect to their Hewett curves in Figure 1 are derived from such data. Note that about 50 years ago the U.S. was in the position that the U.S.S.R. is in today, as regards imports of nonferrous mineral resources. (Data from U.S. Bureau of Mines, Minerals Yearbook.)

genesis is already emerging. Conformity of features between deposits implies conformity of the formative process or processes. The closer one looks at deposits as one seeks variations within and between them, and the larger the pool examined, the more apparent it becomes that conformity of process is indeed present. But, as the test of conformity continues, another—somewhat surprising—picture seems to be emerging. Quite different deposit classes apparently can arise from a single process operating in different environments. For example, it seems probable that some volcanogenic massive sulfide deposits form from the same hydrothermal system, at the same time, and in the same magmatic province, as certain porphyry copper and epithermal gold deposits. Ore-forming systems, therefore, may be vastly larger than we have heretofore recognized. If that conclusion is proved correct

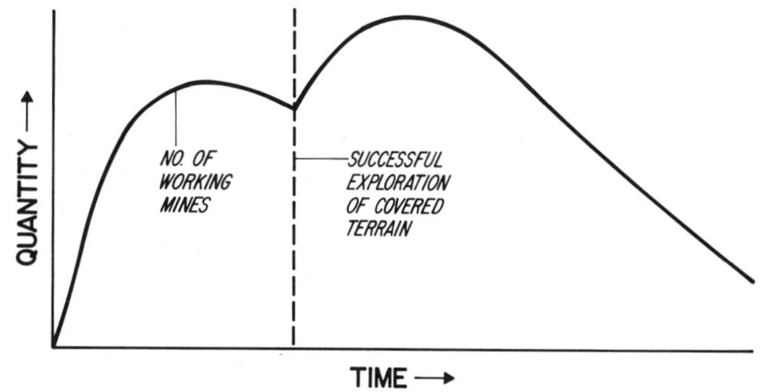

Figure 3. How a technological change can affect a Hewett curve. When a successful method of prospecting at depths up to 1.5 km is developed, the curve defining the changing number of working mines with time will move sharply up.

TABLE 1. LOGIC TREE USED BY COX AND SINGER (1986) TO DEFINE THE BROAD GEOLOGIC-TECTONIC ENVIRONMENTS WITHIN WHICH THE 39 DEPOSIT MODELS (OR CLASSES) AND 99 SUB-CLASSES ARE ORDERED AND CLASSIFIED

Geologic Environment				No. of Deposit Models
Igneous	Intrusive	Mafic and Ultramafic	Stable Region	4
			Unstable Region	6
		Alkaline and basic		2
		Felsic	Phanerocrystalline	3
			Porphyrocrystalline	7
	Extrusive	Mafic and Ultramafic		2
		Felsic-mafic		4
Sedimentary	Clastic rocks			3
	Carbonate rock			1
	Chemical sediments			3
Regional Metamorphic	Metavolcanic and metasedimentary			1
	Metapelite and meta-arenite			1
Surficial	Residual			1
	Depositional			1

through such tests as continental deep drilling programs, and if isotopic, trace element, and other signatures characteristic of a multideposit ore-forming system can be recognized, prospecting in covered terrain will be aided because much larger initial targets can be sought. Models of deposit-containing terranes, and the signatures of giant ore-forming systems that formed the terranes, may well be the next step forward in studies of mineral deposits.

PROSPECTING IN NORTH AMERICA IN THE 21ST CENTURY

In discussing the future of prospecting in North America, only the broadest geologic provinces can be considered. There are five such provinces—the Canadian Shield, the Grenville Orogen, the Appalachian–Ouachita and Innuitian Orogens, the Cordilleran Province, and the Caribbean Province (Fig. 4).

The Canadian Shield and its cover rocks

The core of North America, and the largest of the five geologic provinces, is an assemblage of small cratons and orogens, all older than 1.6 Ga (Hoffman, 1988). The assemblage outcrops most extensively in the eastern half of Canada; to the west the shield is covered by a thick section of Paleozoic sediment. To the south, in the United States and the northernmost part of Mexico, the shield is largely covered by little-deformed sedimentary rocks, principally Phanerozoic in age. The cover rocks are generally less than 5 km thick, but in places up to 15 km of sediment is present.

Mineral deposits of many kinds have been found in the shield where it outcrops. Many of Canada's most famous mineral districts and deposit types are located there (Fig. 5). Examples are banded iron formations, paleoplacer deposits of uranium, chemical-sediment–hosted gold deposits, volcanic-hosted massive sulfide deposits, volcanic-associated vein deposits of gold, ultramafic-and mafic-associated nickel and copper deposits, and many more.

There is every reason to believe that the collage of shield terranes is as mineralogically diverse and rich beneath the Phanerozoic cover as it is in the region of outcrop. The covered region is approximately the same size as the exposed shield area. Relatively modest technological advances could open a significant fraction of the region that is covered by 1.5 km of sedimentary strata or less to prospecting (Fig. 6). Those same technological advances would also open the upper 1.5 km of the outcropping shield to prospecting, and as a result, the entire Canadian shield must be viewed as the most important region for future mineral exploration in North America.

The Phanerozoic strata that cover the basement rocks also contain some famous kinds of mineral deposits both in Canada and the United States. Foremost among them is the Mississippi Valley type deposit. The potential for discoveries of new districts is high. Thus, both the covered portion of the Canadian Shield and its Phanerozoic cover must be considered likely regions for future prospecting successes.

The Grenville Orogen

Surrounding the continental core of rocks older than 1.6 Ga is a series of younger orogens, all younger than 1.2 Ga. The oldest and most extensive of these, the Grenville, bounds the shield to the east and south. It contains rocks deformed between about 1.2 and 0.9 Ga, and within those rocks are some unique and highly unusual deposits. Examples are the ilmenite and related anorthosites of the Adirondacks, and the remarkable zinc-manganese-iron deposits at Franklin Furnace and Sterling Hill in New Jersey.

Where best exposed in southwestern Quebec, southeastern Ontario, and northern New York, the Grenville Supergroup is a series of now-metamorphosed volcanic rocks overlain by marbles and clastic sedimentary rocks. Several suites of intrusive igneous rocks cut the Grenville Supergroup.

Stratabound ores of zinc, lead, and iron are widespread throughout the orogen, but only three deposits have been major producers of base metals; each is in the United States. These are the zinc deposits at Balmat-Edwards in New York and the previously mentioned two deposits in northern New Jersey. Each is stratabound, enclosed in marble, and complexly folded. While the potential for additional stratiform deposits exists in parts of the Grenville covered by younger rocks, the difficulty of finding such deposits seems so great it is unlikely that the covered Grenville will have a high status as a likely site for future exploration. The situation is different to the north and east of Ontario, in Quebec and Newfoundland, where the Grenville outcrops, or is thinly covered. Recent prospecting discoveries in Newfoundland suggest that mineralization potential in the region is good.

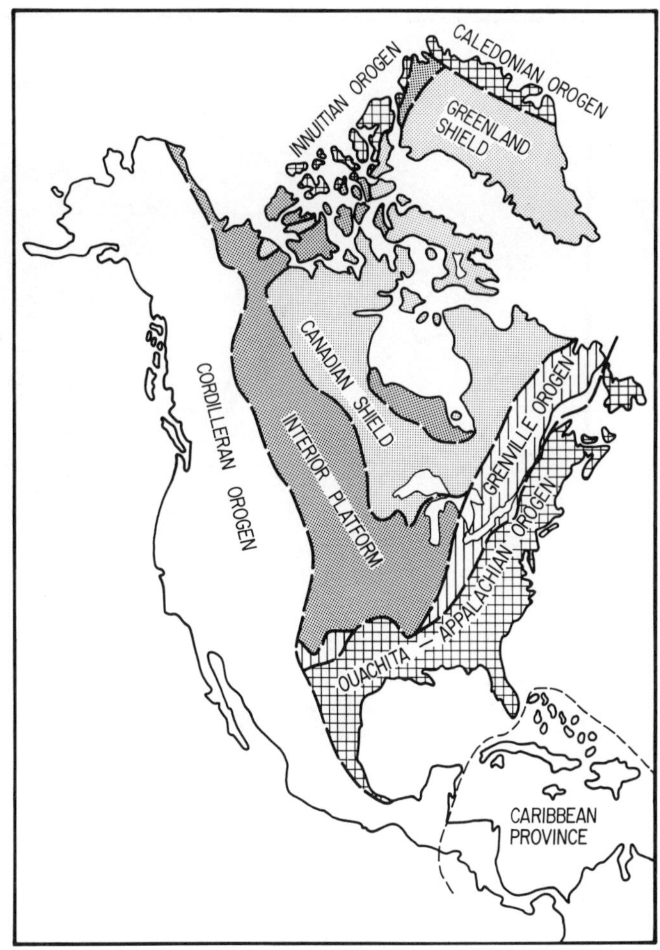

Figure 4. The principal mineral-producing geological provinces in North America.

The Appalachian–Ouachita, and Innuitian Orogens

Bordering the Canadian Shield to the north is a fragment of an orogen of Phanerozoic age, the Innuitian. It has been little prospected because it is a difficult climatic zone. Prospects for substantial mineral finds in the orogen are good, but the region is small and thus will probably not play a major role in meeting future demands for metals.

To the east and south of the Grenville Orogen, North America is flanked by the Appalachian–Ouachita Orogen and related accreted terranes. In many places, particularly south of New Jersey, the Appalachian–Ouachita Orogen overlies and covers rocks of the Grenville Orogen. Fragments of the orogen also occur in the Caledonides of Scotland, Norway, and Greenland.

More than 70 percent of the Appalachian–Ouachita Orogen in North America is exposed, or thinly covered by glacial till, outwash gravels, and residual soils. This suggests that whatever mineral potential does exist in the upper 1.5 km of the orogen should be accessible to prospecting if the previously mentioned technological advances come to pass. The kinds of deposits likely to be found are similar to those discovered in the past. Numerous small- to medium-sized volcanic- and sediment-hosted stratabound deposits of copper, lead, and zinc have been discovered, but most discoveries happened more than a century ago and much of the mining in the region ceased before the turn of the century. For nearly a century, the Appalachian–Ouachita Orogen has received less attention from prospectors than it deserves. However, recent discoveries of large volcanic-hosted massive sulfide deposits and porphyry-type tin-tungsten deposits in the Canadian maritime provinces indicate that the earlier phase of prospecting

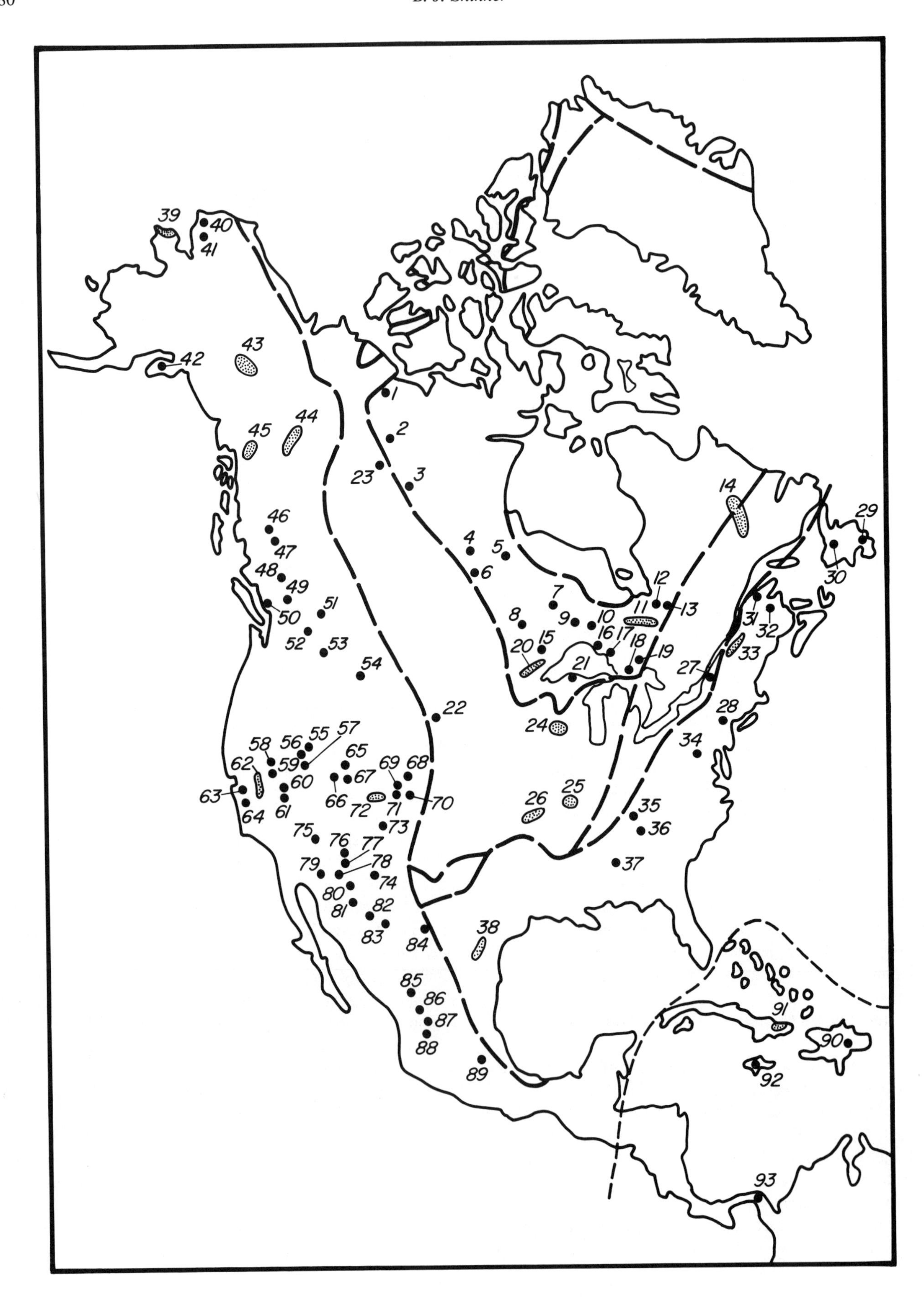
1
2
3
4
5
6
7
8
9
10
11
12
13
14
15
16
17
18
19
20
21
22
23
24
25
26
27
28
29
30
31
32
33
34
35
36
37
38
39
40
41
42
43
44
45
46
47
48
49
50
51
52
53
54
55
56
57
58
59
60
61
62
63
64
65
66
67
68
69
70
71
72
73
74
75
76
77
78
79
80
81
82
83
84
85
86
87
88
89
90
91
92
93

Figure 5. Locations of important mineral deposits and mineral districts in the geologic provinces of North America. Provice boundaries are the same as those shown in Figure 4.

CANADIAN SHIELD AND COVER ROCKS
1. Port Radium, NWT, U
2. Yellowknife, NWT, Au
3. Athabasca, Sask., U
4. Lynn Lake, Man., Ni, Cu, Co
5. Thompson, Man., Ni
6. Flin Flon, Man., Cu, Zn, Au
7. Pickle Crow, Ont., Au
8. Red Lake, Ont., Au
9. Little Long Lac, Ont., Au
10. Gelo, Ont., Cu, Zn, Ag
11. Abitibi Belt, Ont. and Que., Cu, Zn, Au, Ag
12. Mattagami, Que., Zn, Cu, Ag, Au
13. Chibougamau, Que., Cu, Au, Ag
14. Labrador Trough, Que., Fe
15. Steep Rock Lake, Ont., Fe
16. Mishibishu, Ont., Au
17. Hemlo, Ont., Au
18. Elliott Lake, Ont., U
19. Sudbury, Ont., Ni, Cu
20. Mesabi Range, Mich., Fe
21. Keweenaw Copper and White Pine, Mich., Cu
22. Homestake, SD., Au
23. Pine Point, NWT, Zn
24. Upper Mississippi Valley, Zn, fluorite
25. Southeast Missouri distric, Mo, Pb-Zn
26. Tristate district, MO, OK, KS, Zn

GRENVILLE OROGEN
27. Sanford Lake, NY, Ti
28. Franklin Furnace–Sterling Hill, NJ., Zn

APPALACHIAN-OUCHITA OROGEN
29. Wabana, Nfld., Fe
30. Buchans, Nfld., Zn, Pb, Cu
31. Gaspé Copper, Que., Cu
32. Bathurst district, N.B., Pb-Zn
33. Thetford, Que., asbestos
34. Cornwall, PA, Fe
35. Mascot–Jefferson City, TN, Zn
36. Ducktown, TN, Cu
37. Birmingham, AL, Fe
38. South Texas uranium district, TX, U

CORDILLERAN PROVINCE
39. Kougarok district, AK, Sn
40. Red Dog, AK, Cu, Zn, Pb
41. Ambler district, AK, Cu, Zn, Pb
42. Kennecott, AK, Cu
43. Klondike, Yukon, Au
44. Cassiar district, B. C. and Yukon, W
45. Atlin, B.C., Au
46. Granisle, B.C., Cu

CORDILLERAN PROVINCE (continued)
47. Endako, B.C., Mo
48. Boss Mountain, B.C., Mo
49. Bethlehem, B.C., Cu, Ag, Au, Mo
50. Britannia, B.C., Cu, Zn, Au, Ag
51. Sullivan, B.C., Pb, Zn, Ag
52. Metaline district, WA, Pb-Zn
53. Coeur d'Alene, ID, Ag, Pb
54. Butte, MT, Cu
55. Carlin, NV, Au
56. Cortez, NV, Au
57. Eureka, NV, Ag
58. Comstock Lode, NV, Ag
59. Yerington, NV, Cu
60. Tonopah, NV, Ag
61. Goldfield, NV, Ag, Au
62. Mother Lode, CA, Au
63. New Almaden, CA, Hg
64. New Idria, CA, Hg
65. Bingham Canyon, UT, Au
66. Spor Mountain., UT, Be
67. Tintic District, UT, Pb-Zn
68. Henderson-Urad, CO, Mo
69. Climax, CO, Mo
70. Cripple Creek, CO, Au, Ag
71. Leadville, CO, Ag
72. Uravan district, CO, U, V
73. Grants, NM, U
74. Santa Rita, NM, Cu
75. Bagdad, AZ, Cu
76. Globe-Miami, AZ, Cu
77. San Manuel–Kalamazoo, AZ, Cu
78. Twin Buttes, AZ, Cu
79. Ajo, AZ, Cu
80. Bisbee, AZ, Cu
81. Cananea, Mexico, Cu
82. La Caridad, Mexico, Cu
83. Santa Eulalia, Mexico, Ag
84. Terlingua, TX, Hg
85. Cerro Mercardo, Mexico, Fe
86. Fresnillo, Mexico, Ag, Pb, Zn
87. San Luis Potosi, Mexico, Ag
88. Guanjuato, Mexico, Ag
89. Pachuca, Mexico, Ag

CARIBBEAN PROVINCE
90. Pueblo Viejo, Dominican Republic, Au
91. Moa Bay, Cuba, Ni
92. Jamaica, Bauxite
93. Cerro Colorado, Panama, Cu

did not exhaust the potential of the region. Thus, it is likely that the orogen will again be the focus of intensive prospecting sometime in the future. Deposits most likely to be sought, besides volcanic-hosted massive sulfide deposits, are bedded barite, gold-quartz veins, pegmatites containing minerals of lithium and beryllium, sedimentary ironstone, disseminated molybdenite deposits in porphyritic igneous rocks, chromite associated with ultramafic rock, and skarns. However, despite the apparent potential for prospecting, the orogen has a major drawback—it contains many large cities and has a high population density. Whether large-scale mining operations would be tolerated in much of the orogen is an unanswered question.

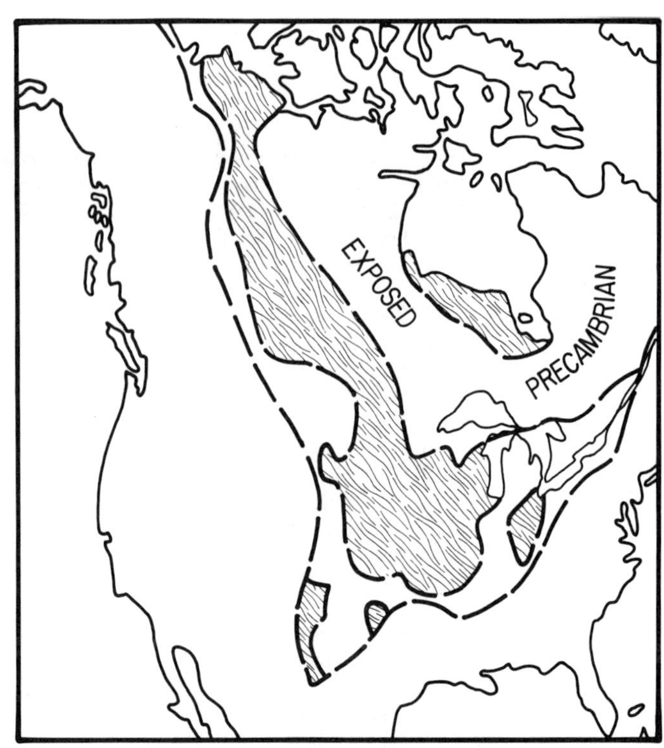

Figure 6. Precambrian rocks of the Canadian shield (inside the outer dashed line) are covered to the south and west by younger sedimentary rocks. Where the shield crops out in Canada and the northern U.S., it is richly mineralized. Most of the cover is less than 5 km thick; the patterned area is covered by less than 1.5 km of sedimentary rocks.

The Cordilleran Province

Running from the southern edge of Mexico to the western tip of Alaska, and bounding the shield along its western margin, is a large, structurally complex region loosely called the Cordilleran Province. The name recognizes the topographic diversity of the region, but the geological diversity is equally great: a highly deformed continental selvedge of Precambrian rocks, onto which volcanic arcs and other terranes of many kinds have been accreted; a covering of miogeoclinal sediments, now strongly deformed; sediment-filled rift basins; and extensive volcanic fields.

The Cordilleran region is geologically complex because each terrane is distinct from its neighbors, so it is nearly impossible to describe its mineralogical heritage as an entity. Within the strata of the ancestral North American miogeocline there are numerous stratiform deposits of zinc, lead, copper, and barium; where the strata have been intruded by sequences of felsic igneous rocks, skarn deposits of tungsten, tin, zinc, lead, and molybdenum have formed. Porphyry-related deposits of copper and molybdenum have been located throughout the region; indeed, some of the largest porphyry copper systems ever discovered are found in the region.

The historic productions of silver, gold, copper, molybdenum, and mercury from the Cordilleran Province have been enormous. The North American Cordillera in Mexico and the United States has been the world's largest silver-producing region for many years. It was also the world's largest producer of copper and molybdenum. At least 50 percent of the region is blanketed by a covering of younger rock or unconsolidated sediment. A few deposits hidden by shallow cover have already been discovered in several places. More discoveries can be expected.

Because the Cordilleran Province is so large, and its historic yield of mineral deposits so great, the region ranks close to the Canadian shield as a likely site for future prospecting.

The Caribbean Province

The Caribbean Province was the site of the first mining by Europeans in the New World. Pueblo Viejo in the Dominican Republic was operated by the Spanish as early as 1505. The region is still a major producer of nickel (Cuba), bauxite (Jamaica), and gold (Dominican Republic). In addition, several large deposits of copper are known but are not yet productive because of disputes between governments and investors. These include the Rio Vivi-Tanama porphyry copper deposits in Puerto Rico, and the Cerro Colorada deposit in Panama.

Mineralization is widespread throughout the region. Many obducted fragments of oceanic crust are present; these contain ophiolite-related chromite deposits and volcanic-hosted massive sulfide deposits. Fragments of island arcs are also present and contain gold and base-metal vein deposits as well as the previously mentioned porphyry coppers.

Although the Caribbean Province is extensively mineralized and the region has much promise for prospecting, it is limited in area and thus is unlikely to be more than a minor contributor to long-term metal production. In addition, the region is politically diverse, a fact that is likely to slow exploration.

CONCLUSION

North America continues to hold great potential for the discovery of metallic mineral resources. Prospecting, up to the 1980s, has effectively been limited to regions with 100 m or less of cover rocks. In special cases, where local geology is known in sufficient detail, exploration can be carried on at greater depths; for most circumstances, however, approximately 100 m is the practical limit. Two things stand in the way of deeper prospecting. First, the resolution of geological, geophysical, and geochemical prospecting techniques declines rapidly at depths greater than about 100 m. Increasing resolution, and thereby increasing prospecting success, requires technological advances, at least in part. Second, the cost and speed of remote sampling by drilling through hard rocks limits testing of deep prospects. If technological advances reduce drilling costs, deep prospecting will move rapidly ahead. It is my belief that both geophysical sensing and drilling technology are likely to enjoy major advances in the decades ahead.

The countries most likely to respond rapidly and effectively to improved prospecting and drilling technologies are the ones with the best three-dimensional geological maps. Mapping the third dimension is the goal of programs such as COCORP, LITHOPROBE, and DOSECC in North America, and equivalent programs in Europe. I suspect that mining activities in the 21st century will return to many of the industrial countries from which they moved in the past century. Technology, when advances are made, will start the countries of North America on new Hewett cycles.

REFERENCES CITED

Some entries have not been specifically cited in the text. They are included as source documents for those who wish to read further on the topics briefly mentioned in the text. Reference should also be made to appropriate volumes of this series on The Geology of North America.

Albers, J. P., 1981, A lithologic-tectonic framework for the metallogenic provinces of California: Economic Geology, v. 76, p. 765–790.

Case, J. E., Holcombe, T. L., and Martin, R. G., 1984, Map of geologic provinces in the Caribbean region: Geological Society of America Memoir 162, p. 1–30.

Cox, D. P., and Singer, eds., 1986, Mineral deposit models: U.S. Geological Survey Bulletin 1693, 379 p.

Davison, K. M., 1984, Mineral deposits and principal mineral occurrences of the Canadian Cordillera and adjacent parts of the United States of America: Geological Survey of Canada Map 1513A.

Demeny, P., 1984, A perspective on long-term population growth: Population and Development Review, v. 10, no. 1, p. 103–126.

Eaton, G. P., 1984, Mineral abundance in the North American Cordillera: American Scientist, v. 72, p. 368–377.

Eckstrand, O. R., ed., 1984, Canadian mineral deposit types; A geological synopsis: Geological Survey of Canada Economic Geology Report 36, 86 p.

Franklin, J. M., and Thorpe, R. I., 1982, Comparative metallogeny of the Superior, Slave, and Churchill Provinces: Geological Association of Canada Special Paper 25, p. 3–90.

Hewett, D. F., 1929, Cycles in metal production: American Institute of Mining and Metallurgical Engineers Yearbook, p. 65–98.

Hoffman, P. F., 1988, United plates of America; The birth of a craton; Early Proterozoic assembly and growth of Laurentia: Annual Review of Earth and Planetary Science, v. 16, p. 543–603.

Kesler, S. E., 1978, Metallogenesis of the Caribbean region: Journal of the Geological Society of London, v. 135, p. 429–441.

Lindgren, W., 1913, Mineral Deposits: New York, New York, McGraw-Hill, 883 p.

Lovering, T. S., 1943, Minerals in world affairs: Englewood Cliffs, New Jersey, Prentice Hall, 394 p.

McLaren, D. J., and Skinner, B. J., eds., 1987, Resources and world development: New York, Wiley-Interscience, Dahlem Workshop Report, 940 p.

Paterson, D. F., 1988, Metallic mineral occurrences in or under the Phanerozoic rocks of Saskatchewan: Geoscience Canada, v. 15, p. 103–105.

Sangster, A. L., and Bourne, J., 1982, Geology of the Grenville Province, and the regional metallogenesis of the Grenville Supergroup: Geological Association of Canada Special Paper 25, p. 91–125.

Sims, P. K., 1985, Metallogeny of Archean and Proterozoic terranes in the Great Lakes region: A brief overview: U.S. Geological Survey Bulletin, 1694, p. 56–74.

Sims, P. K., Kisvarsanyi, E. B., and Morey, G. G., 1987, Geology and metallogeny of Archean and Proterozoic basement terranes in the northern midcontinent, U.S.A.; An overview: U.S. Geological Survey Bulletin 1815, 51 p.

U.S. Bureau of Mines, Annual Publications 1932 to 1988; Minerals yearbook: Washington, D.C., U.S. Government Printing Office.

Manuscript Accepted by the Society December 28, 1988

Printed in U.S.A.

Appendix A. Contents of All Volumes of The Geology of North America

Volume A. *The Geology of North America; An overview*

A. W. Bally and A. R. Palmer, eds.

1. **North America; Plate tectonic setting and tectonic elements**—*A. W. Bally, C. R. Scotese, and M. I. Ross*
2. **The Gravity Anomaly Map of North America**—*W. F. Hanna, and 5 others*
3. **The Magnetic Anomaly Map of North America; A new tool for regional geologic mapping**—*W. J. Hinze and P. J. Hood*
4. **The seismic structure of the continental crust and upper mantle of North America**—*W. D. Mooney and L. W. Braile*
5. **North Atlantic ocean basin; Aspects of structure and evolution**—*P. R. Vogt and B. E. Tucholke*
6. **The Atlantic passive margin**—*R. E. Sheridan*
7. **Evolution of the northern Gulf of Mexico Basin, with emphasis on Cenozoic growth faulting and the role of salt**—*D. M. Worrall and S. Snelson*
8. **Phanerozoic evolution of the North American Cordillera; United States and Canada**—*J. S. Oldow, A. W. Bally, H. G. Avé Lallemant, W. P. Leeman*
9. **An outline of the geology of Mexico**—*Z. de Cserna*
10. **The northeastern Pacific Ocean and Hawaii**—*E. L. Winterer, T. Atwater, and R. W. Decker*
11. **Geologic history of the Caribbean and Central America**—*T. W. Donnelly*
12. **The evolution of the Appalachian chain**—*N. Rast*
13. **The Arctic Islands**—*H. P. Trettin*
14. **The Ouachita System**—*J. K. Arbenz*
15. **Phanerozoic basins of North America**—*A. W. Bally*
16. **Precambrian geology and tectonic history of North America**—*P. F. Hoffman*
17. **The Quaternary**—*H. E. Wright, Jr.*
18. **Fresh water of North America; A profile**—*G. Meyer*
19. **North American fossil fuels**—*K. J. Bird*
20. **Mineral resources of North America**—*B. J. Skinner*

Volume B. *Geology of Canada; Summary*

J. O. Wheeler, P. F. Hoffman, and M. J. Keen, eds.

(contents not yet outlined)

Volume C-1. *Precambrian craton of Canada and Greenland*

P. F. Hoffman, K. D. Card and A. Davidson, eds.

Introduction

1. **Introduction**—*P. F. Hoffman*

Archean

2. **Introduction**—*K. D. Card*
3. **Superior Province**—*K. D. Card*
4. **Slave Province**—*P. F. Hoffman*
5. **North Atlantic Craton; Greenland and Labrador**—*K. D. Card*
6. **Kaminak**—*A. Davidson*
7. **Northwest Churchill province**—*P. F. Hoffman*
8. **Syntheses**—*P. F. Hoffman*

Lower Proterozoic

9. **Introduction**—*P. F. Hoffman*
10. **Huronian**—*K. D. Card*
11. **Ungava**—*P. F. Hoffman*
12. **Penokean Fold Belt**—*P. F. Hoffman and K. D. Card*
13. **Sudbury Structure**—*K. D. Card*
14. **Mistassini-Otish Region**—*P. F. Hoffman and K. D. Card*
15. **Makkovik-Ketilidian**—*A. Davidson*
16. **Trans-Hudson orogen; Foxe Fold Belt, Ketilidian-Rinkian, Chantrey, Amer, Coronation Belt-East Arm, Bathurst, Dubawnt-Thelon, Athabasca**—*P. F. Hoffman*
17. **Synthesis**—*P. F. Hoffman*

Middle and Upper Proterozoic

18. **Introduction**—*P. F. Hoffman and A. Davidson*
19. **Trans-Labrador Belt**—*A. Davidson*
20. **"Nain" anorogenic suite, Gardar, Seal Lake**—*A. Davidson*
21. **Southern Region**—*P. F. Hoffman and K. D. Card*
22. **Coppermine North Baffin Region**—*P. F. Hoffman*
23. **Grenville Province**—*A. Davidson*
24. **Synthesis**—*A. Davidson and P. F. Hoffman*

Post-Precambrian

25. **Post-Precambrian History**—*P. F. Hoffman, K. D. Card and A. Davidson*

Synthesis and Summary

26. **Synthesis and Summary**—*P. F. Hoffman and others*

Volume C-2. *Precambrian–Conterminous U.S.*

J. C. Reed, Jr., M. E. Bickford, R. S. Houston, P. K. Link, D. W. Rankin, P. K. Sims, and W. R. Van Schmus, eds.

1. **Introduction**—*J. C. Reed, Jr.*
2. **The Lake Superior region and Trans-Hudson orogen**
   - **Introduction**—*P. K. Sims and G. B. Morey*
   - **Archean craton and associated Archean rocks**
     - **Greenstone-granite terrane**—*D. L. Southwick, K. J. Schulz, R. W. Ojakangas, R. L. Bauer, S. B. Shirey, and G. N. Hanson*
   - **Gneiss Terrane**
     - **Minnesota River Valley**—*R. L. Bauer and G. R. Himmelberg*
     - **Northern Michigan**—*P. K. Sims, K. J. Schulz, and Z. E. Peterman*
     - **Central Wisconsin**—*P. K. Sims and W. R. Van Schmus*
     - **The Great Lakes tectonic zone**—*D. L. Southwick and P. K. Sims*
   - **Penokean and related epicratonic rocks**
     - **Introduction**—*P. K. Sims and G. B. Morey*
     - **Early Proterozoic epicratonic rocks**—*G. B. Morey*
     - **Wisconsin magmatic terrane**—*P. K. Sims, K. J. Schulz, and Z. E. Peterman*
     - **Tectonic synthesis**—*K. J. Schulz, P. K. Sims, and G. B. Morey*
   - **Intracratonic igneous and sedimentary rocks**
     - **1,760 Ma rhyolite and granite**—*E. I. Smith*
     - **Quartzites**—*R. W. Ojakangas*
     - **The Wolf River Batholith**—*J. L. Anderson*
     - **Midcontinent rift system**—*P. W. Weiblen*
     - **Geophysical characteristics**—*V. W. Chandler*
     - **Metallogeny**—*M. G. Mudrey, Jr., and J. Kalliokoski*
     - **Tectonostratigraphic evolution and problems**—*P. K. Sims, Z. E. Peterman, and D. L. Southwick*
     - **Trans-Hudson orogen**—*Z. E. Peterman and P. K. Sims*
3. **The Wyoming Province**
   - **Location and boundaries**—*R. S. Houston and K. E. Karlstrom*
   - **History of investigations**—*R. S. Houston*
   - **Archean**
     - **Beartooth Mountains and southwest Montana**—*E. A. Erslev*
     - **Bighorn Mountains**—*Z. E. Peterman and R. S. Houston*
     - **Owl Creek Mountains**—*R. S. Houston and K. E. Karlstrom*
     - **Teton and Gros Ventre Ranges**—*J. C. Reed, Jr., and R. S. Houston*
     - **Wind River Range**—*R. G. Worl and R. S. Houston*
     - **Granite, Ferris, and Seminoe Mountains**—*R. S. Houston, K. E. Karlstrom, and M. W. Reynolds*
     - **Medicine Bow Mountains**—*R. S. Houston and K. E. Karlstrom*
     - **Sierra Madre**—*R. S. Houston*
     - **Laramie Mountains and Casper Mountains**—*G. L. Snyder*
     - **Hartville Uplift**—*R. S. Houston*
     - **Black Hills**—*R. S. Houston and K. E. Karlstrom*
     - **Albion and Raft River Ranges**—*R. S. Houston*
     - **Wasatch Mountains and Antelope Island**—*B. Bryant*
     - **Northeastern Uinta Mountains**—*R. S. Houston and K. E. Karlstrom*
     - **Little Belt and Rocky Mountains**—*R. S. Houston*
     - **Mineral deposits in Archean rocks**—*R. S. Houston*
   - **Proterozoic rocks**
     - **Snowy Pass Supergroup of the Medicine Bow Mountains**—*R. S. Houston and K. E. Karlstrom*
     - **Snowy Pass Group of the Sierra Madre**—*R. S. Houston and K. E. Karlstrom*
     - **Red Creek Quartzite**—*R. S. Houston*
     - **Proterozoic rocks of the Black Hills**—*R. S. Houston*
     - **Mineral deposits in Proterozoic rocks**—*R. S. Houston and J. C. Reed, Jr.*
     - **Mafic and ultramafic intrusive rocks**—*G. L. Snyder and R. S. Houston*
     - **Cheyenne Belt**—*R. S. Houston and K. E. Karlstrom*
     - **Geophysical features**—*K. E. Karlstrom*
     - **Tectonic models**—*R. S. Houston, K. E. Karlstrom, and E. A. Erslev*
4. **Transcontinental Proterozoic provinces**
   - **Introduction and overview**—*W. R. Van Schmus and M. E. Bickford*
   - **Older accretionary terranes; Colorado Province**—*M. E. Bickford, J. C. Reed, Jr., and K. C. Condie*
   - **Transitional terranes; Yavapai and Mazatzal Provinces,** *Arizona—K. E. Karlstrom and S. A. Bowring*
   - **Younger accretional Terranes; New Mexico**—*J. Robertson, S. A. Bowring, M. L. Williams, J. A. Grambling, and L. T. Silver*
   - **Western transitional zones; California-Nevada-Arizona**—*J. L. Anderson and J. Wooden*
   - **Central Plains Oregon; Western Midcontinent**—*W. R. Van Schmus and P. K. Sims*
   - **Middle Proterozoic granite-rhyolite provinces**—*M. E. Bickford, W. R. Van Schmus, E. B. Kisvarsanyi, and S. Mosher*
   - **Eastern midcontinent and Grenville transition**—*E. G. Lidiak*
   - **Midcontinent Rift System**—*W. R. Van Schmus and W. J. Hinze*
   - **Middle Cambrian crystalline basement, Oklahoma**—*M. C. Gilbert and R. E. Denison*
   - **General synthesis**—*M. E. Bickford and others*
5. **Proterozoic rocks east and southeast of the Grenville front**
   - **Introduction**—*D. W. Rankin*
   - **Adirondack massif**—*J. McLelland, Y. W. Isachsen, L. M. Hall, and R. W. Weiner*
   - **Subsurface Grenville-age rocks between the Adirondack massif and the Black Warrior basin**—*E. G. Lidiak and W. J. Hinze*
   - **Western extensions of Grenville-age rocks; Texas**—*S. Mosher*
   - **Proterozoic North American (Laurentian) rocks of the Appalachian orogen**—*D. W. Rankin, A. A. Drake, Jr., and N. M. Ratcliffe*
   - **Proterozoic rocks of accreted terranes**—*R. Goldsmith and D. T. Secor*
6. **Precambrian rocks of the northern Rocky Mountains and the Basin and Range Province**
   - **Introduction**—*P. K. Link*
   - **Middle Proterozoic basement**—*P. K. Link*
   - **Middle Proterozoic rocks of Utah; Uinta Mountain Group and Big Cottonwood Formation**—*P. K. Link*
   - **Middle Proterozoic rocks of southeastern California; Pahrump Group**—*L. W Wright*
   - **Middle and Late Proterozoic Grand Canyon Supergroup, northern Arizona**—*D. P. Elston*
   - **Middle Proterozoic rocks of central and southern Arizona; Apache Group, Troy Quartzite, and diabase**—*C. T. Wrucke and L. T. Middleton*
   - **Late Proterozoic rocks of the United States Cordillera**—*J. H. Stewart, P. K. Link, N. Christie-Blick, and L. A. Wright*
   - **Correlation of Middle and Late Proterozoic rocks of the western United States**—*D. P. Elston, D. Winston, and P. K. Link*
   - **Mineral deposits in Middle and Late Proterozoic strata in the United States Cordilleran region**—*R. C. Pearson*
   - **Paleobiology of Middle and Late Proterozoic rocks of the western United States**—*R. J. Horodyski*
   - **Summary and remaining problems**—*P. K. Link*
7. **Discussion and synthesis**—*J. C. Reed, Jr., and 6 others*

Volume D-1. *Sedimentary cover of the Craton; Canada*
D. F. Stott and J. D. Aitken, eds.

1. **Introduction**—*D. F. Stott and J. D. Aitken*

INTERIOR PLATFORM, WESTERN BASINS, AND EASTERN CORDILLERA

2. **Introduction**
   General statement—*D. F. Stott and J. D. Aitken*
   Physiography—*D. F. Stott and and R. W. Klassen*
   History of exploration, geological investigations— *D. F. Stott and J. D. Aitken*
   Tectonic framework—*J. D. Aitken*
3. **Geophysical and petrologic characteristics of the basement rocks**
   Introduction—*R. A. Burwash*
   Structural domains—*R. A. Burwash*
   Magnetic and gravity data—*A. G. Green*
   Deep seismic profiles—*E. R. Kanasewich*
   Heat flow—*A. M. Jessop*
   Geochronology—*R. A. Burwash*
   Lithostructural domains of the buried shield—*R. A. Burwash*
4. **Stratigraphy**
   Proterozoic sedimentary rocks—*J. D. Aitken*
   Cambrian-Lower Ordovician; Sauk Sequence—*J. D. Aitken*
   Ordovician-Silurian—*M. P. Cecile and B. S. Norford*
   Devonian—*P. F. Moore*
   Carboniferous—*B. C. Richards, E. W. Bamber, A. C. Higgins and J. Utting*
   Permian—*C. M. Henderson, E. W. Bamber, B. C. Richards, A. C. Higgins, and A. McGugan*
   Triassic—*D. W. Gibson*
   Jurassic—*T. P. Poulton, W. K. Braun, M. M. Brooke, and E. H. Davies*
   Cretaceous—*D. F. Stott, W.G.E. Caldwell, D. J. Cant, J. E. Christopher, J. Dixon, E. H. Koster, D. H. McNeil and F. Simpson*
   Tertiary—*D. F. Stott, J. Dixon, J. R. Dietrich, D. H. McNeil, L. S. Russell, and A. D. Sweet*
   Quaternary—*A. M. Stalker and J-S. Vincent*
5. **Tectonic evolution and basin history**—*J. D. Aitken*
6. **Economic Geology**
   Petroleum and natural gas—*R. D. Johnson and N. J. McMillan*
   Coal—*A. R. Cameron*
   Geothermal energy—*A. M. Jessop*
   Industrial minerals—*P. Guliov*
   Metals—*J. D. Aitken and D. F. Stott*
   Groundwater—*D. H. Lennox*

HUDSON PLATFORM

7. **Introduction**
   General statement—*A. W. Norris*
   Physiography—*A. W. Norris*
   History of exploration and geological investigations—*A. W. Norris*
8. **Geology**
   Tectonic framework—*A. W. Norris*
   Crustal geophysics—*A. C. Grant and B. V. Sanford*
   Tectonostratigraphic assemblages—*A. W. Norris*
   Biostratigraphy: Ordovician, Silurian, Devonian, Mesozoic—*A. W. Norris*
   Lithostratigraphy: Ordovician, Silurian, Silurian and Devonian, Devonian, Mesozoic—*A. W. Norris*
   Recent advances in the geology of Hudson Platform—*B. V. Sanford and A. C. Grant*
   Lithostratigraphy; Quaternary—*W. R. Cowan*
   Tectonic evolution and paleogeography; Ordovician, Silurian, Devonian, Mesozoic—*A. W. Norris*
9. **Economic Geology**
   Petroleum—*A. W. Norris*
   Oil Shale—*A. W. Norris*
   Industrial minerals—*A. W. Norris*

ST. LAWRENCE PLATFORM

10. **Introduction**
    General statement—*B. V. Sanford*
    Regional elements—*B. V. Sanford*
    History of geological exploration—*B. V. Sanford*
    Physiographic elements—*B. V. Sanford*
11. **Geology**
    Evolution of tectonic framework—*B. V. Sanford*
    Geophysical characteristics—*B. V. Sanford*
    Diagnostic shelly faunas and conodont biostratigraphy—*B. V. Sanford*
    Depositional cycles and lithostratigraphy—*B. V. Sanford*
    The Monteregian intrusions—*K. L. Currie*
    Summary of basin history—*B. V. Sanford*
    Quaternary period— *W. R. Cowan*
12. **Economic Geology**
    Petroleum—*B. V. Sanford*
    Industrial minerals—*B. V. Sanford*
    Metals—*B. V. Sanford*
    Economic aspects of Monteregian intrusions—*K. L. Currie*

SYNTHESIS

13. **Evolutionary models and tectonic comparisons**—*J. D. Aitken*

Volume D-2. *Sedimentary cover—North American Craton: U.S.*

L. L. Sloss, ed.

INTRODUCTION

1. **Introduction**—*L. L. Sloss*
2. **Geophysical aspects of the craton: U.S.**—*W. J. Hinze and L. W. Braile*
3. **Tectonic evolution of the craton in Phanerozoic time**—*L. L. Sloss*

THE ROCKY MOUNTAIN REGION

4. **Triassic and older stratigraphy: Southern Rocky Mountains**—*D. L. Baars*
5. **A synthesis of the Jurassic system in the southern Rocky Mountain region**—*F. Peterson*
6. **Cretaceous rocks of the Western Interior Basin**—*C. M. Molenaar and D. D. Rice*
7. **Phanerozoic stratigraphy of the northern Rocky Mountain region**—*J. A. Peterson*
8. **Basins of the Rocky Mountain region**—*D. L. Baars and 15 others*

THE WESTERN MID-CONTINENT REGION

9. **Geology of the Williston Basin (United States portion)**—*L. C. Gerhard and S. B. Anderson*
10. **Phanerozoic history of the central midcontinent, United States**—*B. J. Bunker, B. J. Witzke, W. L. Watney, and G. A. Ludvigson*
11. **The Permian Basin region**—*H. N. Frenzel and 13 others*
12. **Southern Midcontinent region**—*K. S. Johnson and 7 others*

THE EASTERN MID-CONTINENT REGION

13. **Michigan Basin**—*J. H. Fisher, M. W. Barratt, J. B. Droste, and R. H. Shaver*
14. **Illinois Basin region**—*C. Collinson, M. L. Sargent, and J. R. Jennings*
15. **The Appalachian Basin**—*R. C. Milici and W. deWitt, Jr.*
16. **The Black Warrior basin**—*W. A. Thomas*

CONCLUSIONS

17. **Conclusions**—*L. L. Sloss*

Volume E. *Innuitian Orogen and Arctic Platform: Canada and Greenland*

H. P. Trettin, ed.

1. **Introduction**—*H. P. Trettin*
2. **Geographic and geologic exploration**—*R. L. Christie and P. R. Dawes*
3. **Geomorphic regions**—*P. R. Dawes and R. L. Christie*
4. **Tectonic Framework**—*H. P. Trettin*
5. **Geophysical Characteristics**
   - **Gravity field**—*L. W. Sobczak*
   - **Crustal structure from seismic and gravity studies**—*L. W. Sobczak, D. A. Forsyth, and A. Overton*
   - **Seismicity**—*D. A. Forsyth, H. S. Hasegawa, and R. J. Wetmiller*
   - **Aeromagnetic field**—*R. L. Coles*
   - **Conductivity anomalies**—*E. R. Niblett and R. D. Kurtz*
   - **Motions of the north magnetic pole**—*L. R. Newitt and E. R. Niblett*
   - **Heat flow**—*A. M. Jessop*
6. **Precambrian successions in the northernmost part of the Canadian Shield**—*T. Frisch and H. P. Trettin*
7. **Cambrian to Silurian basin development and sedimentation, and North Greenland**—*A. K. Higgins, J. R. Ineson, J. S. Peel, F. Surlyk, and M. Sonderholm*
8. **Cambrian to Early Devonian basin development, sedimentation, and volcanism, Arctic islands**—*H. P. Trettin, U. Mayr, G.D.F. Long, and J. J. Packard*
9. **The Proterozoic to Late Silurian record of Pearya**—*H. P. Trettin*
10. **Middle-Upper Devonian clastic wedge of the Arctic Islands**—*A. F. Embry*
11. **Devonian-Early Carboniferous deformation and metamorphism, North Greenland**
   - **Deformation**—*N. J. Soper and A. K. Higgins*
   - **Metamorphism**—*A. K. Higgins and N. J. Soper*
12. **Silurian-Early Carboniferous deformation phases and associated metamorphism and plutonism, Arctic islands**
   - **Introduction**—*H. P. Trettin*
   - **Late Silurian-Early Devonian movements of the Boothia Uplift**—*A. V. Okulitch, J. J. Packard, and A. I. Zolnai*
   - **Early Devonian movements of the Inglefield Uplift**—*G. P. Smith and A. V. Okulitch*
   - **Middle Devonian to Early Carboniferous deformations, northern Ellesmere and Axel Heiberg islands**—*H. P. Trettin*
   - **Late Devonian-Early Carboniferous deformation of the Parry Islands and Canrobert Hills fold belts, Bathurst and Melville Islands**—*J. C. Harrison, F. G. Fox, and A. V. Okulitch*
   - **Late Devonian-Early Carboniferous deformation, Prince Patrick and Banks Islands**—*J. C. Harrison and T. Brent*
   - **Summary**—*H. P. Trettin*
13. **Carboniferous and Permian history of the Sverdrup Basin, Arctic Islands**—*G. R. Davies and W. W. Nassichuk*
14. **Mesozoic history of the Arctic Islands**—*A. F. Embry*
15. **Late Cretaceous-Tertiary basin development and sedimentation, Arctic Islands**—*A. D. Miall*
16. **Late Cretaceous-early Tertiary deformation, North Greenland**—*N. J. Soper and A. K. Higgins*
17. **Cretaceous-early Tertiary deformation, Arctic Islands**—*A. V. Okulitch and H. P. Trettin*
18. **Middle and late Tertiary tectonic and physiographic developments**—*H. P. Trettin*
19. **The Quaternary record**—*D. A. Hodgson*
20. **Resources**
   - **Petroleum resources, Arctic Islands**—*A. F. Embry, T. G. Powell and U. Mayr*
   - **Petroleum resources, North Greenland**—*F. G. Christiansen, S. Piasecki and L. Stemmerik*
   - **Coal resources, Arctic Islands**—*R. M. Bustin and A. D. Miall*
   - **Economic mineral resources, Arctic Islands**—*W. A. Gibbins*
   - **Economic mineral resources, North Greenland**—*A. Steenfelt*
21. **Summary and remaining problems**—*H. P. Trettin*

Volume F-1. *Appalachian Orogen: Canada and Greenland*

H. Williams and E.R.W. Neale, eds.

1. **Introduction**—*H. Williams*
2. **Temporal and spatial subdivision of rocks of the Canadian Appalachians**—*H. Williams*
3. **Stratigraphy and tectonic analysis**—*H. Williams and 15 others*
4. **Geophysical features of the Canadian Appalachian region**—*H. G. Miller*
5. **Structural styles**—*D. Keppie*
6. **Metamorphism**—*H. Williams and others*
7. **Plutonism**—*K. L. Currie*
8. **Volcanic regimes**—*S. Barr*
9. **Metallogeny and mineral resources**—*P. Dean, S. Swinden, and others*
10. **Ophiolites and mélanges**—*J. Malpas*
11. **Geochronology and thermal history**—*H. Williams and others*
12. **Faunas and faunal provinces**—*R. B. Neuman and G. S. Nowlan*
13. **Offshore extensions**—*J. S. Bell, R. D. Howie, and H. Williams*
14. **Correlation and comparison between the Canadian and U.S. Appalachian regions**—*H. Williams*
15. **The Caledonides of East Greenland and part of the North American Plate**—*A. K. Higgins*
16. **North Atlantic borderlands and Appalachian connections**—*H. Williams*
17. **Synthesis, models, trends, outlook, reflections**—*H. Williams*

Volume F-2. *Appalachian-Ouachita Orogen in the United States*

R. D. Hatcher, Jr., G. W. Viele, and W. A. Thomas, eds.

THE APPALACHIAN REGION

1. **Introduction—R. D. Hatcher, Jr.**

Time slice analysis

2. **Pre-orogenic terranes**—*D. W. Rankin and 9 others*
3. **The Taconic Orogen**—*A. A. Drake, A. K. Sinha, J. Laird, and R. E. Guy*
4. **The Acadian Orogeny**—*P. H. Osberg, J. F. Tull, P. Robinson, R. Hon, and J. R. Butler*
5. **The Alleghanian Orogeny**—*R. D. Hatcher, Jr., and 6 others*
6. **Post-Paleozoic activity**—*W. Manspeizer and 8 others*

Regional geology and geophysics

7. **Paleontological contributions to Paleozoic paleogeographic reconstructions of the Appalachians**—*R. B. Neuman, A. R. Palmer, and J. T. Dutro, Jr.*
8. **Crustal characteristics**—*J. K. Costain and 5 others*
9. **Late Paleozoic thermal evolution of crystalline terranes within parts of the U.S. Appalachian Orogen**—*R. D. Dallmeyer*
10. **The subsurface Appalachians beneath the Atlantic and Gulf Coastal Plains**—*W. A. Thomas and 5 others*
11. **Geomorphology of the Appalachian highlands**—*J. T. Hack*

Economic geology

12. **Mineral deposits of the U.S. Appalachians**—*P. G. Feiss and J. F. Slack*
13. **Energy resources of the Appalachian orogen**—*W. de Witt, Jr., and R. C. Milici*

Tectonic synthesis

14. **Tectonic synthesis of the U.S. Appalachians**—*R. D. Hatcher, Jr.*

THE APPALACHIAN/OUACHITA CONNECTION

15. **The Appalachian/Ouachita connection**—*W. A. Thomas*

THE OUACHITA OROGENIC BELT

16. **Introduction**—*G. W. Viele*

Regional stratigraphy

17. **Biostratigraphy of the Paleozoic rocks of the Ouachita Orogen, Arkansas, Oklahoma, west Texas**—*R. L. Ethington, S. C. Finney, and J. E. Repetski*
18. **Stratigraphy, sedimentology, and depositional setting of pre-orogenic rocks of the Ouachita Mountains**—*D. R. Lowe*
19. **Stratigraphy and sedimentary history of post-novaculite Carboniferous rocks of the Ouachita Mountains**—*R. C. Morris*
20. **Stratigraphy and sedimentary history of pre-Permian Paleozoic rocks of the Marathon Uplift**—*E. F. McBride*

Tectonics

21. **The Ouachita thrust belt and Arkoma Basin**—*J. K. Arbenz*
22. **Structural setting of the Benton-Broken Bow Uplifts**—*K. C. Nielsen, G. W. Viele, and J. Zimmerman*
23. **The Ouachita system in the subsurface of Texas, Arkansas, and Louisiana**—*R. L. Nicholas and D. E. Waddell*
24. **The Marathon fold and thrust belt, West Texas**—*W. R. Muehlberger and P. R. Tauvers*
25. **Foreland structure adjacent to the Ouachita Foldbelt**—*R. E. Denison*
26. **The Ouachita System: A geophysical overview**—*G. R. Keller, J. M. Kruger, K. J. Smith, and W. M. Voigt*

Tectonic synthesis

27. **Tectonic synthesis of the Ouachita orogenic belt**—*G. W. Viele and W. A. Thomas*

Economic geology

28. **Mineral deposits and resources of the Ouachita Mountains**—*K. L. Shelton*
29. **Hydrocarbons of the Ouachita Trend**—*P. A. Chenoweth*

Epilogue

30. **Epilogue**—*G. W. Viele*

Volume G-1. *The Cordilleran Orogen: Alaska*
G. Plafker, D. L. Jones, and H. C. Berg, eds.

INTRODUCTION

1. **Overview of Alaskan geology**—*G. Plafker and D. L. Jones*
2. **History of earth sciences research in Alaska**—*R. M. Chapman and G. Gryc*

MAJOR TECTONOSTRATIGRAPHIC ELEMENTS BY REGION

3. **Geology of northern Alaska**—*T. E. Moore and 5 others*
4. **Geology of Seward Peninsula and St. Lawrence Island**—*A. B. Till and J. Dumoulin*
5. **Geology of part of east-central Alaska**—*J. Dover*
6. **Geology of the Yukon-Tanana area of east-central Alaska**—*H. L. Foster, T.E.C. Keith, and W. D. Menzie*
7. **Geology of west-central Alaska**—*W. W. Patton, Jr., S. E. Box, E. J. Moll-Stalcup, and T. P. Miller*
8. **Geology of southwestern Alaska**—*J. E. Decker, Jr., and 10 others*
9. **Geology of south-central Alaska**—*D. L. Jones*
10. **Geology of the Aleutian structural arc**—*T. L. Vallier and 5 others*
11. **Geology of the southern Alaskan continental margin**—*G. Plafker, J. C. Moore, G. R. Winkler, and J. E. Decker, Jr.*
12. **Geology of southeastern Alaska**—*G. E. Gehrels and H. C. Berg*

SUCCESSOR BASINS

13. **Geology of the northern Alaska continental margin**—*A. Grantz*
14. **Basins of the eastern Bering Sea continental shelf**—*M. S. Marlow, A. K. Cooper, and M. A. Fisher*
15. **Interior basins of Alaska**—*C. E. Kirschner*

FLYSCH BASINS, OPHIOLITES AND PALEOMAGNETISM

16. **Deformed flysch basins of Alaska**—*D. L. Jones*
17. **Ophiolites and other mafic-ultramafic complexes in Alaska**—*W. W. Patton, Jr., S. E. Box, and D. Grybeck*
18. **Paleomagnetic data from Alaska**—*J. W. Hillhouse and R. S. Coe*

CRYSTALLINE ROCKS

19. **Metamorphism in Alaska**—*C. Dusel-Bacon*
20. **Pre-Cenozoic plutons of Alaska**—*T. P. Miller*
21. **Crustal melting events in Alaska**—*T. Hudson*
22. **Some accreted volcanic rocks of Alaska and their elemental abundances**—*F. Barker and 14 others*
23. **Latest Mesozoic and Cenozoic magmatism in southeastern Alaska**—*D. Brew*
24. **Late Cretaceous and Cenozoic volcanic rocks of mainland Alaska**—*E. J. Moll-Stalcup*
25. **Age, character, and significance of Aleutian arc volcanic rocks**—*B. D. Marsh*
26. **Aleutian magmas in space and time**—*R. W. Kay and S. Mahlburg-Kay*
27. **Isotopic composition of the igneous rocks of Alaska**—*J. Arth*
28. **Quaternary volcanism in the eastern Aleutian arc**—*T. P. Miller and D. H. Richter*

RESOURCES

28. **Metallogeny and major mineral resources**—*W. J. Nokelberg and 8 others*
29. **Petroleum resources of Alaska**—*L. B. Magoon III*
30. **Coal in Alaska**—*S. Bartsch-Winkler, C. Wahrhaftig, and G. D. Stricker*
31. **Geothermal resources**—*T. P. Miller*

QUATERNARY GEOLOGY

32. **Late Cenozoic glaciation of Alaska**—*T. D. Hamilton*
33. **Permafrost maps of Alaska**—*O. Ferrians*
34. **Neotectonics of Alaska**—*G. Plafker*

Volume G-2. *The Cordilleran Orogen: Canada*
H. Gabrielse and C. J. Yorath, eds.

1. **Introduction**—*H. Gabrielse and C. J. Yorath*
2. **Tectonic Framework**
   - **Morphogeological belts, tectonic assemblages and terranes**—*H. Gabrielse, J.W.H. Monger, J. O. Wheeler, and C. J. Yorath*
   - **Paleontological signatures of terranes**—*E. S. Carter and 5 others*
   - **Crustal geophysics**—*J. F. Sweeney, R. A. Stephenson, R. G. Currie, and J. M. DeLaurier*
3. **Paleomagnetism: Review and tectonic implications**—*E. Irving and P. J. Wynne*
4. **Precambrian basement rocks of the Canadian Cordillera**—*R. R. Parrish*
5. **Middle Proterozoic assemblages**—*J. D. Aitken and M. E. McMechan*
6. **Upper Proterozoic assemblages**—*H. Gabrielse and R. B. Campbell*
7. **Cambrian to Middle Devonian assemblages**—*W. H. Fritz and 4 others*
8. **Upper Devonian to Middle Jurassic assemblages**
   - **Ancestral North America**—*S. P. Gordey and 8 others*
   - **Cordilleran terranes**—*J.W.H. Monger and 9 others*
9. **Upper Jurassic to Paleogene assemblages**—*C. J. Yorath and 11 others*
10. **Neogene assemblages**—*J. G. Souther and C. J. Yorath*
11. **Physiographic evolution of the Canadian Cordillera**—*W. H. Mathews*
12. **Quaternary glaciation and sedimentation**—*J. J. Clague*
13. **The modern plate tectonic regime of the western Canadian continental margin**—*R. P. Riddihough and R. D. Hyndman*
14. **Volcanic regimes**—*J. G. Souther*
15. **Plutonic regimes**—*G. J. Woodworth and 4 others*
16. **Metamorphism**—*H. J. Greenwood and 4 others*
17. **Structural styles**—*H. Gabrielse and 27 others*
18. **Tectonic synthesis**—*H. Gabrielse and C. J. Yorath*
19. **Regional metallogeny**—*K. M. Dawson, A. Panteleyev, A. Sutherland Brown, and G. J. Woodsworth*
20. **Energy and groundwater resources of the Canadian Cordillera**
   - **Petroleum**—*C. J. Yorath, P. L. Gordy, and G. K. Williams*
   - **Coal**—*R. M. Bustin*
   - **Uranium and thorium**—*R. T. Bell*
   - **Geothermal**—*J. G. Souther*
   - **Groundwater**—*E. C. Halstead*
21. **Natural Hazards**—*J. J. Clague*
22. **Outstanding problems**—*H. Gabrielse and C. J. Yorath*

Volume G-3. *Cordilleran Orogen: U.S.*

B. C. Burchfiel, P. W. Lipman, and M. L. Zoback, eds.

INTRODUCTION

1. **Introduction—***B. C. Burchfiel, P. W. Lipman, and M. L. Zoback*

TIME SLICE ANALYSIS

2. **Latest Precambrian to latest Devonian time: Development of a continental margin—***F. G. Poole and 8 others*
3. **Late Paleozoic tectonic evolution of the western United States—***E. L. Miller, M. M. Miller, C. F. Stevens, J. E. Wright, and R. Madrid*
4. **Early Mesozoic tectonic evolution of the western U.S. Cordillera—***J. B. Saleeby and 7 others*
5. **Late Jurassic to Early Cretaceous geology of the U.S. Cordillera—***D. S. Cowan and R. L. Bruhn*
6. **Late Cretaceous and Eocene time—***D. M. Miller*
7. **Post-Laramide geology of the Cordilleran region—***R. L. Christiansen and R. S. Yeats*
8. **Lithosphere structure, seismicity, and contemporary deformation of the United States Cordillera—***R. B. Smith*

INTERPRETIVE SYNTHESIS

9. **Tectonic framework of the western U.S. Cordillera: General overview—***B. C. Burchfiel, G. A. Davis, and D. S. Cowan*
10. **Magmatism in the Cordilleran United States: Progress and problems—***P. W. Lipman*
12. **Metamorphism of the western Cordillera and its relationship to tectonics—***W. G. Ernst*
11. **Cordilleran sedimentary assemblages—***W. R. Dickinson*
12. **Extensional tectonics of the Cordillera—***B. P. Wernicke*
13. **Fold and thrust tectonics of the western United States, exclusive of the accreted terranes—***R. W. Allmendinger*
14. **Strike-slip regimes in the western U.S.—***J. H. Stewart and J. C. Crowell*
15. **Metallogenic evolution of the Cordilleran region of the western United States—***R. W. Hutchinson and J. P. Albers*
16. **Ophiolite summary—***J. B. Saleeby*
17. **Tectonic significance of paleomagnetic results for the western conterminous United States—***M. E. Beck, Jr.*

Volume H. *The Caribbean Region*

G. Dengo and J. E. Case, eds.

INTRODUCTION

1. **History of geological investigation in the Caribbean Region—***G. Draper and G. Dengo*
2. **Caribbean crustal provinces: Seismic and gravity evidence—***J. Case, W. D. MacDonald, and P. J. Fox*
3. **Northern Central America: The Maya and Chortis Blocks—***T. W. Donnelly, G. S. Horne, R. C. Finch, and E. López-Ramos*

REGIONAL GEOLOGY

4. **Geology and tectonic evolution of the northern Caribbean margin—***J. F. Lewis and 7 others*
5. **Geology of the Lesser Antilles—***R. C. Maury, G. K. Westbrook, P. E. Baker, Ph. Bouysse, and D. Westercamp*
6. **The Santa Marta prong and adjacent areas of eastern Colombia and western Venezuela—***R. Shagam, R. F. Geigenack, H. Duque-Caro, and R. Towle*
7. **The Caribbean Mountain system in the northern part of South America—***A. Bellizzia*
8. **The geology of southern Central America and western Colombia—***G. Escalante*
9. **Caribbean marine geology: Ridges and interior basins of the plate interior—***T. L. Holcombe, J. W. Ladd, G. K. Westbrook, N. T. Edgar, and C. L. Bowland*
10. **Caribbean marine geology: Active margins of the plate boundary—***J. W. Ladd, T. L. Holcombe, G. K. Westbrook, and N. T. Edgar*

REGIONAL GEOPHYSICS AND GEOCHEMISTRY

11. **Seismicity, large earthquakes, and the margin of the Caribbean plate—***W. McCann and W. Pennington*
12. **Review of Caribbean neotectonics—***P. Mann, C. Schubert, and K. Burke*
13. **History and tectonic setting of Caribbean magmatism—***T. W. Donnelly and 11 others*
14. **Volcanism—***M. J. Carr and R. E. Stoiber*
15. **Survey of Caribbean paleomagnetism—***W. D. MacDonald*

GEOLOGICAL EVOLUTION

16. **Geological evolution of the Caribbean: A plate tectonic perspective—***J. L. Pindell and S. F. Barrett*
17. **Tectonic evolution of the Caribbean region: Alternative hypothesis—***A.E.L. Morris, I. Taner, H. A. Meyerhoff, and A. A. Meyerhoff*
18. **Metallogenic evolution of the Caribbean region—***S. E. Kesler, E. Levy, and C. Martin F.*
19. **Energy resources of the Caribbean region—***A.E.L. Morris, R. Bueno-Salazar, A. A. Meyerhoff, I. Taner, G. A. Young*

SUMMARY

20. **Summary—***J. E. Case and G. Dengo*

Volume I-1. *Geology of the Continental Margin of Eastern Canada*
M. J. Keen and G. L. Williams, eds.

INTRODUCTION
1. **Geological and historical perspective**—*M. J. Keen, D.J.W. Piper, J. S. Bell, and K. Moran*
2. **Tectonic and geophysical overview**—*C. E. Keen and 5 others,* **with contributions on Igneous Rocks**—*G. Pe-Piper and 3 others*
3. **Biostratigraphy and related studies**—*G. L. Williams and 5 others*

REGIONAL GEOLOGY
4. **Paleozoic geology**—*J. S. Bell and R. D. Howie*
5. **The geology of the southeastern margin of Canada**
   The stratigraphy of Georges Bank Basin and relationships to the Scotia Basin—*J. A. Wade*
   Aspects of the geology of the Scotian Basin from recent seismic and well data—*J. A. Wade and B. C. MacLean*
6. **The continental margin around Newfoundland**—*A. C. Grant and K. D. McAlpine*
7. **Geology of the Labrador Shelf, Baffin Bay, and Davis Strait**—*H. R. Balkwill and 4 others*

MARGIN EVOLUTION
8. **Aspects of North Atlantic paleo-oceanography**—*F. Gradstein and 5 others*
9. **Geodynamics of rifted continental margins**—*C. E. Keen and C. Beaumont*

QUATERNARY STUDIES
10. **Quaternary geology**—*D.J.W. Piper and 5 others,* **with contributions by** *A. E. Aksu and 14 others*
11. **Modern sedimentary processes**—*C. L. Amos and 14 others*

RESOURCES
12. **Petroleum resources**—*J. S. Bell and G. R. Campbell*
13. **Mineral resources**—*P. B. Hale*
14. **Constraints to development**—*C.F.M. Lewis and M. J. Keen* **with contributions by** *J. Adams and 20 others*

POSTSCRIPT
15. **The future: A view of marine geology and geophysics in 1987**—*M. J. Keen*

Volume I-2. *The Atlantic Continental Margin: U.S.*
R. E. Sheridan and J. A. Grow, eds.

INTRODUCTION
1. **U.S. Atlantic Continental Margin; A typical Atlantic-type or passive continental margin**—*J. A. Grow and R. E. Sheridan*
2. **Marine physiography of the U.S. Atlantic margin**—*A. N. Shor and C. E. McClennen*
3. **U.S. Atlantic continental margin; Structural and tectonic framework**—*K. D. Klitgord, D. R. Hutchinson, and H. Schouten*
4. **History of studies of the Atlantic margin of the United States**—*C. L. Drake*

STRATIGRAPHY, DEPOSITIONAL PROCESSES, AND DEPOSITIONAL HISTORY
5. **Mesozoic and Cenozoic stratigraphy of the United States Atlantic continental shelf and slope**—*C. W. Poag and P. C. Valentine*
6. **Geology of the northern Atlantic coastal plain: Long Island to Virginia**—*R. K. Olsson, T. G. Gibson, H. J. Hansen, and J. P. Owens*
7. **Late Mesozoic and early Cenozoic geology of the Atlantic coastal plain: North Carolina to Florida**—*G. S. Gohn*
8. **Upper Cenozoic processes and environments of continental margin sedimentation: Eastern United States**—*S. R. Riggs and D. F. Belknap*

BASIN SYNTHESIS
9. **Geophysical data**—*R. E. Sheridan, J. A. Grow, and K. D. Klitgord*
10. **Late Triassic–Early Jurassic synrift basins of the U.S. Atlantic margin**—*W. Manspeizer and H. L. Cousminer*
11. **Mesozoic and Cenozoic magmatism**—*J. Z. deBoer, J. G. McHone, J. H. Puffer, P. C. Ragland, and D. Whittington*
12. **Georges Bank Basin: A regional synthesis**—*J. S. Schlee and K. D. Klitgord*
13. **Structure and evolution of Baltimore Canyon Trough**—*J. A. Grow, K. D. Klitgord, and J. S. Schlee*
14. **The Blake Plateau Basin and Carolina Trough**—*W. P. Dillon and P. Popenoe*
15. **Geology and geophysics of the Bahamas**—*R. E. Sheridan, H. T. Mullins, J. A. Austin, Jr., M. M. Ball, and J. W. Ladd*
16. **Paleoenvironments: Offshore Atlantic U.S. Margin**—*J. S. Schlee, W. Manspeizer, and S. R. Riggs*

DEEP CRUSTAL STRUCTURE: RIFTING AND SUBSIDENCE THEORY
17. **A large aperture seismic experiment in the Baltimore Canyon Trough**—*J. B. Diebold, P. L. Stoffa, and The LASE study group*
18. **Subsidence and basin modeling at the U.S. Atlantic passive margin**—*M. S. Steckler, A. B. Watts, and J. A. Thorne*
19. **Thermal evolution**—*D. S. Sawyer*
20. **Sea-level changes and their effect on the stratigraphy of Atlantic-type margins**—*W. C. Pitman and X. Golovchenko*
21. **Seismic stratigraphic and geohistory analysis of Tertiary strata from the continental shelf off New Jersey; Calculation of eustatic fluctuations from stratigraphic data**—*S. M. Greenlee, F. W. Schroeder, and P. R. Vail*

GEOLOGICAL RESOURCES
22. **Petroleum geology of the United States Atlantic continental margin**—*R. E. Mattick and J. Libby-French*
23. **Hydrogeology of the Atlantic continental margin**—*F. A. Kohout and 5 others*
24. **Sand and gravel resources: U.S. Atlantic continental shelf**—*D. B. Duane and W. L. Stubblefield*
25. **Mineral resources of the U.S. Atlantic continental margin**—*S. R. Riggs and F. T. Manheim*
26. **Heat flow and geothermal resource potential of the Atlantic Coastal Plain**—*J. K. Costain and J. A. Speer*

ENVIRONMENTAL HAZARDS
27. **Geologic hazards on the Atlantic continental margin**—*D. W. Folger*
28. **Coastal geologic hazards**—*O. H. Pilkey and W. J. Neal*
29. **Cretaceous and Cenozoic tectonism on the Atlantic coastal margin**—*D. C. Prowell*
30. **Seismicity along the Atlantic Seaboard of the U.S.; Intraplate neotectonics and earthquake hazards**—*L. Seeber and J. G. Armbruster*
31. **Waste disposal in the Atlantic continental margin**—*H. D. Palmer*

CONCLUSIONS
32. **Synthesis and unanswered questions**—*R. E. Sheridan and J. A. Grow*

Volume J. *The Gulf of Mexico Basin*

A. Salvador, ed.

1. **Introduction**—*A. Salvador*
2. **Physiography and bathymetry**—*W. R. Bryant and C. D. Winker*
3. **Tectonic features**—*T. E. Ewing*
4. **The crust under the Gulf of Mexico Basin**—*D. S. Sawyer, R. T. Buffler, and R. H. Pilger, Jr.*
5. **Evolution of tectonic features**—*M.P.A. Jackson*
6. **Igneous activity**—*G. R. Byerly*
7. **Pre-Triassic**—*R. D. Woods, A. E. Miles, and A. Salvador*
8. **Triassic-Jurassic**—*A. Salvador*
9. **Lower Cretaceous**—*E. McFarlan, Jr., and S. Menes*
10. **Upper Cretaceous**—*N. F. Sohl, E. Martinez, P. Salmeron, and F. Soto*
11. **Cenozoic**—*W. E. Galloway, D. G. Bebout, J. B. Dunlap, Jr., and W. L. Fisher*
12. **Late Quaternary sedimentation**—*J. M. Coleman, H. H. Roberts, and W. R. Bryant*
13. **Seismic stratigraphy of the central Gulf of Mexico Basin**—*R. T. Buffler*
14. **Origin and evolution of the Gulf of Mexico Basin**—*A. Salvador*
15. **Oil and gas resources**—*R. Nehring*
16. **Other natural resources: Phosphate, lignite, sulfur, uranium and geopressured-geothermal energy**—*S. R. Riggs and 4 others*
17. **Concluding remarks and unresolved problems**—*A. Salvador*

Volume K-1. *Quaternary Geology of Canada and Greenland*

R. J. Fulton, ed.

Regional Quaternary Geology of Canada

1. **Quaternary geology of the Canadian Cordillera**—*J. J. Clague and 7 others*
2. **Quaternary geology of the Canadian Interior Plains**—*R. J. Fulton, R. W. Klassen, and J-S. Vincent*
3. **Quaternary geology of the Canadian Shield**—*R. J. Fulton and 4 others*
4. **Quaternary geology of the St. Lawrence Lowlands of Canada**—*P. F. Karrow and S. Occhietti*
5. **Quaternary geology of the Atlantic Appalachian region of Canada**—*D. R. Grant*
6. **Quaternary geology of the Queen Elizabeth Islands**—*D. A. Hodgson, J. Bednarski, J. England, and R. M. Koerner*

Applied Quaternary Geology of Canada

7. **Quaternary environments in Canada as documented by paleobotanical case histories**—*J. V. Matthews, Jr., and 8 others*
8. **Quaternary geodynamics in Canada**—*J. T. Andrews and W. R. Peltier*
9. **A survey of geomorphic processes in Canada**—*J. A. Heginbottom and 12 others*
10. **Terrain geochemistry in Canada**—*R.N.W. DiLabio*
11. **Quaternary resources in Canada**—*L. E. Jackson, Jr., and 7 others*
12. **Influence of the Quaternary geology of Canada on man's environment**—*L. E. Jackson, Jr., and 6 others*

Quaternary Geology of Greenland

13. **Quaternary geology of the ice-free areas and adjacent shelves of Greenland**—*S. Funder, B. Fredskild, and H. C. Larsen*
14. **Dynamic and climatic history of the Greenland Ice Sheet**—*N. Reeh*

Volume K-2. *Quaternary Non-glacial Geology: Conterminous U.S.*

R. B. Morrison, ed.

Introduction

1. **Introduction**—*R. B. Morrison*

Topical Summaries

2. **Quaternary paleoclimates**—*T. L. Smiley, R. A. Bryson, J. E. King, G. J. Kukla, and G. I. Smith*
3. **Dating methods applicable to the Quaternary**—*J. N. Rosholt and 10 others*
4. **Quaternary volcanism in the western conterminous United States**—*R. G. Leudke and R. L. Smith*
5. **Quaternary tephrochronology**—*J. O. Davis*
6. **Tephrochronologic correlation of upper Neogene sediments along the Pacific margin, conterminous United States**—*A. M. Sarna-Wojcseki, K. R. Lajoie, C. E. Meyer, D. P. Adam, and H. J. Riek*

Regional Synthesis

7. **The Pacific Margin**—*R. B. Morrison and 15 others*
8. **The Columbia Plateau**—*V. R. Baker and 8 others*
9. **Quaternary geology and structural history of the Snake River Plain, Idaho and Oregon**—*H. E. Malde*
10. **Northern Basin and Range**—*R. B. Morrison and J. O. Davis*
11. **Southwestern Basin and Range**—*J. C. Dohrenwend and 6 others*
12. **Southeastern Basin and Range**—*J. Hawley and 2 others*
13. **Colorado Plateau**—*P. Patton and 7 others*
14. **Quaternary history of some southern and central Rocky Mountain basins**—*M. C. Reheis and 7 others*
15. **Northern Great Plains**—*W. Wayne and 14 others*
16. **Quaternary geology of the southern Great Plains and an adjacent segment of the Rolling Plains**—*T. C. Gustavson and 6 others*
17. **Osage Plains and interior highlands**—*R. F. Madole, C. R. Ferring, M. J. Guccione, S. A. Hall, W. C. Johnson, and C. J. Sorenson*
18. **Quaternary geology of the Lower Mississippi Valley**—*W. J. Autin, S. F. Burns, B. J. Miller, R. T. Saucier, and J. I. Snead*
19. **Gulf of Mexico Coastal Plain**—*J. R. DuBar, T. E. Ewing, E. L. Lundelius, Jr., E. G. Otvos, and C. D. Winker*
20. **Appalachian highlands and interior low plateaus**—*H. H. Mills and P. A. Delcourt*
21. **Atlantic Coastal Plain**—*D. J. Colquhoun and 2 others*

Volume K-3. *North America and Adjacent Oceans during the Last Deglaciation*

W. F. Ruddiman and H. E. Wright, Jr., eds.

1. **Introduction**—*W. F. Ruddiman and H. E. Wright, Jr.*

NORTH AMERICAN ICE SHEETS: CHRONOLOGY OF DISINTEGRATION

2. **The Late Wisconsin glaciation and deglaciation of the Laurentide Ice Sheet**—*J. T. Andrews*
3. **Proglacial lakes and the southern margin of the Laurentide Ice Sheet**—*J. T. Teller*
4. **Timing and processes of deglaciation along the southern margin of the Cordilleran ice sheet**—*D. B. Booth*

ICE CORE AND OOTHER GLACIOLOGICAL DATA

5. **Ice core and other glaciologial data**—*W.S.B. Paterson and C. U. Hammer*
6. **The oxygen-isotope record of glaciation**—*A. C. Mix*
7. **Northern oceans**—*W. F. Ruddiman*
8. **Glacial isotasy, mantle viscosity, and Pleistocene climatic change**—*W. R. Peltier*
9. **Ice dynamics and deglaciation models when ice sheets collapsed**—*T. Hughes*

THE NON-GLACIAL PHYSICAL RECORD IN THE CONTINENT

10. **River responses**—*S. A. Schumm and G. R. Brakenridge*
11. **The physical record of lakes in the Great Basin**—*L. Benson and R. S. Thompson*
12. **Late Quaternary paleoclimate records from lacustrine ostracodes**—*R. M. Forester*

THE BIOLOGICAL RECORD ON THE CONTINENT

13. **Patterns and rates of vegetation change during the deglaciation of eastern North America**—*G. L. Jacobson, Jr., T. Webb III., and E. C. Grimm*
14. **The northwestern U.S. during deglaciation; Vegetational history and paleoclimatic implications**—*C. W. Barnosky, P. M. Anderson, and P. J. Bartlein*
15. **Vegetation history of the deserts of southwestern North America: The nature and timing of the Late Wisconsin–Holocene transition**—*T. R. VanDevender, R. S. Thompson, and J. L. Betancourt*
16. **Late Wisconsin and early Holocene paleoenvironments of east-central North America based on assemblages of fossil Coleoptera**—*A. V. Morgan*
17. **Environmental fluctuations and evolution of mammalian faunas during the last deglaciation in North America**—*R. W. Graham and J. I. Mead*
18. **Environmental change and developmental history of human adaptive patterns: The Paleoindian case**—*R. Bonnichsen, D. Stanford, and J. L. Fastook*

ANALYSIS AND SUMMARY

19. **Model simulations of the climatic patterns during the deglaciation of North America**—*J. E. Kutzbach*
20. **Climatic change in eastern North America during the past 18,000 years: Comparisons of pollen data with model results**—*T. Webb III., P. J. Bartlein, and J. E. Kutzbach*
21. **Synthesis; The ocean/ice sheet record**—*W. F. Ruddiman*
22. **Synthesis; Land south of the ice sheets**—*H. E. Wright, Jr.*

Volume L. *The Arctic Ocean Region*

A. Grantz, J. F. Sweeney, and G. L. Johnson, eds.

1. **Introduction**—*J. F. Sweeney, G. L. Johnson, and A. Grantz*
2. **Historical background: Exploration, concepts, and observations**—*J. R. Weber and E. F. Roots*

ARCTIC OCEAN ICE COVER

3. **Structure and dynamics of the Arctic Ocean ice cover**—*N. Untersteiner*
4. **Arctic Ocean ice cover: Geologic history and climatic significance**—*D. L. Clark*

BATHYMETRY AND PHYSIOGRAPHY

5. **Bathymetry and physiography**—*G. L. Johnson, A. Grantz, and J. R. Weber*

GEOPHYSICAL DATA

6. **Seismicity and focal mechanisms of the Arctic region, and the North American Plate boundary in Asia**—*K. Fujita, D. B. Cook, H. Hasegawa, D. Forsyth, and R. Wetmiller*
7. **Gravity from 64°N to the North Pole**—*L. W. Sobczak and 5 others*
8. **Magnetic anomalies**—*R. L. Coles and P. T. Taylor*
9. **Geothermal observations in the Arctic region**—*M. G. Langseth, A. H. Lachenbruch, and V. Marshall*
10. **Seismic reflection and refraction**—*H. R. Jackson, D. A. Forsyth, J. K. Hall, and A. Overton*

THE NORTH AMERICAN PLATE BOUNDARY

11. **The North American Plate Boundary**—*O. Eldholm, A. M. Karasik, and P. A. Reksnes*

CONTINENTAL MARGINS

12. **The East Greenland Shelf**—*H. C. Larsen*
13. **The North Greenland continental margin**—*P. R. Dawes*
14. **The continental margin northwest of the Queen Elizabeth Islands**—*J. F. Sweeney, L. W. Sobczak, and D. A. Forsyth*
15. **Canadian Beaufort Sea and adjacent land areas**—*J. Dixon and J. R. Dietrich*
16. **Alaska**—*A. Grantz and S. May*
17. **The Arctic Continental margin of eastern Siberia**—*K. Fujita and D. B. Cook*

RIDGES AND BORDERLANDS

18. **Ridges and basins in the central Arctic Ocean**—*J. R. Weber and J. F. Sweeney*
19. **Chukchi Borderland**—*J. K. Hall*
20. **The Norwegian-Greenland Sea**—*O. Eldholm, J. Skogseid, E. Sundvor, and A. M. Myhre*
21. **Eurasia Basin**—*Y. Kristofferson*
22. **Canada Basin**—*A. Grantz, S. D. May, and L. A. Lawver*

ARCTIC BASIN SEDIMENTS, FOSSILS, PALEOCLIMATE, AND HISTORY

23. **Late Mesozoic and Cenozoic paleogeographic and paleoclimatic history of the Arctic Ocean basin, based on shallow-water marine faunas and terrestrial vertebrates**—*L. Marincovich, Jr., E. M. Brouwers, D. M. Hopkins, and M. C. McKenna*
24. **Late Mesozoic and Cenozoic paleoceanography of the northern Polar oceans**—*J. Thiede, D. L. Clark, and Y. Herman*

(Continued on p. 595)

Volume L. *The Arctic Ocean Region (Continued from page 594)*

A. Grantz, J. f. Sweeney, and G. L. Johnson, eds.

QUATERNARY GEOLOGY

25. **Late Cenozoic geologic evolution of the Alaska North slope and adjacent continental shelves**—*D. A. Dinter, L. D. Carter, and J. Brigham-Grette*

MINERAL RESOURCES

26. **Petroleum**—*N. Heimela*
27. **Gas hydrates of the Arctic Ocean Basin**—*K. Kvenvolden and A. Grantz*
28. **Offshore hard minerals**—*P. B. Hale*

ORIGIN OF THE ARCTIC BASIN

29. **Paleomagnetic and Plate Tectonic constraints on the evolution of the Alaskan-Eastern Siberian Arctic**—*W. Harbert, L. Frei, R. Jarrad, S. Halgedahl, and D. Engebretson*
30. **A review of tectonic models for the evolution of the Canada Basin**—*L. A. Lawver and C. R. Scotese*

SUMMARY

31. **Summary**—*J. F. Sweeney, G. L. Johnson, and A. Grantz*

Volume M. *The Western North Atlantic Region*

P. R. Vogt and B. E. Tucholke, eds.

INTRODUCTION

1. **Perspective on the geology of the North Atlantic Ocean**—*B. E. Tucholke and P. R. Vogt*
2. **Imaging the ocean floor: History and state of the art**—*P. R. Vogt and B. E. Tucholke*
3. **A Jurassic to recent chronology**—*D. V. Kent and F. M. Gradstein*

PRESENT ACCRETION AXIS

4. **The crest of the Mid-Atlantic Ridge: Models for crustal generation, processes, and tectonics**—*K. C. Macdonald*
5. **Subaerial volcanism in the western North Atlantic**—*K. Saemundsson*
6. **Model of crustal formation in Iceland, and application to submarine mid-ocean ridges**—*G. Pálmason*
7. **Seismicity along the eastern margin of the North Atlantic Plate**—*P. Einarsson*
8. **"Zero-age" variations in the composition of abyssal volcanic rocks along the axial zone of the Mid-Atlantic Ridge**—*W. G. Melson and T. O'Hearn*
9. **Geochemical and isotopic variation along the Mid-Atlantic Ridge axis from 79°N to 0°N**—*J.-G. Schilling*
10. **The geology of North Atlantic transform plate boundaries and their aseismic extensions**—*P. J. Fox and D. G. Gallo*
11. **Hydrothermal activity in the North Atlantic**—*J. M. Edmond*
12. **The present plate boundary configuration**—*P. R. Vogt*

REGIONAL GEOLOGY AND GEOPHYSICS

13. **Gravity anomalies in the western North Atlantic Ocean**—*P. D. Rabinowitz and W-Y Jung*
14. **Geoid undulations mapped by spaceborne radar altimetry**—*P. R. Vogt*
15. **Magnetic anomalies and crustal magnetization**—*P. R. Vogt*
16. **The relationship between depth and age and heat flow and age in the western North Atlantic**—*J. C. Sclater and L. Wixon*
17. **Petrologic and geochemical evolution of pre-1 Ma western North Atlantic lithosphere**—*W. B. Bryan and F. A. Frey*
18. **Mid-plate stress, deformation, and seismicity**—*M L. Zoback, S. P. Nishenko, R. M. Richardson, H. S. Hasegawa, and M. D. Zoback*
19. **Seismic structure of the ocean crust**—*G. M. Purdy and J. Ewing*
20. **Structure of basement and distribution of sediments in the western North Atlantic Ocean**—*B. E. Tucholke*
21. **Subduction of Atlantic lithosphere beneath the Caribbean**—*G. K. Westbrook and W. R. McCann*

PLATE TECTONIC EVOLUTION

22. **Plate kinematics of the central Atlantic**—*K. D. Klitgord and H. Schouten*
23. **Plate kinematics of the North Atlantic**—*S. P. Srivastava and C. R. Tapscott*
24. **Plate kinematics during the last 20 m.y., and the problem of "present" motions**—*P. R. Vogt*

SURFICIAL SEDIMENTATION

25. **Surficial sedimentary processes revealed by echo-character mapping in the western North Atlantic Ocean**—*E. P. Laine, J. E. Damuth, and R. Jacobi*
26. **Turbidite sedimentation in the northwestern Atlantic Ocean basin**—*O. H. Pilkey and W. J. Cleary*
27. **Deep current-controlled sedimentation in the western North Atlantic**—*I. N. McCave and B. E. Tucholke*
28. **Oceanic particles and pelagic sedimentation in the western North Atlantic Ocean**—*S. Honjo*
29. **Mass wasting in the western North Atlantic**—*R. M. Embley and R. Jacobi*
30. **Seabed geotechnical properties and seafloor utilization**—*A. J. Silva and J. S. Booth*

BIOFACIES

31. **Northwestern Atlantic Mesozoic biostratigraphy**—*F. M. Gradstein*
32. **Paleogene biofacies of the western North Atlantic Ocean**—*I. Premoli-Silva and A. Boersma*
33. **Neogene marine microfossil biofacies of the western North Atlantic**—*C. W. Poag and K. G. Miller*
34. **North Atlantic Mesozoic and Cenozoic paleobiogeography**—*W. A. Berggren and R. K. Olsson*

PALEOCEANOGRAPHY

35. **Paleogeographic and paleobathymetric evolution of the North Atlantic Ocean**—*B. E. Tucholke and F. W. McCoy*
36. **Paleoceanography and evolution of the North Atlantic Ocean basin during the Jurassic**—*L. F. Jansa*
37. **Cretaceous paleoceanography of the western North Atlantic Ocean**—*M. A. Arthur and W. E. Dean*
38. **Tertiary paleoceanography of the western North Atlantic Ocean**—*B. E. Tucholke and G. S. Mountain*

RESOURCES AND LAW OF THE SEA

39. **Space systems as marine geologic sensors**—*R. J. Anderle*
40. **Resource potential of the western North Atlantic Basin**—*W. P. Dillon and 5 others*
41. **The juridicial ocean basin**—*J. A. Knauss*

Volume N. *The Eastern Pacific Region*

E. L. Winterer, D. M. Hussong, and R. W. Decker, eds.

INTRODUCTION

1. **Introduction**—*E. L. Winterer, D. M. Hussong, and R. W. Decker*
2. **Large scale undersea features of the northeast Pacific**—*J. Mammerickx*
3. **Sediment thickness maps of the northeastern Pacific**—*E. L. Winterer*

PLATE KINEMATICS

4. **Tectonic maps of the northeast Pacific**—*T. Atwater and J. Severinghaus*
5. **Plate tectonic history of the northeast Pacific**—*T. Atwater*

ACTIVE RIDGES

6. **Evolution in plate tectonics; The Juan de Fuca Ridge**—*H. P. Johnson and M. L. Holmes*
7. **Tectonic and magmatic processes on the East Pacific Rise**—*K. C. Macdonald*
8. **Transforms of the eastern central Pacific**—*P. J. Fox*
9. **Hydrothermal processes and products on the Galapagos Rift and East Pacific Rise**—*R. M. Haymon*
10. **Petrology and geochemistry of the eastern Pacific spreading centers**—*R. Batiza*
11. **Propagating rifts and spreading centers**—*R. N. Hey, J. M. Stinton, and F. K. Duennebier*

MID-PLATE VOLCANISM

13. **The Hawaii–Emperor Chain**
    Tectonics, geochronology, and origin of the Hawaiian–Emperor volcanic chain—*D. A. Clague and G. B. Dalrymple*
    Petrology of Hawaiian lava—*T. L. Wright and D. A. Clague*
    The seismicity and tectonics of Hawaii—*F. W. Klein and R. Y. Koyanagi*
    Magma and eruption dynamics—*R. W. Decker*
    Hydrothermal systems in Hawaii—*D. M. Thomas*
14. **Seamounts and seamount chains of the eastern Pacific**—*R. Batiza*

SEDIMENTARY REGIMES

15. **The late Cenozoic stratigraphic record and hiatuses of the northeast Pacific; Results from the Deep Sea Drilling Project**—*J. A. Barron*
16. **The pelagic clay province of the North Pacific Ocean**—*M. Leinen*
17. **Hydrogenous sediments**—*D. Z. Piper and G. R. Heath*
18. **Sedimentation and paleoceanography of the central equatorial Pacific**—*F. Theyer, E. Vincent, and L. A. Mayer*
19. **Major submarine fans of the California continental rise**—*W. R. Normark and C. E. Gutmacher*

CONTINENTAL MARGIN

20. **Continental margins around the Gulf of Alaska**—*R. von Huene*
21. **Queen Charlotte Islands margin**—*R. Riddihough and R. D. Hyndman*
22. **Plate tectonic evolution of the Cascade arc-subduction complex**—*R. A. Duncan and L. D. Kulm*
23. **Evolution of the offshore central California region**—*D. S. McCulloch*
24. **The California continental borderland**—*D. S. Gorsline and L. S-Y. Teng*
25. **Neogene plate-tectonic evolution of the Baja California Sur continental borderland and the southern Gulf of California**—*J. E. Spencer and W. R. Normark*
26. **Geology and tectonic history of the Gulf of California**—*P. Lonsdale*
27. **The Middle America Trench off southern Mexico**—*J. S. Watkins*
28. **The Middle America convergent plate boundary**—*R. von Huene*

Volume O-1. *Surface Water Hydrology*

M. G. Wolman and H. C. Riggs, eds.

1. **Introduction**—*H. C. Riggs and M. G. Wolman*
2. **Influence of atmosphere on stream flow**—*F. K. Hare and K. P. Singh*
3. **Influence of land and vegetation on stream flow**—*K. E. Saxton and S. Y. Shiau*
4. **Temporal and spatial variability of streamflow**—*H. C. Riggs and K. D. Harvey*
5. **Floods**—*H. F. Matthai*
6. **Low flows and hydrologic drought**—*J. D. Rogers and J. T. Armbruster*
7. **Snow and ice**—*M. F. Meier*
8. **Hydrology of lakes and wetlands**—*T. C. Winter and M-K. Woo*
9. **Hydrogeochemistry of rivers and lakes**—*J. Hem, A. Demayo, and R. A. Smith*
10. **Aquatic biota in North America**—*R. Patrick and D. D. Williams*
11. **Movement and storage of sediment in rivers of the United States and Canada**—*R. H. Meade, T. R. Yuzyk, and T. J. Day*
12. **The riverscape**—*M. G. Wolman and 9 others*
13. **The influence of Man on hydrologic systems**—*R. M. Hirsch, J. C. Day and R. Kallio*

Volume O-2. *Hydrogeology*

W. R. Back, J. S. Rosenshein, P. R. Seaber, eds.

I. INTRODUCTION

1. **Historical perspective**—*G. Meyer, G. Davis, and P. E. LaMoreaux*
2. **Hydrostratigraphic units**—*P. R. Seaber*

II. HYDROGEOLOGIC REGIONS

3. **Hydrogeologic setting of regions**—*R. C. Heath*

Cordilleran Sector

4. **Region 1, Western mountain ranges**—*B. L. Foxworthy, D. L. Hanneman, D. L. Coffin, and E. C. Halstead*
5. **Region 2, Columbia Lava Plateau**—*G. F. Lindholm and J. J. Vaccaro*
6. **Region 3, Colorado Plateau and Wyoming Basin**—*O. J. Taylor and J. W. Hood*
7. **Region 4, Central Valley and Pacific Coast Ranges**—*C. D. Farrar and G. L. Bertoldi*
8. **Region 5, Great Basin**—*M. D. Mifflin*
9. **Region 6, Coastal Alluvial Basins**—*W. F. Hardt*
10. **Region 7, Central Alluvial Basins**—*T. W. Anderson, G. E. Welder, G. Lesser, and A. Trujillo*
11. **Region 8, Sierra Madre Occidental**—*J. J. Carrillo R.*
12. **Region 9, Sierra Madre Oriental**—*J. M. Lesser and G. Lesser*
13. **Region 10, Faja Volcanica Transmexicana**—*R. Chavez*
14. **Region 11, Sierra Madre del Sur**—*R. R. Palacio*

Central Cratonic Sector

15. **Region 12, Precambrian Shield**—*R. N. Farvolden, O. Pfannkuch, R. Pearson, and P. Fritz*
16. **Region 13, Western Glaciated Plains**—*D. H. Lennox, H. Maathuis, and D. Pederson*
17. **Region 14, Central Glaciated Plains**—*N. C. Krothe and J. P. Kempton*
18. **Region 15, St. Lawrence Lowland**—*R. N. Farvolden and J. A. Cherry*
19. **Region 16, Central Nonglaciated Plains**—*D. G. Jorgensen, J. Downey, A. R. Dutton, and R. W. Mcclay*
20. **Region 17, High Plains**—*J. B. Weeks and E. D. Gutentag*
21. **Region 18, Alluvial valleys**—*J. S. Rosenshein*

Appalachian Sector

22. **Region 19, Northeastern Appalachians**—*A. D. Randall, R. M. Francis, M. H. Frimpter, and J. M. Emery*
23. **Region 20, Appalachian Plateaus and Valley and Ridge**—*P. R. Seaber, J. V. Brahana, and E. F. Hollyday*
24. **Region 21, Piedmont and Blue Ridge**—*H. E. LeGrand*

Coastal Plain Sector

25. **Region 22, Atlantic and eastern Gulf Coastal Plain**—*H. Meisler, J. A. Miller, L. L. Knobel, and R. L. Wait*
26. **Region 23, Gulf of Mexico Coastal Plain**—*H. F. Grubb and J. J. Carrillo R.*
27. **Region 24, Southeastern United States**—*R. H. Johnston and J. A. Miller*
28. **Region 25, Yucatan Peninsula**—*J. M. Lesser and A. E. Weidie*

Island Sector

29. **Region 26, West Indies**—*W. Back*
30. **Region 27, Hawaiian Islands**—*C. D. Hunt, Jr., C. J. Ewart, and C. I. Voss*

Permafrost

31. **Region 28, Permafrost region**—*C. E. Sloan and R. O. van Everdingen*

III. COMPARATIVE HYDROGEOLOGY

32. **Nature of comparative hydrogeology**—*S. N. Davis*
33. **Alluvial aquifers along major rivers**—*J. M. Sharp, Jr.*
34. **Western alluvial valleys and the High Plains**—*G. H. Davis*
35. **Glacial deposits**—*D. A. Stephenson, A. H. Fleming, and D. M. Mickelson*
36. **Coastal Plain deposits**—*J. A. Miller*
37. **Sandstones and shales**—*S. N. Davis*
38. **Carbonate rocks**—*J. V. Brahana, J. Thrailkill, T. Freeman, and W. C. Ward*
39. **Volcanic rocks**—*W. W. Wood and L. A. Fernandez*
40. **Plutonic and metamorphic rocks**—*F. W. Trainer*

IV. GROUND WATER AND GEOLOGIC PROCESSES

41. **Ground water as a geologic agent**—*P. A. Domenico*
42. **Landform development**—*C. G. Higgins and 12 others*
43. **Landform development; Karst**—*D. C. Ford, A. N. Palmer, and W. B. White*
44. **Ground water and clastic diagenesis**—*F. W. Schwartz and F. J. Longstaffe*
45. **The generation and dissipation of abnormal fluid pressures in active depositional environments**—*P. A. Domenico and V. V. Palciauskas*
46. **Ground water and fault strength**—*S. A. Rojstaczer and J. D. Bredehoeft*
47. **The role of ground-water processes in the formation of ore deposits**—*J. M. Sharp, Jr., and J. R. Kyle*
48. **Ground water and hydrocarbon migration**—*J. Toth*

V. OUTLINE FOR THE FUTURE

49. **Scientific problems**—*L. F. Konikow and S. S. Papadopulos*
50. **Epilogue; Societal problems**—*J. S. Rosenshein and W. Back*

Volume P-1. *Mineral Deposits of Canada*

R. I. Thorpe and O. R. Eckstrand, eds.

1. **Introduction**—*R. I. Thorpe and others*
2. **Canadian mineral deposit types**—*O. R. Eckstrand and 19 others*
3. **Metallogenic concepts**—*R. I. Thorpe and others*
4. **Regional metallogeny of the Canadian Shield**—*K. D. Card, J. M. Franklin, and others*
5. **Summary**—*R. I. Thorpe and O. R. Eckstrand*

Volume P-2. *Economic Geology: U.S.*

Mineral Deposits, *R. B. Taylor, ed.*

1. **Introduction**—*R. B. Taylor*

METALS

2. **Gold and silver deposits of the United States**—*R. P. Ashley*
3. **Copper and molybdenum deposits of the United States**—*E. W. Tooker*
4. **Lead and zinc deposits**—*E. L. Ohle*
5. **Iron and manganese**—*G. B. Sidder*
6. **Deposits containing nickel, cobalt, chromium, and platinum-group elements**—*M. P. Foose*
7. **Uranium and vanadium deposits**—*D. R. Shawe, J. T. Nash, and W. L. Chenoweth*
8. **The other metals**—*R. G. Worl*

INDUSTRIAL MINERALS

9. **Phosphate deposits of the United States; Discovery, development, economic geology, and outlook for the future**—*J. B. Cathcart*
10. **Evaporites and brines**—*O. B. Raup and M. W. Bodine, Jr.*
11. **Oil shale**—*J. R. Donnell*
12. **Other selected industrial deposits**—*D. A. Brobst*

SYNTHESIS

13. **Perspectives**—*R. B. Taylor*

Oil and Gas, *D. D. Rice, ed.*

INTRODUCTION

14. **Introduction**—*D. D. Rice*
15. **Generation, expulsion, and migration of hydrocarbons**—*F. Meissner*
16. **Pore system aspects of hydrocarbon trapping**—*W. R. Almon and J. B. Thomas*

GEOLOGY OF PETROLEUM

17. **Exploration techniques**—*E. A. Beaumont, G. R. Curtis, and N. H. Foster*

REGIONAL SYNTHESIS OF SELECTED PROVINCES

18. **Petroleum geology of the Appalachian Basin**—*W. de Witt, Jr., and R. C. Milici*
19. **The Michigan Basin**—*C. R. Reszka, Jr.*
20. **The northern Gulf of Mexico Basin**—*D. M. Curtis*
21. **Petroleum geology of the Greater Anadarko Basin**—*H. G. Davis, R. A. Northcutt, and R. E. Espach, Jr.*
22. **The Permian Basin**—*B. M. Hanson and 10 others*
23. **Oil and gas resources of the San Juan basin, New Mexico and Colorado**—*J. E. Fassett*
24. **Powder River Basin**—*J. E. Fox, G. L. Dolton, and J. L. Clayton*
25. **Geologic controls on hydrocarbon occurrence, Fossil Basin area, Cordilleran thrust belt**—*M. A. Warner*
26. **Basin and Range**—*N. H. Foster*
27. **San Joaquin Basin, California**—*D. C. Callaway and E. W. Rennie, Jr.*
28. **Geologic controls on hydrocarbon occurrence within the Santa Maria basin of western California**—*J. B. Dunham, B. W. Bromley, and V. J. Rosato*
29. **North slope of Alaska**—*K. Bird*

Coal, *H. J. Gluskoter, ed.*

INTRODUCTION

30. **Coal geology of the U.S.; Introduction**—*H. J. Gluskoter*

GEOLOGY OF COAL

31. **Tectonic, climatic, and paleogeographic setting of coal**—*T. Cross and A. Ziegler*
32. **Environments of deposition**—*P. J. McCabe*
33. **Paleobotany and paleoecology of coal**—*T. L. Phillips and A. T. Cross*
34. **Coalification in North American coal fields**—*H. H. Damberger*

REGIONAL SYNTHESIS OF MAJOR U.S. COALS

35. **Pennsylvanian coals of central and eastern United States**—*A. C. Donaldson and C. F. Eble*
36. **Cretaceous and Tertiary coals of the Rocky Mountains and Great Plains**—*R. Flores and T. Cross*
37. **Tertiary coals of the Gulf Coast**—*J. A. Breyer*
38. **Mesozoic and Cenozoic coals of far western U.S.**—*A. Cross*
39. **Alaska**—*G. Stricker*

Volume P-3. *The Economic Geology of Mexico*

G. P. Salas, ed.

1. **Economic geology of Mexico**—*G. P. Salas*
2. **National Hydroelectric Plan (1982–2000)**—*Hydroelectric Projects Management, Federal Commission on Electricity (Mexico)*
3. **Economic geology of geothermal reservoirs in Mexico**—*A. Razo, V. P. Reyes, and O. Palma*
4. **Geothermal resources and provinces in Mexico**—*A. Razo and F. Romero*
5. **Main geothermal fields of Mexico; Cerro Preito (B. C.) geothermal field**—*A. Pelayo and 5 others*
6. **Los Azufres geothermal field, Michoacán**—*G. Huitrón and 7 others*
7. **Los Humeros geothermal field, Puebla**—*F. Romero*
8. **La Primavera geothermal field, Jalisco**—*S. Venegas and 6 others*
9. **Geologic report on the Fuentes-Rio Escondido coal basin, Coahuila**—*F. Verdugo and C. Ariciaga*
10. **Summary of exploration and development activities at Rio Escondido**—*F. Verdugo and C. Ariciaga*
11. **Geology of coal deposits and reserves in the Republic of Mexico**—*E. Flores*
12. **Geology of uranium deposits in Mexico**—*G. P. Salas and F. Castillo N.*
13. **Geohydrogeology**—*G. P. Salas and C. García H.*
14. **Metallic and non-metallic mineral deposits; Introduction to the geology of the Metallogenic Provinces**—*G. P. Salas*
15. **Baja California Peninsula Metallogenic Province**—*G. P. Salas*
16. **Summary of stratigraphic and structural information on the Monterrey Formation outcrops of the San Hilario area, Baja California Sur**—*J. Ojeda R.*
17. **Geology and mineral deposits of the El Boleo copper district, Baja California Sur**—*I. F. Wilson and V. S. Rocha*
18. **Sierra Madre Occidental Metallogenic Province**—*G. P. Salas*
19. **Cananea copper deposit, Sonora**—*G. P. Salas and R. H. Sillitoe*
20. **"La Caridad" disseminated copper deposits, Sonora**—*G. P. Salas and R. H. Sillitoe*
21. **Gochico mineral deposits; Geology, environment, and tectonics**—*A. Rosas*
22. **Geology and mineralization of the Topia Mining District, Durango**—*H. Monje*
23. **Geology of the Tayoltita Mine, San Dimas District, Durango**—*M. Clark*
24. **Development of the Tayoltita Mine, San Dimas District, Durango**—*T. Martínez P.*
25. **Economic geology of the San Martín Mining District**—*P. Olivares R.*
26. **Sierra Madre Oriental Province**—*G. P. Salas*
27. **Economic geology of the Santa Eulalia Mining District, Chihuahua**—*E. D. Maldonado*
28. **Geology and mineralization of the La Ecantada Mining District, Coahuila**—*R. B. Solano*
29. **Geology and genesis of the Naica mineral deposits, Chihuahua**—*H. A. Palacios, F. Querol, and G. K. Lowther*
30. **San Francisco del Oro Mining District, Chihuahua**—*G. P. Salas*
31. **Geology and mineralization of the Minera Antares zinc-bearing body, Velardeña, Durango**—*J. I. Figueroa S.*
32. **Economic geology of the Velardeña Mining Department, Durango**—*I. Herná C.*
33. **Economic geology of the Charcas Mining District, San Luis Potosí**—*F. Castañeda A.*
34. **Geology and mineralization of the El Realito Mining Unit, Victoria Township, Guanajuato, Mexico**—*P. Fraga M.*
35. **Geology and mineralization of the La Negra Mining Unit, Cadereyta Township, Queretaro**—*P. Fraga M.*
36. **Description of some Zimapán District deposits, Zimapán, Hidalgo**—*G. García G. and F. Querol S.*
37. **Geology of the Nolango manganese district, Hidalgo**—*R. Alexandri R. and A. Martínez V.*
38. **Pachuca-Real del Monte District, State of Hidalgo**—*C. Fries and others*
39. **Mining-geological report on the Santa Fe Mine, Chiapas**—*J. Pantoja A.*
40. **Antimony deposits in the Los Tecojotes area, San Juan Miztepec Township, State of Oaxaca**—*R. Guízar Jr., and D. E. White*
41. **Sierra Madre del Sur Metallogenic Province**—*G. P. Salas*
42. **Geology and genesis of the La Minita deposit, Coalcoman Township, Michoacán**—*J. De la Campa G.*
43. **Iron deposits, Las Truchas, Michoacán**—*E. Mapes*
44. **Geology of the Pegaso asbestos deposit, Concepcion Papalo, Cuicatlán, Oaxaca**—*J. C. Ramírez*
45. **Titanium deposit at Huitzo and Telixtlahuaca, Oaxaco**—*F. J. Díaz T.*
46. **Metallogenic Province of the Neovolcanic axis**—*G. P. Salas*
47. **Geological description of the Cuale District mineral deposits, Jalisco, Mexico**—*G. Gerrocal L. and F. Querol S.*
48. **Economic geology of the Inguarán Mining District, Michoacán**—*A. Osorio H., N. Leija V., and R. Esquivel*
49. **El Oro and Tlalpujahua Mining District, State of Mexico**—*G. P. Salas*
50. **The Zacualpan Mining District, State of Mexico**—*B. Noguez A., J. Flores M., and A. Toscano F.*
51. **Geology of the Tizapa Ag, Zn, Pb, Cu, Cd, and Au poly-metallic massive sulphides, Zacazonapan, Mexico**—*J. de J. Parga P., and J. de J. Rodríguez S.*
52. **Taxco Mining District, State of Guerrero**—*G. P. Salas*
53. **The Central Mesas Metallogenic Province**—*G. P. Salas*
54. **Geology of the Fresnillo Mining District, Zacatecas**—*E. García M., F. Querol S., and G. K. Lowther*
55. **Geology of the Real de Angeles deposit, Noria de Angeles Township, Zacatecas**—*J. Bravo N.*
56. **Mineral deposits of the Guanajuato District, Guanajuato**—*F. Querol S., G. K. Lowther, and E. Navarro*
57. **History of exploration for sulphur in southeast Mexico**—*G. P. Salas*

Volume P-4. *The petroleum geology of Mexico*

(details not yet available)

Appendix B

List of published COSUNA (Correlation of Stratigraphic Units of North America) charts. Available from American Association of Petroleum Geologists, Tulsa, Oklahoma.

Northern Rockies/Williston Basin Region—*William W. Ballard, J. P. Bluemle, and L. C. Gerhard, regional coordinators, 1983*

Southwest/Southwest Mid-Continent Region—*John M. Hills, and Frank E. Kottlowski, regional coordinators, 1983*

Atlantic Coastal Plain—*Robert R. Jordan and Richard V. Smith, regional coordinators, 1983*

Northern California Region—*Charles C. Bishop and James F. Davis, regional coordinators, 1983*

Central California Region—*Charles C. Bishop and James F. Davis, regional coordinators, 1984*

Southern California Region—*Charles C. Bishop and James F. Davis, regional coordinators, 1984*

Northern Mid-Continent Region—*D. J. Bergstrom and G. B. Morey, regional coordinators, 1985*

Southern Appalachian Region—*Douglas G. Patchen, Katharine Lee Avary, and Robert Erwin, regional coordinators, 1985*

Northern Appalachian Region—*Douglas G. Patchen, Katharine Lee Avery, and Robert B. Erwin, regional coordinators, 1985*

Midwestern Basin and Arches Region—*Robert H. Shaver, regional coordinator, 1985*

Great Basin Region—*Lehi F. Hintze, regional coordinator, 1985*

New England Region—*James W. Skehan, regional coordinator, 1985*

Mid-Continent Region—*Frank J. Adler, regional coordinator, 1987*

Texas–Oklahoma Tectonic Region—*Charles J. Mankin, regional coordinator, 1987*

Northern Alaska Region—*Ross G. Schaff and Wyatt G. Gilbert, regional coordinator, 1987*

Southern Alaska Region—*Ross G. Schaff and Wyatt G. Gilbert, regional coordinators, 1987*

Piedmont/Blue Ridge Region—*Michael Higgins, regional coordinator, 1987*

DECADE OF NORTH AMERICAN GEOLOGY
GEOLOGIC TIME SCALE

DECADE OF NORTH AMERICAN GEOLOGY 1980 1989

DNAG

GEOLOGICAL SOCIETY OF AMERICA

THE GEOLOGICAL SOCIETY OF AMERICA 1888

CENOZOIC

Period		Epoch		Age	Picks (Ma)
QUATERNARY		HOLOCENE			0.01
QUATERNARY		PLEISTOCENE		CALABRIAN	1.6
TERTIARY	NEOGENE	PLIOCENE	L	PIACENZIAN	3.4
		PLIOCENE	E	ZANCLEAN	5.3
		MIOCENE	L	MESSINIAN	6.5
		MIOCENE	L	TORTONIAN	11.2
		MIOCENE	M	SERRAVALLIAN	15.1
		MIOCENE	M	LANGHIAN	16.6
		MIOCENE	E	BURDIGALIAN	21.8
		MIOCENE	E	AQUITANIAN	23.7
	PALEOGENE	OLIGOCENE	L	CHATTIAN	30.0
		OLIGOCENE	E	RUPELIAN	36.6
		EOCENE	L	PRIABONIAN	40.0
		EOCENE	M	BARTONIAN	43.6
		EOCENE	M	LUTETIAN	52.0
		EOCENE	E	YPRESIAN	57.8
		PALEOCENE	L	SELANDIAN – THANETIAN	60.6
		PALEOCENE	L	SELANDIAN – UNNAMED	63.6
		PALEOCENE	E	DANIAN	66.4

Magnetic polarity, anomalies: 1, 2, 2A, 3, 3A, 4, 4A, 5, 5A, 5B, 5C, 5D, 5E, 6, 6A, 6B, 6C, 7, 7A, 8, 9, 10, 11, 12, 13, 15, 16, 17, 18, 19, 20, 21, 22, 23, 24, 25, 26, 27, 28, 29

Chrons: C1, C2, C2A, C3, C3A, C4, C4A, C5, C5A, C5B, C5C, C5D, C5E, C6, C6A, C6B, C6C, C7, C7A, C8, C9, C10, C11, C12, C13, C15, C16, C17, C18, C19, C20, C21, C22, C23, C24, C25, C26, C27, C28, C29

MESOZOIC

Period	Epoch	Age	Picks (Ma)	Uncert. (m.y.)
CRETACEOUS			66.4	
	LATE	MAASTRICHTIAN	74.5	4
	LATE	CAMPANIAN	84.0	4.5
	LATE	SANTONIAN	87.5	
	LATE	CONIACIAN	88.5	2.5
	LATE	TURONIAN	91	
	LATE	CENOMANIAN	97.5	2.5
	EARLY	ALBIAN	113	4
	EARLY	APTIAN	119	9
	EARLY (NEOCOMIAN)	BARREMIAN	124	9
	EARLY (NEOCOMIAN)	HAUTERIVIAN	131	8
	EARLY (NEOCOMIAN)	VALANGINIAN	138	5
	EARLY (NEOCOMIAN)	BERRIASIAN	144	5
JURASSIC	LATE	TITHONIAN	152	12
	LATE	KIMMERIDGIAN	156	6
	LATE	OXFORDIAN	163	15
	MIDDLE	CALLOVIAN	169	15
	MIDDLE	BATHONIAN	176	34
	MIDDLE	BAJOCIAN	183	34
	MIDDLE	AALENIAN	187	34
	EARLY	TOARCIAN	193	28
	EARLY	PLIENSBACHIAN	198	32
	EARLY	SINEMURIAN	204	18
	EARLY	HETTANGIAN	208	18
TRIASSIC	LATE	NORIAN	225	8
	LATE	CARNIAN	230	22
	MIDDLE	LADINIAN	235	10
	MIDDLE	ANISIAN	240	22
	EARLY	SCYTHIAN	245	20

Magnetic polarity, anomalies: 29, 30, 31, 32, 33, M0, M1, M3, M5, M10, M12, M14, M16, M18, M20, M22, M25, M29; RAPID POLARITY CHANGES

Chrons: C29, C30, C31, C32, C33

PALEOZOIC

Period		Epoch	Age		Picks (Ma)	Uncert. (m.y.)
PERMIAN		LATE	TATARIAN		245	20
		LATE	KAZANIAN		253	20
		LATE	UFIMIAN		258	24
		LATE	KUNGURIAN		263	22
		EARLY	ARTINSKIAN		268	12
		EARLY	SAKMARIAN			
		EARLY	ASSELIAN		286	12
CARBONIFEROUS	PENNSYLVANIAN	LATE	GZELIAN	S.		
		LATE	KASIMOVIAN	S.	296	10
		LATE	MOSCOVIAN	W.		
		LATE	BASHKIRIAN	W.	315	20
	MISSISSIPPIAN	EARLY	SERPUKHOVIAN	N.	320	
		EARLY			333	22
		EARLY	VISEAN		352	8
		EARLY	TOURNAISIAN		360	10
DEVONIAN		LATE	FAMENNIAN		367	12
		LATE	FRASNIAN		374	18
		MIDDLE	GIVETIAN		380	18
		MIDDLE	EIFELIAN		387	28
		EARLY	EMSIAN		394	22
		EARLY	SIEGENIAN		401	18
		EARLY	GEDINNIAN		408	12
SILURIAN		LATE	PRIDOLIAN		414	12
		LATE	LUDLOVIAN		421	12
		EARLY	WENLOCKIAN		428	8
		EARLY	LLANDOVERIAN		438	12
ORDOVICIAN		LATE	ASHGILLIAN		448	12
		LATE	CARADOCIAN		458	16
		MIDDLE	LLANDEILAN		468	16
		MIDDLE	LLANVIRNIAN		478	16
		EARLY	ARENIGIAN		488	20
		EARLY	TREMADOCIAN		505	32
CAMBRIAN		LATE	TREMPEALEAUAN FRANCONIAN DRESBACHIAN		523	36
		MIDDLE			540	28
		EARLY			570	

PRECAMBRIAN

Eon	Era	Bdy. Ages (Ma)
		570
PROTEROZOIC	LATE	900
PROTEROZOIC	MIDDLE	1600
PROTEROZOIC	EARLY	2500
ARCHEAN	LATE	3000
ARCHEAN	MIDDLE	3400
ARCHEAN	EARLY	3800?

Compiled 1983

Published by: The Geological Society of America, Inc.
3300 Penrose Place, P.O. Box 9140
Boulder, Colorado 80301

MAP AND CHART SERIES MC-50

Index

[Italic page numbers indicate major references]

A-subduction, 406
Abitibi island-arc terrane, *451*
Abitibi terrane, 451
Abloviak shear zone, 465
Absaroka field, 219
Absaroka sequence, *427*
Absaroka subsequences, *427*, *429*, *431*
Acadian orogeny, 3, *335*, 336, 337, 506
Acapulco region, 259
acid rain, 538
adamellites, 244
Adirondack terrane, 500
Aegir Ridge, 61
agglomerates, 245, 249
Agnew Lake area, 568
Agua Blanca fault, 246
Aillik Group, 481
air masses, *540*
Alabama Piedmont, 340
Alaska, 3, 7, 18, 20, 151, 152, 154, 158, 159, 164, 174, 177, 185, 187, 197, *219*, *220*, *221*, 278, 280, 281, 427, 434, 560, 565
  active margin, 200
  airborne moisture, 540
Alaska-Aleutians batholith, 219
Alaska Arctic shelf, 408
Alaska North Slope, 157, 427, 432, 433, 434
Alaska North Slope basin, *407*
Alaska Peninsula, 219, 221, 541
Alaska Range, 20
Alberta, Canada, 164, 170, 200, 433, 474, 526
Alberta basin, 559, 562
Alberta corridor, 525
Alberta plains, 151, 178
Alberta Rockies, 149
Albion Range, *213*
Aldrich Formation, 492
Aleutian arc, 18, 200, 220, 221
Aleutian basin, 200
Aleutian deep-sea trench, 201
Aleutian Island arc, 13
Aleutian Islands, 280
Aleutian margin, 280, *281*
Aleutian thrust, 201
Aleutian Trench, 281
Aleutian volcanic arc complex, 201
Aleutians, 200
Alexander Archipelago, 201
Alexander terrane, 151, 152, 154, 176, 177, 181, 194, 201
Alisitos Formation, 244, 246
Alisitos volcanic activity, 244
Alleghanian orogenic cycle, 343
Alleghanian period, *337*
Alleröd/Younger Dryas climactic fluctuation, 520
alluvium, 550
Alpha-Mendeleyev Ridge, 364
Alpine glaciation, 515
Alsate, 374
Altar Desert, 246
Alum Fork fault, 386
Amarillo-Witchita-Arbuckle uplift, 428
Amerasian basin, 7, 189, *363*, 364, 435
American Southwest, 526, 527
Amina-Maimón, 305
Amitsoq gneisses, *458*
ammonites, 181, 197, 248
Ampferer, 7
amphibolite, 151, 250, 305, 313, 356, 360, 451, 458, 460, 481, 501
Amundsen basin, 488
Amundsen Gulf, 491
Anadarko basin, 161, 390, 423, 426, *428*
Anadyr basin, 200
Anahim belt, 221
Anahuac Formation, 104, 115
Ancestral Rocky Mountains, 149, *161*, 425, 428, 429, 559
andalusite, 246
Andean Mountains, 7
Andean system, 13
Anderson Plain, 156
Andes, 518
andesite, 159, 162, 163, 222, 249, 262
Angayucham terrane, 154, 163, 175, 195
Angayucham-Tozitna terrane, 163
Angelina-Caldwell hinge zone, 103, 104
anhydrite, 86, 256, 257, 362
Animikie, 480
anions, 551
anomalies
  Bouguer gravity, *20*
  free-air gravity, *18*
  gravity, 18, 386, 456
  magnetic, *33*, 313, 364
  marine magnetic, 34
  negative, 18, 20, 21, 33, 34
  positive, 18, 20, 34
  sources, *31*
anorthosite, 328, 494
Antarctic bottom water, 68
Antarctica, 273, 532
  interior, 520
Antigonish Highland, 506
Antigua, 306
Antillean island arc, 304
Antler basin, *159*
Antler belt, 149, 158, 162
Antler foredeep, 159
Antler orogeny, 149, *158*, 173
Antler-Prophet foredeep, 427
Antoinette Formation, 362
Apache Group, 493
Apishapa-Sierra Grande-Front Range, 428
Appalachian basin, 407, 427, 430
Appalachian chain, *328*
  basement, *328*
  evolution, *323*, 340
  tectonic divisions, *325*
Appalachian foredeep, 410, 411, 426, 435
Appalachian-Mauritanide megasuture, 97, 98
Appalachian Mountains, 22, 55, *323*, *423*, *501*, *502*, *505*, 564
  anticlinoria, 325
  central, 328, 423, 430, 504
  eastern, 505
  northern, 325, 326, 328, 330, 332, 334, 335, 337, 340, 425
  southern, 47, 98, 327, 328, 332, 335, 337, 340, 371, 423, 503
  synclinoria, 325
Appalachian orogen, 324
Appalachian-Ouachita orogen, mineral deposits, *579*
Appalachian Plateau, 325, 338
Appalachian province, *564*
Appalachian uplands, 324
aquifers, 541
Arbuckle, 373
Arbuckle Mountains, 372, 390
arc system, Lesser Antilles, 19
Archean, *506*
Archean crust, *506*
Archean provinces, *448*
Archean Rae province, 494
Archer Fiord, 354
Arctic Alaska, 192
Arctic Archipelago, 158, 161, *349*, 360
Arctic Canada, 526
  permafrost, 540
Arctic Coastal Plain, 349
Arctic Islands, 3, *349*, 352, 361, *367*
  northeastern, *366*
  southeastern, *364*
Arctic Islands Shelf, 360
Arctic National Wildlife Refuge, 560
Arctic Ocean, 13, 57, 158, 189, 191, 349, 364, 560
Arctic Ocean basin, 3, 55
Arctic passive margin, 432, 434
Arctic platform, 158, 349, 350, *352*
  western, *488*, 497
Arctic Polar Front, 68
Arctic Slope, 541
Arctic Slope basin, *560*
Arctic tectonic belts, 189
Ardmore basin, 389, 390
arenite, 493
Arenque field, 559
argillite, 81, 150, 154, 155, 159, 161, 492
Arizona, 167, 209, 214, 220, 249,

487, 493, 568
Arkansas, 371
southern, 115
Arkansas Novaculite Formation, *377*
Arkoma basin, 407, *410*, 411, 426, 427, 428, 564
southern, 388
arkosic, 372
Armorica, *341*
Arteaga area, 259
Aruba, 307, 315
ash
flows, 484, 496
volcanic, 281, 289, 515
Ashe Formation, 335
ashrock, magnesian, 454
Ashuanipi granulite gneiss complex, 456
assemblages
faunal, 524
floral, 524
flysch, 377
overlap, *487*
pollen, 524
Assistance Formation, 362
asthenosphere, 48
Aston Formation, 488
Astoria Fan, 281
Athabasca basin, 568
Atlantic Coastal Plain, 100, 324
Atlantic Ocean, 541
central, 431, 433
early, 95
greater, *57*, 61
Atlantic passive margin, *81*
Atlantic shelf, 323
Atoka Formation, 381
atols, living, 290
Audhild Formation, 362
aulacogen, 22
Austin Chalk, 434
Austin Group, 103
Avalon belt, 326
Avalon plate, 325
Avalon Sea, 332, 335
Avalon succession, 332
Avalon superterrane, 327, *330*, 332, 341
Avalon terranes, 325, *326*, 328, 506
Avalonia, 3
Avalonian orogeny, *332*
Aves Island, 315
Aves Ridge, 314, *315*
Axel Heiberg Island, 352, 354, 358, 360, 364, 369
Axelgold pluton, 180
Azuero Peninsula, 309

Badshot Formation, 152
Baffin Bay, 5, 35, 72, 74, 349, 364, 367, 488
Baffin Island, *35*, 367, 369, 462, 474, 523
Bahama Platform, 5
Bahamas, 20, 74, 86, 87
Bahoruco, 305
Baie Verte-Brompton line, 334
Baja California, 181, 194, 197, 203, 218, 221, 237, 239, *243*, 244, 277
southern, *283*
Baja California Norte, 244
Baja California seamount province, 237
Baja California syncline, 245, 246
Baker basin, 474
Baker terrane, 155, 175
balance, torsion, 17
Balcones fault zone, 103, *115*
Balmat-Edwards, New York, 579
Balsas River, 257, 260
Baltic Shield, 44, 506
Baltica, 3
Baltimore Canyon area, 434
Baltimore Canyon Trough, 55, 61, 81, 86, 88, 91, 92
Banco de Campeche, 242
Bancroft terrane, *500*
Banks Island, 191, 369
banks, carbonate, 62, 86, 333
Baraboo Quartzite, 494
Baranof Fan, 281
Barbados, *306*, 515
Barbados marine terraces, 521
Bárcena Volcano, 237
Barents Sea margin, 55
Barents Shelf, 3, 367
barite, 290
Barkerville terrane, 151
Barn Mountains, 150, 189
Barron Quartzite, 494
basalt, 21, 100, 152, 154, 163, 210, 209, 221, 223, 305, 307, 309, 311, 315, 316, 324, 330, 350, 357, 448, 455, 461, 471, 488, 490, 494, 500, 504, 505, 550
alkalic, 221, 222
complex, 313
dikes, 154
eruptive centers, 314
flood, 222, 509
flows, 488, 493
oceanic, 307, 309, 310
pillow, 468
subalkaline, 222
tholeiitic, 222, 364, 454, 455, 468, 478, 480
basement, *474*
continental, 412
crystalline, 146, 248, *349*, 366
Basin and Range Province, 7, 13, 42, 46, 167, 173, 192, 209, 216, 222, 224, 402, 436
southern, *219*, *220*
basins
classifications, *397*
cratonic, 397, *403*, 438
deep-water, 352, *354*, 390
drift-stage, *85*
episutural, *412*
extensional, 278, *400*
flexural, *402*
models, *400*
passive margin, *436*
Permian, west Texas, 430
Phanerozoic, North America, *397*
push-together, 207
rift, *81*
salt, 113
sedimentary, *397*, 448
Tertiary, North America, *435*
Bathurst fault, 474
Bathurst Inlet area, 490
Bathurst Island, 361, 364
Bathurst transcurrent fault, 474
bathymetry, multibeam, *73*
Baucarit Formation, 248
Baumann Fiord, 353
Bay Fiord, 353
Bay of Biscay, 61
Bay of Campeche, 100
Bear Creek Group, 474
Bearpaw Mountains, potassic center, 219
Beck Spring Formation, 493
beds
boulder, 374, 379, *381*
hydrocarbon source, 374
lake, 173
volcanic-ash, 477
Belcher Channel Formation, 362
Belcher fold belt, 468
Belcher Islands, 468
Belcher thrust belt, 468
Belize, 301, 302
Belt Supergroup, 156
Belt/Purcell basin, 493
Belt/Purcell Supergroup, 492
belts
evaporite, 100
folded, *7*
magmatic, 187
tectonic, *164*
Benioff, 7
Benton uplift 374, 375, 377, *386*, 387
Berens plutonic complex, *454*
Bering Sea, 18
Bering shelf, 200, 219
Berkshires, 328
Bermeja Complex, 305, 316
Bermuda, 20
Bermuda Rise, 20, 74
Bermudez field, 559
Bessemer Quartzite, 494
Bienville plutonic complex, *456*
Big Cottonwood Formation, 493
Big Horn Mountains, 21
Bigfork Foundation, 377
biotite, 180, 213, 259, 497
bioturbation, benthic, 72
Birmingham basement fault, 372
Bishop Suite, 478
bivalves, 197
Bjorne Formation, 363
Blaa Mountain Formation, 363
Black Hills, 172, 219, 471
Black Knob Ridge, 374
Black Sea, 72
Black Warrior basin, 388, 426, 427, 428, 562
Bladen volcanic series, 302
Blake escarpment, 87
Blake Plateau, 19
Blake Plateau basin, 81, 86, *87*
Blake Spur fracture zone, 72
Blake Spur magnetic anomaly, 81, 94

Blakely Sandstone, 374, 381
Blaylock Sandstone, *374*
Blind Fiord Formation, 363
Blow-Me-Down Massif, 55
Blue Mountains, 175
Blue Mountains block, 155
Blue Mountains province, 174
Blue Ridge anticlinorium, 502
Blue Ridge belt, 334
Blue Rige massifs, 328
blueschist 155, 175, 305
Bogota plain, 518
bolide impacts, 69
Bölling/Alleröd interval, 527
Bonaire, 307, 312, 315
Boothia uplift, 350, 354, 358, 361, 488
Boothia uplift–Bell Arch, *424*
Borden basin, *488*
Border Ranges fault, 154
Borup Fiord Formation, 362
Bouguer anomaly, *20*
Bowers ridge, 18
Bowser basin, 176
Brandon, Vermont, 324
brannerite, 570
breccia, fallback, 479
Brevard fault, 335
Briery fault, 386
Brigham Group, 505
British Columbia, 146, 151, 152, 155, 159, 164, 170, 175, 177, 201, 278, 290, 212, 221, 504
British Mountains, 150, 158, 159, 164, 189, 191
Broken Bow uplift, *374*, 377, *386*
Bronson Hill anticlinorium, 334
Brookian sequence, 150
Brooks Range, 20, 150, 154, 157, 158, 159, 161, 163, 164, 167, 170, 174, 175, 177, 191, 192, 193, 194, 541
  shortening, 185
Broxson Gulch thrust system, 178
Bruce River Group, 484
Buckner, 101
Burwell province, *447*, *464*
Bylot Island, 366

Cabaiguán, 304
Caballos Formation, *377*, 381
Cabañas fault, 313
Caborca region, 247
Cabot fault, 337
Cacagua-Tinaco belt, 307
Cacaguapa, 302
Cache Creek melange, 162
Cache Creek terrane, 152, 162, 175, 181, 196
Cactus-Nispero field, 559
Calaveras Formation, 155
calc-alkalic rocks, 250, 478
calc-silicates, 258
calcarenites, 375, 377
calcisiltites, 375, 377
calcite compensation depth (CCD), 281
Caledonian fold belt, 21
Caledonian Mountains, 354
Caledonides, east Greenland, *501*, 503
California, 7, 46, 149, 155, 158, 187, 201, *202*, *205*, *207*, 214, 218, *277*, 423, 493, 505, 518, 546, 560, 570
  coastal province, *221*
California Borderland, 155, 243, 278, 281
California current, 289
California margin, *283*
Camajuaní, 304
Cameron Island, 368
Cameron line, 330
Camp Century core, 519
Campeche Bank, 242, 243
Campeche Canyon, 243
Campeche Escarpment, 20, 103, 242
Campeche Sound, 559
Canada, 158, 176, 191, *221*, 508
  airborne moisture, *540*
  anomaly data, *30*
  eastern arctic, *487*
  northwestern, *477*
  See also specific locations
Canada basin, 18, 158, *189*, 364, 560
Canadian Arctic, 423, 424, 425, 431
Canadian Arctic Archipelago, 18, *349*
Canadian Arctic Islands, 189, *190*
Canadian Cordillera, *139*, 221, 423, 508
  northern, *491*, 501
  southern, 47
Canadian Maritime provinces, 337, 412
Canadian passive margin, 93
Canadian Platform, 45
Canadian Rocky Mountains, 434
  southern, 170
Canadian Shield, 7, 34, 35, 146, 156, 330, *349*, 423, 425, 477, 496, 497, 506
  crystalline basement, *349*
  mineral deposits, *578*
  sedimentary succession, *349*
  southern, *493*
  volcanic succession, *349*
  western, *487*
Canary Current, 63
Canrobert Formation, 354
Canrobert Hills fold belt, 360
Cantarell Field, 242, 559
Canyon Fiord, 362
Caopas region, 251
Cape Breton Islands, 506
Cape Mendocino, California, 200, 278
Cape Phillips Formation, 354
Cape San Lucas, 243
Cape Smith klippe, 465
Cape Viscaino, 283
Captains Cove pluton, 180
Caracas, 307
carbon, organic, 283
carbonate
  banks, 62, 86, 333, 334
  complexes, 434
  deposition, 157
  marine, 150
  ocean, 62
  platform, 88, 102, *372*, 392, 412, 434
  reefs, 62
  sequence, 190
  shallow-water, 423
  shelves, 102, 146, 251
  stromatolitic, 455
carbonates, 86, 88, 89, 98, 101, 150, 151, 152, 154, 190, 200, 243, 250, 289, 301, 303, 304, 332, 335, 337, 338, 352, 354, 372, 404, 408, *431*, 455, 456, 488, 492, 503, 504, 517, 552
carbonatites, 103, 500
Cariaco trench, 72
Caribbean Basin, *36*
Caribbean plate, 5, 13, 20, 300, *309*, 310, 314, 318
Caribbean province, mineral deposits, *582*
Caribbean Sea, 36, 57, 243, *299*, 310
  eastern, *314*
  sea floor, *243*
  stratigraphy, *301*
  tectonic history, *300*, *312*
  terranes, *300*
Caribou Group, 504
Carolina Platform, 86
Carolina Slate Belt, 327, 506
Carolina terrane, 327, 506
Carolina Trough, 81, 86, *88*
Carolinas, 570
Carrizo Mountain Group, 501
Carson-Bonnition basin, 90
Carthage-Colton mylonite zone, 500
Cascade arc, *220*, *221*
Cascade forearc, *201*
Cascade Island arc system, 200
Cascade Mountains, 21, 42, 45, 176, 201
Cascade thrust, 20
Cascade volcanic arc system, 201, 220
Cason, 373
Cassiar terrane, 151, 152, 170, 174
Catalina basin, 206
Catoctin Basalt, 503
Catoctin Formation, 503
Catoctin Volcanics, 330
Catskill delta complex, 337
Cayman Ridge, 314
Cayman trough, 5, *313*, 319
Cayo Cocos, 304
Cedar Creek anticline, 172, 405
Cedar Creek fault system, 405
Cedros Deep, 283
Cedros Island, 238, 245
Cenozoic, *104*, *105*
  early, 218, 225
Central America, *299*, 310, 316, 318, 542
  airborne moisture, 541
  northern, *302*
  southern, *309*, *310*
Central Atlantic, passive margin, 432, 434

Central Basin platform, 428, 429
Central belt, 164, *174*, 176, 179, 194, 195
Central Depression, *260*
Central fault system, 178, 193
Central Louisiana shelfal sags, 103
Central Metamorphic belt, 159
Central Mobile Belt, 333, *334*
Central Plains orogen, 448, 494
Central Rocky Mountain trench, 178
Cerro Colorado deposits, 582
Cerro de la Bandera, 245
Cerro de la Giganta, 245
Cerro del Potosí, 250
Chain Lakes massif, 330
chalk, 103, 104, 290
  water marine, 104
Challenger salt, 100
Challis belt, 219
Challis field, 219
Challis volcanic field, 150
Channel Islands, 204
Charlie Transform fault, 85
Charlie-Gibbs fracture zone, 68
Charlotte belt, 506
charnockites, 258, 328
Chatham Strait fault, 176, 178, 179, 192
Chattanooga-Woodford transgression, 373
Chedabucto fault zone, 84, 336
chert, 150, 159, 163, 177, 245, 289, 316, 274, 275, 277, 354, 356, 361, 387
  nodules, 290
  radiolarian, 162
chert-argillite, 152
Chesapeake Bay, 541
Cheyenne belt, 36, 460, *485*
Chiapas, Mexico, 260, 302
Chiapas Highlands, 260
Chiapas Massif, *260*, 261
Chichonal volcano, 261
Chicontepec field, 559
Chihuahua, 249, 250
Chilhowee Group, 330, 502, 503
Chinook trough, 266
Chioak Formation, 471
chlorite, 288, 361
chlorite schists, 258
Chocolay Group, 480
Chortis block, Central America, 300, 301, *302*, 314, 316, 317
Choyal Formation, 245
Chuar Group, 493
Chugach Mountains, 201
Chugach terrane, 154, 177, 194, 201
Chukotat Group, 468
Chupaxeros Caldera, 249
Churchill craton, 21
Cifuentes, 304
Cincinnati Arch, 425
circulation, atmospheric, 526
Circum-Pacific ring-of-fire, 13
Claiborne, 104
clams, 271
Clarion fault zone, 20
Clarion fracture zone, 238
Clarno field, 219
clastics, 150, 200, 201, 301, 303, 503
clays, 281, 283, 288, 289
  brown, 287, 288, 289, 290
  silty, 242
Clear Lake, 518
Cleaver diabase, 491
Clemente-Tomas fault, 118
Clements Markham fold belt, 354, 356, 358, 361
climates, reconstruction, 519
climatic changes, short-term, *527*
clinoptilolite, 290
clinopyroxenite, 357
Clovis culture, 525
Coahuila Peninsula, 251, 252
coal, 251, 259, 367, 368, *562*
  classification scheme, *562*
  geographic distribution, *564*
  geologic distribution, *564*
  lignite, 324
  resources, *562*
  seams, 362
Coast Plutonic complex, *176*
Coast Ranges, 21, 46, 221
Coastal belt, 164, 174, *177*, 181, 195, 197
Coastal Maine Belt, 335
Coastal Plain, 81, 86
Coates Lake Group, 491
Coatzacoalcos, 242
Coatzacoalcos-Grijalva-Usumacinta Embayment, *257*
cobalt, 479
Coban/Ixcoy, 302
Cobequid Highlands, 506
Cobequid-Chedabucto fault, 337
coccolithophorids, 280
coccoliths, 281, 288
Cocos plate, 13, 20, 237, 238, 239, 280
coffinite, 568
Colima graben, 262
Colima region, 262
collapse, gravitational, *118*
Collier Shale, 374
Colombia, 22, 307
Coloradito Formation, 245
Colorado, 161, 170, 220, 275, 487, 568
Colorado delta, 244
Colorado Front Range, 570
Colorado Plateau, 146, 164, *170*, 209, 212, *216*, 222, 434, 570
Colorado River, 239, 244
Columbia, 301
  northern, 309
Columbia belt, 164, 174, *176*, 179, 195, 197
Columbia Mountains, 504
Columbia Plateau, 21, 42
Columbia River basalt, 222
Columbia River Plateau, 209, 222
Columbian Andes, 518
Colville basin, 408
Colville foredeep, 7, *407*, 411, *435*
Comalcalco, 257
Comondu Formation, 245
Comondu Group, 245
compaction, shale, 97, 118
complexes
  alkaline, 451
  dolomite reef, 471
  transpressional, 164, *174*
Concho arch, 372
conglomerates, 101, 156, 159, 163, 245, 247, 248, 251, 256, 258, 311, 354, 360, 362, 366, 374, 375, 377, 453, 454, 456, 493, 504, 568
continental crust, 20, *39*, *44*, 47, 61, *81*, 86, 390, *506*
continental divide, 325
continental glaciation, 515, 517
continental margin, 13, 62, 113, *157*, 159, *189*, 203, 243, 280, 281, 371, 372, 388, 448, 500, 503
  tectonism, 158
continental shelf, 201, 242, 325, 237, 243
continental slope, 242
Continental Thrust, 238
contourites, 326
convergence, oblique, *141*
copper, 479
Coppermine area, 490
Coppermine homocline, 502
corals, 515
cordierite-sillimanite, 246
Cordillera de Mérida, 307
Cordillera, *7*, *139*, 222, 225, 425, 434, 491, *504*
  accretionary history, *192*
  Cretaceous-Paleocene, *193*
  Early Jurassic, *196*
  kinematics, 164, 174
  Late Triassic, *196*
  magmatic evolution, *216*
  mid-Cretaceous, *194*
  mid-Eocene, *192*
  middle, *492*
  North American units, 164
  northern, *219*
  northern Canadian, *491*
  southern, 222, *493*
  structure, 164, 174
  tectonism, *198*
  volcanism, *198*
  western, 45, 432, *433*
Cordilleran belt, 541
Cordilleran foredeep, *435*
Cordilleran orogen, eastern, 371
Cordilleran province, mineral deposits, *582*
Cordilleran shelf, 434
Cordilleran transpression, 185
cores
  Camp Century, 519
  Dye 3, 520, 532
  ice, *519*
  North Atlantic Ocean, 517
  ocean, *514*
  Southern Ocean, 521
  Vostok, 520, 531, 534
Coriolis effect, 63, 288
Cornwall arch, 366
Coronation Supergroup, 477

Corsair fault, 105, 118, *122*
COST well, 89
Costa Rica, 22, 309, 311, 316
Cotton Valley Formation, 101
Cotton Valley strata, 115, 129, 132
Cozumel, 243
Crater Lake, Oregon, 546
cratons, 7
  North American, 371, 408, 419, *421*, *423*, *425*, *427*, *429*, *431*
Crazy Mountains, potassic center, 219
Cretaceous-Paleocene, *193*
Criner Hills-Wichita Mountains, 390
Crossnore Plutonic Series, 332
crust, 7, 90, 316, *447*, *449*, 460, 462, *477*, 487, 517
  Archean, *506*
  continental, 20, 39, *44*, 47, 51, 81, 86, 172, 371, 386, 506
  crystalline, 189
  extension, *215*
  growth, 508
  juvenile, 508
  oceanic, 19, 34, 35, 39, 43, 55, *57*, 68, 159, 189, 200, 239, 280, 281, 305, 309, 316, 364, 468
  stretching, 91
  structure, 44, *75*
  thickness, *39*, *43*
  transitional, 39, 55, 88, 94
  velocity, *43*
Crystal Mountain Sandstone, 374, 381
Crystal Spring Formation, 493
Cuba, 22, 300, 301, 304, 314, 319
Cuban orogeny, 87
Cumberland unit, 325
Curaçao, 307, 315
Curaçao Lava, 307
currents
  bottom, 281
  ocean, 63
  thermohaline, 63
  traction, 104
  turbidity, 72, 283, 281, 288, 290, 374, 375
Cuyama basin, 205, 206
cyclothems, 427

dacite, 159, 252
Dagger Flat Sandstone, 374
Dakota segment, *471*
Dakotas, 565
Danley Bay, 21
dating, radiocarbon, *514*
Davis Straits, 35, 472
Death Valley region, 149, 213, 493, 505
décollement
  crustal, 193
  regional, 226
  zones, 143
Deep Sea Drilling Project, 72
deformation, salt, *101*, 129
Degerböls Formation, 362
Delaware, 325
Delaware Aulacogen, 372
Delaware basin, 428, 429
Delaware-Midland basin, *559*
Delaware rift, 372
Delgado Pan, 283
Denali fault system, 178, 179, 183, 192
Denver basin, 173
deposits
  barite, 388
  carbonate, 86, 423
  clastic, 335
  coal-bearing, 337
  conglomerate, quartz-pebble, *568*
  continental, 203
  copper, 491
  deep-marine, 158
  deep-water, 374
  evaporate, 559
  fluvial, 283, 364
  flysch-type, 428
  glacial, 90, 547, 550
  glaciogenic, 356
  iron ore, 249
  iron, 260, 367
  lake, 81, 173
  limestone, 162
  marine, 104, 115, 244
  mineral, *576*
  model, *576*
  molasse, 244, 246
  neritic, 111
  nonmarine, 100
  pipe, 570
  red bed, 301, 316
  rift, 100, 503
  sandstone, 568
  shallow-water, 434, 492
  siliciclastic, 89
  submarine volcanic, 306
  surficial uranium, 570
  turbiditic, 208, 327
  unconsolidated, 552
  uranium, sandstone-hosted, *568*
  volcanic, 303, 309, 515
depth, calcite compensation (CCD), 281
Des Moines lobe, 523
Desierto de Vizcaíno, 245
devals, 271
Devils Kitchen Conglomerate, 389
Devils River uplift, 387
Devon Island, 353, 362, 367
diabase, 100
diabases, tholeiitic, 332
Diablo platform, 373, 429
diamictites, 356, 487, 504
Diamond Peak Formation, 427
diapirs, 88
  evaporite, 361
  salt, 97
  shale, 97, 200
diatoms, 280, 283, 288
dike swarms, *332*
dikes, alkaline xenolithic, 332
Dimple Formation, 381
Dimple Limestone, 379
dinosaur, footprints, 260
diorites, 152, 163, 357, 455, 484, 496
  quartz, 244
Dismal Lakes Group, 492, 502
displacements
  salt, 128
  thrust, 142
  transcurrent, 177, 181, 214
  transpressive, *187*, 196
Dixie Valley, 214
docking, 13, 163, 326
dolines, 546
dolomite, 86, 87, 150, 247, 251, 257, 302, 303, 460, 480, 487, 491, 492, 505
dolostone, 353, 356, 367
domes, salt, 100, 106, 111, 129, 132, 242, 256, 257
Domingo, 304
Doonerak window, 164, 170
Dorset fold belt, 462
drilling, deep, *74*
dropstones, 504
drought, *544*
Duarte, 305
Duke of York high, 350
Dumisseau, 305
Dunnage belt, 330, 334
Dunnage terrane, 337
Durango City, 249
Dye 3 core, 520, 532

Eagle basin, 428, 429
Eagle Ford, 104
Eagle Ford Group, 103
Eagle Mills Formation, 98, 100
Early Cretaceous, *195*, *316*
Early Jurassic, *196*
earthquakes, 1, 75, 403
  Charleston, 1
  intraplate, *1*
  New England, 1
  New Madrid, 1
  tectonic, 293
  volcanic, 293
East Coast magnetic anomaly (ECMA), *34*, 81, 94, 99
East Coast margin, 55
East Greenland Current, 68
East Humboldt Range, 212
East Pacific rise, 30, 74, 198, 203, 220, 237, 238, 271, 287, 288
East Siberian volcanic arc, 200
East Texas basin, 104
East Texas field, 559
Eau Pleine suture zone, 478, 479
Ebano-Panuco field, 559
Eclipse Sound, 366
eclogite, 155, 175 258
Edwards Plateau, 103
Eel River basin, 202
Ekwi Supergroup, 491
El Antimonio, 247
El Carmén Formation, 307
El Chichón, 261
El Fuerte region, 247
El Niño, 72
El Paso, 373
El Plan, 302
El Tambor, 303
elements, platinum group, 479

Eleonore Bay Group, 503
Elk Hills, 560
Ellesmere Group, 353
Ellesmere Islands, 5, 260, 352, 353, 354, 363, 364, 369, 506
  deformation, *357*
Ellesmerian basement, 164
Ellesmerian orogenic belt, 158, 161, 191
Ellesmerian orogeny, *158*
Ellesmerian sequence, 150
Elliot Lake area, 568
Elmtree inlier, 334
Elzevir terrane, 497, *500*
Emma Fiord Formation, 362
Emperor seamount chain, 273, 288, 291
Emperor trough, 266, 290
English River, 453
  accretionary prism, *454*
environmental changes, 526
episodes, flood-basalt, 69
equator, 287
Eqululik Group, 488
erosion, 21, 62, 88, 89, 191, 216, 243, 248, 250, 291, 324, 337, 362, 366, *430*
  glacial, 89, 403
  sea-floor, 69
  submarine, 436
Esayoo Formation, 362
Eugene Island 175, 112
Eugenia Formation, 245
Euramerica, 3
Eurasian Tethys seaway, 62
Eureka fold belt, 214
Eureka Sound Group, 366, 369
Eureka thrust, 193
Eureka thrust belt, 173
Eurekan orogeny, 349, *366*
evaporite diapirs, 361
evaporites, 62, 86, 89, 100, 156, 170, 243, 253, 337, 352, 361, 362, 405, *432*
  marine, 252
  saline, 167
evapotranspiration, 542, 552
evolution
  Appalachian chain, *323*
  magmatic, Cordillera, *216*
  North American Cordillera, *139*, 156
  North American craton, *421*
  tectonic, *156*
Exclusive Economic Zone, 243
exploration, gas and oil, 256
extensional province, southern Cordillera, *209*
Exterior fault system, 194
External fault system, 178
Externides, 7

Faeroe-Shetland Channel, 63
Falcón basin, 318
Falcón suite, 312
fanglomerates, 81
fans
  submarine, 281, 283
  turbidite, 281, 283, 377, 381, 392
Farallon plate, 13, 202, 266, *270*, 277, 312, 316, 318
  fragmentation, *270*
Farallon slab, *172*
Farmington basement complex, 170
Fashing fault zone, *115*
faults
  antithetic, *126*
  arcuate, 132
  growth, *97*, 113, *115*, 116, 117, 118, 245, 388
  high-angle, 303, 471
  normal, *198*, 212, 213, 214, 222, 242, 245, 250, 364, 480, 504, 505
  reverse, 172, 428
  strike-slip, 205, 278, 305, *344*
  thrust, 172, 176, 202, 204, 304, 366, 381
  transcurrent, 186, 198, 226, 246, 338
  transfer, 214
  transform, 237, 239, 271
  zones, *114*
fauna, 98, 244, 247, 251, 258, 301, 327, 506
  benthic, 205
  Tethyan, 152, 162, 196
Feilden fault zone (FFZ), 356
feldspar, 361
fertility, equatorial, 288
Finley fault system, 192
Finmarkian orogeny, 341
Flemish Cap, 85
float, orogenic, 7, *142*
Flodelle Creek, 570
flooded belts, 7
floods, *544*
Florida, 100, 102, 570
  northern, 506
Florida-Bahama block, 318
Florida-Bahama platform, 304
Florida-Cuba-Bahama carbonate platform, 434
Florida Platform, 86
Florida Straits, 63
flowage, salt, 107
Flowers River peralkaline suite, 496
flows
  andesitic, 248
  ash, 220, 484, 496
  basalt, 248, 488, 493, 494
  debris, 290
  ice, 520, 521
  komatiitic, 451, 468
  komatiitic basalt, 454
  lava, 249, 250, 251, 484
  low, *544*
  salt, 97, 104
  shale, 117
  tholeiitic, 451, 468
flysch, 154, 178, 250, 251, 253, 302, 303, 335, 354, *377*, 411, 474
folded belts, *7*
foldbelt, submarine, 242
folding
  antithetic, 115
  rollover, 115, *126*
foraminifers, 280, 281, 288
Ford Group, 103
foredeep platform, *408*
foredeeps
  development, *406*
  North America, *405*
foreland basins, North America, *405*
Foreland fold belt, *164*
Fort Norman fault, 491
Fort Simpson magnetic high, 478
Fort Union Formation, 565
Forth Worth basin, 428
fossil fuels, North American, *555*
fossils, 162, 163, 244, 301, 302, 322, 324, 374, 375, 505
  plant, American Southwest, 527
Fox River belt, 468
Foxe basin, 352, 366
Foxe orogen, 447
Foxe-Rinkian fold belt, 474
fragments
  ophiolitic, 155, 305, 335
  phyllite, 243
France, 518
Franciscan belt, 155
Franciscan complex, 155, 176
Franklin Furnace, 579
Franklin Mountains, 501
Franklinian mobile belt, *352*
Franklinian orogen, 506
Franklinian sequence, 150
Franklinian shelf, *352*
Franklinides, *503*, *506*
Fraser fault, 192
Fredericksburg Group, 103
French Broad massif, 328
Frio Formation, 104, 115, 129
Front Range uplift, 161
Frontenac terrane, 497, *500*
fuels, fossil, North American, *555*
Fury basin, *488*
fusulinids, 251

gabbro, 22, 163, 244, 258, 357, 455, 484, 493, 494, 496, 500
Galapagos spreading center, 271
Galeana, 251
Gardar suite, *496*
Garibaldi belt, 221
Garlock fault, 36, 204
garnet, 250
Garrapata Formation, 309
gases, 371, 426, 559
  acidic, 539
  development, 242
  greenhouse, 532
geochemistry, basalt, 74
geohydrology
  fresh-water, *542*
  North America, 537
geoid, 18
Georges Bank, 60
Georges Bank basin, 81, *86*, *89*
Georgia, 100, 324, 325, 328, 570
Georgian Bay, 497
geosynclines, *397*
Germany, northern, 518
Gilmer Limestone, 101
Giraldes field, 559

glacial maximum, American
Southwest, 526
glaciation, 13, 62, 288, *521*
abortive, 523
continental, 515, 517
glacier ice, 523
glacierization, instant, 521
Glen Rose reef, 103
gliding, gravity, *118*
gneiss
granite, 328
granitoid, 356, 465
mafic, 465
Golconda allochthon, 150, 161, 162
Golconda terrane, 163
Golden Lane platform, 121
Gondwana, 3
Gondwanide terranes, *505*
Goochland terrane, 330
Gorda plate, 202
grainstones, oolitic carbonate, 101
Gran Cañon Formation, 245
Grand Banks, 68, *81*, 91, 402, 432, 506
Grand Banks basin, 81, 86, *90*
Grand Canyon, 149, 493
Grand Canyon region, 570
Grand Pile, 518
Grand Pitch Formation, 334
Grande Embayment, *257*
granite, 21, 22, 34, 114, 152, 158, 163, 203, 244, 247, 258, 304, 335, 336, *340*, 451, 453, 455, 456, 471, 474, 476, 480, 484, 487, 493, 494, 496, 497, 498, 500, 501, 503
complex, 152
muscovite, 218
granitoids, 152, 259, 261, 302, 332, 340, 476
granodiorite, 244, 357, 360, 451, 455, 484
Grant Land Formation, 354
Grant Land uplift, 358
granulites, 21, 258, 455, 469, 498
graptolites, 375
gravels, 89
gravimeters, 17
gravity anomaly
Bouguer, *20*
map, North America, *17*
gravity gliding, *118*
gravity measurements, *17*
gravity slide, 106
gravity spreading, *118*, 121
graywacke, 150, 154, 155, 156, 251, 259, 471
graywacke-pelite, 462
Great Basin, 21, 149, 164, 177, *209*, *212*, *219*, *220*, *221*, 275
extension, *213*
half-grabens, 214
rotations, 214
strike-slip zones, 214
western, 197
Great Bear Lake, 433, 523
Great Bear magmatic arcs, 477
Great Falls orogen, 447
Great Falls tectonic zone, 462
Great Lakes region, 47, *478*, 541
ice lobes, 524
Great Lakes tectonic zone, 451
Great Salt Lake, Utah, 546
Great Slave Lake, 523
Great Slave Lake shear zone, *36*
Great Valley, California, 21, 560
magnetic anomaly, *36*
Great Valley basin, 155, *203*
Great Valley sequence, 155
Great Valley–Sacramento basin, 206
Greater Antilles, 13, 302, *303*, 312, 314, 316, 317, 318
Greater Antilles arc, 5
Greece, 518
Green Head group, 331
Green Mountains, 328
Green Mountains anticlinorium, 502
Green River Foramtion, 562
greenhouse gases, 532
Greenland, 3, 5, 18, 21, *35*, 63, 352, 366, 435, 447, 456, 465, 474, 532
aeromagnetic data, *31*
northern, *487*
northwestern, 519
southern, *480*, *496*, 520
Greenland platform, *488*
Greenland Shield, 7
Greenland-Scotland Ridge, 68, 69
greenschist, 151, 356, 360, 451, 474, 481, 487
greenstones, 245
Grenada, 306
Grenada basin, 315
Grenadines, 306
Grenville basement province, magnetic paten, 35
Grenville front, 21, 47, 55
Grenville massifs, geologic settings, *330*
Grenville orogen, *448*, 484, 494, *496*, *497*, 579
Appalachians, *501*
Caledonides, *501*
central zone, *498*
Mexico, *501*
mineral deposits, *579*
northwestern zone, *497*
southeastern terranes, *500*
Texas, *501*
Grenville Province, 35
Grenville Supergroup, 330, 579
Grenvillian terranes, *506*
Grijalva River, 260
grit, 152, 504
Groswater Bay terrane, 484
growth fault geometries, *120*
Guadalupe, 306
Guadalupe plate, 270
Guanajuato, 249
Guarico Formation, 309
Guarico trough, 318
Guatemala, 280, 300, 302, 303, 542
Guatemala basin, 239
Guaymas basin, 283
Gulf basin, 115
Gulf Coast, 7, 103, 434
Gulf Coast basin, *558*, 564
ancestal, *412*
Gulf Coast geosyncline, 20
Gulf Coast province, *564*
Gulf Coastal Plain, 22, 115, *257*, 261, 317, 386
Gulf Coastal Plain foreland, *256*
Gulf of Alaska, 300, 281
Gulf of Alaska shelf, 201
Gulf of Alaska–Aleutian Island arc system, *200*
Gulf of California, 203, 207, 222, 237, *239*, 271, 277, *283*
Gulf of Maine, 89
Gulf of Mexico, 3, 13, 20, 57, 121, 434, 436
deep, 102
floor, *242*
northern, *97*
opening, 432
passive margins, 431
Gulf of Mexico basin, *97*, *104*
northern, 100
sediment, 104
Gulf of St. Lawrence, 3, 412
Gulf of Tehuantepec, 283
Gulf region, growth faulting, *106*
Gulf rim, northern, 104
Gulf salt basin, northern, 100
Gulf Shield, 257
Gulf Stream, *63*, 88
guyots, 20, 290
gypsum, 258
gypsum-units, 302

halite, 86, 362
Har Fiord Formation, 362
Harp Lake complex, 496
Harper Group, 504
Hartville uplift, 460
Hassel Formation, 364
Hatillo thrust, 305
Hatton Bank margin, 55
Haughton Crater, 367
Havallah basin, 162, 197
Havallah sequence, 162
Hawaiian Islands, *265*, *291*
hydrothermal systems, *294*
lava, *291*
seismicity, *293*
tectonics, *293*
Hawaiian Ridge, 291
Hawaiian seamount chain, 273, 388, 290, 291
Hawaiian swell, 291
Hawaiian-Emperor volcanic chain, 291
Hayesville fault line, 330
Hayfork terrane, 155
Haymond Formation, 379, 381
Haynesville Formation, 101
Hazen fold belt, 358
Hazen Formation, 354
Hearne province, 447, *462*, 487
heat flux, geothermal, 68
Hebgen Lake, 546
Hecla basin, *488*
Helena Embayment, 156, 408
Helena/Wallace Formation, 492
Hess rise, 266, 288, 290

Hibernia well, 90
Hidalgo, 250
Highwood Mountains, potassic
center, 219
Himalaya-Tibetan region, uplift, 518
Himalayas, 518
Hines Creek stand, 179
Hispaniola, 22, *304*, 311, 314, 319
Hispaniola fault zone, 305
Honduras, 13, 301, 302, 309, 319
Honduras Group, 302
Hooiberg pluton, 315
hornblende, 180, 497
hornblendite, 357
Hornby Bay Group, 491
Horseshoe basin, 90
Horsethief Creek Group, 505
Hosston-Sligo cycle, 103
hot spots, 269, 273, 290, 291, 295, 310
  mantle, 73
  mechanism, *291*
Hottah arc terrane, 476, 477
Hottah magmatic arc, 477
Hozameen fault zone, 185, 192
Huayacocotla anticlinorium, 250, 251
Hudson Bay, 21, 462
Hudson Bay basin, *403*, 423, 436, 468
Hudson Bay hinterland, 468
Hudson Bay lowland, dome, 521
Hudson Bay segment, *468*
Hudson Strait, marine embayment, 524
Hueco Mountains, 501
Huizachal-Peregrina anticlinorium, 251
Humboldt plate, 278
Hunting Formation, 488
Hunton, 373
Huron Supergroup, *480*
Hurricane Mountain terrane, 334
hyaloclastites, 311
hydrates, 200
hydrocarbon, 104, 105, 386, 426
hydrogeochemistry, *550*
hydrogeology, *546*
Hyland Group, 504

Iapetus Ocean, 55, 331, 332, 341
Ibbett Bay Formation, 354
ice
  cores, *519*
  domes, 523
  flow, 520, 521
  glacial, 21, 523
  rafts, 281
  sheets, 72, 515, *516*, 518, 521, 524, *526*, 532
Iceland, 74
Iceland–Faeroe Ridge crest, 68
Iceland front, 68
Iceland hotspot, 74
Iceland-Scotland Ridge, 68
Idaho, 45, 150, 154, 156, 212, 214, 505, 570
Idaho batholith, 21, 150, 193, 219, 492
ignimbrites, 312, 319
  felsic, 250
  rhyolitic, 249
Illinoian, glaciation, 515
Illinois, southern, 518
Illinois basin, *403*, 423, 564
illite, 288
Ilordleq Group, 481
imaging, *75*
  acoustic, *72*
Imperial Formation, 158
Imperial Valley, 244
Independence Fjord Group, 488
Ingenika Group, 504
Inglefield Uplift, 354, 358
Inland Ice, 21
Inner Piedmont, 330
Innuitian fold belt, 149, 157, 191
Innuitian foredeep, 426
Innuitian orogen, 349
  mineral deposits, *579*
Interior province, *564*
Internal fault system 177, 194
Internides, 7
intrusions, granitic, 212, 412
Inuvikian sequence, 150
Iowa, 523
iron, 31, 271, 287, 290, 493
  ore deposits, 249
  formation, 34, 454, 455, 456, 458, 460, 462
ironstone, 468, 480
Isachsen Formation, 364
Isla Mujeres, 243
Isla Tortuga, 239
island arc system, 13
islands
  Venezuelan, 307
  volcanic, 239, *306*
isostasy, 397
Isthmian salt, 100
Isthmus of La Paz, 245, 246
Isthmus of Tehuantepec, 242, 256
Isukasia, 458
Izanagi plate, 266

J-Anomaly Ridge, 61
Jackson, Mississippi, 104
Jackson Dome, 98, 103
Jackson Formation, 104, 129
Jackson Group, 381
Jamaica, 22, *306*, 312, 314, 319
James Bay, terranes, *456*
Jan Mayen Ridge, 61
Jatibonico, 304
Jeanne d'Arc basin, 90
Jemez Mountains, 222
jet stream, 518, 526, 534
John Day belt, 220
John Day inlier, 163
Johnnie Formation, 505
Johnny Hoe gravity high, 478
Johns Valley Formation, 381
Josephine ophiolite, 155
Juan de Fuca margin, 281
Juan de Fuca plate, 270, 280
Juan de Fuca ridge, 74, 200, 201, 271
Juan Griego, 307
Jurassic, *316*

Kalapana earthquake, 293
Kalmath Mountains, 21, 36, 155
Kaltag fault system, 177
Kane Fracture Zone, 53, 61
Kanguk Formation, 364
Kansas, 47
kaolinite, 288
Kapuskasing uplift, *451*
Karnes trough, 115, 129, 132
Kaskaskia sequence, *425*
Kaslo Group, 159, 163
Kaza Group, 504
Keele Formation, 504
Keetlehole lakes arc, 545
Keewatin Arch, *424*
Keewatin district, 523
Kelly-Snyder field, 559
keratophyres, 163, 305
Kern River, 560
Ketilidian orogen, *481*, 496
Keweenawan rift, 42, 44, 403
Kilauea caldera, 293
Kilauea valcano, 291, 293
Killarney belt, 448
kimberlites, 103
Kimerot platform, 474
kinematics, plate, *73*
Kingston Peak Formation, 493, 505
Klamath Mountains, 158, 159, 162, 174, 176, 193, 198, 423
knockers
  amphibolite, 155
  blueschist, 155
  limestone, 162
Knowles Limestone, 102
Kobuk fault system, 177
Komaktorrik shear zone, 465, 472
komatiitic basalt, 455
Kootenay terrane, 151, 159, 163, 196
Korik antiform, 456, 465
Koyukuk basin, 154, 167, 174, 177
Kula ridge, 220
Kula plate, 200, 202, 266, *269*, 295
Kuparuk field, 560
Kure Atoll, 291
Kuujjuaq, 471

La Blanquilla Island, 315
La Boca Formation, 100
La Désirade, 306, 311, 315
La Rinconada, 307
Labrador, 456, 472, *480*, *494*, 498, 521
Labrador basin, *364*
Labrador orogen, 448, *484*, 494
Labrador Sea, 5, 55, 61, 74, 85, 95, 364, 521
Labrador Shelf basins, 81, *90*
Labrador trough, 471
Laguna Salada, 244
lahars, 245
Lake Agassiz, 523
Lake Athabaska, 523
Lake Harbour Group, 462
Lake Hazen fault zone, 366
Lake Huron, 47, 497
Lake Mead shear zone, 214
Lake Michigan, 47

Lake Nicaragua, Nicaragua, 546
Lake Superior, 44, 47, 478, 494
Lake Tahoe, 546
Lake Winnipeg, 21
Lake Yojao, 314
lakes, *545*
  lava, 291
  pluvial, 527
  See also specific lakes
lamphrophyres, 262
lamproite, 103
Lancaster sound, 366, 369
landslides, 545
Laporte Group, 471
Laporte Schist, 471
Laramide anticline, 172
Laramide deformation, 7
Laramide flat slab, 275, 295
Laramide inversion anticline, 405
Laramide orogeny, 172, 275
Laramide uplift. 192
Laramie Range, 21
Lardeau Group, 152
Larder-Cadillac fault, *453*
Las Ovejas Series, 302
Las Vegas region, 212
Las Vegas shear zone, *214*
Las Villas zone, 304
Late Cretaceous, *218*
Late Permian, *197*
Late Triassic, *196*
Laurentia
  Archean protocraton, *447*
  margins, *502*
  passive margin prisms, 502
Laurentian craton, 325, 328, 332, 341, 447
Laurentian Great Lakes, 523
Laurentian shield, 332
Laurentide ice sheet, 515, 521
lavas, 22, 221, 245, 271, 291, 311, 496
  basaltic, 224
  flows, 484
  pillow, 162, 201, 244, 245, 251, 259
lawsonite, 155
lead, 368
Leigh Ridge fault, 491
Lemhi Arch, 425
Lesser Antilles, 13, 22, *306*, 310, 314
  arc system, 19, 20, 58
  northern, 304
  southern, *306*, 319
Letitia Lake Group, 494
limestone, 62, 86, 87, 90, 155, 163, 244, 245, 247, 250, 251, 253, 254, 256, 257, 258, 261, 290, 301, 302, 303, 306, 307, 316, 353, 356, 362, 374, 377, 550
  blocks, 155
  cherty, 247
  cobbles, 381
  marine, 248
Limestone Caribbees, 317, 319
Line Islands, 273
Line Islands chain, 288, 290
lithosphere, *48*, 57, 85, 91, 141, 164, *187*, 189, 192, 195, 197, 204, 205, 219, 225, 287, 288, 294, 325, 406, 448, 507
  defined, 39
  oceanic, 200
Little Belt Mountains, 156
Little Cornwallis Island, 368
Little Ice Age, 521, *531*
Littleton Formation, 335
Llano de Magdalena, 245
Llano de Santa Clara, 245
Llano del Berrendo, 245
Llano uplift, 22, 114, 115, 501
loading
  flexual, 400
  sedimentary, 131
Loihi seamount, 291, 293
Lomi volcano, 293
Lomonosov Ridge, 367
Long Island Platform, 86
Long Range anticlinorium, 502
Long Range massif, 328
Los Angeles basin, 205, *206*, 283, 560
Los Ranchos, *305*, 311
Louann salt, 100, 101, 103, 115, 129, 132
Louisiana, 100, 104, 105, *109*, 132
Louisiana offshore, 113
Louisiana shelf, 105
Luling fault zone, *115*
Luning-Fencemaker fold belt, 214
Luning-Fencemaker thrust belt, 163, 167, 174, 177

Mackenzie delta region, 189
Mackenzie dike swarm, 487
Mackenzie Mountains, 20, *146*, 156, 164, 167, 174, 193, 194, 504
Mackenzie Mountains Supergroup, 491
Macuspana, 257
Madeira-Tore Rise, 61
Magdalen and Sidney basin, *412*
Magdalen Islands, 334
Magdalena Fan, 283
magmas, 271, *294*
  basaltic, 291
magmatism, 203, *216*, 218, *219*, *220*, *223*, 311, 312, 453, 494, 500, 504, 506
  andesitic, 219
  arc, 198
  late Cenozoic, *220*
  New Mexico, 222
  potassic, *219*
magnetic anomaly, East Coast, 34
magnetic anomaly map, North America, *29*
magnetite, *31*, 180
magnetization, *31*, 180
  remanent, 33
Maine, 334, 506, 570
Makarov basin, 364
Makkovik orogen, *481*
Malton Gneiss, 504
manganese, 287, 290
Manitoba-Saskatchewan segment, *468*
Manitoulin Island discontinuity, 497
Manlius Formation, 338
mantle, upper, *39*, *43*, 47
maps, accumulation-rate, 421
maps, gravity anomaly, *17*
maps, magnetic anomaly, *29*
Marathon basin, 392
Marathon belt, 387
Marathon Embayment, 372
Marathon Limestone, 375
Marathon uplift, 98, 371, 373, 375, 379, 381
Maravillas Formation, 375, 377
marble, 152, 243, 250, 258, 259, 302, 304, 331, 356, 460, 471, 473, 474, 500
margins
  active, 164, *200*
  Atlantic passive, *81*
  continental, 13, 62, 113, *157*, *158*, 159, *189*, 203, 243, 280, 281, 372, 388, 448, 500, 503
  convergent, 281
  Laurentia, *502*
  passive, 81, 90, 93, 146, 159, 191, 243, 281, 332, 371, 399, 406, 411, *433*, *434*, 435, *436*
  shelf, 353
  subduction, tectonics, *280*
  transform, *277*, 281, 283
Marias Islands, 238
Maritime basin, 337
Maritime provinces, Canadian, 3
Markham Fiord pluton, 357
marls, 62, 103, 104
marlstone, 290, 362
Marquette Range Supergroup, 478, 479, *480*
Marshfield terrane, 478
Mary River, 367
Mary River Group, 462
Massachusetts, 336
Matagalpa, 303
Maumelle chaotic zone, 388
Mauna Loa volcano, 293
Maya block
  basement, 301
  Central America, 300, *302*, 317
Mazarn Shale, 374
Mazatlan, 247, 248
Mazatzal orogeny, 487
M'Clintock orogeny, *357*
McCloud limestone, 162
McDonald fault, 36, 474
McKinley segment, 178
measurements, gravity, *17*
Medial New England terrane, 335
Medicine Bow Mountains, 485
Medicine Hat block, 462
Medieval Warm period, 532
Mediterranean, 57
megabank, 74
megabreccias, 245, 502, 506
megafaunal extinctions, *525*
megaplumes, 74
megasutures, *7*
Meguma terrane, 336
mélange belt, 335
mélanges, central Appalachians Piedmont, 335

Melville horst, 350
Melville Island, 191, 361, 363
Melville Peninsula, 474
Mendocino fault zone, 20
Mendocino fracture zone, 20
Mendocino transform fault, 201
Mendocino triple junction, 220, *277*, 283
Menihek foredeep, 471
Menihek Formation, 471
meta-anorthosites, 258
meta-argillites, 331
metabasite, 152, 307
metacarbonate, 152
meta-chert, 155
metagraywacke, 155, 473
metamorphism, 13, 152, 203, 212, 244, 256, 304, 310, 335, 340, 356, 360, 386, 449, 458, 474, 480, 497, 506
  blueschist, 154
Metapán, 302
metasediments, 152, 302, 330, 454, 458, 471, 487, 493, 500, 501, 504
metatuffs, 258
metavolcanics, 21, 330, 471
meteorite, 367
Methow-Tyaughton trough, 155
Mexia-Talco fault zone, 115, 129, 132
Mexican Cordillera, 13
Mexican geosyncline, 252
Mexican Gulf Coast, 242
Mexican Ridges, 242
Mexican Ridges fold belt, 106, *121*
Mexican volcanic belt, 42, 45
Mexico, 7, 60, 214, 219, *233*, 280, 301, 413, *501*, 570
  airborne moisture, 541
  east coast, 106
  geology, *233*
  Grenvillian terranes, *506*
  morphotectonic provinces, *236*
  northeastern, 98
  northwestern, 505
  nothern, 371
  onshore, 103
  submarine regions, *237*
micas, 327, 361
Michale gabbro suite, 494
Michigan basin, *403*, 423
micrites, 375
microfossils, planktonic, 288
Mid-America trench, 280
Mid-Atlantic Ridge, *20*, 55, 58, 61, 73
mid-Michigan high, 21
Midcontinent, southern, *485*
Midcontinent platform, *493*
Midcontinent Rift (MCR) System, *35*, 448, *494*
Middle America margin, *283*
Middle America Trench, *238*, 249, 283
Midland basin, 428, 429
Midway, 104
Midway-Sunset, 560
Miette Group, 504
migmatite, 258, 453
migration, air masses, *540*
  volcanic, 221
Milankovitch cycles, 515, 526, 532
Milford Group, 159, 163
Mille Lacs Group, 480
minerals
  authigenic, 281
  ferrimagnetic, 31
  North America, *575*
Minnesota foreland, *451*
Minto arch, 350
Minto gneiss complex, *456*
Misinchinka Group, 504
Mississippi, 100, 104
Mississippi embayment, 21, 36, 103
Missoula Group, 492
Missouri, 494
Missouri gravity low, 21
Missouri Mountain Shale, 374
Mistastin monzogranite batholith, 494
models
  Baja California Peninsula, 239
  Baltimore Canyon Trough, 91
  basin, *400*
  Central belt, 185
  deposit, *576*
  elastic, 402
  flat-slab, Laramide orogeny, 276
  growth fault, *120*
  Kilauea, 294
  kinematic, *181*, 185, *215*
  lithospheric stretching, 400
  magnetic anomaly, 33
  oroclinal, Canada basin, *191*
  paleoclimate, *526*
  passive margin, *90*
  plate tectonic, *273*
  pullapart basin, 207
  seismic, upper mantle, *48*
  terrane migration, *183*, 185
  Tintina-Kaltag fault system, 185
  Transverse Ranges, 204
  viscoelastic, 402
Mogollon-Datil volcanic filed, 220
Mohave Desert area, 527
Mohns Ridge, 68
Moho, *39*, 47, 48, 50, 68, *92*, 187, 192, 402, 405
moisture
  airborne, *540*, *541*
  distribution, continental, *539*
  marine, 540
Mojave Desert, 149, 161, 163, 197
Mojave-Sonora megashear, 60
molasse, 245, 248, 253, 468, 471
Molokai fracture zone, 238, 239
Monashee complex, 176
Monashee Mountains, 146
Monashee terrane, 151, 170, 178, 196
monazite, 570
Monotis, 181
Monroe Uplift, 98, 103
monsonite, quartz, 360
Mont Laurier terrane, *500*
Montana, 156, 164, 214, 218, 219, 460, 462, 546, 565
Monte Cristo fault system, 129
Monterey fan, 283
Montoya, 373
monzodiorite, 357
monzogranites, 494, 496
monzonite, 496
Moral Lake Group, 481
Morin terrane, 500
Mormon Mountains, 222
Motagua fault, *313*
Motagua River, 303
Motagua suture zone, 302, *303*
Mount Bayley Formation, 362
Mount Lassen volcano, 221
Mount Stuart pluton, 180
Mt. Taylor, 222
mudrock, 353, 354, 356, 360, 361, 362, 266
muds, 281, 377
mudstone, 62, 101, 159, 248, 354, 491, 504
Mulberry Rock Gneiss, 328
Murray fault zone, 20
Murray fracture zone, 270
muscovite, 213, 497
Muskwa Group, 492
Muskwa Ranges, 492
mylonites, 174, 196, 212, 214, 461, 468, 474, 498

Nacza plate, 270
Nagssugtoqidian suture zone, 472
Nahanni terrane, *478*
Nain complex, *496*
Nain province, 447, *456*, 494
Nankoweap Formation, 493
Nansan Formation, 362
nappe, salt, 109, 111
Narakay volcanic center, 491
Naranjos–Cerro Azul field, 559
Nares Strait, 5, 95, *366*
Narragansett basin, 337, 344
Nashoba terrane, 335
Nashville, Tennessee, 425
Nashville dome, 372
Nastapoka homocline, 468
Natkusiak Formation, 352
Navarin basin, 200
Navarro Group, 103
Nemaha uplift, 428
Neslin terrane, 151
Nesson anticline, 172
Nevada, 36, 46, 158, 161, 162, 163, 164, 197, *212*, 214, 218, 425, 505, 546
New Brunswick, 331, 332, 338, 506
New England, 324, 344
  southeastern, 506
New Hampshire, 324, 336
New Madrid area, 403
New Madrid rift complex, *35*
New Mexico, 161, 164, 170, 209, 249, 487, 567, 568
  magmatism, 222
New Quebec orogen, 447, *471*, 494
New York, 500
Newark Group, 100
Newark Island, 496
Newfoundland, 55, 324, 332, 334,

423, 432, 434, 506
Newfoundland Shelf, 434
Niagara fault zone, 478
Niagara suture zone, 479, 497
Nicaragua, 13, 22
Nicaraguan rise, 314
nickel, 479
Nicoya Complex, 309, 316
Nipissing diabase, 480
Nixon Fork terrane, 154, 174, 177, 194, 196
nonglaciated areas, terrestrial record, *518*
Noonday Dolomite, 505
Norfolk basin, 337
norites, 21, 496
Norphlet Formation, 101
North American Cordillera, *139*, 189, *192*
  tectonic evolution, *156*
North American craton, 371, 408, 419, *421*, 559
  Absaroka sequence, *427, 429, 431*
  Kaskaskia sequence, *425*
  pre-Kaskaskia unconformity, *423*
  Sauk sequence, *421*
  Tippecanoe sequence, *423*
  Zuni sequence, *431*
North American ice sheet, 526
North American margin, 283
North American plate, 1, 57, 312, 317
North American units, 164
North American Water and Power Alliance (NAWAPA), 538
North Atlantic Deep Water, 68, 531
North Atlantic Leg, 74
North Atlantic Ocean, *20, 57*, 526, 531
  core, 517
North Atlantic Ocean basin, *53*
North Equatorial Current, 182
North Fork terrane, 155
North Greenland, 358, 367
North Pacific, 266
Northeast Channel, 89
Northern Great Plains province, *565*
Northern Heiberg fold belt, 354
Northern Hemisphere, 521, 532, 534
  ice sheets, 518, 521, 534
Northern Nevada rift, 222
Northern Rocky Mountain trench, 177
Northwest Territories, 156, 158, 161, 164, 433
Norton basin, 200
Norway basin, 61
Norwegian Sea, 85
Norwegian-Atlantic current, 68
Norwegian-Greenland Sea, 55, 61, 63
Nova Scotia, 81, 324, 330, 336, 344, 506
Nova Scotia passive margin, 432
novaculites, 375
Nuk gneisses, 458
Nunatsiaq Group, 488
Nuuk region, 456

Oaxaca, 259
Oaxacan Complex, 258
ocean cores, *514*
Ocean Drilling Project, site, 645, 72
ocean sediments, *515*, 518
ocean spreading, *7*, 291
Ocoee Supergroup, 332, 503
offshore flight-track data, *31*
offshore ship-track data, *30*
Ogilvie Mountains, 149, 156, 158, 164, 174, 190, 504
Ohio, 500
oil, 371, 426, 559
oil development, 242
oil well, 257
Okanogan, 212
Okanogan highlands, 154, 219
Okhotsk-Chukotsk volcanic arc, 200
Oklahoma, 371
Oklahoma aulacogen, 372, 390
Oklahoma basin, 372
Oklahoma Rift, 419
Oldhamia, 334
Olds Ferry terrane, 155, 175
Olds Ferry volcanic arc, 163
Olenellus, 247
olistostromes, 379, 392
Olympic Mountains, 201
Omineca crystalline belt, 212
Omineca-Okanogan domain, 209
Omoa, 302
Ontario, 494, 497, 500, 568, 570
Ontong Java Plateau, 311
ooids, 375
ooze
  pelagic, 200, 243
  radiolarian, 287
ophiolites, 13, 246, 258, 304, 311, 335, 506
Oquirrh basin, 161, 428
Ordóñez Cordillera, 242
Oregon, 46, 155, 163, 174, 175, 219, 222, 280
Oregon Cascades, 221
Oregon-Washington Coast Range, 220
organisms
  biosiliceous, 62
  planktonic, 280
Oriente, 304
orogens, collisional, *447, 465*
Orozco fracture zone, 238
Orphan basin, 90, 91
Orphan Knoll, 85
Orpheus Trough, 84
Orr Lake block, 469
Osa Peninsula, 309
Otish/Mistassini basin, 471
Ottawa Islands, 468
Otto Fiord Formation, 362
Ouachita basin, 377, 392, 430
Ouachita Embayment, 372
Ouachita fold belt, 99, 115, 558
Ouachita foredeep, 426
Ouachita foreland, 161
Ouachita-Marathon folded belt, 428
Ouachita Mountains, 371, 373, 374, 379, 387
Ouachita orogeny, *389*
Ouachita system, *371, 381, 390*
  eastern segment, *388*
  western segment, *387*
Ouachita trough, 377
Ouachita-Wichita Mountains, 426
Ouchita Mountains, 98, 161
Owens Valley, 167
Oxec ophiolite, 303
oxhydroxides, 290
oxides, 288, 290
Ozark uplift, 372, 425

Pacific basin, 181, 183
  northeast, 265
Pacific Coast province, *565*
Pacific Coastal Plain, 245, 260
Pacific margin, 319
Pacific margin basins, 564
Pacific Northwest
  active margin, *200*, 220
  glacial maximum, 526
Pacific Ocean
  eastern, *289*
  floor, 237
  northern, *289*, 540
  north-central, *288*
  northeastern, *265, 280, 290*, 365
Pacific plate, 20, 200, 203, 237, 266, 278, 280, 285, 288
Pacific rim, 275
Packsaddle Schist, 501
Padre Miguel, 303, 312
Pahrump Group, 505
paleoecology, *524*
Paleozoic, *3*, 302, *332*
  early, *3*
  late, *3*
palygorskite, 290
Panama, 22, 390, 316
Panama basin, 285
Panama-Columbia margin, *285*
Panama isthmus, 532
Pangea, 3, 97, 99
Pangean suture zone, 386
Pánuco Embayment, *257*
Papagayo River, 259
Papagayo River valley, 258
Papaloapan Embayment, *257*
Paradox basin, 161, 428, 429, 431
paragneiss, 328, 456, 458, 465, 484
Parry Channel, 349, 358
Parry Island, 360
Parry Island fold belt, 425, 433
Parry Sound, 498
passive margins, 159, 81, 90, 93, 146, 191, 243, 371, 406, 411, *433, 434*, 435, *436*
  Atlantic, *81*
  Canadian, 93
  sequences, 146
  subsidence modeling, *90*
Patton terrane, 155
Peace River Arch, 424
Peace River–Keewatin Arch, 438
Peach Spring tuff, 216
Pearya terrane, 354, *356*, 360, *506*
Pedernal-Diablo platform, 372
Pedregosa basin, 152
Peel Sound Formation, 361
pegmatites, 453, 455

pelagites, 306
pelite, 460, 468, 473, 477, 479, 487, 501, 503, 504
Pemberton volcanic belt, 221
Pembina, 559
Pembine-Wausau terrane, 478, 479
Peña Blanca Mountains, 570
Peninsular Ranges, 202, 244
  batholith, 218
  plutons, 244
  subprovince, 246
Peninsular terrane, 152, 154, 177, 200, 201
Pennsylvania, 324
Penobscottian episode, 326, 334
Penokean orogen, *478*, *494*
Penrhyn Group, 474
Peravilla, 305
Perdido fold belt, 114, 122, 129
peridotite, 305
periodicities, 72
permafrost, 540
Perry fault, 156
Perry Formation, 335
Peter Lake terrane, 471
petroleum, 206, 207, 367, *368*, *556*
  forms, *556*
  geographic distribution, *558*
  geological distribution, *558*
  origin, 556
  resources, 556
petrology, Hawaiian lava, *291*
Phanerozoic basins, *397*
phillipsite, 290
Phoenix group, 266
Phoenix plate, 266
phosphorites, 245
phyllite, 177, 243, 259, 307, 487
phyllosilicates, 354
Piedmont belt, 334
Piedmont Province, 325, 328
Piedmont Suture, central, 335
Pikes Peak batholith, 493
Pikwitonei uplift, *455*
Pinacates volcanic field, 248
Pinar del Rio, 304
Pine Mountain belt, 330
Pine Nut fault system, 167, 177, 179, 193, 194, 198, 399
Pioneer fault zone, 20
Pioneer fracture zone, 270
Piscataquis belt, 335
Pittsburg basin, 518
Placer de Guadalupe, 251
Placetas, 304
plagioclase, 288
plagiorhyolite, 478
plankton, shelled, 280
plant fossils, American southwest, 527
plants, progressive immigration, 518
plate reconstructions, *1*
plate-boundary zone, *74*
platform
  carbonate, *372*, 392, 412
  foredeep, *408*
plume, mantle, 69
plutonism, 152, 167, 187, 455
plutons
  calc-alkaline, 500
  Columbia belt, 180
  granitic, 159, 302, 357, 476, 478
  granitoid, 152, 175, 304, 305, 312, 315
Pocatello Group, 505
Point Conception, 283
Point Lake, 460
Polaris, 368
Polk Creek Shale, 374
pollen analysis, 524
pollen sequence, continental, 518
pollen zone, spruce, 525
Pontiac accretionary prism, *453*
Porcupine River, 191
Porcupine shear zone, 191, 192
potash, 493
Potato Hills, 374, 386
Povungnituk Group, 468
Powder River basin, 173, 565
Poza Rica field, 559
Prairie Evaporite, 425
pre-Kaskaskia unconformity, *423*
pre-Robles, 311
precipitation, 542, 552
  acidic, 538
prehnite, 155
Prichard Formation, 492
primitive island arc (PIA) suite, *311*, 312
Prince Albert Group, 462
Prince Patrick Island, 191, 358, 360
Prince William terrane, 154, 177, 201
Princess Margaret arch, 366
production
  gas, 104, 257
  oil, 104, 257, 562
  sulfur, 257
profiles
  oxygen-isotope, 515
  seismic, *72*
  seismic-refraction, 39, 43, 44, *46*
propagation, rift, *271*
Proterozoic, 3, *156*
  early, *508*
  late, *509*
  middle, *508*
proto-Caribbean Ocean, 5
proto-San Andreas fault system, *202*
protolith, 473
Providencia Island, 314
Prudhoe Bay field, 560
psammitic metasediments, 501
Puckwunge Quartzite, 494
Puebla, 259
Puebla-Oaxaca upland, 258
Pueblo Viejo, 582
Puerto Rico, 20, 22, *305*, 311, 314, 316, 319
Puerto Rico trench, 20
Pump Station Hills, 501
Punta Conchal, 309
Purcell fault, 178
Purcell Mountains, 178, 194, 152
Purcell Supergroup, 492
Purtuniq ophiolite, 468
Pyramid Lake, Nevada, 546
pyroclastics, 244, 311, 357
pyroxenites, 103

Qipisarqo Group, 481
Qorqut granite, 458
Quaternary, *513*
quartz, 288, 354, 361
quartz porphyry, 248
quartz veins, 374, 386
quartzarenite, 468, 487, 488, 491, 494
quartzite, 152, 247, 251, 258, 259, 331, 356, 455, 456, 460, 462, 471, 473, 474, 480, 481, 487, 492, 503, 504, 505
  metabasalt, 481
Quebec, 324, 462, 500, 526
  northern, 21
Quebec segment, northern, *465*
Queen Charlotte basin, 201
Queen Charlotte fault system, 20
Queen Charlotte Island, 183, 201, 278, 281
Queen Charlotte transform, 200, *201*
Queen Charlotte–Fairweather fault system, 201
Queen Elizabeth Islands, 349, 367
Queen Maud uplift, *474*
Quesnellia terrane, 151, 152, 163, 174, 175, 176, 181, 196
Quetico accretionary prism, *453*
Quetico metasedimentary belt, 451
Quetico-Opatica prism, 453

Rabbit Point Formation, 353
Racklan orogeny, 448, 491, *496*, 497, *501*, 502
radial ice flow, 521
radioactive wastes, 571
radiocarbon dating, *514*
radiolarians, 280, 288, 354, 377
radiolarite, 311
Rae province, *447*, *462*, 487
Rae-Nain suture zone, 496
rafts, ice, 281
rain, 542
  acid, 538
Ramah Group, 472
Rapid fault system, 191
Rapitan Group, 504
Raton basin, 173
Ravalli/Creston Group, 492
reconstructions, plate, *1*
recrystallization, 150
Red Wine complex, 494
redbeds, 89, 90, 100, 101, 115, 251, 256, 257, 260, 303, 358, 362, *413*, 471, 477, 494, 559
Redwall Limestone, 570
reefs, 306
  carbonate, 62, 288, 488
  coral, 290
Reelfoot aulacogen, 502
Reelfoot Rift area, 403, 419
Reelfoot-Rome trough rift, 372
Reelfoot–Mississippi Valley basin, 372, 388
Reelfoot–Rough Creek–Rome trough rift, 372
Reform area, 559

Reforma, 257
regimes, tectonic, 415
Remedios zone, 304
reservoirs
  carbonate, 559
  clastic, 559
  sandstone, 559
  storage, 541
resources
  fossil fuels, 397
  mineral, North America, *575*
Revillagigedo Archipelago, 237, 238
Reykjanes Ridge, 69
rhyodacites, 262
rhyolite, 152, 159, 162, 262, 330, 471, 494, 500, 501
rhyolite domes, 249
Richardson fault system, 189, 191
Richardson Mountains, 150, 158, 161, 164, 189, 191
Richmond Gulf Group, 468
rift propagation, *271*
rift system, 3
  midcontinent, *35*
rifting, 5, 58, 61, 81, *100*, 189, 214, *312*, *316*, 327, 330, *332*, 337, 350, 352, 361, 364, 371, 392, 400, 408, 414, 433, 434, *435*, 436, 447, 448, 494, *502*, 509
  crustal, 250
  episodes, 156
  events, 13
Rinkian orogen, 447
Rio Bravo, 242
Rio Conchos, 249, 250
Rio Grande de Santiago, 247
Rio Grande depression, 214
Rio Grande Embayment, 257
Rio Grande region, 104
Rio Grande rift system, 21, 209, *214*, 220, 222, 224, 402, 436
Rio Grande, 220, 242
Rio Nazas, 249
Rio Vivi-Tanama porphyry, 582
Rivera fracture zone, 237
Rivera plate, 237, 238
Rivera triple junction, 220, 277
Roberts Mountains, 150
Roberts Mountains allochthon, 159
Rockall Plateau, 68
Rockall Trough, 61
Rockdale delta, 104
Rockinghorse high, 490
rocks
  basaltic, 88
  basement, 31, 259
  carbonate, 162, 243, 302, 550, 559
  clastic, 150, 388
  consolidated, 547
  crystalline, 251, 280, 497, 542, 550
  gneissic, 456
  granitic, 239, 244, 256, 302
  granitoid, 315
  igneous, 218, 247, 304, 307, 310, 314, 468, 570
  intrusive, 257, 236, 456, 458
  island-arc volcanic, 303
  magmatic, 364
  marine sedimentary, 246
  metaigneous, 151
  metamorphic, 151, 154, 175, 193, 237, 243, 246, 258, 300, 301, 307, 484, 501, 570
  metasedimentary, 151, 244, 302, 328, 454, 456, 460, 552, 568
  metavolcanic, 155, 244, 456, 462, 500
  ophiolitic, 154, 174, 303, 305, 334
  peralkaline, 494
  plutonic, 243, 328, 454, 456, 478, 552
  preorogenic, 374
  sedimentary, 21, 151, 154, 237, 301, 302, 305, 307, 324, 356, 372, 451, 468, 478, 494, 504, 550, 559, 570
  shelf carbonate, 356
  siliceous, 324
  supracrustal, 451, 468
  ultramafic, 163, 458
  volcanic, 33, 150, 151, 152, 154, 155, 158, 161, 162, 218, 239, 244, 246, 249, 257, 302, 305, 311, 324, 327, 330, 356, 451, 453, 454, 478, 494, 504, 550, 552
  volcaniclastic, 327
  water-bearing, *550*
  Yavapai-cycle, 36
Rocky Mountain fold belt, 149
Rocky Mountain foredeep, 7, 432, *435*
Rocky Mountain province, *565*
Rocky Mountain Trench, northern, 5-4
Rocky Mountains, 20, *146*, 164, 425, 559, 565
  shortening, 185
  southern, 149, 161, 164, *170*, 173, 425, 438
Romanzof Mountains, 158, 159, 164, 170, 189
Rome Trough, 408
Rosario Formation, 244
Ruby Mountains, 212, 462
Ruby terrane, 154, *174*
Ruby-Koyukuk succession, 177
runoff, *543*, 552
Ruth Shale, 471
rutile, 497

Saba Bank, 314
Sabana Grande, 309
Sabina Gulf, 252
Sabine Bay Formation, 362
Sabine high, 434
Sabine Uplift, 103, 388
Sachigo Terrane, 455
Sachigo Zone, 455
Sacramento–San Joaquin basin, 206
Saglek basin, 90
sags, shelfal, 103
St. Croix, 314
St. Elias Mountains, 201
St. Francois Mountains, 494
St. Lawrence aulacogen, 502
St. Matthew-Hall basin, 200
St. Paul fracture zone, 74
St. Peter, 373
Salada Formation, 245
Salada Lagoon, 239
Salinia terrane, 202
Salinian block, 203, 205, 206, 278
Salisbury embayment, 87
salt deposit, 90
Salt Lake City, 161
salt, 86, 88, 89, *97*, 104, 106, 109, 256, 432, 518
  allochthonous, 101, 107, 111, 113
  anticlines, 161, 412
  autochthonous, 101, 106, 113, 129
  basins, 388
  beds, 405
  deformation, *101*, 129
  diapirs, 86, 242
  displacement, 128
  domes, 100, 106, 111, 129, 132, 242, 256, 257
  flow, 97, 104, 107
  intrusions, 242
  layer, 86
  mobile, 128, 131
  nappe, 109, 111
  shallow, 105, 129
  stocks, 242
  walls, 100
Saltillo-Monterrey region, 254
Salton Sea, 239, 244
Salton Sea basin, 201, 222
Samari-Cunduacan field, 559
San Andreas fault system, 156, 164, *202*, *203*, 206, 220, *277*
San Andreas strike-slip system, 198, 202
San Antonio Mountains, 213
San Benedicto Island, 237
San Benito, 283
San Diego, 302
San Francisco Peaks, 222
San Hipolito Formation, 245
San Joaquin basin, 209, *560*
San Joaquin Valley, 205
San Jose Canyon, 283
San Juan basin, 173, 562, 567, 568
San Juan Islands, 155, 177
San Juan volcanic area, 21
San Luis Gonzaga, 244
San Luis Potosi, 249
San Marcos Arch, 114, 131, 434
San Miguel–Vallecitos fault, 246
sand, 69, 89, 104, 257, 488
  quartz, 377
  turbidite, 283
sandstone, 81, 90, 150, 151, 159, 161, 244, 247, 248, 250, 251, 256, 257, 258, 259, 260, 261, 302, 333, 353, 354, 356, 360, 361, 362, 366, 368, 372, 454, 468, 488, 493, 560, 568
  aeolian, 101
  carbonate, 374
  marine, 90

quartzose, 101
reservoirs, 559
volcanic, 245
Sans Souci, 307
Santa Ana Magdalena region, 248
Santa Barbara basin, 204
Santa Clara, 304
Santa Cruz basin, 206
Santa Maria basin, 205, 560
Santa Rosa, 302
Santa Ynez Range, 204
Sarasota high, 434
Saskatchewan, 433, 568
Saudi Arabian Shield, 44
Sauk sequence, *421*
Sauratown Mountain belt, 330
Sayunei Formation, 504
Schei Point Group, 363
schist, 155, 250, 257, 258, 302, 356
biotite, 258
mafic, 305
quartz-mica, 152
Scotian Shelf, 86
Scotian Shelf basin, 81, 86, *89*
Scotland, northwest, 447
Sea of Cortez, 239
Seal Lake Group, 494, 496, 509
Seal River Group, 496
seamounts, 20, 73, 237
New England, 68
sediments, *290*
seas, epicontinental, 332
Sebastopol gneiss, 307
sediments
alluvial, 324
arenaceous, 488, 493
basal clastic, 337
biogenous, 281, 287, 288
calcareous, 288
cherty, 373
clastic 350, 353, 360, *361*, 436, 455
coastal plain, 550
deep-water, 371, 392, 491
drift, 61
equatorial, 287
evaporitic, 503
fluvial, 471
flysch, 371
hemipelagic, 281
hydrogenous, *290*
hydrothermal, *290*
indurated, 200
loading, 436
marine, 89, 201, 239, 352, 451, 560
North American continent, *281*
ocean, *515*, 518
pelagic, 281, 283, 309, *310*
seamounts, *290*
shallow-water, 412
shelf, 493
terrestrial, 500
terrigenous, 281, 283, 488
turbidite, 281
seismic properties, 43
seismology, *75*
Selkirk allochthon, 176
Selwyn Mountains, 167, 197
semipelite, 456, 504
sepiolite, 290
sequences
carbonate, 190, 388, 559
clastic, 559
defined, 414
igneous, 13
marine clastic, 302
passive margin, 146
pelitic, 162
sedimentary, 303
shale, 170
stratigraphy, *414*
volcanic, 13, 458
series, metavolcanic, 203
serpentine debris, 309
serpentines, 303
serpentinite, 155, 357, 478
Serrania del Interior, 300, 301
Sevier belt, 164, 193
Sevier fold belt, 214
Sevier foreland, 192
Sevier orogeny, 173
Seward Peninsula, 174
Seward Subgroup, 471
Shabogamo gabbro suite, 494
Shakwak segment, 178
Shakwak-Denali strike-slip fault, 200
Shaler/Rae Group, 490
shales, 62, 81, 89, 104, 152, 170, 177, 190, 200, 244, 245, 247, 250, 251, 256, 258, 259, 261, 302, 326, 333, 334, 338, 372, 374, 377, 379, 471, 480, 491, 504, 552, 560, 568
bathyal, 111
black, 248, 426, *427*
compaction, 97, 118
diapirs, 200
flow, 117
geopressured, 117, 118
marine, 104, 373
red, 248
sedimentation, 103
Sheazal diamictite, 504
Sheepbed Formation, 504
Sheeprock Group, 505
sheets
ash flow, 220
ice, 515, *516*, 524, *526*, 532
ignimbrite, 248
ophiolite, 154
thrust, 173
shelf
continental, 201, 237, 242, 243, 325
Texas continental, 115
Shenandoah massif, 328
shifts, latitudinal, 141
Shoo Fly complex, 159
shortening, 122, 141, 142, 158, *167*, 172, 174, 176, 185, 187, 192, 197, 204, 205, 215, 226, 462
back-arc, 187
coeval, 181
crustal, 222
regional, 143
Shuswap, 193
Siberia, 1, 3, 200
Sibley Group, 494
Sierra de Carrizalillo, *250*
Sierra de Catorce, 251
Sierra de Chiapas, *260*
Sierra de Chuacus, 303
Sierra de Cuerva, 251
Sierra de Guanajuato, 251
Sierra de Juarez, 258
Sierra de la Giganta, 244, 245, *246*
Sierra de las Minas, 303
Sierra de Palomas, 251
Sierra de Perija, 307
Sierra de San Andres, 245
Sierra de San Carlos, 257
Sierra de Santa Rosa, *248*
Sierra de Tamaulipas, 257
Sierra de Victoria, 246
Sierra del Alamo, *247*
Sierra front, 224
Sierra Madre, 20
Sierra Madre del Sur, 249, *257*, *258*, *259*, 260
Sierra Madre Occidental, 13, 22, 219, 239, 247, *248*
Sierra Madre Occidental belt, 219
Sierra Madre Oriental, 22, *250*, 413, 434
Sierra Nevada, 149, 155, 158, 159, 162, 163, 167, 174, 176, 193, 197, 198, 202, 209, 212, 218, 570
Sierra Nevada arc, 150
Sierra Nevada batholith, 21
Sierra-Wasatch belts, 220
Sierran-Idaho arc complex, 155
Sierran-Klamath arc system, 196
Sierran-Klamath volcanic arc, 163
Siete Cabezas, 305
Sigsbee Deep, 20, 243
Sigsbee Escarpment, 101, 107, 109, 113
Sigsbee plain, 103, 243
Sigsbee salt nappe complex, 109, 112, 113, 132
silica, 289
silt, 69, 377
siltstone, 245, 248, 251, 374, 505
silver, 368
Simpson, 373
Sims Formation, 494
Sinaloa, 247, 248
sinkholes, karstic, 324
sinking, 244
Sioux Quartzite, 494
Siquisique ophiolite, 316
Sixtymile Formation, 493
skeletal remains, 280
slate, 258, 260, 334
slate belt, 388
Slaughter-Levelland field, 559
Slave Craton, 36
Slave province, 447, *449*, *458*
Slide Mountain terrane, 151, 152, 163, 174, 196
sliding, gravity, 97, 116, 117
Slocan Group, 152, 163
slope
continental, 242, 243

submarine, 62
slumping, 72, 120
Smackover Formation, 101
Smartsville ophiolite, 155
smectite, 288, 290
Snake River Plain, 21, 42, 150, 460, 550
Snake River Plain graben, 22
Snake River Plain–Yellowstone Plateau province, *222*
snow, accumulation, 520
Snowbird orogen, 447, 487
Snowbird tectonic zone, 474
Snowblind Bay Formation, 361
snowmelt, 540
Snowy Pass Supergroup, 485
Socorro complex, 304
Sokoman ironstone, 471
Solitario, 371
Solitario uplift, 373
Somerset Island, 474
Sonoma orogeny, 150, 162, 163, 197
Sonora, 247, 248, 487
Sonoran Desert, *214*, 527, 541
Sonoran Desert domain, 209
South America
northern, *307*, 316
southern, 301
South American margin, 317
South American plate, 313, 317
South Dakota, 172, 471, 568
South Florida–Bahamas Basin, 81, *86*
South Georgia rift basin, 99
Southeast Georgia embayment, 87
Southeast Newfoundland Ridge, 61
Southern Alaska Superterrane, 154
Southern Cape region, 244, *246*
Southern Cordillera, *222*
Southern Ocean cores, 521
Southern Oklahoma aulacogen, 502
Southern Rocky Mountains, 7
Southern Rocky Mountains foredeep, 411
Southwest America, 526, 527
spicules, sponge, 377
spilites, 305
Spirit Lake trend, 479
Split Lake blocks, 469
spreading centers, *271*
spreading
gravity, 113, 118, 121
internal, *319*
ocean, 7, 291
sea-floor, 189, 222, 238, 239, 364, 432
young, 313
Springerville-Raton lineament, 222
spruce pollen zone, 524
Spuzzum pluton, 180, 181
Stallworthy Formation, 361
Stanley Group, 381
Steep Rock Group, 454
Stellarton basin, 344
Sterling Hill, 579
Stikinia terrane, 151, 155, 175, 176, 181, 196
Stirling Formation, 505
Stockton arch, 206
Stolz thrust, 366
strain, Great basin, 212
stratigraphy
seismic, 414
sequence, *414*
stream, jet, 518, 526, 534
streamflow, changes, 546
stress field, 1
stress, shear, 293
stromatolitic structures, 375
Stuart City reef, 103
Stuart Fork terrane, 155
subbasins, 90
subbottom, sedimentary, 68
subduction, western United States, *275*
subgreenschist, 356
Subinal Formation, 303, 313
Sudbury intrusion, 479
Sugluk terrane, 465
suites
calc-alkaline, *312*, 451
igneous, 448
primitive island arc (PIA), 311
supercontinent, *419*
Superior craton, 21
Superior lobe, 523
Superior Province, 44, 447, 494
supersequences, *61*
Superterrane I, 151, *152*, 179, 181, 194
Superterrane II, 151, *152*, 179, 181, 195, 197
Surreyor fault zone, 20
Surveyor Fan, 281
Sverdrup basin, 3, *349*, *361*, *363*, 368, *412*, 431, 432
Sverdrup rim, 361
Swampy Bay Subgroup, 471
Swan Hills, 559
swarms, dike, *332*
Sweetgrass Arch, ancestral, 425
syenites, 103, 474, 493, 496
syenogranites, 487, 494, 501
Sylvan, 373

Tabasco, 242, 243
Tacagua, 307
Tacaná Volcano, 261
Taconian, 334
Taconic klippen, 334
Talladega terrane, 335
Tallahassee-Suwannee terrane, 327, 341
Taltson magmatic zone, 474, 475
Tamarack River Formation, 471
Tamaulipas Arch, 434
Tamaulipas, 251
Tamaulipas Peninsula, 252
Tamayo fracture zone, 238
Tampico Embayment, *559*
Tanquary Formation, 362
Tanquary high, 361
Tatonduk River area, 504
Taylor Group, 103
tectonics, *1*, *7*, *140*, *447*
continental margin, *161*
intra-plate, *161*
strike-slip, 7
transcurrent, *202*
tectonism, 57, *198*
continental margin, 158
Tehuantepec fracture zone, 238, 239
Tehuantepec Ridge, 283
Tenaghi Pillippon, 518
Tepalcatepec River, 257
terraces, uplifted marine, 514
terranes
accreted, 141, *476*, *487*
Alaskan, *154*
Canadian, *151*
composite, 326
conterminous United States, 154
exotic, 302, *505*
granite-greenstone, 508
migration model, *183*, 185
permafrost, 546
suspect, 141, 142, *146*, 151, 158, 326
transpressional, 197
Tertiary, *5*, *435*
Teslin fault system, 174, 183
Tesnus Formation, 379, 381
Tethyan seaway, 84
Texarkana platform, 388
Texas, 103, 105, 114, 120, 219, 371, *501*, 565, 568
central, 114, 129
east, 100, 103
offshore, 121, *122*, *128*
onshore, 129
south, 117, 132
west, 371, 428, 429
Texas Coastal Plain, 115
Texas Gulf Coast, 104
Texas shelf, 105, 122
Texas slope, 122
The Tuxtlas volcanic massif, 257
Thelon basin, 36
Thelon magmatic zone, *474*, 475
Thelon orogen, 447, 474, 488
thermal cooling, 436
tholeiites, 451, 478
Thompson belt, *455*, 469
Thores Suite, *357*
thorianite, 570
thorite, 570
thorium, *567*, *570*
thrust belts, progressive development, *145*
Thrust, Continental, 238
Thule basin, *488*
Ti Valley fault, 386
Tiara, 315
Tiara Lava, 307
Tibetan Plateau, 518
Tillite, Group, 503
tilts, 179, 515
Tindir Group, 504
Tintina fault, 177, 183, 185, 192, 193
Tippecanoe sequence, *423*, *424*
titanite, 497
titanium, 271
Tobacco Root Range, 462
Tobago, 307, 311, 315
Tobosa basin, 372, 423
Todos Santos, 302

Tofino basin, 201
tonalite, 244, 451, 453, 455, 471, 484, 500
Tonopah belt, 220
Topolobampo, 247
Torngat orogen, 447, *472*, 494
Torok Formation, 410
Tosco-Abreojos fault zone, 277, 283
Tozitna terrane, 154, 163, 175
tradewinds, 63
Trans-Hudson orogen, 21, 447, *465*
  Hudson Bay segment, *468*
  Manitoba-Saskatchewan segment, *468*
  northern Quebec segment, *465*
Trans-Labrador batholith, 484, 497
Trans-Mexico neovolcanic belt, 249, *261*
Trans-Pecos Texas region, 250
Transcontinental Arch, 161, 423, 438
transcurrent displacements, *177*
transport, downslope, 281
transpression, *185*
  kinematic model, *181*
Transpressional complex, 164, *174*, 177
Transverse Ranges, 187, 203, 204, 206, 221, 278
Tres Marias Islands, 277
Tres Virgenes volcanic field, 246
Triassic, *156*
trilobites, 258
Trinidad, 207, 311, 315
Trinity Group, 103
Trinity-Fredericksburg-Washita cycle, 103
Trold Fiord Formation, 362
trondjhemite, 311, 357
trough, deep-water, 388
Troy quartzite, 493
Tucutunemo Limestone, 307
tuffs, 155, 245
  ash flow, 220, 494
  rhyodacite, 377
turbidites, 69, 155, 162, 163, 242, 243, 283, 326, 335, 334, 338, 361, 363, 453, 454, 456, 458, 468, 471, 477, 479, 480, 488, 504, 506
  carbonate, 162
  fans, 377, 381, 392
  quartz-rich, 306
turbidity, 104
Turtle structures, 100
Tuscaloosa Formation, 104
Tuscarora belt, 220
Tuxpan Platform, 256
Tuxtlas volcanic massif, 242, 243, 256
Twitya Formation, 504
Tyaughton-Methow trough, 177

Uchi zone, 455
Uchi-Sachigo island-arc, *454*
Uchi-Sachigo terrane, 451
Uinta basins, 156
Uinta Mountains, 172
Ulaksan Group, 488
ultramylonite, 258
Uncompaghre uplift, 161, 428
unconformities, foredeep, 438
Unita Mountain Group, 493
United States
  airborne moisture, *541*
  anomaly data, *30*
  central western, *36*
  Cordillera, *139*, 222
  southeastern, *485*
  southwestern, *493*
  western, *275*
  See also specific states
Unkar Group, 493
uplift, thermal, 204
uraninite, 568
uranium, *567, 568*
uranothorite, 570
Usumacinta River, 260
Utah, 164, 170, 212, 493, 505, 568

Valle de Angeles, 302
Valle Formation, 245
Valley and Ridge Province, 325, 335, 338, 340
Valley Spring Gneiss, 501
Valverde-Marfa basin, 428
Van Horn, 501
Van Horn Conglomerate, 501
Vancouver Island, 152, 201
Vancouver plate, 270
variability
  temporal, 69
  vertical spatial, 68
Variscan, 338, 343
velocity, crustal, *43*
Vema fracture zone, 57, 68
Vendom Fiord Formation, 361
Venezuela, 22, *307*, 309, 311, 312, 315, 316, 319
  coastal belt, *307*
  northern, 300, 301
Venezuelan basin, 309, 310, 315, 316
Venezuelan islands, 307
vents, hydrothermal, *74*, 271, 287
Ventura basin, *204*, 206, 283, 560
Vermillion Sea, 239
Vicksburg, 120
Vicksburg fault system, 104, 117, 129
Vicksburg flexure, 117
Vicksburg Formation, 115
Victoria Island, 350, 352
Villa de Cura allochthon, 315
Villa de Cura belt, 307
Villa de Cura nappe, 307, 309, 318
Viola, 373
Virgin Islands, *305*, 311, 319
Viscaíno Peninsula, 245, 283
Volcan low, 462
Volcan Pico de Orizaba, 261
volcanics, 13, 150, 152, 156, 177, 197, 202, 204, 212, 219, 244, 246, 248, 251, 260, 312, 352, 356, 412, 413, 455, 461, 468, 471, 474, 479, 480, 481, 496, 500, 502, 504
  ashes, 281, 289, 515
  basaltic, 155, 162, 201
  cones, 246
  deposits, 515
  detritus, 104, 150
  epiclastic, 244
  mafic, 152
  migration, 221
  regions, 42
  sills, 283
  tholeiitic, 159
  tuffs, 388
volcanism, 22, 44, 57, 98, 159, 162, *198*, 201, 206, 212, 455, 458, 462, 468, 487, 494, 505, 506
  arc, 219
  intraplate, 291
  island-arc, 302, 305
  silicic, 221
  submarine, 68, 104
volcano fields, 262
volcanoes, 13, 201, 221, 288, 290
  calc-alkaline, 310
  mud, 200
Voring Plateau, 74
Vostok core, 520, 531, 534

Wabigoon island-arc terrane, *453*
Wabigoon terrane, 451
Waco uplift, 387
Wagwater trough, 312, 318
Wakeham terrane, 500
Walker Lane, *214*
Wallowa arc, 163
Wallowa terrane, 155, 175
walls, salt, 200
Wanda fault system, 122, *126*
warping, lithospheric, 425
Wasatch Mountains, 493
Wasatch segment, 173
Washikemba, 307
Washikemba Formation, 311
Washington, 46, 154, 201, 209, 212, 280, 504, 570
Washita Group, 103
Wason field, 559
wastes, radioactive, 571
Water Island, 305, 311
waters
  deep, 410
  fresh, *537*, 546
  fresh-surface, *550, 551*
  ground, 397, *546, 547*, 551
  marine, 62
  meteoric, 295
  ocean, *63*
  redistribution, *538*
  regional transfer, *538*
  saline, 295
  surface, *542*
Wathaman-Chipewyan batholith, 470
Wawa island-arc terrane, *451*
Wawa terrane, 451
weathering, 518
wedges
  accretionary, 13, *200*
  clastic, 361, *410*, 426
wehrlite, 357
Wellington high, 350
Welsh graben, 341
Wernecke Mountains, 504

Wernecke Supergroup, 491, 502
West Floria escarpment, 20
West Pacific backarc system, 158
West Siberia basin, 156
Western Boundary Undercurrent, 63, 68
Western Canada basin, *407*, *410*
Western Cascades arc volcanism, 220
Western Channel diabase, 491
wetlands, *545*
Wheeler Ridge area, 204
Wiberns-Ellenburger, 373
Wichita-Ancestral Rocky Mountain system, 7
Wichita-Arbuckle uplift, 428
Wichita Mountains, 161, 372
Wiggins arch, 103
Wiggins high, 434
Wilcox, 104, 120, 129
Wilcox faults, 129, 132
Wilcox flexure, 117
Williston basin, 42, 172, *403*, *405*, 423, 425, 565
Willow Creek thrust, 193
Wilson cycle, 69, 371
Wind River Mountains, 170
Wind River Range, 461
Windermere Supergroup, 146, 491, 504
Winisk trough, 468
Winnipeg plutonic complex, 454
Wisconsin, 478
  glaciation, 515
Wisconsin arch, 21
Wisconsin magmatic terrane, *478*
Wishart Quartzite, 471
Wolf River batholith, 21
Womble Shale, *374*
Wood Canyon Formation, 505
Woodbine Formation, 104
Woodbine Group, 103
Woodburn Group, 462
Woods Hollow, 374
Wopmay orogen, 447, *477*, 488, 508
worms, 271
Wrangell arc, 45
Wrangell Mountains, 42
Wrangellia terrane, 151, 152, 154, 176, 177, 181, 194, 201
Wyoming, 36, 164, 170, 172, 192, 214, 219, 460, 565, 568
Wyoming/Hearne province boundary, *461*
Wyoming province, 36, 447, *460*, 492, 493
Wyoming-Utah thrust belt, 174

xenoliths, 456, 496
  volcanic, 216
Xilitla-Jacala, 254

Y-City fault, 386
Yakutat and Queen Charlotte Islands margin, *281*
Yakutat basin, 201
Yakutat block, 278
Yakutat terrane, 201
Yates field, 559
Yavapai orogeny, 487
Yavapai-Mazatzal orogen, 448
Yegua, 104
Yellowstone Plateau, 515
Yerington district, 213
Younger Dryas, 520
Younger Dryas oscillation, *527*
Yucatán , 102, *256*
Yucatán Bank, 256
Yucatán basin, 243, *313*
Yucatán Carribean margin, 94
Yucatán Channel, 243
Yucatán Peninsula, 242, 256, *257*
Yucatán Platform, 22, 434
Yukon, 158, 161, 164, 221, 425, 427
Yukon fault system, 185
Yukon-Tanana terrane, 151, 152, 159, 170, 174, 194
Yukon Territory, 151, 159, 504, 541

Zacatecas City, 251
Zaza, 304
Zechstein basin, 3
zenoliths, 256
zeolite, 290
Zig-zag Dal Formation, 488
zinc, 367, 368
zircons, 159
Zodiac Fan, 281
Zuluenta, 304
Zuni sequence, *431*

Typeset by WESType Publishing Services, Inc., Boulder, Colorado
Printed in U.S.A. by Malloy Lithographing, Inc., Ann Arbor, Michigan

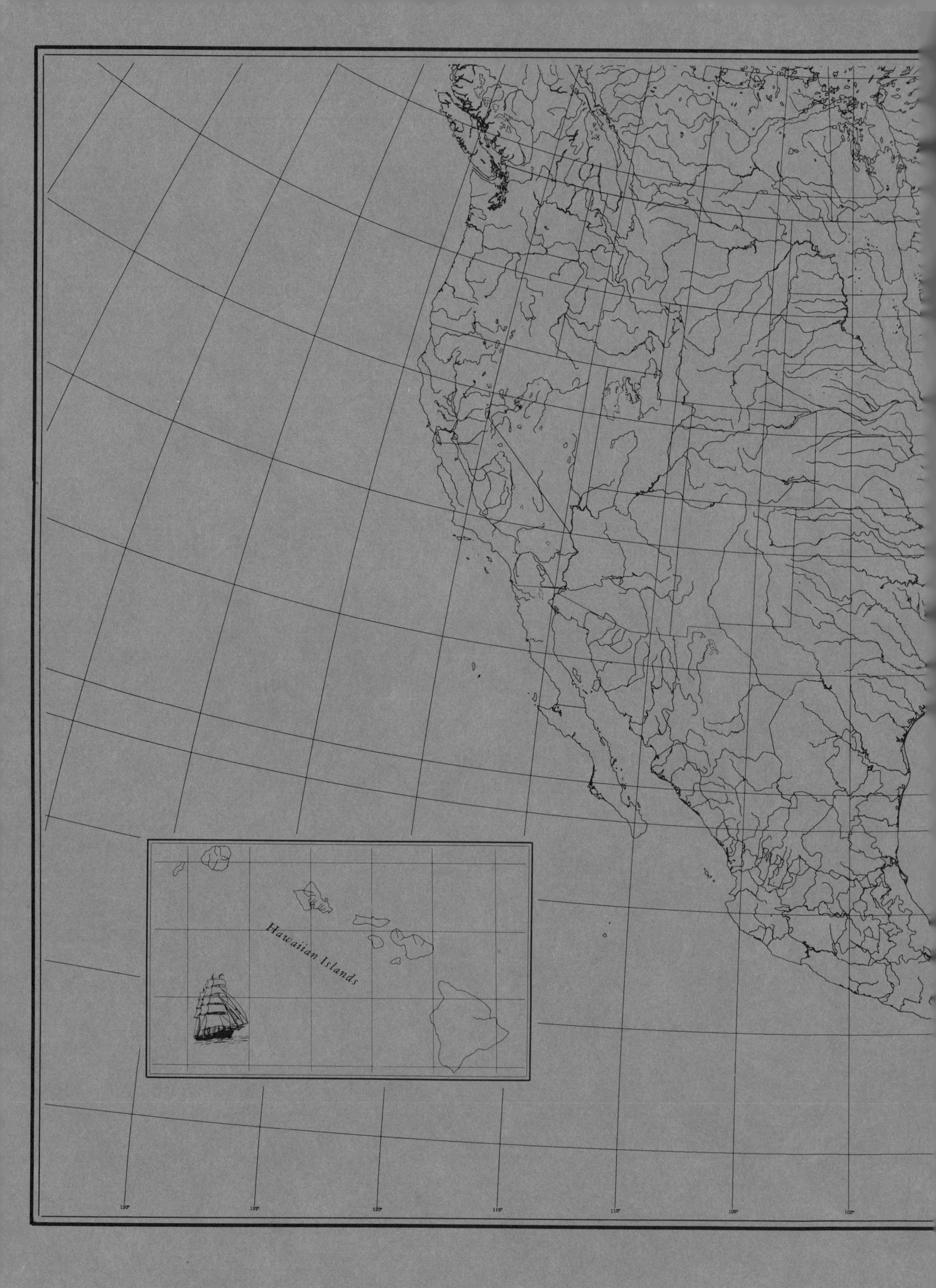
Hawaiian Islands
130°
125°
120°
115°
110°
105°
100°